President and Publisher
IRA SHAPIRO

Executive Vice President
ANN MIDDLEBROOK

Controller
BRENDA MASSY

Director of Marketing
and Sales
ERICA STURDEVANT

Director of Production
and Manufacturing
ZULEMA RODRIGUEZ

Art Director
JILL BLUMING

Front Cover & Spine Illustrations
LAURA SUSANNE BAILEY

ADVERTISING SALES

Client Services Manager
RANDY PUDDU

Sales Coordinator
CLAIRE MISSANELLI

Sales Representatives
JOHN BERGSTROM
JO ANN MILLER
JOE SAFFERSON

MARKETING

Marketing Administration Manager
LISA WILKER

CREATIVE

Designers
JOHN TROCHE
LAURA BERKOWITZ

PRODUCTION

Production/Client Relations Manager
CHUCK ROSENOW

Production Coordinator
JUSTINE KEEFE

Traffic Coordinator
CURT SWEDIN

DISTRIBUTION

Distribution Manager
JAMES KRAVITZ

Labels To Go Coordinator
KAREN WRIGHT

Distribution Assistant
THERESA AFFUSO

ADMINISTRATION

Office Manager
JACQUELINE ILDEFONSO

Senior Accounting Assistant
MICHELLE ROBERTS

Accounting Assistant
ALEXANDRIA MANIATAKIS

Digital Communications Consultant
JASON ELLIS

Receptionist
TIFFANY KAMARA

SPECIAL THANKS TO

EDSON AVELAR
CASSANDRA COOK
JAMES DAHER
DAN DYKSEN
EDUARDO FAUSTI
JOE KRAVITZ
RAFAEL MEDINA

Publisher and U.S. Book Trade Distributor   American Showcase, Inc. 915 Broadway, 14th Floor, New York, NY 10010   Tel 212.673.6600 or 800.894.7469
Fax 212.673.9795   email info@amshow.com url www.theispot.com

For Sales Outside the U.S.   Rotovision SA   Sheridan House, 112/116A, Western Road, Hove BN3 2AA, England   Tel 44 1273 72 72 68   Fax 44 1273 72 72 69

Color Separation   PrintPro Ltd., Hong Kong

Printing and Manufacturing   Dai Nippon Printing Co., (Hong Kong) Ltd.

American Illustration Showcase 24   BOOK 2 of 2   ISBN 1-887165-35-5   ISSN 0278-8128

AMERICAN SHOWCASE

ILLUSTRATION

american **showcase**

TWENTY—FOURTH EDITION

CONTENTS

ART PAGES

ADVERTISERS' INDICES

DIRECTORY

ILLUSTRATORS & DESIGNERS

ILLUSTRATORS & DESIGNERS

ILLUSTRATORS & DESIGNERS

ILLUSTRATORS & DESIGNERS

ILLUSTRATORS & DESIGNERS

the*i*spot·showcase™

the *illustration* internet site

© 2000 CAMPBELL LAIRD

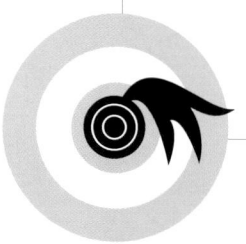

Your

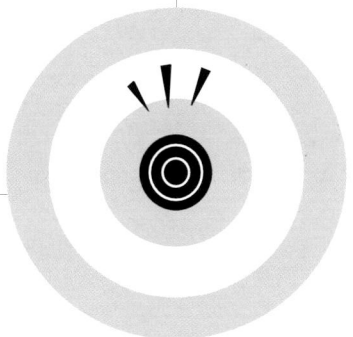

*Visit Theispot-Showcase™ to find even
more work from the worlds top illustrators.*

Browse through over 700 portfolios by name, or use our search engine to review
a variety of samples that match the style, subject and medium you need.
e-mail: info@theispot.com   toll free: 888.834.7768

www.theispot.com

illustration source...online!

NEIL BRENNAN

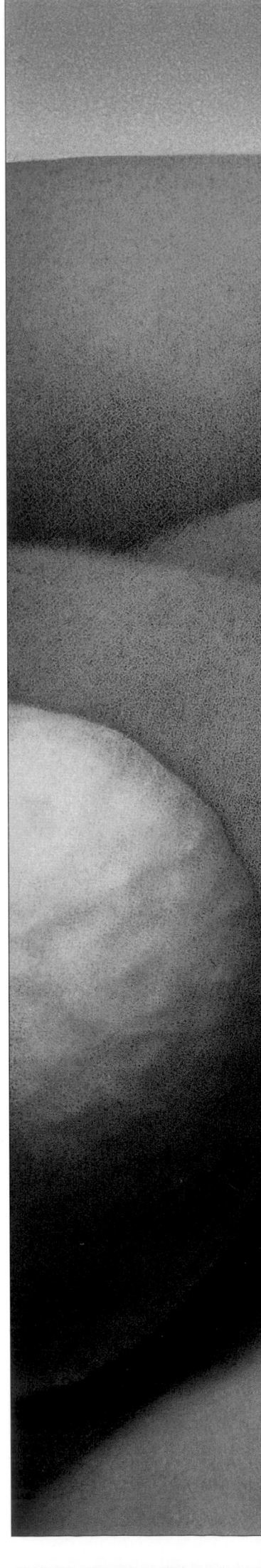

terry**allen** 914 238 1422 terryallen.com

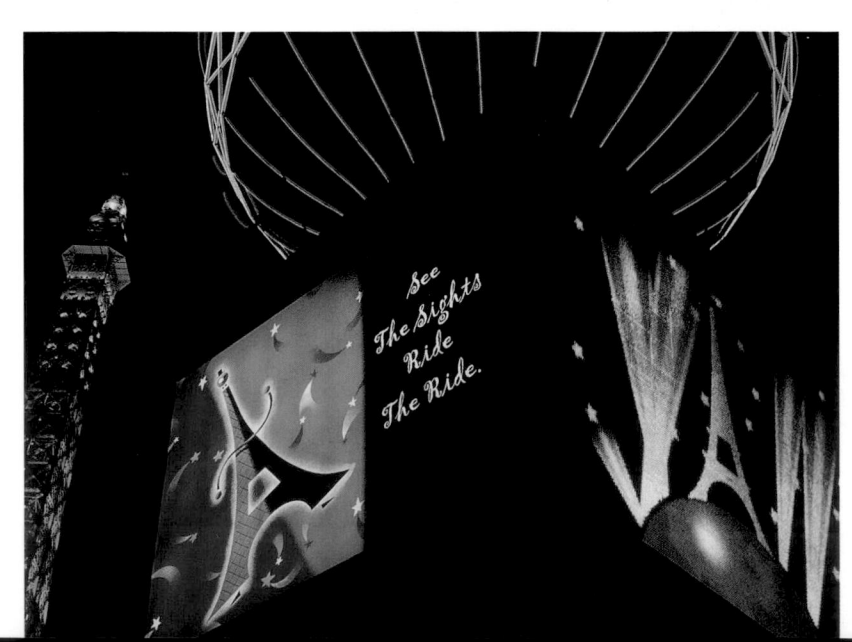

this page, top: three posters for
paris las vegas casino; bottom: animated
marquee, las vegas blvd.
next page: year of the dragon watch
for swatch; three posters for elnet, japan

566

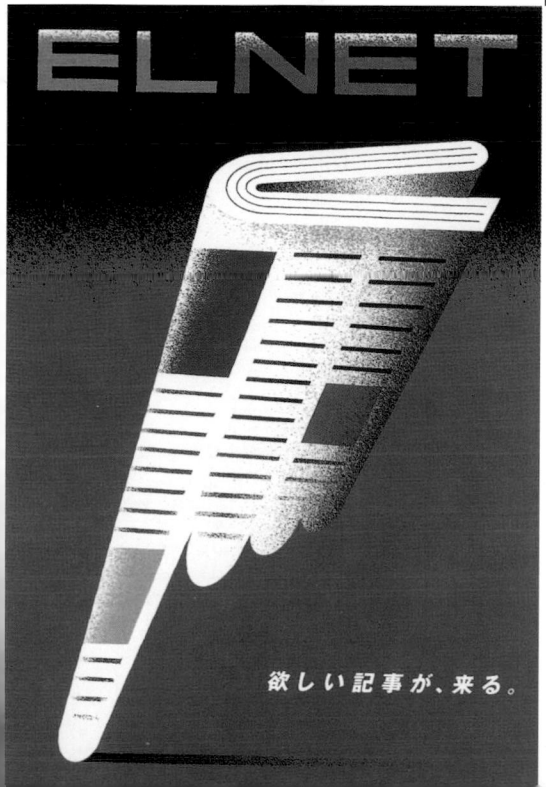

Steve Björkman
Studio 949.261.1411   Fax 949.261.7528
www.stevebjorkman.com

Steve Björkman
Studio 949.261.1411   Fax 949.261.7528
www.stevebjorkman.com

GUY BILLOUT

TEL 212.786.4352 FAX 786.4180

voice: 415.431.1069 fax: 415.431.1719
e-mail: hoeyart@earthlink.net
www.peterhoey.com

ALLEN GARNS

611 South Loma Vista Circle

Mesa, Arizona 85204

480 854 3121

ALLEN GARNS

611 South Loma Vista Circle

Mesa, Arizona 85204

480 854 3121

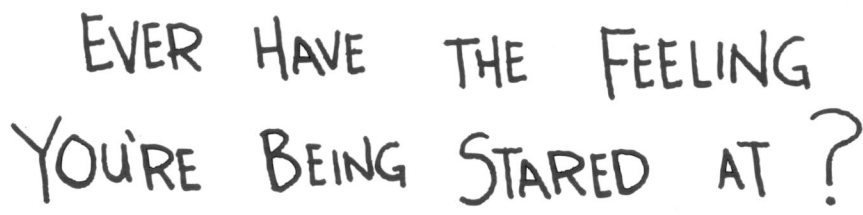

JEFFMOORES.COM   716 229-4603

"THAT'S NOT ART, THAT'S ILLUSTRATION"

Everybody is an artist these days. Rock and Roll singers are artists. So are movie directors, performance artists, make-up artists, tattoo artists, con artists and rap artists. Madonna is an artist because she explores her own sexuality. Snoop Doggy Dogg is an artist because he explores other people's sexuality. Victims who express their pain are artists. So are guys in prison who express themselves on shirt cardboard. Even consumers are artists when they express themselves in their selection of commodities. The only people left who seem not to be artists are illustrators.

HOLLAND

tom white.images • *phone* 212 866 7841 • *e-mail* tom@twimages.com • *website* http://www.twimages.com

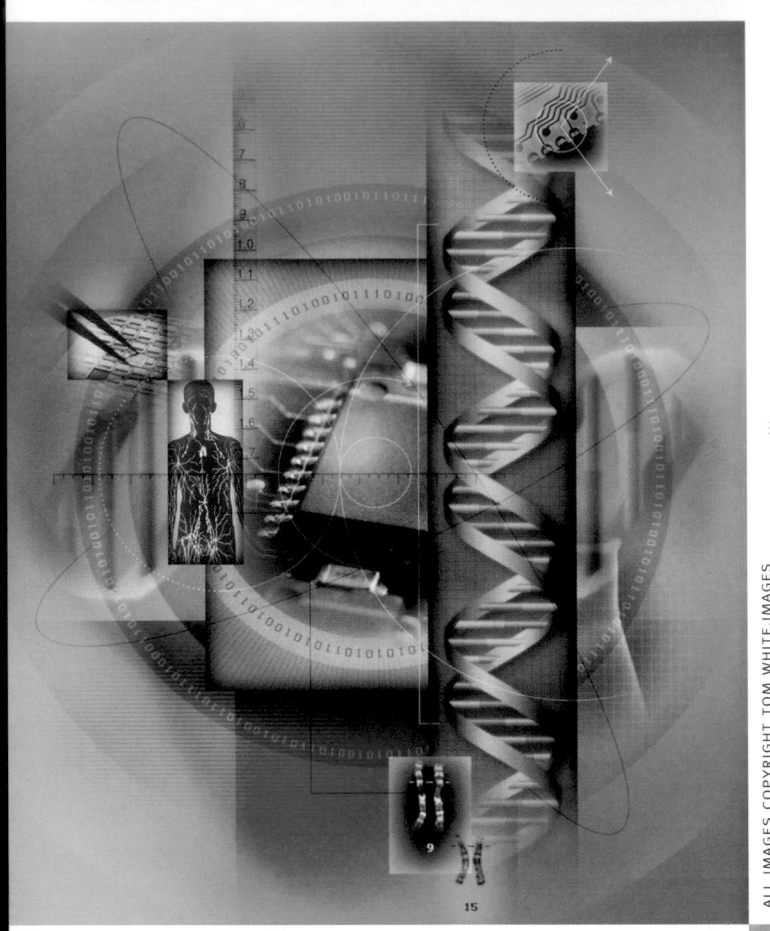

ALL IMAGES COPYRIGHT TOM WHITE.IMAGES

Transition

tom white.images *phone* 212.866.7841 *website* www.twimages.com • • •

rené **milot**

416] 425-7726

Peter SiU

650.692.1839 FAX 650.697.3306

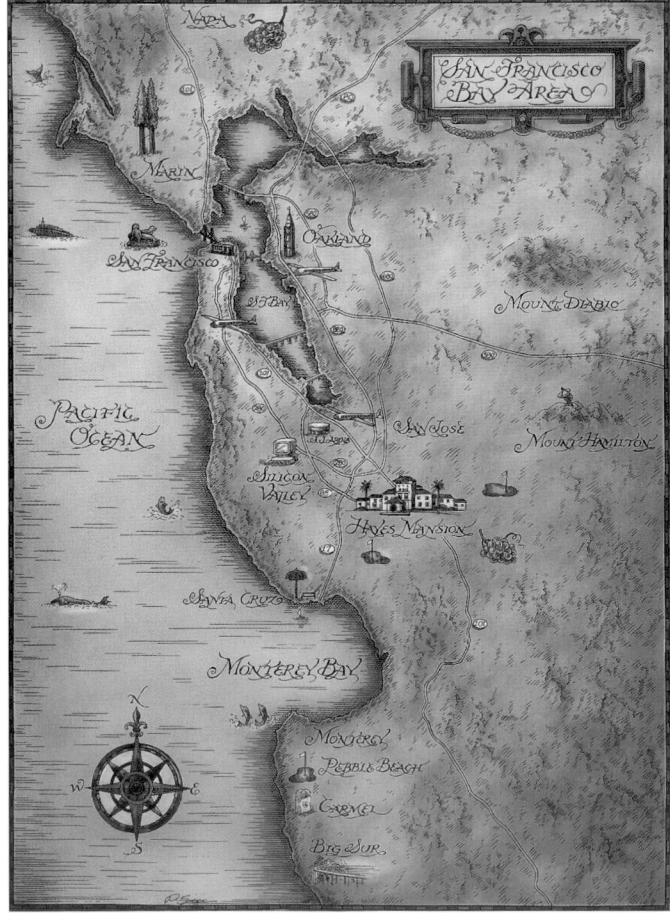

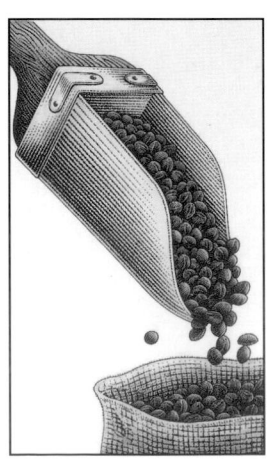

www.theispot.com/artist/petersiu

In New York: Artworks Inc. 212.627.1554

Peter SiU 650.692.1839 FAX 650.697.3306

www.theispot.com/artist/petersiu

In New York: Artworks Inc. 212.627.1554

BILL MAYER (404)378-0686 FAX(404)373-1759 240 FORKNER DR. DECATUR, GA 30030

ken orvidas

tel 425 867 3072
fax 425 867 3092
www.theispot.com/artist/korvidas
www.orvidas.com
email ken@orvidas.com

marketeer

ken orvidas

tel 425 867 3072
fax 425 867 3092
www.theispot.com/artist/korvidas
www.orvidas.com
email ken@orvidas.com

growth

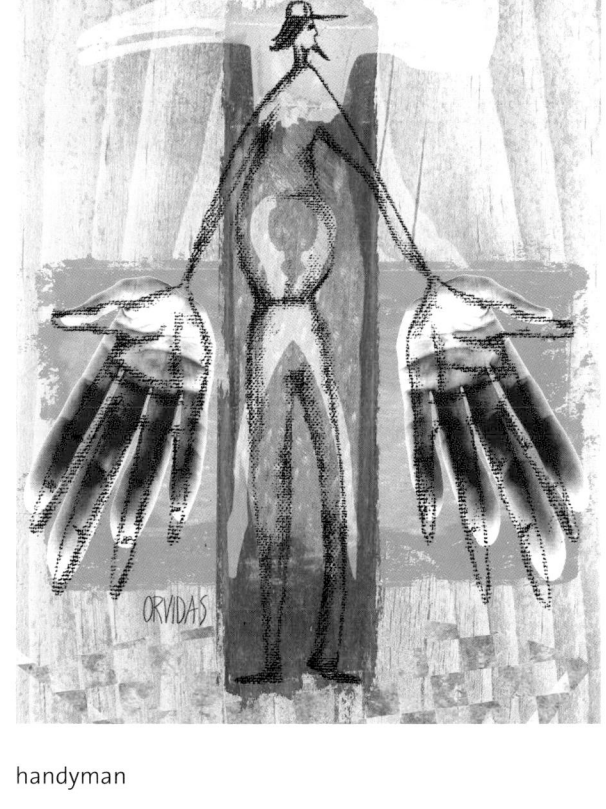

handyman

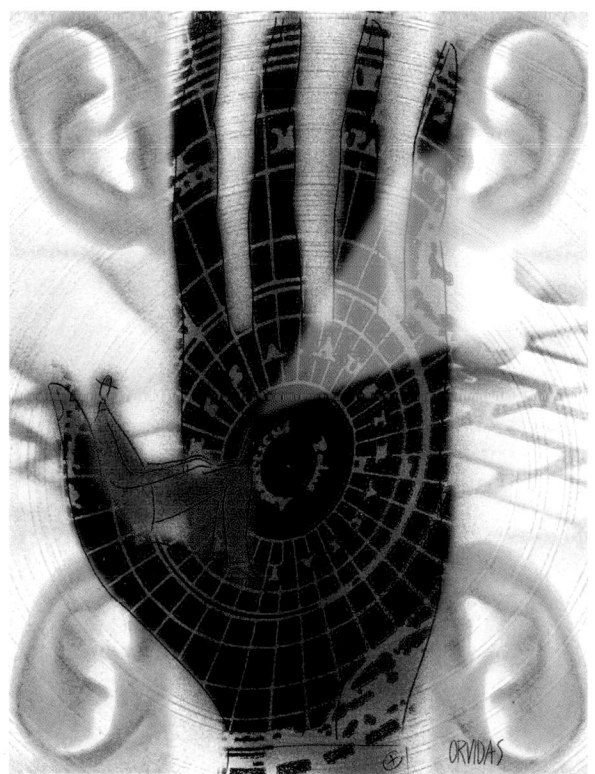

internet security

waiting

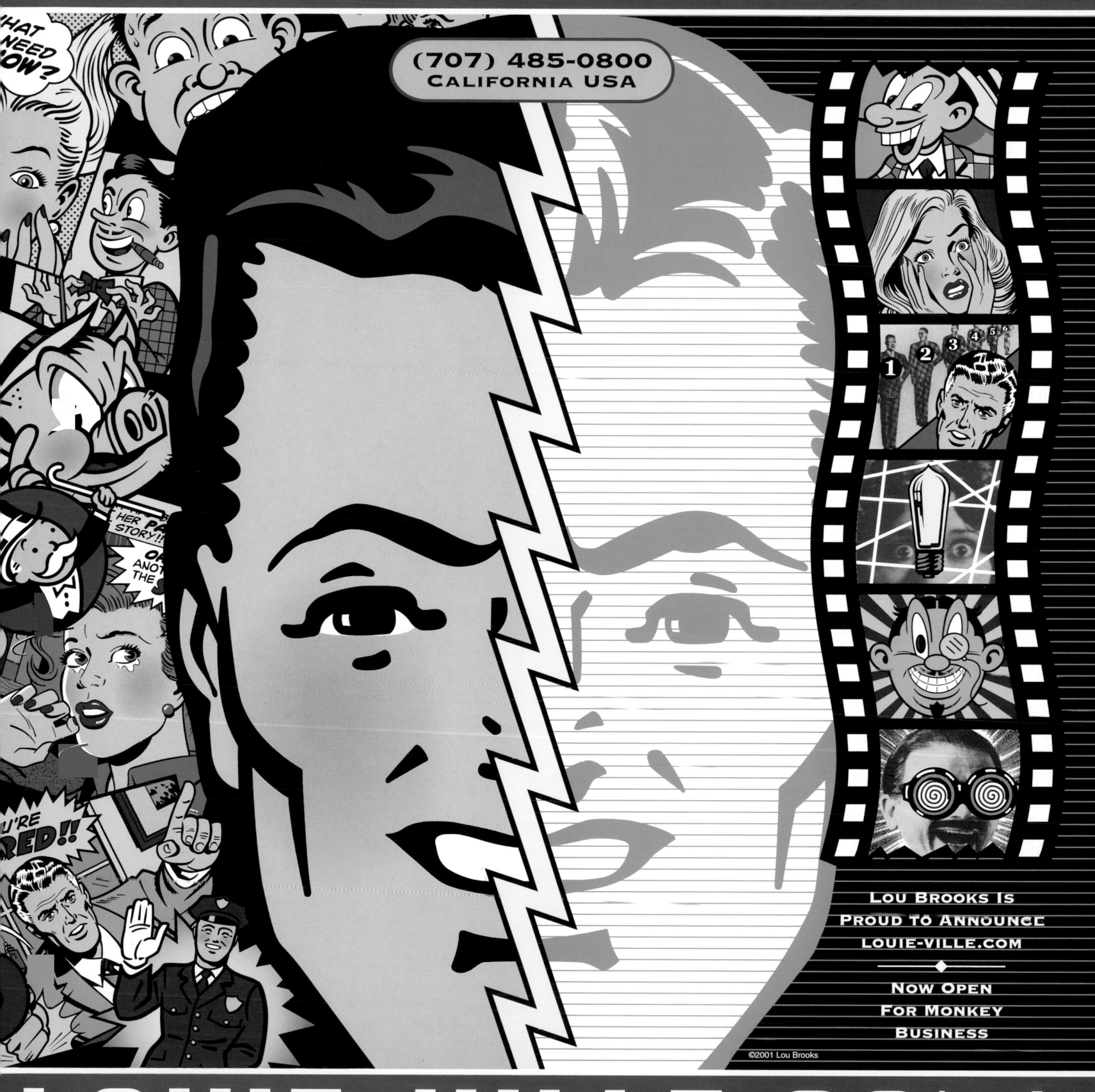

Sandy Haight

PHONE: 206-343-0656   FAX: 206-343-5697

www.showcase.com/artist/sandyhaight

Association of Trial Lawyers of America, Bellevue Square Mall, Caravali Coffee, Estee Lauder, Houghton Mifflin Publishers, John Hancock Mutual Life, Microsoft Magazine, National Kidney Foundation

PHONE: 206-343-0656 **Sandy Haight** FAX: 206-343-5697

www.showcase.com/artist/sandyhaight

Gary Baseman

Represented by Jan Collier (415) 383-9026 (415) 383-9037 fax collierreps.com
East & Editorial (323) 934-5567 (323) 934-5516 fax

Gary Baseman Represented by Jan Collier (415) 383-9026 (415) 383-9037 fax collierreps.com
East & Editorial (323) 934-5567 (323) 934-5516 fax

CATHLEEN
TOELKE.COM

RHINEBECK NY
▪
PH 845.876.8776

FX 845.758.2784
▪
ADVERTISING

CORPORATE

& EDITORIAL

ILLUSTRATION
▪
REUSE IMAGES

CATHLEEN TOELKE

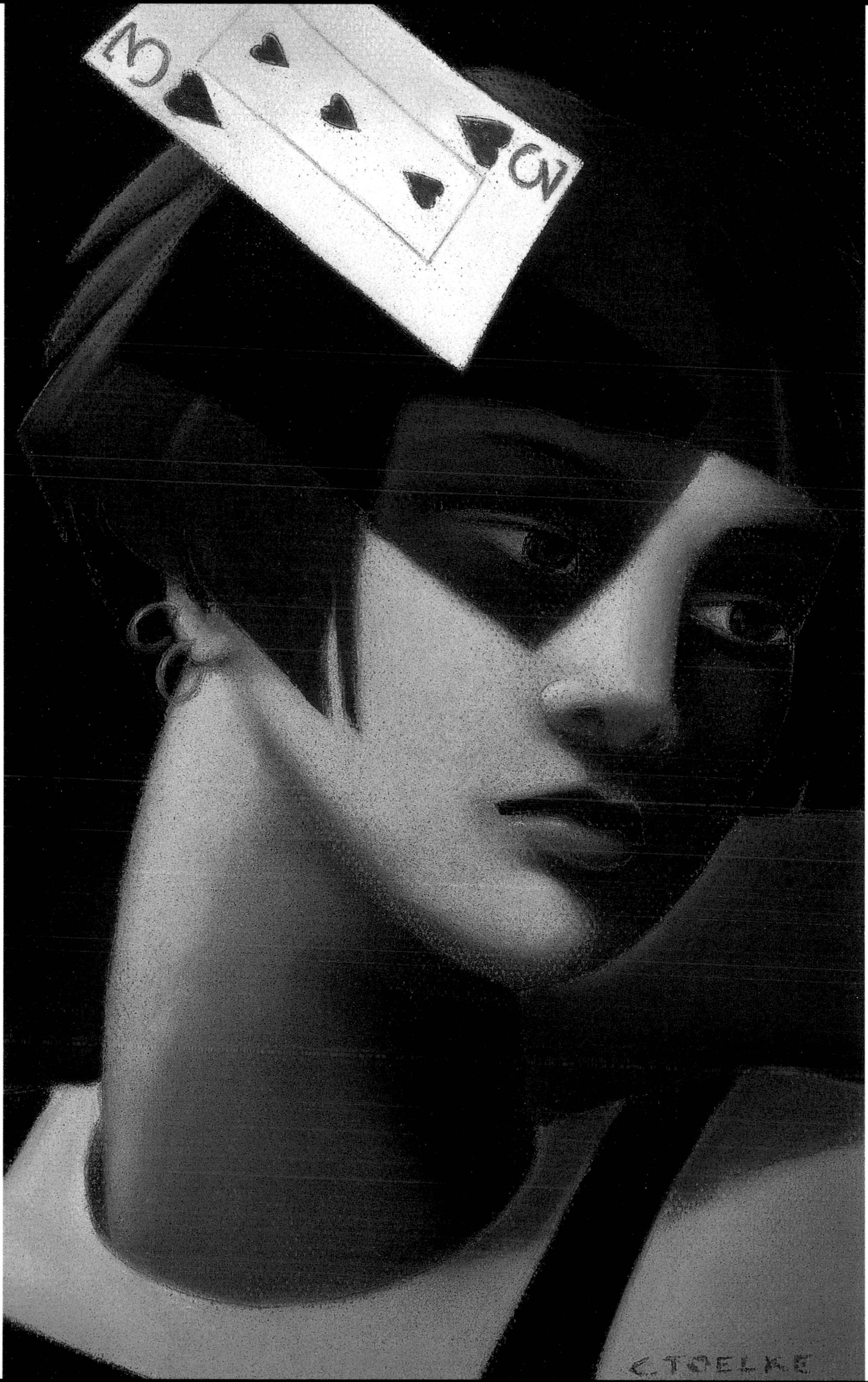

CATHLEEN
TOELKE.COM

RHINEBECK NY

PH 845.876.8776

FX 845.758.2784

ADVERTISING

CORPORATE

& EDITORIAL

ILLUSTRATION

REUSE IMAGES

WARD ANNUALS ▪ AMERICAN ILLUSTRATION ▪ PRINT'S REGIONAL ▪ CA ILLUSTRATION ▪ GRAPHIS DESIGN
HE SOCIETY OF ILLUSTRATORS ▪ ▪ SAMPLES ON THE WEB ▪ http://www.zaks.com/illustrators/toelke

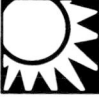

(513) 932-2154
FAX (513) 932-9389

www.theispot.com/artist/jaredlee
www.workbook.com/portfolios/lee_j
E-MAIL JLeeStudio@AOL.COM

JARED LEE
ILLUSTRATOR

2942 Hamilton Road
Lebanon, Ohio 45036

VALUE GOLF

VALUE GOLF

JOHN MacDONALD

Digitally colored scratchboard. Delivered on-line, on Zip, CD or FTP.

Bozell Kamstra (People's Heritage Financial Group)

Mutual Funds Magazine

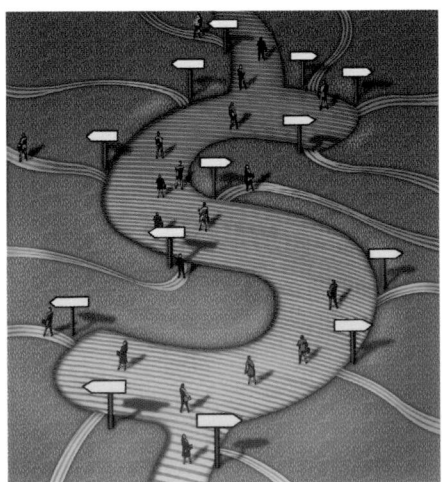

The Wall Street Journal

Mutual Funds Magazine

1021 Hancock Rd, Williamstown MA 01267 • Tel: 413-458-0056 • Fax: 413-458-5379 • e-mail: john@jmacdonald.com

JOHN MacDONALD

G.A.G. 12 thru 17 • Showcase 19 thru 22 • Black Book 1997 thru 2000 • On-line portolio: http://www.jmacdonald.com

Der Speigel

Business Supply Chain Review Magazine

Windows Magazine

Windows Magazine

1021 Hancock Rd, Williamstown MA 01267 • Tel: 413-458-0056 • Fax: 413-458-5379 • e-mail: john@jmacdonald.com

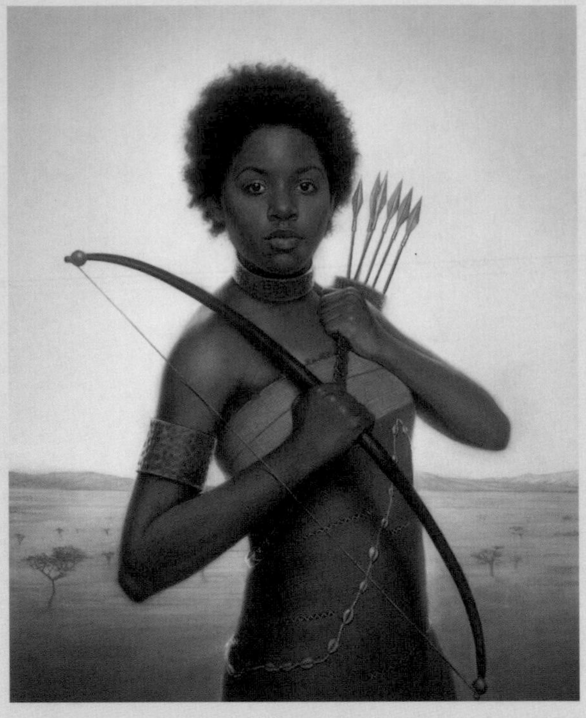
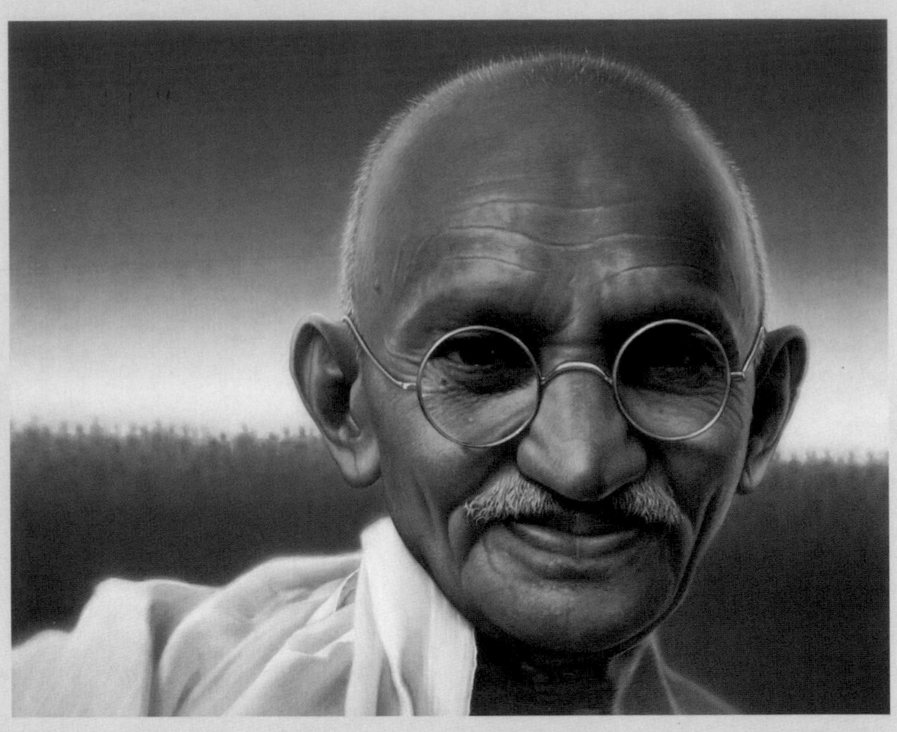
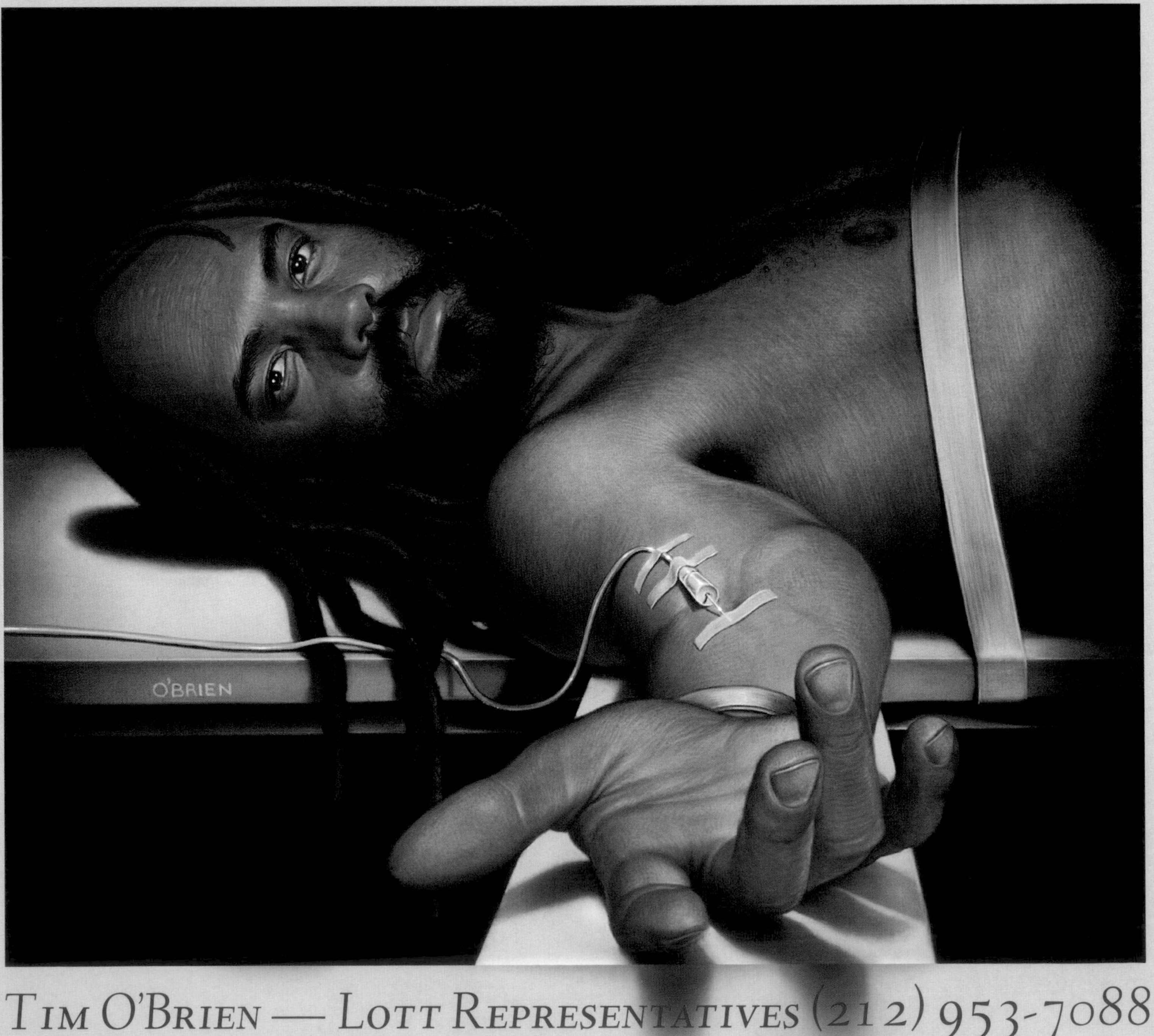

TIM O'BRIEN — LOTT REPRESENTATIVES (212) 953-7088

TIM O'BRIEN

LOTT REPRESENTATIVES
60 EAST 42ND STREET, SUITE 1146
NEW YORK, NY 10165
(212) 953-7088

Min Jae Hong • 845-986-8040 • Fax: 845-987-1002 • Email: mj@minjaehong.com • www.minjaehong.com

Min Jae Hong • 845-986-8040 • Fax: 845-987-1002 • Email: mj@minjaehong.com • www.minjaehong.com

WWW.BONNIERIESER.COM

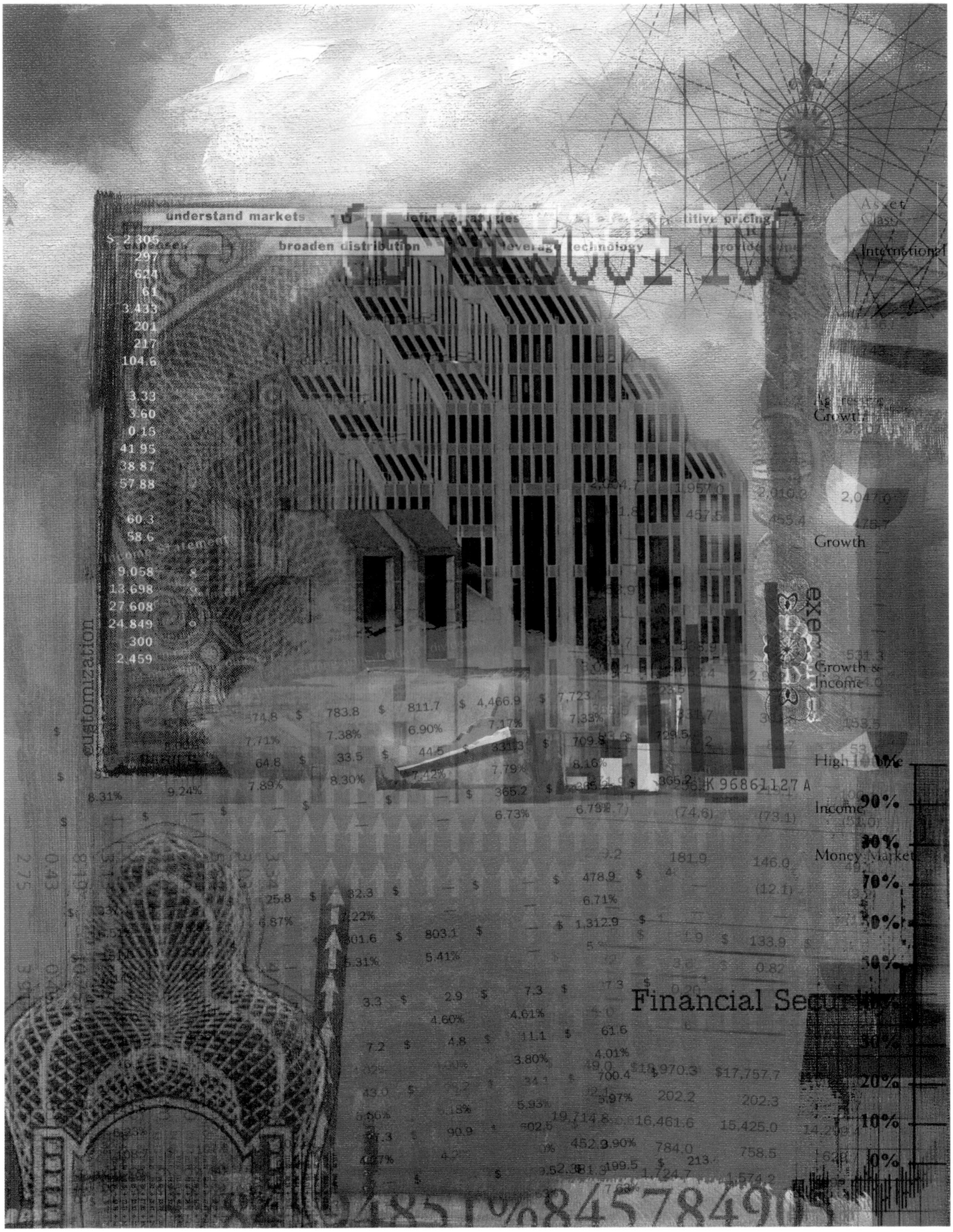

Bonnie Rieser

[206] 633-2334

Adobe American Lung Association Apco
Chicago Mercantile Exchange GenRad
Japan Airlines Simon & Schuster Tektronix

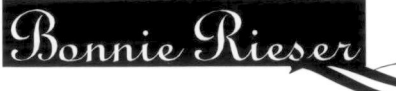

FUTURES

Butter

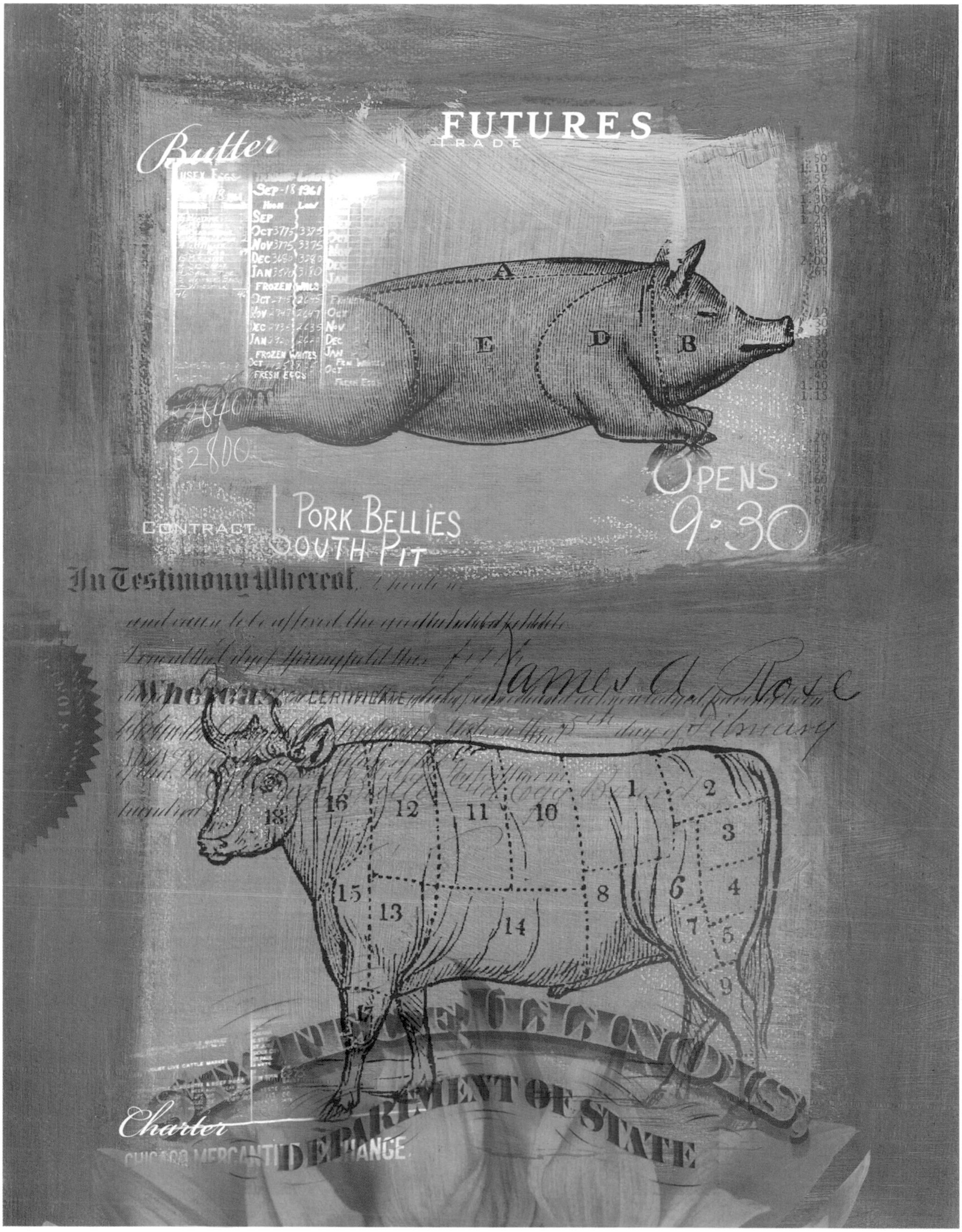

FUTURES

PORK BELLIES
SOUTH PIT

OPENS
9:30

CONTRACT

Charter

CHICAGO MERCANTILE EXCHANGE

Nicholas Wilton

Represented by Jan Collier (415) 383-9026 (415) 383-9037 fax collierreps.com

WILTON

Nicholas Wilton Represented by Jan Collier (415) 383-9026 (415) 383-9037 fax collierreps.com

john jinks

1 888 240 9568

for additional images see Showcase 14-23 or www.jjinks.com

1 888 240 9568

john jinks

John **Rowe Illustration**

Mendola Artists *New York and the east*
212.986.5680 · *f* 212.818.1246

See our portfolio website
www.theispot.com/artist/jrowe
or www.john-rowe.com

"First View of the World," from the children's book, She is Born. 24 x 24, oil.

Artwork delivered as digital file or as transparency. See additional work: Workbook #22, Showcase #21 and #22, Directory of Illustration #16

"Memories of Loved Ones," from the children's book, She is Born. 24 x 24, oil.

John **Rowe Illustration**

Mendola Artists *New York and the east*
212.986.5680 · *f* 212.818.1246

See our portfolio website
www.theispot.com / artist / jrowe
or www.john-rowe.com

indubitably incorrectly

INCORPORATE INSPIRATION

John S. Dykes 203·254·7180 www.theispot.com/artist/dykes

John S. Dykes 203·254·7180   email:jsdart@freewwweb.com

FRANK STURGES *artist representative*

Ph. 740-369-9702

Fax 740-369-0547

www.Sturgesreps.com

franklin
HAMMOND

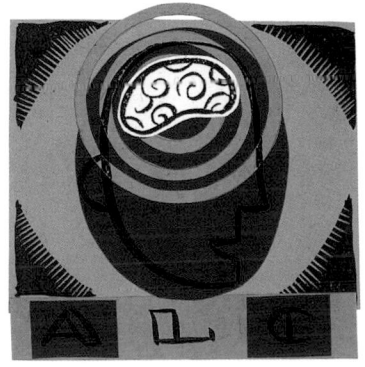

rich **LILLASH**

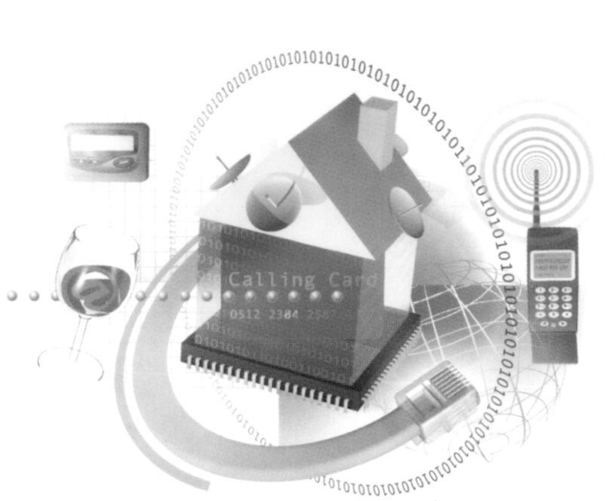

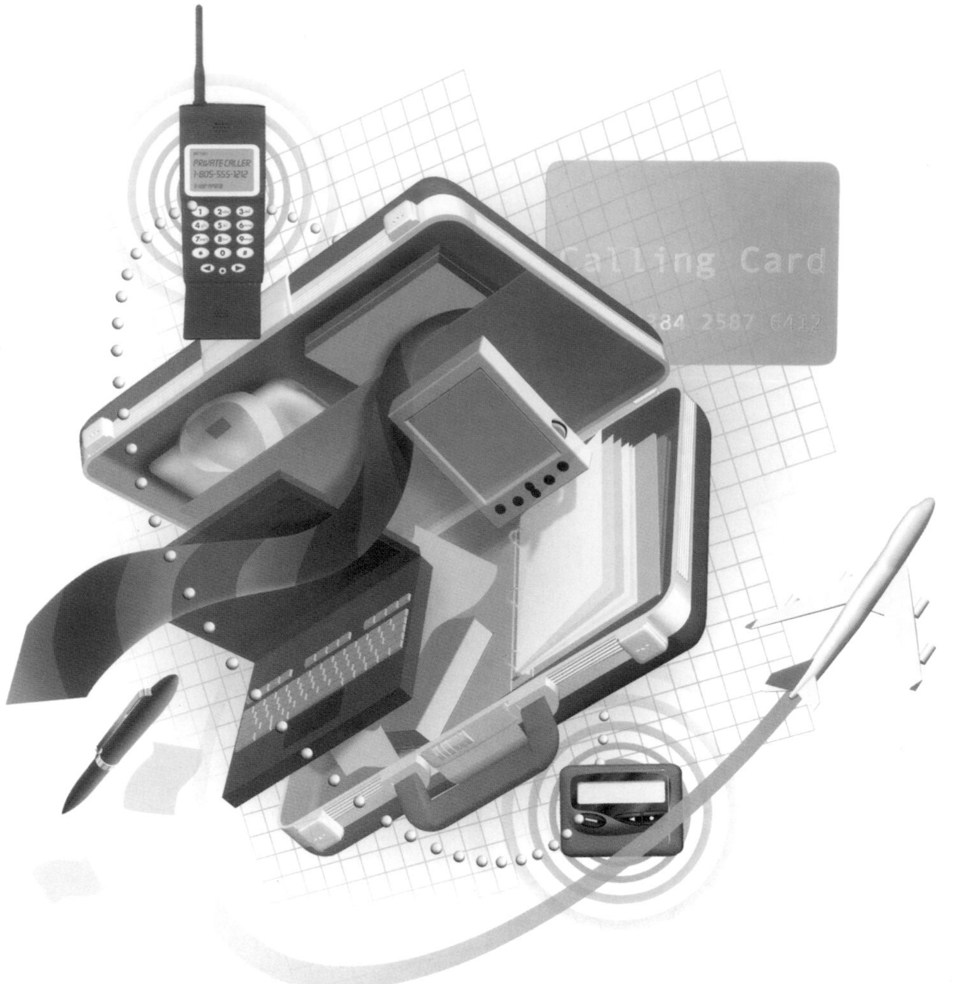

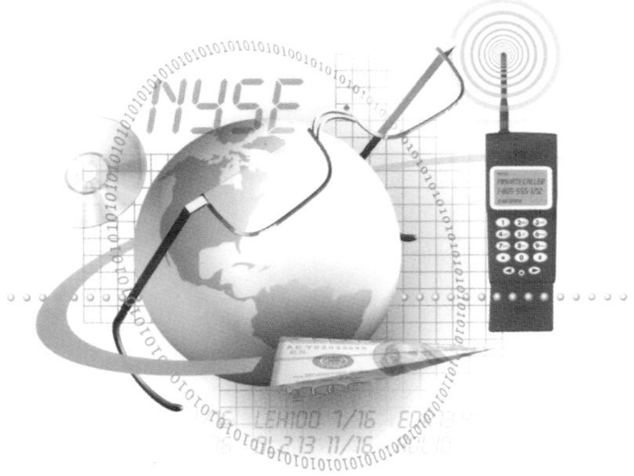

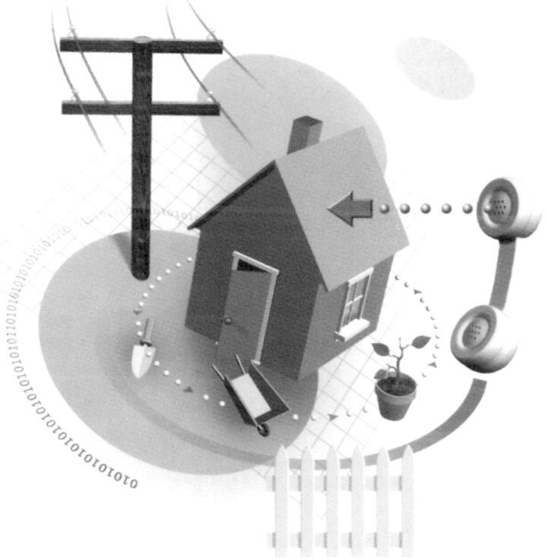

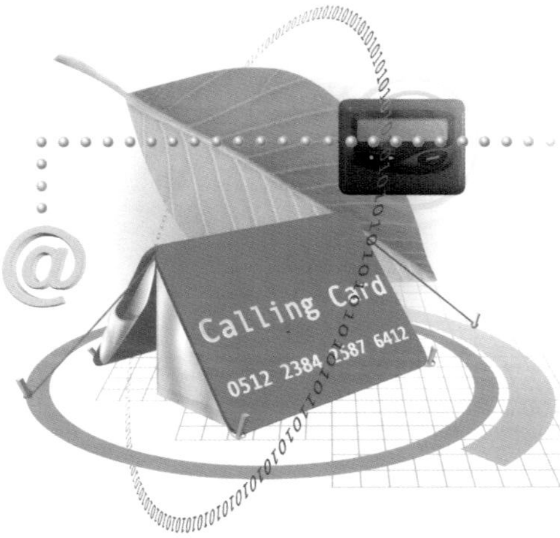

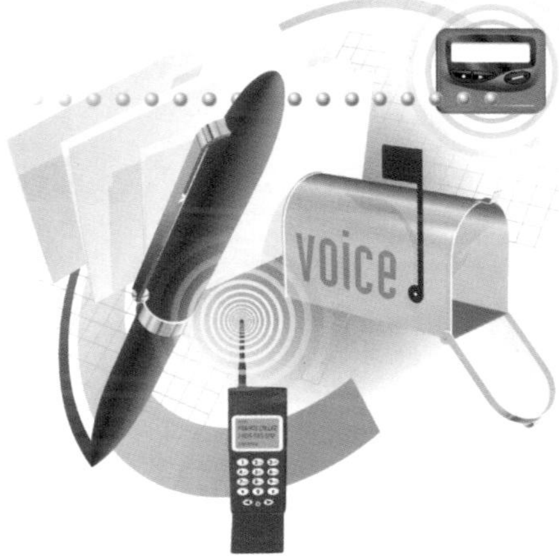

DamanStudio **1.888.213.6852** *website:* **www.DamanStudio.com** *email:* **DamanStudio@mindspring.com**

View more images in these publications: American Showcase 23, and 22, Directory of Illustration 16 and 17.

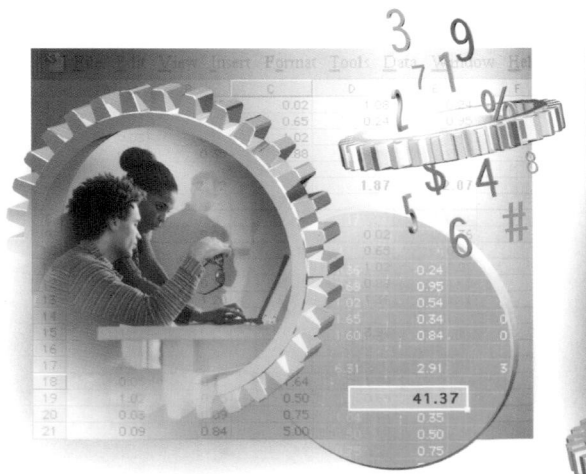

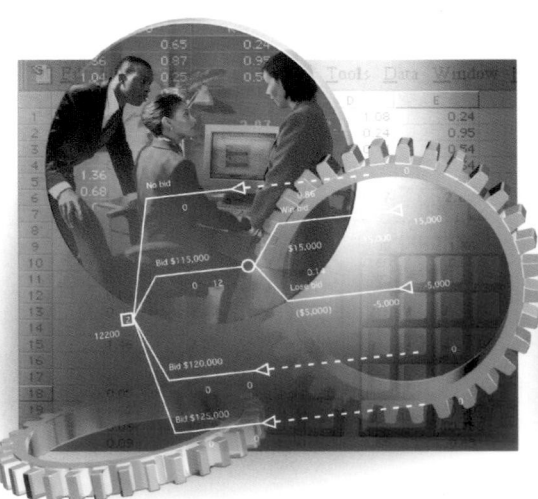

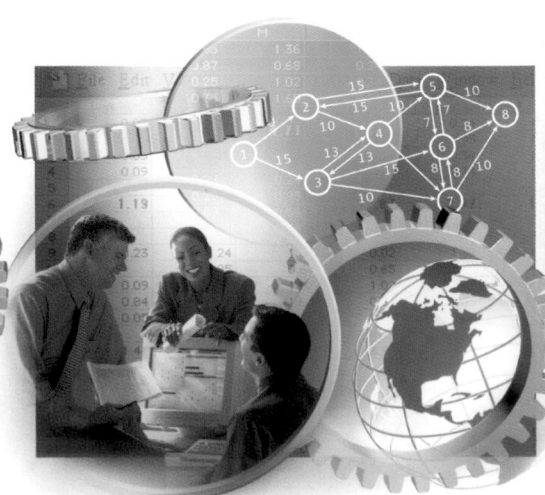

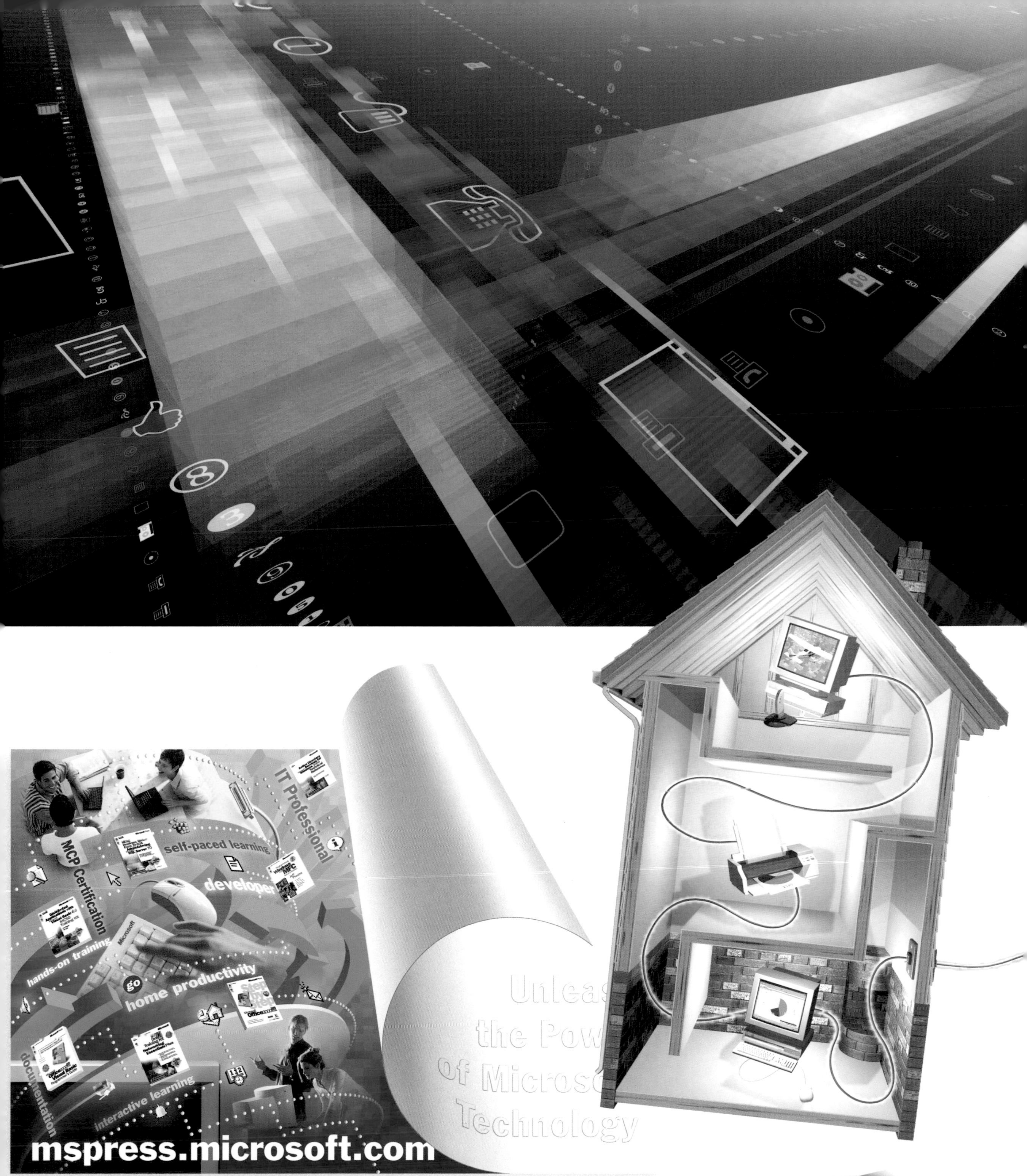

mspress.microsoft.com

Unleash the Power of Microsoft Technology

John Berg

110 Cottage Street • Buffalo, New York 14201 • 716.884.8003 • Fax 716.885.4281

For additional samples see Showcase 14-23, or call. © 2000 John Berg

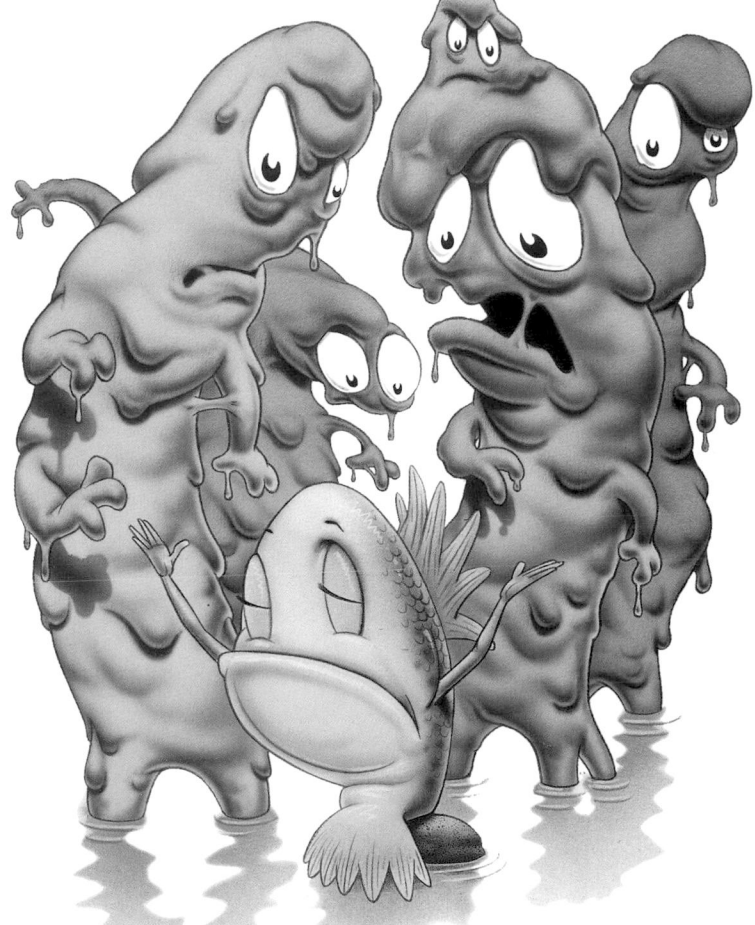

625

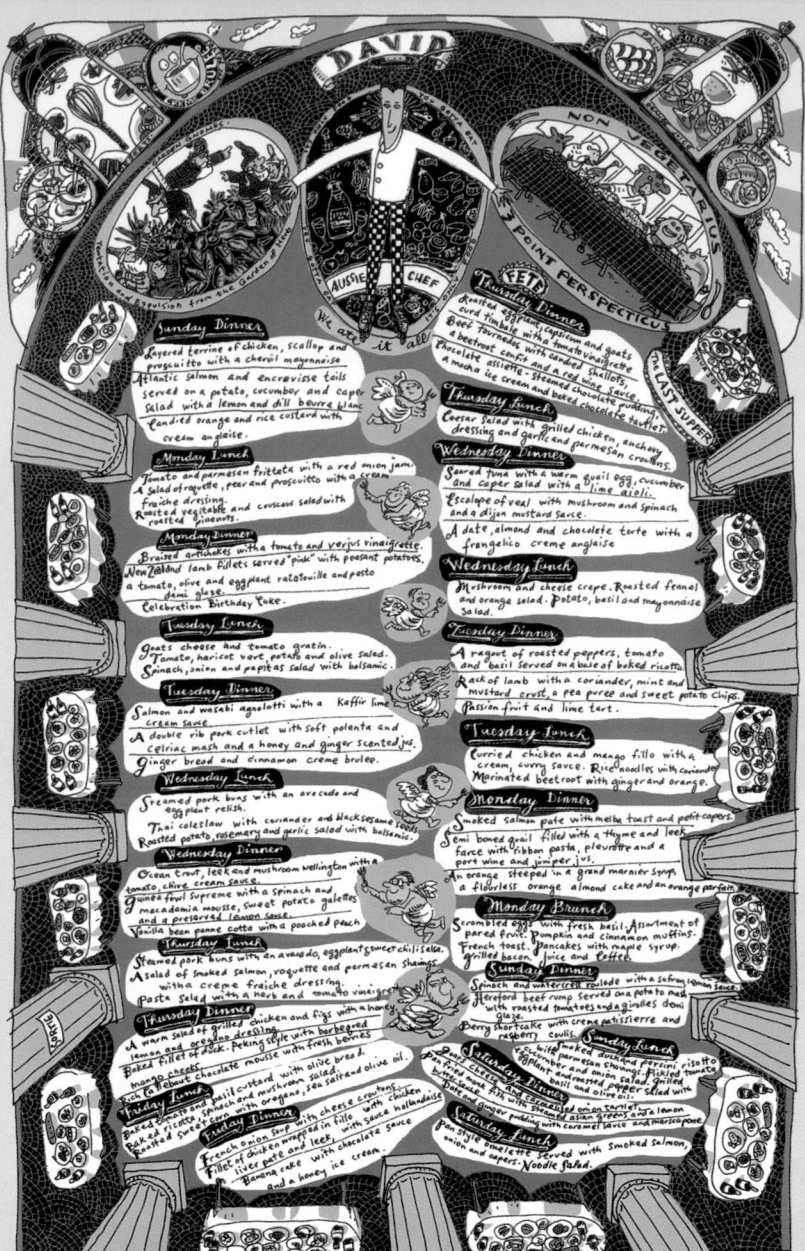

Doors to the Museo Archeologico looking out onto San Marco Square
Venice 10·14·97

ILLUSTRATION BY
MIKE MℭCONNELL

mike@wetinc.com

410-527-0055

www.wetinc.com

titus

CLIENTS INCLUDE:

GRAMMY AWARDS

WALL STREET JOURNAL

CHILDREN'S TELEVISION
WORKSHOP

NETSCAPE

MACROMEDIA

AOL

INTUIT

MCGRAW-HILL

XPLANE
The Visual Thinking Company
Tel 800.750.6467 Fax 314.436.0506
We make things clear and easy to
use by making them more visual.
www.xplane.com

The Fiber Crunch

Long-distance carriers have been adding capacity to their networks by adding new signals on different wavelengths using Dense Wavelength Division Multiplexing technology. Where those heavily packed fiber cables intersect, however, there's a wavelength pileup. According to AT&T's figures, when four fiber routes - one each from the east, west, north and south, and each consisting of four cable sheaths housing a total of 48 fiber-optic cables (packed with 80 wavelengths per cable) come together, that's roughly 15,000 different signals to track, manage and route accurately.

80 wavelengths per cable
N
48
48
15,000+ signals
48
fiber-optic
48

Construction site
Garage

Train tracks

Haynes' parked car

Home of Charles Stroupe, CEO of Wesley-Jessen, maker of blue-tinted contact lenses.

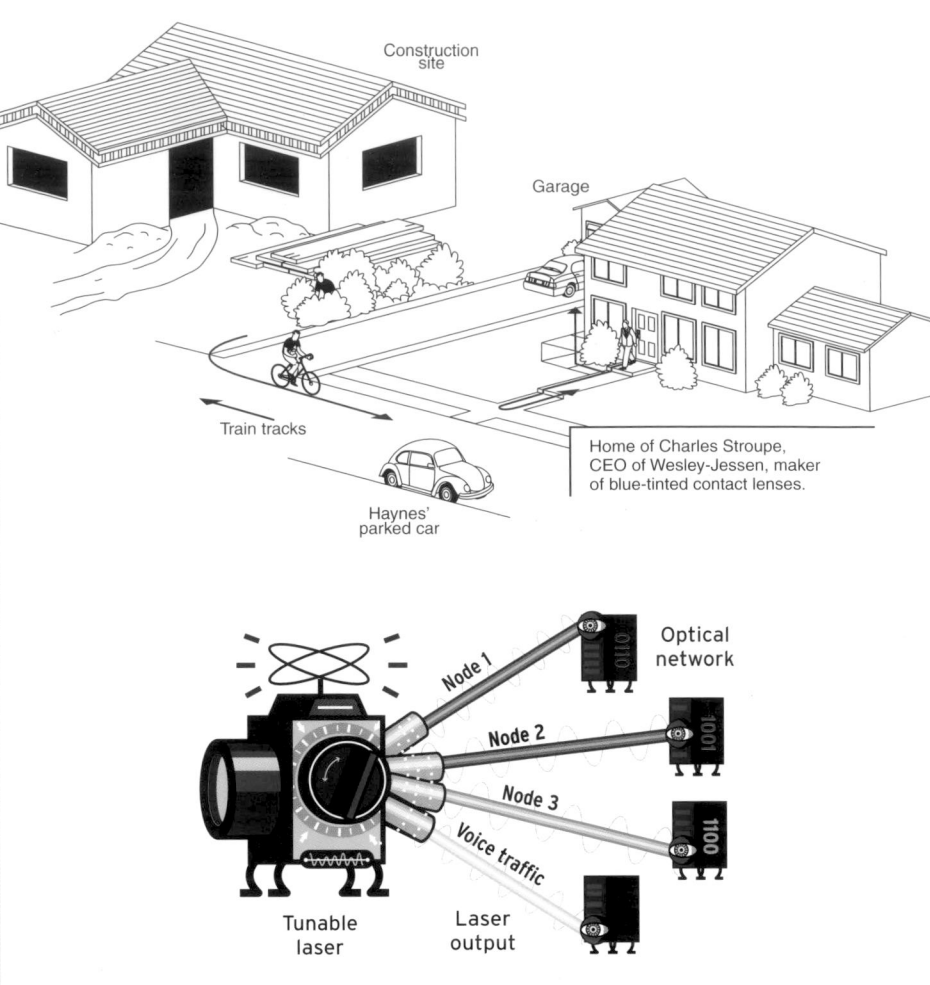

Optical network
Node 1
Node 2
Node 3
Voice traffic
Tunable laser
Laser output

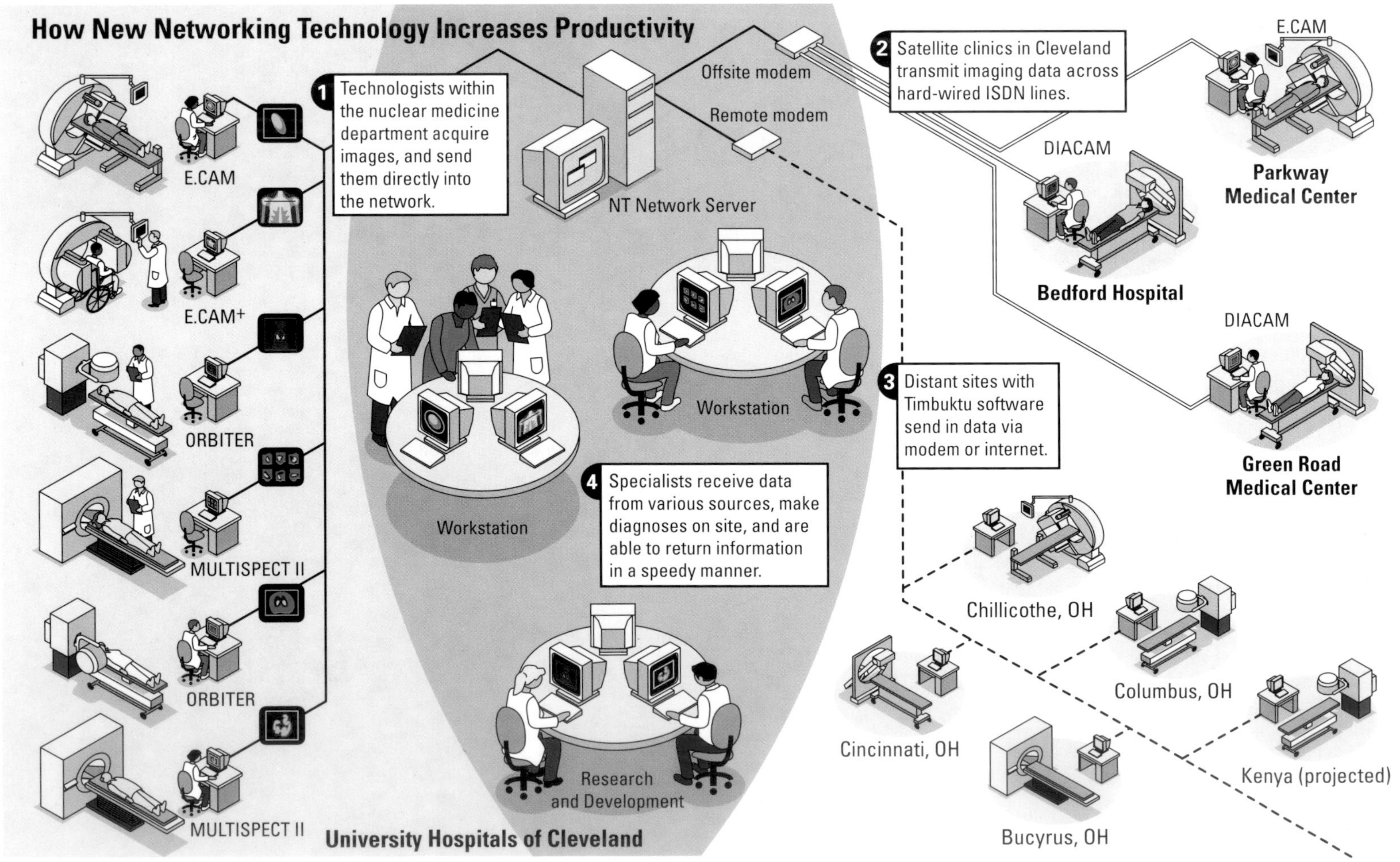

How New Networking Technology Increases Productivity

E.CAM

E.CAM
E.CAM+
ORBITER
MULTISPECT II
ORBITER
MULTISPECT II

1 Technologists within the nuclear medicine department acquire images, and send them directly into the network.

Offsite modem
Remote modem
NT Network Server

2 Satellite clinics in Cleveland transmit imaging data across hard-wired ISDN lines.

E.CAM
DIACAM
Parkway Medical Center
Bedford Hospital

DIACAM
Green Road Medical Center

Workstation
Workstation

3 Distant sites with Timbuktu software send in data via modem or internet.

4 Specialists receive data from various sources, make diagnoses on site, and are able to return information in a speedy manner.

Research and Development
University Hospitals of Cleveland

Chillicothe, OH
Columbus, OH
Cincinnati, OH
Kenya (projected)
Bucyrus, OH

630

XPLANE

The Visual Thinking Company
Tel 800.750.6467 Fax 314.436.0506

We make things clear and easy to
use by making them more visual.

www.xplane.com

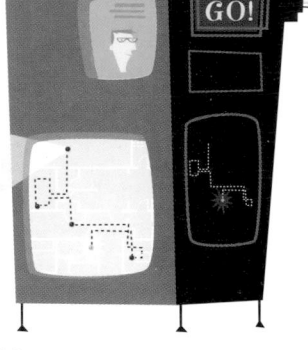

Visitors to your Web site are scored
against your business rules and their
behavior is mapped.

"access"

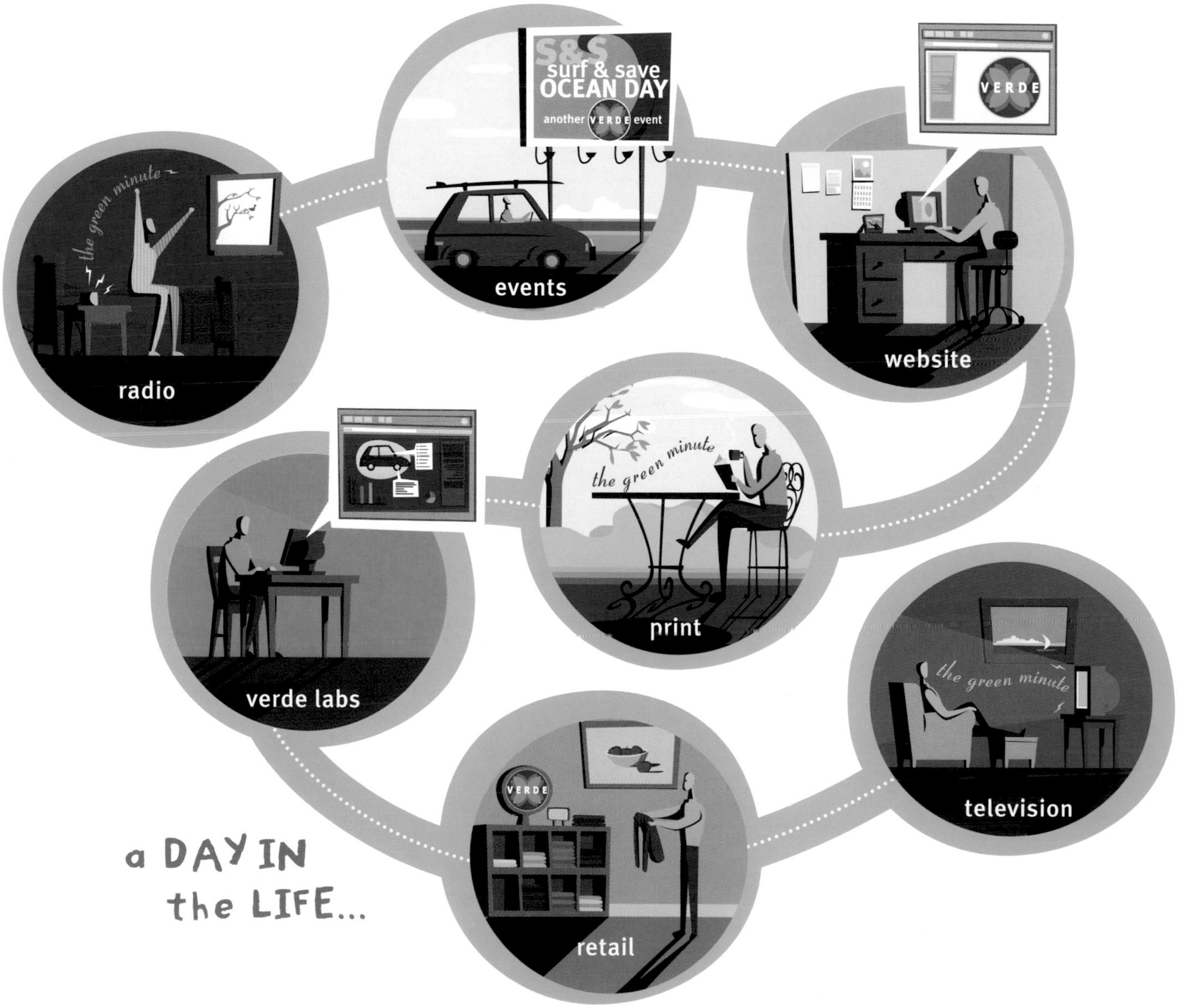

events

website

radio

verde labs

print

television

retail

a DAY IN
the LIFE...

632

Gerber

Café du Port – Paraza, France

Ryerson Tull

LINDA FENNIMORE
ILLUSTRATION
808 WEST END AVE. #801
NEW YORK, NEW YORK 10025
(212) 866-0279

635

Moonlight Press Studio
Chris Spollen
362 Cromwell Ave
Ocean Breeze NY 10305-2304
Phone: 718 979 9695
Fax: 718 979 8919

Web: Spollen.com
E Mail : cspollen@ inch.com
Design Illustration
Three Stock Catalogs: Free
Deluxe Sample Kit on Request

Studio by the Ocean

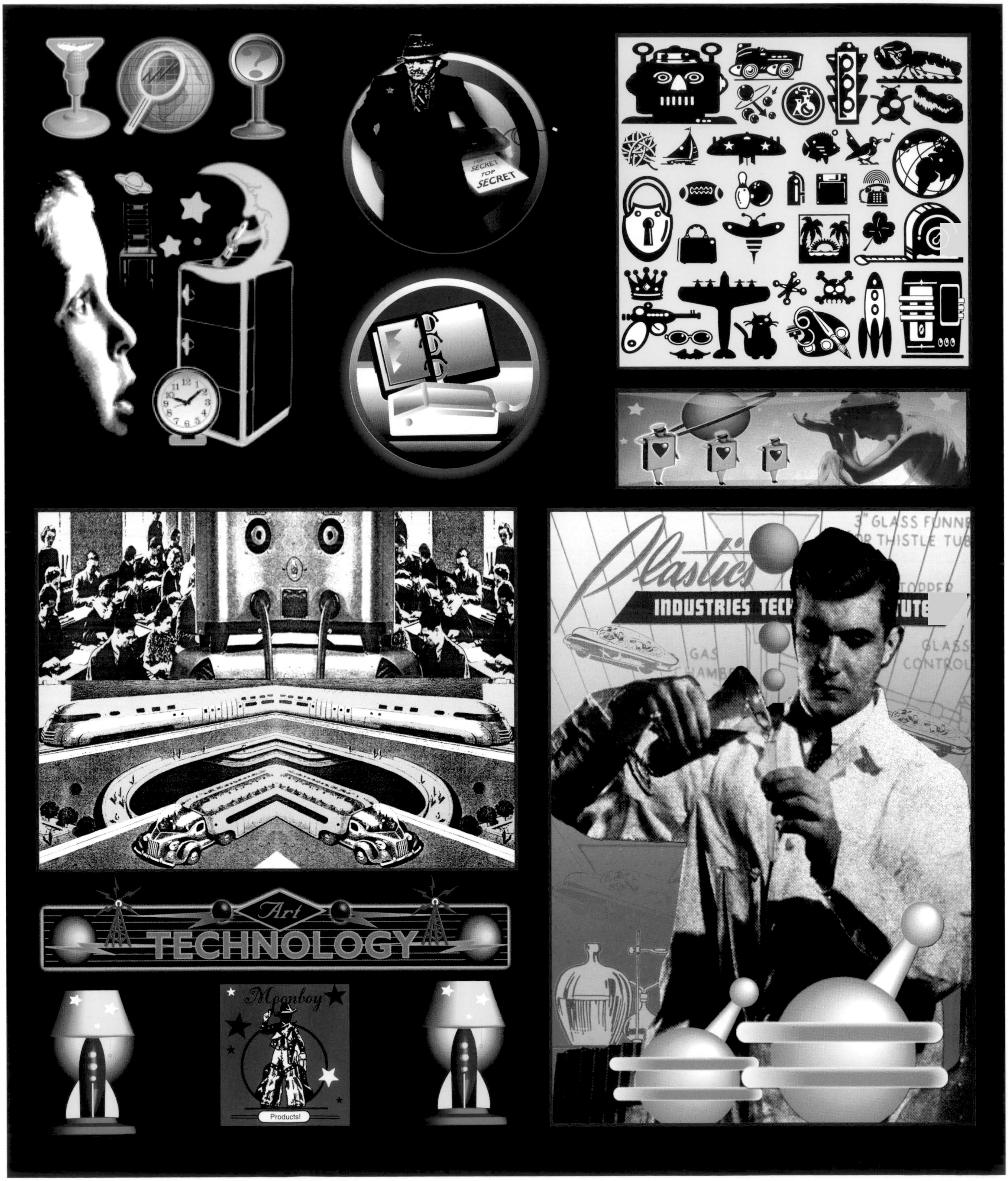

Moonlight Press Studio
Chris Spollen
362 Cromwell Ave
Ocean Breeze NY 10305-2304
Phone: 718 979 9695
Fax: 718 979 8919

Web: Spollen.com
E Mail : cspollen@ inch.com
Design Illustration
Three Stock Catalogs: Free
Deluxe Sample Kit on Request

Studio by the Ocean

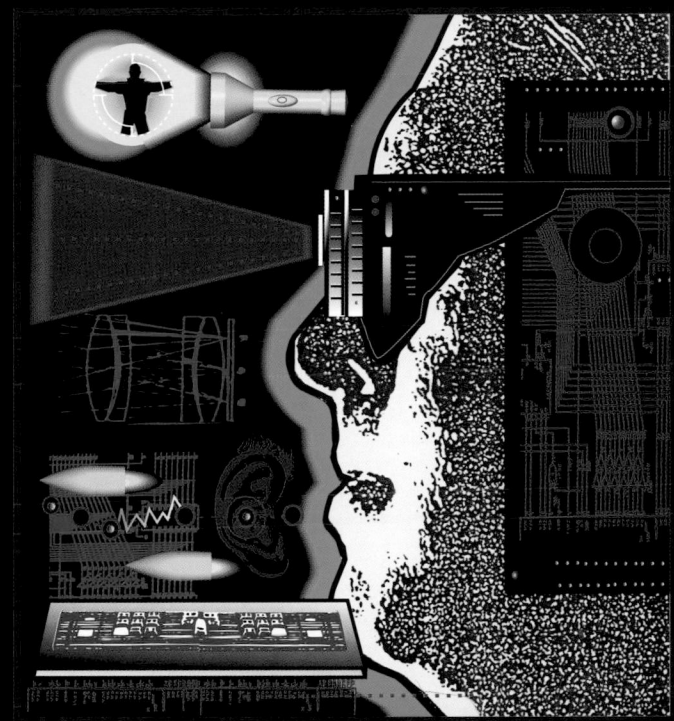

JUN PARK

T: 416-441-9422 • F: 416-441-1328

E: JUNPARK@HOME.COM • WWW.JUNPARK.COM

Cappuccino

T: 416-441-9422 • F: 416-441-1328 • JUN PARK

E: JUNPARK@HOME.COM • WWW.JUNPARK.COM

PASCAL MILELLI

Client British Columbia Securities Commission • Annual Report

609-402 WEST PENDER STREET
VANCOUVER BC CANADA V6B 1T6
TEL:604.608.2708 FAX:604.682.6086
EMAIL: PASCAL@PASCALMILELLI.COM

PASCAL MILELLI

Client Raincoast Books · Spread from **Rainbow Bay**

Gemini appeared on the cover of Communication Arts Illustration Annual 1994

Client Kneipp Netherlands · Tea package

609-402 WEST PENDER STREET
VANCOUVER BC CANADA V6B 1T6
TEL:604.608.2708 FAX:604.682.6086
EMAIL: PASCAL@PASCALMILELLI.COM

LAKE MERRITT

SPRINTS

Alan Claude

ALAN CLAUDE   DIGITAL ILLUSTRATIONS   415.371.0067

ispot website: http://www.theispot.com/artist/aclaude

email: ac@acesdesign.com

visit the studio at: **www.acesdesign.com**

A C E S
DESIGN

Michelle
Angers

2453 OLIVE RD, WINDSOR ONTARIO CANADA N8T 3N4
TEL: (519) 948-7853 • FAX: (519) 948-2418 • EMAIL: mangers@mnsi.net • WEB: www.michelleangers.com

MARC GABBANA

2453 OLIVE RD. WINDSOR ONTARIO CANADA N8T 3N4 PHONE / FAX (519) 948-2418 EMAIL: mgabbana@mnsi.net WEB: www.marcgabbana.com

Group Five Creative

4600 S. Syracuse
Ninth Floor
Denver, CO 80237

303-256-6335 office
303-932-8759 studio

Mark Bremmer

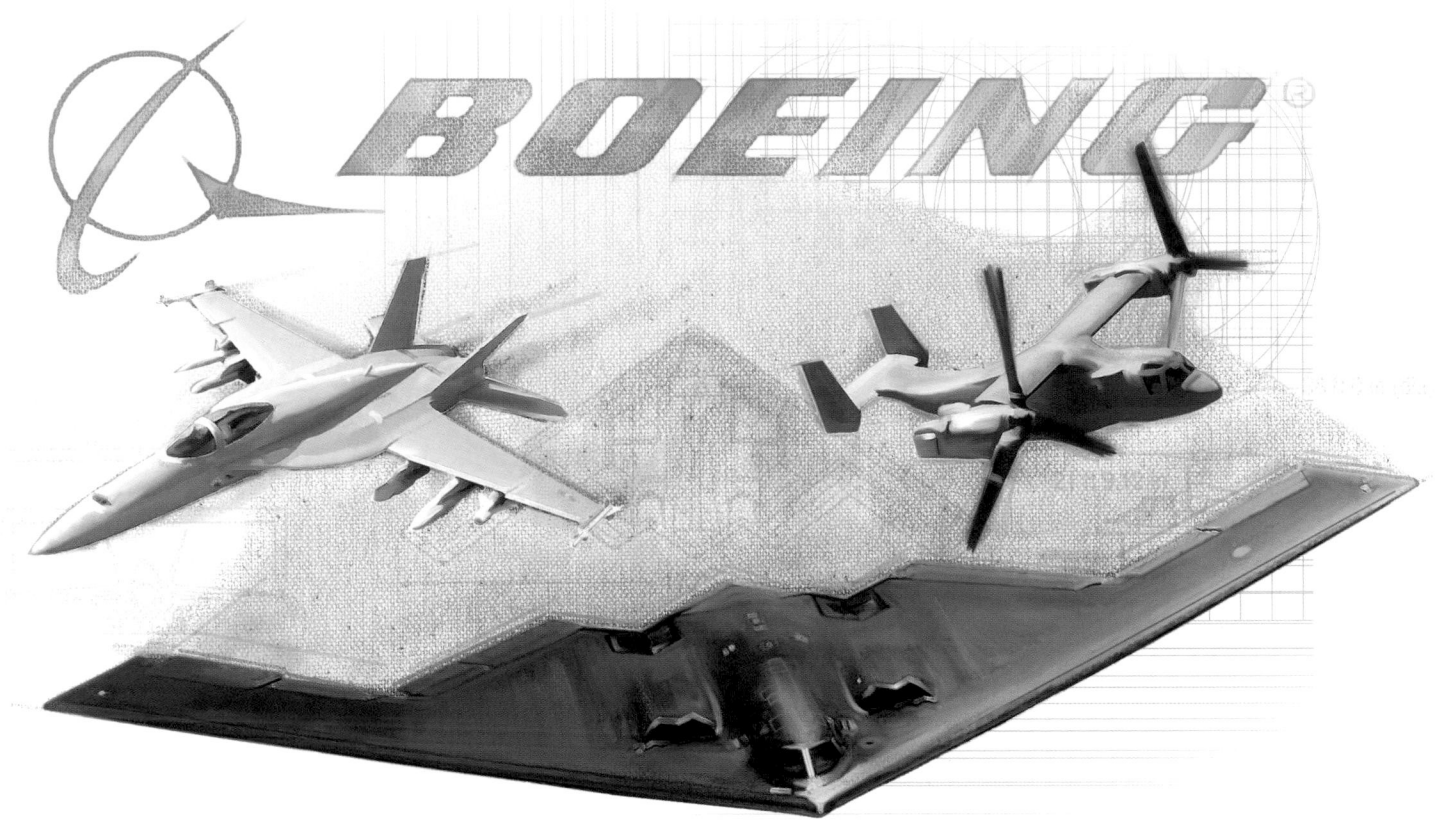

Summit International

Group Five Creative

4600 S. Syracuse
Ninth Floor
Denver, CO 80237

303-256-6335 office
303-979-9527 studio

Michael Hite

GROUP FIVE
Creative

Delta Airlines

TSI Software International

Information Handling Services, Inc.

Sirius Computer Solutions, Inc.

HEALTHeCAREERS.COM

michael sloan | 212.253.2047

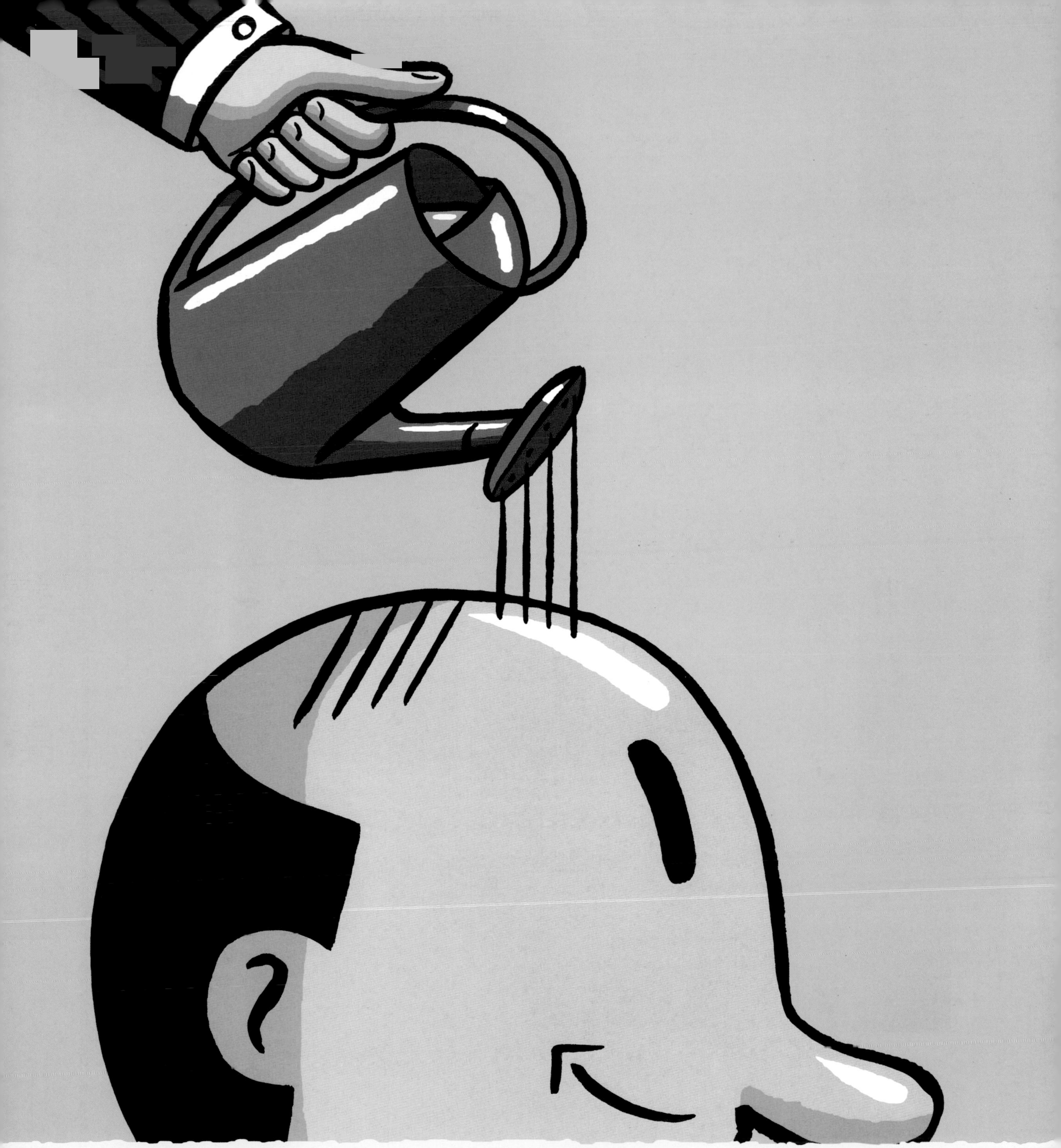

michael sloan   212.253.2047   SLOAN

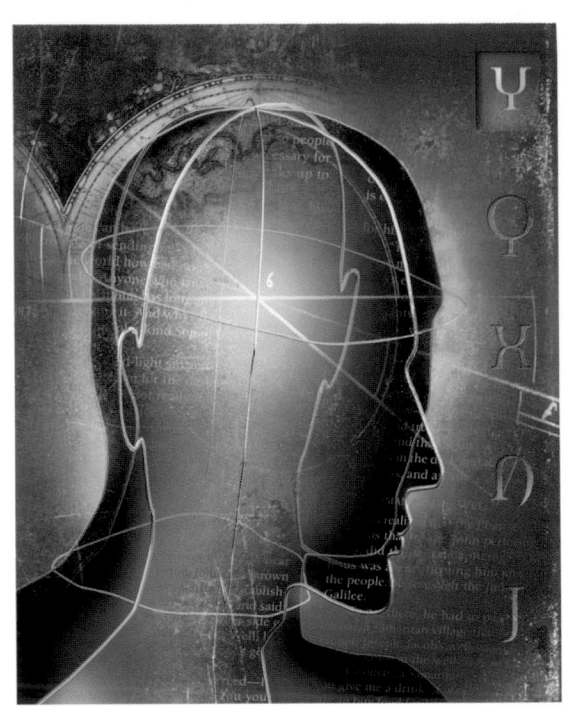

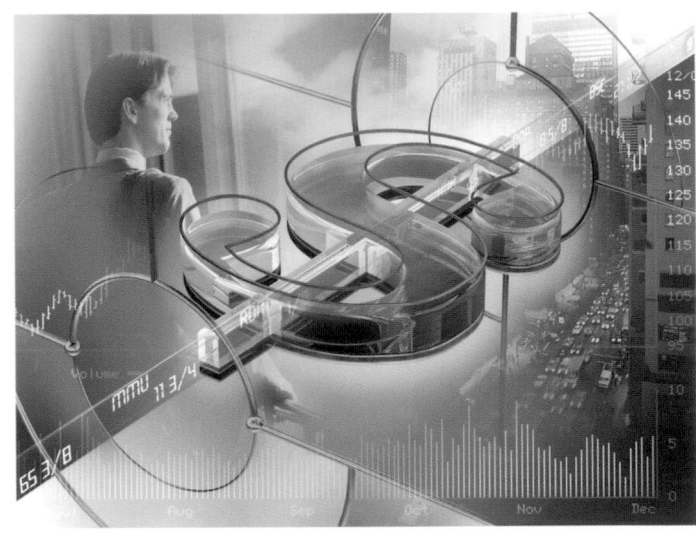

henk **DAWSON**
425·882·3303
d 3 d . c o m

henk

DAWSON

4 2 5 · 8 8 2 · 3 3 0 3

d 3 d . c o m

Fred Rix Illustration

212-674-4842

www.fredrix.com

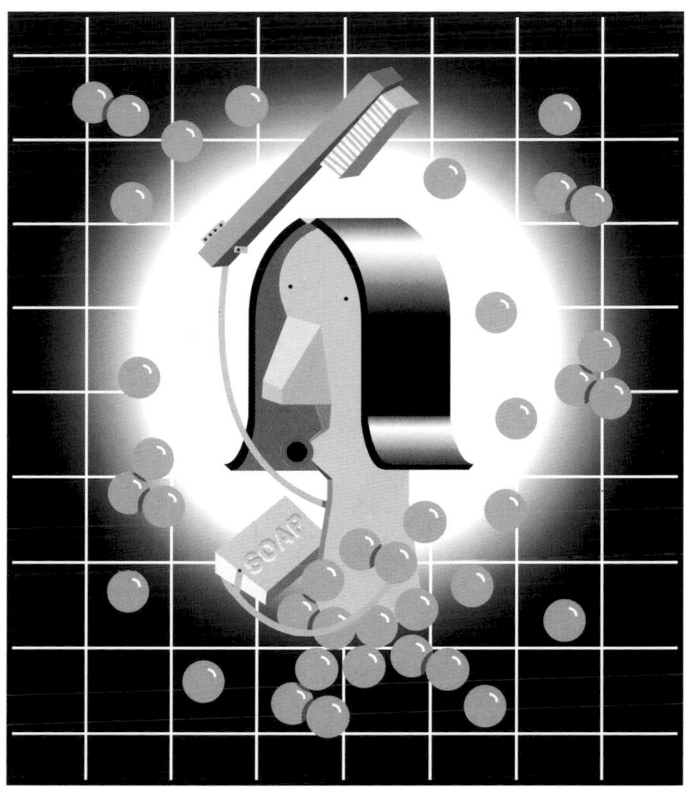

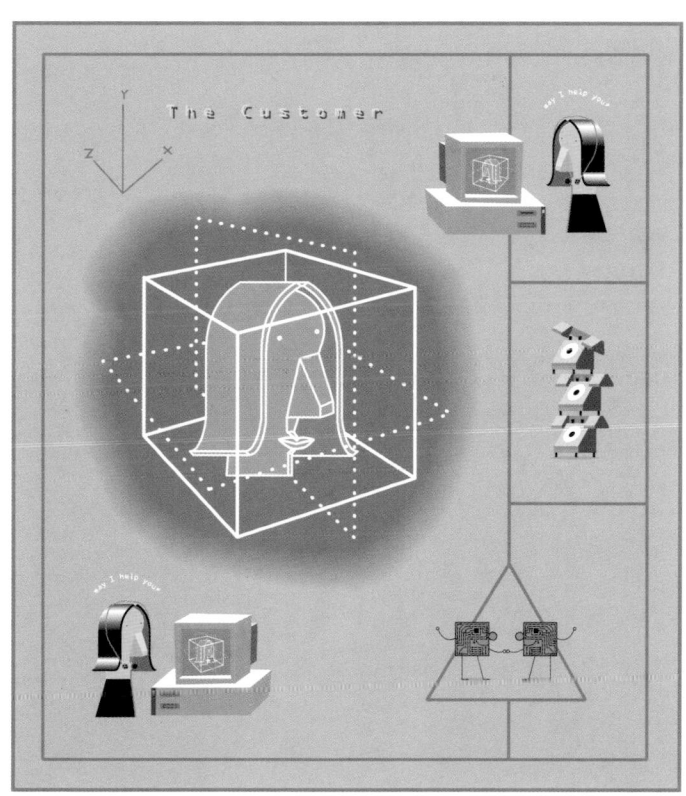

Award winning digital illustration by Dave Cutler • T203 938 7067 • F203 938 7077 • dcutler@optonline.net • See more in the SOI Annuals, Directory of Illustration, Blackbook and Workbook • Online portfolio available at www.theispot.com/artist/cutler • Stock images available • Member, SOI

Award winning digital illustration by Dave Cutler • T203 938 7067 • F203 938 7077 • dcutler@optonline.net • See more in the SOI Annuals, Directory of Illustration, Blackbook and Workbook • Online portfolio available at www.theispot.com/artist/cutler • Stock images available • Member, SOI

DAN

GARROW

Tel: 302-651-0179

2013 West 17th
Street
Wilmington ,
Delaware 19806

DAN GARROW

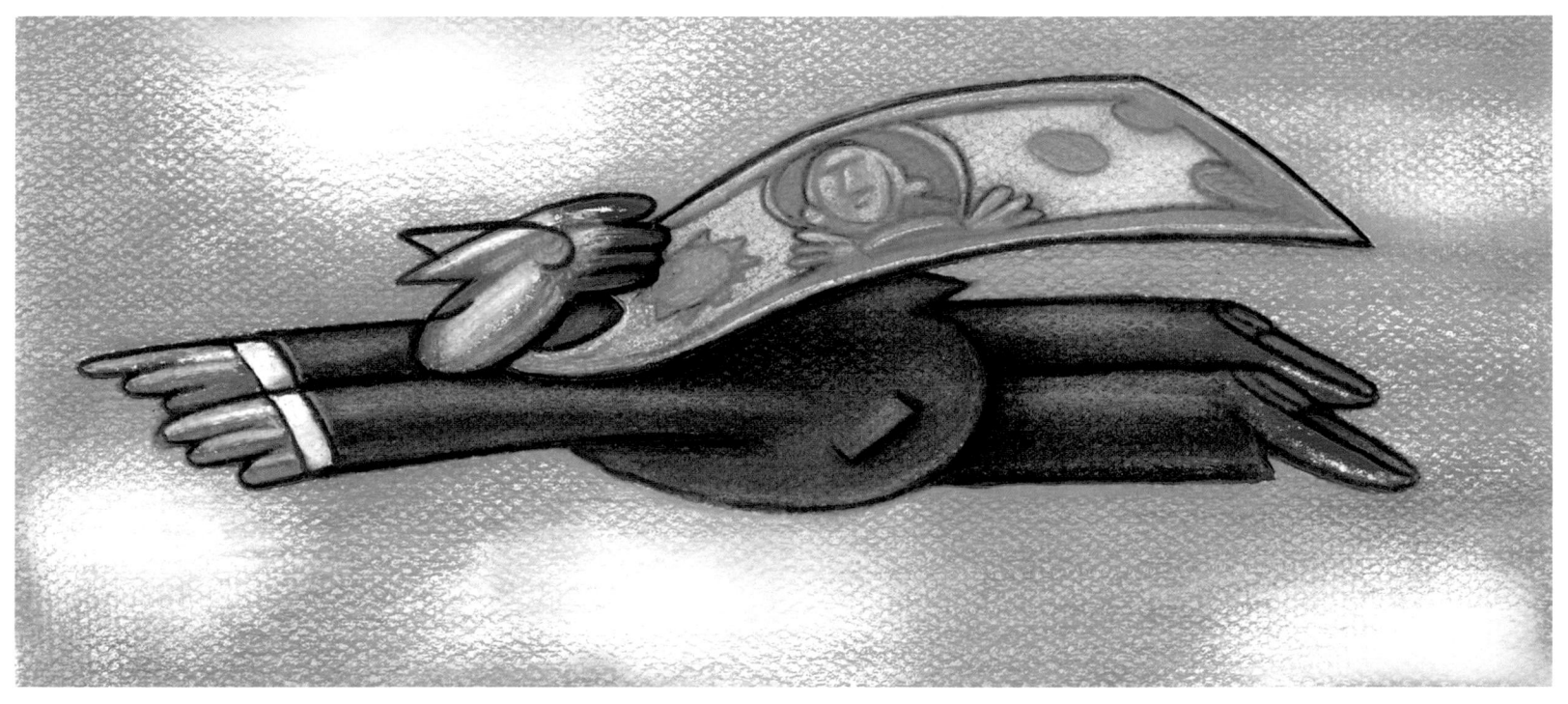

Tel: 302-651-0179   2013 West 17th Street   Wilmington, Delaware 19806

MICHAEL "THE CANNIBAL" TYSON
for Mad Magazine
A.D.: Sam Viviano

SANDRA BERNHARDT

'ZOWIE' HOWIE STERN FOR MAD MAGAZINE

1561 NARVA RD. MISSISSAUGA **SAM SISCO** ONTARIO L5H 3H4 905-278-2716 (PH & FAX)
samsisco@home.com

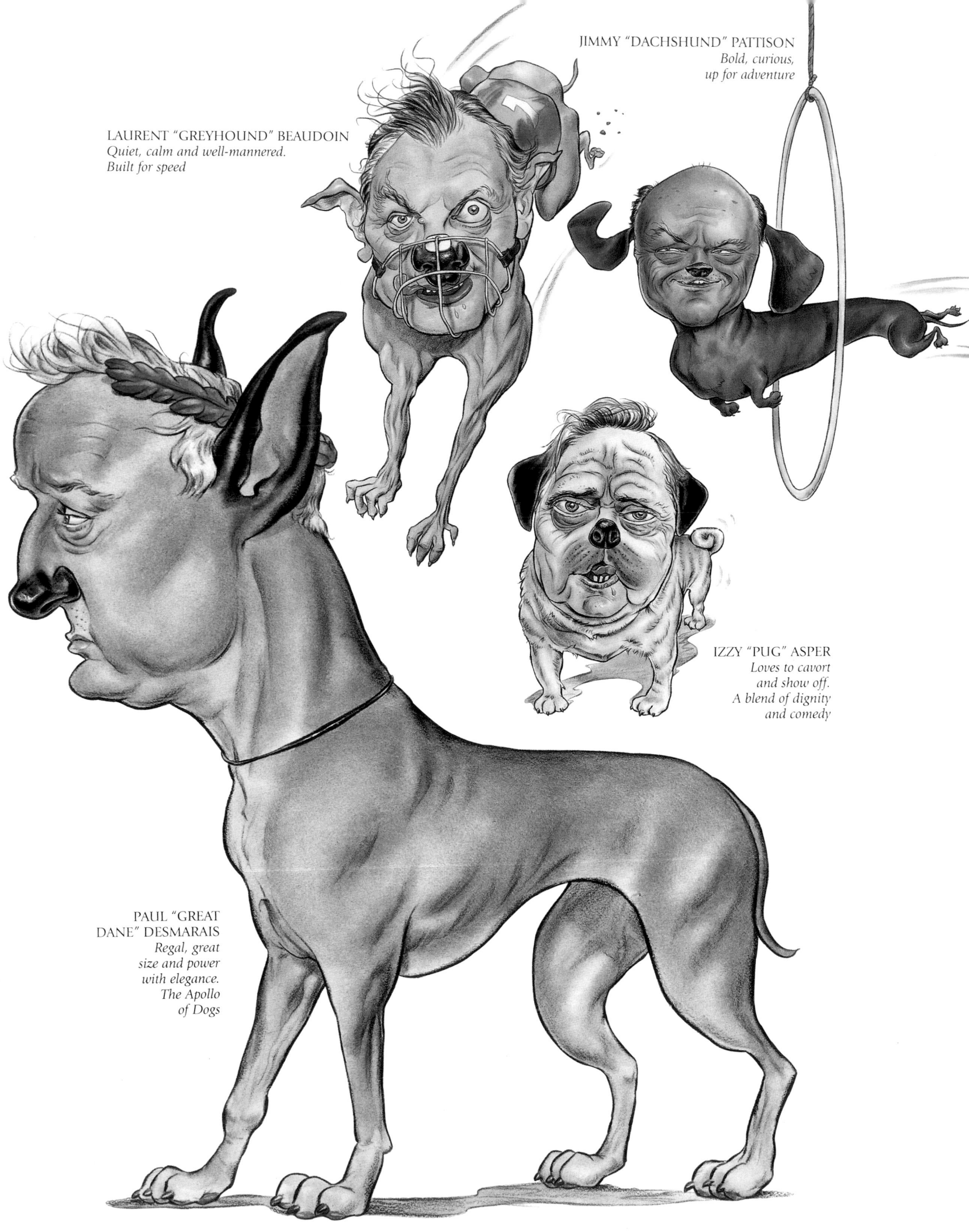

LAURENT "GREYHOUND" BEAUDOIN
Quiet, calm and well-mannered.
Built for speed

JIMMY "DACHSHUND" PATTISON
Bold, curious,
up for adventure

IZZY "PUG" ASPER
Loves to cavort
and show off.
A blend of dignity
and comedy

PAUL "GREAT
DANE" DESMARAIS
Regal, great
size and power
with elegance.
The Apollo
of Dogs

1561 NARVA RD. MISSISSAUGA **SAM SISCO** ONTARIO L5H 3H4 905-278-2716 (PH & FAX)
samsisco@home.com

we are   f   l   a   s

VROOM
to move

we are   m   o   t   i   o

we are   e   f   f   e   c   t

we are   s   h   o   c   k   e

CATERPILLAR

we are   www.flashimation.co

but we are still   Daniels and Daniels

tel. 805 498 1923

fax 805 499 8344

www.beaudaniels.com

e-mail daniels@beaudaniels.com

DANIELS ≠ DANIELS

14 South Madrid Ave, Newbury Park, Ca. 91320
Tel. 805 498-1923 Fax. 805 499-8344 E-mail ariaart@aol.com
Web sites   www.beaudaniels.com   www.flashimation.com

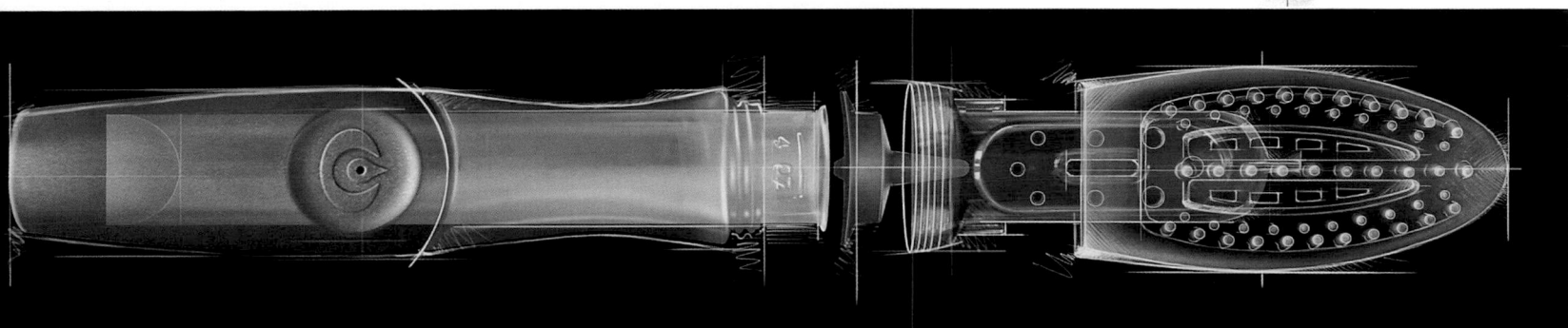

TSUKUSHI

LOTT
REPRESENTATIVES

60 E. 42 ST. #1146 • N.Y., N.Y. 10165 • (212) 953-7088

TSUKUSHI

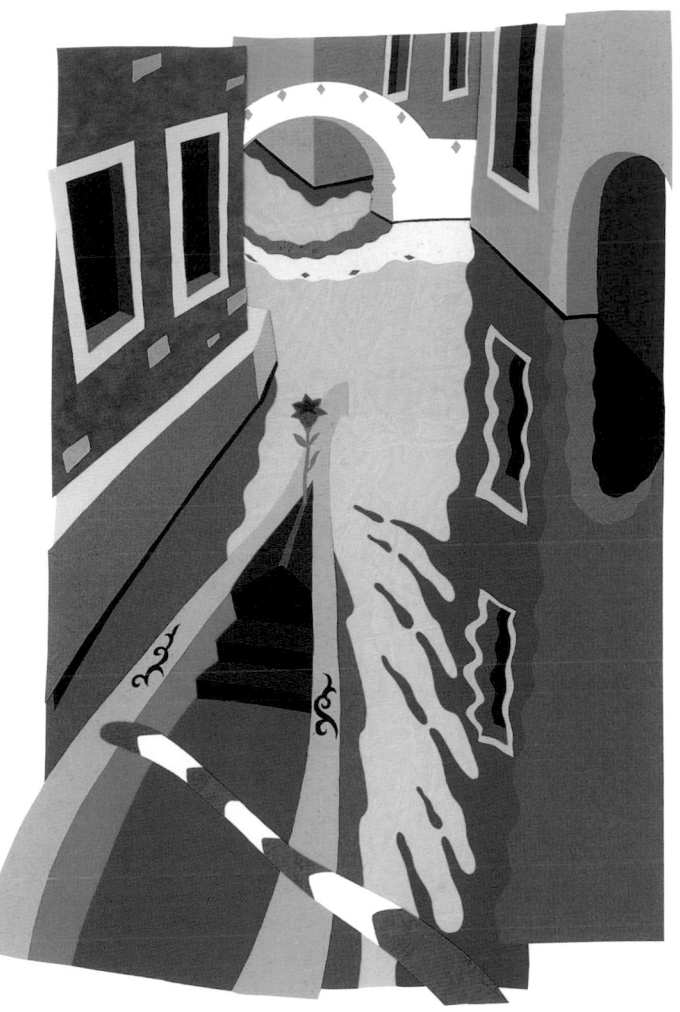

LOTT
REPRESENTATIVES

60 E. 42 ST. #1146 • N.Y., N.Y. 10165 • (212) 953-7088

www.cocotos.com

tom nick cocotos

www.cocotos.com

tom nick cocotos

212.620.7556

e:tom@cocotos.com

665

RICHARD
ELY

212 874 4816

CHRIS McALLISTER ILLUSTRATION
218 · 828 · 8786

CHRIS McALLISTER ILLUSTRATION

218·828·8786

 718 783 1488 **MARK TODD** mtodd.net

ESTHER PEARL WATSON

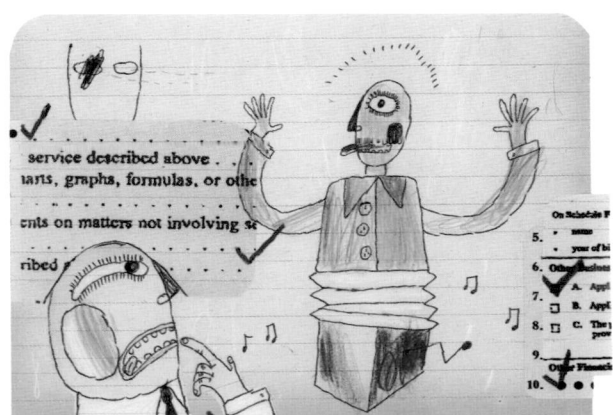

123 PROSPECT PL. #1 BROOKLYN, NY 11217 (718) 783-1488 FAX 9590   ESTHERWATSON.COM

STEVEN NOBLE

St. George slaying the dragon

Ortho Vitros

STUDIO: 415.897.6961 / FAX: 415.892.4449

ADDITIONAL SAMPLES CAN BE VIEWED @ WORKBOOK VOL. 19-23 & BLACKBOOK '99-2001 WWW.BLACKBOOK.COM

SPICE WORLD

QUALITY SINCE 1949

Spiceworld

FIAN ARROYO

ILLUSTRATION

T:305.866.6370

F:305.866.1192

E:fianarroyo@aol.com

W:www.fian.com

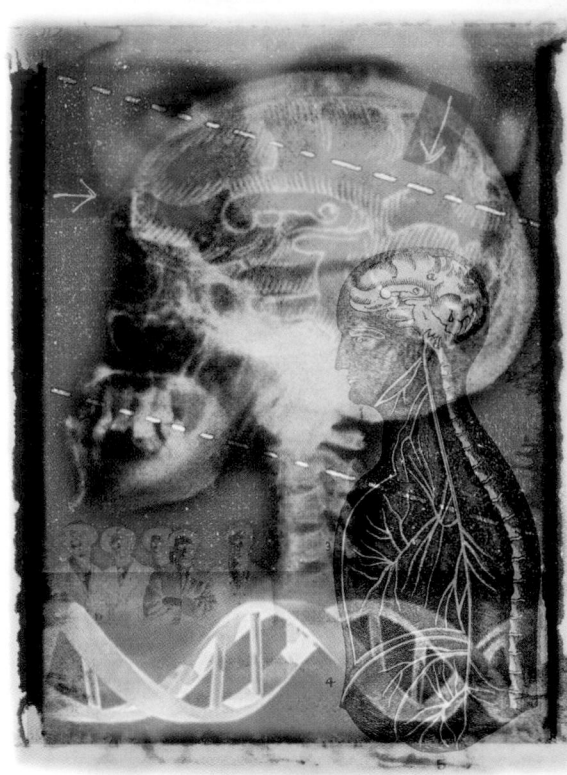
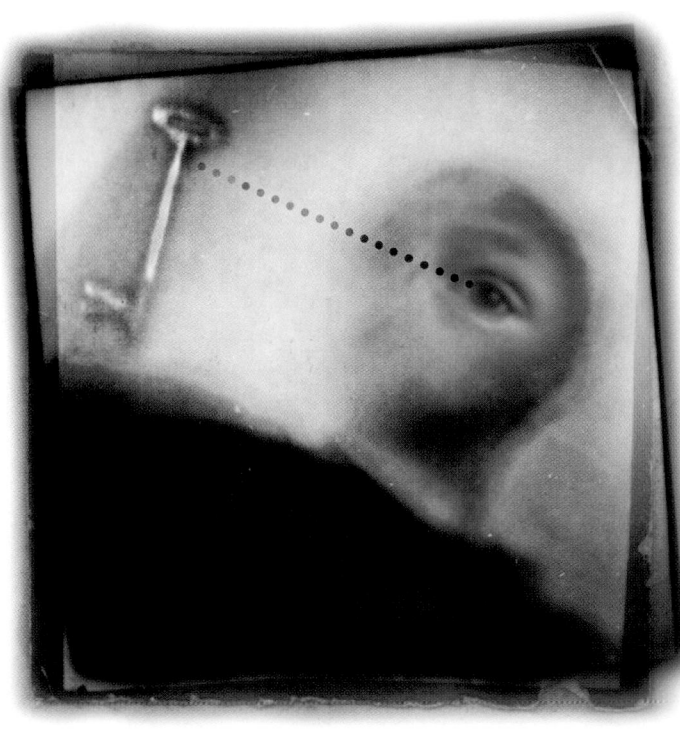

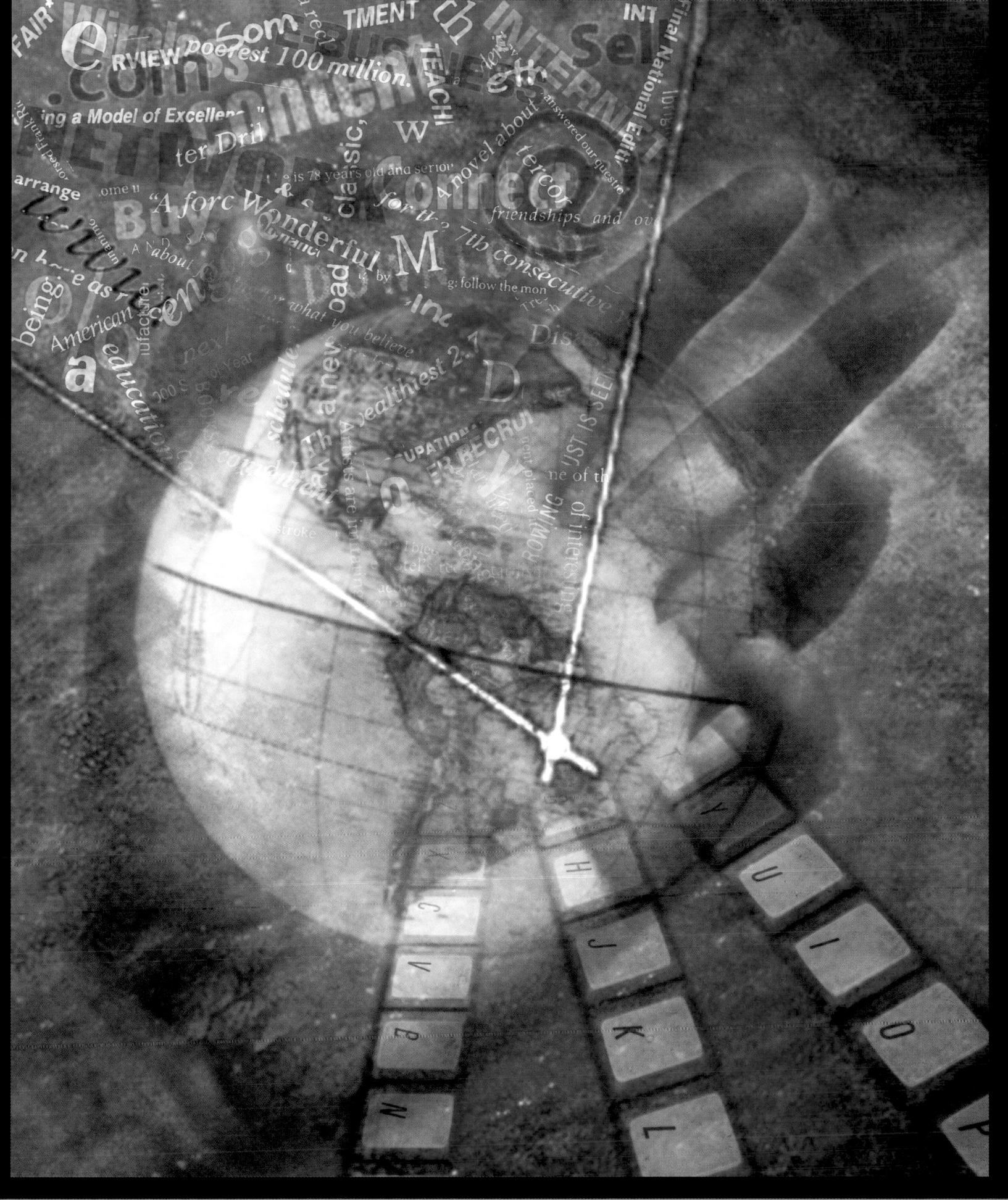

Represented in Europe by
ART CONNECTION
TEL: +31(0)20-6449011
FAX: +31(0)20-6758839
E-MAIL: twac@artconnection.nl
www.artconnection.nl

1) Self Promotion
2) Graco
3) Unisys

Jan-willem Boer
the new Dutch Master

Represented by
Nancy Bacher
Phone/Fax: 763-786-1200
E-mail: nbacher@visi.com
Homepage:nancybacher.com

For additional work see Showcase #23, pages 882 & 883

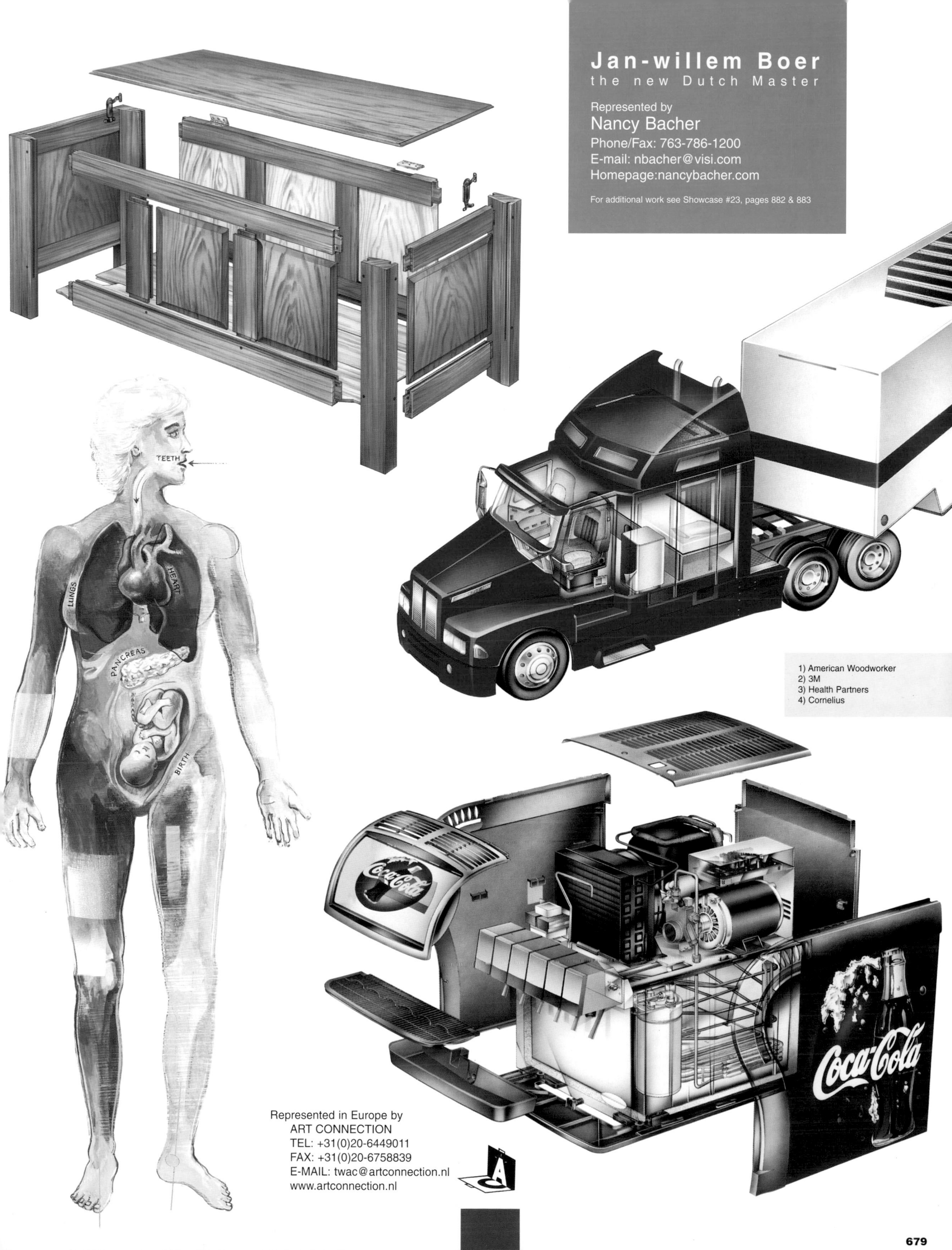

Jan-willem Boer
the new Dutch Master

Represented by
Nancy Bacher
Phone/Fax: 763-786-1200
E-mail: nbacher@visi.com
Homepage:nancybacher.com

For additional work see Showcase #23, pages 882 & 883

1) American Woodworker
2) 3M
3) Health Partners
4) Cornelius

Represented in Europe by
ART CONNECTION
TEL: +31(0)20-6449011
FAX: +31(0)20-6758839
E-MAIL: twac@artconnection.nl
www.artconnection.nl

visit Lynn's Flash site www.FellmanStudio.com to see animation, interface design and illustration for the web

PLAY PAUSE SO...

ON

© 2001 Fellman Stud...

THE AMAZING SOYBEAN

Make Your Selection on the Touch Plate

Welcome Center

Cyber Study Hall

Library

Interactive Lecture Hall

Fellman Studio Inc.
IMAGES for PRINT and SCREEN

www.FellmanStudio.com
Lynn@FellmanStudio.com
tele 952.975.0296
fax 952.975.0297

Director animation
for an educational kiosk

Flash animation for a
chip manufacturer's web site

Graphics for Cigna's
Cyber Academy web site

© 2001 Fellman Studio Inc.

Illustration for a
financial print brochure

Illustration for a magazine
article about land developers

Illustration for a book
about dreaming

Fellman Studio Inc.
IMAGES for PRINT and SCREEN

www.FellmanStudio.com
Lynn@FellmanStudio.com
tele 952.975.0296
fax 952.975.0297

Viv Eisner
157 Joseph Ct.
Warwick RI 02886

401-884-3424   Vivincorporated@earthlink.net

Viv Eisner
157 Joseph Ct.
Warwick RI 02886

401-884-3424

Vivincorporated @ earthlink.net

© Viv 2000

RACOON ILLUSTRATION, INC.
Ismael Roldan

1 Beechwood Road
Bedford Hills, NY 10507

Tel: Toll Free 1-877-RACOON1

E-mail: roldancari@aol.com

RACOON ILLUSTRATION, INC.
Wilma Sanchez

1 Beechwood Road
Bedford Hills, NY 10507

Tel: Toll Free 1-877-RACOON1

E-mail: sanchezwj@aol.com

WILMA SANCHEZ

ADVERTISING Joe Rocco EDITORIAL

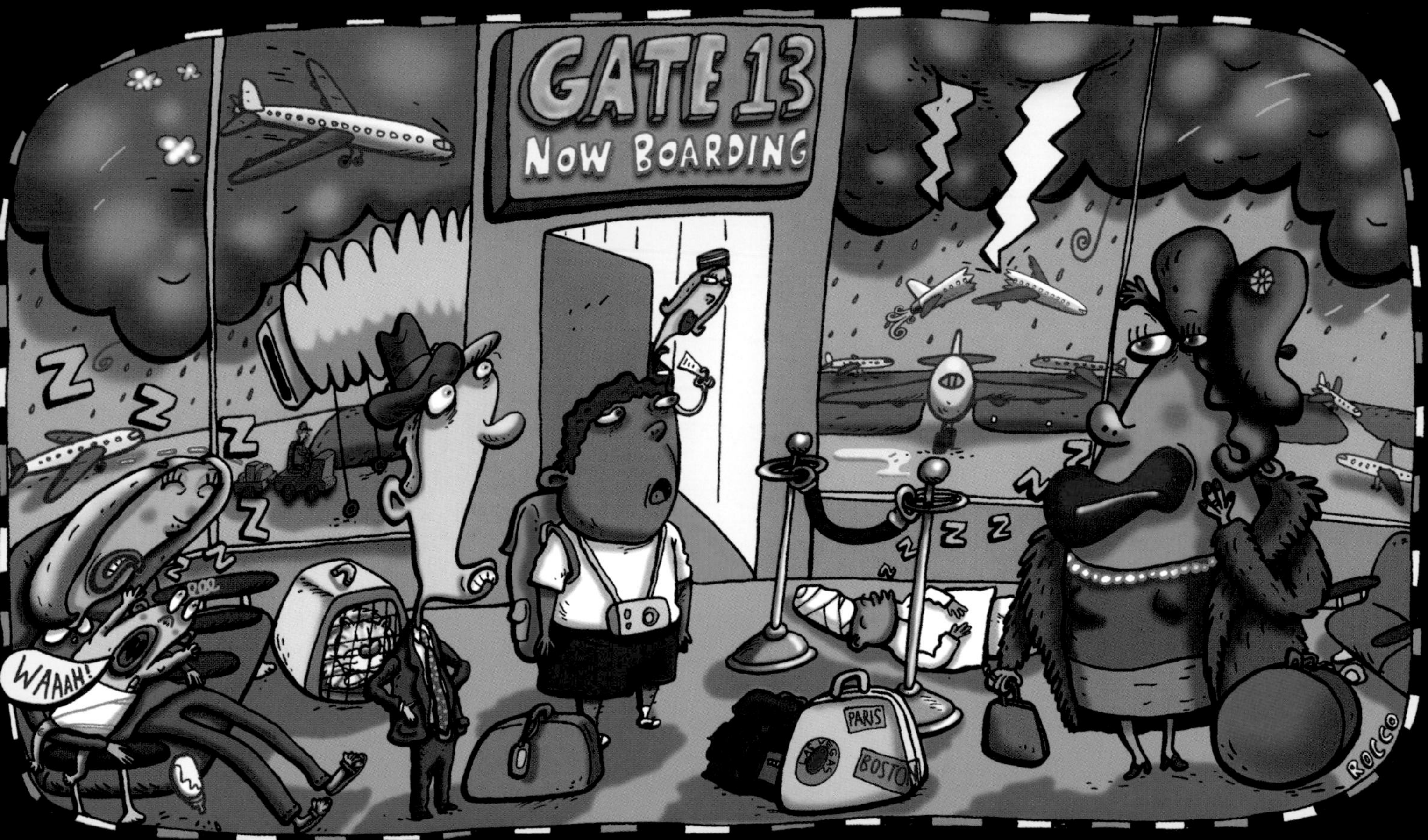

Congratulations

Car of the Future

ROCCO

GATE 13
NOW BOARDING

WAAAH!

PARIS
BOSTON

peter hamlin

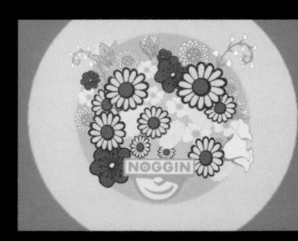

Secret Sauce Studio

animated countdown for Nickelodeon

STEVE GRAY...
310·318·3844
31(FAX)·318·3296

689

CHRIS·BUTLER

303·494·4118
Fax: 303·530·5036

E-mail: artzguy@serve.com

Online portfolio: www.artzguy.com

More samples in: showcase 22 & 23

If you would like to see printed samples of over 160 illustrations, call me and I'll send them to you. These are for you to keep.

All illustrations on these two pages are for a children's book to be released in March of 2001. The book is called **The Moon & Riddles Diner and Sunnyside Café** written by Nancy Willard and published by Harcourt, Inc.

Los Angeles Times
Magazine

Fast Company

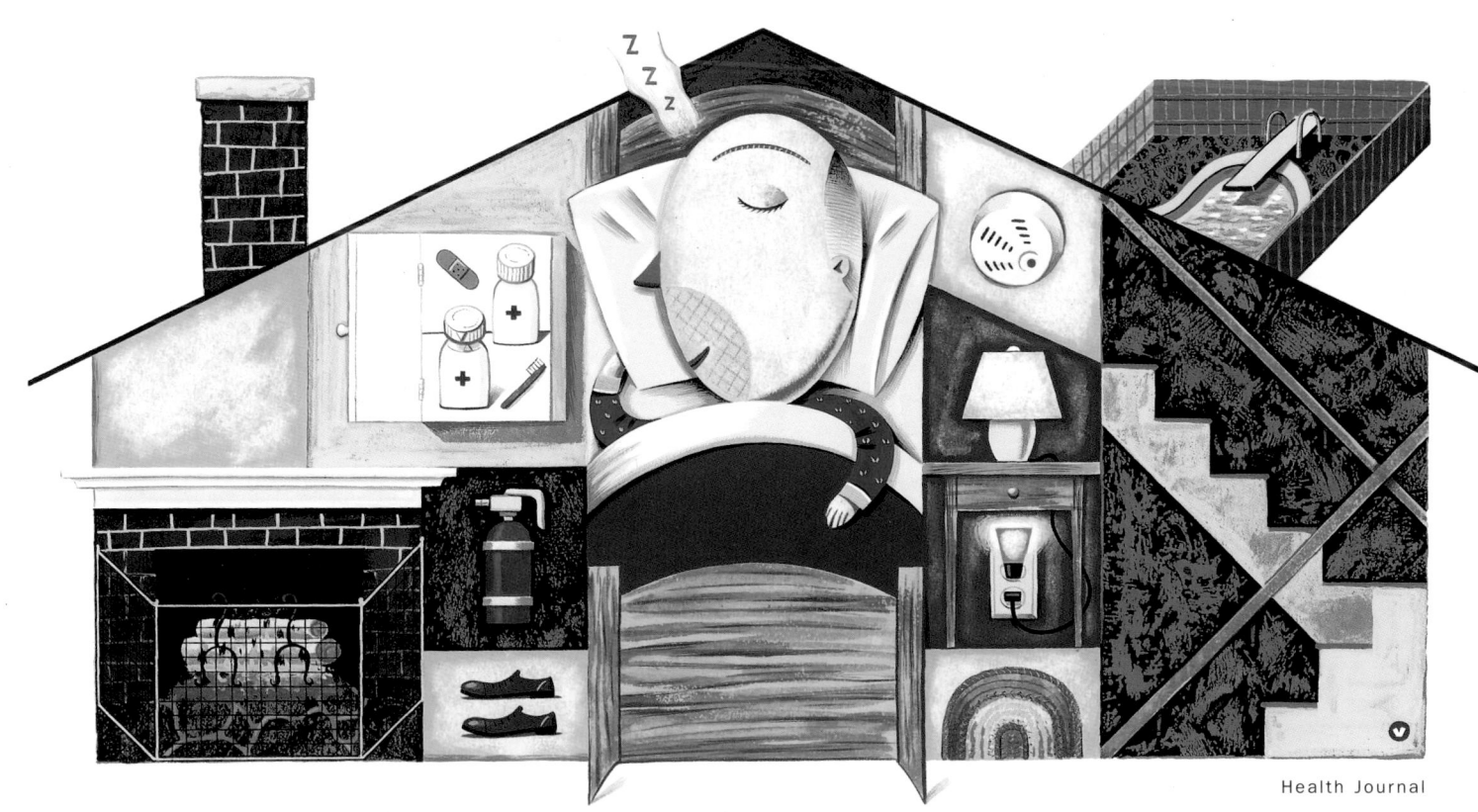

Health Journal

Texas Monthly

Web Icons

phone 207.236.2961  **CHRIS VAN DUSEN** www.chrisvandusen.com

LEZA Anthenien
www.theispot.com/artist/lanthenien
www.leza.com
lia@leza.com

P.O. Box 191 • Glenbrook, NV 89413   **Voice** 775/588-1982 • **Fax** 775/588-9775

LEZA Anthenien

CARY HENRIE

PH 801.298.2044

FAX 801.299.1919

CARY HENRIE

PH   801.298.2044

FAX 801.299.1919

HoGAn braun

marty braun / illustrator

265 PLEASANT AVE
PEAKS ISLAND
MAINE 04108
207·766·9726
www.hoganbraun.com

JEFF JONES

STUDIO   602.331.4599
FAX   602.331.4799

Geoffrey
ZIPOLI

STUDIO 602.331.4599   FAX 602.331.4799

EQUAL OPPORTUNITY JOURNAL

BUSINESS WEEK

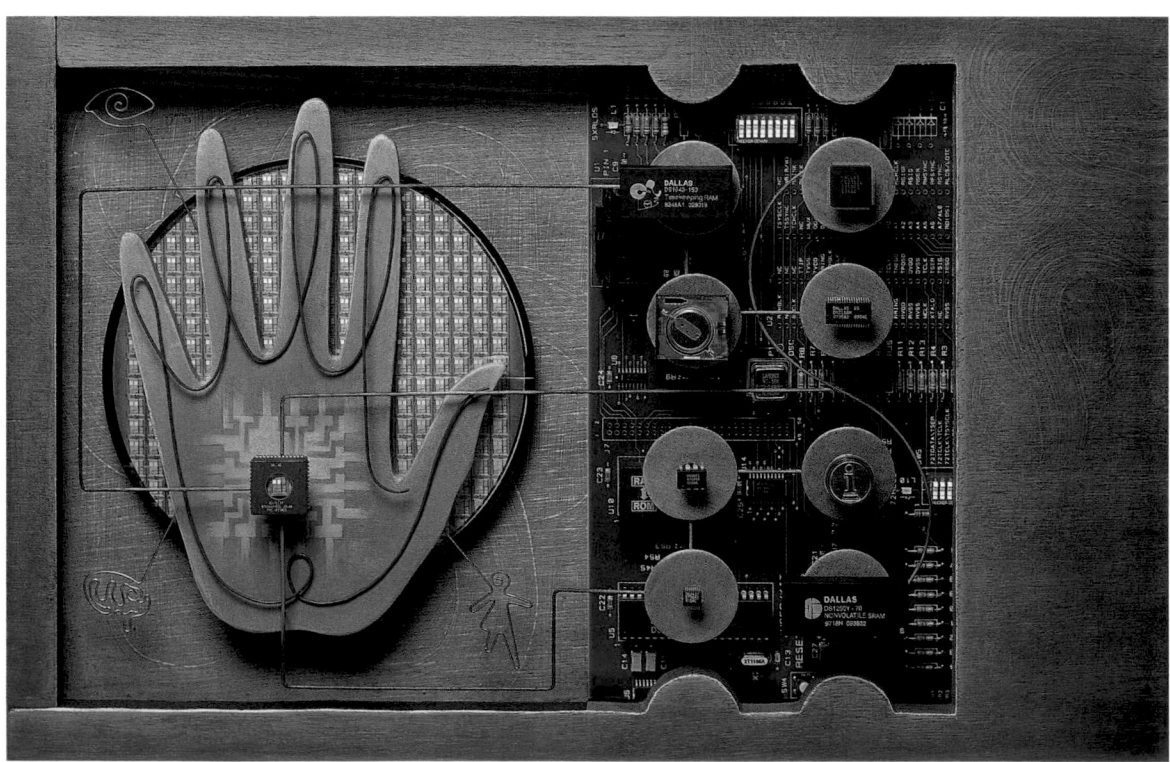

DALLAS SEMICONDUCTOR

ROX

ROXANA ◆ VILLA

818.992.0490 roxanavilla.com

JOHN

ILLUSTRATION

MATTOS

415.397.2138

Studio Phone Number
415.397.2138
Studio Fax Number
415.397.1174
email
mattos@sirius.com

Represented in the
Southern Midwest
and Southeast by
JettReps
502.228.9427
www.jettreps.com

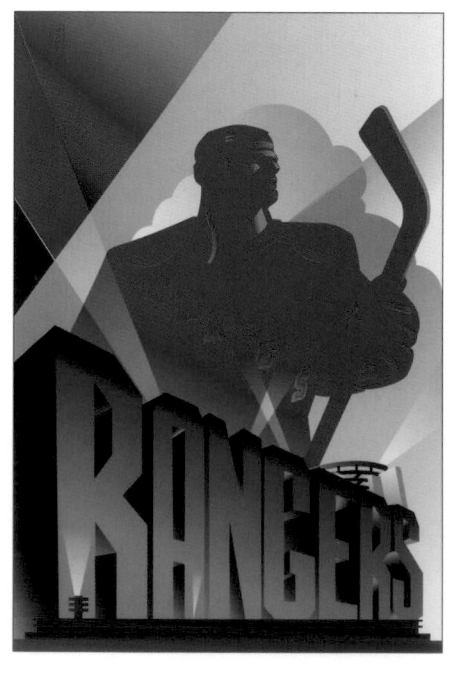

Jon Conrad Stock and Assignment Illustration 60 East Magnolia Boulevard Burbank California 91502 Phone: 818-526-0075 www.jonconrad.com

West Coast: Corey Graham Reps 415-956-4750

Karen Forkish

888 • 686 • 8863   karen@forkish.com   www.forkish.com

WEB SIGHT!

© 2000 E.H. SMITH

CHECK OUT THE OTHER STUFF ON THE WEB:
www.elwoodsmith.com
www.theispot.com/artist/esmith
www.showcase.com/artist/esmith

41 LOCUST GROVE ROAD RHINEBECK, NY 12572

NOT JUST DUCKS

INK

ELWOOD H. SMITH IS REPRESENTED BY MAGGIE PICKARD
845·876·2358
FAX: 845·876·5931
e-mail:
elwood@pojonews.infi.net

Glinka   Beethoven   Hindemith   Holst   Saint-Saëns   Haydn   Respighi

Strauss

Rimsky-Korsakov

ELIZABETH WOLF

3303 NORTH MOUNTAIN LANE • BOISE, IDAHO 83702
PHONE: 208-387-0031 • FAX: 208-387-0119 • E-MAIL: LizWolf13@AOL.COM

DIGITAL ART ®

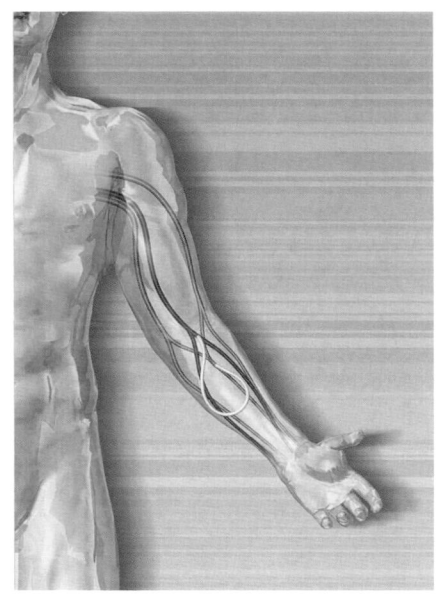
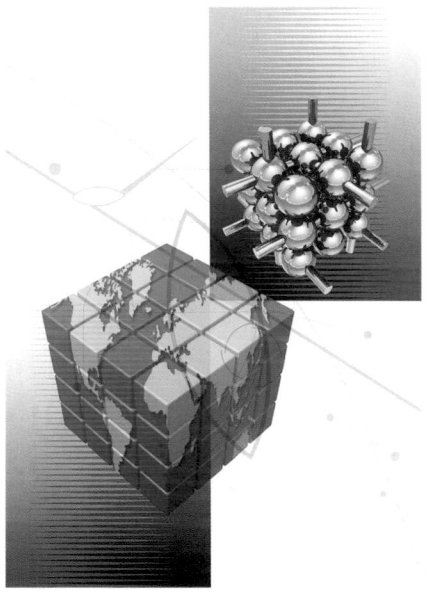
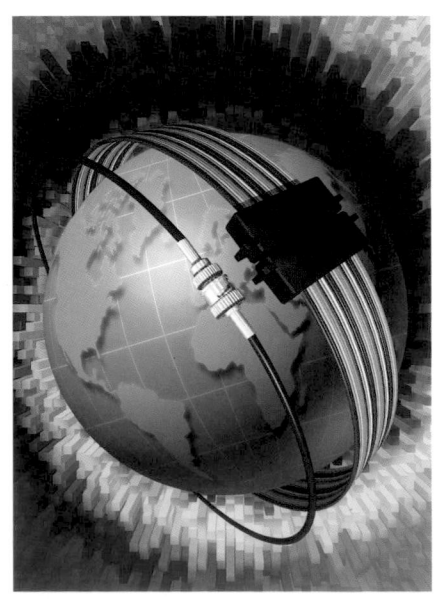

(661) 265-8092   FAX (661) 265-8095
3166 East Palmdale Blvd., Suite 120   Palmdale, CA 93550
PORTFOLIO: digitalart1.com

TREASURE FREY
212 726 3262

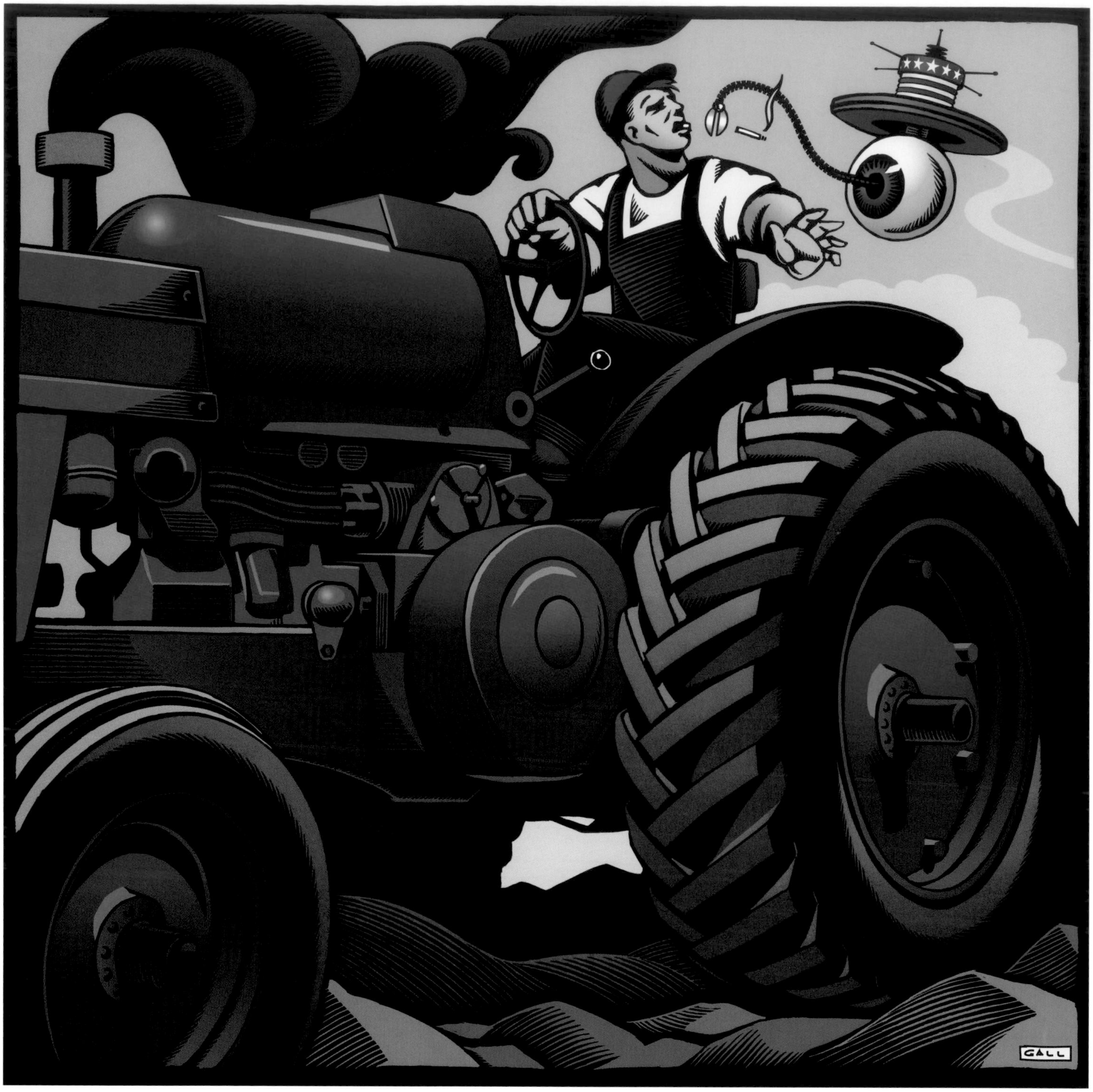

CHRIS GALL

520-299-4454   FAX 520-299-4662

tel. 718.387 9570 Ingo Fast fax. 718.387 5970

FAST LN

13th AVE

www.ingofast.com   ingo@ingofast.com

STORAGE SOLUTION

EATON ANNUAL REPORT - TRUCKING

EATON ANNUAL REPORT - AEROSPACE

DON ARDAY

DIGITAL ILLUSTRATION   972 223 6235

REPRESENTED BY: PHOTOCOM INC.   PHONE 214 526 2020   FAX 214 526 2062

ONLINE PORTFOLIO AT WWW.DONARDAY.COM

dan yaccarino

reel available

212-675-5335

www.danyaccarino.com

ADAIR PAYNE

480.641.7345   FAX 480.641.7779   1824 NORTH SOMERSET MESA ARIZONA 85205

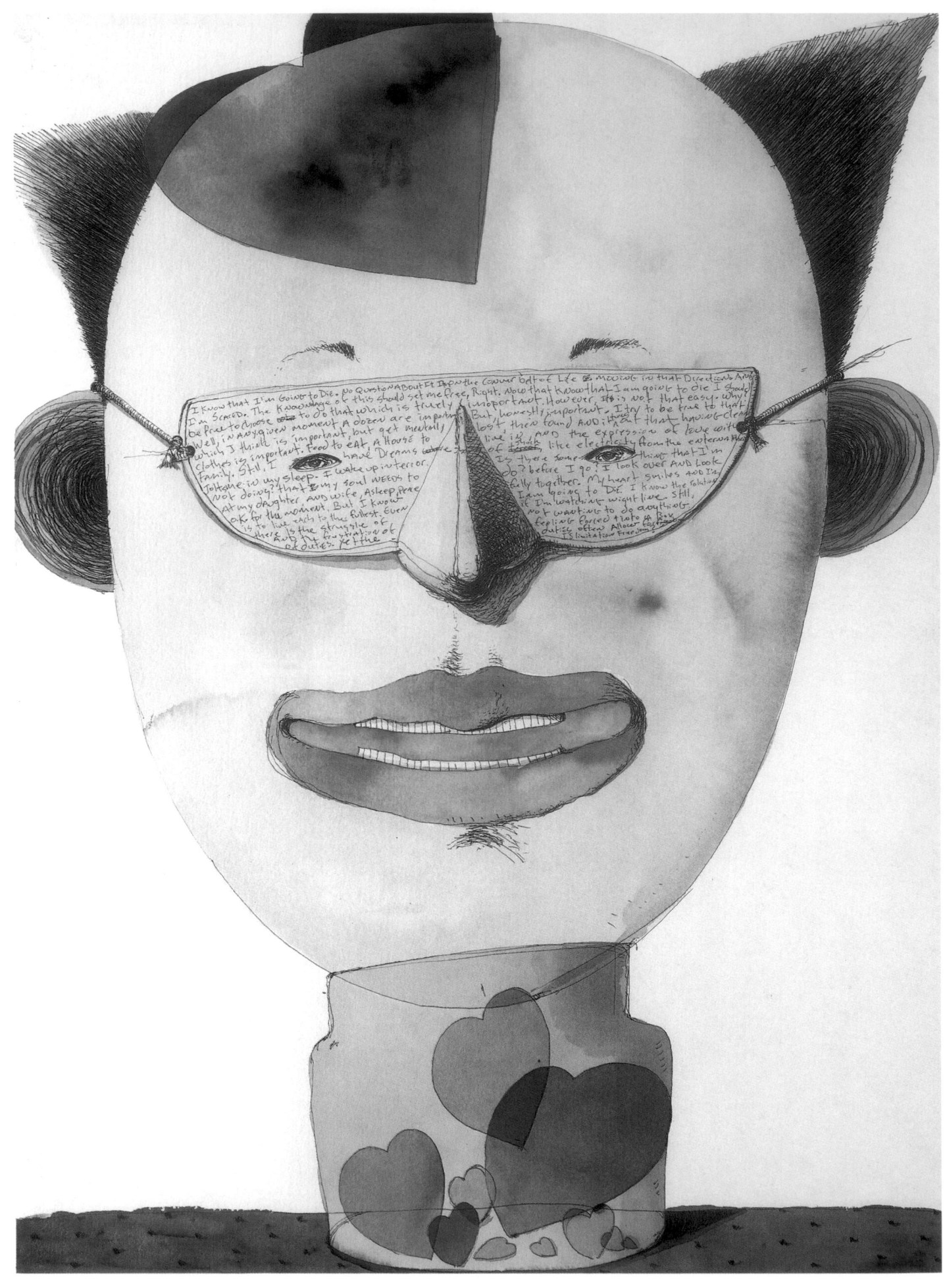

See more images at www.billjaynes.com

SUSAN SMITH ISHIGE
TEL: 781-449-7761
FAX: 781-449-9092

MICROSOFT

NEW ENGLAND ELECTRIC

DREYFUS FUND

MSN.COM

BE SURE TO VISIT MY NEW WEBSITE AT WWW.SMITHISHIGE.COM

TANA POWELL

Tel 415|759.6453   Fax 415|759.6380   Email artana@concentric.net

Additional images: www.workbook.com/portfolios/powell
Stock images: www.theispot.com   www.workbook.com/stock   www.images.com
Showcase Stock Premier Illustration   Stock Workbook Illustration

MICHAEL J DEAS

illustrator

5 0 4 · 5 2 4 · 3 9 5 7

JOHN MANTHA

Toronto telephone/fax (416) 778 5089

jmantha@netcom.ca

Vincent McIndoe 416.967.2840 fax 416.967.5414 www.vince.on.ca webmaster@vince.on.ca

LINDA FOUNTAIN   716.624.1405   FAX 716.624.2624

Kazuhiko Sano

Studio (415) 381-6377   Fax (415) 381-3847

JANET CLELAND

ILLUSTRATOR

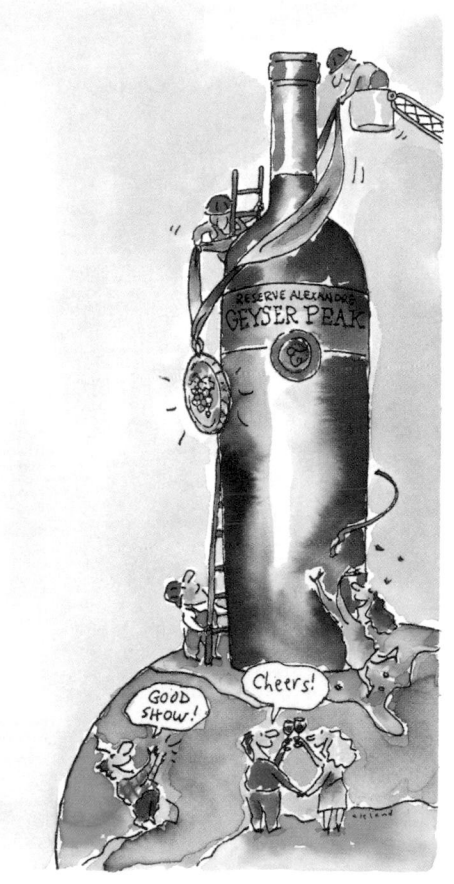

tel 415.457.1049 • fax 415.453.5851 • www.theispot.com/artist/jcleland

LINDA BLECK

PHONE 877·607·0599

WEB www.lindableck.com

VERSATILITY
editorial
corporate
packaging & display
conceptual sketching
stock

david bishop/san francisco

415 558 9532

http://www.dbsf.com

Brad Pitt

Quentin Tarantino

Bruce Willis

LESLIE COBER - GENTRY
224 SHERWOOD FARM
FAIRFIELD, CT
06430
203 · 255 · 9780 PHONE + FAX
www.theispot.com/artist
cober-gentry

t a n y a   b r o k a w   310 394 8456   www.tanyabrokaw.com

Arden von Haeger 7100 Patten Lane Nashville, Tennessee p615.646.7022 f615.662.9997 e:vonhaeger@aol.com

www.vonhaeger.com

aaron meshon

hello from

AUCKLAND

NEW ZEAL-AND

AUSTRALIA
"Shrimp On the Barbi"

WELLINGTON

PACIFIC OCEAN

CHRISTCHURCH

DUNEDIN

ANTARCTICA

MESHON

I LIVE IN

NEW YORK CITY

always a free call

(212) 253-1350 or (800) 753-7513

visit aaronmeshon.com

Rebecca Lyon

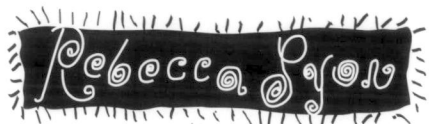

[415] 751 • 7343/e-mail: reblyon@earthlink.net

www.rebeccalyon.com

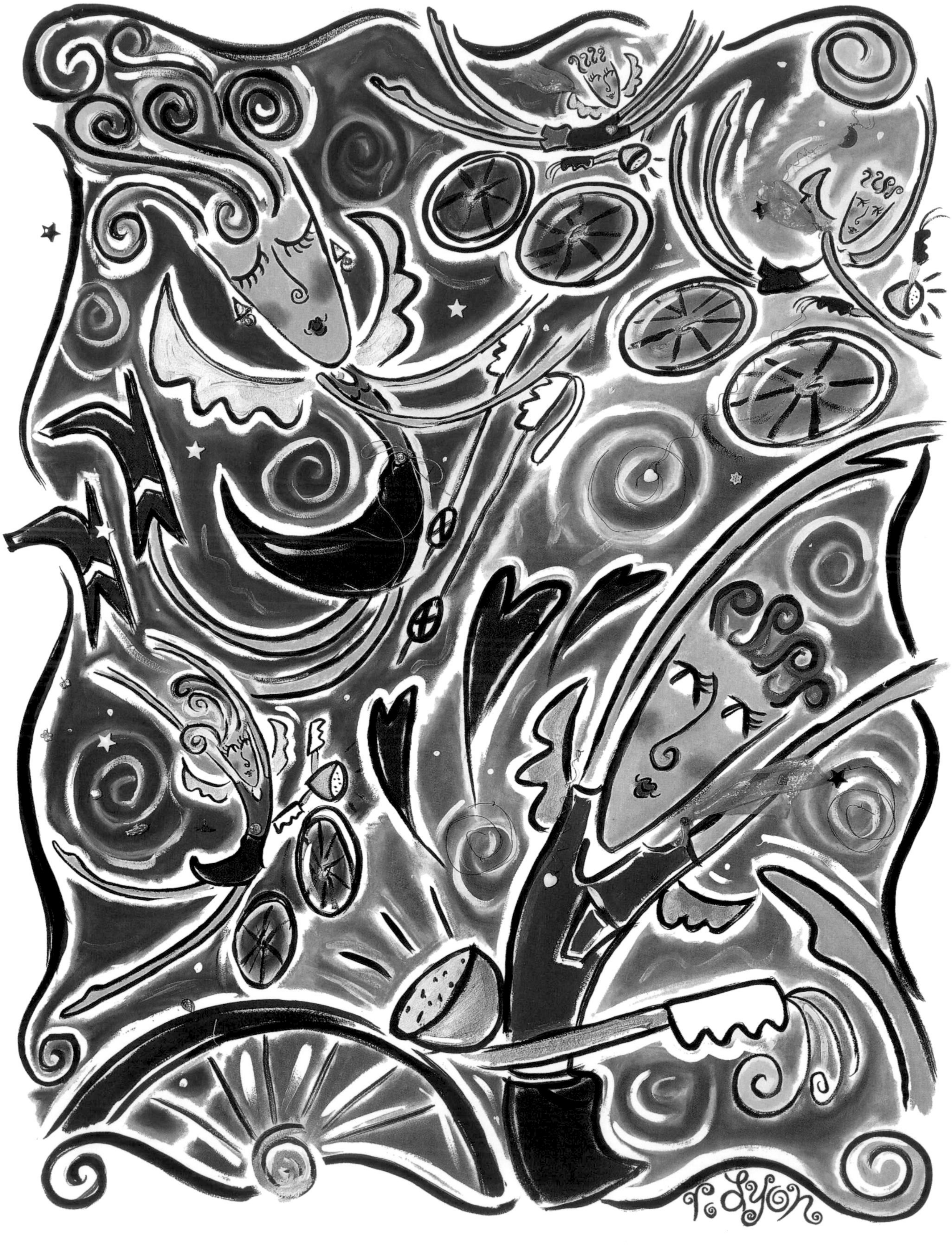

client list includes: Cost Plus World Market, Starbucks Coffee, Robert Mondavi, Stoufers...

OPRAH

TED KOPPEL

clients include:
Rhino Records,
Harper/Collins
Publisher, The
Chicago Tribune,
The Washington
Post, The Los
Angeles Times

R.Genn

Represented by Barbara Markowitz
323. 939-5927

www.theispot.com/artist/rgenn & www.rgenn.com

REGIS PHILBIN

KENNETH BATELMAN
1-888-532-0612
batelman.com

Digital Illustration for use in advertising, educational books, editorial, technical, products & packaging, covers & interiors of books & magazines, info-graphics, illustrated charts & maps, annual reports, internet

All art created using Adobe Illustrator

Clients:
McGraw Hill, Macmillan, Harcourt Brace, Silver Burdett Ginn Inc., Prentice Hall, Scholastic, Simon & Schuster, Allstate, Young & Rubicam, Newsweek, Revlon, Businessweek, Readers Digest, Clinique, Woman's Day, Popular Science, Mayo Clinic, Coca-Cola

Additional work samples:
Black Book
Directory Of Illustration
New Media Showcase
Stock Illustration Source
California Image
Book Production Buyer's Guide
www.theispot.com

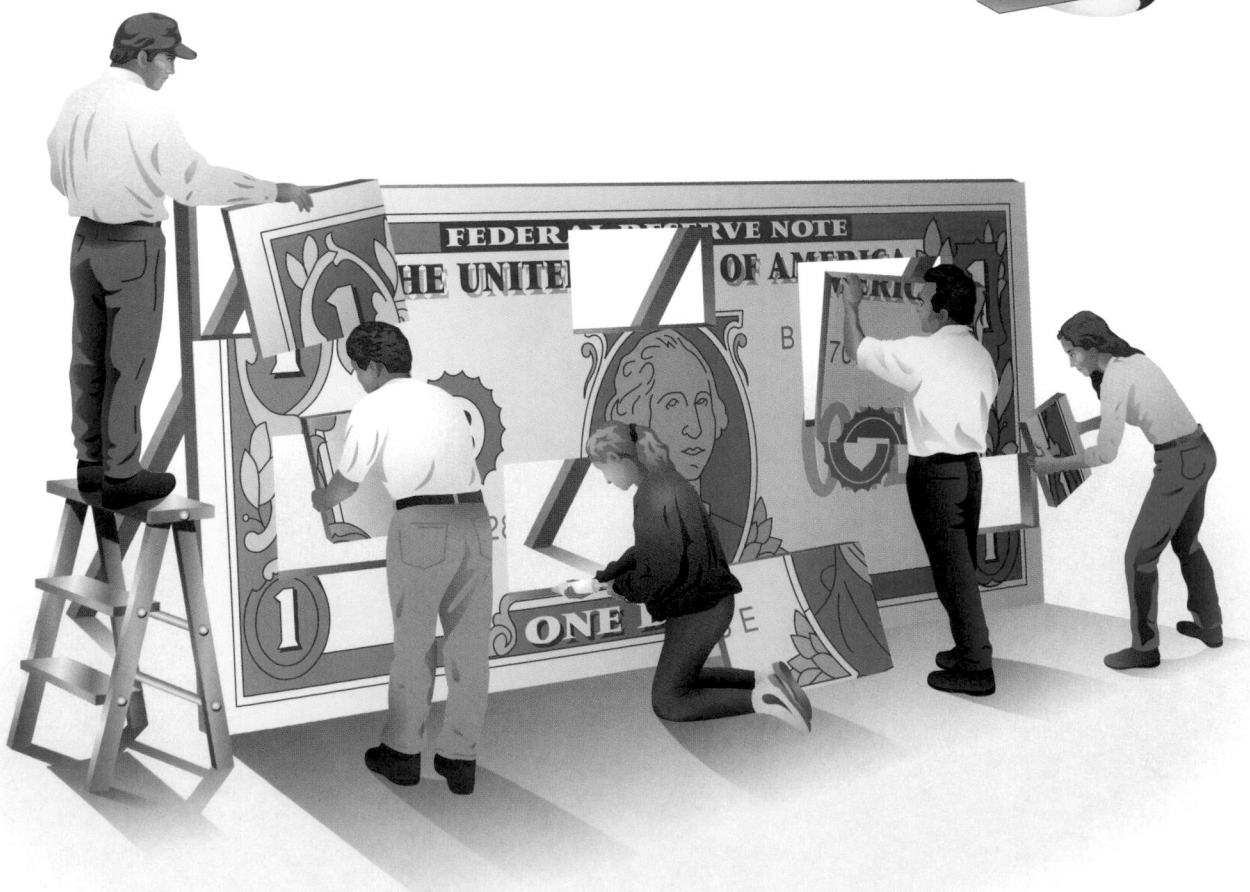

Victoria Kann

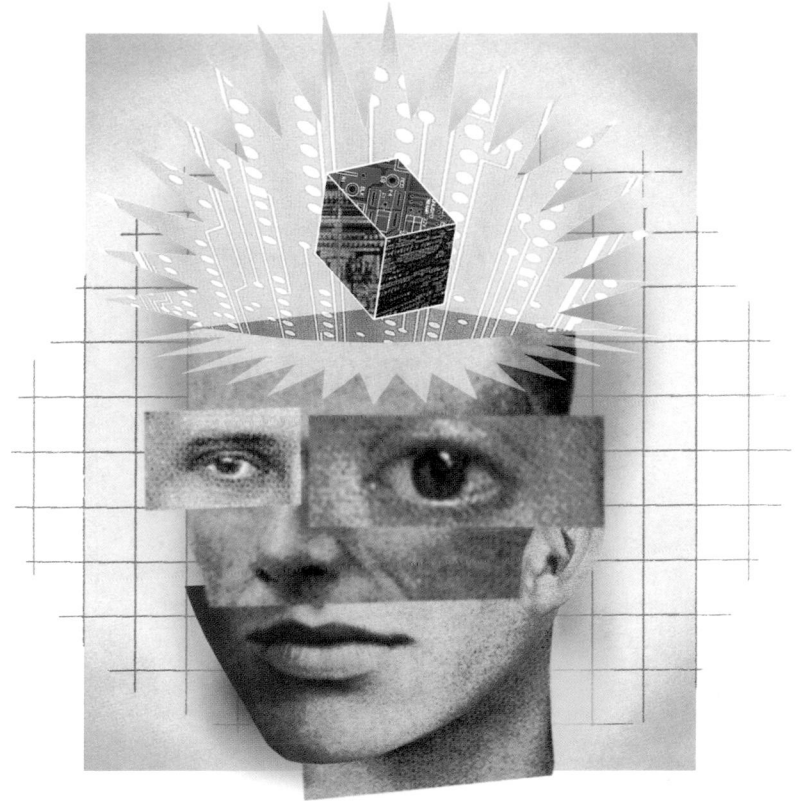

Phone: 212 979-0988   **Fax:** 212 979-7066   **Web:** www.IlikeArt.com   **E-mail:** VKStudio@aol.com

124 Hoyt Street, Brooklyn, New York 11217-2215
718.237.0145 e-mail: cusackart@aol.com
website: MargaretCusack.com

Stitched artwork: embroidered samplers, quilts,
soft sculpture, props, and mixed media.
Stock illustration available.

MARGARET CUSACK

Clients: The Wall Street Journal, Time Magazine,
Avon, Fisher Price, Lord & Taylor, Reader's Digest,
Forbes Magazine, The Village Voice, Texaco,
Seagram's, and The New York Times.

Also: American Showcase: 23, 22, 21, 20,
and Showcase Stock. ©2000 Margaret Cusack

Thanksgiving 2001 United States Postage Stamp ©USPS 1999

Print Magazine Regional Design Annual Cover

Fisher Price Catalog Cover

THOMAS B. ALLEN
The Journey of an
AMERICAN ILLUSTRATOR

Thomas B. Allen
941-358-0073   thomasballen.com   TBAjourney@aol.com
830 Indian Beach Drive • Sarasota, FL 34234

Robert Saunders

45 Bartlett Crescent, Brookline, MA 02446
Vox: (617) 566-4464   Fax: (617) 739-0040
www.theispot.com/artist/rsaunders
rob@robertsaunders.com
www.robertsaunders.com

GRAPHIC ARTISTS GUILD NEWS

THE ATLANTIC MONTHLY

FORTUNE SMALL BUSINESS

744

LISA ADAMS

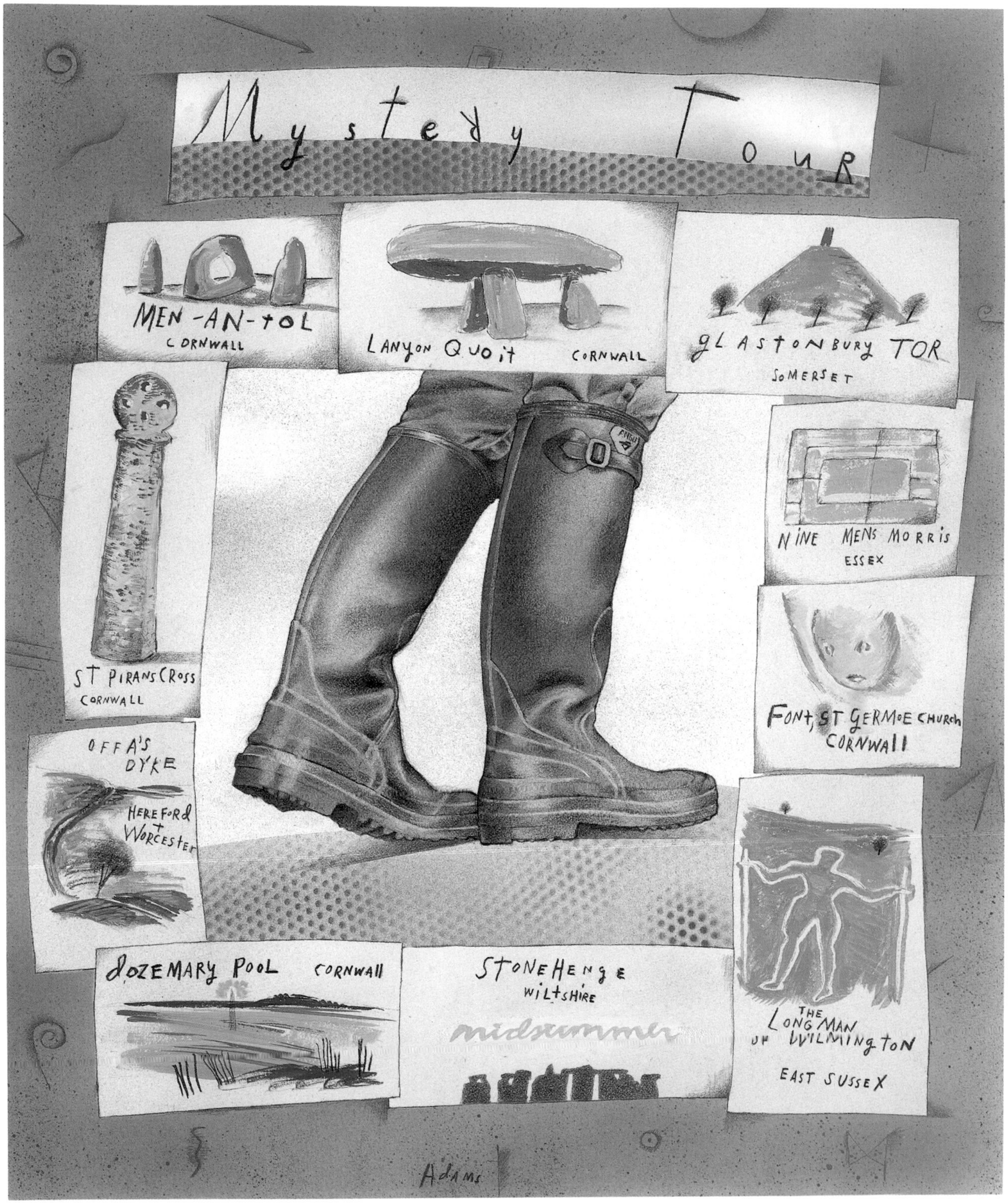

40 Harrison Street | № 29f | **NYC** | **10013** | tel: **212.385.8189** | fax: **212.385.9630**
view more work: www.workbook.com   workbook   the blackbook   www.sharpshooterinc.com

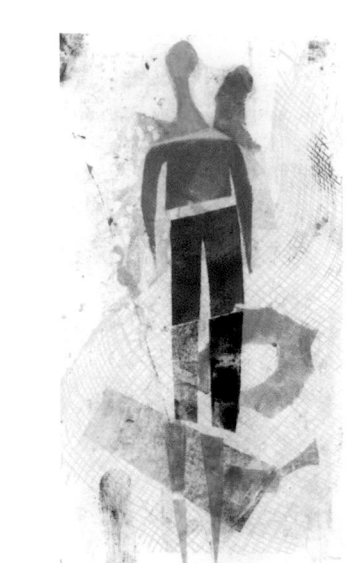

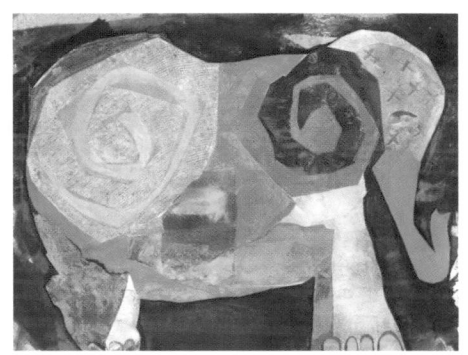

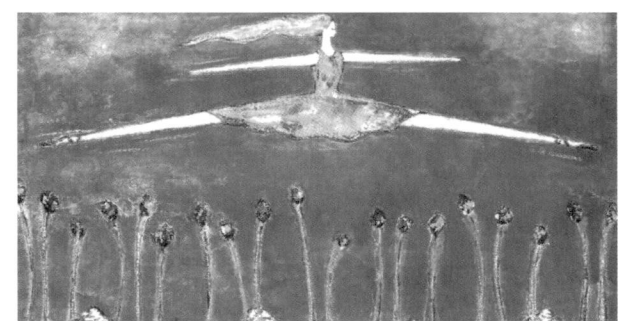

Sharon Wells • 970.925.6701 • swdesign@rof.net

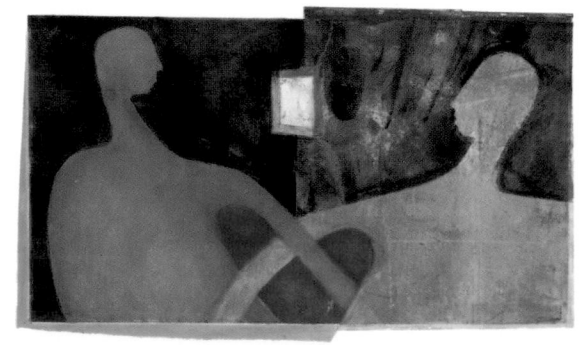

Signing of the Declaration of Independence, commissioned by *Fast Company*

Poster image for the Long Wharf Theatre, New Haven, Connecticut

Poster for the Wyoming Business Council; Lettering: Michael Doret

Portrait of American Colonist, Myles Standish, commissioned by *Smithsonian Magazine*

STEPHEN SAVAGE | 444 SACKETT STREET
BROOKLYN, NY   11231
TEL/FAX (718) 624-5435

zohar lazar

718-852-2293 102 Luquer St., #1L, Brooklyn, NY 11231

e-mail: zlazar@earthlink.net www.zoharlazar.com

Shelly Meridith 55 mercer street Floor 4 nyc 10013
212 · 941 · 1905   Fax 212·226·3227

ShellyM@Shellyadventures.com   www.Shellyadventures.com

Rick Calomino

phone 303 455 6561 • fax 303 455 1162 • email calominostudio@compuserve.com
www.theispot.com/artist/rcalomino

sean
KAPITAIN

416.923.8215
www.kapitain.com

R O B E R T   J O H A N N S E N

Robert Johannsen 1088 Diamond Ct, Mississauga   Ontario, Canada L5V·1J5   Phone: 905·567·1493

9 0 5 · 5 6 7 · 1 4 9 3

Fresh From the Garden!

SueMell 415.436.8865
www.suemell.com

John Courtney
79 11th Avenue, #5-D
Paterson, NJ 07514
973.345.7652 home
201.599.7340 office

MARK BOWERS
(719) ◆ 683 ◆ 2729

5695 Renneberger Road
Peyton, Colorado 80831

www.theispot.com/artist/mbowers

mlbowers@earthlink.net

jeff shelly

www.jeffshelly.com

2330 San Marco Dr. Los Angeles, CA 90068 (800)318-3244 (323)460-4604 Fax(323)464-6630 you can view my portfolio at

www.PollyPowell.com

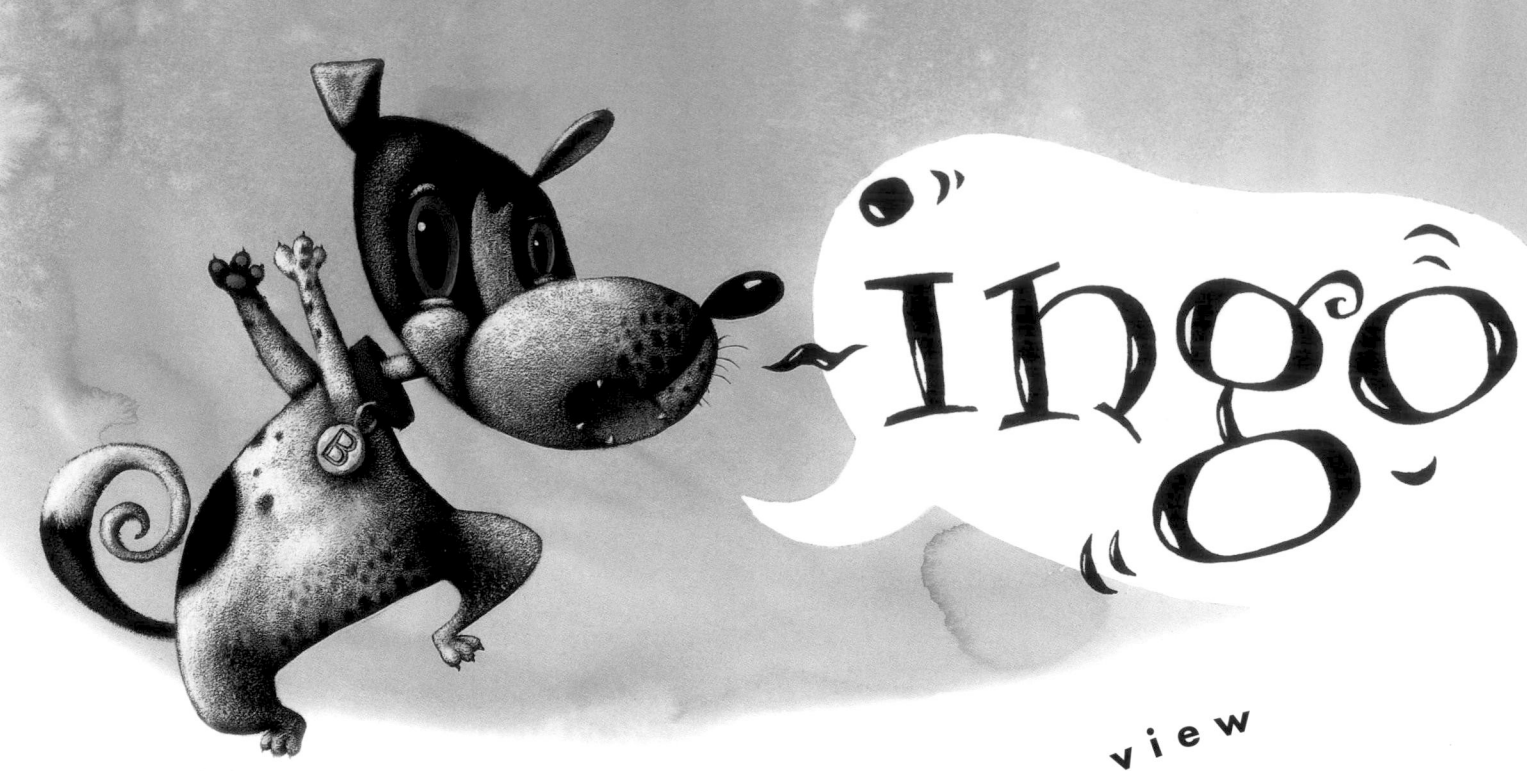

Polly Powell

916.444.1646

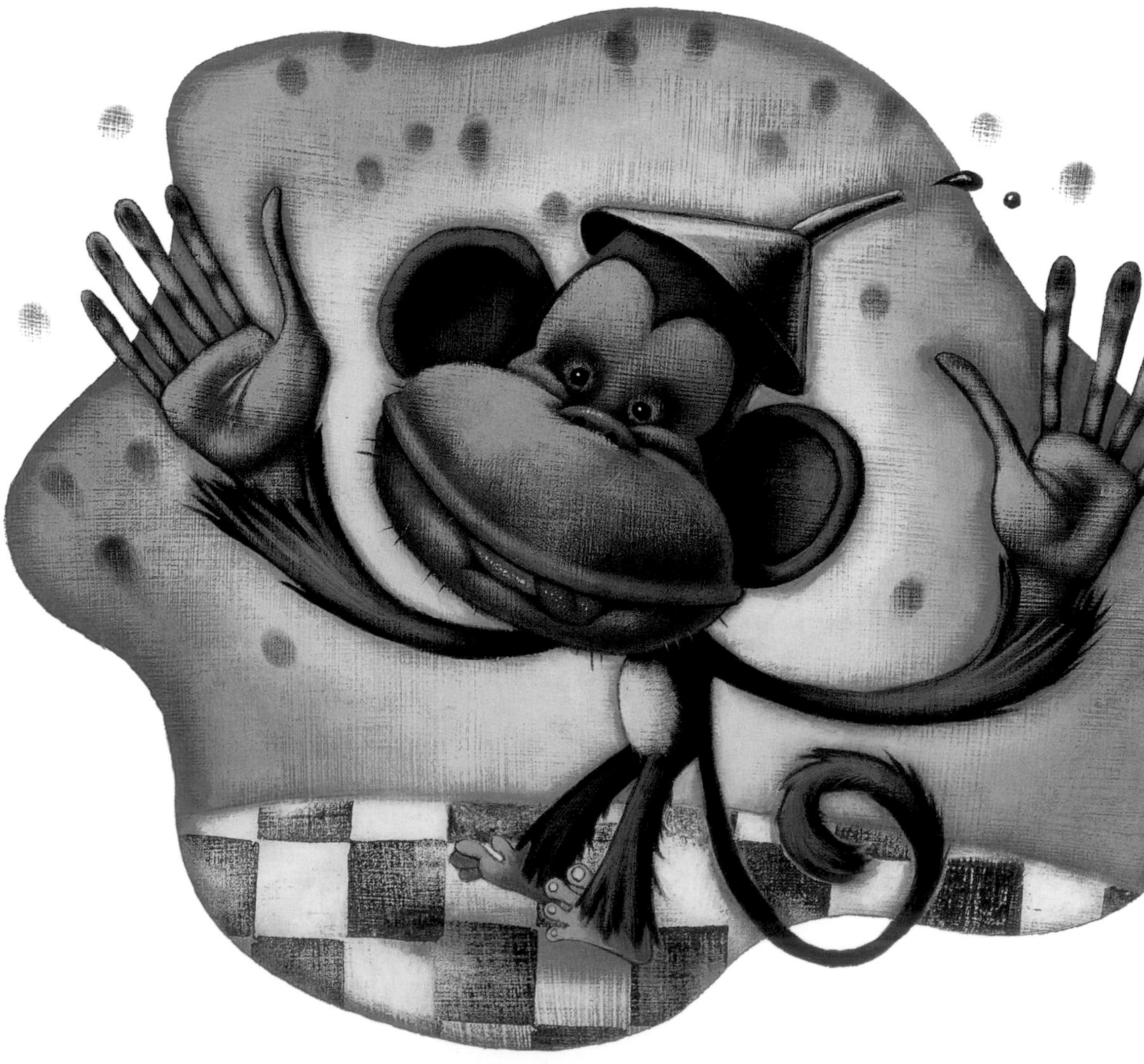

POLLY

QUIET   MEDIUM   LOUD

I CAN MAKE ANYONE DO ANYTHING YOU WANT THEM TO DO!

1·888·403·1004
F–1·562·989·9539

RICHARD
EWING
DRAWINGS

888·403·1004   F – 562·989·9539
See Also Showcase 18, 19, 21, 22, 23 & Workbook 22
www.theispot.com/artist/rewing

Guy Smalley
maker of happy drawings

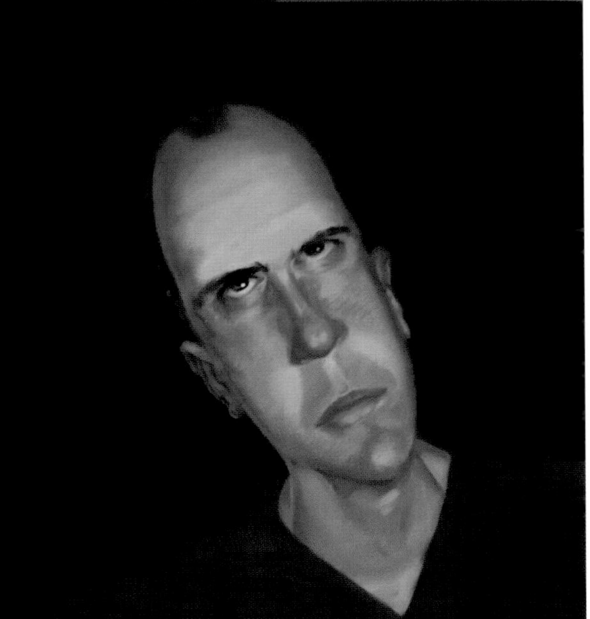

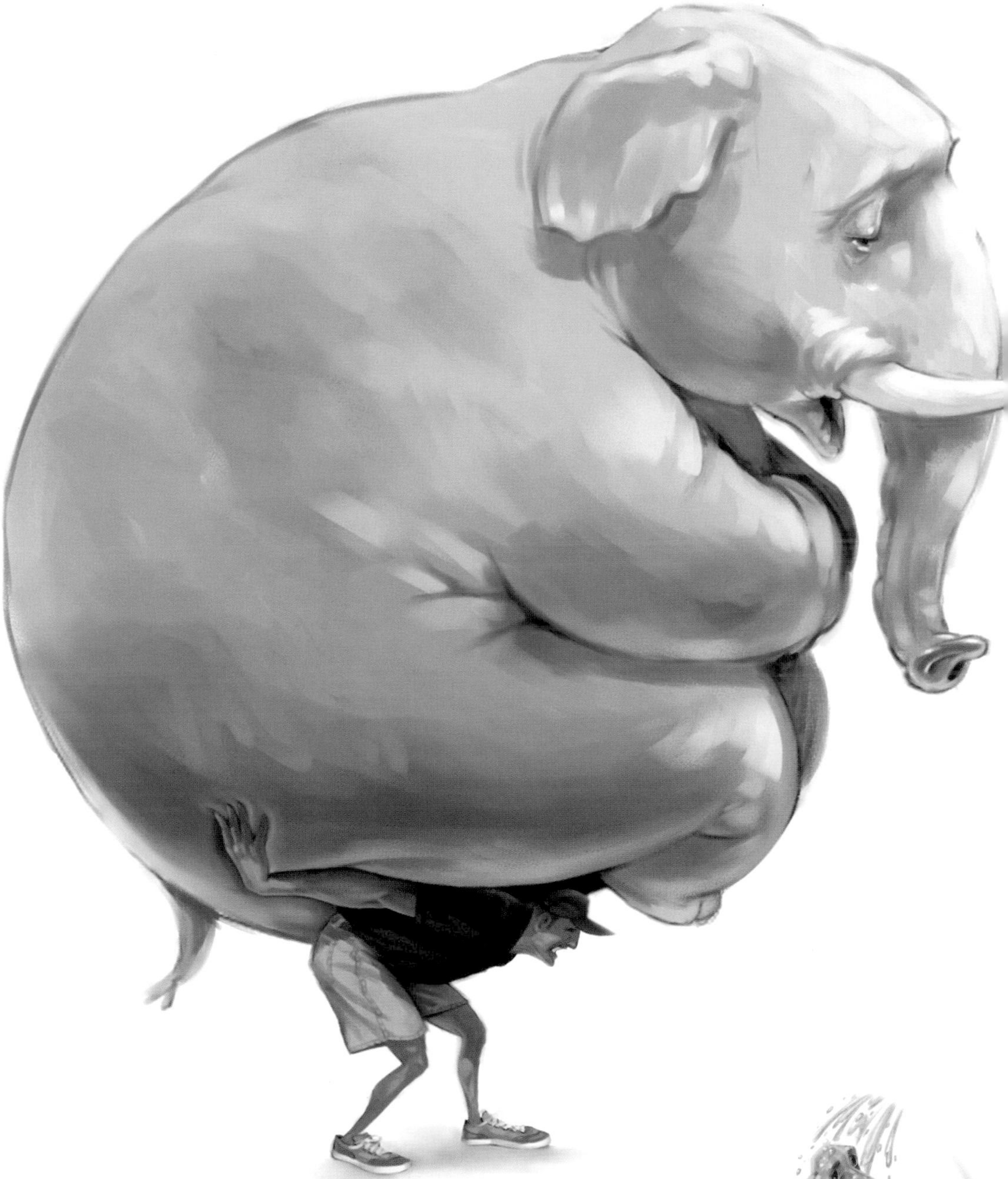

[PHONE] – 903.565.4900

[FAX] – 903.566.4958

[EMAIL] – artog@tyler.net

[ADDRESS] – 3505 Melanie Court
Tyler, Texas 75707

MITCHGREENBLATT.COM

718.624.6361

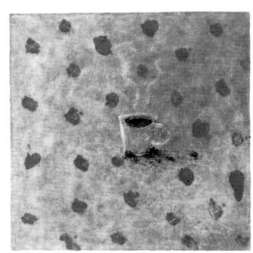

Susan Gross

illustrations & monotypes
415.751.5879
www.susangross.com

212 · 775 · 1484

jody wheeler

375 south end ave. · 12t · n.y. n.y. · 10280

See Directory of Illustration #9, 11, 12, 14, 15, 16 for additional work.

HARRY BRIGGS

ILLUSTRATION

P/F 831 393 9433   P.O. BOX 51266 PACIFIC GROVE CA 93950
HARRY@HAIRBALLDESIGN.COM   THEISPOT.COM

DIAZ ICON

760 . 438 . 0070

800 . 474 . ICON

FAX 760 . 438 . 0315

www . diazicon . com

NEW ⊙ ILLUSTRATION ⊙

⊙ STOCK ⊙ PROMOTIONS ⊙

⊙ SAMPLES ⊙ BOOKS ⊙ FONTS

⊙ CD OF 300 EPS IMAGES $250. ⊙

DARA GOLDMAN

978.440.8636

NED SHAW STUDIO

Fat-Free All Digital Illustration!

©NED 2000 Portions © Synopsys

To hear voices: 812-333-2181 • To send faxes: 812-331-0420
To view portfolio: www.nedshaw.com

Janet Hamlin

phone: 718·768·3647
fax: 718·768·3675

website: www.janethamlin.com

nicholas chubay 973 822 8912 fax 973 822 2027

Call Jim Bradshaw
856.459.3990

Guida Studio

Liisa Chauncy Guida

STUDIO 970 845 0771 FAX 970 949 0633 www.theispot.com/artist/lguida
REPRESENTED IN NEW YORK BY MENDOLA ARTISTS 212 986 5680

DANIELLE JONES

416 - 968 - 6277

Paul Schulenburg
508 432.0994
www.elbowpond.com

Illustrating
corporate hi-jinx
for over a decade.

MELISSA SWEET

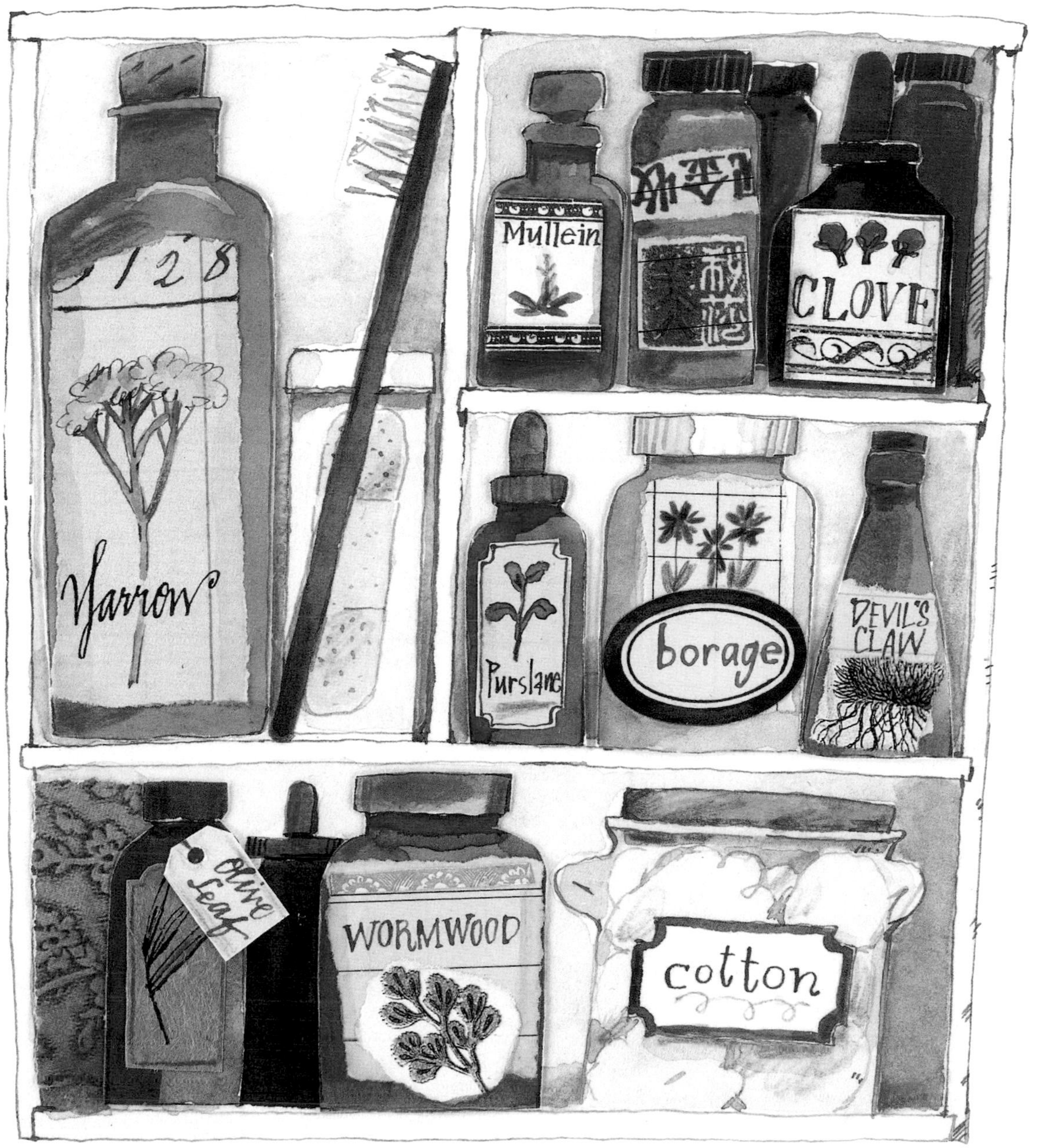

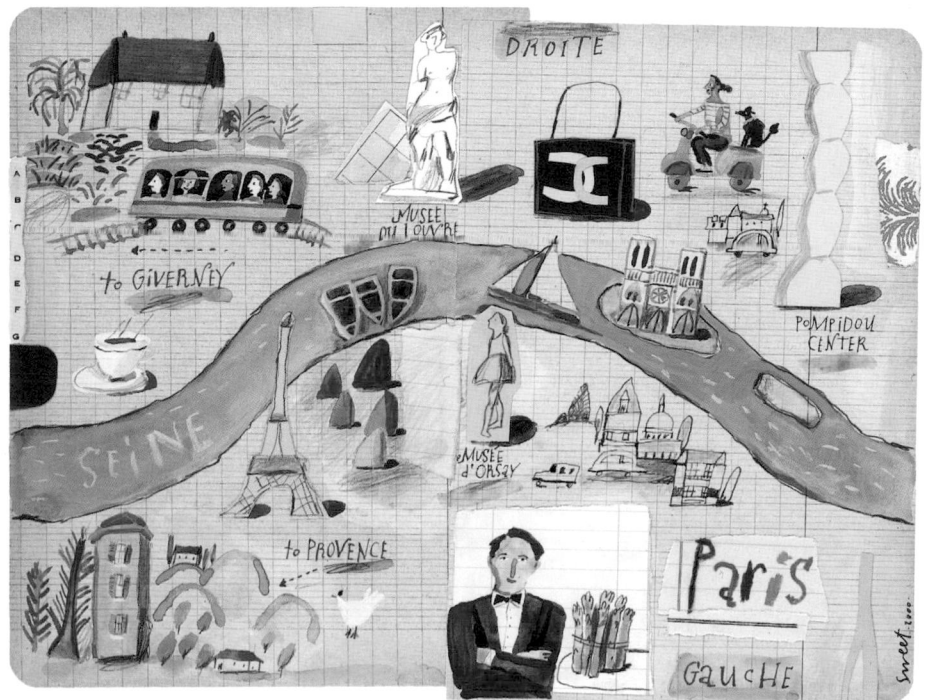

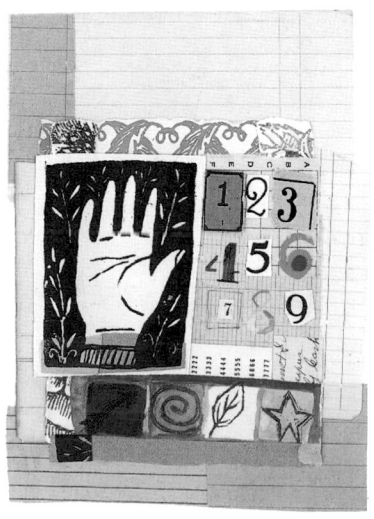

voice 207.236.0348
fax 207.236.0350
www.melissasweet.net

Sachiko Yoshikawa

mixed media • collage • traditional illustration

Bon jour! Alice goes to Paris

When the Giant ate a Carrot

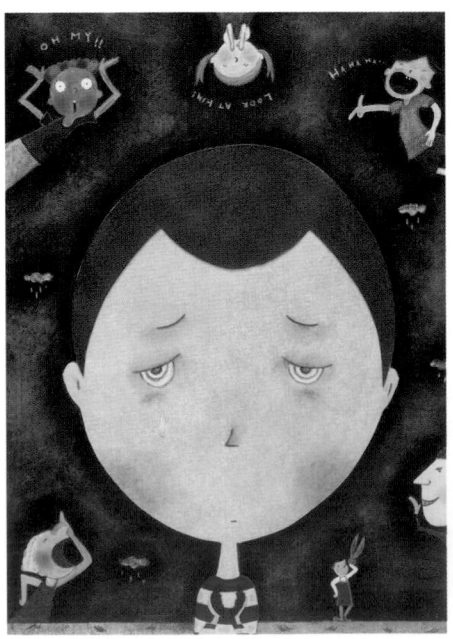

The day I cut my hair

14155 SW Wilson Dr., Beaverton, OR 97008 Phone • Fax 503.626.7271 www.studiosachiko.com

JOHN BURGOYNE

Northern Goshawk

Cooper's Hawk

Peregrine Falcon

Red-tailed Hawk

Osprey

CALL JOHN AT HIS STUDIO 617.489.4960   FX 617.489.0629
26 STATLER RD BELMONT MA 02478   LEVEL9@THECIA.NET
WWW.THEISPOT.COM/ARTIST/BURGOYNE
WWW.JOHNBURGOYNE.COM

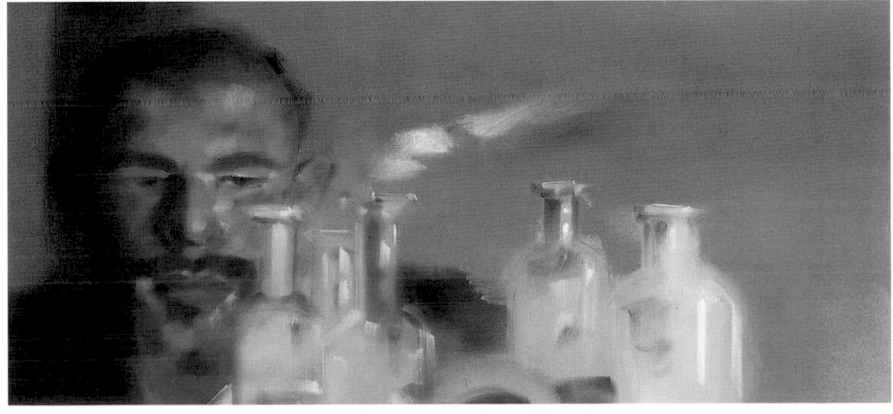

TRACI HAYMANS

601 WALTHOUR ROAD • SAVANNAH, GEORGIA 31410
912-897-0902 • fax: 912-897-6142
email: thaymans@earthlink.net

illustrations
infographics

LESSON #1

WWW.

OPEN

HOLLYWO

How to Yo-yo

❶

❷

❸

DSL

Managing Risk

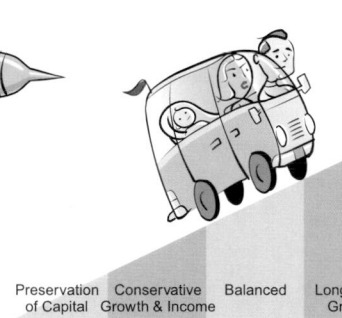

REWARD

Preservation of Capital | Conservative Growth & Income | Balanced | Long-Term Growth | Aggressive Growth

RISK   Low   Average   High

Richard Sheppard

Richard Sheppard
707•433•9641
artstudios.com

786

Suling Wang

✿   ✿   ✿

(415) 474-0259
2885 Bush Street #9
San Francisco, CA 94115

suling_wang@mindspring.com
http://www.best.com/~sulingw/

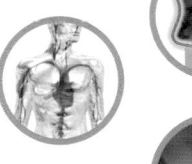
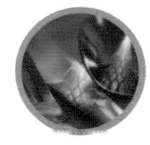
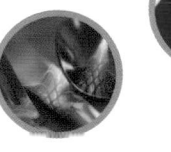

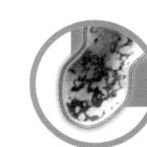

digital illustration

stephen mclean

command i

T: 973.857.8110

F: 973.857.8109

E: smclean@command-i.com

Digital portfolio at www.command-i.com

TAYLOR BRUCE
tel/fax 707 857-3373 or 360 378-9561

Kathyjean Boise

Get your dream illustration!

K.Boise © 2000

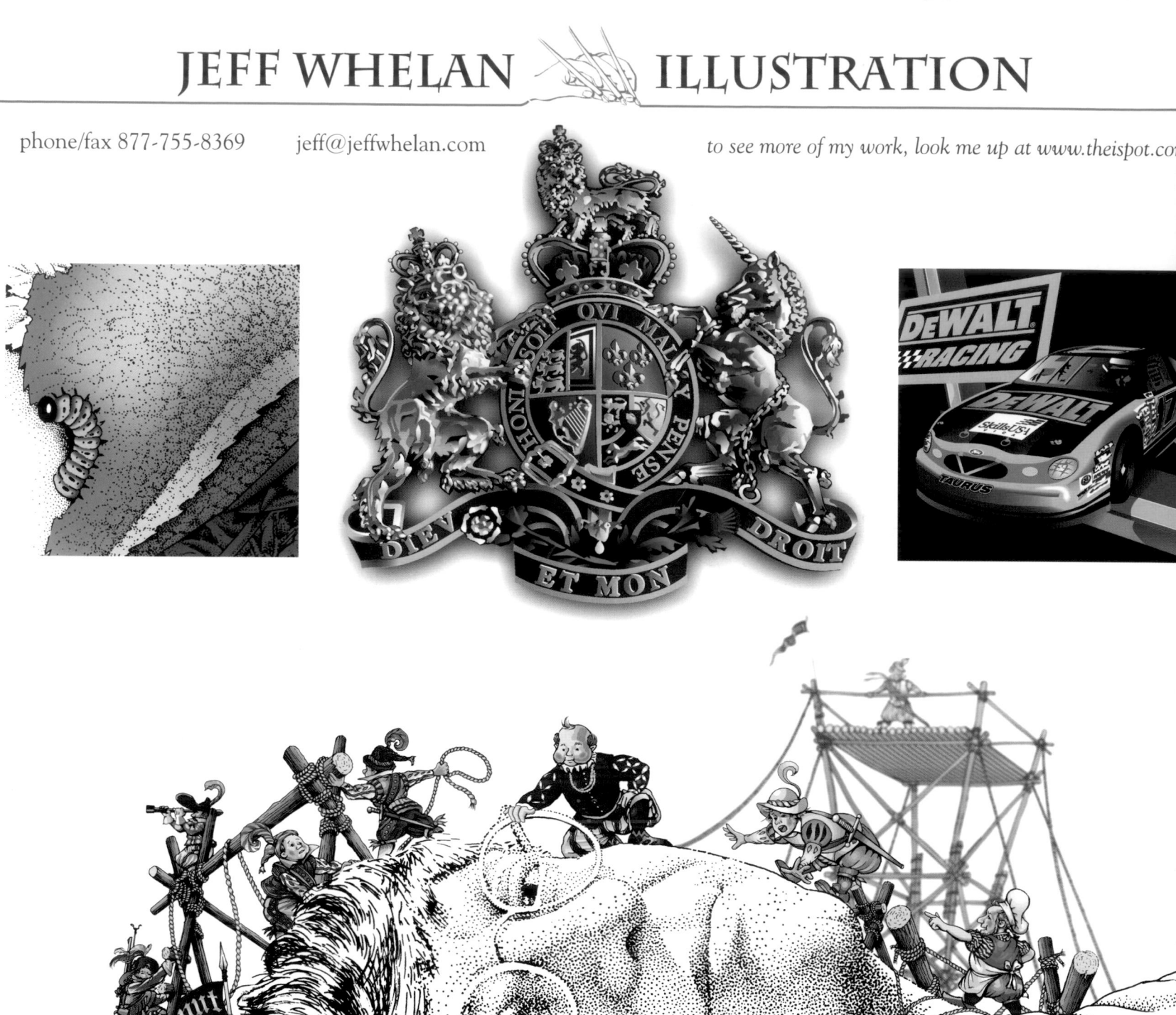

Brian **Jensen**

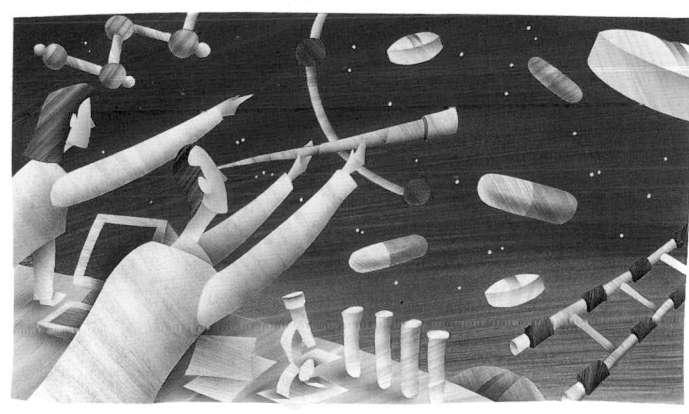

marc phares

please visit our online portfolios

www.epicstudios.com

908-879-6583

www.theispot.com

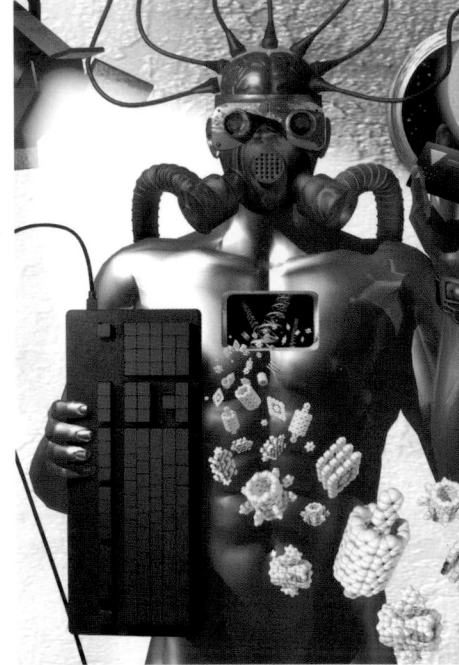

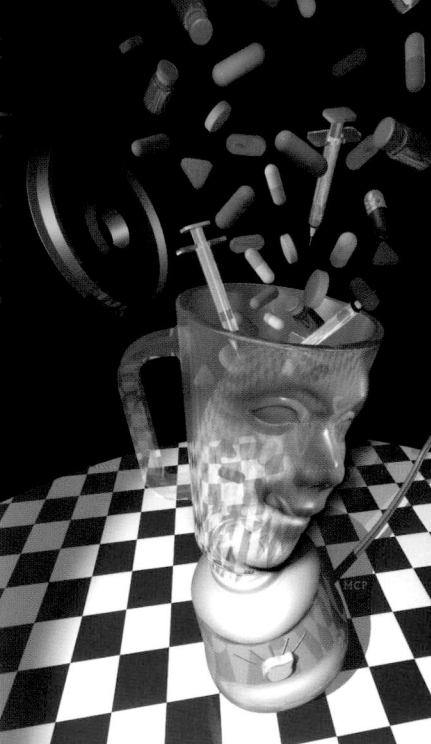

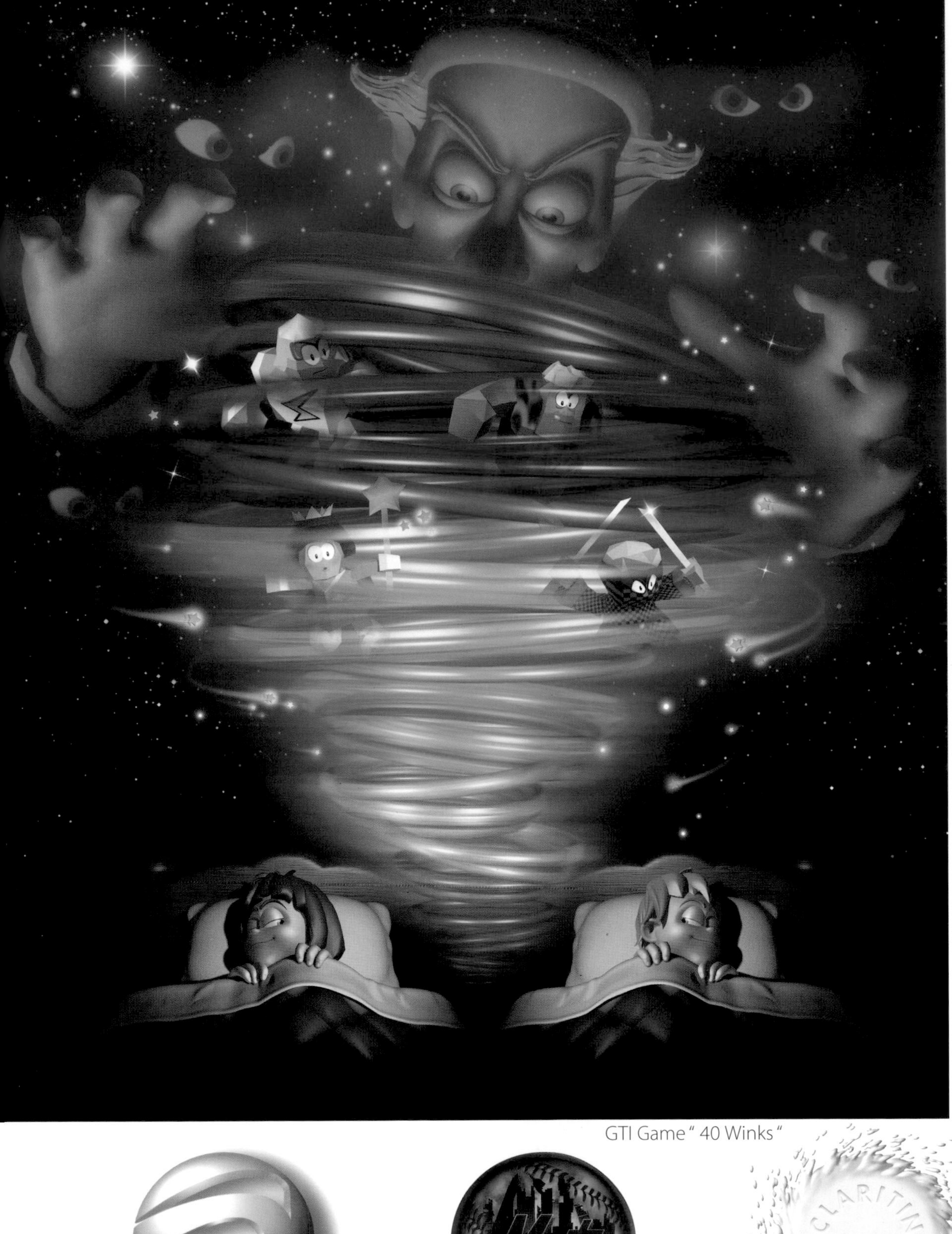

GTI Game " 40 Winks "

The Source Magazine

The Village Voice

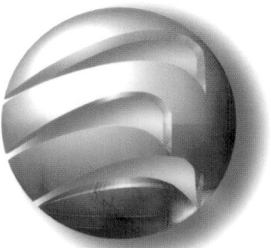

Epic Studios, Inc.

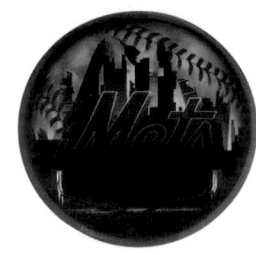

ESPN Magazine

Schering-Plough

Bristol-Myers Squibb

Epic Studios, Inc. Voice: 908-879-6583 Fax: 908-879-6579 Email: marc@epicstudios.com

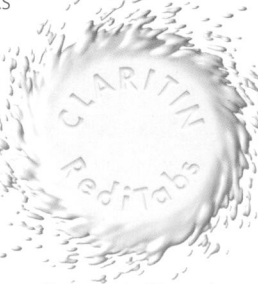

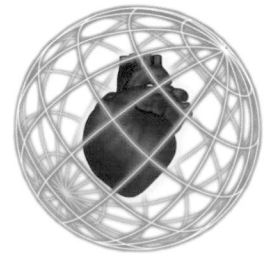

Maral Sassouni Illustration

1416 Queens Road, West Hollywood, California 90069 • (323) 650-5865 • marals@starnet.fr • www.theispot.com/artist/msassouni

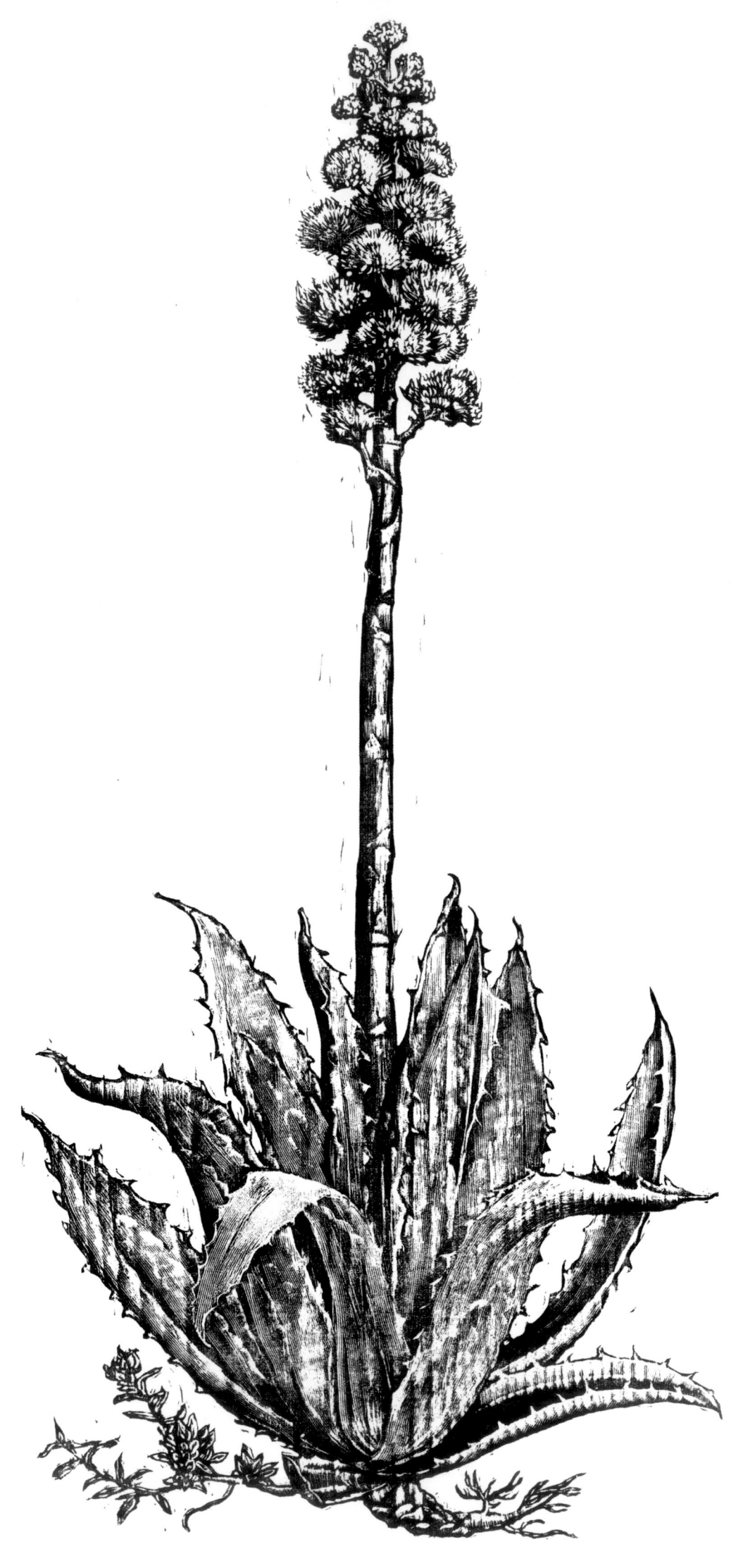

THE AGAVE
AMERICANA
OR CENTURY
PLANT GROWS
IN ROSETTES
OF SPINE-
MARGINED
THICKENED
LEAVES,
PERSISTING
FOR SEVERAL
YEARS UNTIL
A FLOWERING
STALK IS
PRODUCED.
AFTER
FLOWERING
THE PLANT
DIES
TO STAND
FLAG-LIKE
WHILE YOUNG
PLANTS
PRODUCED
FROM ITS
BASE
CONTINUE
TO LIVE.

Carla Bauer
156 Fifth Avenue
Suite 1100
New York City
10010

212.807.8305 phone
212.727.8094 fax
carlabauer@earthlink.net

Woodcut illustration

website
www.juliagran.com
email granny@juliagran.com
julia gran
telephone
718.601.8820
3240 henry hudson pkwy.
Suite 6h
bronx, ny 10463
© julia gran 2000

Roxanna Baer

Roxanna Baer

I L L U S T R A T I O N

TEL 212·496·5495

FAX 212·496·5498

WEB www.roxyillustration.com

Clients include: The New York Times, The Gap,
Child Magazine, Houghton Mifflin, Seventeen Magazine

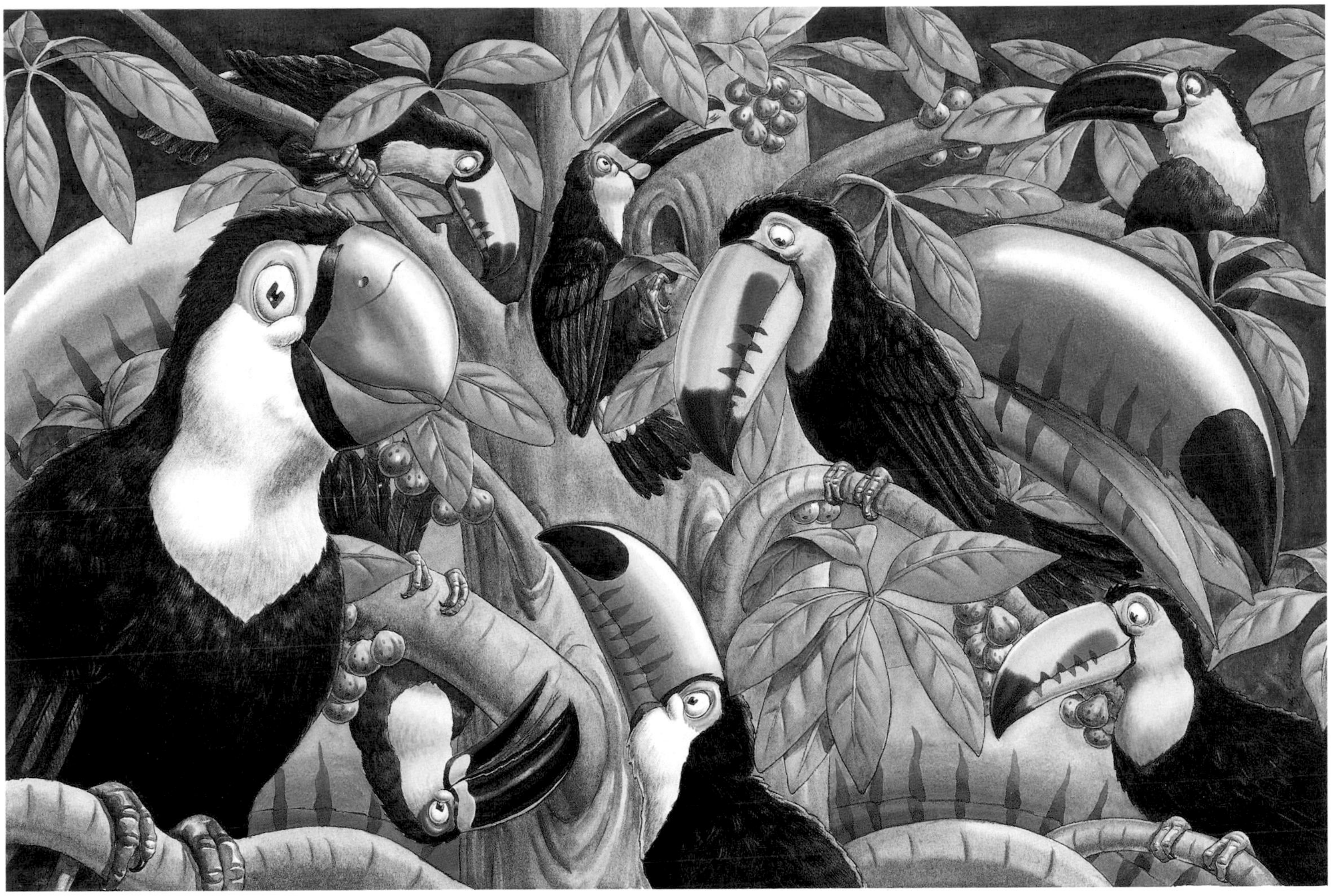

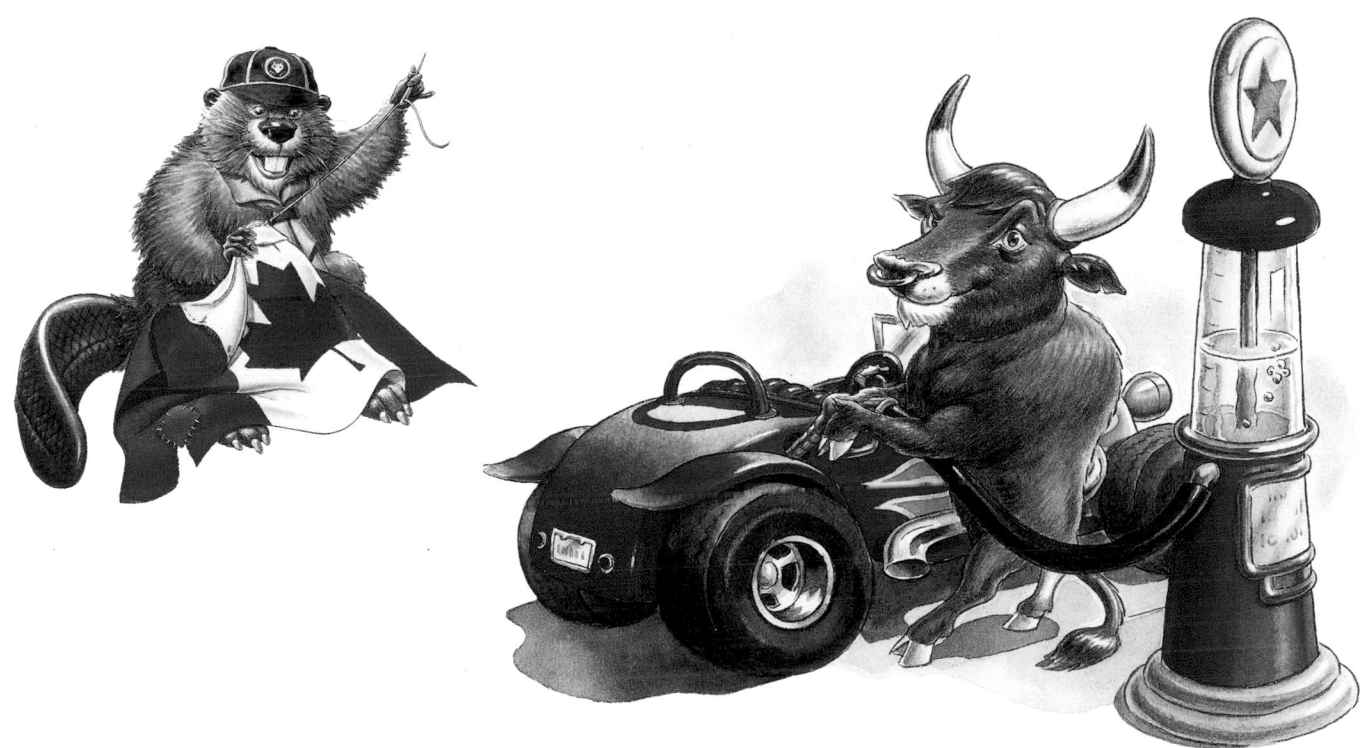

BARBARA SPURLL PHONE 1·800·989·3123 OR 416·594·6594

Showcase 19 - 23, Workbook 22 & 23, Directory of Illustration 17, Society of Illustrators 40. Call for fax number, email, website, portfolio, samples.

Forbes Magazine

Nuveen

Ad Pages in: Showcase 19, 20, 21, 22 and 23; Workbook 19 and 20; Directory of Illustration 12, 13, 14, and 15.

Online Portfolio and Stock Imagery available at ROBERTPASTRANA.COM

ROBERT PASTRANA
818 • 548 • 6083

SASHA RUBEL

773•525-3075

3421 N. Marshfield
Chicago, IL 60657

www.sasharubel.com
sasha@sasharubel.com

Mural for Kit Cole Investment Advisory Services

Tina Vey 212·460·9697

M.E. Cohen's
SM**ART** ART
"Leave the thinking to us"

Camera on a chip monitors internal body. — **PC Magazine**

Phenomenal cable franchise growth. — **Ameritech**

The PC itself is only part of what you need for personal computing. — **Fortune**

Phone
973-783-1171

Fax
973-783-2182

Mail
28 Aubrey Road
Upper Montclair, NJ 07043

E-mail
smartart@home.com

Web
www.theispot.com/
artist/mecohen

Cli**ents** Pizza Hut, Time Warner, Walt Disney, AT&T, Andrews & McNeel, Ameritech, Gibson Greetings, Standard & Poors, Forbes, E.D.S., N.Y.Times, Nickelodeon, Barrons, Scholastic, Sesame Street, Wall Street Journal, U.S. News & World Report, Newsweek, Bell Atlantic, DDB Needham, Ogilvy & Mather, A.M.A., CNA Insurance, National Law Journal, Washington Post

www.happypix.com

barbara
POLLaK
415.550.0551
digital illustration

Michael Garland
79 Manor Road
Patterson, NY 12563
845.878.4347
FAX: 845.878.4349
email:garlandmp@aol.com
www.bestweb.net/~artmtn/

Last Night at the ZOO

Michael Garlan

patton brothers illustration • 619.463.4562
www.pattonbros.com

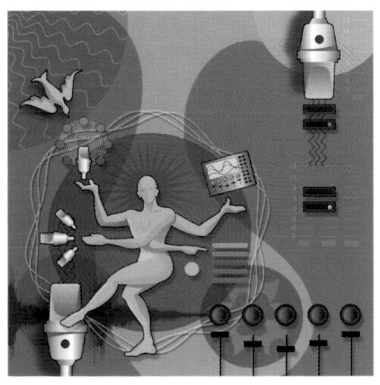

lisa@itsalooloo.com

lisa parett

860.669.4045

RICK POWELL

PHONE 757-440-1723, FAX 757-440-0952   PORTFOLIO & STOCK studiopowell.com

illustrations

JOSEPH
DAVIDSON
5 2 0 / 7 7 1 / 9 4 7 5

Post / Office / Box
1 9 8 8
Prescott / Arizona
8 6 3 0 2

FAX / 520 / 445 / 1583

Blandino

Carmelo Blandino tel. 514.934.5583   fax. 514.934.0267

JOHN STEVEN GURNEY

710 Western Avenue, Brattleboro, Vermont 05301   802.258.2654   fax 802.258.2654   jsgurney@cheshire.net
visit more samples at http://atom.cheshire.net/~jsgurney

R O B E R T   H U N T

Jeff Grunewald
Digital Illustration

Architectural, Retail, Trade Show
and Museum Visualization
Technical Illustration
Conceptual Illustration

Judy Francis
212.866.7204
212.734.6113
FAX 212.734.3263

Members Society of Illustrators
Members Graphic Artists Guild
Member Fashion Art Source
www.theispot.com

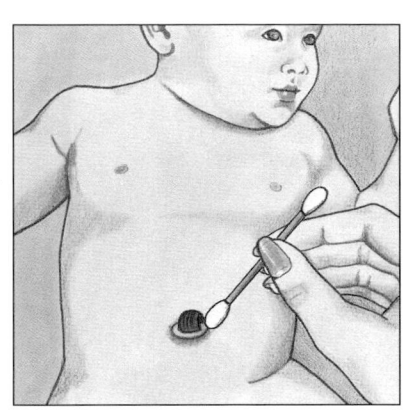
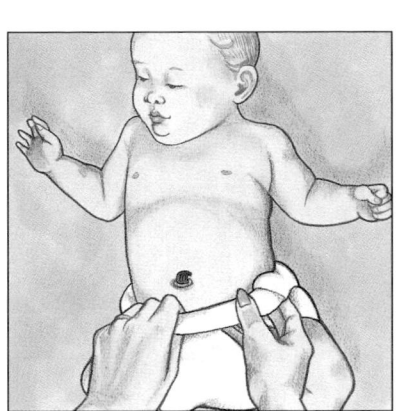

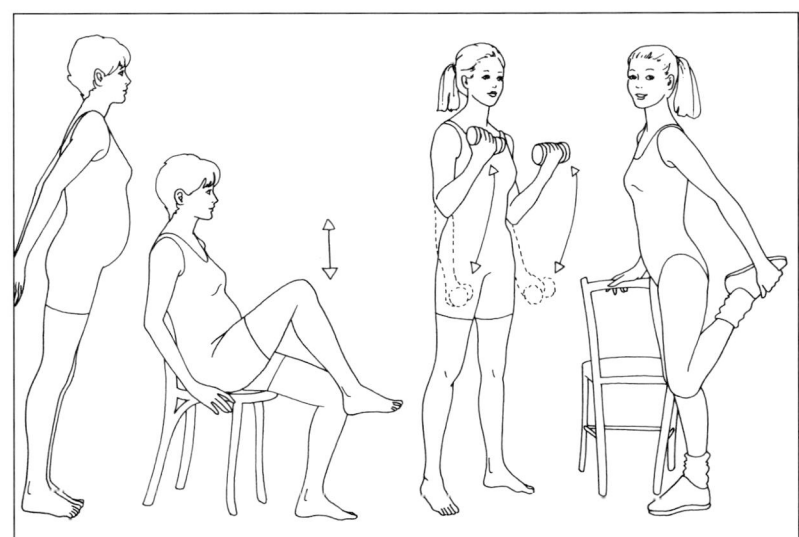
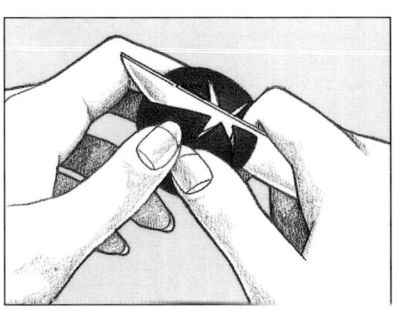
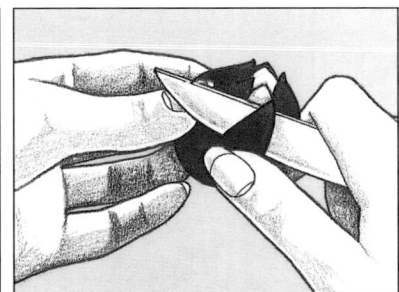

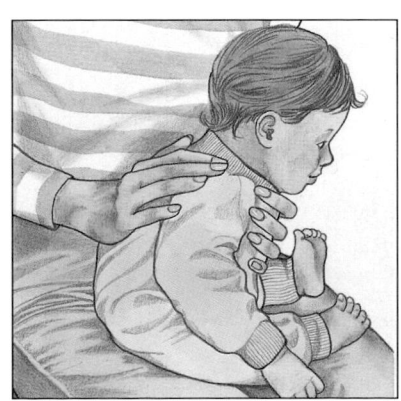

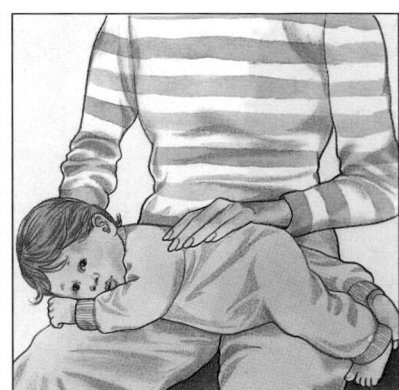

CATHERINE PARR

1888 288 2794
PORTFOLIO STOCK
WWW.THEISPOT.COM/ARTIST/PARR

jeff welch

415.337.1640

www.jeffwelch.net

MARINA THOMPSON

digital illustration   www.marinathompson.com   fax 781 581 5808   voice 781 581 1725

Providing Professional Artwork For Quite Some Time Now!

STEPHEN SCHUDLICH

ILLUSTRATION + DESIGN

303.575.9014 | 24 HOUR FACSIMILE .9015 | WWW.SSID.COM

call for your free gift!

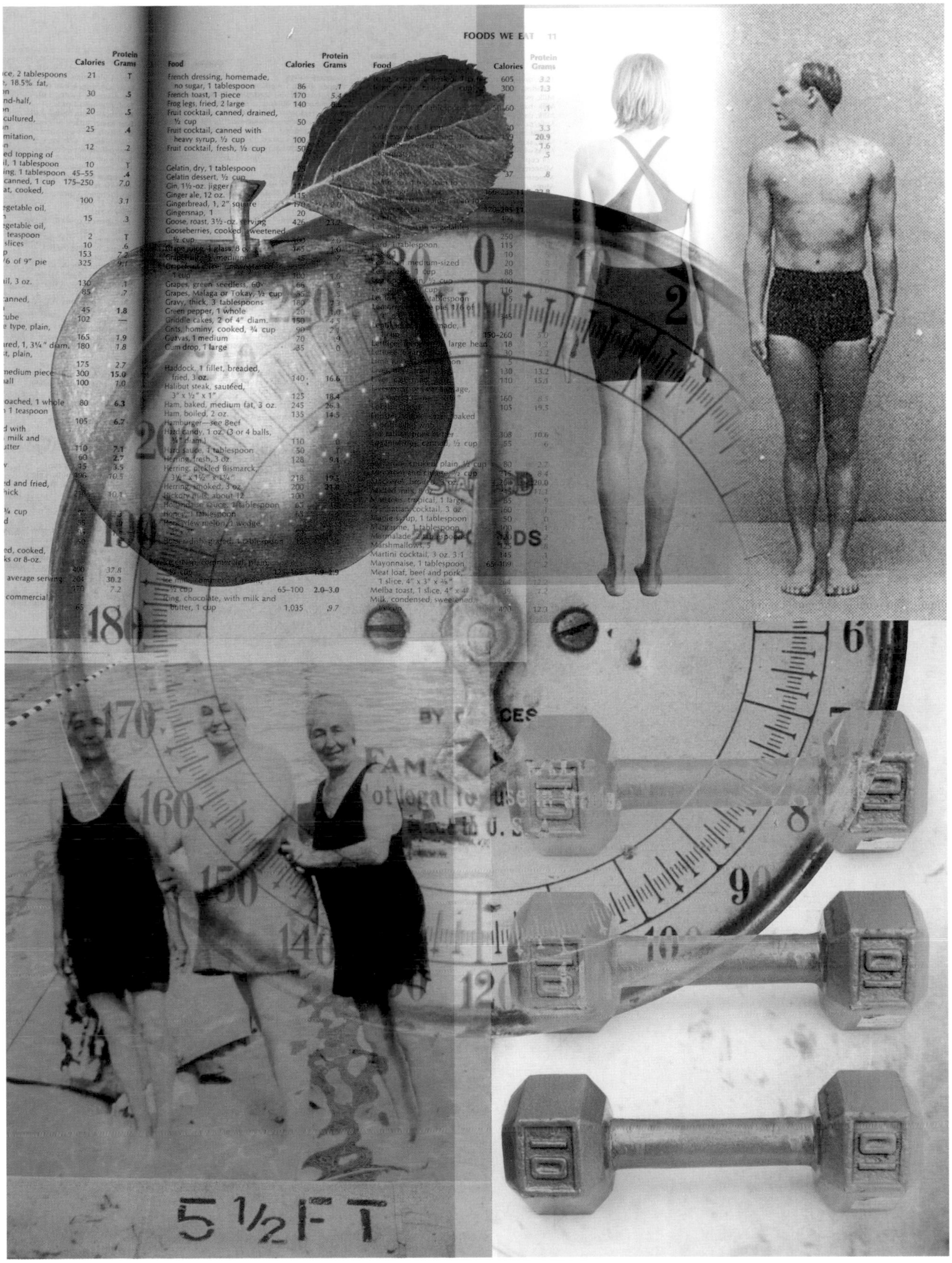

RIEGELART

MARGARET RIEGEL ✳ 800 WEST END AVENUE APT 8D NEW YORK NY 10025 ✳ 212.866.8466 T 212.662.2881 F RIEGELART@AOL.COM

SHANE REISWIG

TEL. 206.523.9579   FAX. 206.524.0831   shane@speakeasy.org   www.shanereiswig.com

Andrew Faulkner Illustration

415.332.3521

"Look! You can either back up your hard drive with our new, fully warrantied GT250 Turbomax system or risk losing all your data—it's up to you, mom!"

"Wait a minute!...I just bought that one!"

"Finally! Abacus 2.0!"

COLIN POOLE
1-800-808-5005

Rob Gregoretti

PHONE/FAX **718.779.7913** 41-07 56TH STREET, WOODSIDE, NEW YORK 11377 **www.theispot.com**

david weisman

70 e 10th st., #8g
ny, ny 10003
212-387-7805
dudesicl@interport.net

Clients include Adobe Press, Apple Computer Inc., CMP Publications, Electronic Arts Inc., Forbes ASAP, Guitar Player, The Hudson Valley Children's Museum, Henry Holt, IBM inc., Interactivity, M.I.T.'s Leonardo, Musician, NewMedia, Prentice Hall, Publish, Simon & Schuster, Success. Awards received are from the Art Director's Club, Print, Macromedia, and Publish. Group exhibitions include the Forbes Gallery, New York Digital Salon, School of Visual Arts Gallery, and Faculty Show at UC Berkeley.

About the Artist:
With his computer as his paintbrush , David works in his Greenwich Village studio, creating award-winning, dynamic style has appeared in publications world-wide, ranging from Forbes to the Hudson Valley Children's Museum. David enjoys working with editorial, problem/solution assignments utilizing metaphors, allegorical concepts, geometric shapes, and pattern fills. Additionally, David is a course instructor at the School of Visual Arts.

TIM SPOSATO
ILLUSTRATION
1.877.839.2509

For additional work, see Showcase 23,
Directory of Illustration #16.
See my portfolio at
www.theispot.com/artist/tsposato

©2000 C. Michael N

C. Michael Neely
mn@caveartstudios.com
3D Illustration & Animation

Cave Art Studios, Inc. - Animation, Illustration, & Interactive Design
phone 912.898-1501   web http://www.caveartstudios.com

DAVID JULIAN

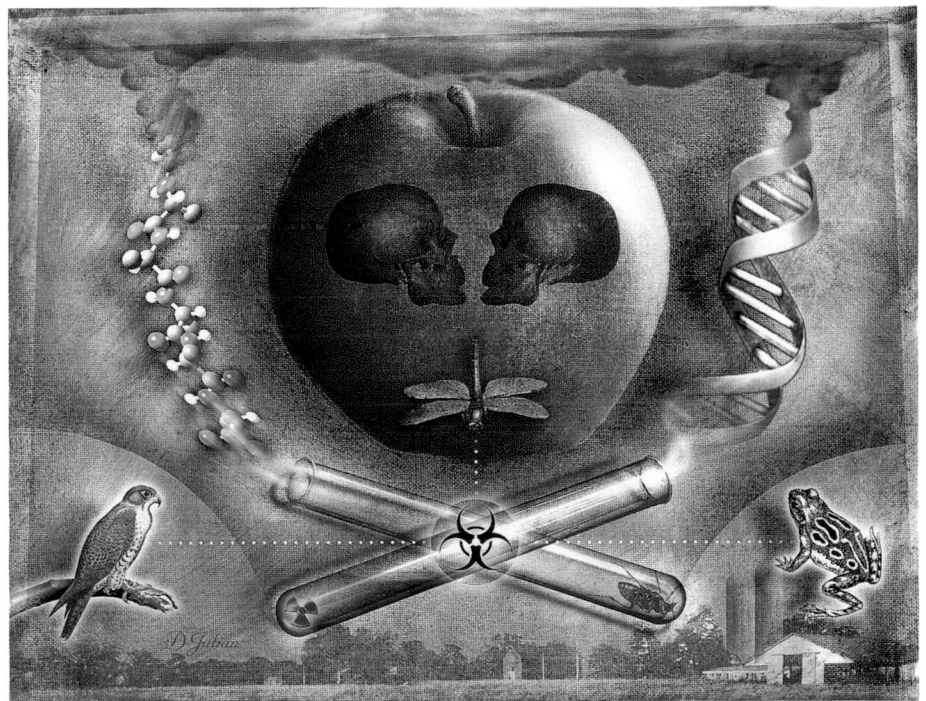

anatoly chernishov
4 Willowbank Court, Mahwah, NJ 07430-2909
tel: 201.327.2377 fax: 201.236.9469
e-mail: chern@usa.com

HARRY CAMPBELL

410-889-1100   harry@hspot.com   www.hspot.com

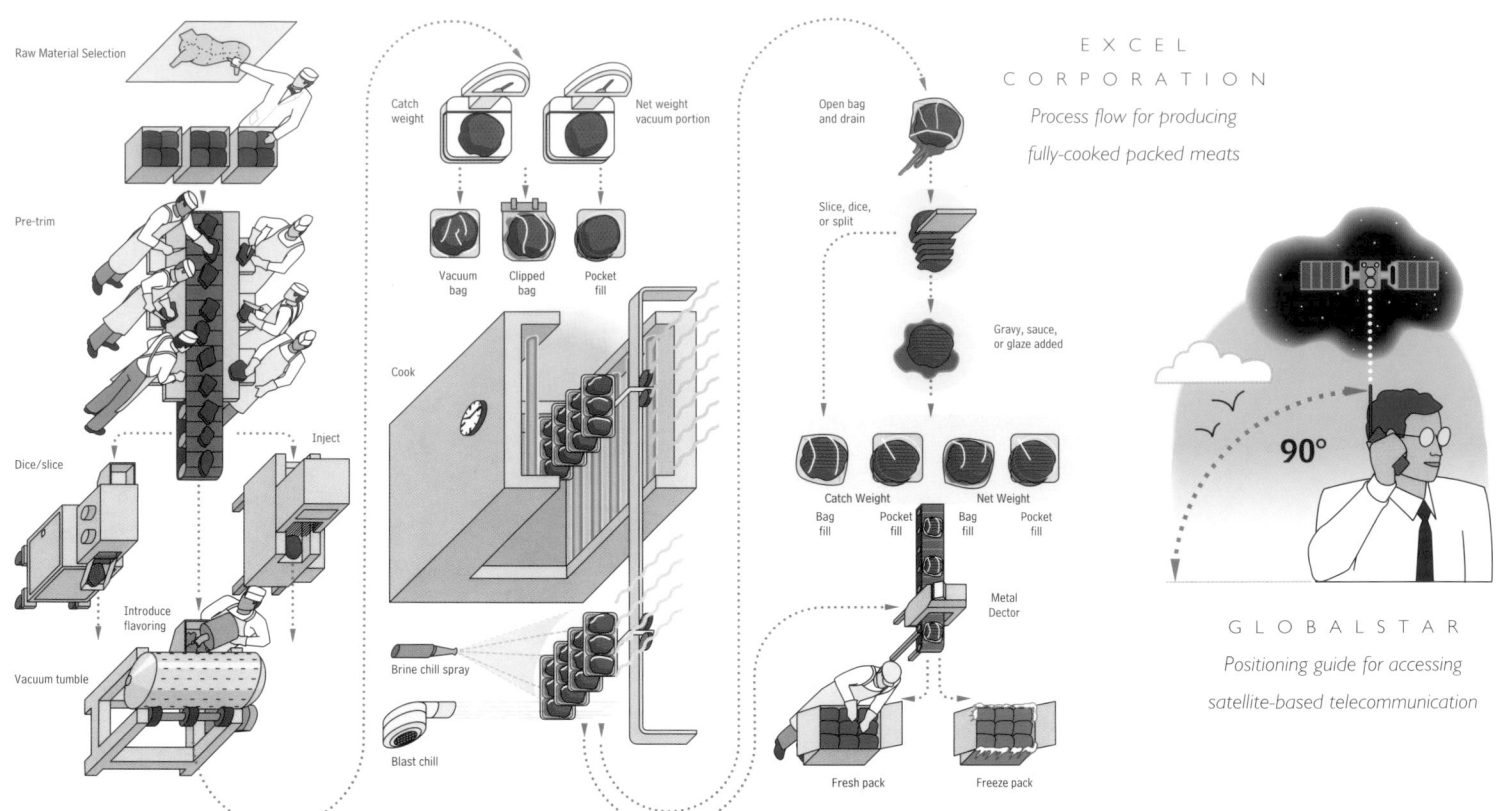

Raw Material Selection
Pre-trim
Dice/slice
Inject
Introduce flavoring
Vacuum tumble
Catch weight
Net weight vacuum portion
Vacuum bag
Clipped bag
Pocket fill
Cook
Brine chill spray
Blast chill
Open bag and drain
Slice, dice, or split
Gravy, sauce, or glaze added
Catch Weight
Net Weight
Bag fill
Pocket fill
Bag fill
Pocket fill
Metal Dector
Fresh pack
Freeze pack

E X C E L
C O R P O R A T I O N
Process flow for producing fully-cooked packed meats

90°

G L O B A L S T A R
Positioning guide for accessing satellite-based telecommunication

S I G N O R E
E R G O N O M I C S
A view of an ergonomic "Heaven and Hell" in an office environment

Jeff West

INFORMATION DESIGN AND ILLUSTRATION

Diagrams, Anatomies, Processes, Concept Models, Maps, Hierarchies, Structures, Relationships, Explanations, Narratives, Pictures, Interfaces, Icons, and Imagery

☎ **831.688.6075** fax 831.688.6072

View other samples at **www.jwestdesign.com**

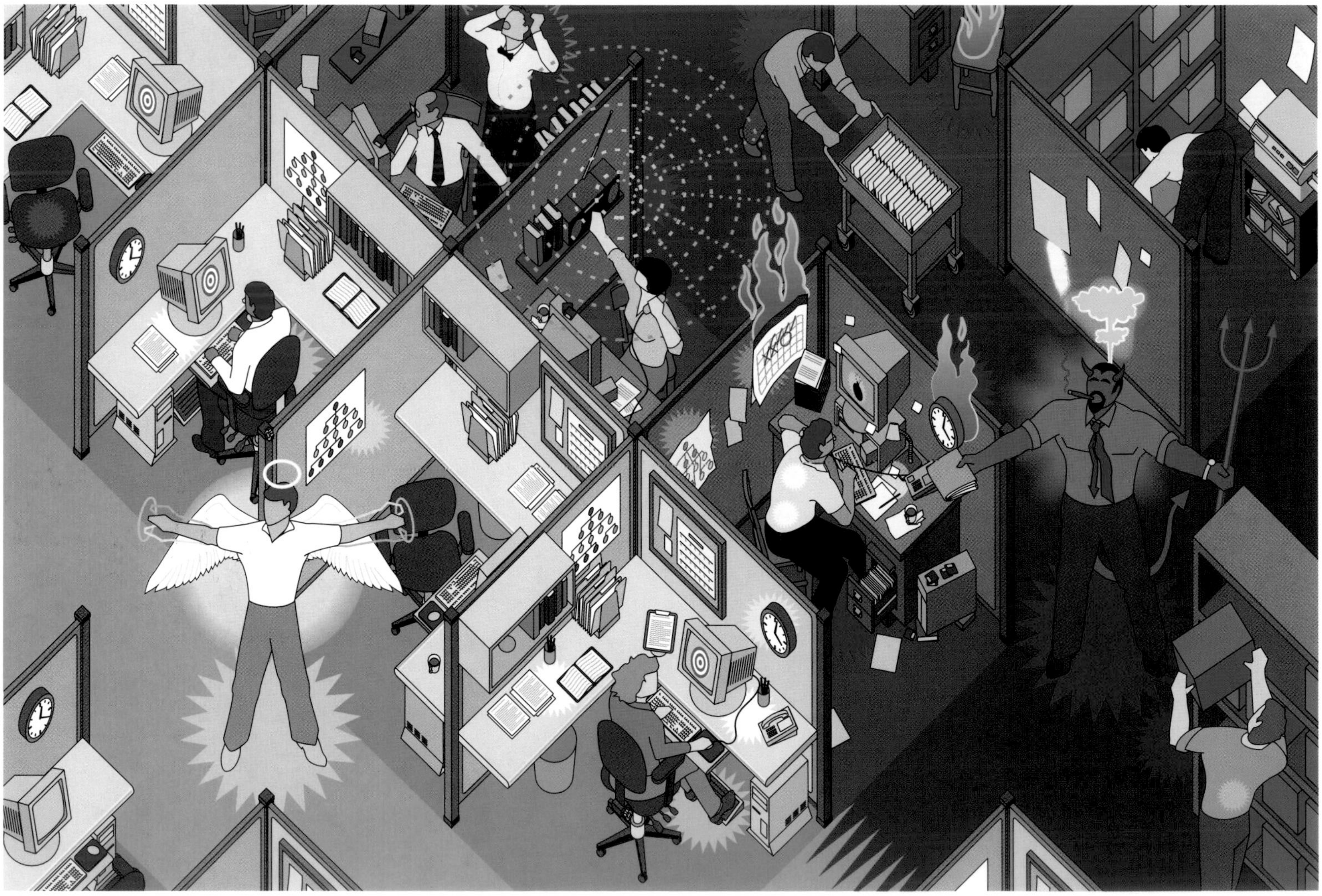

Marian Nixon

t: (773) 588 - 8640
f: (773) 588 - 7640
e: nixonm @ enteract.com

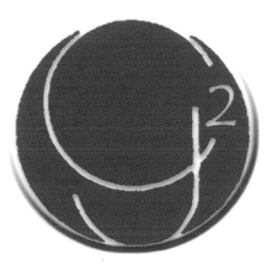

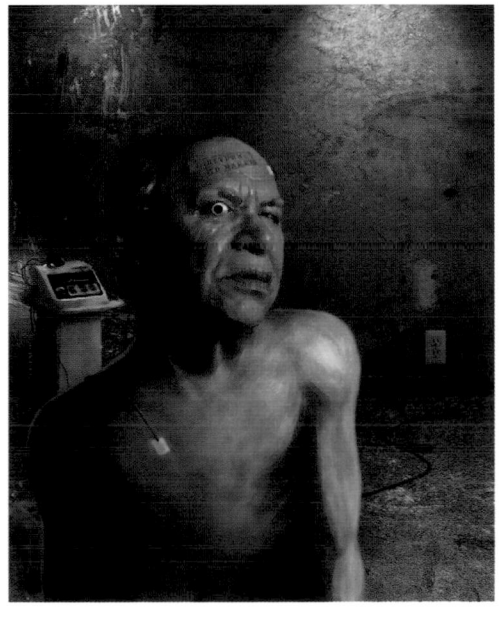

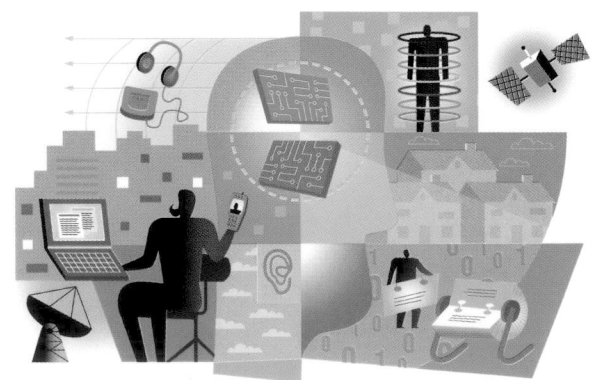

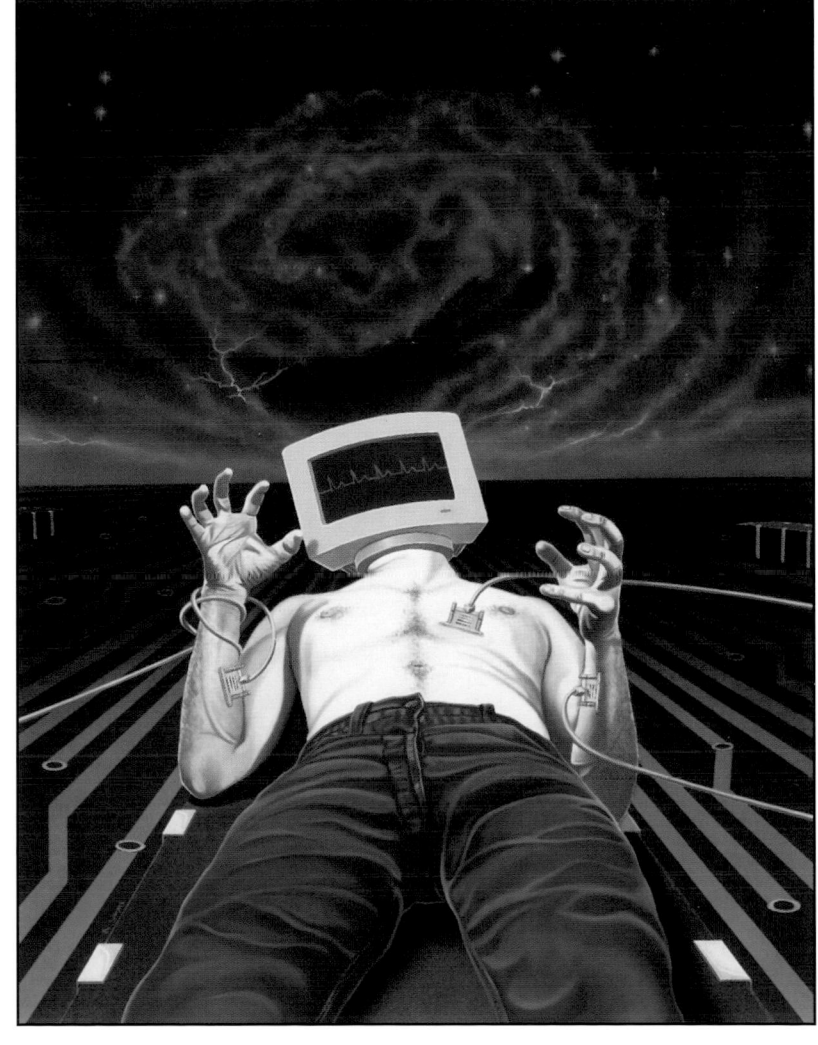

tel 916 929 477
fax 916 929 173
e-mail shull@hullhoneycutt.c

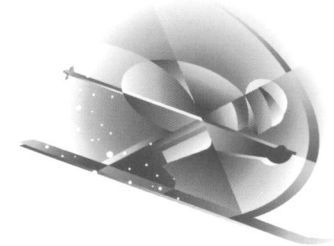

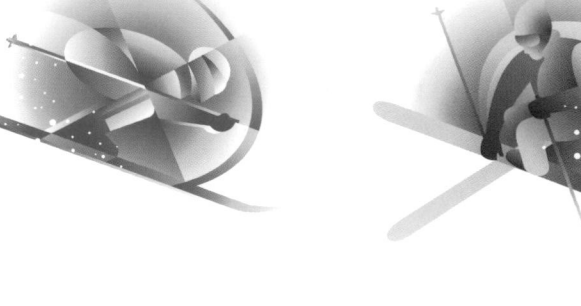

DIGITAL ILLUSTRATION+DESIGN

another
color

Creative Photo-Illustration.
Superior Image Modification.
SAM HALTOM
970.871.0151 voice
970.871.0150 fax
sam@digitalnation.com
www.anothercolor.com

Clients include:
IBM, Bell Atlantic, NASA,
Time Life Books/Video,
Lockheed Martin,
American College of Radiology,
Steamboat Ski & Resort

Shenandoah Dreamer

Elizabeth Pollie

Phone 810.629.8855 Fax 810.629.7374 www.epollie.com

TERRY SHOFFNER ILLUSTRATOR INC.
(416) 967-6717

marc stolfi
blackbird studio

203 • 439 • 0674
34 flagler avenue
cheshire, ct 06410
www.marcstolfi.com

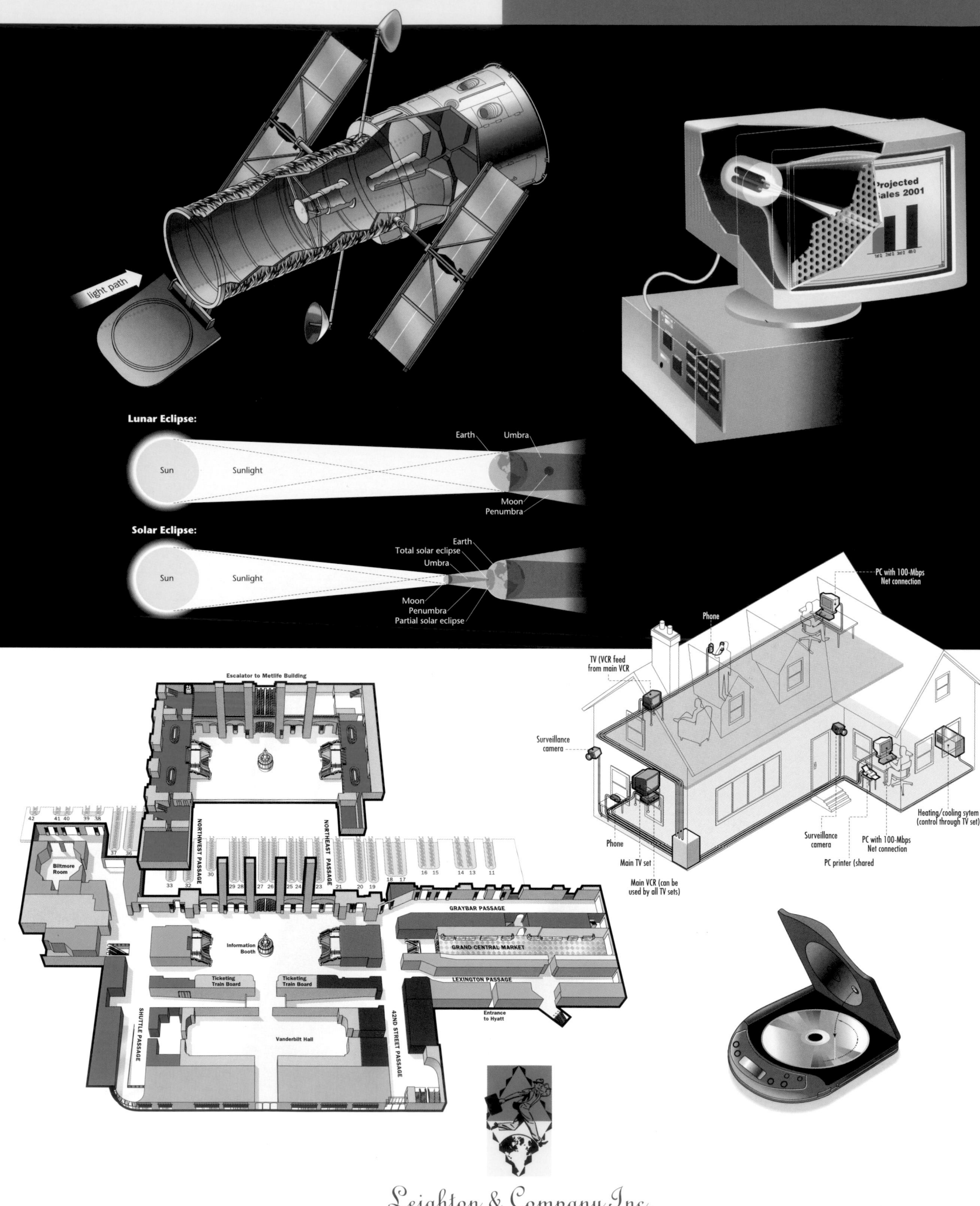

steven stankiewicz

Lunar Eclipse:

Sun · Sunlight · Earth · Umbra · Moon · Penumbra

Solar Eclipse:

Sun · Sunlight · Earth · Total solar eclipse · Umbra · Moon · Penumbra · Partial solar eclipse

light path

Projected Sales 2001

Escalator to Metlife Building

NORTHWEST PASSAGE · NORTHEAST PASSAGE

Biltmore Room

42 41 40 39 38 37 36 35 34 33 32 31 30 29 28 27 26 25 24 23 22 21 20 19 18 17 16 15 14 13 11

GRAYBAR PASSAGE

Information Booth

GRAND CENTRAL MARKET

Ticketing Train Board · Ticketing Train Board

LEXINGTON PASSAGE

SHUTTLE PASSAGE · 42ND STREET PASSAGE

Vanderbilt Hall

Entrance to Hyatt

PC with 100-Mbps Net connection

Phone

TV (VCR feed from main VCR)

Surveillance camera

Heating/cooling sytem (control through TV set)

Surveillance camera

Phone

Main TV set

Main VCR (can be used by all TV sets)

PC printer (shared

PC with 100-Mbps Net connection

978 • 921 • 0887 phone
978 • 921 • 0223 fax

Leighton & Company Inc.
ARTISTS' REPRESENTATIVES
http://www.leightonreps.com

in New York City call:
212 • 477 • 4229

Michael Kirkbride • Illustration • Phone & Fax: 415. 924. 3839

Portfolio available at : www.theispot.com

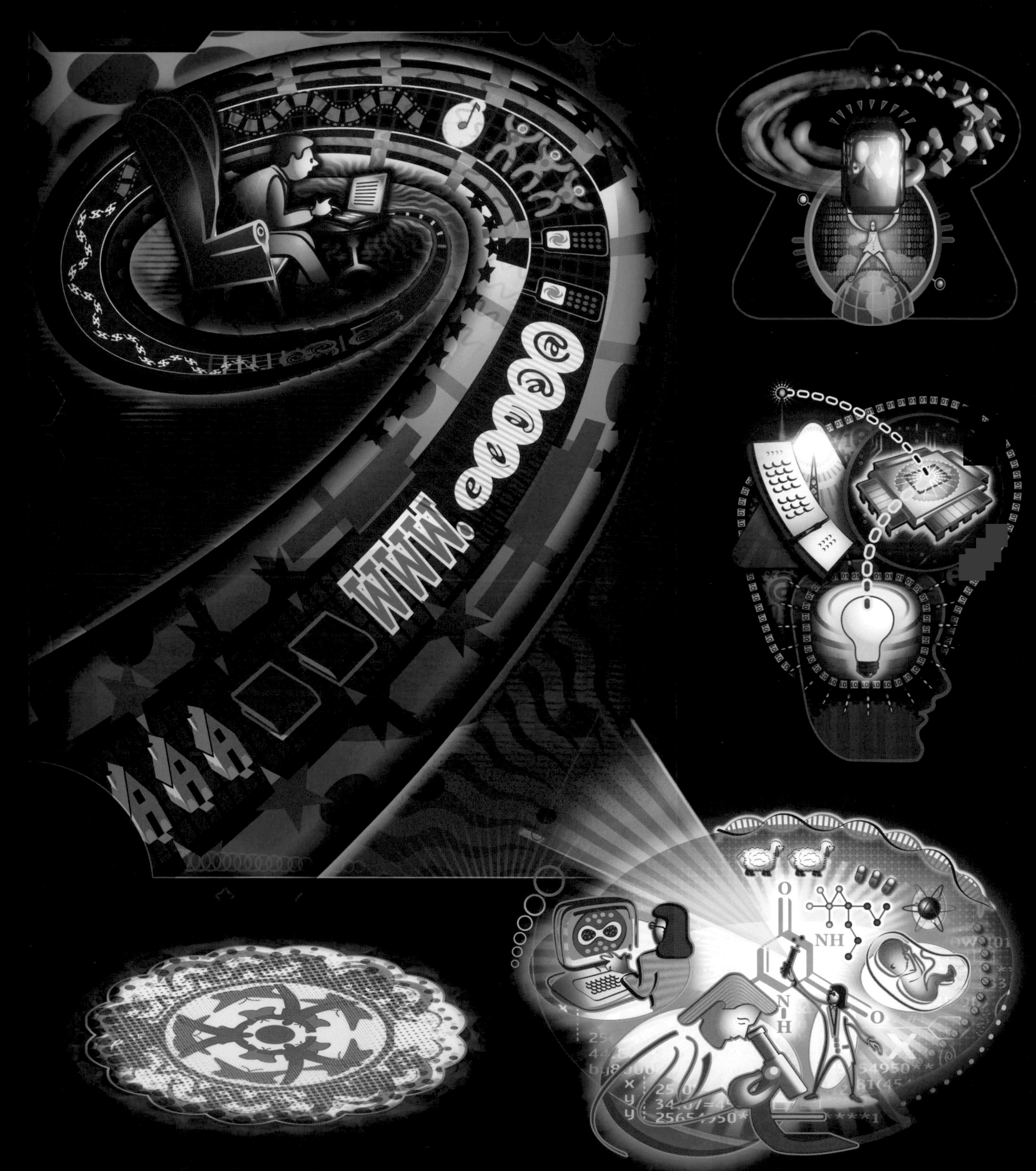

John Martin Illustration
37276 Chelsea Court
Farmington Hills, MI 48331
(248) 848-1388
FAX: (248) 848-1161
www.flash.net/~jamartn
e-mail - jamartn@flash.net

Clients:
Chrysler, Ford, General Motors,
Big Boy, Little Ceasars, UAW,
McDonalds, Taco Bell, Valassis,
Wendy's, White Castle, Nextel,
U-Save, Anchor Bay
Entertainment, Farmer Jack

Awards:
Detroit Creative Council (CADDY)
Detroit Scarab Club Award
PIA Graphic Arts Award
P.O.P.A.I.-OMA Gold Award

Mike Flint
20 Levesque Lane
Mont Vernon, NH 03057
603.673.6234

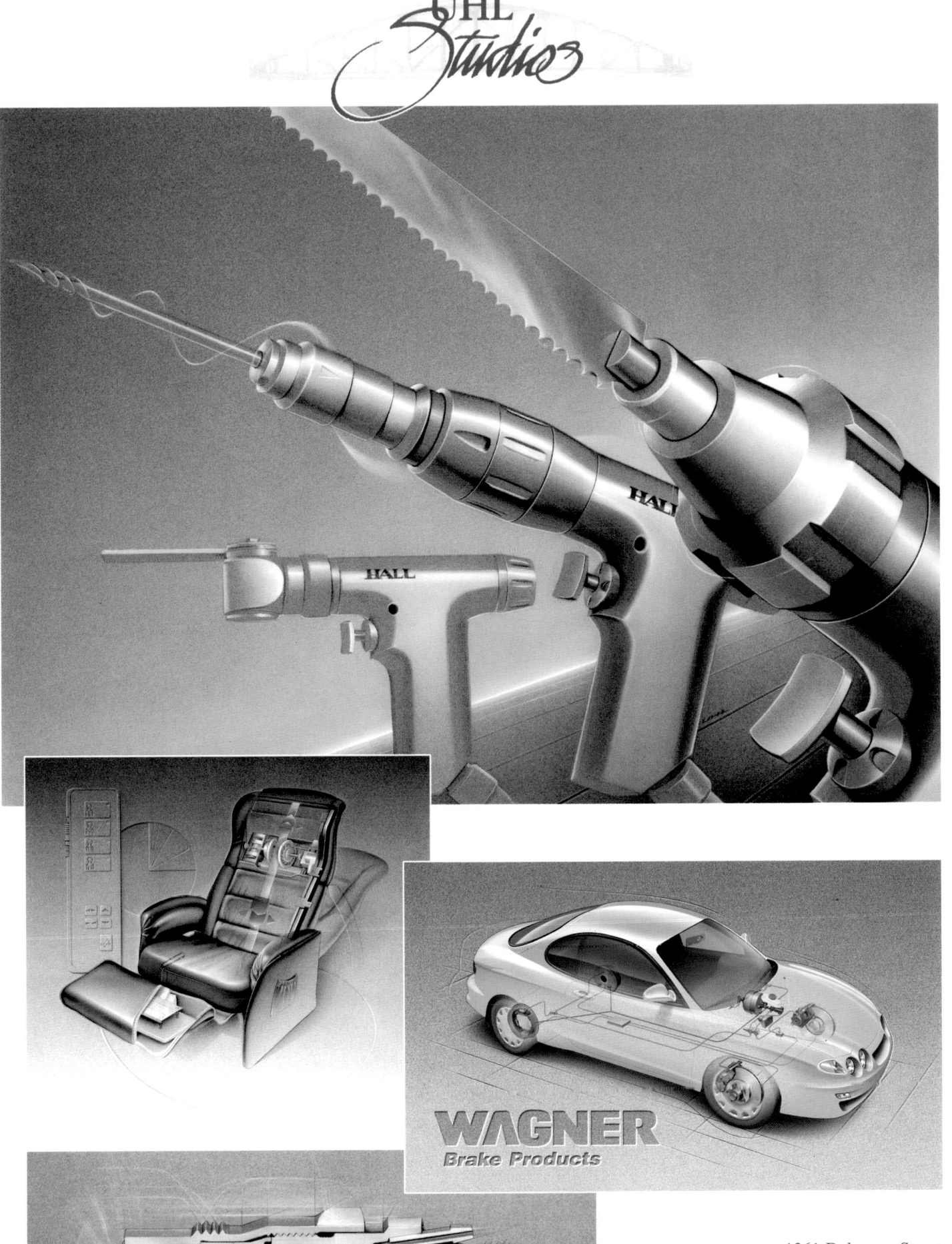

UHL
Studios

1261 Delaware Street
Denver, Colorado 80204
ph. 303.534.2054
fax. 303.534.2056
email-daviduhl@sni.net
www.uhlstudios.com
www.theispot.com/artist/duhl

At the wet end of the paper machine, our starches are used in the sheet forming process for strength and drainage.

For a coated finish, our starches help adhere the coating minerals to the base sheet.

To impart a finished surface for better printing, our sizing starches are applied after pressing and drying the paper.

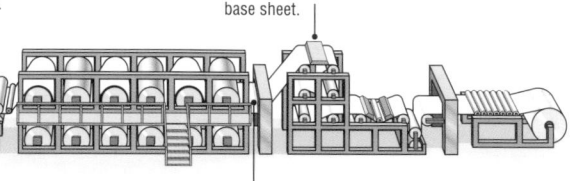

Penford starches and dextrins are used in the batter applicator. The starches and dextrins are dry-blended with other ingredients and flavors then hydrated to approximately 60% moisture. The wet batter is pumped into the batter applicator. The french fries pass through the batter prior to par frying. The batter improves the finished product texture and increases the in-store hold time of the french fries.

peel   wash   cut   dry   par fry   freeze

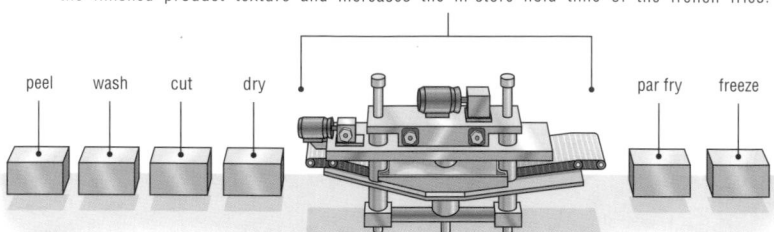

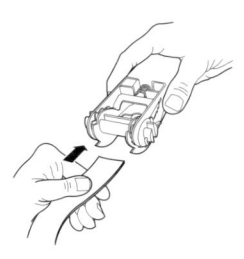

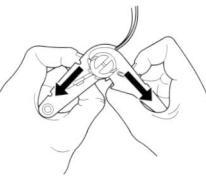

14.4k

❶

MSC

❷

BTS

❸ ❹

IWF

❺

Public Switched Telephone Network

❻

Microsoft Point-to-Point Compression software loaded on end-user's laptop

provides data throughput equivalent to landline modems

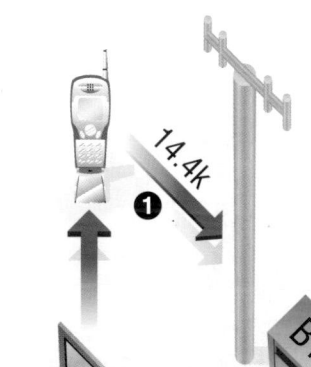

Corporate Server(s)

Must have **Windows NT** RAS Server

RAS Server

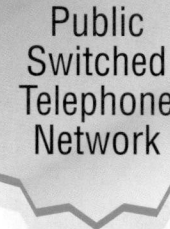

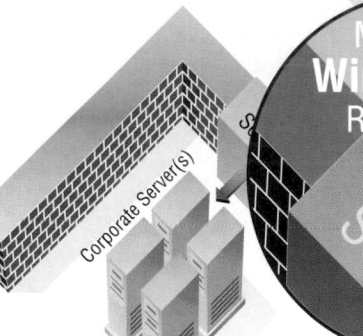

Motherboard
Ribbon cable
Power supply
RAM chips
Expansion slot card

Disk drive
CD ROM drive
ZIP drive
Hard drive

ENCRYPTION PROCESS

Dear Max   X1XMVPQ2

INTERNET HACKER

X1XMVPQ2

Dear Max

PRIVATE KEY

COLIN HAYES
ILLUSTRATOR
(425) 338-5452
colinhayes@aol.com

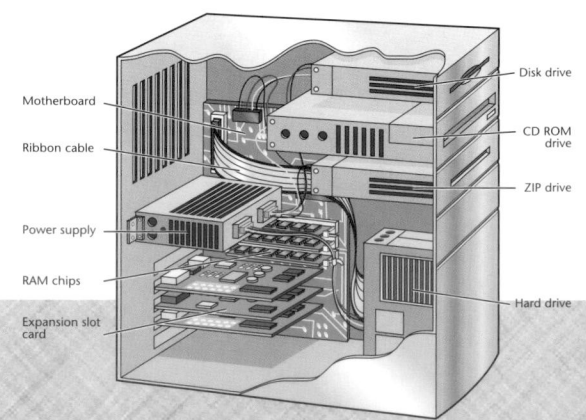

mikecressy@earthlink.net

MIKE CRESSY

ILLUSTRATION

On-line Portfolio

http://home.earthlink.net/~mikecressy

853

Amy Vangsgard

 **Tel:** (323) 461-3094

 **Portfolio:** www.theispot.com/artist/vangsgard

www.spark-y.co.uk
mail@spark-y.co.uk

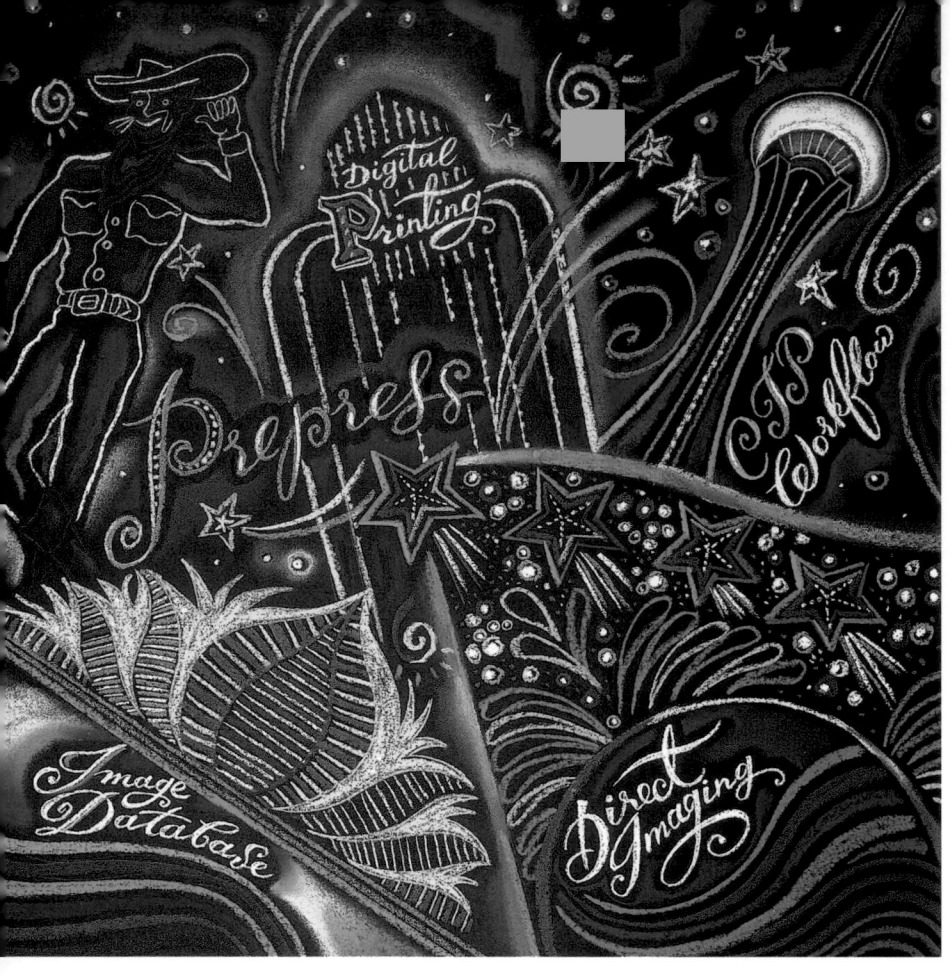

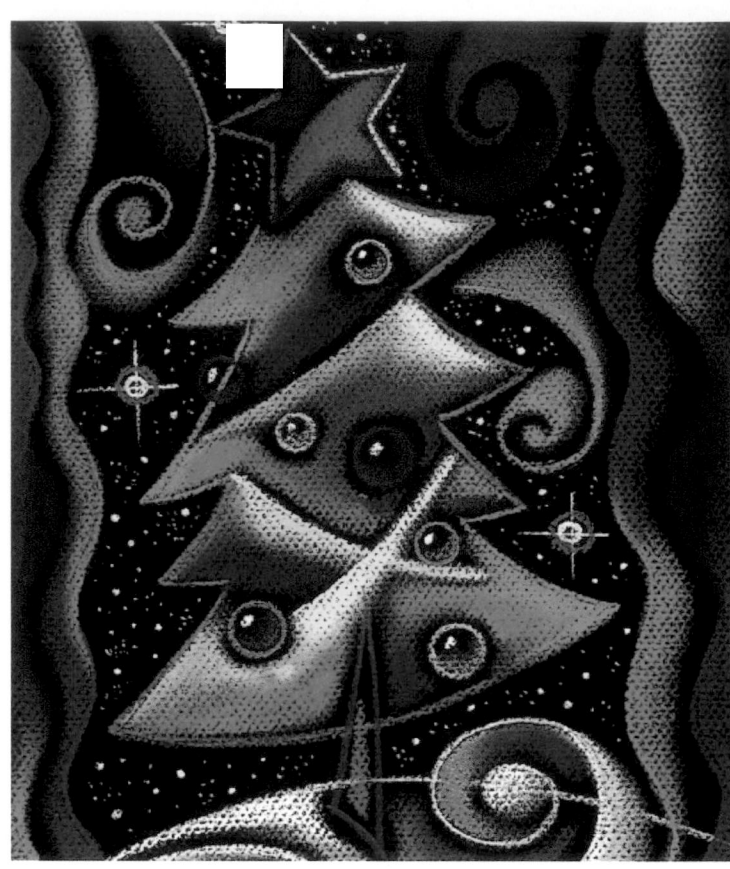

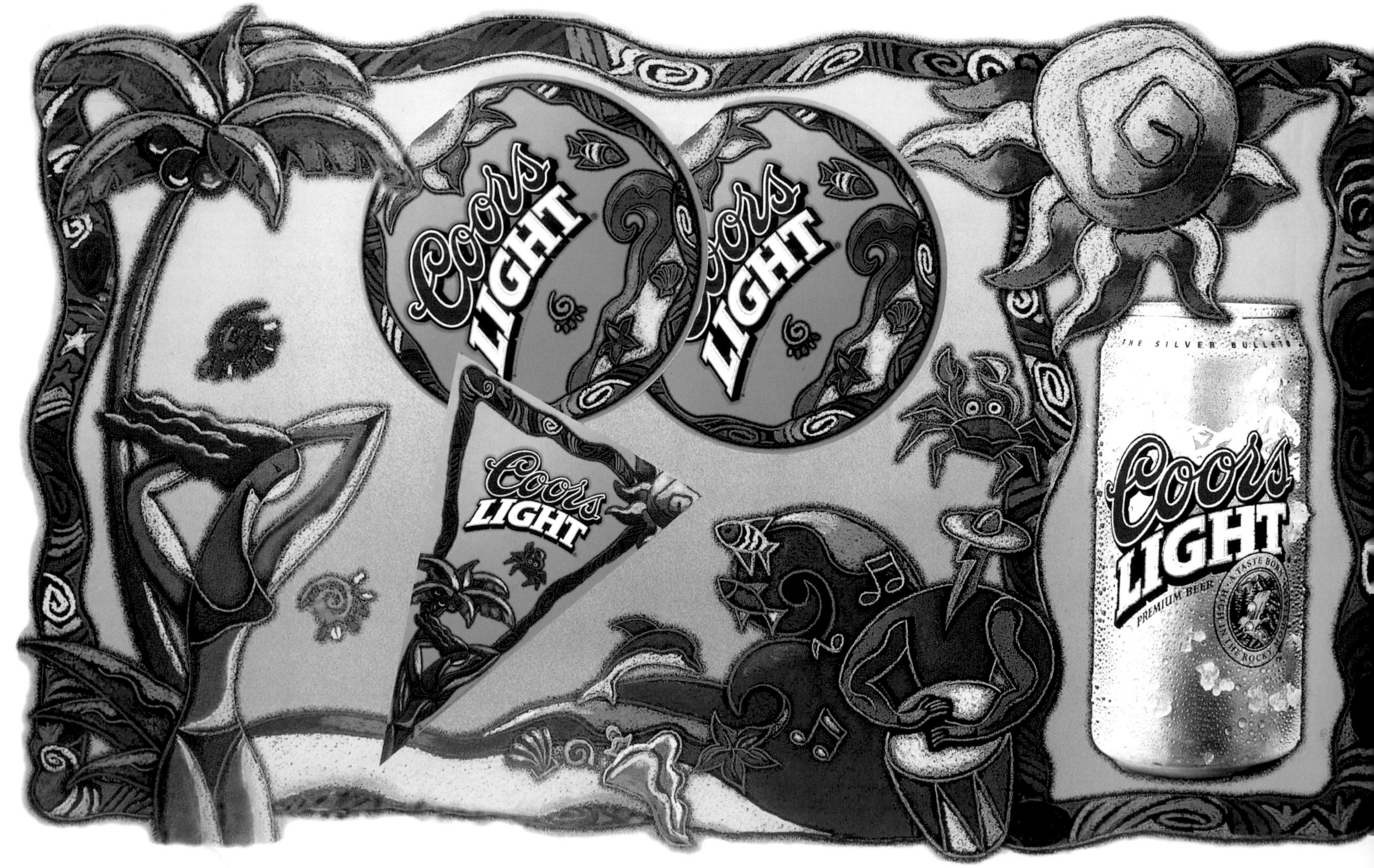

Leon Zernitsky
tel:905.770.2199 fax:905.770.9798

See more at:
www.leonzernitsky.com

Staywell

Delta Air Lines

American Express

Jimmy Holder

1452 El Miradero Ave.
Glendale, CA 91201

www.**jimmyholder**.com
(818) 244-6707

FAX 818 244-6766

Edith L. Bingham
ILLUSTRATION
831-636-8397

482 South Street, Hollister, California 95023

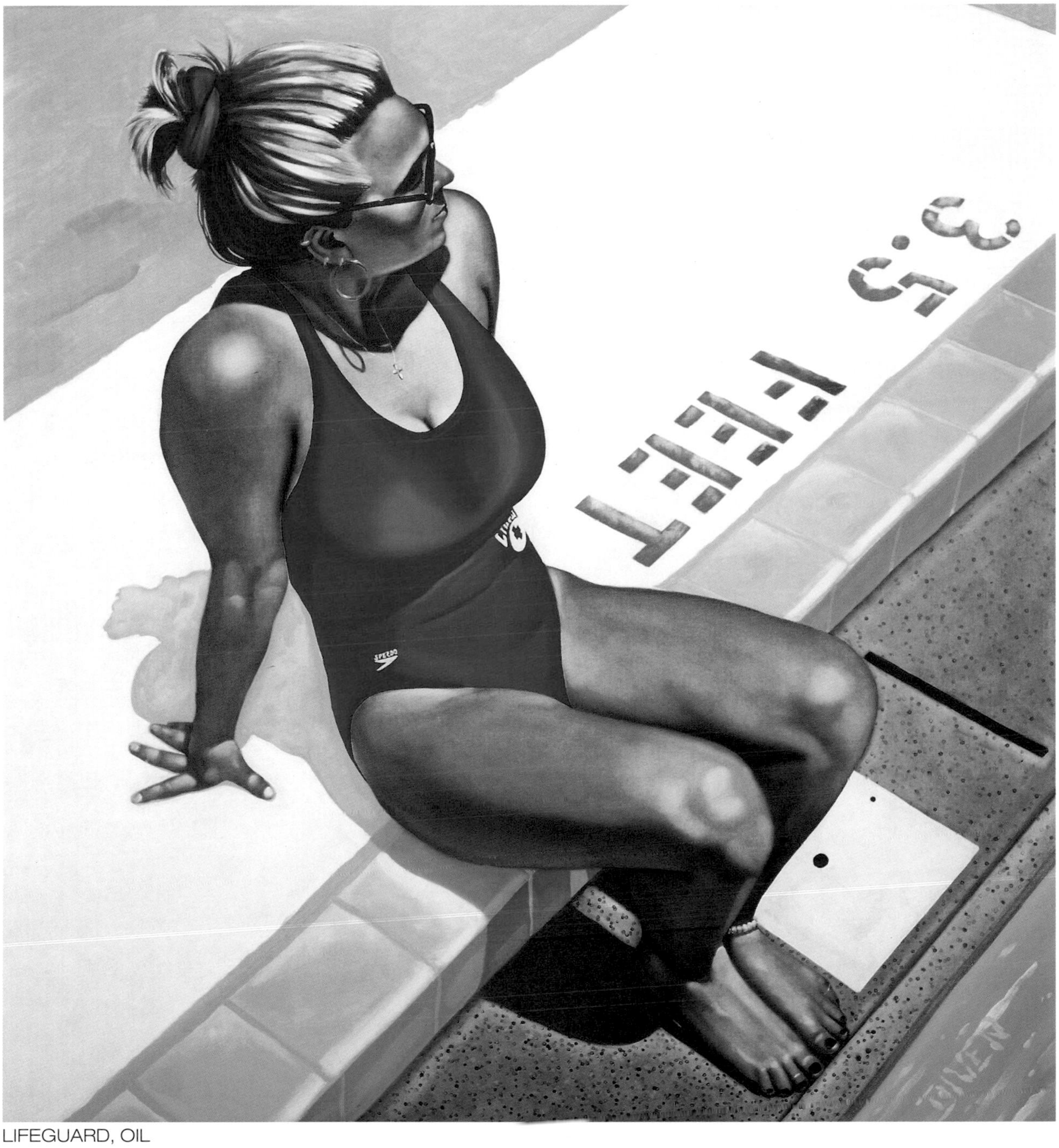

Howard Cruse ● 88-11 34th Avenue #5D ● Jackson Heights, NY 11372 ● (718)639-4951 ● Fax: (718)639-40 95

Funny Funnels

©'85 CRUSE

HCruse1816@aol.com
www.howardcruse.com

©1998 CRUSE

Joseph
Demaree

(408) 297-8332

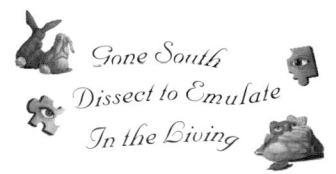
Gone South
Dissect to Emulate
In the Living

2538 la mirada dr. san jose, ca. 95125 ~ www.nothingenterprises.com

Comparison Shopping Mall
Washington Mutual Bank
ink & watercolor

Savertooth Tiger
Boeing Employees Credit Union
ink & Photoshop

www.samday.com

SAM DAY
I Draw Pictures.

206.382.7413

P.O.Box 4425 Seattle, WA 98104

862

MICHELE AMATRULA

Phone: 212•255•7413   www.illustrators.net/amatrula/   Fax: 212•989•4374

142 West 26th Street • Suite #12B • New York, New York • 10001

Tim Schneider
(626) 683-0648

to see more work go to timschneiderillustration.com

Mark E. Verna

66 Martinot Ave.
Rochester, NY 14609-3803
845 288-5762 *phone/fax*
verna@localnet.com *e-mail*
www.theispot.com

Winky Adam   370 Central Park West   New York, NY 10025   212.423.0746

CHUCK TODD ILLUSTRATION (925) 691-8541

www.chucktodd.net

CHUCK TODD

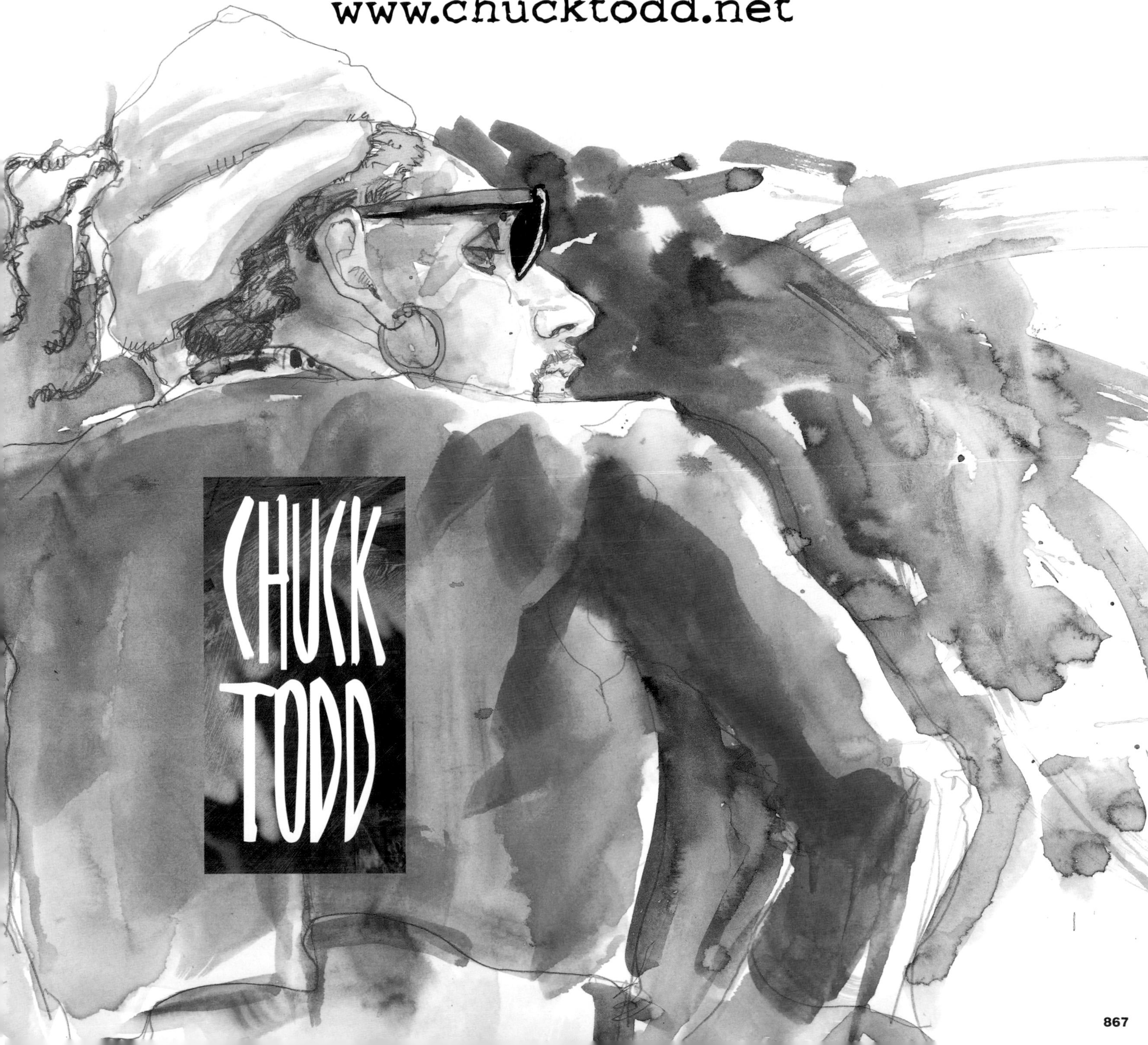

LINDA BILD
310-444-9962
e-mail: LBild16658@aol.com

"DRAGONHEART" for Universal Studios and Sound Source Interactive

"BABE" for Universal Studios and Sound Source Interactive

SCOTT GWILLIAMS

TEL (416) 929-8432

FAX (416) 926-8875

G I O V A N N I N A   C O L A L I L L O

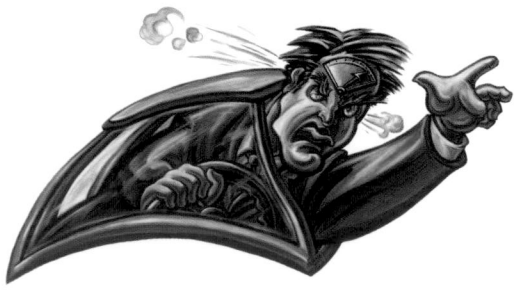

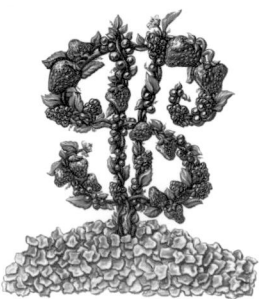

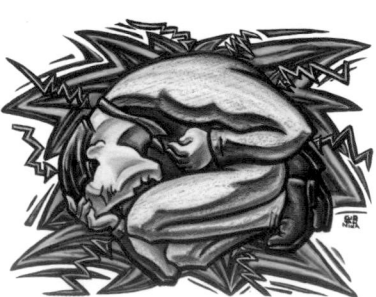

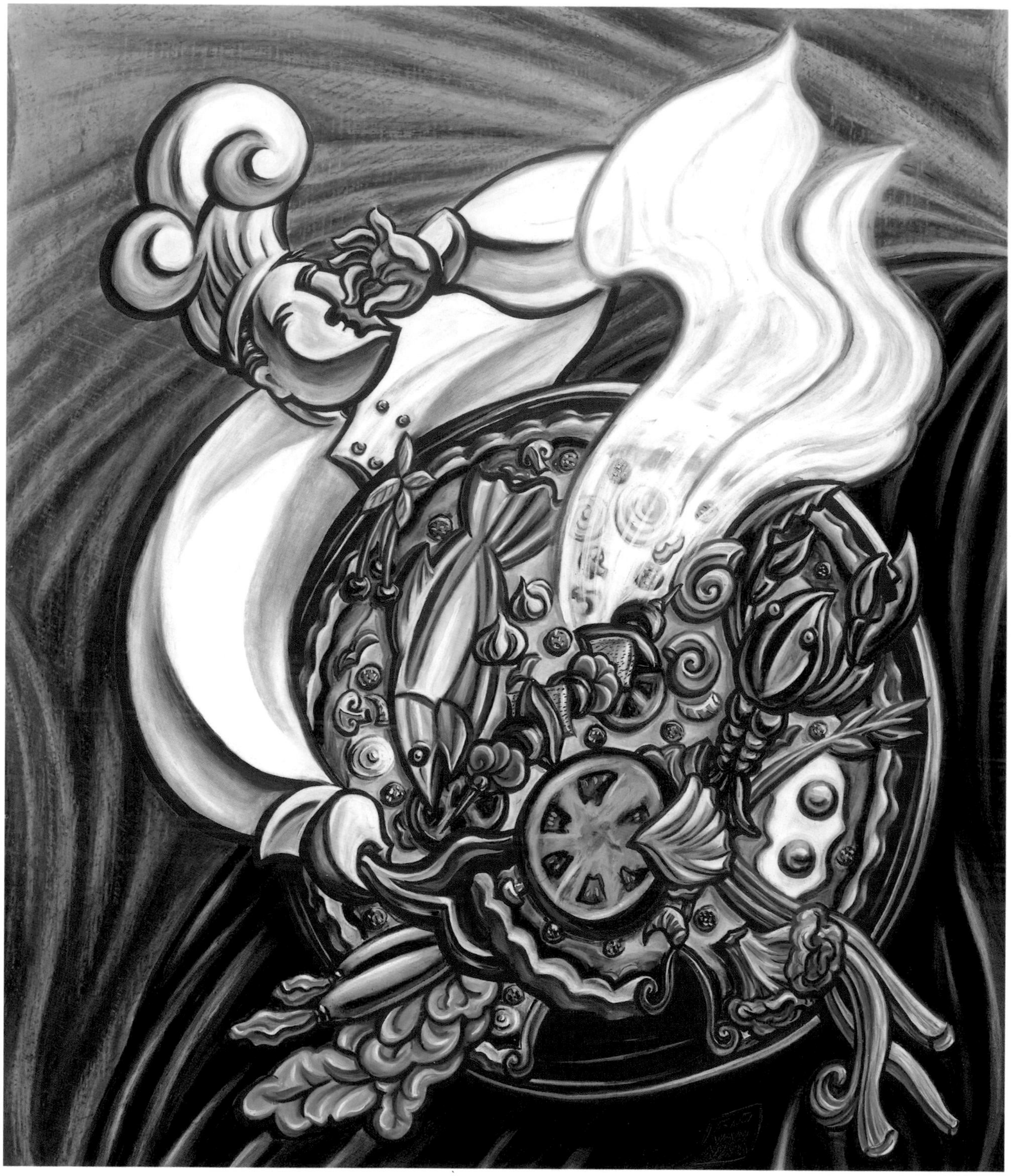

GIO VAN NINA ILLUSTRATION

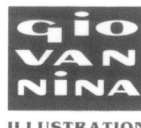

PHONE 905~939~1156 • FAX 905~939~2128

nyc

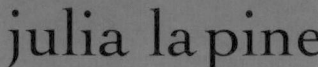

julia la pine

represented by

Eastcoast/Midwest

carolyn potts

and associates

888.546.7688

or 773.935.8840

Westcoast

sharon dodge

and associates

206.284.4701

fax 206.282.3499

BOBBYE COCHRAN

studio
773.404.0375

fax
773.404.0377

COZAAR CUP

Keiko Motoyama

1607 East Glenhaven Drive
Phoenix, AZ 85048
Phone/fax 480.460.2743
Phone 877.251.9663
email: mokkun@aol.com

Artist agent: Christina A. Tugeau
203.438.7307

For additional work see:
American Showcase 21, 22, 23

STEPHANIE DALTON COWAN

Foot leads eye, eye instructs foot, alternatingly. Walking takes on the movement of soul because, as the great philosopher Plotinus said, the soul's motion is not direct

mittens

and 86,297 other things that begin with "M" cheerfully illustrated by Megan Montague Cash*

clients:

Barnes & Noble
Big Apple Circus
Brooklyn Children's Museum
Children's Museum of Manhattan
Disney Enterprises
eeBoo Corporation
Elektra Entertainment
Family Fun Magazine

Family Life Magazine
Galison Books
Graphique de France
Just Play In Furniture
Museum of Modern Art
New York Kids, WNYC
Nick Jr. Magazine
Nickelodeon

Parenting Magazine
Parents Magazine
Silicon Graphics
Simon & Schuster
South Street Seaport Museum
Scholastic
Stewart, Tabori & Chang
They Might Be Giants

**Call for samples
or just to say hello:**
(718) 388-3473
(718) 388-0043/fax
Brooklyn, NY 11211
www.megancash.com
megan@megancash.com

*Many other letters of the
alphabet accommodated.
Please inquire about
your favorites.

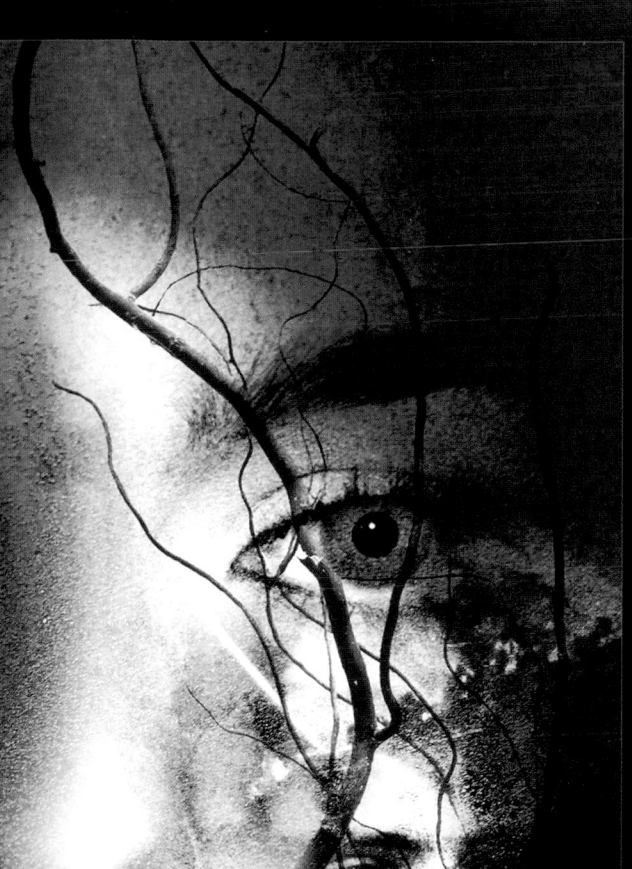

SANDY YOUNG

www.studio-y.com 707.939.1131

Photo-Illustration / Digital Imagery
Current Portfolio Online: www.studio-y.com
e-mail: ideas@studio-y.com

See also Showcase 23
The Alternative Pick 8, 9, 10

"Lost in Love" – Guideposts for Teens Magazine

<u>*Dark Secrets*</u> *– Pocketbooks / Simon & Schuster*

"Cancer Survivor" – Guideposts for Teens Magazine

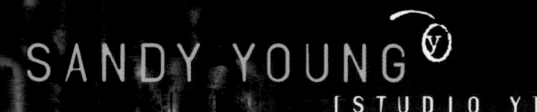

SANDY YOUNG
[STUDIO Y]

"New Visions for a New Millenium" – Independent School (cover)

OGDEMLI/FELDMAN DESIGN & ILLUSTRATION

818•760•1759   FAX: 818•760•1582

E-MAIL: daniel@ogdemlifeldman.com

http://www.ogdemlifeldman.com

LOGOS/LETTERING • PACKAGING

BROCHURES/COLLATERAL • SIGNAGE

PRODUCT DESIGN • ILLUSTRATION

SEE SHOWCASE 22 & 23, WORKBOOK 19-22

cindy couling
Illustrator

408.431.0675
www.couling.com

879

ERIC JOYNER

ZAMMARCHI

www.zammarchi.com

NANCY GIBSON NASH

TELEPHONE 207·766·5761

nancygibsonnash.com

FAX 207·766·4472

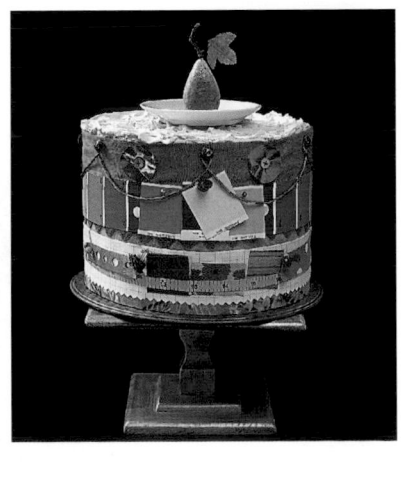

Time (Asia)

SI for Kids

Cool & Strange Music

Mac Addict (3)

daryll collins   513.683-9335   fax 513.683-9345
darylla1c@aol.com

Adam Hart

678-560-8506 (STUDIO)

WWW. ADAM-HART .COM

E-MAIL: ADAM.HART@MINDSPRING.COM

James Montgomery Flagg

Toni Morrison

Celestine Sibley

John Cage

Debbie Hanley

Daisy Art Studio

500 Aurora Ave N #405
Seattle, WA 98109
fone/phax: 206.621.0410
e.mail: daiseyart@aol.com

So call today and you'll be able to say "I got it at Daisy Art!"

Eddie Young ph: 562 429-2513 fx: 562 429-1400
e-mail: youngeddie@eddieyoung.com Web Site: www.eddieyoung.com

allen ginsberg for east bay express

free goodies, yummy artwork!

wertzateria.com
michael s. wertz illustration

{415} 824-5542

mykl@wertzateria.com

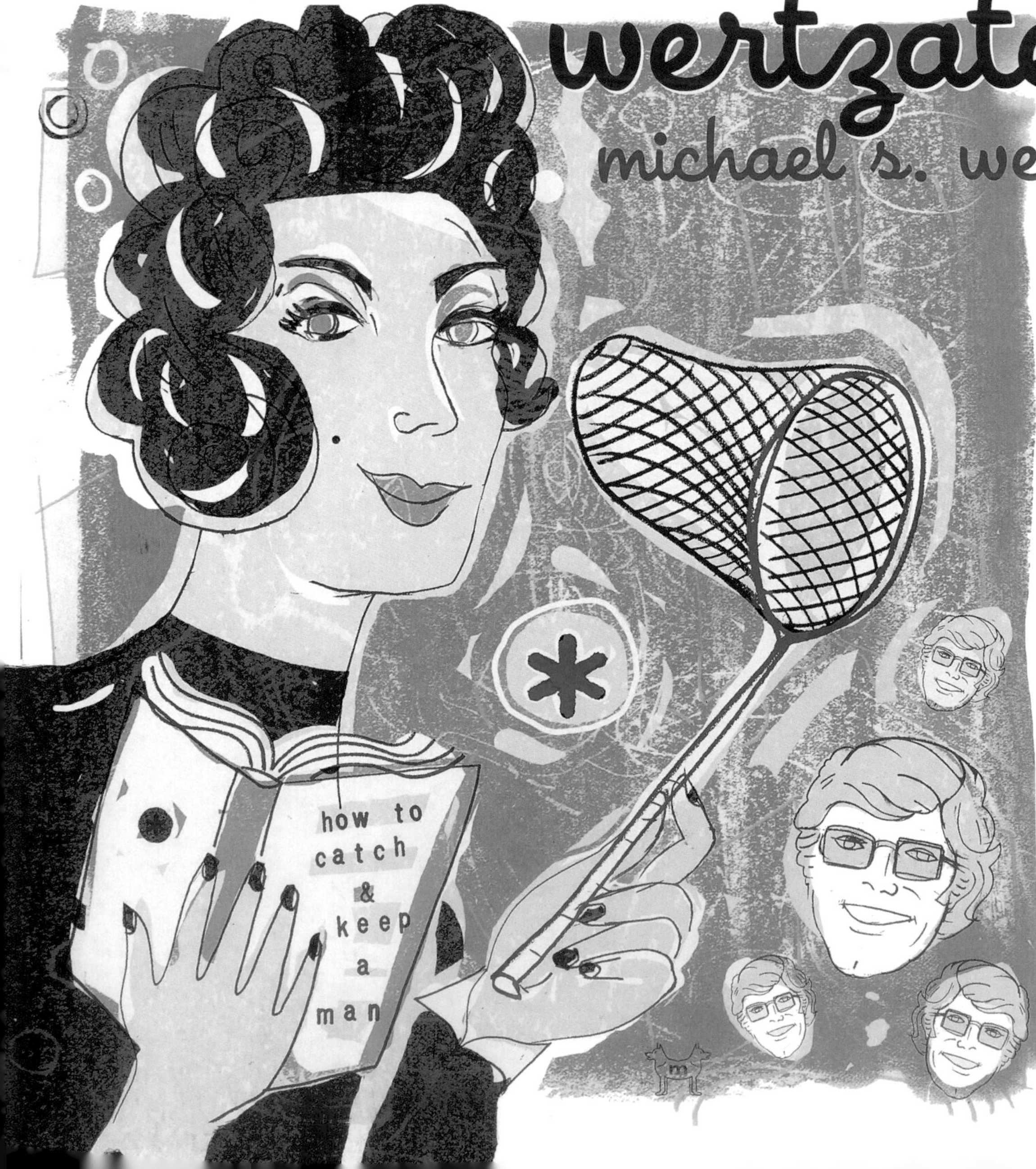

how to catch & keep a man

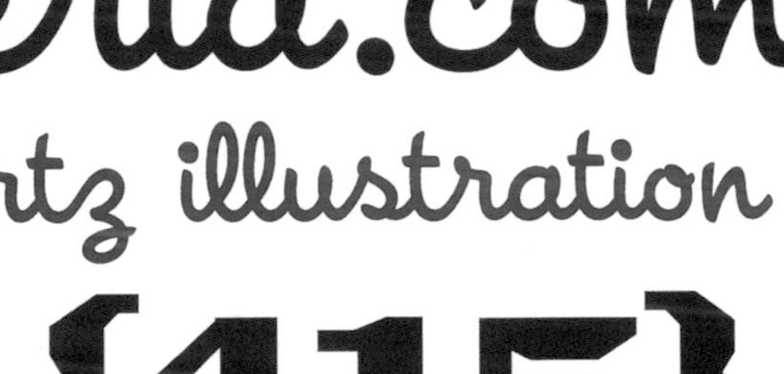

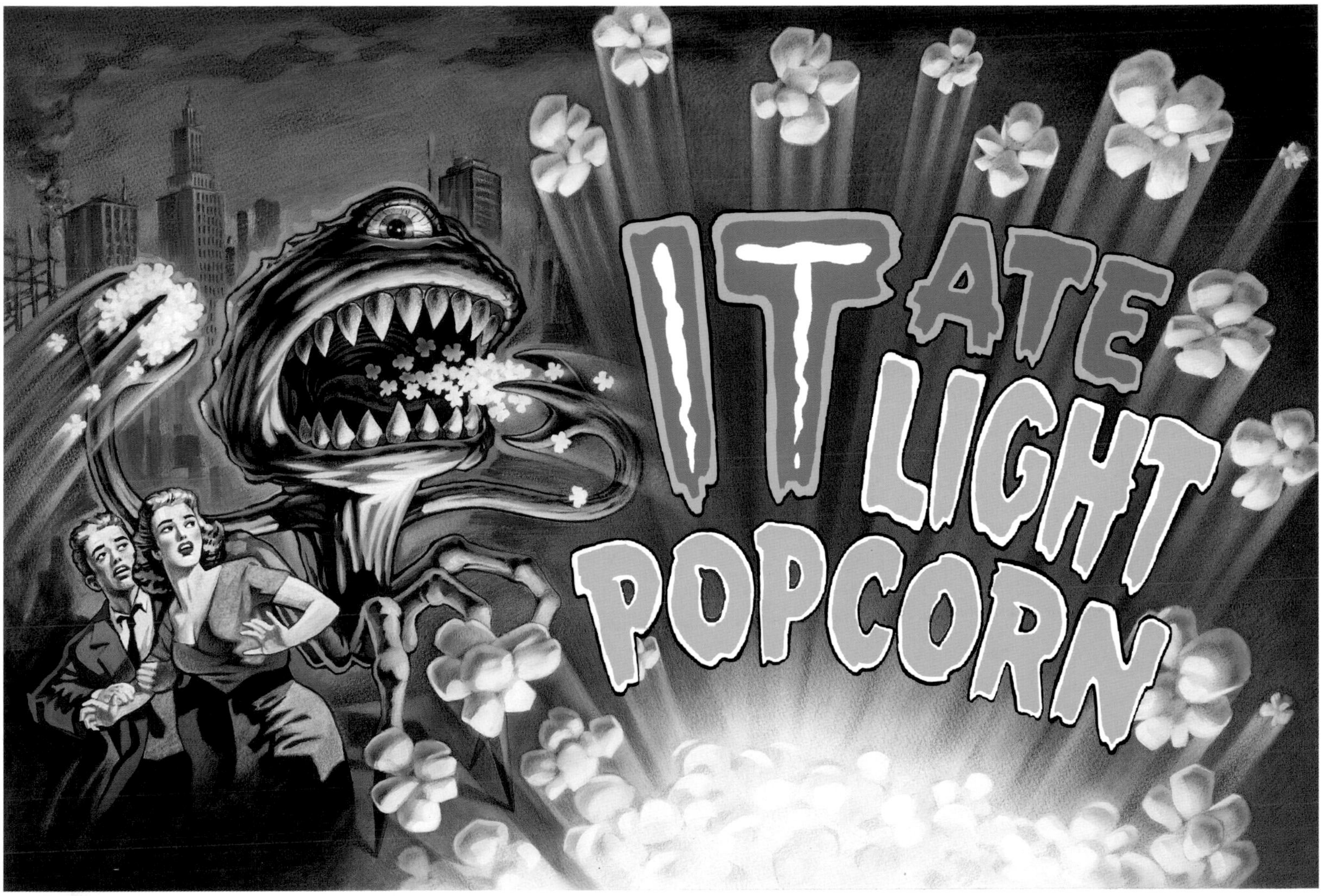

Hollywood Video movie poster packaging campaign. To see more stuff, log onto my web site.

ANNIE BISSETT

SPECIALIZING IN INFORMATION GRAPHICS

www.anniebissett.com
for more samples

1-800-515-1060

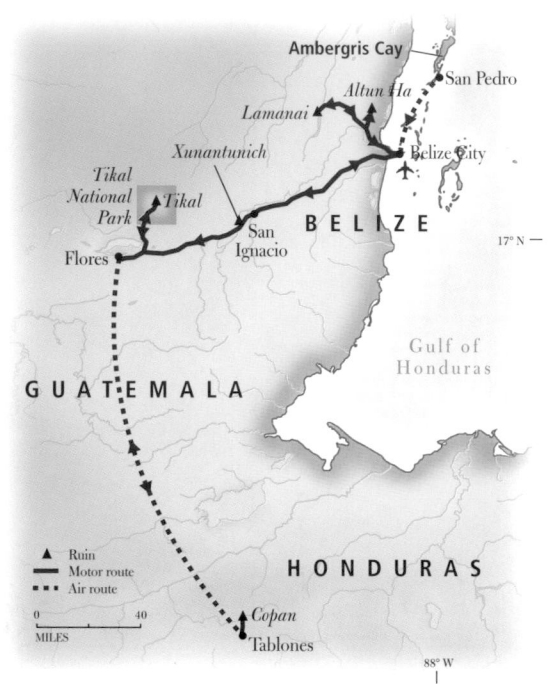

Ambergris Cay
San Pedro
Altun Ha
Lamanai
Xunantunich
Belize City
Tikal National Park
Tikal
San Ignacio
B E L I Z E
17° N —
Flores
Gulf of Honduras

G U A T E M A L A

H O N D U R A S

▲ Ruin
— Motor route
···· Air route

0   40
MILES

Copan
Tablones

88° W

Food Prep
2.8 hours

Household Maintenance
1.3 hours

Personal Hygiene
0.8 hours

On the Road
3.1 hours

Sleep
5.5 hours

Childcare
3.2 hours

Paid Work
7.3 hours

Domestic Goddess

How the Average American Woman Spends Her Day

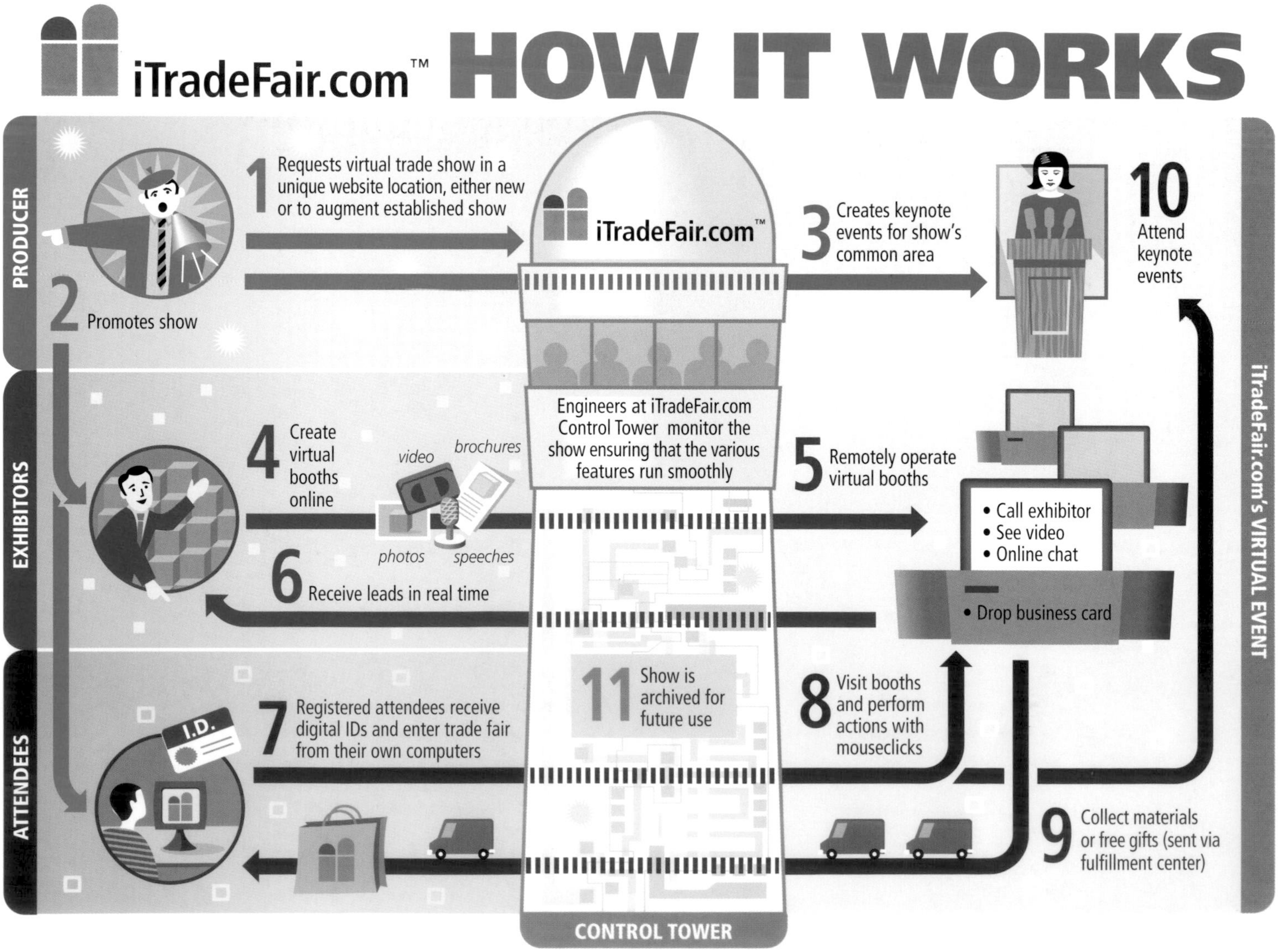

---

iTradeFair.com™ HOW IT WORKS

PRODUCER

1 Requests virtual trade show in a unique website location, either new or to augment established show

2 Promotes show

iTradeFair.com™

3 Creates keynote events for show's common area

10 Attend keynote events

Engineers at iTradeFair.com Control Tower monitor the show ensuring that the various features run smoothly

EXHIBITORS

4 Create virtual booths online

video *brochures*
photos *speeches*

5 Remotely operate virtual booths

• Call exhibitor
• See video
• Online chat

• Drop business card

6 Receive leads in real time

ATTENDEES

7 Registered attendees receive digital IDs and enter trade fair from their own computers

I.D.

11 Show is archived for future use

8 Visit booths and perform actions with mouseclicks

9 Collect materials or free gifts (sent via fulfillment center)

iTradeFair.com's VIRTUAL EVENT

CONTROL TOWER

people

gadgets

critters

1112 north hoyne • no. 2 • chicago 60622

patty O'friel • fōn & fax 773.384.3496

food

financial

to bump into more work, check out black books '96-00, directory of illustration 17

come play at www.pattyo.com

BABYGAP

BABYGAP

BABYGAP

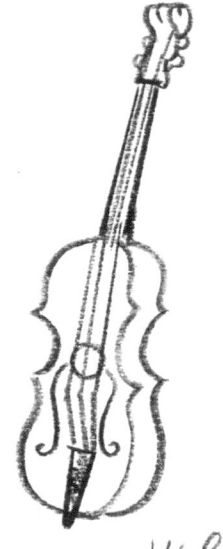

Violin

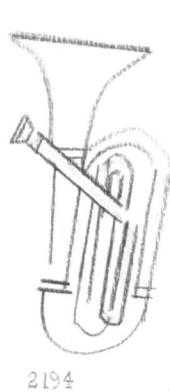

2194

MARCI ROTH

503·284·2978 ✺ www.theispot.com/artist/mroth

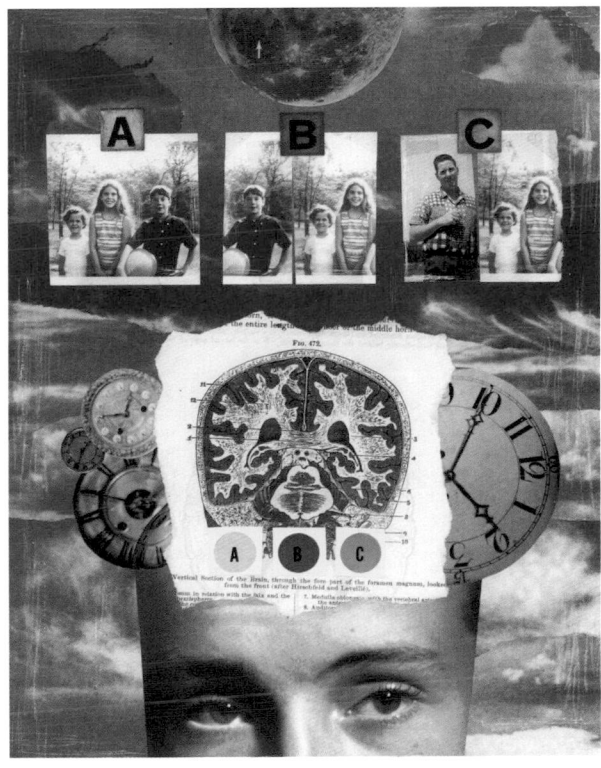

DOUGLAS BUCHMAN
a.k.a. The Big Pixel

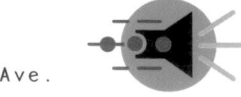

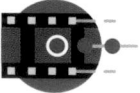

3183 Airway Ave.

Suite G

OFFICE/Sparrow

714-444-1904

studio tel/fax

714-979-8001
www.thebigpixelstudios.com

Costa Mesa, CA

E-MAIL

92626-4611

bigpixels@aol.com

894

[creative conspiracy inc.]

ph 970.247.2262

creativeconspiracy.com

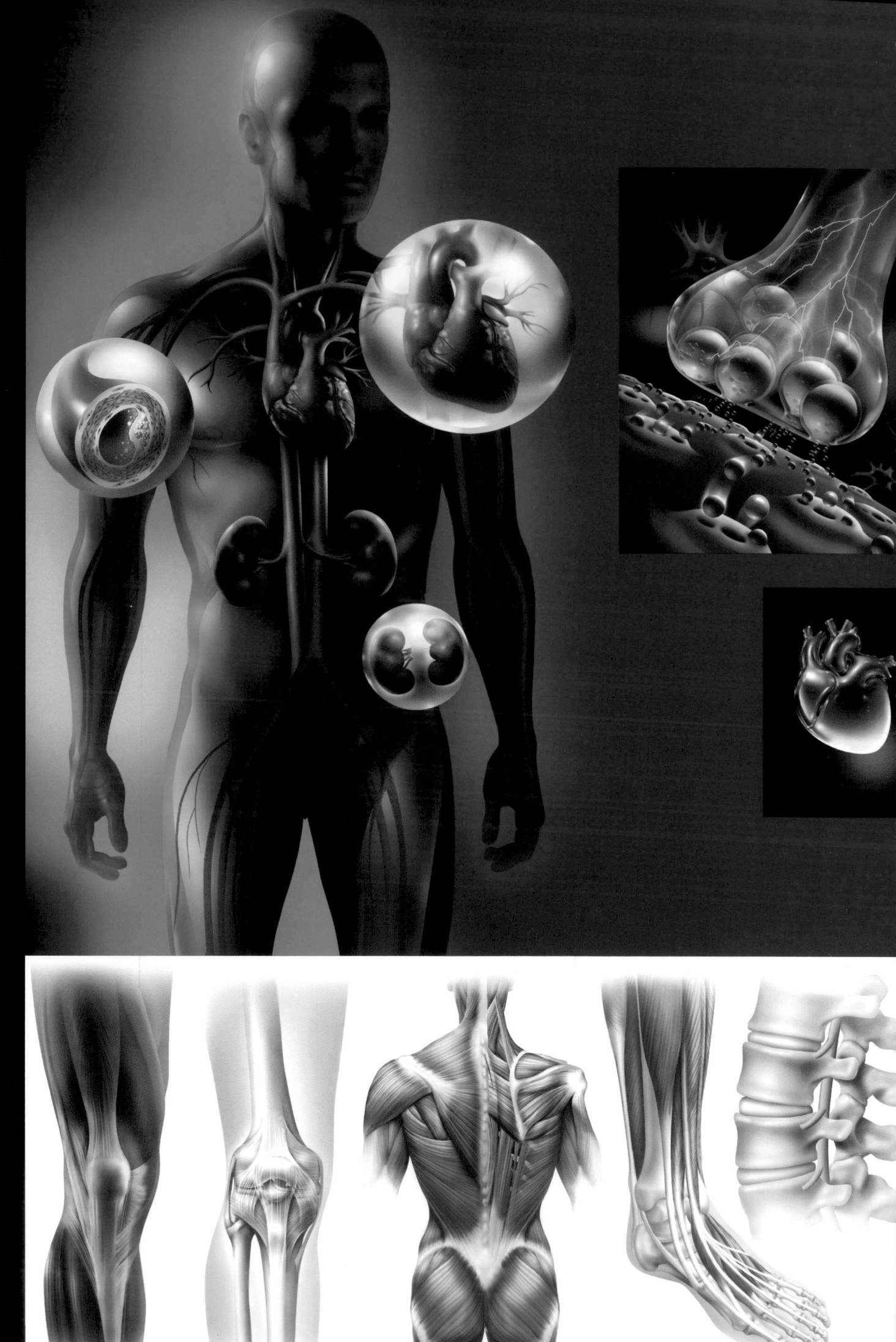

www.johneeBee.com

the johnee bee show!

ILLUSTRATION | WEB ICONS | FLASH ANIMATION

TRAFFIC 411.com

small/medium business

ip device

policy server

IP/ATM/TDM

NETWORK with

IP CONTROL

base service providers

augmented service providers

ipVerse ControlSwitch

trunking gateway

ras – different vendors

access gateway

ss7

pstn & wireless networks

home/soho

enterprise

FLASH INTROS

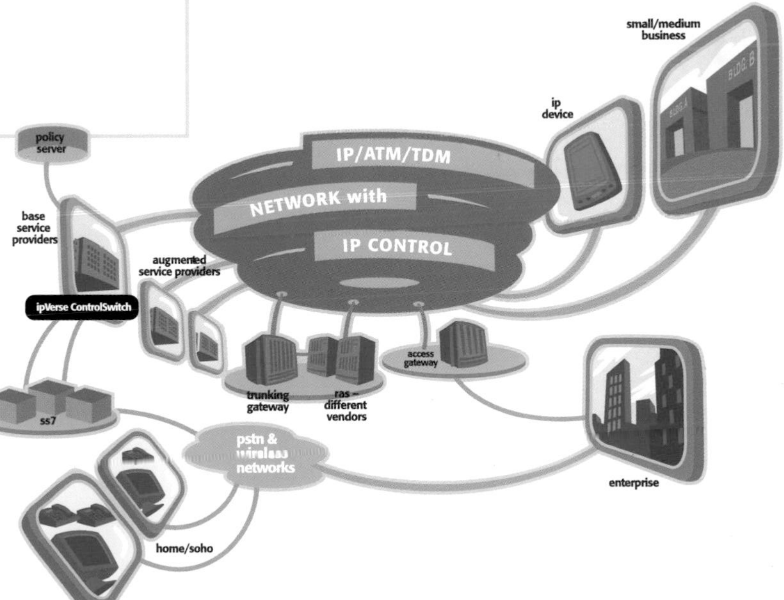

netscape 4.0
or higher works best
to see my flash site

• the bee studio 949-642-2789 • fax 949-642-1400 • e-mail jb@johneebee.com

WWW.JOHNEEBEE.COM

897

ArtRampage.com

Graphic Design and Illustration for Web and Print

JOHN CHUI

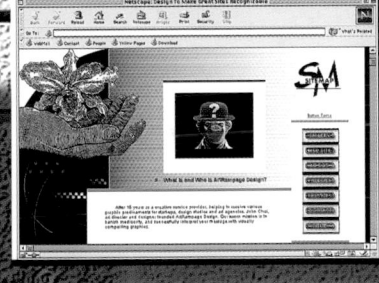

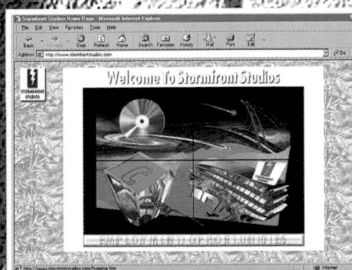

johnc@artrampage.com   510-918-2333   www.artrampage.com

Todd Leonardo

510 · 728 · 1076

☎ 773-264-1152

DAVE MILLER

FAX 773-264-0916

John Francis

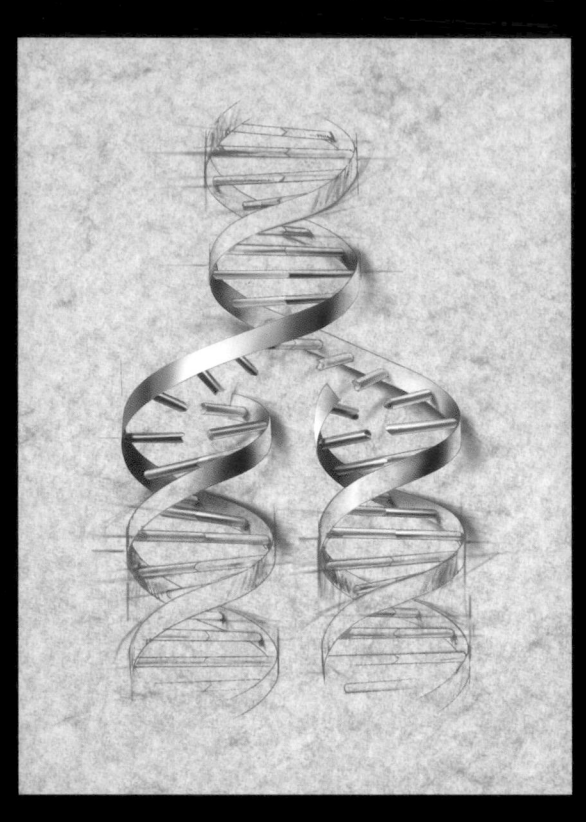

Sally Springer
1510 N. Thumb Point Drive
Fort Pierce, FL 34949
561.467.0095
www.theispot.com/artist/springer

Dorothy Remington

632 Commercial Street

San Francisco, CA 94111

tel 415.397.4668

fax 415.392.8354

www.akagiremington.com/dr.html

harrietgolden

01. webstyle

connection connection
communication
connection
unitedkingdomchinaparisisraelgermanyitalyaustraliaspaingreecerussiajapan
connection

corporate

STATUS   TAX PLANNING

strategies

tax tips

outsourcing

BENEFITS

TRAVEL

PAYROLL

goldenhr@earthlink.net + 212.249.4194 + www.harrietgolden.com

FLASH MOTION GRAPHICS   COLLAGE ILLUSTRATION

Cathleen Earle

233 N. MacKenzie St.
Sarnia, Ontario, N7T 6L2
Canada
T 519.383.1668
F 519.383.8835

Doglight Studios   www.doglight.com   323 222-1928

Tracey Corinne
800-848-9364
www.Traceyart.com

908

RICK UNRUH ILLUSTRATIONS

395 BROADWAY SUITE 3A NEW YORK NY. 10013 ~ PH: (212)966-5569 FAX: (212)966-3117 E-MAIL: RICKUNRUH@aol.com

bob scott

804.320.0007   bob@bscott.com   www.bscott.com

Bert Monroy

Creating what you see

- Illustration
- Animation
- Interactive Media
- Web Visuals

11 Latham Lane
Berkeley, CA 94708
voice: 510.524.9412
fax: 510.524.2514
e-mail: bert@bertmonroy.com
www.bertmonroy.com

All images created without the use of scans

Laura Bailey
314.352.4752
lsbaile@aol.com

eric yang digital illustrations

phone: 626-284-4727 fax: 626-282-5536 e-mail: etyang@pacbell.net
http://www.eric-yang.com

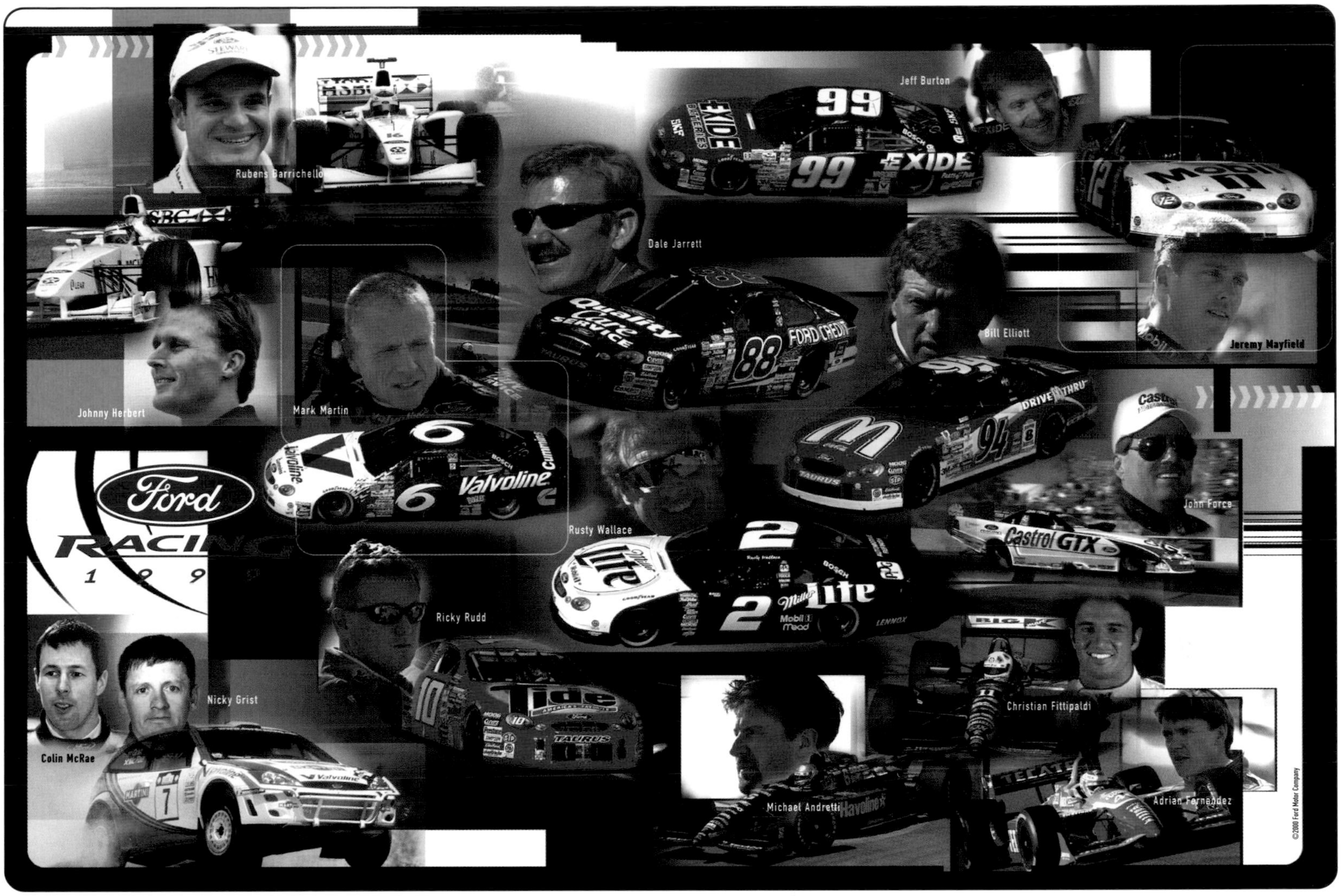

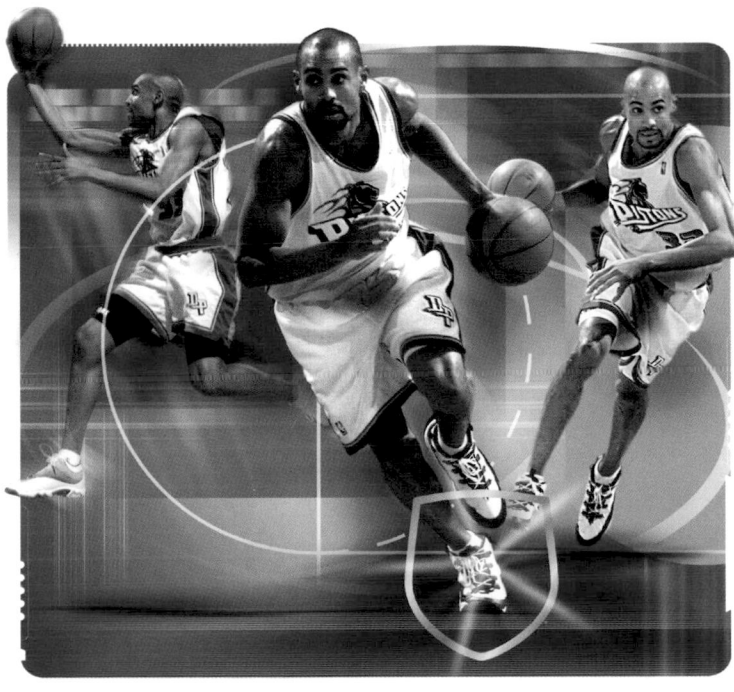

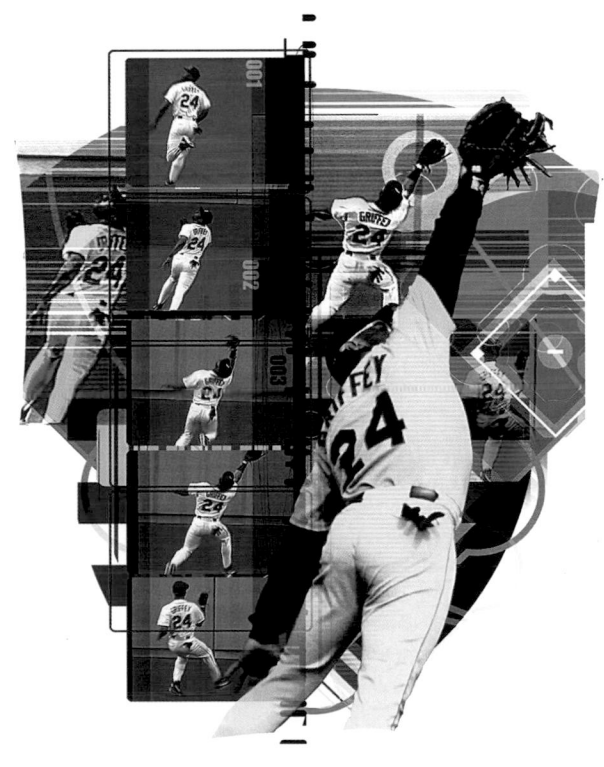

Personal Journal Cover

LAURA TARRISH

Laura Tarrish has relocated to
London, England for the next two
years. Please contact me at my
new address:

11 South Lodge
Circus Road off Abbey Road
London NW8 9ER   UK

Phone: 011.44.207.266.5485
email: lauratarrish@earthlink.net

One of series for boxed set of cards   Galison/New York

MARC SASSO

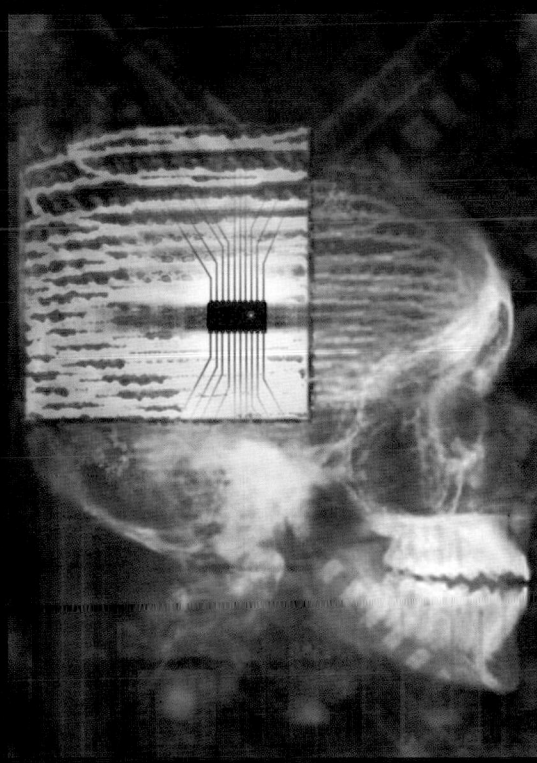

Marc Sasso
27 General Heath Avenue
North White Plains, N.Y. 10603
914.949.1949
Fax: 914.949.1966
e-mail: BLKMETAL1@aol.com

on-line portfolio at www.marcsasso.com

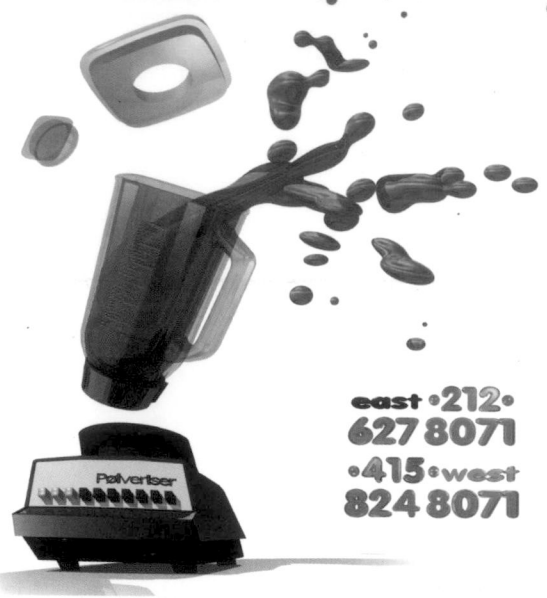

east •212•
627 8071
•415• west
824 8071

07:02
am

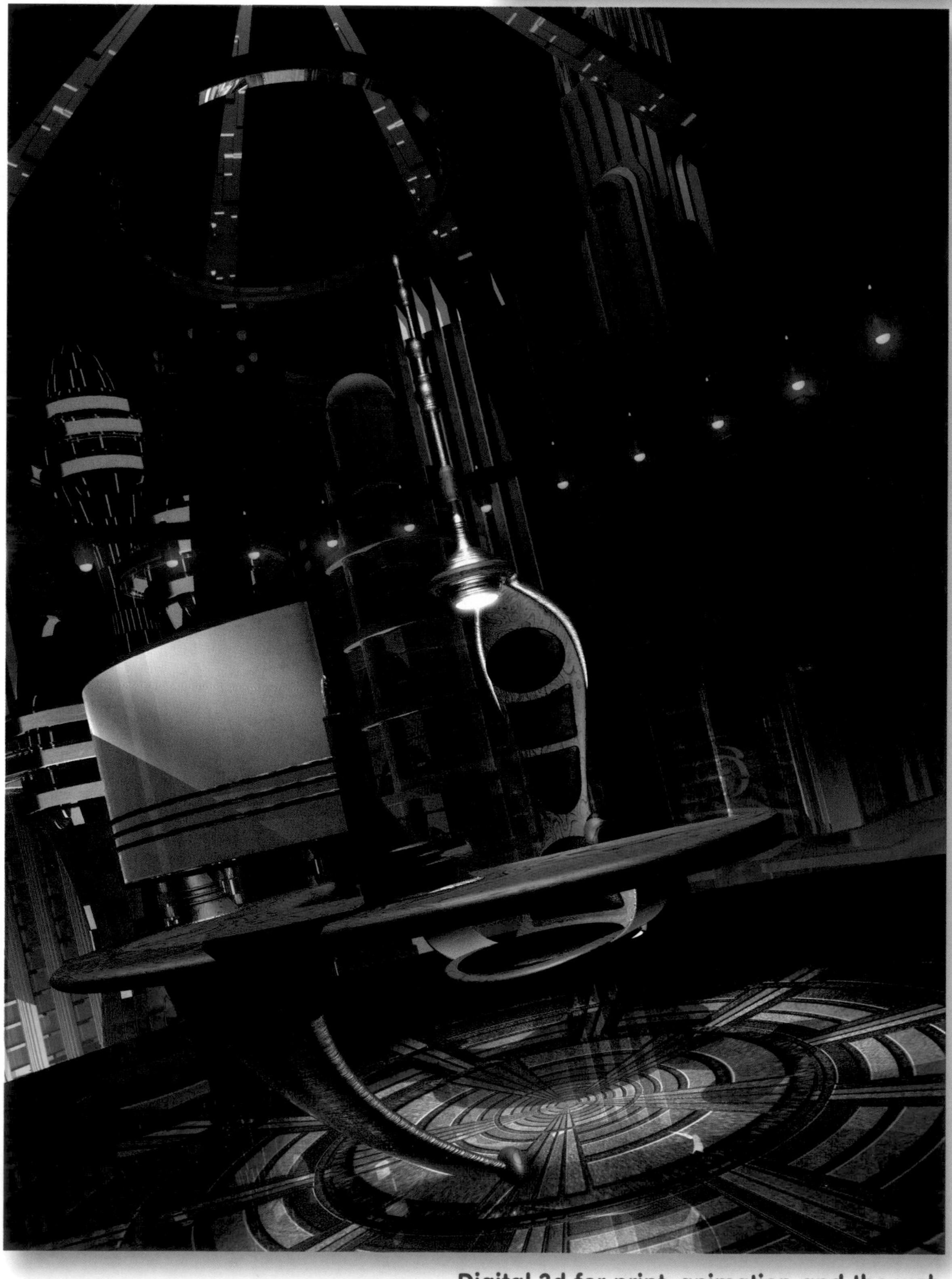

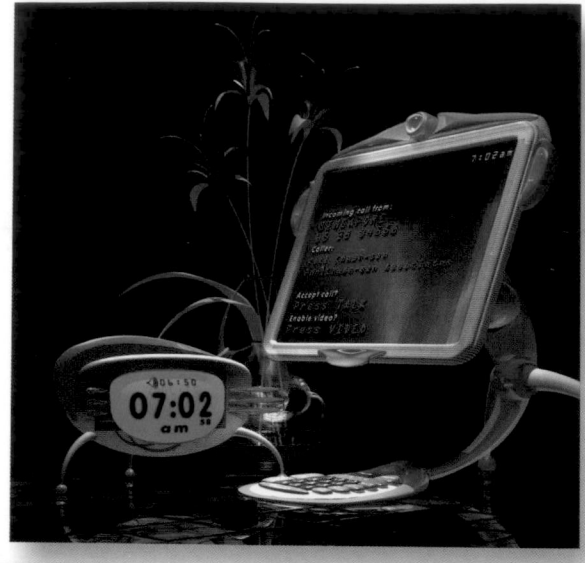

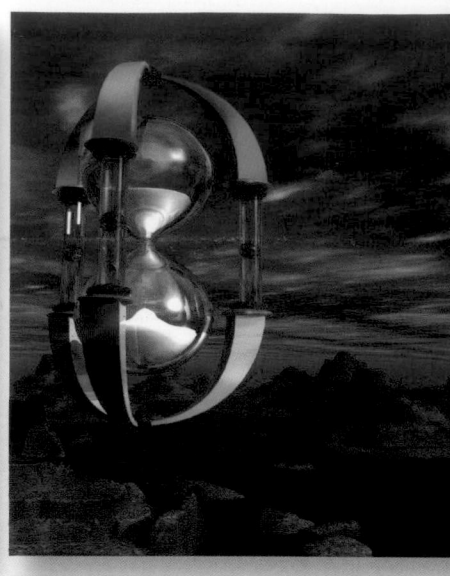

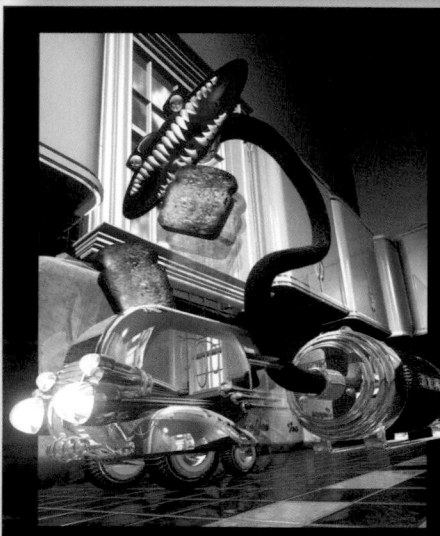

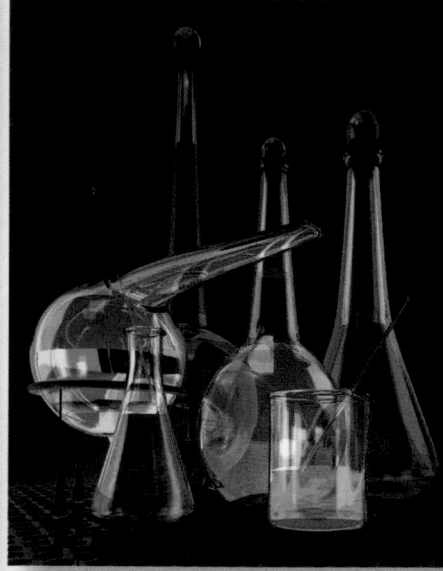

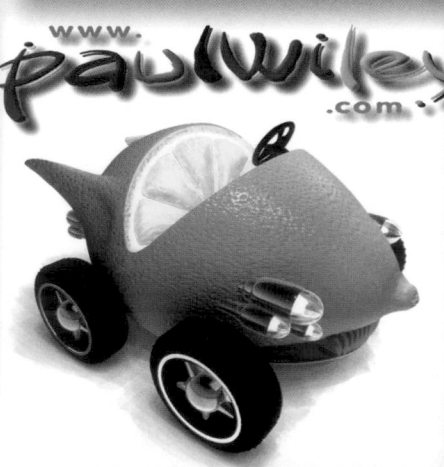

www.paulwiley.com

Digital 3d for print, animation and the web.

DESIGN & LETTERING

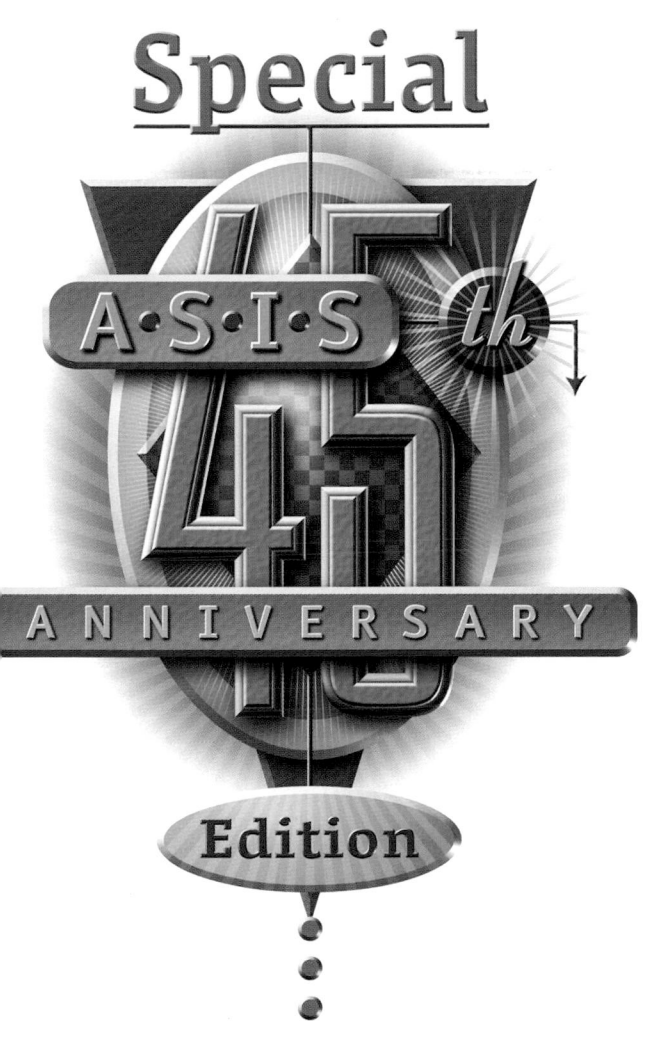

Special

A·S·I·S 45th

ANNIVERSARY

Edition

CUSTOMER

SMA

INTERACTION

AWARD

ALL IMAGES COPYRIGHT 9 SURF STUDIOS

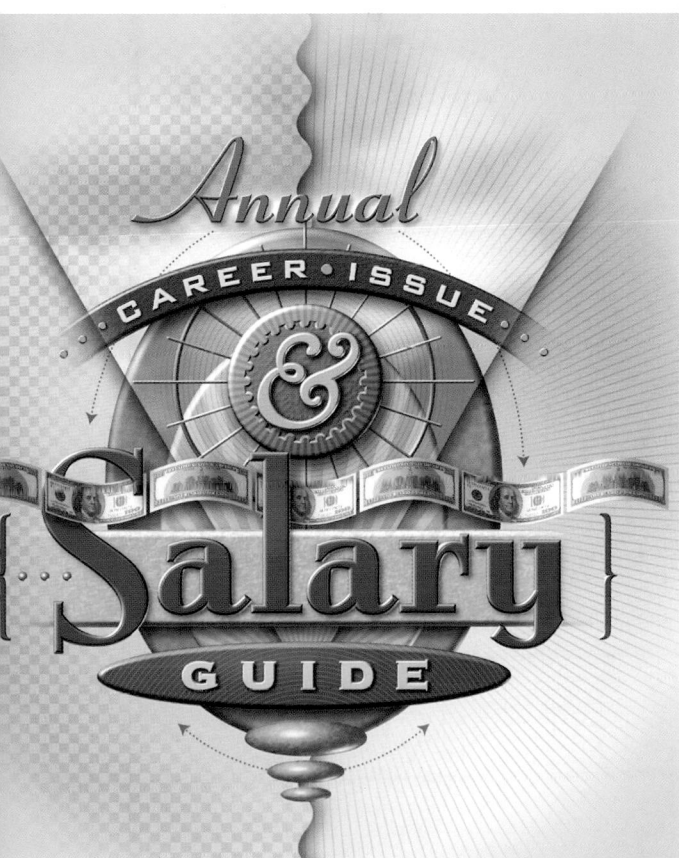

Annual

CAREER · ISSUE

&

Salary

GUIDE

NT Runs

WALL ST.

SELF PROMOTION

CARRABBA'S RESTAURANT CHAIN / DESIGNER AT LARGE, TAMPA, FL

PANACOM, INC

ICON DESIGN, RWJ HOSPITAL GROUP / WINNING STRATEGIES ADV.

CHILDREN'S SPECIALIZED
H O S P I T A L

ICON DESIGN, RWJ HOSPITAL / WINNING STRATEGIES AD AGENCY

SPECIAL EVENTS GROUP

ANELLE FONT
The quick brown fox jumped
over the lazy dog.

ORIGENS / CUSTOM TYPEFACE

HOLED UP
IN AN OLD
Funeral Home
THE MAN BEHIND
NINE INCH NAILS
HAS SPENT THE LAST
FOUR YEARS
coping with loss e
CONSTRUCTING A
DELICATE
&
BRUTAL
MASTERPIECE

ROLLING STONE MAGAZINE

ESTEE LAUDER

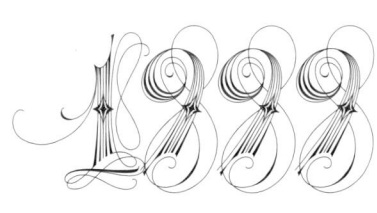

SELF PROMOTION

Organic

DANNON YOGURT / CORNERSTONE DESIGN ASSOCIATES, INC.

ROBERT WOOD JOHNSON
UNIVERSITY HOSPITAL
AT HAMILTON

ICON DESIGN, RWJ HOSPITAL / WINNING STRATEGIES ADV.

LIFESAVERS / CORNERSTONE DESIGN ASSOCIATES, INC.

CUSTOM TYPEFACE DESIGN
STOUFFERS FOODS / THE COLEMAN GROUP

HARPER COLLINS PUBLISHERS

GLAXO PHARMACEUTICALS / NATREL COMMUNICATIONS

ANTHONY BLOCH, 718/274-6064, FAX/274-1826, abld@mindspring.com, www.anthonybloch.com

TAVERN ON THE GREEN, NYC

TERRY W SANDERS

PRESENTS

AN OUTSTANDING DISPLAY of

Photo Illustration & Design Manifested as

DIGITAL PRESTIDIGITATION

AND

VISUAL ASTONISHMENT

Terry W Sanders (212) 980.1893 lonelaser@aol.com
New York City, New York

Gerald & Cullen Rapp, Inc., 108 East 35 St., NYC 10016 Phone: (212)889-3337 Fax: (212)889-3341 e-mail:BMaisner@aol.com

Hairworks VOLUMIZING SHAMPOO

Hairworks CONDITIONER

APTIVA

IBM.

NOW CONCER TRY OUT AN IDEA FOR YOUR NEXT VIDEO. STILL HAVE TO TRASH HOTEL ROO

IT'S THE SOFT WHITE, COMFORTING LIGHT YOU'RE FAMILIAR WITH. BUT IT'S A COMPACT FLUORESCENT. IT TURNS ON WITHOUT ANY DELAY. IT COMES IN A VERSATILE, COMPACT SIZE. IT'S INCREDIBLY ENERGY EFFICIENT. AND IT LASTS 10 TIMES LONGER THAN AN ORDINARY INCANDESCENT LIGHT BULB. IT'S THE NEW SYLVANIA SOFT WHITE DULUX EL.

SYLVANIA
BRILLIANT LIGHT

Signs of the Times

London $292.50
World Offers
Call 1-800-AIRWAYS.

Where is everybody?

naturellement.

ORPHÉE, furieux — CHUT !

Than for transferring your balanc

CHOICE

Mirror, Mirror

She's gone to Capri and she's not coming back

EXECUTIVE PRODUCERS ROBERT REDFORD and PA

GRAND AVENU

Made with Tender Loving Care By Bernard Maisner

TELARC JAZZ

Jeremy Davenport

A COMPLETE COMPANION TO LISTENING, LEARNING, AND PLAYING

The Living Piano

Scarlatti Bach

OSCAR PETERSON

TELARC JAZZ

Capri Superslims

CAPRI

l. socco FINE WOOLLENS

A PIZZA is a CANVAS AND you CAN PAINT on it ALL DaY long

Pizza Kitchen menu. That's American Express Cards all over the world
s us freedom and comfort
because we like Why in the world would
limitations. Peop customer?
our restaurants f American Express is welcom
experimental

Daniel Pelavin • 212 941-7418 • Fax 212 431-7138 • daniel@pelavin.com
Lettering • Logos • Illustration • Typographic Design • www.pelavin.com

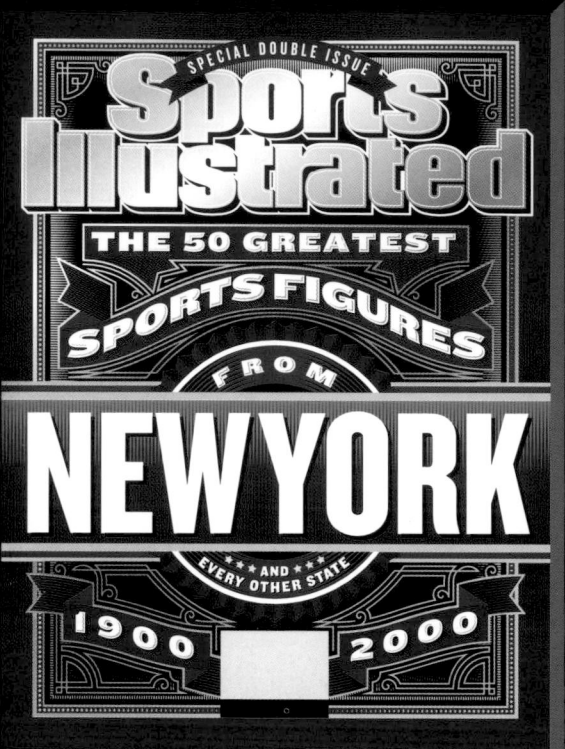

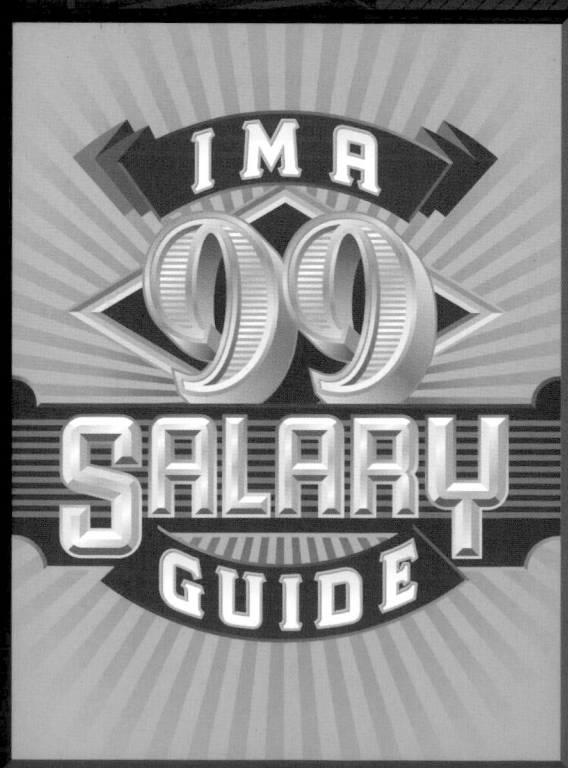

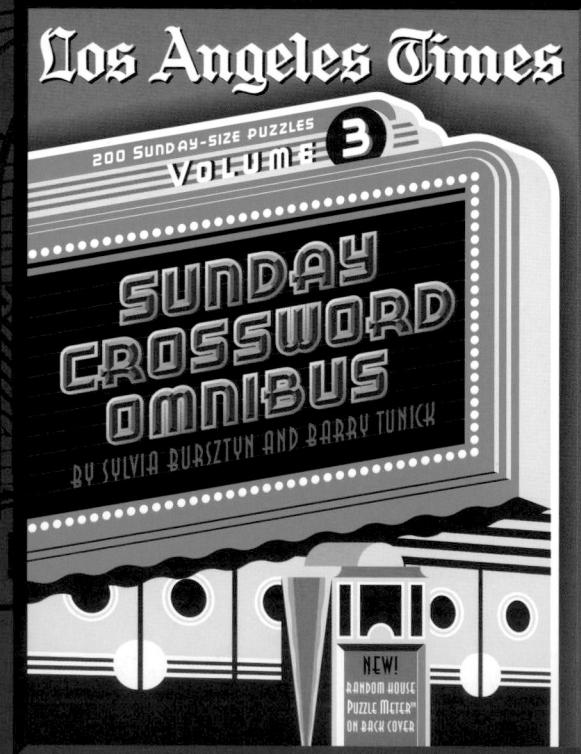

Chocolate Truffles

B

BARBARA CALLOW CALLIGRAPHY

C

American Express · Banana Republic · British Airways · Bulgari · Chanel · Clorox · DDB Needham · Digitas · Fraser Papers · Macy's · Microsoft · Modern Maturity · Oldsmobile · SBG Enterprise · Charles Schwab · SFMOMA · Sony · Sun Microsystems

Performing Arts

aztec

organic

hysteria

Cabaret

thrill

fabulous

Gold

Linda de Moreta

Mecca Studios

166 5th Avenue New York, NY 10010

212. 633. 1999

info@meccastudios.com

New York Knicks

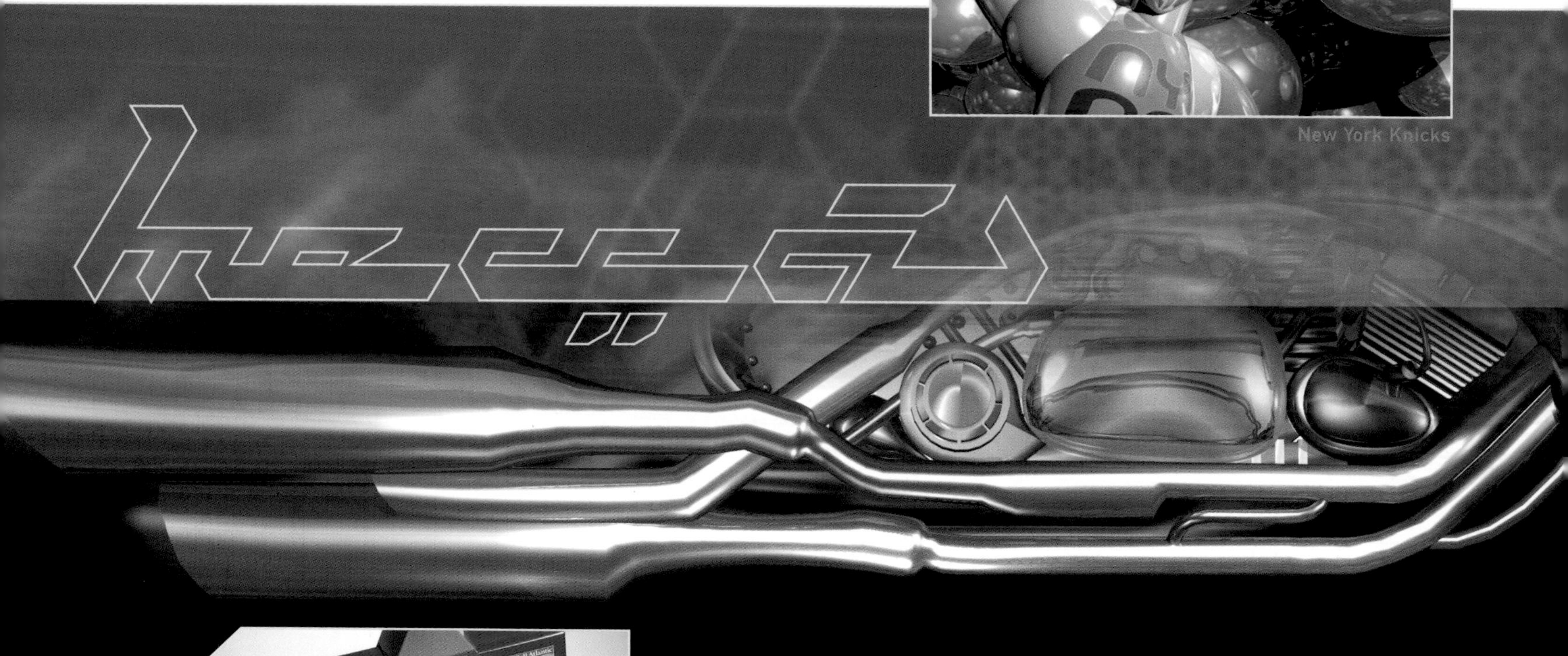

Bell Atlantic

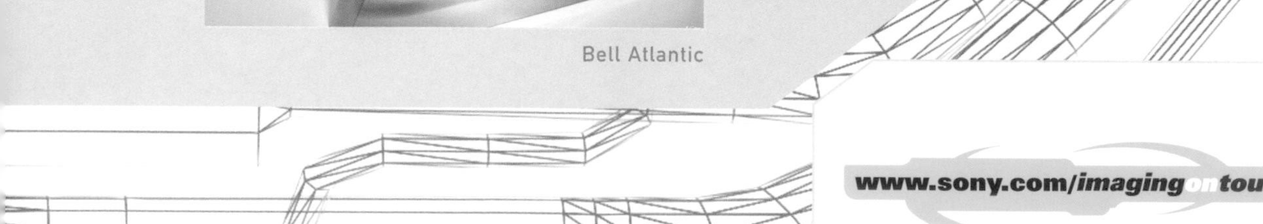

www.sony.com/*imaging* on *tour*

SONY Mavica

Hasb

www.meccastudios.com

www.meccastudios.com

New York Rangers

Hasbro

designeroffice.com

dosomething.com

Parlo.com

Mecca Studios 212. 633. 1999

LAURA KAY DESIGN

Phone 800 497-1752
http://opendoor.com/laurakaydesign/
email: laurakaydesign@opendoor.com

Logos, Trademarks, Icons
Corporate Identity Packages
37 international & national design awards

iFind

VanVleet

InTransit

ELCOR

SPECIALTY DESIGN

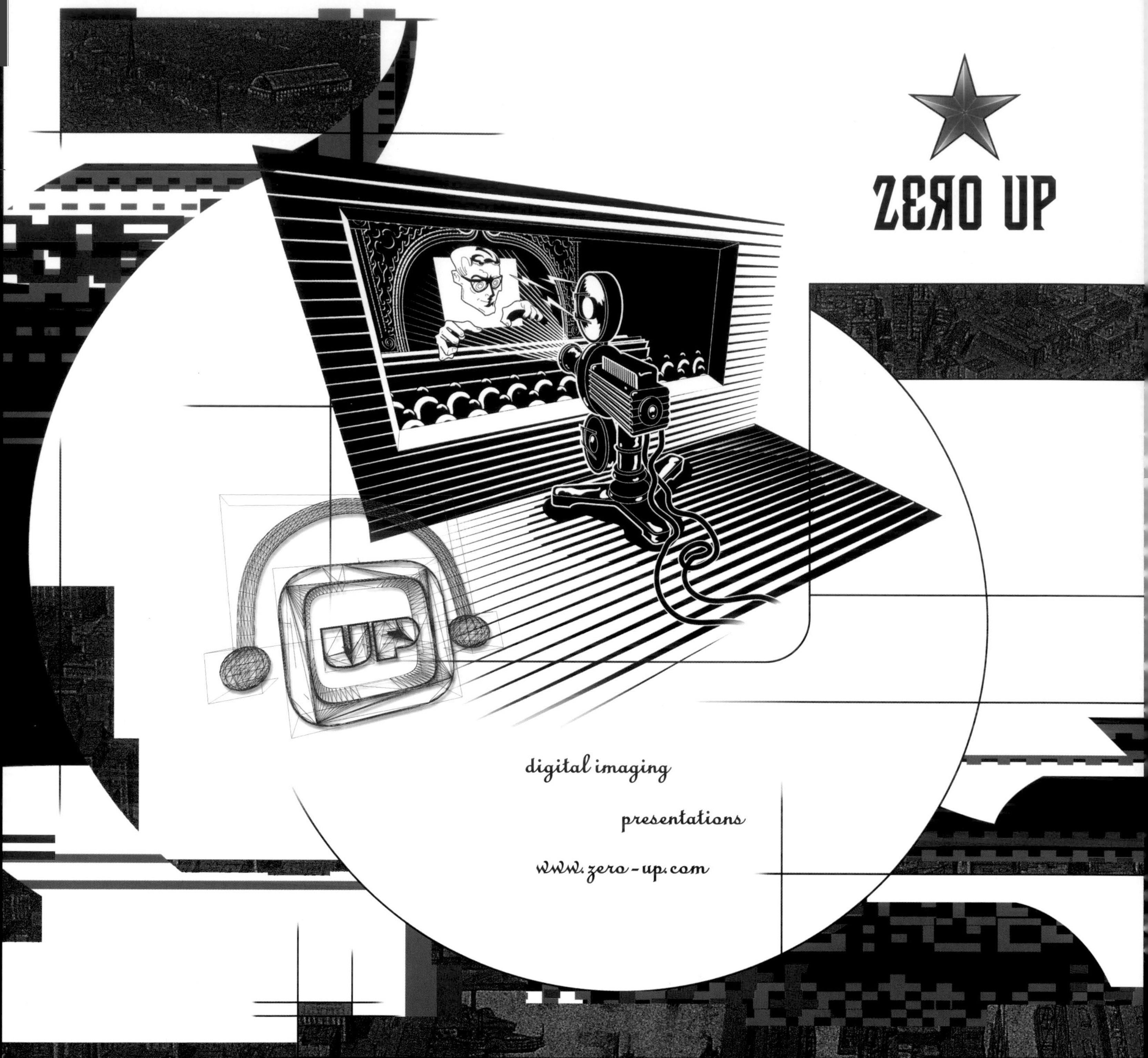

ZERO UP

digital imaging

presentations

www.zero-up.com

Digital Imaging
- *Professional Film Processing*
- *Prepress Quality Batch Scanning*
- *Custom Scanning*
- *Photo Retouching/Restoration*
- *Digital Illustration*

Presentation Services
- *Trade Show Demos*
- *Shareholder Meetings*
- *Sales Presentations*
- *Business Meetings*
- *Award Ceremonies*

**Check our web site
for great specials
and current prices
on our digital
imaging services.**

Call **Chris Barnes** at
800.570.5204 or
877.614.3492

At zeroUp we forge interactive presentations from the latest
media technologies. Using a mix of Macromedia, QuickTime, and
DVD technologies we create rich presentations which can be
delivered through a variety of channels. Through analysis of your
needs, budget, and timeframe we develop the presentations that
will make a significant impact on your audience.

ZERO UP

post office box 20828
baltimore, maryland 21209
showcase@zero-up.com
www.zero-up.com

Holly Dickens

LETTERING AND DESIGN   **P** 312.280.0777   **F** 312.280.1725   **E** holly@hollydickens.com   www.hollydickens.com

intel inside

Remember when those guys said customers would never buy this stuff. They did.
—the Future

ACXIOM.COM

say something real. fresh ink.™

HALLMARK

PLANTERS™
Relax. Go Nuts.

NABISCO

KRAFT

Fa la la la la la la la la

GRANT A WISH
FOUNDATION

the Victoria
use of lace ups. Th
in chocolate brown
find them for about s
Kinney. That
fashion is

is Sound

ISSOUND CORP.

Does Estee Lauder still deserve to be A GLAMOUR STOCK?

BARRONS

american **showcase**

INDEX

INDEX

INDEX

INDEX

INDEX

INDEX

COMPING IS USAGE
PLEASE ASK FIRST

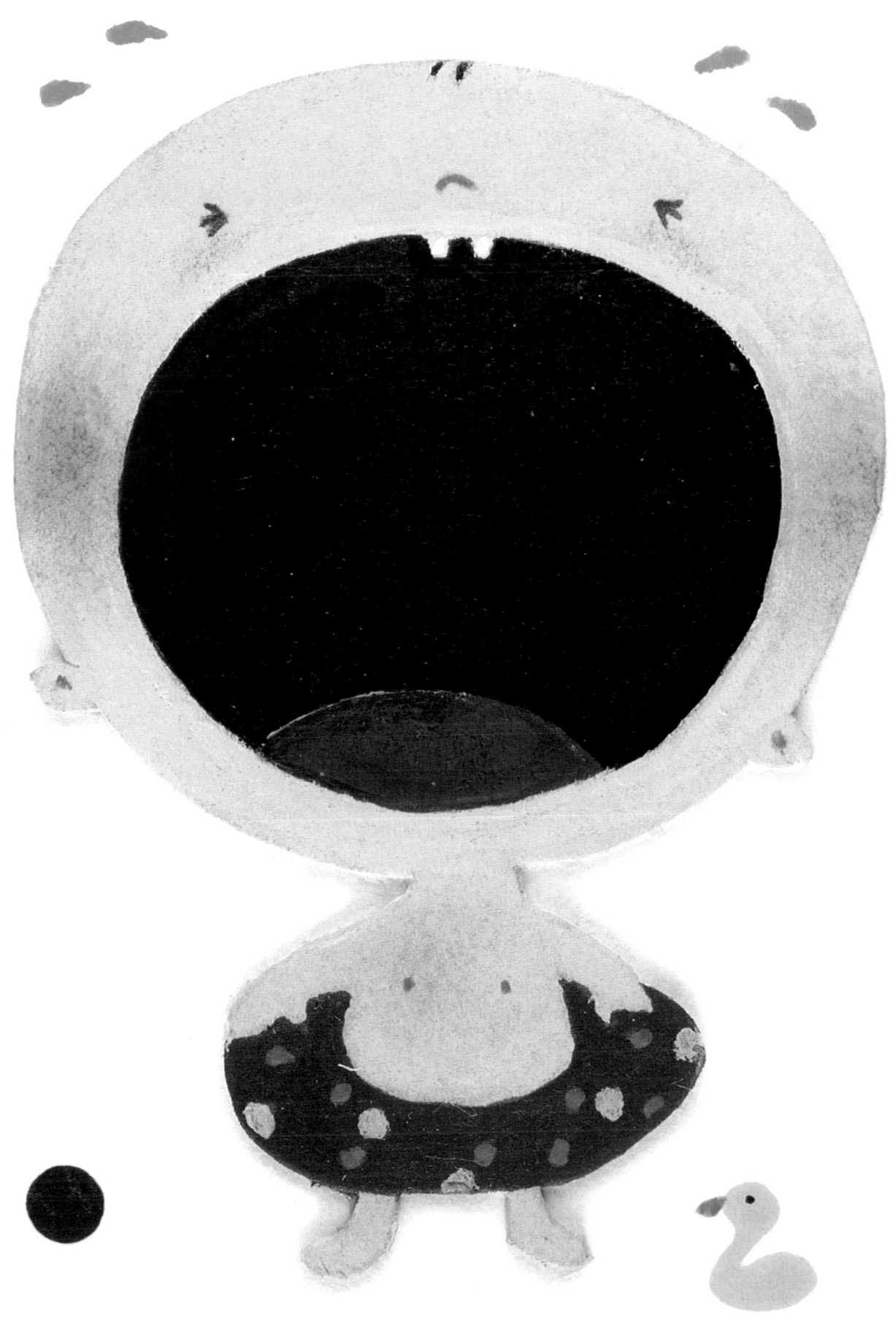

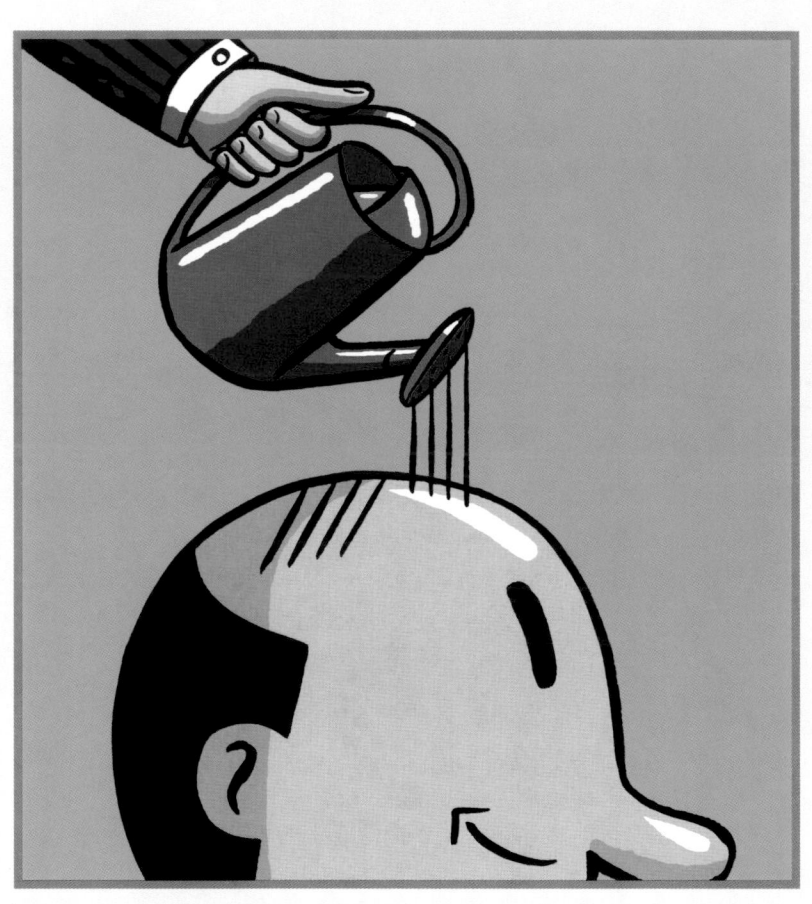

DIRECTORY

PHONE & ADDRESS
LISTINGS

REPRESENTATIVES

A

Alexander/Pollard, Inc:
848 Greenwood Ave NE, Atlanta, GA 30306 404-875-1363
Illustrator:
Lindy Burnett, Karen Strelecki, Cheryl Cooper, Diane Dempsey, Chris Ellithorpe,
Thomas Gonzalez, Kathy Lengyel, Don Morris, Brian Otto, Nip Rogers, James Soukup,
Karen Strelecki, Kate Thomssen, Mark Weakley, Stephen Wells
Photographer:
David Guggenheim

• **American Artists Reps, Inc: pg 534,535**
353 W 53rd St #1W, New York, NY 10019 212-582-0023
e-mail: info@aareps.com / url: www.aareps.com / fax: 212-582-0090
Film:
Arcana Digital
Illustrator:
Don Almquist, John Alvin, Arcana Digital, Nick Backes, Keith Batcheller,
Roger Bergendorff, Don Bishop, Barbara Bond Higgins, Robert Burger, Steve Celmer,
John Churchman, Gary Ciccarelli, Andrew Condron, Bob Depew,
Lane Du Pont, Jim Effler, Jacques Fabre, Malcolm Farley, Russell Farrell, Bob Fisher,
Brian Fyffe, Kent Gamble, Bill Garland, Annie France Giroud, Garth Glazier,
Scott Grimando, Grg Grucel, Pamela Hamilton, Brian Harrold, Doug Henry,
Michael Hill, John Holm, John & Phillip Hom, Chris Hopkins, Sandy Huffaker,
John Hull, Kelly Hume, Mitch Hyatt, Mike Jaroszko, Alan Leiner, Neil Leslie,
Maurice Lewis, Jerry Lofaro, Madoka, Ron Mahoney, Alan Male, Andrzej Malinowski,
Jean-Claude Michel, Chuck Passarelli, Tony Randazzo, Bot Roda, Joe Scrofani,
Jim Starr, Studio Liddell, Ezra Tucker, Rod Vass, Rhonda Voo, Stan Watts,
Jonathan Wright, Eddie Young, Andy Zito
Photographer:
Lynn Butler, Rob Gage

Art Agency, The:
2405 NW Thurman St, Portland, OR 97210 503-203-8300
Illustrator:
Robin Ator, Peter Beach, Diana Rice Bonin, Dale Champlin, Debra Spina Dixon,
Stephen F Hayes, Laure Heinz, Craig Holmes, Bruce MacPherson, Joanne Radmilovich,
Ben Killen Rosenberg, Gary Whitley, Matt Wuerker, Jane Zwinger
Photographer:
Jim Lommasson, Brad Ness, Brandy Pace

Art Bunch Inc, The:
180 N Michigan Ave #1720, Chicago, IL 60601 312-368-8777
Illustrator:
Phil Babb, Randy Chaffee, Jay Fisher, Rich Lo, Tak Murakami, Jerry Salinas

Art Factory Ltd:
925 Elm Grove Rd, Elm Grove, WI 53122 414-785-1940
Illustrator:
Amanda Aquino, Chuck Boie, Tom Buchs, Todd Dakins, Linda Godrey, Terry Herman,
Larry Mikec, Tom Nachreiner, Bill Scott, Stewart Zastrow

Art Source/Diane Barkley:
PO Box 257, Pleasantville, NY 10570 914-747-2220

Art Staff, Inc:
1000 John R Rd #201, Troy, MI 48083 248-583-6070
Illustrator:
Paul Chen, Pam Colecchia, Larry Cory, Heiner Hertling, Ben Jaroslaw, Rainer Laubach,
Dick Meissner, Linda Nagle, Gary Richardson, Jeff Ridky, Ken Taylor, Alan Wilson

• **Artco: pg 423-434**
232 Madison Ave #512, New York, NY 10016 212-889-8777
e-mail: jp@artcoreps.com / url: www.artcoreps.com / fax: 212-447-1475
227 Godfrey Rd, Weston, CT 06883 203-222-8777
e-mail: artco1@mindspring.com / url: www.artcoreps.com / fax: 203-454-9940
Graphic Designer:
Michael Sullivan
Illustrator:
Alexander & Turner, Ed Acuna, George Angelini, Tim Barnes, Doron Ben-Ami,
Bruce Bowles, Steven Belchér, Brian Berley, Eric Bowman, Gary Carlson,
Daniels & Daniels, Mort Drucker, Suzanne Duranceau, Michael Edholm, Electric Soup,
Kevin Eslinger, Jason Farris, Cheri Freund, Aline Gauthier, Stan Gorman,
Lisa Henderling, Sue Hughes, Inkwell Studios, Kirkland Studios, Rick McCollum,
Kevin Lyman, Bret Meredith, Yishai Minkin, Wendy Morris, Shawn Murphy,
Todd Partridge, Dimitrios Patelis, Randy Pollak, David Poole, Lisa Rivard,
Philip St Jacques, Broeck Steadman, Joe St Pierre, Studio 212, Michael Sullivan,
Ken Susynski, Dale Stephanos, John Stephens, Studio Macbeth, Jason Sutton,
Larry Taugher, Alex Tiani, Victor Vaccaro, Sally Vitsky, Matthew Wygant

Artisan:
1950 S Sawtelle Ave #320, Los Angeles, CA 90025 310-312-2062

Artisan Professional Freelance Reps, Inc:
10 E 40th St #2902, New York, NY 10016 212-448-0200

Artists Associates:
4416 La Jolla Dr, Bradenton, FL 34210 941-756-8445
Shrub Oak, NY 212-755-1365
Illustrator:
Norman Adams, Michael C Dudash, Mark English Robert Heindel, Steve Karchin, Dick
Krepel, Fred Otnes

Artists International:
134 Christian St, New Preston, CT 06777 . . . . 860-868-1011 Michael Brodie
Illustrator:
Peter Barrett, David Chestnut, Gino, Jerry Harston, Barbara Lanza, Julius Lisi,
Victoria Lisi, Victoria Poyser Lisi, John Lunch, John Lund, Jane Maday, Kathy Mitchell,
John Nez, Anne Thornburgh, Richard Walz

Artline:
439 S Tryon St, Charlotte, NC 28202 704-376-7609
Film:
Herb Schartz, Shadowbach Productions
Illustrator:
Steve Barbaria, Eric Joyner, David Wink
Photographer:
Alex Bee Photography, Jim Fiscus, Steve Murray, William Thompson
Stock:
Picturesque

Arts Counsel, Inc:
853 Broadway #606, New York, NY 10003 212-777-6777
Illustrator:
James Dignan, Bill Donovan, Matt Downs, Chuck Gonzales, Glen Hanson,
Doreen Kibler, Steve Klamm, Pamela Kogen, Mark Korsak, Barbara McGregor,
David McGrievey, Jackie Pardo, Sally Sturman, Annalisa Vivarelli, Jenny Williams

ARTS Resource:
545 Sutter St #305, San Francisco, CA 94102 415-956-2133
Illustrator:
Arthur Bell, Don Dylan, Scott Seidman, John Wotipka

• **Artworks Illustration: pg 372-385**
89 Fifth Ave #901, New York, NY 10003 212-627-1554
e-mail: artworksillustration@earthlink.net / url: www.artworksillustration.com
fax: 212-627-1719
Illustrator:
Paul Bachem, Dan Brown, Harry Burman, Deborah Chabrian, Adrian Chesterman,
Christopher Clarke, Bob Dombrowski, Peter Fiore, Mike Harper, Rick Lovell,
Dennis Lyall, Molly O'Gorman, Peter Peebles, Jerry Vanderstelt, Victoria Vebell

Asciutto Art Reps:
1712 E Butler Cir, Chandler, AZ 85225 602-899-0600
Film:
Elaine Garvin, Pat Lucas-Morris, Gary Undercuffler
Illustrator:
Anthony Accardo, Alex Bloch, Deborah Borgo, Olivia Cole, Mark Corcoran,
Jack Crompton, Susanne DeMarco, Len Epstein, Kersti Frigell, Meryl Henderson,
Alan Leiner, Loretta Lustig, Charles Peale, Jan Pyk

• **Baker, Kolea: pg 436-445**
7205 28th Ave NW, Seattle, WA 98117 206-784-1136
e-mail: kolea@kolea.com / url: www.kolea.com / fax: 206-784-1171
Film:
Jeff Brice
Illustrator:
George Abe, Don Baker, Jeff Brice, Margaret Chodos-Irvine, Tom Collicott, Brant Day,
Nelson Hilber, Riccardo Stampatori
Photographer:
Tom Collicott

Bancroft & Friends, Carol:
121 Dodgingtown Rd Box 266, Bethel, CT 06801 203-748-4823
Illustrator:
Gary Bialke, Gioro Carmi, Mena Dolobowsky, Cliff Faust, Linda Graves,
Catherine Huerte, Karen Loccisano, Steve Marchesi, Yoshi Miyake, Frank Ordaz,
Robin Roraback, Don Weller, Linda Weller

Baranski Art Reps, Sue:
3200 N Lake Shore Dr #2310, Chicago, IL 60657 773-477-3188
Illustrator:
Storyboard Studio
Photographer:
Wayne Cable, Greg Heck

Barracca, Sal:
22 Seminary Ln, Granite Springs, NY 10527   914-248-4870
Illustrator:
Alan Ayers, Franklin Ayers, Andrea Baruffi, Bradley Clark, Cynthia Watts Clark,
Donato Giancola, Rich Grote, Tim Jacobus, Roger Loveless, Greg Roman,
Peter Scanlan, Larry Selman, Matt Stawicki, Patrick Whelan

Bartels & Assocs/Studio 612, Ceci:
612 N 2nd St, St Louis, MO 63102 314-781-7377
Illustrator:
Bill Bruning, Lindy Burnett, Kevin Conran, Robert Craig, Chris Dellorco, Sheryl Dickert,
Dave Ember, Jonathan Evans, Mary Flock-Lempa, Mike Gardner, Leland Klanderman,
Shannon Kriegshauser, Larry McEntire, Rollin McGrail, Raphael Montoliu,
Kevin Newman, Deborah Palen, Charlie Podrebarac, Guy Porfirio, Jean Probert,
Kyle Raetz, Chris Sharp, Stephen Thompson, Jon Ward, Wayne Watford, Stan Watts,
Russ Widstrand, Ted Wright
Photographer:
Chris Amaral, Jacques Barbey

Bartholomew, Gillian:
One Captain Dr #D358, Emeryville, CA 94608 510-653-3996
Illustrator:
Patrick Réault

Bates & Assocs, Pat:
300 W 12th St #3-I, New York, NY 10014 212-807-8420
Photographer:
Francesca Galliani, Ted Hartshorn, Stewart Heir

Baugher Assocs, Liz:
300 N State St # 4511, Chicago, IL 60610 312-832-9888
Illustrator:
Shock Digital Art, Somers Studio
Photographer:
Richard Avedon, Dave Jordano Studio, Mark Luinenburg, Thomas Smugala,
Lisa Spindler, Peter Zander

Beate Works:
2400 Shenandoah St, Los Angeles, CA 90034 310-558-1100
Graphic Designer:
Maura McCarthy
Photographer:
Larry Bartholomew, Grey Crawford, Guido Flueck
Bender, Brenda:
4170 S Arbor Cir, Marietta, GA 30066 770-924-4793
Graphic Designer:
Thomas Cleveland
Illustrator:
Art Factory, Stephen Gallegos, Hellman Assoc, Richard Edward Hicks, Paul Lackner,
Marc Rochon, Geo Sipp, Kyle Stone, Keith Witmer
Photographer:
Jon Mazey, Chuck St John, Debrah Wihitlau
Beranbaum, Sheryl:
934 Williamsburg Circle, Warwick, RI 02886 401-737-8591
Illustrator:
Doug Bowles, Michael Brennan, Beth Buffington, Richard Cook, James Edwards,
John Kastner, Manuel King, Mary King, Albert Molnar, Stephen Moscowitz,
Brock Nicol, Matthew Pippin, Susan Seed, Gary Symington, Erin Terry, Tim Yearington
Berendsen & Assocs, Inc:
2233 Kemper Ln, Cincinnati, OH 45206 513-861-1400
Illustrator:
David Aikins, Bruce Armstrong, Jeffrey Bedrick, MIchael Bonilla, Linda Buckley,
Doug Chaffee, David Chestnutt, Jake Ellison, Dan Farris, Bill Fox, Judy Hand,
George Hardebeck, Marcia Hartsock, Jeff Holbrook, Alfred Kamajian, Mike Kreffel,
Daniel Krovatin, Doug Lemker, Mahammad Mansoor, Misty Maxwell, Paul Miller,
Frank Ordaz, Duff Orlemann, Jack Pennington, Tong Poole, Dave Reed,
Gary Richardson, Randy Rogers, Robert Schuster, Kevin Torline, Christina Wald,
Dave Warren, Wendy Wassink-Ackison, Randy Wazzola, Jim Williams,
Archie Williamson, Lee Woolery, Judy Workman
Photographer:
Jim Callaway, Dan Patterson, Don Ventre
Bernstein & Andriulli:
58 W 40th St 6th Fl, New York, NY 10018 212-682-1490
Illustrator:
Tony Antonios, Pat Bailey, Johnathon Barkat, James Frisino, Cheryl Griesbach,
Jacques Brady, Don Brautigam, Neil Brennan, Gregory Bridges, Rick Brown,
Leonello Calvetti, Barbara Camp, Karen Chandler, Cloe Cheese, The CIA,
Haydn Cornner, Creative Capers Ent. Inc., Grant Delin, Grace DeVito, Anatoly Dverin,
Julia Eggeringhaus, Pauline Ellison, Ronald Finger, Dean Fleming, Ron Fleming,
Victor Gadino, Fred Gambino, Joe Genova, Lynda Gray, Brian Grimwood,
John Harwood, Bryan Haynes, David Holmes, Peter Horridge, Catherine Huerta,
Daniel Kirk, Thea Kliros, Peter Kramer, Mary Ann Lasher, John Lawrence, Vicki Lowe,
Lee MacLeod, Jacqueline Mair, Charles Masters, Darlene Olivia McElroy,
David McMacken, Paul Micich, Frances Middendorf, Chris Moore, Pete Mueller,
Fabian Negrin, Craig Nelson, Jeff Nishinaka, Neil Packer, Leah Palmer Preiss,
Larry Paulsen, Greg Petan, Laura Phillips, Michael Plank, Peggi Roberts,
Paul S Robinson, Jeremy Sancha, Goro Sasaki, Robert Shadbolt, Sandra Shap,
Michael Sheehy, Erwin Sherman, Simon Spilsbury, Peter Stallard, Tommy Stubbs,
Thomas Thewes Jr, Jean-Paul Tibbles, Russell Walker, Pam Wall, Matt Warford,
Brent Watkinson, Catherine Wessel, Bryan Wiggins, David Wilgus, Leslie Wu,
Farida Zamas, Matt Zumbo
Photographer:
Melanie Acevedo, David Bartolomi, Dean Freeman, Brett Froomer, Philip Habib,
Stuart Hall, Gregory Heisler, Thibault Jeanson, Jock McDonald, Hans Neleman,
Pete Seward, Daniella Stallinger, Paul Wakefield
Birenbaum, Molly:
127 White Birch Dr, Guilford, CT 06437 203-453-9333
Illustrator:
Bill Thomson
Photographer:
Sean Kernan Studio, Frank Moscati, Joanne Schmaltz
Black, Inc:
2512 E Thomas Rd #2, Phoenix, AZ 85016 602-381-1332
Illustrator:
Greta Buchart, Giovannina Colalillo, Bob Diercksmeier, Brad Goodell, John Huxtable,
Alan Neider, Angela Simon, Tad Smith
Photographer:
George Bernal, Coni Bourin, Dan Coogan, Reddie Henderson, Bill McKellar,
Tim Pannell, Richard Petrillo, Dave Siegel, Lonna Tucker
Boege, Atelier Kimberly:
PO Box 7544, Phoenix, AZ 85011 602-265-4389
Illustrator:
Robert Case, Joann Daley, Matt Foster, Roberta Hancock, Tracy Hill, Paul Janovsky,
John Lambert, Jim McDonald, John Nelson, Adair Payne, Howard Post, Kevin Short,
Dale C Verzaal, Charles Wilkin
Photographer:
Jacques Barbey, Kevin Cruff, Rick Gayle
Bookmakers Ltd:
PO Box 1086, Taos, NM 87571 505-776-5435
Illustrator:
Susan Banta, Andrea Barrett, Lloyd Birmingham, Tami Boehle, David Brickman,
Barbara Cousins, Deirdre Griffin, Lydia Halverson, David Hohn, Marion Hull Hammel,
Melinda Levine, Kathleen McCord, Ted Mcneil, Judith Mitchell, Karen Pellaton,
Marsha Serafin, Dick Smolinski, Rosiland Solomon
Photographer:
David Brooks
Braun, Kathy:
2925 Griffith St, San Francisco, CA 94124 800-755-3380
Illustrator:
Pat Allen, Vivian Wu Browning, Scott Matthews, Sudi McCollum, Stephen Osborn
Brenneman, Cindy:
1856 Elba Cir, Costa Mesa, CA 92626 714-641-9700

• **Brewster Creative Services, John: pg 500-503**
597 Riverside Ave, Westport, CT 06880 203-226-4724
e-mail: creative.svcs@snet.net / url: www.brewstercreative.com / fax: 203-454-9044
Illustrator:
Kevin Callahan, Roger Chandler, Lane Du Pont, Tom Garcia, Glenn Gustafson,
Steve Harrington, Reggie Holladay, Seth Larson, Dolph LeMoult, Mike Lester,
Alan Neider, Steve Osborne, Miles Parnell, Jack Pennington, Chris Peterson,
Robert Prince, Jonathan & Georgina Rosenbaum, RM Schneider Illustration,
Stuart Simons, Cliff Spohn, Sharif Tarabay
Photographer:
Larry Ash, Frederick Charles, Dan Lenore, Bruce Plotkin
Brody, Sam:
77 Winfield St #4, E Norwalk, CT 06855 203-854-0805
Brown & Assocs, Shelley:
116 Spadina Ave Ste 400, Toronto, ON M5V 2K6 416-505-9522
Illustrator:
Philippe Beha, Harvey Chan, Dannille Collignon, Helen D'Souza, Joe Fleming,
Kevin Ghiglione, Laurie Lafrance, Matsu, Glenn Ryan, Thom Sevalrud, Remy Simard,
Tracy Walker, Tim Zeltner
Brown, Regina:
307 S Trooper Rd, Norristown, PA 19403 610-539-1130
Illustrator:
Jean Bryer van Dornick, Max Garcia, Jeff Holewski, Linda S Nye, Terry Watkinson
Lettering:
Luis Sola
• **Bruck & Moss: pg 524,525**
333 E 49th St, New York, NY 10017 212-980-8061
url: www.bruckandmoss.com or www.repstock.com / fax: 212-832-8778
100 Bleecker St, New York, NY 10012 212-982-6533
url: www.bruckandmoss.com or www.repstock.com / fax: 212-358-1586
Illustrator:
Dave Black, Tom Curry, Barbara Hranilovich, DB Johnson, Elizabeth Lada,
Susan LeVan, Adam Niklewicz, Rebecca Rüegger, Wiktor Sadowski
Buck & Kane:
481 8th Ave #E24, New York, NY 10001 212-631-0009
Illustrator:
Shawn Banner, Jay Belmore, Ken Call, Michel Canetti, Mario Henri Chakkour,
Dee Densmore D'amico, Natalie Fabian, Mark Kaufman, Bob Lapsley, Bertrand Le
Pautremat, Robert Melendez, Robert Passantino, Joanie Popeo, Dave Redl,
Jerry Schurr, Kevin Serwacki, Kevin Spaulding, Eva Sullivan, Roman Szolkowski,
Glenn Tunstull, Ron Victor, Marcia Yerman
Bundi, Kori:
246 W 108th St #1E, New York, NY 10025 212-980-9060
Burnett, Yolanda:
6478 Chestnut Hill Rd, Flowery Branch, GA 30542 770-967-0039
Illustrator:
Jill Arena, Joe Beauchamp, Clem Bedwell, Vince Chiaramonte, Barbara Emmons,
Jack Graham, Pamela Hamilton, Paul Johnson, Tim Jonke, Nobee Kanayama,
Nancy Kurtz, Don Margolis, Jeff Meyer, Jeff O'Connor, James Shepherd, Keith Skeen,
Jay Smith, Luis Sola, Tim Spransy, Gary Swift, Susan Tolonen, Keith Ward,
Xavier Wynn, Matt Zumbo
Photographer:
Al Clayton, Mike Granberry
• **Buzz: pg 446-455**
Sam Francisco, CA 415-441-4384
Illustrator:
Ron Chan, Glenn Mitsui, Bud Peen, Jeffrey Pelo, Gordon Suder

C

Cary & Co:
PO Box 711820, Salt Lake City, UT 84171 404-296-9666
Illustrator:
Robert August, Howard & Margie Fullmer, Mike Hodges, Kevin Hulsey, David Marks,
Shawn McKelvey, Charlie Mitchell, Greg Olsen
Photographer:
Axiom Imaging, Chuck Carlton, Peter Fownes
Caton, Chip:
15 Warrenton Ave, Hartford, CT 06105 860-523-4562
Illustrator:
Jeff Albrecht, Diana Minisci Appleton, Doug Besser, Mark Busacca, Ken Condon,
Gary Davis, Phillip Dvorak, Jeff Faria, Steve Fuller, Manuel Geerinck, Andy Giarnella,
Joe Klim, Terry Lennox, Roger Leyonmark, Jon Lezinsky, Michelle Lougee,
Michael McCurdy, Vince Perez, Nikolai Punin, Aina Roman, Linda Schiwall,
Marty Smith, Jim Smola, Janet Street, Jon Valk, Randall Zwingler
Photographer:
Melanie Eve Barocas, Peter Barrett, Alan Epstein, David Mendelsohn, Robert Reichert,
Peter Weidlein

Coleman Presents Inc, Woody:
490 Rockside Rd, Cleveland, OH 44131 800-486-1248
Electronic Imaging:
Royce Fitzgerald, Bill Morse
Illustrator:
Paul Abrams, Tom Antonishak, Eric Apel, Uwe Arendt, Michael Arnold, Charles Black,
Andi Boediman, Alex Bostic, Bruce Bowles, Mark Brown, Robert Brünz, Eric Bryant,
Mark Busacca, John Churchman, Mike Corcoran, Birck Cox, Denise Cuttitta,
Jack Doherty, JC Duffy, John Dzedzy, Larry Elmore, Sid Evans, Wes Feathers,
Larry Feign, Sean Fitzgibbon, Mike Fleishman, Mark Forrer, Robert Fraser, Gary Glover,
Stan Gorman, Jenny Graham, Andrew Grivas, Abe Gurvin Festive Illustrations,
Julie Hartman, R Hartzler, Bella Hollingworth, Bruce Holwerda, David House,
Thomas Hudson, Greg Hurley, Herb James, David Jermann, Thomas Jester,
Buena Johnson, Dana Johnstone, Reginald Jones, Eric Joyner, David Kelley,
Toni Kurrasch, John Letostak, Roger Leyonmark, Cindy Lorimer, Bob Lynch,
Charles Manus, Camille McBride, Larry Milam, Cheryl Nobens, Bob Novak,
Fred Padberg, Joani Pakula, Marshall Peck, Vincent Perez, Fanista Petron,
Sally Pogwizd, Elizabeth Prager, Chris Pribanic, Peter Quidley, Bob Radigan,
Rick Reeves, Jesse Reisch, Brian Rood, Gerry Saent-Johns, Jerry Sandefur,
Tim Scoggins, Natalie Sehn, James Seward, Steven Seward, Marla Shega,
Tom Shephard, William Silvers, Jae Song, Victor Stabin, Wayne Still, Ann Stookey,
Alan Studt, James Swanson, Jeff Swarts, Jim Szczodrowski, Robert Tanenbaum,
David Taylor, Ezra Tucker, Victor Valla, Barry Waldman, Lawrence Walker, Tim Webb,
Mark Weber, David Wenzel, Eric Williams, Steve Williams, Steve Windmiller,
Bruce Wolfe, Greg Wray, Roger Xavier, Bob Ziering

Collier, Jan:
PO Box 470818, San Francisco, CA 94147 415-383-9026
Illustrator:
Gary Baseman, Rich Borge, Gerald Bustamante, Katherine Dunn, Rae Ecklund,
Travis Foster, Douglas Fraser, Craig Frazier, Michele Manning, Jennie Oppenheimer,
Marti Somers, Robert Gantt Steele, Nicholas Wilton

• **Collignon, Daniele: pg 538**
200 W 15th St, New York, NY 10011. 212-243-4209
url: www.danielecollignon-reps.com
Illustrator:
Dianne Bennett, Dan Cosgrove, Jean Manuel Duvivier, Matt Foster, Bill Frampton,
Ken Jacobsen, Kevin Newman, Michael Stepanek, Alex Tiani, Don Weller,
Vicki Yiannias, Dennis Ziemienski

Conrad Represents:
2149 Lyon St #5, San Francisco, CA 94115 415-921-7140
Illustrator:
Paul Anderson, Neal Aspinall, Charles Bell, Guy Billout, Jerry Blank,
Christopher Buzelli, David Chen, Phil Cheung, David Clar, Adam Cohen Illustration,
Jim Cohen, Robert Crawford, Tom Curry, James Endicott, James Frisino, Michael Gibbs,
Richard Goldberg, Yolanda Gonzales, David W Groff, Rich Grote, Lydia Hess,
Danuta Jarecka, Jeff Jones, Andrew Judd, Joyce Kitchell, Leland Klanderman,
Jerzy Kolacz, Tim Lee, Lance Lekander, Larry Limnidis, Rafael Lopez, Michael Maydak,
Messi & Schmidt, Robin Moline, Gerald Nelson, Gavin Orpen, Eric Peterson,
Tana Powell, David Regan, David Renner, David Ridley, Scott Roberts, Carlos Sanchez,
Max Seabaugh, Eve Steccati, Dave Stevenson, Ron Tanovitz, Ellen Thompson,
Roxanna Villa, Paul Vismara
Photographer:
Sue Carlson

Cornell & Co:
737 Milwood Ave, Venice, CA 90291 310-301-8059
Film:
Crossroads Films, Nomad Editorial, Taylormade Editorial, X-1 Films, X-Ray Films
Illustrator:
Joe Saputo
Photographer:
Charles Hopkins

Cornell & McCarthy:
2D Cross Hwy, Westport, CT 06880 203-454-4210
Illustrator:
Elizabeth Sayles

Corporate Art Planning:
27 Union Square West ste 407, New York, NY 10003 212-242-8995
Electronic Imaging:
Suzanne Brookens, Caroline Corey, Nebraska Gifford Shestak, Richard Rockwell
Photographer:
Michael Friedman

• **Craig Represents, Suzanne: pg 520,521**
4015 E 53rd St, Tulsa, OK 74135 918-749-9424
url: www.suzannecraig.com / fax: 918-749-5165
Photographer:
Jim Davies
Illustrator:
Gil Adams, Martha Anne Booth, Cameron Clement, Jim Davies, Scoll Dawson,
Bruce Eagle, Michael Hogue, Tim Jessell, Robin Kachantones, Gary Locke, Keith Locke,
Genevieve Meek, Richard Merchan, David Merrell, Aletha Reppel

Creative Advantage, Inc:
620 Union St, Schenectady, NY 12305 518-370-0312
Illustrator:
Jack Graber

Creative Freelancers:
99 Park Ave #210A, New York, NY 10016 800-398-9544
Illustrator:
Gil Ashby, Cary Austin, Marcel Bordei, Stephen Bornstein, Lloyd Brimingham,
Henry Buerckholz, Wende Caporale, Carolyn Carpenter, Chris Celusniak,
Roger Chandler, James Cooper MD, Jim DeLapine, John Edens, Clifford Faust,
Anne Feiza, John Gampert, Rick Geary, Gary Hanna, Traci Harmon, Phil Howe,
Chet Jezierski, Sandy Kossin, Salem Krieger, Rob Lawson, Frank McShane,
AJ Miller, Greg Newbold, Jan North, Jim Owens, Elena Poladin, Meryl Rosner,
Reg Sandland, Glen Schofield, Scott Snow, Steve Sullivan, David Tamura,
Winson Trang, Lou Vaccaro, David Wink, Yemi
Photographer:
Greg Newbold

Creative Network:
100 Wyndham Cir W, New Brighton, MN 55112 612-631-2353
Illustrator:
Tim Blouch, Terry Boles, Dave Danz, Virginia Kylberg, Keith Lango, C Spencer Morris,
Chris Nye, Linda O'Leary, Bryon Vollman

Creative Network South:
4316 Cynthia St, Bellaire, TX 77401 281-870-1102
Illustrator:
Brad Gaber
Photographer:
Ken Childress, Rocky Kneten, Hal Lott, Beryl Striewski

Creative Options, Inc:
208 Harbor Dr Bldg #1, Stanford, CT 06902 203-854-9393

D

Darnell, Jim, The Art Source:
2820 Rainforest Ct, Southlake, TX 76092 817-481-2212

Das Group:
311 Avenue H #D, Redondo Beach, CA 90277 310-540-5958
Illustrator:
Loudvik Akopyan, Mona Daly, Brian Fujimori, Ray Goudey, John Hull, Jui Ishida,
Jeff Labbe, Rachael McCampbell, Mercedes McDonald, Robert Rodriguez,
Brad Weinman, Michael Wepplo
Photographer:
Richard Rendon

Davis, Brooke:
4911 N Hanover, Dallas, TX 75209 214-352-9192
Illustrator:
Bryan Haynes, Gary Head, Mike Reed, Carol Zuber-Mallison
Photographer:
Walt Denson, Chip Henderson, David Lyles, Richard Seagraves

• **DeMoreta Represents, Linda: pg 465-467**
1839 Ninth St, Alameda, CA 94501 510-769-1421
e-mail: ldmreps@prodigy.net
Illustrator:
Shannon K Abbey, Monica Dengo, Diane Hays, Tina Healey, Janet Hyun, Peter
McDonnell, Colin Poole, Charles Pyle, Tina Rachelle, Richard Sheppard, Rosiland
Soloman
Lettering:
Barbara Callow, Monica Dengo
Photographer:
James Chiang, John Lund, Ron Miller, Susan Vogel

• **Dedell, Inc, Jacqueline: pg 332-356**
58 W 15th St, New York, NY 10011. 212-741-2539
url: www.jdedell.com or www.theispot.com / fax: 212-741-4660
Illustrator:
Scott Baldwin, Richard Beards, Amy Binder, Philip Brooker, Alicia Buelow,
Kelly Brother, Piero Corva, Judd Guitteau, Cornel Rubin, Alicia Buelow,
Kimberly Bulken Root, Brian Cairns, Ivan Chermayeff, Christopher Corr, Nancy Davis,
Sandra Filippucci, Louis Fishauf, David Frampton, Linda Frichtel, Wendy Grossman,
Jud Guitteau, Bryan Leister, Frank Miller, Paula Munck, Nigel Owen, Chang Park,
Ed Parker, Cornel Rubino, Fletcher Sibthorp, Karen Tenenbaum, Jim Tsinganos,
Richard Tuschman, Alexandra Weems, Mick Wiggins, Heidi Younger

Dimension Creative :
9801 DuPont Ave S #168, Minneapolis, MN 55431 612-884-4045
Electronic Imaging:
Jennifer Vee
Film:
Wobat Interactive, Frank Ordaz, Marshall Woksa
Illustrator:
Fred Dingler, Fran Gregory, Keith Grove, Linda O'Leary, Dennis Rogers, Kathy Rogers,
Don Salmela, Meg Smith, Rebbeca Stenstrom-Leblanc
Photographer:
Posl Photography

Dodge + Assocs, Sharon:
3033 13th Ave W, Seattle, WA 98119 206-284-4701
Illustrator:
Bart Bemus, Bill Brown, Jonathan Evans, Chris Gall, Allen Garns, Jud Guitteau,
G Brian Karas, Mike Kowalski, Gennady Kurbat, Julia Lapine, Stephanie Morgan
Rogers, Mark Schofield, Kevin Short, Beata Szpura, Keith Witmer
Photographer:
Robin Bartholick, Patricia Ridenour

Douraghy, Jamie:
1950 S Sawtelle Blvd #333, Los Angeles, CA 90025 310-312-2062

Dubois, Dennis Reps, Francoise:
305 Newbury Ln, Newbury Park, CA 91320 805-376-9738
Photographer:
Michael Baciu, Andrew Bernstein, Ron Derhacopian, Stephen Lee, Eric Sander

Dunham, Jennie:
50 W 29th St, New York, NY 10001 212-684-6050

E

Edsey & Sons, Steve:
401 N Wabash, Chicago, IL 60611. 312-527-0351
Graphic Designer:
Roberts Barnes, Kelly Hume
Illustrator:
Keith Batcheller, Michael Carroll, Mike Dammer, Lary Day, Tom Durfee, Dennis Dzielak,
Michael Edsey, Dennis Franzen, Bryan Friel, Gene Givan, George Hamblin,
Seitu Hayden, Mitchell Heinze, Tim Huhn, Victor Kennedy, Doug Knutson, Gary Krejca,
Rick Lieder, David Loew, Dan Lotts, Rick Lundeen, Rob Magiera, Ron Mahoney,
Betty Maxey, Tom McKee, Jay Moore, Manuel Morales, Terry Olson, Matt Paoletti,
Mike Philips, Harlan Scheffler, Mike Sobey, Richard Stergulz, Don Stinson, Bobbi Tull,
Jim Wisniewski, John Zielinski
Photographer:
Robert Barnes, Steve Liss

Embler, Jennifer:
10 Fairway Dr #212, Deerfield Beach, FL 33441. 954-760-4195
Illustrator:
Sid Daniels, David FeBland, Lisa Henderling, Reggie Holladay, Dick Mahoney,
Bruce Montecalvo, Colin Poole, Bob Radigan, Jim Stillwell

Envoy Creative Consultants, Inc:
1523 King St, Alexandria, VA 22314. 703-706-5729
Illustrator:
Debra Schaeffer
Photographer:
Fred Dana Photography, Aaron Goodman, Mark Lee, Stephen Spartana,
Vecchione Print & Film Inc, Mark Wieland

Ericson, William:
1020 Mission St #C, S Pasadena, CA 91030. 323-461-4969

Evelyne Johnson Assocs:
201 E 28th St, New York, NY 10016   212-532-0928
Illustrator:
Lynn Adams, Cathy Beylon, Nanette Hilton, Kristine Bollinger, Lisa Bonforte,
Joanne Cannon, Larry Daste, Jill Dubin, Carolyn Ewing, Bill Finewood, Lia Frasinetti,
Mel Gaefinger, Simon Galkin, June Golsborough, Marsha Halleck, Turi MacCombie,
Darcy May, Cheryl Nathan, Joan O'Brien, John O'Brien, Heidi Petach, Steven Petruccio,
Barbara Soloff-Levy, Barbara Steadman, Pat Stewart, Tom Tierney, Sylvia Walker

F

Famous Frames:
5855 Green Valley Cir #308, Culver City, CA 90230. 310-642-2721
Illustrator:
Bill Angresano, Jennifer Baker, Paul Bananno, Kathy Bieck, Paul Binkley, Ted Blackall,
Mark Bloom, George Booker, Vonnie Brenno, Walter Brogan, Jason Brubaker,
Pierre Chanty, Gary Ciccati, Rick Clubb, Philippe Collot, Gus DeGuzman, Paul Didier,
Cash Donovan, Patty Dryden, Rod Dryden, Phil Dunlap, Gabriella Farkas, Kevin Farrell,
James Fogle, Trevor Goring, Collin Grant, Ramon Gregorio, Mark Harris, Reggie Hendrix,
Ron Hicinbothem, Shannon Hogan, Chuck Hom, Jim Hopkins, Tak Ioka, Al Johnson,
Meredith Johnson, Merle Keller, Jeff Kronen, Andy Lee, Michael Lee, Walter Lee,
Hector Lopez, Meridee Mandio, Chad McGown, Hogie Mcmurtrie, Alex McOwan,
Davd Melloni, Martin Mercer, Marc Messenger, Stanley Miller, Mark Millicent,
Luis Molina, Alex Morris, Duff Moses, Chris Muller, Brian Murray, John Killian Nelson,
Jeanne Norman, Scott Ownbey, Neal Parrow, Ivan Pavlovits, Charles Pecoraro,
Colin Pennock, Howard Perlin, Bill Perry, Steve Pica, Manuel Plank, Debon Repos,
Mike Rider, Ruben Sarkissian, Miro Sinovcic, Chris Stiles, Michael Swift,
Dave Threadgold, Thomas Tonkin, Bob Towner, Jerry Viviit, Mark Wagner,
Steve Werblun, Shari Wickstrom, Brian Wilcox, Ed Wolfe, Steve Worthington,
Nob Yamashita, Mark Yates, Debbie Young

Fiat & Assocs, Randi:
918 Sheridan Rd, Glencoe, IL 60022. 312-663-5300
Illustrator:
Jon Conrad
Photographer:
Carrie Branovan, Daniel Malka, Victor John Penner, Laurie Rubin, Sandro, Todd Winters

Fishback Illus, Inc, Lee:
350 W 21st St, New York, NY 10011. 212-929-2951
Illustrator:
Peter Attard, Andrew Bacha, Nancy Cheadle, Mac Conner, Bruce Eagle, Trini Eiche,
Samson Pollen, Mike Russell, Barbara Siegel, Joseph Taffo, Bryna Waldman,
Kevin Wasden, George Wilson

Fisher Reps, Bunny:
320 W Illinois Ste 2212, Chicago, IL 60610. 312-280-1961
Illustrator:
Jennifer Riggler
Photographer:
Kevin Banna, James Caulfield, Tony Glaser, John McArthur

Flanders, Shelley:
1424 Las Positas Place, Santa Barbara, CA 93105. 805-682-6775
Illustrator:
Andrea Barrett, Anne Dayal, Tinka Anjali Sloss, Michele Zuzalek

Fleming, Laird Tyler:
2214 Fox Hills Dr, Los Angeles, CA 90064. 310-556-0541

Folio:
PO Box 1251, New York, NY 10023. 212-774-4271
Graphic Designer:
Steve Jones
Illustrator:
Bayo Akinsiku, Richard Allen, Mark Arundale, David Atkinson, Paul Bateman,
Katherine Baxter, Claudio Berni, Malcolm Bird, Michael Bishop, Kay Boyce,
John Bradley, Syd Brak, Jane Brewster, Judy Byford, Paul Campion, Reg Cartwright,
Chris Coady, Jonathan Cooper, Don Cordery, Eddie Corkery, Sydney Couldridge,
David Cutter, John Davis, Nina Davis, Mike Delany, Simon Dewey, Jovan Djoedevic,
Christophe Drochon, Jacques Fabre, David Farren, Steve Fricker, Manuel Geerinck,
Tim Gill, Jo Goodberry, Charlotte Grann, Alex Green, Roger Harris, Robert Heesom,
Paul Hogarth, Andrew Ingamells, Kevin Jones, Tim Jonke, Sophie Joyce, David Juniper,
JC Knaff, David Lawrence, Andy Lawson, Larry Learmonth, Stewart Lees, Gary Long,
Alyson MacNeill, Martin Macrae, Chandraa Manga, Helen Manning, David McAllister,
John McIlvancy, Stuart McKay, Ed McLachlan, Tony Meeuwissen, Jonathan Milne,
Bekah O'Neill, Roger O'Reilly, Micheal Ogden, Viv Oxley, Nick Pace, Andrew Pepworth,
Alan Preston, Graham Redfern, John Reilly, Larry Richmond, David Riley, David Russell,
Jonathan Satchell, Nick Schon, Anne Sharp, Mike Sharp, Tony Spaul,
Tamara Sternberg, Leo Stevenson, Gay Sturrock, Tim Taylor, Mike Terry, Ken Thompson,
Nancy Tolford, Michael Toohig, George Underwood, Chris Vine, Diz Wallis, Andy Ward,
Povl Webb, Laurence Whiteley, Sue Williams, Ray Winder, Stephan Wohlgemuth,
Andela Wood, Murray Zanoni

Folio London:
10 Gate St Lincoln Inn Fields, London, England, UK WC2 A. 171-242-9562

• **Foster Artists' Representative, Pat: pg 522-523**
32 W. 40th St #2 South, NYC, NY 10018. 212-575-6887
url: www.patfosterartrep.com
Illustrator:
Franco Accornero, Dru Blair

Foster Reps, Teenuh:
1051 S Big Bend Blvd #210, St Louis, MO 63117. 314-647-7377
Illustrator:
Sandy Appleoff, Paul Blakey, Matt Foster, Mark Frueh, Tuko Fujisaki, Ian Greathead,
Jim Hancock, Bryan Haynes, Michael P Haynes, Daphne Hewett, Kelly Hume,
Mark Langeneckert, Jeff May, Mark Oakley, Brian Otto, Harlan Scheffler, Jim Steck,
Frank Steiner, Terry Tidwell, Beth Tipton, Arden von Haeger
Photographer:
Scott Ferguson, Robert Grimm, Mark Katzman, Jim Olvera, Greg Rannells

Fox Art Inc, Marsha:
3363 Barham Blvd, Los Angeles, CA 90068. 323-662-0020
Illustrator:
Mike Bryan, Bruce Eagle, Abe Gurvin, Sue Rother, Joe Spencer
Photographer:
Chapman Baehler, Reggie Casagrande, Roger Erickson, Storm Hale, Tim Hale,
Poruchai Mittongtare, Robert Mizano, Sean Murphy, Bill Pack, James Sorensen

Freeman, Lisa:
740 E 52nd St #8, Indianapolis, IN 46205. 317-920-0068
Illustrator:
Julie Baker, Brian Behnke, Calef Brown, Don Carney, Kim Colwell, Barbara Friedman,
Liz Grace, Todd Graveline, Terry Julien, Sara Love, Tracey Mitchell, Carol O'Malia,
Emily Pearlman, Einat Peled, Chris Pyle, TIm Schneider, Jerry Velasco, David Wong

Friedman Creative Showcase, Eric:
16 Oak Pkwy, Sparta, NJ 07871. 212-689-2343

Friend & Johnson:
137 W 14th St #204, New York, NY 10011. 212-337-0055
325 Wilson Way, Larkspur, CA 94939. 415-927-4500
3100 Carlisle #210, Dallas, TX 75204. 214-969-0026
Illustrator:
Robert Forsbach

G

Garafola Reps, Lorraine:
206 Linda Ln, Edison, NJ 08820. 908-756-9254
Illustrator:
Ralph Garafola, Bob Hardin, Don Martinetti, Peter Neumann, Robert Nicol

• **Gatlin Represents Inc, Rita: pg 485-487**
83 Walnut Ave Corte Nadera, CA 94925. . . . . **415-924-7881**
. . . . **800-924-7881**
e-mail gatlin@ritareps.com / url: www.ritareps.com / fax: 415-924-7891
Illustrator:
Andrew Boerger, Russ Charpentier, Anne Crosse, Chris Dellorco, Tom Hennessy, Elizabeth Hinshan,
Jack Lutzow, Stephanie Langley, Sudi McCollum, Delro Rosco, Mary Ross, Matthew Squillante,
Kirk Waren
Photographer:
Jackson Vereen

• **Gaynin, Gail: pg 386-399**
194 Third Ave, New York, NY 10003. . . . . **212-475-0440**
see Morgan Gaynin Inc

Gem Studio, Inc:
420 Lexington Ave #220, New York, NY 10170. 212-687-3460

Glenn, Chris :
340 Diversey St, Chicago, IL 60657. 312-829-4201
Illustrator:
Tom Bachtell, Alex Boies, Chuck Gonzales, Carlos Marrero
Photographer:
Jim Krantz Studio, Jack Perna, Victor Skrebneski, Dave Slivinski

Glick & Assocs, Ivy:
San Francisco, CA 415-543-6056
Illustrator:
Catherine Rose Crowther, Jerry Dadds, Derek Grinnell, Matthew Holmes, Terence Lawlor, Map Makers, Tony Morse, John Roman
Lettering:
Jane Dill

Godfrey, Dennis:
201 W 21st St #10G, New York, NY 10001 212-807-0840
Illustrator:
Jeffrey Adams, John Blackford, David Parker, Wendy Popp, David Stimson, Michael Wepplo
Photographer:
John Blackford

• **Goldman Agency, David: pg 496-499**
41 Union Square W #918, New York, NY 10003 212-807-6627
e-mail: dgagency@idt.com / url: www.davidgoldmanagency.com / fax: 212-463-8175
Illustrator:
Nishan Akgulian, Michelle Barnes, Norm Bendell, Steve Dininno, Rosemary Fox, Mazemaster David Anson Russo, Kazu Nitta, Jeffrey Oh, Teofilo Olivieri, Kurt Vargo, Mark Wiener, James Yang

Gordon Assocs, Barbara:
165 E 32nd St, New York, NY 10016 212-686-3514
Illustrator:
Susan Avishai, Ron Barry, Robin Brickman, Valerie Constantino, Ben Craner, Michael D'Antuono, Jim Dietz, Bob Dorsey, Douglas Dowd, Gary Glover, Glenn Harrington, Robert Hunt, Nenad Jakesevic, George Ladas, Tim Lundgren, Cynthia Samul, Jim Smola, John Suh

• **Graham Represents, Corey: pg 480-484**
Pier 33 North, San Francisco, CA 94111 415-956-4750
e-mail: cgr@slip.net / url: www.coreygrahamreps.com
Illustrator:
Frank Ansley, Andrea Brooks, Kirk Caldwell, Tim Clark, Jon Conrad, Jim Coon, Manuel Geerinck, Pat Hilliard-Barry, Ken Jacobsen, Joel Nakamura, John Nelson, Bill Rieser, Brian Rea, Sammy Silverstein, David Tillinghast, Robin Zingone
Photographer:
Zoe Danae Falliers, Giles Hancock, Nick Pavloff, Allan Rosenberg, Deborah Roundtree

• **Grien, Anita: pg 435**
155 E 38th St, New York, NY 10016 212-697-6170
url: www.anitagrien.com / fax: 212-697-6177
Illustrator:
Dolores Bego, Fanny Mellet Berry, Julie Johnson, Hal Just, Mona Mark, Jerry McDaniel, Don Morrison, Alan Neider, Alan Reingold, Alex Zwarenstein

Gross Assocs, Lee:
119 W 57th Street ste 1215, New York, NY 10019 212-582-0440

• **Guenzi Agents, Inc, Carol: pg 474-479**
865 Delaware St, Denver, CO 80204 303-820-2599
. . . . 800-417-5120
url: www.artagent.com / fax: 303-820-2598
Film:
Alweis Productions, Sanford Baran, Daniel Clawson, Dan Thomas, Tom Ward, Visual Approach
Illustrator:
Gus Alavezos, Shelly Bartek, Marc Brown, Dan Bulleit, John Ceballos, Jim Chow, Dave Ember, Christer Eriksson, Brian Evans, Michael Fisher, Greg Hargreaves, Kelly Hume, Jeff Jones, Dean Kennedy, Todd Lockwood, Jason Lynch, Joe McDermott, Heidi Merscher, Sue Rother, Ryle Smith, Don Sullivan, Tatjana, Marina Tito, Tom Ward, Randall Zwingler
Photographer:
Jay Dickman, Nora Feller, Jason Lynch, Brian Mark, Priscilla Montaya, Carl Yarbrough

H

Hackett Artist Representation, Pat:
1809 7th Ave #1710, Seattle, WA 98101 206-447-1600
Illustrator:
Bryan Ballinger, Ken Barnes, Janice Kooch Campbell, Jonathan Combs, Steve Coppin, Eldon Doty, Larry Duke, Edwin Fotheringham, Martin French, John Fretz, David Harto, Celeste June Henriquez, Chris Hopkins, Lilly Lee, Daniel McGowan, Bill Meyer, Leo Monahan, Dennis Ochsner, Chuck Pyle, Elizabeth Read, Laurie Rosenwald, Yutaka Sasaki, Kathlyn Shadle, Chuck Solway, Bobbi Tull, Kris Wiltse, Ted Witus, Mark Zingarelli
Photographer:
Bill Cannon, Diane Padys, Marco Prozzo

Hahn [H2 & Co], Holly:
837 W Grand Ave 3rd Fl, Chicago, IL 60622 . . . . 312 633-0500
Illustrator:
Nan Brooks, Lina Chesak, Doug Githens, Tim Peterson, Diane Sudyka, Kirsten Ulve
Photographer:
Stephen Hamilton, Jeff Sciortino, Kipling Swehla, Greg Whitaker

Hall & Assocs:
606 N Larchmont Blvd #4C, Los Angeles, CA 90004 323-962-2500

Hankins & Tegenborg Ltd, Artists Reps:
60 E 42nd St, New York, NY 10165 212-867-8092
Illustrator:
Matt Archambault, Jeff Barson, Bob Berran, Paul Blumstein, Joe Burleson, Dan Burr, Warren Chang, Chris Cocozza, David Cook, John B Crane, Pino Daeni, Vittorio Dangelico, Donna Diamond, Bill Dodge, John Dzedzy, Bryant Eastman, Jon Paul Ferrara, David Gaadt, Antonio J Gabrielle, Mark Garro, Kerri Gibbs, William Giese, Sergio Giovine, Donna Gorson, Jim Griffin, Phil Heffeman, Edwin Herder, Michael Herring, Tony Hertz, Philip Howe, Aleta Jenks, Rick Johnson, Jean-Kves Kervevan, Uldis Klavins, Rick Lieder, Kei Masuda, Linda Messier, Cliff Miller, Rudy Muller, Keith Newton, Ernie Norcia, Kevin Odhner, Gary Penca, Walter Rane, Sergio Roffo, Larry Roibal, Ken Rosenberg, Robert Sabin, Mitzura Salgian, Harry Schaare, Bill Schmidt, Rob Schuster, Miro Sinovcic, Diane Sivavec, Ted Sizemore, John W Sledd, Victor Stabin, Don Stewart, Robert Swanson, Jean Targete, Peter Van Ryzin, Richard Waldrep, Jeff Walker, Anne Wertheim, Judy York, John Youssi

Hanson, Jim:
777 N Michigan Ave Ste 706, Chicago, IL 60611 312-337-7770
Illustrator:
Michael Dinges, Rob Porazinski, Craig Smallish .
Photographer:
Leonard Gertz, Glen Gyssler, Maria Krajcirovic, Drew Reynolds, Derek Snape

Harlib Assocs, Joel:
10 E Ontario #4708, Chicago, IL 60611 312-573-1370
Illustrator:
Richard Anderson, Nick Backes, Julie Bell, Rick Brown, Gerry Chapleski, Russell Cobane, Michael Dean, Lawrence Duke, Alex Ebel, Chuck Eckert, Abe Gurvin Festive Illustrations, Abe Gurvin, Karel Havlicek, Joe & Kathy Heiner, Tim Langenderfer, Kent Leech & Associates, Fred Pepera, Buc Rogers, Delro Rosco, RV2, Tim Stout, Robert Tyrrell, Boris Vallejo, Ron Villani, Kim Whitesides, Bruce Wolfe
Photographer:
Marty Evans, Robert Farber, Jean Moss Studio, Steve Nozicka

Harris & Assocs, Gretchen:
5230 13th Ave S, Minneapolis, MN 55417 612-822-0650
Illustrator:
Matt Coffin, Ken Jacobsen, John Kleber, Jane Mjolsness, Eric Mueller, Jody Winger, Mary Worcester
Photographer:
Russell Brannon, Graham Brown

Hart, Vikki:
780 Bryant St, San Francisco, CA 94107 415-495-4278
Illustrator:
Kevin Hulsey, Aleta Jenks, Jonathan Wright
Photographer:
GK Hart

Head Productions:
42 Delavan St, Brooklyn, NY 11231 718-624-1906

Hedge, Joanne:
1415 Garden St, Glendale, CA 91201 818-244-0110
Illustrator:
Tony De Luz, Greg Epkes, Rick McCollum, David McMacken, Victoria Miller, David Mollering, Marjorie Muns, Ken Perkins, Laura Phillips, Ken Rosenberg, Jim Salvati, David Schweitzer, Tsuchiya Sloneker Comms, Brent Watkinson

Hedleston/Sharpe & Assocs, Colleen:
25 W 68th St #9A, New York, NY 10023 212-595-1125
Illustrator:
Peter Simpson Cook, Greg Morales, Dan Richards, Judy Reed Silver
Photographer:
Neal Brown, Ann Cutting Photography, Hugh Kretschmer, Lise Metzger, Jamey Stillings Photography Inc, Eric Tucker, Everard Williams Jr

Hellman Assocs, Inc:
1225 W 4th St, Waterloo, IA 50702 319-234-2089

Herman, Ronnie Ann:
350 Central Park West, New York, NY 10025 212-749-4907
Illustrator:
Dawn Apperley, Mary M Bono, Thierry Courtin, Barry Gott, Gideon Kendall, Sonja Lamut, Tomas Leszczynski, Jill Newton, Betina Ogden, Michael Rex, David Sheldon

Heyl Assocs, Fran:
230 Park Ave ste 2525, New York, NY 10169 800-327-0333

Hillman, Betsy:
PO Box 77644, San Francisco, CA 94107 415-381-4728
Illustrator:
Istvan Banyai, Doug Bowles, Cathy Deeter, John S Dykes, Jud Guitteau, Bruce Pope, Randy South, Greg Spalenka, Joe Spencer, Jeremy Thornton
Photographer:
Gordon Edwardes, Dennis Gray, Randy Schwartz, Holly Stewart

• **HK Portfolio: pg 504-507**
666 Greenwich St #860, New York, NY 10014 212-675-5719
e-mail: harriet@hkportfolio.com / url: www.hkportfolio.com / fax: 212-675-6341
Illustrator:
John Bendall-Brunello, Nan Brooks, Lindy Burnett, Anthony Carnabuci, Abby Carter, Randy Chewning, David Austin Clar, Steve Cox, Renée Daily, Jack E Davis, Eldon Doty, Kathi Ember, Leonid Gore, Amanda Harvey, Shelly Hehenberger, Laura Huliska-Beith, Susan Keeter, Anne Kennedy, Kristin Kest, Anthony Lewis, Stephen Lewis, Katherine Lodge, Margeaux Lucas, John Manders, Paul Meisel, Jan Palmer, Valeria Petrone, Mike Reed, Michael Reid, Clive Scruton, Remy Simard, Jamie Smith, Kristina Stephenson, Peggy Tagel, George Ulrich, John Wallace
Photographer:
Stephen Lewis

Hodges, Jeanette:
12401 Bellwood Rd, Los Alamitos, CA 90720 562-431-4343
Illustrator:
Ken Hodges

Holland & Co, Mary:
6638 N 13th St, Phoenix, AZ 85014 602-263-8990
Illustrator:
Shelly Bartek, Heather Bednorz, Jack Crompton, Jack Graham, Doug Horne,
Rose Johnson, Jeff Jones, Julie Pace, Scott Picunko, Pepper Tharpe, Cathy Trachok
Photographer:
Patrick Darby/Studio X, Marc Feldman, Paul Loven, Judy Miller

• **Holmberg, Irmeli: pg 357-371**
280 Madison Ave #1110, New York, NY 10016. 212-545-9155
url: www.irmeliholmberg.com / fax 212-545-9462
Illustrator:
Mike Aarestrup, Kaz Aizawa, Melanie Barnes, Alexander Barsky, Kristen Barr,
Louise Baker, Tivadar Bote, Dan Bridy, Bob Byrd, Maria Cardelli, Rita Chow, Lo Cole,
Sylvie Daigneault, Jim Dandy, Peter De Freitas, Donna Delich, William Ersland,
Linda Fong, Susan Gal, Anna-Liisa Hakkarainen, Carolyn Holman, Laurie Keller,
Barbara Kelley, Mir Lada, Ken Laidlaw, Roger Leyonmark, Tina Bela Limer,
Suzanne Mogensen, Wally Neibart, John Nelson, Meredith Nieves, Steven Noble,
Ann Mari Olsson, Takumasa Ono, Doug Panton, Melisande Potter, Bob Radigan,
Linda Schiwall, Thom Sevalrud, Clare Schaumann, Melissa Sweet, Lydia Taranovic,
Kat Thacker, Hannele Vanha-Aho

Hopson Reps, Melissa:
1605 Stemmons Freeway #C, Dallas, TX 75207 214-747-3122
Illustrator:
Pat Binder, Bill Jenkins, Cody Lucido, Kevin Mishak, Peggy Mozley, Colin Poole,
Keith Steiger, Studio 212 °

Hunter, Nadine:
PO Box 307, Ross, CA 94957 415-456-7711
Illustrator:
Rebecca Archey, M Kathryn Thompson Illustration, M Kathryn Thompson, Liz Wheaton

• **Hull Associates, Scott: pg 518-519**
Dayton, OH 937-433-8383
San Francisco, CA. 415-285-3808
New York, NY 212-966-3604
url: www.scotthull.com / fax 937-433-0434
Illustrators:
Dave Albers, Rob Blackard, David Bowers, Tracy Britt, Andy Buttram, John Ceballos,
Young Sook Cho, Greg Dearth, Andrea Eberback, Doug Fryer, Clint Hansen, Stacey Innerst,
Greg Lafever, Jon Lezinsky, John Maggard, Larry Martin, Larry Moore, Noma, Curtis Parker,
John Patrick, Ted Pitts, Andrew Powell, Mark Riedy, Amiee Sicuro, Geoffrey Smith, Tammy Smith,
Lorraine Tuson

I

• **Inman, E.W., Ltd.: pg 539**
300 N State St #3302, Chicago, IL 60610 773-792-9169
e-mail: ewinman@aol.com / fax: 773-792-9189
Illustrator:
Chris Sheban, Russell Thurston
Photographer:
Barbara Karant, Jeff Kauck, John Payne, Greg Rannells, John Wagner

Intermarketing Group, The:
29 Holt Rd, Amherst, NH 03031 603-672-0499

International Fine Arts:
One Timber Ln, Westport, CT 06880. 203-227-5687

Ivy League of Artists:
1133 Broadway Ste 825, New York, NY 10010 212-243-1333
Illustrator:
Cheryl Chalmers, Ric Del Rossi, John Dyess, John Paul Genzo, Paula Goodman,
Chris Murphy, Justin Novak, Tom Powers, Tanya Rebelo, John Rice, Steve Smallwood

J

Jameson, Diane:
231 Humbercrest Blvd, Toronto, ON M6S 4L5 416-530-1500
Illustrator:
Ninonq Barroux, Nina Berkson, Mike Constable, Katrin Dockrill, Clancy Gibson,
Grant Innis, Aaron Leighton, Pierre Pratt, Paul Rivoche

Jaz & Jaz, The Artists' Rep:
810 NE 102nd St, Seattle, WA 98125 206-526-7171
Illustrator:
Todd Connor, Lisa Johnston, Dev Madan, Larry Milam, Shawn Ogle, Craig Orback,
Julie Paschkis, Heather Scholl
Photographer:
Martin Bydalek, Rick Etkin, Robert Tran, Mitch Craig, Ted Grudowski, Bobby Houghram

Jenni & Assocs, Jane:
472 Portland Ave, St Paul, MN 55102 651-224-6763
Illustrator:
Amy Butler, Julie Delton, Joelle Nelson

• **Jett Reps: pg 412-422**
7118 Upper River Rd, Prospect, KY 40059 502-228-9427
url: www.jettreps.com / fax: 502-228-8857
Illustrator:
Lu Beach, Mark Betcher, Jennifer Bolten, Dan Brawner, Annette Cable, Antonio Cangemi,
Cameron Eagle, Robert Felker, Jesica Flick, Claudia Hammer, Dave Jonason, Patricia Languedoc,
John Mattos, Jacqui Morgan, Monica Rangne, Billie Renkl, Lori Siebert, Carla Siboldi,
Kelly Romer, Roy Wiemann, M.P. Wiggins

Jorgensen/Barrett:
PO Box 19412, Seattle, WA 98109 206-634-1880
Illustrator:
Fred Birchman, Sharon Dahl, Debbie Hanley/Daisy Art Studio, Colin Hayes,
Fred Hilliard, Kurt Hollomon, Mits Katayama, Richard Kehl, Stephanie Langley,
David Lund, Greg MacDonald, Cheri Ryan, Jane Shasky, Theresa Wingert
Photographer:
Angie Norwood Browne, Mel Curtis, Donna Day

K

Kahn Artists:
4317 Cornelia Cir, Minneapolis, MN 55435 612-925-1699
Illustrator:
Tom Lochray Inc., Mike McMillen, Brian Otto, Rick Peterson, Cindy Wrobel

Kahn, Harvey:
155 Millburn Ave, Millburn, NJ 07041 212-752-8490
Illustrator:
Bernie Fuchs, Gerry Gersten

Kalish, Renee:
203 N Wabash Ave #900, Chicago, IL 60601 312-704-0010
Illustrator:
Gary Glover, Bob Krogle, Greg Loudon, Karen Snave, Jim Sutton

Kamin & Assocs, Vince:
260 E Chestnut Ste 3005, Chicago, IL 60611 312-787-8834
Illustrator:
Jim Allen, Steve Bjorkman, Paul Bond, Andrzej Dudzinski, Eddie Guy, Mark Mille,
Gail Greenfield Randall, James Swanson, David Tillinghast
Photographer:
James Balog, Ernie Block, Tom Burazin, Walt Denson, Michael Deuson, Susan Drinker,
Dick Durrance, Marko Lavrisha, Dorit Lombroso, Jim Secreto, Gil Smith, Andrew Terzes,
Bill Tucker, Jim Veccioni, Jim White, Mark Wiens

• **Kasak, Harriet: pg 504-507**
666 Greenwich St #860, New York, NY 10014 212-675-5719
(see HK Portfolio)

Kastaris & Assocs, Harriet:
3301A S Jefferson Ave, St Louis, MO 63118 314-773-2600
Illustrator:
Sarah Beise, Jim Carroll, Gary Ciccarelli, Eric Dinyer, Greg Johannes, Rip Kastaris,
Michael Kilfoy, Darin Murray, Christian Musselman, Nikolai Punin, Terry Ravanelli,
Carlos Sanchez, RJ Shay, Joseph Taylor, Doug Thompson, Jenny Vainisi,
Amanda Warren, Linda Webb, April Goodman Willy, Keith Witner, Cindy Wrobel

Kaurala & Assocs, Ed:
903 N Main St, Royal Oak, MI 48067 248-548-4500
Photographer:
Kevin Cruff

Keating, Peggy:
30 Horatio St #3B, New York, NY 10014 212-691-4654
Illustrator:
Charles Dillon, Carol Vennell, Sylvia Walker

Kimche, Tania:
137 Fifth Ave 11th Fl, New York, NY 10010 212-529-3556
Illustrator:
Paul Blakey, Bill Brandon, Kirk Caldwell, Lisa Grothman, Ken McMillan, Rafal Olbinski

• **Kirsch Represents: pg 541**
4541 Highway 47 N, Rhinelander, WI 54501 715-369-2130
Illustrator:
David Kimble
Photographer:
Todd Smith

Klein Represents, Jane:
1635 E 22nd St, Oakland, CA 94606 510-535-0495
Illustrator:
Jannine Cabossel, Tuko Fujisaki
Photographer:
Kirk Amyx, Reid Ashton, Marshall Gordon, Christian Peacock

Klimt Represents, Bill & Maurine:
15 W 72nd St, New York, NY 10023 212-799-2231
Illustrator:
David Blattel, Paul Henry, Katherine Manzo, Frank Morris, Vince Natale, Tom Patrick,
Ben Stahl, Rachel Stuart, Tsukushi

Knable & Assocs, Ellen:
1233 S La Cienega Blvd, Los Angeles, CA 90035 310-855-8855
Animator:
Roger Chouinard
Photographer:
Dean Siracusa, Kirk Weddle

Knecht, Cliff:
309 Walnut Rd, Pittsburgh, PA 15202 412-761-5666
Illustrator:
Michael Aveto, Pamela Becker, Mark Bender, Janet Darby, Debra Drummond,
Milan Kecman, Melinda Levine, Lauren Ling, Ron Magnes, Lyn Martin,
Robert Meganck, James Mravec, Mark Murphy, Lori Osiecki, Phil Parks,
Wayne Parmenter, Debbie Pinkney, Karen Pritchett, George Schill, Lee Steadman,
Jim Trusilo, Phil Wilson

Koeffler, Ann:
5015 Clinton St #306, Los Angeles, CA 90004 323-957-2327
Illustrator:
Ron Barry, Beverly Bigwood, Linda Blackwell Design, Roger Chouinard, Dick Cole,
Bob Commander, Catherine Deeter, Duck Soup, Edem Elesh, Jan Evans, Gary W Glover,
Bruce Helander, Kyle Hollinger, Paul Jermann, Judy Koenig, Rob Lawson,
Patricia Logan, Constance McLennan, Eugene Mitta, Burton Morris, Juliana Morris,
Will Nelson, Rik Olson, Ann Pickard, Randy South, Kevin Spaulding, James Stagg,
Charles Thomas, Jenny Vainisi, Teresa Woodward

Koralik Assocs:
343 Rocky Hill Rd, Galena, IL 61036 815-777-0420
Illustrator:
Randal Birkey, Carmelo Blandino, Tim Campell, Ron Criswell, Tony Crakovich,
Joann Daley, Susan Edison, Pam Eklund, Lori Nelson Field, Arthur Friedman,
Bill Graham, Myron Grossman, Loren Kirkwood, Salem Kreiger, Karen Kuchar,
Jim Lange, Rob Lawson, Chuck Ludeke, Dan McCreehan, Joe McDermott,
Michele Noiset, LS Pierce, Tom Price, Ilene Robinette, Dennis Soderstrom,
T Starrett, Ken Tiessen, Ralph Voltz, Marshall Woksa, Andy Zito
Photographer:
Robert Keeling

• **Korn & Associates, Pamela: pg 540**
PO Box 521, Canadensis, PA 18325 570-595-9298
e-mail: pamkorn@ptd.net / fax: 570-595-9392
Illustrator:
Brian Ajhar

Kramer, Ina:
928 Broadway, New York, NY 10010 212-614-0616

Kuehnel & Assocs, Peter:
30 E Huron Plaza #2108, Chicago, IL 60611 312-642-6499
Electronic Imaging:
TOPIX Mad Dog
Illustrator:
Phoenix Studio Inc

• **Kurlansky Associates, Sharon: pg 526,527**
192 Southville Rd, Southborough, MA 01772 508-872-4549
e-mail: laughstoc@aol.com / url: www.laughing-stock.com / fax: 508-480-9221
Illustrator:
Tim Lewis, Blair Thornley

L

Lachapelle Reps, Linda:
420 E 54th St, New York, NY 10022 212-838-3170
Photographer:
Carlo Dalla Chiesa, Richard Dunkley, Pieter Estersohn, Linda Farwell, James Galloway,
Tim Geaney, Thom Jackson, Jean-Noel L'harmeroult, Andrew Williams

Langley Artist Rep, Sharon:
333 N Michigan Ave #400, Chicago, IL 60601 312-782-0244
Illustrator:
Jill Arena, Vince Chiaramonte, Eddie Corkey, Mona Daly, Jack Graham, Tim Jonke,
Nobee Kanayama, Don Margolis, Jeff O'Connor, Gary Smith, Brian White, Xaviar Wynn,
William Illus Group Zumbo

• **Lavaty, Frank & Jeff: pg 310-331**
217 E 86th St #212, New York, NY 10028 212-427-5632
e-mail: jeff@lavatyart.com / url: www.lavatyart.com / fax: 212-427-6372
Illustrator:
Steven Adler, Lori Anzalone, Craig Attebery, David Biedrzycki, Dom D'Andrea,
Don Demers, Chris Duke, Gervasio Gallardo, Neal Hughes, Grant Jerding,
David McCall Johnston, Yuan Lee, Robert LoGrippo, Don Mannes, Kevin Murphy,
Carlos Ochagavia, Rick Reeves, Ben Verkaaik

• **Lehmen Dabney, Inc: pg 528,529**
1431 35th Ave S, Seattle, WA 98144 206-325-8595
url: ldabneyinc@home.com / fax: 206-325-8594
Film:
Debi Lee Mandel, Sachiko Yoshikawa
Illustrator:
Cherie Bender, Ruben De Anda, Jim Deal, Rolf Goetzinger, Jeremy Kidd, Kong Lu,
Debbie Lee Mandel, Julie Pace, Stan Shaw, Carla Siboldi, Steve Slaske,
Kirk Richard Smith, Debra Solomon, David Wink, Allen Yamashiro,
Sachiko Yoshikawa, Jeff Yeomans

• **Leighton & Co, Inc: pg 530,531**
7 Washington St, Beverly, MA 01915 978-921-0887
e-mail: leighton@leightonreps.com / url: www.leightonreps.com / fax: 978-921-0223
Illustrator:
Scott Angle, Jon Berkeley, Rob Bolster, Marty Braun, Linda Bronson, Stephen Costanza,
Laura DeSantis, Kyle Dreier, Jamie Fogle, Jamie Hogan, Danuta Jarecka,
Annette Kraus, Anne Lambert, Mary Anne Lloyd, Michael Lotenero, Fred Lynch,
Lisa Manning, Steve Meek, Scott Nash, Tim Nihoff, Fran O'Neill, Traci O'Very Covey,
Ami Plasse, Bruce Sanders, Rod Savely, Steven Stankiewicz, August Stein,
Paul Stoddard, Julia Talcott, Jennifer Thermes, Art Valero, Cam Wilson, Jane Winsor,
Charlie Woglom

Lesli-Art, Inc:
PO Box 6693, Woodland Hills, CA 91365 818-999-9228
Illustrator:
Kurt Anderson, Raymond Bayless, John Bruce, Frank Caldwell, Don Clark, Jim Daly,
Thomas Darro, Bob Fassl, Walter Graham, Gregory Harris, Al Helner, Christa Kieffer,
Roger La Manna, Richard Pionk, Jan Saether, Bob Schmalzried, Albert Sharp,
John Stephens, George Thompson, Edward Turner, James Verdugo, SZ Wang,
Alexander Yelagin

• **Levy Creative Management: pg 456-464**
300 E 46th St #4G, New York, NY 10017 212-687-6463
url: www.levycreative.com / fax: 212-661-4839
Illustrator:
Alan Dingman, Shane Evans, Thomas Fluharty, Max Grafe, Chris Hargis, Rob Magiera,
Tim Okamura, Roberto Parada, David Rankin, Oren Sherman, Doug Struthers,
Jonathan Weiner

Leyden Diversified:
976 Old Huntingdon Pike, Huntingdon Valley, PA 19006 215-663-0587
Illustrator:
Animates/Hellman Assoc Animation, Kim Behm, Deb Bovy, Bob Byrd, John Emil
Cymerman, Donna Bair Delich, Len Epstein, Bruce Evans, Alex Forbes, Than Geehr,
Greg Hargreaves, Dan Hatala, Robert Hochgertel, Steve Hunter, Kathleen King,
John Langdon, Tony Mascio, Marcos Monteiro, Pat Muchmore, Wayne Parmenter,
Matt Scharle, John Miles Simon, Craig Simpson, Jon Simpson, Carol Stolvoort,
John Thompson, Todd Treadway, Mary Wilsbach
Photographer:
Ed Marco, Gary Mattie, Scott Nibauer, Christopher Smith

• **Lilie, Jim: pg 512-514**
728 Castro St, San Francisco, CA 94114 415-441-4384
e-mail: jimlilie@aol.com / url: www.planetpoint.com/jim_lilie
Illustrator:
Eric Bowman, Armandina Lozano, Dugald Stermer, Ezra Tucker, Dennis Ziemienski

• **Lindgren & Smith: pg 244-283**
250 W 57th St #521, New York, NY 10107 212-397-7330
San Francisco 415-788-8552
url: www.lindgrensmith.com
Illustrator:
Stéphan Daigle, Regan Dunnick, Joseph Daniel Fielder, Douglas Fraser, Audra Geras,
Bob Hambly, Joe & Kathy Heiner, Jennifer Herbert, Matthew Holmes, Matsu,
Miles Hyman, Jeff Jackson, Kim Johnson, Susan Leopold, Francis Livingston,
Lori Lohstoeter, Matsu, Bill Mayer, Jonny Mendelsson, Yan Nascimbene, Chris O'Leary,
Michael Paraskevas, Charles Pyle, Tim Raglin, Robert Rodriguez, Steven Salerno,
Valerie Sinclair, Valerie Sokolova, Robert Gantt Steele, JW Stewart, Yasuo Tanaka,
Mary Thelen, Stefano Vitale, Cynthia von Buhler, Robert Wagt

Lindgren, Patricia: pg 244-283
250 W 57th St #521 New York, NY 10107 212-397-7330
San Francisco, CA 415-788-8552
url: www.lindgrensmith.com
(see Lindgren & Smith for client list)

• **Link Associates: pg 532,533**
 416-530-1500
url: www.linkartists.com / fax: 416-530-1401
Illustrator:
Nina Berkson, Mike Constable, Clancy Gibson, Aaron Leighton, Ninon Pelletier, Pierre Pratt

Lorraine & Assocs:
2311 Farrington St, Dallas, TX 75207 214-688-1540
Illustrator:
Jacques Lamy, Mary Thelen
Photographer:
David Bullock, Lee Gordon, Keith Madigian

Lott Reps:
60 E 42nd St #1146, New York, NY 10165 212-953-7088
Illustrator:
Sean Beavers, Tony Cove, Ed Kurtzman, Eric JW Lee, Mark Nagata, Tim O'Brien,
Tsukushi, Barbara Tyler, Craig White

Lulu Creatives:
4645 Colfax Ave South, Minneapolis, MN 55409 612-825-7564
Illustrator:
Alan Brunettin, Tina Lee Hill, Fran O'Neill, Virginia Peck

Lurie Fine Arts:
8657 Wonderland Ave, Los Angeles, CA 90046 213-654-8983
Illustrator:
Daniel Brice, Agop Gemdjian, Greg Gronowski, Alfonce Pagano, David Serrano,
Rene Vasquez
Photographer:
Steve Olson, Ben Sedererowsky

• **Lynch Artists, Alan: pg 131**
11 Kings Ridge Rd, Long Valley, NJ 07853 908-813-8718
e-mail: alartists@aol.com / url: www.arenaworks.com / fax: 908-813-0076
Illustrator:
Martin Andrews, Arena, Michael Armson, A. Azpiri, Colin Backhouse, Simon Bartram,
John Peter Brown, Jim Burns, Nigel Chamberlain, Oscar Chichoni, John Clementson,
Brigid Collins, Gordon Crabb, Carla Daly, Merritt Dekle, Les Edwards, Faranak,
Chris Gibbs, Yvonne Gilbert, Peter Gudynas, Elizabeth Harbour, John Harris,
Matilda Harrison, Susan Hellard, Paul Hess, David Hitch, John Howe, Diane Lumley,
Edward Miller, Mark Oldroyo, Liane Payne, Hood Philip, Adrian Johnson, Koveck,
Neal Layton, Milo Manara, Terry Oakes, MA Prado, Tony Roberts, Luis Royo,
Liz & Brian Sanders, Leonie Shearing, Jon Sullivan, Brain Sweet, Daniel Torres,
Jenny Tylden-Wright, Bob Warner, Ben Warner, Jim Warren, David Williams,
Janet Woolley, Paul Wright, Paul Youll

M

Maloney, Tom:
307 N Michigan Ave #1006, Chicago, IL 60601 312-704-0500
Illustrator:
Rex Bohn, Steve Bondurant, Dennis J Carmichael, PD Cooper, Dennas Davis,
Jeanne de la Houssaye, Greg Dye, Scott Ernster, Bruce Helander, Dale Joritz,
Kelly Kennedy, John Margeson, David McMacken, Keith Meehan, Margery Mintz,
Mitch O'Connell, David Olmstead, Rik Olson, Julie Pace, George Peters, Oscar Senn,
Miro Sinovcic, Kevin Spaulding
Photographer:
Axiom Imaging, Jeff Burke, Chuck Carlton, Nick Faltage, Raif-Finn Hestoft,
Roarke Johnson, Vito Palmisano, Bill Schild

Manasse, Michele:
2134 Aquetong Rd, New Hope, PA 18938 215-862-2091
Illustrator:
Eric Dever, Sheldon Greenberg, Carol Inouye, Genevieve Leloup, Ger & Barbara Quinn,
Mike Reagan, Leslie Stall, Matthew Trueman, Sharon Watts, Terry Widener

Marlena Agency:
145 Witherspoon St, Princeton, NJ 08542 609-252-9405

Martha Productions, Inc:
11936 W Jefferson Blvd #C, Culver City, CA 90230 310-390-8663
Illustrator:
Bob Brugger, Bradley Clark, Royce Fitzgerald, Allen Garns, Byron Gin, Joe & Kathy Heiner, Nathan Kane, Steve Keller, Hiro Kimura, Catherine Leary, Mike Meaker, Bill Morrison, Mukai Studio, Peter Siu, Steve Vance, Eric Westbrook

Mason Illus:
3810 Edmund Blvd, Minneapolis, MN 55406 612-729-1774
Illustrator:
Neal Aspinall, Kenn Backhaus, Patrick Faricy, Paul Fricke, Glenn Gustafson, Joe Heffron, Dan Lotts, Jeff Meyer, Mark Mille, Christine Monroe, Tom Rosborough, Harlan Scheffler, Dan Wiemer

Maslov, Norman
608 York St San Francisco, CA 94110 415-641-4736
Photographer:
Davis Allan Brandt, Christiana Ceppas, Michele Clement, Deborah Jones, David Maisel, Mika Manninen

• Maslov/Weinberg pg 468-473
608 York St San Francisco, CA 94119 415-641-1285
url: www.theispot.com/rep/weinberg
Illustrator:
Stuart Bradford, Sean Flanagan, Stefan Gutermuth, Pamela Hobbs, Tatiana Krizmanic, Mark Matcho, Jason Mecier, Adam MCauley, Bill Russel, Caroline S, Susan Sanford, Maarcos Sorrensen, Mandy Tritty, Mark Urliksen, Eric White

Matson Reps, Marla:
1429 N 1st Street, Phoenix, AZ 85004 602-252-5072
Illustrator:
Michael Carroll, Mark Fredrickson, Chris Gall, Allen Garns, Mike Gushock, Rick Kirkman, John Kleber, Darrel Kolosta, Julia La pine, Ann Morton, Curtis Parker, Walter Porter, Barbara Samanich
Photographer:
Ellen Barnes, Scott Baxter, William McKellar, Mark Segal Photography, John Wagner

Mattelson Assocs Ltd:
37 Cary Rd, Great Neck, NY 11021 516-487-1323
Illustrator:
Karen Kluglein, Marvin Mattelson, Phill Singer

McCusker, Kathleen
3178 Belgrade St, Philadelphia, PA 19134 215-427-6114
Illustrator:
Ken Hobson, Connie Kennedy, Keith Neely, Steve Smallwood, Thalia Stratton, Victor Valla

McLean & Friends Reps:
2460 Peachtree Rd NW #1705, Atlanta, GA 30305 404-881-6627
Illustrator:
Martin Pate

McMahon & Co, Eileen:
PO Box 1062, Bayonne, NJ 07002 201-436-4362
Illustrator:
Mark Bannerman, Michael Foreman, Andre Francois, Edward Gorey, Neil Gower, Clare Mackie, George Riemann, Ronald Searle

McMahon, Brian:
1535 N Western Ave, Chicago, IL 60622 773-227-6778

Meiklejohn Illustration:
32 Shelton St, Covent Garden, London, England, UK WC2H 442072402077
Illustrator:
Alan Cracknell, Matt Eastwood, Andrew Farley, Jake Rickwood, Paul Sample

• Mendola Artists: pg 132-188
420 Lexington Ave, New York, NY 10170 212-986-5680
e-mail: mendolaart@aol.com / url: www.mendolaart.com / fax: 212-818-1246
Film:
Dave Henderson, Charlie Hill, Tim Lee, Wayne McLoughlin, Richard Newton
Illustrator:
Acme Pixel, TL Ary, Rowan Barnes-Murphy, Russell Benfanti, Ron Berg, Doug Chezem, Steven Chorney, Garry Colby, Michael Crampton, Mona Daly, Chris Dellorco, Digital Dimensions, John Taylor Dismukes, Lisa Chauncy Guida, Dave Henderson, Charlie Hill, Robert Hynes, Kenny Kiernan, Joyce Kitchell, Robert Krogle, Tim Lee, Jeffrey Mangiat, Bill Maughan, Mick McGinty, Wayne McLoughlin, Tom Newsom, Richard Newton, Kevin Rechin, Frank Riccio, Linda Richards, Francesco Santalucia, Joe Saputo, Heidi Schmidt, Kyle Still, Jim Talbot, Robert Tanenbaum, Wayne Tannenbaum, Joseph Taylor, Wayne Vincent, Jeff Wack, Sam Ward, Don Wieland, Dean Williams, Mike Wimmer, Keith Witmer, Boris Zlotsky,

Mills & Co, Jane:
1117 N Caterbury Ct, Dallas, TX 75208 214-946-6569
Illustrator:
Bob Shema
Photographer:
Eric Pearle

Mizuno, Barbara:
23548 Calabasas Rd #207, Calabasas, CA 91302 818-223-0082

Montagano & Assocs, David:
11 E Hubbard 7th Fl, Chicago, IL 60611 312-527-3283
Electronic Imaging:
Joseph Taylor
Illustrator:
Joel Heinz, John Hyatt, Mary Jones, Jason Millet, Burton Morris, Bruno Paciulli, Larry Paulsen, Mike Randall
Photographer:
Douglas Bening, Hans Rott

Moore & Assocs, Gigante:
360 N Michigan Ave #904, Chicago, IL 60601 312-541-9595
Animator:
Will Vinton Studios
Film:
Compulsive, Industrial Light & Magic
Photographer:
Wilson Griak Productions, Silent Partner

• Morgan Gaynin Inc: pg 386-399
194 Third Ave , New York, NY 10003 212-475-0440
url: www.morgangaynin.com / fax: 212-353-8538
Illustrator:
Nanette Biers, Karen Blessen, Dave Calver, Tom Christopher, Raúl Colón, Nicholas Gaetano, Beppe Giacobbe, Jean-Claude Götting, Sandra Kaplan, Joan Landis, William Low, Michael Morgenstern, Joyce Patti, Anne Pundyk, Elizabeth Rosen, Robert Sauber, Guido Scarabottolo, Joanie Schwarz, Joel Spector, Dahl Taylor, Kris Wiltse, Jessica Daryl Winer, Bruce Wolfe, Wendy Wray

• Morgan, Vicki: pg 386-399
194 Third Ave, New York, NY 10003 212-475-0440
see Morgan Gaynin Inc

Morin & Assocs, Jacqueline:
725 Millwood Rd, Toronto, ON M4G 1V7 416-488-6759

Moskowitz Reps, Inc, Marion:
315 E 68 St, New York, NY 10021 212-517-4919
Illustrator:
Phillip Dvorak, Diane Teske Harris, Beth McCash, Geoffrey Moss, Roger Roth

Motion Artists:
1400 N Hayworth Ave #36, Los Angeles, CA 90046 323-851-7737
Film:
Patrick Tatopoulos
Illustrator:
Gabriel Abraham, Jim Bandsuh, Harold Belker, Ted Boonthanakit, Mauro Borelli, Jim Byrkit, Raymond Consing, Robert Consing, John Coven, Juan Diaz, Mariano Diaz, Christiano Donzelli, Guy Dyas, Giacomo Ghiazza, Chad Glass, Christopher Glass, Darek Gogol, Peter Heer, Marc Hurtado, Bruton Jones, Petko Kadiev, Phil Keller, Joseph Musso, Emily Owens, Scot Ritchie, Louise Russo, Jim Salvati, Christian Scheuerer, Oliver Scholl, Joshua Sheppard, Jeffrey Starling, Tracey Wilson

Munro Campagna:
332 Bleecker St, New York, NY 10014 212-691-2667
4 E Ohio Studio B, Chicago, IL 60611 312-321-1336
Illustrator:
Shelly Bartek, Tom Bookwalter, Mark Chickinelli, Sally Wern Comport, Philip Dunlap, Pat Dypold, Malcolm Farley, Tom Foty, Ben Garvie Illustration, Clint Hansen, Greg Hargreaves, Greg Harreaves, Dan Hatala, Iskra Johnson, Mike Kasun Illustration, Douglas Klauba, Tatjana Krizmanic, Paul Lackner, Ben Luce, Jack A Molloy, Bryan Peterson, Tim Robinson, David Schweitzer, Steve Shock, Ryle Smith, Michael Steirnagle, Uhl Studios/David Uhl, Peter Wells, Mark Wiener, Corey Wilkinson

N

Nachreiner Boie Art Factory Ltd, Tom:
925 Elm Grove Rd, Elm Grove, WI 53122 414-785-1940

• Neis Group, The: pg 493-495
11440 Oak Dr PO Box 174 Shelbyville, MI 49344 616-672-5756
e-mail: neisgroup@wmis.net / url: www.neisgroup.com / fax: 616-672-5757
Illustrator:
Tom Bookwalter, Lyn Boyer-Nelles, G William Cole, Liz Conrad, Clint Hansen, Michael Inglo, Erika LeBarre, Matt LeBarre, Peg Magovern, Don McLean, Laura Meadows, Bill Ross, David Schweitzer, Joyce Shelton, John White, Danny Wilson
Lettering:
Ruth Pettis
Photographer:
Fred Bender, Phil Gray

Newborn Group, The:
115 West 23rd St , New York, NY 10011 212-989-4600
Illustrator:
David Beck, Roy Carruthers, Teresa Fasolino, Robert Giusti, Robert Goldstrom, Mark Hess, John H Howard, Victor Juhasz, James Marsh, Wilson McLean, John Rowe, David Wilcox, Christopher Zacharow

Newman & Assocs, Carole:
13756 Ventura Blvd #201, Sherman Oaks, CA 91423 310-394-5031
Electronic Imaging:
Tim Petros, Phaedrus Productions, Tom Slatky
Graphic Designer:
Joe Cibere, Lynda Modaff
Illustrator:
Joy Allen, Scott Angle, Ted Burn, Roger Chandler, Allen Coulter, Leslie Crofford, Christian Ellithorpe, Gino Hasler, Tim Huhn, Michael Jackson, Gino McIntyre, Larry Reinhart, Larry Taugher
Photographer:
John Bauer, Mike Granberry, Knight/Bilham, Kaz Kurisu, Robert Mayer, Gabriela Ortuzar

Nittolo Studio, Mary:
216 E 45th St 14th Fl, New York, NY 10017 212-661-1363

• Nowicki & Assocs, Lori: pg 508-511
310 W 97th St #24, New York, NY 10025 212-243-5888
e-mail: lori@lorinowicki.com / url: www.lorinowicki.com / fax: 212-243-5955
Illustrator:
Barroux, John Bleck, Martha Anne Booth, John Huxtable, Mellissa McGill, Burton Morris, Hank Osuna, Tony Persiani, Stacie Peterson, Doug Ross, Bryon Thompson, Dona Turner, Cecilia Waxberg, Cecilia Waxberg

Nygreen, Ann:
250-A Seaview Ave, Piedmont, CA 94610 510-653-1744
Illustrator:
Keith W Criss

O

Oasis Art Studio:
952 Medina Rd, Wayzata, MN 55391 612-860-1701
Illustrator:
Bill Bruning, Ronald Finger, Corbert Gauthier, Leland Klanderman

Ogden Represents, Robin:
4409 Washburn Ave S, Minneapolis, MN 55410 612-925-4174
Illustrator:
Dianne Bennett, Charlie Griak
Lettering:
Kelly Hume
Photographer:
John Reed Forsman, Richard Hamitlon-Smith, Jeff Johnson

Organisation, The:
42 Delavan St, Brooklyn, NY 11231 718-624-1906
Illustrator:
Harry Brockway, Paul Cemmick, Yvonne Chambers, Becky Cole, Steve Dell,
Maxwell Lawrence Dorsey, David Eaton, Mark Entwisle, Cathie Felstead, Mickey Finn,
Francois Gervais, Neil Gower, Adam Graff, Becky Halls, Stephanie Hawken,
Susan Hellard, Nicholas Hely-Hutchinson, Michael Hill, Allison Jay, Natacha Ledwidge,
Domanic Li, Darren Lock, Dave Luscombe, Alan Mcgowan, Shane Mcgowan,
Mark Morgan, Jayne Morris, Michael Munday, Claudio Munoz, Robert Nelmes,
Dean Paget, Janet Pontin, Mark Preston, Ruth Rivers, Benjamin Russell Warner, Mattew
Russell, Dave Smith, Ray Smith, Andrew Steward, Lee Stinton, Peter Sutton,
Chris Swee, Fred Van Deelen, Kelly Waldek, Amanda Ward, Nadine Wickenden,
Matthew Williams, Stuart Williams, Jonathan Wolstenholme, Dave Wood

Oscard Agency, Fifi:
24 W 40th St, New York, NY 10018 212-764-1100
Illustrator:
Joe Farris
Photographer:
William Claxton, Jeanne Moutousammy-Ashe, Mark Newman, Carole Reiff,
Henri Silverman, Edmond Van Hoorick

P

Palulian Reps, Joanne:
18 McKinley St, Rowayton, CT 06853 203-866-3734
Illustrator:
Philippe Beha, Greg Couch, David Goldin, Bonnie Hofkin, Gayle Kabaker, Peter Kitchell,
Dick Palulian, Trip Park, Tom Saecher, David Sheldon, Bonnie Timmons

Parios Studio:
21 Toledo Dr, Brick, NJ 08723 908-477-5529

Payne Assocs:
32 W 31st St 5th Fl, New York, NY 10001 212-239-4283
Illustrator:
Ronald Slabbers

Pema Browne Ltd:
Pine Rd HCR Box 104B, Neversink, NY 12765 914-985-2936
Illustrator:
Robert Barrett, Robin Crumbacher, Todd Doney, Bob Dorsey, Richard Hull,
Charles Jordan, Dilleen Marsh, John Sandford, Bob Schochet, Maren Scott

Penny & Stermer Group, The:
2031 Holly Dr, Prescott, AZ 86305 520-708-9446
Illustrator:
Steve Ellis, Scott Gordley, John Mantha, Glynnis Osher, Tom Payne, Delro Rosco,
T Starrett, Rick Stromoski

Perlow, Carrie:
311 Ave H #D, Redondo Beach, CA 90277 310-540-5958
Illustrator:
Barbara Cummings, Mona Daly, Ray Goudey, Greg Hally, John Hull, Jui Ishida,
Nora Koerber, Rachael McCampbell, Mercedes McDonald, Robert Rodriguez,
Chuck Schmidt, Michael Wepplo
Photographer:
Richard Rendon

PG Reps:
211 Monson Turnpike Rd, Ware, MA 01082 413-967-9855
Illustrator:
Robbie Short

Photocom, Inc:
3922 Gilbert Ave #106, Dallas, TX 75219 214-526-2020
Illustrator:
Don Arday, Jon Flaming, Michael Steirnagle
Photographer:
Abrams/Lacagnina, Ric Cohn, Phillip Esparza, Nancy Moran, Rick Wahlstrom

Pinnacle Creative Co:
8136 Mullen Rd, Lenexa, KS 66215 913-438-1888
Illustrator:
Peter Cole, Chris Willey

Planet Rep-Williams Group West:
7376 Cliffton, Cliffton, VA 20124 800-847-5101
Illustrator:
John F. Martin

Poje, Elizabeth:
1001 S Alfred St, Los Angeles, CA 90035 310-556-1439
Illustrator:
Mark Bussaca, Frank Kozik, Dave Woodman
Photographer:
Jack Anderson, Robert Butler, Tony Garcia, Joseph Ilan, John Konkal, Dorit Lombroso,
Bill Robbins, Eric Schmidt, Carl Schneider, Jeff Sedlik

Potts & Assocs, Carolyn:
1872 N Clybourn #404, Chicago, IL 60614 773-935-8840
Illustrator:
Karen Bell, John Craig, Byron Gin, Greg Huber, Julia Lapine, Rhonda Voo
Lettering:
Joe Plume
Photographer:
Terry Collier, Ralph Daniel, Debra Doffing, Paul Goirand, Stuart Schwartz,
Derek Seaward, Craig van der Lende

Potts, Vicki:
PO Box 13518, Chicago, IL 60613 773-296-2940

Powditch Assocs, Michael:
863 Hartglen Ave, Westlake Village, CA 91361 805-497-0069
Illustrator:
Denny Osborn
Photographer:
Steve Cooper, Bo Hylen, Bud Lammers, O'Brien & Schridde, Bob Williams

Pred, Becky:
10012 Perry Dr, Overland Pk, MO 66212 913-438-7733
Graphic Designer:
Margaret Carsello
Illustrator:
Jean Holmgren, Angela Moore, Jim Paillot, Tom Patrick, Rick Richter
Photographer:
Donovan Reese

Prentice Assocs, Inc, Vicki:
630 Fifth Ave 20th Fl, Rockefeller Ctr, New York, NY 10111 212-332-3460
Illustrator:
Rocco Baviera, Robert Byrne, Tom Edgarton, Joan Farber, David Mckenzie,
Masaaki Ogai, Marjorie E Pesek, Hisashi Sekine, Mary Spencer, Tom Voss,
Lawrence Walker
Photographer:
Jack Neith, Reuben Njaa, Al Rubin

Prentice, Nancy:
2917 N Fulton Dr NE, Atlanta, GA 30305 404-266-0088
Illustrator:
Steve McAfee, Mark E Schuler, Robbie Short, Bruce Young

Publishers Graphics:
231 Judd Rd, Easton, CT 06612 203-445-1511
Illustrator:
Joann Adinolfi, RW Alley, Dan Andreasen, Paige Billin-Frye, Eric Brace, Susan Calitri,
Jean Cassels, Eulala Conner, Jane Conteh-Morgan, Lynne Crowath, Shelley Dieterichs,
Bert Dodson, Julie Durrell, Alan Eitzen, Nate Evans, Gioia Fiammenghi, Cynthia Fisher,
Teresa Flavin, Brian Floca, Patrick Girouard, Joan Holub, Berrei Huang,
Pamela G Johnson, G Brian Karas, Lisa McCue, Debbie Palen, Pam Paparona,
RA Parker, Cary Pillo, Dana C. Regan, SD Schindler, Rebecca Thornburgh,
Lucia Wasburn, James Watling, Terry Weidner, Jenny Williams, Vik Woodworth

Pushpin Group Inc, The:
18 E 16th St 7th Fl, New York, NY 10003 212-255-6456
Illustrator:
Seymour Chwast

Putscher, Terry:
PO Box 461, Narberth, PA 19072 610-667-8890
Illustrator:
Tracie Aretz, Dale Crawford, Marie Garafano, Tom Herbert, Neal Hughes,
Heidi Merscher, Bot Roda

R

Ramin, Linda:
6239 Elizabeth Ave, St Louis, MO 63139 314-781-8851
Illustrator:
Robert Barnum, Phil Benson, Richard Bernal, Tom Buttner, Carol Carter, Donald Curran,
Hans Droog, Brian Fine, William O'Donnell, Righard High, Miro Sinovic, Richele Garcia
Slecke, Roy Smith, Linda Solovic, Jim Turgeon, Jack Whitney, Mike Whitney,
Terry Ziegelman, John Zielinski

• **Rapp, Inc, Gerald & Cullen: pg 48-130**
108 E 35th St , New York, NY 10016 212-889-3337
e-mail: gerald@rappart.com / url: www.theispot.com/rep/rapp / fax: 212-889-3341
Illustrator:
Philip Anderson, Natalie Ascencios, Garin Baker, Stuart Briers, Lon Busch,
Jonathan Carlson, Michelle Chang, R Gregory Christie, Jack Davis, Robert deMichiell,
Bill Devlin, The Dynamic Duo Studio Inc, Randall Enos, Leo Espinosa, Phil Foster,
Mark Fredrickson, Mark Gagnon, Eliza Gran, Gene Greif, Thomas Hart, Peter Horjus,
Peter Horvath, Celia Johnson, Douglas B Jones, James Kaczman, John Kascht,
Steve Keller, JD King, Laszlo Kubinyi, Scott Laumann, Davy Liu, Lee Lorenz,
PJ Loughran, Bernard Maisner, Hal Mayforth, David McLimans, Alex Murawski,
Marlies Merk Najaka, James Robert O'Brien, Jerry Pinkney, John Pirman,
Jean-Francois Podevin, Marc Rosenthal, Alison Seiffer, Seth, Whitney Sherman,
Jeffrey Smith, James Steinberg, Drew Struzan, Elizabeth Traynor, Michael Witte,
Noah Woods, Brad Yeo

Ravenhill Reps:
1215 W 67th St, Kansas City, MO 64108 816-333-0744
Illustrator:
Sandy Appleoff, Kelli Everett, Jim Fanning, CB Mordan, Darryl Shelton, Steve Skelton
Photographer:
Jim Krantz Studio

Reactor Art & Design:
51 Camden St, Toronto, ON M5V 1V2 416-703-1913
Illustrator:
Jaime Bennett, Roxanna Bikadoroff, Federico Botana, Blair Drawson, Henrik Drescher,
Louis Fishauf, Bob Fortier, Gail Geltner, Carolyn Gowdy, Steven Guarnaccia,
Margaret Hathaway, Tom Hunt, Huntley/Muir, Jerzy Kolacz, James Marsh, Simon Ng,
Tomio Nitto, Alain Pilon, Stephanie Power, Bill Russell, Fiona Smyth, James Turner,
Jean Tuttle, Maurice Vellekoop, Tracey Wood, Rene Zamic

Reilly Reps, Kerry:
1826 Asheville Pl, Charlotte, NC 28203 704-372-6007
Cartoonist:
Alex Tiani
Illustrator:
Ken Bowser, Alan Brunettin, Sally Wern Comport, Richard Cowdrey, Gary Crane,
Ernie Eldredge, Jerry Frazee, Marsha Grossman, Michael Hagel, John Huxtable,
Reid Icard, John Luck, Gary Palmer, Ben Perini, Chuck Rancorn, Greg Rudd,
Skidmore Inc, Walter Stanford, Dave Stevenson, Jack Vaughan, David Wariner,
David Wilgus, Robin Wilgus
Lettering:
Mike McMahon
Photographer:
Gerin Choiniere, Jim McGuire

Remen-Willis Design Group:
2964 Colton Rd, Pebble Beach, CA 93953 831-655-1407

Renard Reps:
501 Fifth Ave, New York, NY 10017 212-490-2450
Illustrator:
Steve Bjorkman, James Bozzini, Rob Brooks, Bill Cigliano, Stéphan Daigle,
Carol Donner, Gary Eldridge, Dan Garrow, Audra Geras, Wendy Grossman,
Jud Guitteau, William Harrison, Matthew Holmes, Tim Lee, John MacDonald,
John Martin, Matsu, Michael McGurl, Wayne McLoughlin, René Milot, Richard Newton,
Jeffrey Pelo, Kevin Pope, Robert Rodriguez, Theo Rudnak, Kazuhiko Sano,
Valerie Sinclair

Rep Art:
2491 W 22nd Ave, Vancouver, BC V62 1M3 604-684-6826
Film:
Gerard Dubois
Illustrator:
Robin Arkell, Charles Bell, Peter Bishop, John Bolesky, Kelly Brooks, Jeff Burgess,
Lorne Carnes, Margaret Hathaway, Mark Heine, Steven Hepburn, Barbara Klunder,
Michael Knox, Kim LaFave, Dedtrich Madsen, Michael McKinnell, Gary McLaughlin,
Mark Schofield, Elizabeth Simpson, Sharon Smith, Ernie Thomsen, Brad Yeo
Photographer:
Ed Gifford, Raymond Lum, Anthony Redpath, Storme, Brad Stringer

Repertoire:
2029 Custer Pkwy, Richardson, TX 75080 972-761-0500
Illustrator:
Amy Bryant, Lisa Cargill, Denise Crawford, Eric Dinyer, Matt Foster, Marianne Garcia,
Jennifer Harris, Jeff Holter, Frederico Jordan, Dave Kramer, C B Mordan,
Ambrose Rivera, RJ Shay, Steve Verriest, Rhonda Voo, Maranda Worley
Photographer:
Robie Capps, John Dasilva, Elecric Soup, Charlie Freeman, Skeeter Hagler,
Marc Hauser, Aaron Jones, Ed Lallo

Repertory:
847A Second Ave #150, New York, NY 10017 212-486-0177
Illustrator:
Richard Arruda, Kirk Botero, Tom Cristopher, Rhonda Burns, Cristos, John Hanley,
Hom & Hom, Haruo Ishioka, Philip Knowles, Paul Kratter, Teresa Powers, Don Stewart,
Jackie Urbanovic, Steve Walters
Photographer:
Tom O'Brien, Karl Parry, Don Saban

Reps in the West:
17 Osgood Pl, San Francisco, CA 94133 415-283-2400

Ridgeway, Inc, Ronald:
530 Broadway 4th Fl, New York, NY 10012 212-966-9696

Riley Illustration:
155 W 15th St #4C, New York, NY 10011 212-989-8770
Illustrator:
Benoit, Juliette Borda, William Bramhall, Paul Degen, Isabelle Dervaux, Jeffrey Fisher,
Rebecca Gibbon, Edward Koren, Pierre Le-Tan, Warren Linn, Kathy Osborn,
Robert Andrew Parker, Liz Pyle, Victoria Roberts, Marina Sagona, Jean Jacques Sempe,
Danny Shanahan, Gretchen Dow Simpson, Mark Von Ulrich, Philippe Weisbecker,
Sarah Wilkins

Ring Creative Rep, Thomas:
1015 N Central Ave , Phoenix, AZ 85004 602-447-9186
Illustrator:
Keith Biele, Karen Strelecki, Russ Wall
Photographer:
Arthur A Holeman Photo, Norton Photography

• **Rogers Studio, Lilla: pg 400-411**
6 Parker Rd, Arlington, MA 02474 781-641-2787
e-mail: info@lillarogers.com / url: www.lillarogers.com / fax: 781-641-2244
Illustrator:
Makiko Azakami, Diane Bigda, Julia Binfield, Ann Boyajian, Maria Carluccio,
Susan Farrington, SaraJo Frieden, Janell Genovese, Donna Ingemanson,
Tracy McGuinness, Lilla Rogers, Anne Smith, Susy Pilgrim Waters
Photographer:
Maria Carluccio

Rohani, Mushka:
9229 215th St SW, Edmonds, WA 98020 425-771-2905
Illustrator:
Michael Sours Rohani
Photographer:
Richard DeWeese

Roland Group, Inc:
4948 St Elmo Ave #201, Bethesda, MD 20814 301-718-7955
Illustrator:
Max Altekruse, Ivan Angelic, Tungwai Chau, Michael Crampton, Garth Glazier,
Ralph Hughes, Kurt Krebs, Rainer Laubach, Paul Manz, Karen Stolper, Mark Weber
Photographer:
Michael Pohuski

Rosen, Donna:
15209 Rockport Dr, Silver Spring, MD 20905 301-384-8925
Illustrator:
Dennis Auth, Lew Azzinaro, Matthew Baek, William Brown, Jim Haynes, Jack Hornaby,
Rob Johnson, James Kowalski, Bruce MacPherson, Steve Pica, Jo Rivers,
Renata Roberts, Dale Rutter, Bruce Sharp, Steve Sweny, Eric Tunnéll

Rosenthal Reps:
3850 Eddingham Ave, Calabasas, CA 91302 818-222-5445
Film:
Terry Anderson, Catherine Huerta, Judy Koenig, Dirk J Wunderlich
Illustrator:
Nan Brooks, Marjory Buckley, Teddy Edinjiklian, Steven Michael Gardner,
John Paul Genzo, Bill Hall, Ken Kotik, Roger Leyonmark, Mary Jane Mitchell,
Rae Russell, Kim Simons, June Sobel, Larry Taugher, Russell Ucker, Bill Vann

Roth-Karpe, Michele:
11959 Woodbridge St, Studio City, CA 91604 818-760-0491
Illustrator:
Greg Spalenka
Photographer:
David Nagel, Victoria Pearson, Horst Stasny, Michal Venera

Rutt Assocs, Dick:
669 Pelican Ave , Myrtle Beach, SC 29577 843-238-9556
Illustrator:
Kim Behm, Deb Bovy, Gary Ciccarelli, Linda Clark, Mike Hagel, Greg Hargreaves,
Dan Hatala, Lu Matthews, Randall McKissick, John Thompson, Todd Treadway,
Scott Travers Wright

S

Salzman Int'l:
824 Edwards PO Box 41, Trinidad, CA 95570 707-677-0241
Illustrator:
Denise Hilton Campbell, Kristen Funkhouser, Manuel Garcia, Rhoda Grossman,
Marty Gunsaullus, Dirk Hagner, Dan Jones, Nancy Gibson Nash, Everett Peck,
Robert Rayevsky, Greg Shed, Walter Stuart, Debbie Tilley

Sanders Agency, Liz:
16 Phaedra, Laguna Niguel, CA 92677 949-495-3664
Illustrator:
Johnee Bee, Gina Binkley, Bruce Carnes, Martha Collins, Carol Cottone, Sarah Eisler,
Zoe Danae Falliers, Jack Gallagher, Jud Guitteau, Johanna Hantel, Margaret Hewitt,
Chris Lensch, Bachrun LoMele, Janet McLeod, Pete Mueller, Kevin Newman, Amy Ning,
Tom Pansini, Pierre-Paul Pariseau, Kim Passey, Judy Pedersen, Dorothy Reinhardt,
Mark Shaver, Cameron Wasson, Roger Xavier
Photographer:
Michael Lariche

Sands Artist Rep, Trudy:
2410 Farrington, Dallas, TX 75207 214-905-9037
Illustrator:
John Cook, Beth McCash, Tim McClure, Michael Sours Rohani
Photographer:
Richard DeWeese

Santa-Donato Studio:
42 W 38th St, New York, NY 10018 212-921-1550

Schmidbauer, Michele:
PO Box 1197, Lake Zurich, IL 60047 847-438-7128
Illustrator:
Phil Kirchmeier, Terry Schmidbauer

Schumann & Co:
1009 West 6th St #207, Austin, TX 78703 512-481-0907
Illustrator:
Pearl Beach, Anthony Butkouich, Larry Goode, David Kampa, Chris Lockwood,
John Rutkowski, Gregory Smith Truett, Brian White
Photographer:
Paul Bardagjy, Robb Kendrick, Terry Vine

Schuna Group, Inc, The:
1503 Briar Knoll Dr, Arden Hills, MN 55112 651-631-8480
Illustrator:
Pete Bastiansen, Cindy Berglund, Neverne Covington, Theresa Cox, Jim Dryden,
Tom Foty, Tony Griego, Warren Hanson, Beth Hatlen, Cathy Lundeen Huber,
Kristen Miller, Anastasia Mitchell, Joe Nordstrom, Faye Passow, Ruth Pettis, Will Terry

Scott, Freda:
1015-B Battery St, San Francisco, CA 94111 415-398-9121
Illustrator:
Kelly Burke, Debra Spina Dixon, Diane Fenster, Cynthia Fitting, Matt Foster, Abe Gurvin,
Terry Hoff, Francis Livingston, Alan Mazzetti, Nancy Nimoy, Jeffrey Pelo, Thorina Rose,
Sue Rother, Randy South, Carolyn Vibbert, Filip Yip
Photographer:
Ty Allison, Leigh Beisch, Bruce Brown, Lon Clark Photography, Walt Denson, Edward Holub,
Kevin Irby, Christopher Irion, Stan Musilek Photography Studio, Katrine Naldid, Penina,
Susan Schelling, Robert Schlatter, Stuart Schwartz, Ron Starr Photography, Liz Steketee,
Elizabet Zeilon, Bill Zemanek

Seigel, Fran:
160 West End Ave #23-S, New York, NY 10023 212-486-9644
Illustrator:
Kinuko Y Craft, John Dawson, Catherine Deeter, Mark Harrison, Hokanson/Cichetti,
Earl Keleny, Ron Miller, Myles Pinkney, Dan Sneberger

Sell, Inc, Dan:
333 N Michigan Ave Ste 800, Chicago, IL 60601 312-578-8844
Illustrator:
Bob Boyd, Lee Lee Brazeal, Daryl Cagle, James Carlson, Bobbye Cochran, Sally Wern
Comport, Robert Crawford, Jerry Dadds, Bill Ersland, Lynn Fellman, Dick Flood,
Bill Gerhold, Bill Harrison, Jeffrey Jones, Frank Manzo-Morris, Kathryn Manzo-Morris,
Bill Mayer, Mike McMillen, Gary Overacre, WB Park, Roy Pendleton, Ian Ross, RJ Shay,
Tom Siebers, Heidi Smith, Alec Syme, Bill Vann, Dale Verzaal, Arden von Haeger,
Richard Waldrep, Phil Wende, Scott T Wright, John Youssi
Photographer:
Don Carstens, Miles Lowry, Denis Scott

• **Shannon Associates L.L.C: pg 189-243**
Chicago, IL **312-364-0244**
London **011-44-207-636-1064**
New York, NY **212-333-2551**
Los Angeles **323-874-5700**
Washington, DC **410-349-8669**
url: www.shannonassociates.com
Graphic Designer:
Mike Koelsch, Cliff Nielsen, Dave Seeley, Peter Bollinger
Illustrator:
Amy Bates, James Bernardin, Peter Bollinger, Eddie Bowen, Steve Brodner,
Andrew Burward-Hoy, Sally Wern Comport, Matthew Cooper, Peter Crowther,
Glin Dibley, Mark Elliott, Patrick Faricy, Gone Loco, Dave Gordon, Glenn Harrington,
Jack Harris, Stuart Haygarth, Brett Helquist, Jonathan Herbert, Nannette Hoogslag,
Sterling Hundley, Mirko Ilic, Jacey, Mike Koelsch, Dave Lafleur, Robert Neubecker,
David Newton, Cliff Nielsen, Chris Nurse, Paul Price, Steve Rawlings, Redseal,
Dave Seeley, Mike Shepherd, Silver Kid, John Sosnovsky, Spalenka, Greg Swearingen,
James Way, Hala Wittwer, Yücel

Sharpe & Assocs/John Sharpe:
7536 Ogelsby Ave, Los Angeles, CA 90045 310-641-8556
Illustrator:
Robert Case, Peter Simpson Cook, Judy Reed Silver, Dan Richards
Photographer:
Neal Brown, Ann Cutting Photography, Ann E Cutting, Hugh Kretschmer, Lise Metzger,
Jamey Stillings, Eric Tucker, Everard Jr. Williams

Sharpshooter Creative, Inc:
49 Spadina Ave Ste 309, Toronto , ON M5V 2P1 416-205-9995
Illustrator:
Shelajh Armstrong, Bill Boylco, Christine Bunn, Stephanie Carter, Frederic Eibner,
Norman Eyolfson, Nancy Ruth Jackson, Jacobson/Fernandez, Olena Kassian, JC Knaff,
Anita Kunz, Neil MacLachlan, Stuart Mclachlan, K C Rasmussen, Gordon Sauve,
Jason Walker, Laura Wallace, Rick Zettler
Photographer:
Francois Robert, Brian Smale, Lorelia Zanetti

Sheehan, Betsy:
19 Ruxview Ct #301, Baltimore, MD 21204 410-828-4020
Illustrator:
Don Dudley, RJ Shay
Photographer:
Steve Uzzell

Shemesh, Colleen:
431 W Colfax Ave #540, Denver, CO 80204 303-446-2611
Cartoonist:
John Dearstyne, Don Dudley
Illustrator:
Mark/Group Five Creative Bremmer, Thomas Buchanan, Paul Dempsey, Malcolm Farley,
Lisa Haughton, Laura Hesse, Ron Hicks, Jeffery Hitch, John Hull, John Huxtable,
Steve Keller, Clare Kelly, Tammie Lane, Darlene Olivia McElroy, Mathew McFarren,
Jill McIntyre, David Moyers, Elizabeth Read, Jeff Slemons, Uhl Studios/David Uhl,
Keith Witmer
Lettering:
Sandy Marvin

SI Int'l:
43 E 19th St, New York, NY 10003 212-254-4996
Illustrator:
Carolyn Bracken, Cardona Studio, Mario Cortes, Ted Enik, Segundo Garcia, Mel Grant,
Holly Hannon, Steve Haskamp, Jane Kurisu, John Kurtz, Franc Mateu, Isdre Mones,
Carlos Nine, Bob Ostrom, Gabriel Picart, Jesus Redondo, Francesc Rigol,
Gusti Rosenefet, Martin Salvador, Sanjulian, Serrat-Sans, Ortiz Tafalla, Dana Thompson,
Del Thompson
Photographer:
Karen Baumann, Horacio Elena, Pepe Gonzalez, Steve Haefele, Nick Jainschigg, Fred
Marvin, Ed Tadiello, Del & Dana Thompson

Siegel, Tema:
234 Fifth Ave 4th Fl, New York, NY 10001 212-696-4680

Skidmore, Inc:
29580 Northwestern Hwy, Southfield, MI 48034 248-353-7722
Illustrator:
Bob Andrews, Wayne Appleton, John Ball, Ann Bauer, Rob Burman, Larry Dodge,
Stephen Magsig, Jerry Monley, Dave O'Connell, Scott Olds

• **Smith, Piper: pg 244-283**
250 W 57th St #521, New York, NY 10107 212-397-7330
San Francisco, CA 415-788-8552
(see Lingren & Smith for client)

Snyder, Deborah:
5321 W 62nd St, Edina, MN 55436 612-922-3462
Illustrator:
Scott Buchschacher, Mike Carina, John Clarke, Doug Horne, Mark Jarman, Gary Keith,
Steve Mark, Terri Mitchelson, Glenn Quist, Bob Winberry

• **Solomon, Richard: pg 12-47**
New York, NY 212-223-9545
url: www.richardsolomon.com / fax: 212-223-9633
Illustrator:
Kent Barton, James Bennett, John Collier, Paul Cox, John Dawson, Dan Giancola,
David Johnson, Stephen Johnson, Gary Kelley, Murray Kimber, Loren Long,
Gregory Manchess, Bill Nelson, CF Payne, Douglas Smith, Mark Summers,
Andrea Ventura, Raymond Verdaguer,

Sonneville, Dane:
67 Upper Mountain Ave, Montclair, NJ 07042 973-744-4465
Illustrator:
Jack Balnave, Bryn Barnard, Tim Barrall, Jim Fanning, Pierre Fortin, Rich Grote,
Jeff Holewski, Art Kretzschmar, Alex Leonard, Leonard Morgan,
Steve & Jacqui Osborne, Earl Parker, Jared Phillips, Kevin Somerville, Gregory Voth,
Pam Voth
Photographer:
Barry Blackman, John F Cooper, Joseph Sachs

• **Spectrum Studio Inc: pg 542,543**
1503 Washington Ave S, Minneapolis, MN 55454 612-332-2361
e-mail: erep@spectrumstudio.net / url: www.spectrumstudio.net / fax: 612-332-2364
Illustrator:
Marty Harris, Anthony Hilscher, Mark Jensen, Roger Lundquist, Cliff Nielsen,
Preston Palmer, Jim Rownd, Larry Ruppert, John Schreiner, Blair Thornley

Spencer, Torrey:
11201 Valley Spring Ln, Studio City, CA 91602 818-505-1124
Illustrator:
Robert August, Cam DeLeon, Rob Magiera
Photographer:
Stephanie Ellis, Rick Rickman, Holly Stewart, Paul Taylor

• **Stefanski Represents, Janice: pg 536**
990 Filbert St, San Francisco, CA 94133 415-928-0457
fax: 415-785-8887
Illustrator:
Phil Carroll, Barbara Kelley, Maria Korusiewicz, Beth Whybrow Leeds, Jeffrey Oh,
Katherine Salentine

Stemrich, J David:
1334 W Hamilton St, Allentown, PA 18102 610-776-0825

Stieglitz, Clifford:
1985 Swarthmore Ave, Lakewood, NJ 08701 732-364-2111

Stock Art.Com/Iconomics:
155 N College Ave #225, Ft Collins, CO 80524 970-493-0087

Storyboards Inc:
1426 Main St, Venice, CA 90291 310-581-4050

Streeters USA Inc:
568 Broadway #504A, New York, NY 10012 212-219-9566
Photographer:
Miles Aldridge, Kim Andreolli, Chris Sturman

Sullivan & Assocs:
3805 Maple Ct, Marietta, GA 30066 770-971-6782
Illustrator:
Terry Buchanan, Joann Daley, PJ Meacham, Henry Patton, Phil Perry, Charles Scogins,
Simon Sholnik, Anne Teisher
Photographer:
Ken Chesler, Alan David, Sylvia Martin, Harrison Northcutt, Ron Sherman, Ed Wolkis

Susan & Co:
5002 92nd Ave SE, Mercer Island, WA 98040 206-232-7873
Illustrator:
Linda Ayriss, Bryn Barnard, Bob Bredemeler, George Cheney, Wendy Edelson,
Lisa Henderling, Chris Henrichs, Ken Huey, Kelly Hume, Fred Ingram, Larry Jost,
Nina Laden, Eric Larsen, Mark Monlux, Stephen Peringer, Douglas Schneider,
Greg Simanson, Greg Stadler, Carolyn Vibbert, Rosemary Woods
Photographer:
Don Mason Photography

• **Sweet Represents, Ron: pg 309**
716 Montgomery St, San Francisco, CA 94111 415-433-1222
url: www.sweetreps.com / fax: 415-433-9560
Illustrator:
Dick Cole, Jonathan Combs, Marc Ericksen, Robert Evans, Ben Garvie, Randy Glass,
Bryan Haynes, Roger Hill, Kent Leech, Derek Mueller, Will Nelson, Jim Nichols,
Steven Noble, Todd Nordling, Scott Sawyer, Bruce Wolfe
Photographer:
Curt Fischer

T

T-Square Etc:
1426 Main St, Venice, CA 90291 310-581-2200

Teri O:
1045 Diamond Ave NE, Grand Rapids, MI 49503 616-454-1278
Illustrator:
Nell Floeter, Tim Foley, Rob Lawson, Ed Wong Ligta
Photographer:
Roger Hill, Julie Lang

The Pred Group:
10012 Perry Dr., Overland Park, KS 66212 913-438-7733

• **THEARTWORKS, USA: pg 488-492**
455 W 23rd St #8D, New York, NY 10011 212-366-1893
e-mail: sally@theartworksinc.com / fax 212-604-9643
Film:
Charlotte Knox, Anthony Russo
Illustrator:
Peter Allen, Sophie Allport, Marcin Baranski, Dorvat Bennahum, Christian Birmingham,
Greg Clarke, Izhar Cohen, Matthew Cook, Penny Dann, Andrew Davidson,
Jeffrey Decoster, Graham Evernden, Sarah Gibb, Chris Gents, Giles Greenfield,
Jody Hewgill, Charlotte Knox, Laura Levine, Peter Malone, Sarah McMenemy,
Anton Morris, Joe Morse, Hanoch Piven, Paul Rogers, Anthony Russo, Ian Smith,
Meilo So, Mark Ulriksen, Rupert van Wyk, Marco Ventura, Jane Watkins, Mary Woodin,
Christopher Wormell
Photographer:
Tatsuro Kiuchi, Marco J Ventura

Those Three Reps:
2909 Cole Ave #118, Dallas, TX 75204 214-871-1316
Illustrator:
Artfix, Dave Albers, Art Gecko, Phil Boatwright, Mark Chickinelli, Gary Ciccarelli,
Ray-Mel Conelius, Michael Crampton, Michael Fisher, Keith Graves, Arthur James,
Neal Taylor, George Toomer, Terry Widener
Photographer:
Art Gecko, Tom Hussey, Craig Kuhner, Sean McCormick, White Packert, Toby Threadgill

Three:
236 W 26th St #805, New York, NY 10001 212-463-7025
Illustrator:
Max Tokyo

Tiffany Represents:
19524 23rd Ave NE, Seattle, WA 98155 206-365-7500
Illustrator:
Jill Arena, Clem Bedwell, Vince Chiaramonte, Eddy Corkery, Barbara Emmons,
Jack Graham, Tim Jonke, Nobee Kanayama, Maria Knier, Nancy Kurtz-Schoettel,
John Lambert, Don Margolis, Jeff Meyer, Jeff Nishinaka, Jeff O'Connor, Tom Price,
Jim Shepherd, Keith Skeen, Jay Smith, Tim Spransy, Susan Tolonen, Keith Ward,
Peter Wells, Brian White, Matt Zumbo

Tonal Values, Inc:
133 N Montclair Ave, Dallas, TX 75208 214-943-2569
Illustrator:
Nigel Buchanan, Anatoly Chernishov, Kyle Dreier, Karen L Greenberg, D Mark Kingsley,
Kyle Lane, Jane Mjolsness, Joe Murray, Mike Schroeder, Pauline Cilmi Speers, Superlux,
Russell Tate, Mark Tremlett, Gus Van Eck, Carol Wyatt

Tugeau, Christina A:
110 Rising Ridge Rd, Ridgefield, CT 06877 203-438-7307
Illustrator:
Winky Adam, Ann Barrow, Sarah Beise, James Bernardin, Karen Brooks, Craig Brown,
Jonathan Bumas, Priscilla Burris, Lisa Carlson, Larry Day, Bill Farnsworth, Crista Forest,
Nancy Pelham Foulke, Nancy Giffy, Carla Golembe, Laurie Harden, Heather Harms
Maione, Stephen Harrington, Nancy Hayashi, Naomi Howland, Melissa Iwal, Karen A
Jerome, John Kanzler, Cheryl Kirk Noll, Lauren Klementz-Harte, Paul Kratter, Jan
Machalek, Erin Mauterer, Keiko Motoyama, Cheryl Kirk Noll, Kathleen O'Malley, Daniel
Powers, Susan Simon, Teri Sloat, Frank Soto, Sally Springer, Karen Stormer-Brooks,
Meryl Treatner, Jeremy Tugeau, Weather Warms Mainone, Jason Wolff

Tuke, Joni:
325 W Huron , Chicago, IL 60610 312-787-6826
Illustrator:
Kaz Aizawa, Fian Arroyo, Gary Ciccarelli, Brian Fujimori, Jud Guitteau, Chris Hopkins,
John Hull, Kitty Meek, Cyd Moore, Gary Penca, Terry Sirrell, Ted Tamburo, Ezra Tucker,
Pam Wall, DL Warfield
Photographer:
Eric Klein

Turk, Melissa:
9 Babbling Brook Ln, Suffern, NY 10901 845-368-8606
Illustrator:
Barbara Bash, Ka Botzis, Nancy Didion, Drew-Brook-Cormack Assoc, Robert Frank,
Dara Goldman, Pedro Julio Gonzalez, Joe LeMonnier, Kevin O'Malley, Claudia Karabaic
Sargent, Wendy Smith, BK Taylor, Bridget Starr Taylor, Mary Teichman, Neecy Twinem,
Elsa Warnick, Jane Chambless Wright

V

Vargo/Bockos:
211 E Ohio Suite 2404, Chicago, IL 60611 312-661-1717
Illustrator:
Barbara Samanich
Photographer:
Greg Heck, David Leach, Brian Lipchik

Veloric Associates, Philip M:
200 S Roberts Rd #F6, Bryn Mawr, PA 19010 610-520-3470
Illustrator:
Susan Avishai, Beatrice Bork, Rick L Cooley, Jack Crane, Sherry L Fissel,
Deborah Healy, John Holder, Robert R Jackson, Rebecca A Merrilees, Keith Neely,
Vivien Ryan, Dennis Schofield, Nina Wallace, Stephen Wells, Jennifer Wharton,
Lane Yerkes

Virnig, Janet:
5236 W 56th St, Minneapolis, MN 55436 612-926-5585
Illustrator:
Rick Allen, Tom Casmer, Kara Fellows, Mary GrandPre, Cindy Lindgren, Bill Reynolds,
Adam Ritchie, Kate Thomssen

W

W/C Studio Inc:
208 Providence Rd, Annapolis, MD 21401 410-349-8669
Illustrator:
Lori Bilter, Sally Wern Comport, Vicki Gullickson, Stan Makowski, Chuck Rancorn

Wagoner, Jae:
654 Pier Ave #C, Santa Monica, CA 90405 310-392-4877
Illustrator:
Rick Allen, Dennis Doheny, Stephen Durke, Eva Ashley Emmert, William Harrison,
Gary Johnson, Moline Kramer, Maurice Lewis, Brad McMahon, Jane Mjolsness,
Leo Monahan, Derek Mueller, Jeff Nishinaka, Miles Parnell, Don Weller, Paul Yalowitz

Wagonheim, Rick:
350 W 39th St, New York, NY 10018 212-946-4000

Walters, Gwen:
50 Fuller Brook Rd, Wellesley, MA 02482 781-235-8658
Illustrator:
Tom Barrett, Dee DeLoy, Alain Espinoza, Arthur Friedman, Dave Garbo, Lane Gregory,
Larry Johnson, Dan Krovatin, Pat Paris, Judith Pfeiffer, L S Pierce, Sally Shadeler,
Janise Skivington, Requel Soysa, Susan Spellman, Gerardo Suzan, Gary Torrisi,
Rosario Valderrama, Fabrisio Vandenbroeck, Joe Veno, Deborah White, Jane Wright

• **Washington Artists Rep/Dick Washington: pg 537**
San Antonio, TX 210-698-1409
url: www.uscreative.com / fax: 210-698-1603
Illustrator:
Fian Arroyo, Walt Curlee, Darius Detwiler, Stephen Durke, Mark Harlien, Jay Mercado,
Kevin Peake, Herb Schnabel, Jim Steck, Michelle Wilby, John A Wilson

Watson & Spierman:
636 Broadway, Ste 708, New York, NY 10012 212-253-9991
Illustrator:
Jim Allen, Dan Cotton, Monica Lind, Andrew Mockett
Photographer:
Marc Antoni, Kan Phtography, Rob Lewine, Frank Siteman, North Sullivan, Steve
Vaccariello, Louis Wallach

• **Weber, Tricia: pg 244-283**
250 W 57th St #521, New York, NY 10107 212-397-7330
San Francisco 415-788-8552
url: www.lindgrensmith.com or www.stocklillustration.com
(see Lindgren & Smith for client list)

Weinberg, Larry:
608 York St, San Francisco, CA 94110 415-641-1285

Wells, Karen:
14027 Memorial #125, Houston, TX 77079 281-579-3220
Illustrator:
Karen Bell, Bill Firestone, Daphne McCormack, Sharron O'Neil, Stephen Wells

Wells, Susan:
5134 Timber Trail NE, Atlanta, GA 30342 888-255-1490
Illustrator:
Mark Andresen, Ted Burn, Chad Cameron, David Clegg, Ethan Conner, Jon Nelson,
Matt Phillips, Colin Poole, Bob Radigan, Lynne Riding, Tommy Stubbs, Jack Unruh
Lettering:
Elaine Dillard

West End Studio:
28020 Sea Lane, Malibu, CA 90265 310-664-9200
Animator:
Robert Blair
Illustrator:
Joe Cibere, Jim Krogle, Ken Roberts

• **Wiley Represents: pg 515-517**
94 Natoma St #233, San Francisco, CA 94105 415-442-1822
url: www.wileyreps.com / fax: 415-442-1823
Illustrator:
Steve Forney, Charlie Hill, Elliott Park, Rick Parks, Barbara Perdiguera, Miyuki Sakai,
Ken Toyama, Garry Williams, Keith Witmer
Photographer:
Marc Simon

Williams Group, The:
731 Stovall Blvd NE, Atlanta, GA 30342 800-791-1189
Illustrator:
Luis Fernandez, Abe Gurvin Festive Illustrations, Abe Gurvin, Rick Lovell, Bill Mayer,
Steve McAfee, David McKelvey, Tom Patrick, John Robinette, Jim Theodore,
Carlos Torres, Dale Verzaal, Russ Wilson
Photographer:
Boris Pittman

Winners Circle:
520 Murray Canyon Dr Ste 316, Palm Springs, CA 92264 760-327-6916

• **Wolfe Ltd, Deborah: pg 284-308**
731 N 24th St, Philadelphia, PA 19130 215-232-6666
url: www.deborahwolfeltd.com / fax: 215-232-6585
Illustrator:
Debra Spina Dixon, Felipe Echevarria, Dave Garbot, Bruce Garrity, Patrick Gnan,
Sharon & Joel Harris, Nancy Harrison, Mark Heine, Lynn Jeffery, Bob Kayganich,
Michael Kerr, Alan King, Harry Moore, JT Morrow, Leif Peng, Paine Proffitt,
Jesse Reisch, Irena Roman, Nick Rotondo, Simon Shaw, Marcia Staimer, Jo Tronc,
Chris Van Es, Richard Waldrep, Amy Wummer

Wolter, Bob:
440 N Wabash #1909, Chicago, IL 60611 312-670-8770
Illustrator:
Susan Aiells, Sandy Ostroff, Marty Roper, Sandbox Digital Playground
Photographer:
Dennis Galcante, Ralph Mercer, Kathy Sanders, Joel Sheagren, John Welzenbach, Art Wise

Y

Yantis, Day:
5706 Sprinter Ln, Bonita, CA 91902 619-479-2622
Illustrator:
Ken Joudrey

ILLUSTRATORS

ILLUSTRATORS

Andresen, Mark: 5134 Timber Trail NE, Atlanta, GA 30342 888-255-1490
Andrews, Bob: 29580 Northwestern Hwy, Southfield, MI 48034 248-353-7722
Andrews, Chris: 1515 N Beverly Ave, Tucson, AZ 85712 520-325-5126
Andrews, Joanne: 5 Falcon Trail, Pittsford, NY 14534 716-218-9187
Andriani, Vince: 2815 W 82nd St, Leawood, KS 66206 913-341-7169
Ang, Thomas: 766 N Mentor Ave, Pasadena, CA 91104 818-296-6808
Angel Art: 1224 Biscayne Blvd, Union, NJ 07083. 908-686-8645
Angelagraphics: 529 S Seventh St Suite #440, Minneapolis, MN 55415 612-332-1832
Angelic, Ivan: 4948 St Elmo Ave, Bethesda, MD 20814 301-718-7955
Angelini, George: 227 Godfrey Rd, Weston, CT 06883 203-222-8777
Angelo, Peter: 99 Park Ave #210A, New York, NY 10016 800-398-9544
Angeloch, Eric: 8 Manor Dr, Woodstock, NY 12498. 914-679-6175
Angerman, Judith: 356 N McCadden Pl, Los Angeles, CA 90004 213-857-0894
• **Angers, Michelle: pg 644** 2453 Olive Rd, Windsor, ON N8T 3N4. . . . . **519-948-7853**
e-mail: mangers@mnsi.net / url: www.michelleangers.com / fax: 519-948-2418
Angle, Scott: 7 Washington St, Beverly, MA 01915 978-921-0887
Angotti, Michael: 100 Longport Rd, Wayne, NJ 07470 201-831-7662
Angresano, Bill: 135 E Clinton Ave #6B, Bergenfield, NJ 07621 212-708-7943
Angrisani, Chris: 6095 N 9th Rd, Arlington, VA 22205 703-241-3739
Angry Cow: 164 Colbeck St, Toronto, ON M6S 1V9. 416-767-6035
Annaleo Studio: 175 W 90th St #3K, New York, NY 10024. 212-496-5185
Annis, Scott: 26099 McCiver Cir, Conifer, CO 80433. 303-674-1151
• **Another Color: pg 841** PO Box 775909 Steamboat Springs, CO 80477. . . . . **970-871-0151**
e-mail sam@anothercolor.com / www.anothercolor.com / fax: 970-871-0150
Ansley, Frank: Pier 33 North, San Francisco, CA 94111 415-956-4750
• **Anthenien, Leza: pg 694,695** PO Box 191, Glenbrook, NV 89413. . . . . **775-588-1982**
e-mail: lia@leza.com / url: www.leza.com & www.theispot.com/artist/lanthenien
fax: 775-588-9775
Anthony, Cheryl: 2525 Shadow Chaser Dr, Springfield, IL 62707. 217-793-7303
Antkowiak Design Group Inc, Jeff: 7440 Ritchie Hwy #A, Glen Burnie, MD 21061 . . . 410-360-2535
Antolic, Rick: 5742 Northumberland St #300, Pittsburgh, PA 15217 724-733-8546
Anton, Jean: PO Box 2038, Natick, MA 01760 . . . .
Antonio: 31 Magnolia St, Framingham, MA 01701 508-872-8180
Antonio Illustration: 7118 Upper River Rd, Prospect, KY 40059 502-228-9427
Antonios, Tony: 58 W 40th St 6th Fl, New York, NY 10018 212-682-1490
Anx, Inc: PO Box 550, New Windsor, MD 21776 410-875-9174
• **Anzalone, Lori: pg 312,313** 217 E 86th St #212, New York, NY 10028 . . . . . . **212-427-5632**
e-mail: jeff@lavatyart.com / url: www.lavatyart.com / fax: 212-427-6372
Anzovin, Steven: 162 Farview Way, Amherst, MA 01002 413-549-4030
Apice, Michael: 3419 Lindbergh Ave, Oceanside, NY 11572. 516-678-3735
Apjones, Todd: 2821 Colfax Ave S, Minneapolis, MN 55408. 612-871-3719
Apperley, Dawn: 350 Central Park West, New York, NY 10025 212-749-4907
Apple, Margot: March Rd, Ashfield, MA 01330. 413-625-9514
Appleoff, Sandy: 2029 Custer Pkwy, Richardson, TX 75080 972-761-0500
Appleton, Diana Minisci: 15 Warrenton Ave, Hartford, CT 06105. 860-523-4562
Appleton, Doug: 360 S Los Robles Ave #2, Pasadena, CA 91101 818-304-1054
Appleton, Wayne: 29580 Northwestern Hwy, Southfield, MI 48034. 248-353-7722
Aqua Images: PO Box 290055, Minneapolis, MN 55429. 888-658-5211
Aquilino, John: 38 W 21st St 3rd Fl, New York, NY 10010 212-268-9400
Aquino, Ervic: 2042 43rd Ave, San Francisco, CA 94116. 415-681-6755
Aragones, Sergio: 4948 St Elmo Ave #201, Bethesda, MD 20814 301-718-7955
Arcelle, Joan: 430 W 24th St, New York, NY 10011 212-924-1865
Archer, Doug: 2031 Holly Dr, Prescott, AZ 86305 520-708-9446
Archey, Rebecca: PO Box 307, Ross, CA 94957 415-456-7711
Architectural Art Inc: 150 S Washington St #500, Falls Church, VA 22046 703-533-2300
Arculus, Callie: 119 St John St, Cannington, ON L0E 1E0 705-432-2789
• **Arday, Don: pg 714** 3922 Gilbert Ave #106, Dallas, TX 75219 . . . . **214-526-2020**
616 Arbor Creek Dr, DeSoto, TX 75115 . . . . **972-223-6235**
url: www.donarday.com
Arena, Jill: 4137 N LeClaire Ave, Chicago, IL 60641. 773-283-9885
Arendt Graphics: 15908 82nd Pl NE, Kenmore, WA 98028 425-488-2573
Arenson, Robbie: 1647 Oregon Ave, Prescott, AZ 86301 520-776-8128
Arentsen, Carolina: 169 10th St, Providence, RI 02906. 401-454-4219
Argus: 37 W 20th St #902, New York, NY 10011. 617-497-5336
Arihara, Shino: 789 E California Blvd, Pasadena, CA 91106. 626-795-3287
Arion, Katherine: 1162 N Orange Grove #6, W Hollywood, CA 90046. 310-476-3227
Aris, David: 3170 Rue Saint-Antoine O, Montreal, QU H4C 1A6 514-931-6482
Arizona Media: 4840 South 35th St, Phoenix, AZ 85040. 602-276-7776
Arledge Studio: 6024 Pierson St, Arrada, CO 80004 303-421-1404
Armandina, Lozano: 2 Buckhorn St, Irvine, CA 92604 714-559-1397
Armano, David: 5360 N Lowell Ave #306, Chicago, IL 60630 773-478-4556
Armantrout, Linda: 817 Pine St, Leinisville, CO 80027 303-664-0086
Armes, Steve: 731 N 24th St, Philadelphia, PA 19130 215-232-6666
Armstrong, Bruce: 2233 Kemper Ln, Cincinnati, OH 45206. 513-861-1400
Armstrong, Shelagh: 120 Movety St, Toronto, ON M6P 2L9 416-762-4987
Armstrong, Stuart: 9312 Harvey Rd, Silver Spring, MD 20910 301-585-8723
Arnold, Jean: 1220 E 400 S, Salt Lake City, UT 84102 801-582-4148
Arnold, Michael: 225 Park Pl #2-D, Brooklyn, NY 11238 718-398-9039
Arnston, Amy: N 6475 Shorewood Hills Rd, Lake Mills, WI 53551 414-648-5255
Aronoff, Susan: 201 E 25th St #11C, New York, NY 10010. 212-889-0942
Aronow, Murielle Rodin: 188-04 64th Ave #F, Fresh Meadows, NY 11365. 718-454-0415
Aronson, Ben: 33 Wayside Inn Rd, Framingham, MA 01701. 508-788-1455
Aronson, Larry: 35 W 20th St #2, New York, NY 10011 212-807-8561
Arrasmith, Patrick: 309 Sixth St #3, Brooklyn, NY 11215 718-499-4101
• **Arroyo, Fian: pg 674,675** 901 Surfside Blvd, Surfside, FL 33154 . . . . **305-866-6370**
e-mail: fianarroyo@aol.com / url: www.fian.com / fax: 305-866-1192
Arscott, Steve: 7895 Tranmere Dr #4, Mississauga, ON L5S 1V9 416-678-6596
Art Associates: 4635 W Alexis Rd, Toledo, OH 43623 419-537-1303
Art Factory Ltd: 925 Elm Grove Rd, Elm Grove, WI 53122. 414-785-1940
Art Gecko: 2909 Cole Ave #118, Dallas, TX 75204 214-871-1316
Art Machine Inc, The: 2224 N 38th Ave, Hollywood, FL 33021 954-967-0409
Art of the Pen, The: 1220 S Bedford St, Los Angeles, CA 90035. 310-271-4909
• **Art Studios: pg 786** 1728 Spur Ridge Lane Healdsburg, CA 95448 . . . . **707-433-9641**
url: www.artstudios.com
Artell, Michael: PO Box 1819, Covington, LA 70434. 504-626-3420
Arturo: 534 1/2 S Coronado St, Los Angeles, CA 90057 213-383-5123
Aruta, Mark: 5115 41st St NW, Washington, DC 20016 202-364-0384
Arvis, Tom: 11228 Troy Rd, Rockville, MD 20852 301-468-0828

• **Ary Illustration, TL: pg 148,149** 420 Lexington Ave, New York, NY 10170 . . . . **212-986-5680**
e-mail: mendolaart@aol.com / url: www.mendolaart.com / fax: 212-818-1246
Aryai, Sia: 837 Traction Ave, Los Angeles, CA 90013 213-617-9001
Asbaghi, Zita: 125-10 Queens Blvd #1023, Kew Gardens, NY 11415. 718-275-1995
Ascencios, N: 108 E 35th St, New York, NY 10016 212-889-3337
Ascroft, Robert: 287 Orchard Creek Ln, Rochester, NY 14612. 716-227-1976
Ash, Susan: 3301A S Jefferson Ave, St Louis, MO 63118 314-773-2600
Ashby, Gil: 99 Park Ave #210A, New York, NY 10016 800-398-9544
Ashtiani, Sholeh: 2434 Olde Sawmill Blvd, Dublin, OH 43017 614-791-9580
Ashton, Rachel: 286 Spring St #301, New York, NY 10013. 212-229-0073
Asmussen, Don: 1903 Broderick St #5, San Francisco, CA 94115 415-885-6195
Aspinall, Neal: 1255 Martha Washington Dr, Wauwatosa, WI 53213 414-774-3808
Aspland, Kurt: 305 N Harbor #215, Fullerton, CA 92832 714-738-5587
Asprino, Donna: 315 Kent Dr, E Greenwich, RI 02818. 401-884-8699
Assel, Steven: 29-54 143rd St, Flushing, NY 11354. 718-539-5776
Athanas, Charlie: 915 Dempster, Evanston, IL 60201 847-332-2136
Atkins, Bill: PO Box 1091, Laguna Beach, CA 92652 949-494-5899
Atkinson, Mike: 23 Ganton St, London, England, UK WIV 1LA 71-287-9191
Atkinson, Steve: 7 Washington St, Beverly, MA 01915. 978-921-0887
Atkinson, Steve: 2100 Ridge Dr #14, Minneapolis, MN 55416. 612-544-6387
Atkinson-Mavilia, Peg: 45 Captain Pierce Rd, Scituate, MA 02066. 617-545-7654
Atomic Imaging: 1501 N Magnolia, Chicago, IL 60622 312-649-1800
Ator, Robin: 2405 NW Thurman St, Portland, OR 97210. 503-203-8300
• **Attebery, Craig: pg 330** 217 E 86th St #212, New York, NY 10028 . . . . **212-427-5632**
e-mail: jeff@lavatyart.com / url: www.lavatyart.com / fax: 212-427-6372
Attilis, Andy: 9710 Days Farm Dr, Vienna, VA 22182 703-759-1519
Atwood, Lucinda: 1435 Commercial Dr, Vancouver, BC V5L 3X8 604-254-3113
Auckland, Jim: 16 Phaedra, Laguna Niguel, CA 92677 949-495-3664
Audette, Cat: 3 W 23rd St, Baltimore, MD 21218. 410-366-3624
Auerbach, Larry: 116 Bedford Ave #1R, Brooklyn, NY 11211. 718-384-5826
August, Robert: 325 Bannock St, Denver, CO 80223. 303-777-1288
Auster, Ken: 2405 Laguna Canyon, Laguna Beach, CA 92651. 714-494-9525
Austin, Cary: 1352 N Formosa Ave Ste 2, Los Angeles, CA 90046. 323-874-5700
Austin, David W: 37440 Hills Tech Dr, Famington Hills, MI 48331 248-553-2474
Austin, Graham: 23 Ganton St, London, England, UK WIV 1LA. 71-287-9191
Austin, Steve: 2500 E Menlo, Fresno, CA 93710 . . . . 209 323 6939
AutoMedia: 3757 S Wallace, Chicago, IL 60609. 312-528-6628
Avanti Studios: 1274 Quincy St, Ashland, OR 97520 800-435-6509
Avary, Beth: 18380 China Grade, Boulder Creek, CA 95006. 408-338-8362
Aveto, Michael: 525 E 14th St #7A, New York, NY 10009 212-460-8494
Avila, Winona: 1739 Comstock Ln, San Jose, CA 95124 408-266-7216
Avishai, Susan: 165 E 32nd St, New York, NY 10016 212-686-3514
Axelrad, Stephen: 293 Ravenna Dr, Long Beach, CA 90803 310-438-4561
Axelrod, Dale: 3415 22nd St, San Francisco, CA 94110 415-824-1549
Axmann, Doug: 16 Schoolhouse Ln, Somerville, NJ 08876. 908-722-1925
Aye, Nila: 32 Shelton Covent Garden, London, England, UK WC2 H. 442074972555
Ayers, Alan: 22 Seminary Ln, Granite Springs, NY 10527. 914-248-4870
Ayers, Franklin: 1430 Georgia Blvd, Orlando, FL 32803. 407-896-6787
Ayers, Marti: 1803 Stratton Cir., Walnut Creek, CA 94598 925-930-9181
Ayriss, Linda Holt: 5002 92nd Ave SE, Mercer Island, WA 98040. 206-232-7873
• **Azakami, Makiko: pg 411** 6 Parker Rd, Arlington, MA 02474. . . . . **781-641-2787**
e-mail: lilla@rcn.com / url: www.lillarogers.com / fax: 781-641-2244
Azar, Joe: 1220 N Pierce St #904, Arlington, VA 22209 703-527-1443
Azzinaro, Lew: 11630 Old Brookville Ct, Reston, VA 20194 703-834-6419

B

Babasin, Pierre: 1504 Gerry Wy, Roseville, CA 95661 916-782-2956
Babboni, Robert: 295 St Johns Pl #3G, Brooklyn, NY 11238 718-230-9647
Bacall, Aaron: 204 Arlene St, Staten Island, NY 10314 . . . . 718 494 0711
• **Bachem, Paul: pg 385** 89 Fifth Ave #901, New York, NY 10003 . . . . **212-627-1554**
fax: 212-627-1719
Bachtell, Tom: 220 South State #1930, Chicago, IL 60604 312-939-6603
Back, Francis: 4706 Rue Marquette St, Montréal, QU H2J 514-527-9536
Backer, Marni: 866 United Nations Plaza, New York, NY 10017 212-644-2020
Backes, Nick: PO Box 421443, San Francisco, CA 94142. 415-647-5660
Bacon, Paul: PO Box 275, Clintondale, NY 12515 914-883-9036
Bad Katz Graphics: 2256 Ewing St, Los Angeles, CA 90039. 323-661-3890
Bader, David A: 3257 Revlon Dr, Kettering, OH 45420 937-298-7516
Badgley, Marcus: 1016 McNear Ave, Petaluma, CA 94952. 707-778-0165
Badlands Media: 165 Larose Ave #1017, Etobicke, ON M9P 3V9. 416-245-3494
Baehr, AIA, Richard C: 217 E 86th St #212, New York, NY 10028. 212-427-5632
• **Baer, Roxanna: pg 798** 64 W 83rd St #3, New York, NY 10024 . . . . **212-496-5495**
e-mail: roxy@roxyillustration.com / url: www.roxyillustration.com
fax: 212-496-5498
Baggs, Mike: 160 E 38th St #20G, New York, NY 10016 800-492-2447
Baglieri, Peter & Mike: 160 E 38th St #20F, New York, NY 10016 212-687-5227
Baher, H Edward: 12 Magnolia Blossom Dr, Bluffton, SC 29910 843-837-8502
Baier, Matt: 30 Second Plc #2, Brooklyn, NY 11231 718-802-9483
Bailey, John: 7709 W Lisbon Ave, Milwauke, WI 53222 414-442-1367
• **Bailey, Laura: pg 912, Front Cover Illustrators' Book** 4317 S 37th St, St Louis, MO 63116 . . **314-352-4752**
e-mail: lsbaile@aol.com
Bailey, Pat: 58 W 40th St 6th Fl, New York, NY 10018. 212-682-1490
Bailey, Phil: 47 Hager St, Marlborough, MA 01752 508-485-4225
Bailey, Sheila: 3050 Wembly Park Rd, Lake Oswego, OR 97035 503-635-4938
Bakal, Scott: PO Box 531, Central Islip, NY 11722. 888-234-4492
Baker, Charissa: 159 John St 6th Fl, New York, NY 10038 212-825-1475
Baker, David B: 1868 Blacksmith Dr, Marriottsville, MD 21104 410-549-7246
• **Baker, Don: pg 436, 437** 7205 28th Ave NW, Seattle, WA 98117. . . . . **206-784-1136**
e-mail: kolea@kolea.com / url: www.kolea.com or www.don-baker.com / fax: 206-784-1171
• **Baker, Garin: pg 50,51** 108 E 35th St, New York, NY 10016 . . . . **212-889-3337**
e-mail: gerald@rappart.com / url: www.theispot.com/rep/rapp / fax: 212-889-3341
Baker, Gary: 4101 Linkwood, Euless, TX 76040. 817-268-4608
Baker, Grahame: 42 Delavan St, Brooklyn, NY 11231 718-624-1906
Baker, Lori: RR1 Box 880, Plainfield, VT 05061 802-426-3800
Baker, Louise : 1640 W Melrose St, Chicago, IL 60657 773-327-7286
Baker, Skip: 731 N 24th St, Philadelphia, PA 19130 215-232-6666
Baker, Spencer: 242 Camino Descanso, Palm Springs, CA 92264 714-724-3870

Baker, Susan Harriet: 315 West Side Dr #303, Gaithersburg, MD 20878 ... 301-258-0126
Bakley, Craig: 68 Madison Ave, Cherry Hill, NJ 08002 ... 609-428-6310
Baldini, Francisco: Rua Mariante, 288 Sala 904, BR 90570 ... 5551346337
Baldwin Jr, Gunnar: RR1 Box 3271, Plymouth, NH 03264 ... 603-536-1836
Baldwin, Christopher: 7205 28th Ave NW, Seattle, WA 98117 ... 206-784-1136
Baldwin, James: 1467 Jordan Ave, Crofton, MD 21114 ... 410-721-1896
Baldwin, Scott: 58 W 15th St, New York, NY 10011 ... 212-741-2539
Balistreri West End Art Co: PO Box 70, Delafield, WI 53018 ... 414-646-8578
Ball, David: 1207 Bush St. #6, San Francisco, CA 94109 ... 415-431-2776
Ball, John: 29580 Northwestern Hwy, Southfield, MI 48034 ... 248-353-7722
Ballard Visual Communication, Dan: PO Box 85187, Seattle, WA 98145 ... 206-634-0084
Ballinger, Bryan: 0 South Madison Street, Windield, IL 60190 ... 630-871-3001
Bamundo, David: 141 Fisk Rd, Staten Island, NY 10314 ... 718-556-3249
Banashek, Jill: 578 29th Ave, San Francisco, CA 94121 ... 415-751-5336
Bandle, Johnna: 7726 Noland Rd, Lenexa, KS 66216 ... 913-962-9595
Bandsuch, Matt: 497 Prentis St #4, Detroit, MI 48201 ... 313-831-7324
Banfield, Elliott: 341 E 10th St, New York, NY 10009 ... 212-473-6772
Bangham, Richard: 351 Scott Dr, Silver Spring, MD 20904 ... 301-649-4919
Banks, Michael: 1109 Foxcroft Rd, Richmond, VA 23229 ... 804-282-6293
Banner, Shawn: 28 Madison St, Saratoga Springs, NY 12866 ... 518-583-7982
Bannerman, Isabella: 41 South Dr, Hastings, NY 10706 ... 914-478-3097
Bannister, Philip: 23 Ganton St, London, England, UK WIV 1LA ... 71-287-9191
Banta, Susan: 17 Magazine St, Cambridge, MA 02139 ... 617-876-8568
Banthien, Barbara: PO Box 470818, San Francisco, CA 94147 ... 415-383-9026
Banyai, Istvan: PO Box 77644, San Francisco, CA 94107 ... 415-381-4728
Baquero, George: 4 Westlay Ln, New Milford, NJ 07646 ... 201-261-6011
Baradat, Sergio: 210 W 70th St #1606, New York, NY 10023 ... 212-721-2588
Baran, Zafer: 42 Delavan St, Brooklyn, NY 11231 ... 718-624-1906
Barancik, Cathy: 18 E 78th St, New York, NY 10021 ... 212-472-3838
• **Baranski, Marcin: pg 489** 455 W 23rd St #8D, New York, NY 10011 ... **212-366-1893**
e-mail: sally@theartworksinc.com / url: www.theartworksinc.com / fax: 212-604-9643
Barbaria, Steve: 1990 Third St #400, Sacramento, CA 95814 ... 916-442-3200
Barbee, Joel: 209 Avenida San Pablo, San Clemente, CA 92627 ... 714-498-0067
Barber, Bert: 290 Charlois Blvd/Box 79, Winston-Salem, NC 27102 ... 800-800-3080
Barber, David: 21 Taft St, Marblehead, MA 01945 ... 617-631-6130
Barber, Rob: 4809 Lincoln Ave, Beltsville, MD 20705 ... 301-931-1157
Barberio, Steve: 2450 S 24th St, Phoenix, AZ 85034 ... 602-275-6565
Barbey, Jacques: 3034 E. Marlette, Phoenix, AZ 85016 ... 602-956-1536
Barbier, Suzette: 124 Winchester St, Newton, MA 02461 ... 617-527-8388
Barbour, Karen: PO Box 1210, Pt Reyes Station, CA 94956 ... 415-663-1100
Barcita, Pamela: 3582 Campion Ave, Virginia Beach, VA 23462 ... 804-463-7619
Barklew, Pete: 110 Alpine Way, Athens, GA 30606 ... 706-546-5058
Barkley, James: 25 Brook Manner, Pleasantville, NY 10570 ... 914-747-2220
Barlow, Jared: 22 N Prospect Ave, Baltimore, MD 21228 ... 410-455-9955
Barlow, Kevin: 2360 Bayless Pl, Saint Paul, MN 55114 ... 612-649-0257
Barnard, Bryn: 5002 92nd Ave SE, Mercer Island, WA 98040 ... 206-232-7873
Barnard, Doug: 28805 S Lakeshore Dr, Agoura Hills, CA 91301 ... 818-991-9328
Barner, Bob: 866 United Nations Plaza, New York, NY 10017 ... 212-644-2020
Barnes, Christopher: pg 932 1801 Falls Rd #2A, Baltimore, MD 21201 ... **410-576-0856**
Barnes, Jeff: 3718 E 83rd, Tulsa, OK 74137 ... 918-496-9598
Barnes, Karen: 17 Pinewood St, Annapolis, MD 21401 ... 410-266-6550
Barnes, Ken: 16006 88th Ave NE, Kenmore, WA 98028 ... 425-481-5848
Barnes, Kim: 89 Fifth Ave #901, New York, NY 10003 ... 212-627-1554
• **Barnes, Melanie: pg 357** 280 Madison Ave #1110, New York, NY 10016 ... **212-545-9155**
url: www.irmeliholmberg.com / fax: 212-545-9462
Barnes, Michelle: 41 Union Square W #918, New York, NY 10003 ... 212-807-6627
Barnes, Richard: 109 Windsor St #7, Cambridge, MA 02139 ... 617-430-5952
• **Barnes, Tim: pg 423** 227 Godfrey Rd, Weston, CT 06883 ... **203-222-8777**
e-mail: jp@artcoreps.com / url: www.artcoreps.com / fax: 203-454-9940
232 Madison Ave #512, New York, NY 10016 ... **212-889-8777**
e-mail: gt@artcoreps.com / url: www.artcoreps.com / fax: 212-447-1475
• **Barnes-Murphy, Rowan: pg 139,140,141** 420 Lexington Ave, New York, NY 10170 **212-986-5680**
e-mail: mendolaart@aol.com / url: www.mendolaart.com / fax: 212-818-1246
Barnet, Nancy: PO Box 9, Elk Grove, CA 95759 ... 916-685-4147
Barr, Elissa: PO Box 470483, Brookline Village, MA 02147 ... 617-731-4487
Barr, Ken: 420 Lexington Ave #2760, New York, NY 10170 ... 212-697-8525
• **Barr, Kristin: pg 362** 280 Madison Ave #1110, New York, NY 10016 ... **212-545-9155**
url: www.irmeliholmberg.com / fax: 212-545-9462
Barr, Loel: 11100 Kensington Blvd, Kensington, MD 20896 ... 301-774-4634
Barr, Marilyn Grant: 5721 Wildberry Dr, Greensboro, NC 27409 ... 910-852-4287
Barrall, Tim: 372 Bleecker St #2, New York, NY 10014 ... 212-243-9003
Barrera, Alberto: 55 Bethune St #914C, New York, NY 10014 ... 212-645-2544
Barrett, Andrea: 1424 La Positas Plaza, Santa Barbara, CA 93105 ... 805-682-6775
Barrett, Anne S: 163 Ocean Ave #6K, Brooklyn, NY 11225 ... 718-940-8133
Barrett, Debby: 49 Hamilton St, Everett, MA 02149 ... 617-387-2031
Barrett, Jennifer: 5510 Glenwood Rd, Bethesda, MD 20817 ... 301-654-4603
Barrett, Kent: 674 Keefer St, Vancouver, BC V6A 1Y4 ... 604-254-6030
Barrett, Rob: 1844 W Wayzata Blvd, Long Lake, MN 55356 ... 612-476-2204
Barrett, Ron: 666 Greenwich St #860, New York, NY 10014 ... 212-675-5719
Barrett, Ron: 2112 Broadway #212, New York, NY 10023 ... 212-874-1370
Barrett, Sabina Crosby: 120 Hudson St, New York, NY 10013 ... 212-343-0631
Barrett, Tom: 18 Central St #4, Marblehead, MA 01945 ... 617-523-4072
Barrette, Doris: 297 rue de Srencois Baillarge, Laval, QU H7L 5E9 ... 514-622-0325
Barris, Beverly: 7-27 Park Ave, Fairlawn, NJ 07410 ... 201-794-9219
Barron, Mary: 3910 Orchard St, Boulder, CO 80304 ... 303-440-0988
• **Barroux: pg 511** 310 W 97th St #902, New York, NY 10025 ... **212-243-5888**
e-mail: lori@lorinowicki.com / url: www.lorinowicki.com / fax: 212-243-5955
Barrows, Scott: 5182 Cypress Ct, Lisle, IL 60532 ... 630-355-4242
Barry, Rick: 1631 W 12th St, Brooklyn, NY 11223 ... 718-232-2484
Barry, Ron: 21005 Tamarack Cir, Southfield, MI 48075 ... 810-356-8946
Barry, Ron: 165 E 32nd St, New York, NY 10016 ... 212-686-3514
• **Barry, Pat Hilliard: pg 484** ... **510-704-4044**
url: www.phb4art.com
Barry-Jansson & Associates, Nancy: PO Box 2628, Cupertino, CA 95015 ... 408-534-1244
Barsky, Alexander: 280 Madison Ave #1110, New York, NY 10016 ... 212-545-9155
Barson, Jeff: 60 E 42nd St, New York, NY 10165 ... 212-867-8092
Barta, Les: 812 Jeffrey Ct, Incline Village, NV 89451 ... 702-831-0430
Bartalos, Michael: 30 Ramona Ave #2, San Francisco, CA 94103 ... 415-863-4569
Bartczak, Peter: PO Box 7709, Santa Cruz, CA 95063 ... 831-429-9980
Bartek, Shelly : 8522 Izand St, Omaha, NE 68114 ... 402-399-5251
Bartholomew, Beth: 486 Graham Ave #21, Brooklyn, NY 11222 ... 718-384-0162
Bartlett, Michael: 45 Bulkley Ave #2, Sausalito, CA 94965 ... 415-331-5127
Bartoli, Yuri: 45-21 45th St #3F, Sunnyside, NY 11104 ... 718-729-0361
• **Barton, Kent: pg 14,15** 305 E 50th St # 1, New York, NY 10022 ... **212-223-9545**
url: www.richardsolomon.com / fax: 212-223-9633
Bartos, Joe: 95 Lexington Ave #5F, New York, NY 10016 ... 212-686-9033
Baruffi, Andrea: 22 Seminary Ln, Granite Springs, NY 10527 ... 914-248-4870
Baruffi, Andrea: 341 Hudson Terr, Piermont, NY 10968 ... 914-359-9542
• **Baseman, Gary: pg 598,599** Los Angeles, CA ... **323-934-5567**
fax: 323-934-5516
PO Box 470818, San Francisco, CA 94147 ... **415-383-9026**
e-mail: jan@collierreps.com / url: www.collierreps.com / fax: 415-383-9037
Bash, Barbara: 9 Babbling Brook Ln, Suffern, NY 10901 ... 845-368-8606
Baskett, Austin H: 4700 Edison Ln, Boulder, CO 80301 ... 303-443-4643
Bass Illustration & Design, Sam: PO Box 646, Concord, NC 28026 ... 704-455-6915
Bassino & Guy: 80 E Hartsdale Ave #623, Hartsdale, NY 10530 ... 914-682-3723
Basso, Bill: 38 Ogden Ln, Englishtown, NJ 07081 ... 908-431-5497
Bastermagian, Avi: 217 S Wm, Mt Prospect, IL 60056 ... 847-259-2928
Batcheller, Keith: 353 W 53rd St #1W, New York, NY 10019 ... 212-682-2462
Batelman, Kenneth: 128 Birch Leaf Dr, Milford, PA 18337 ... 570-296-9926
• **Batelman, Kenneth: pg 740** , Belvedere, NJ ... **888-532-0612**
url: www.batelman.com
Bateman, Paul: UK ... 441392435513
• **Bates, Amy: pg 192** Chicago, IL ... **312-364-0244**
London ... **011-44-207-636-1064**
Los Angeles, CA ... **323-874-5700**
Washington, DC ... **410-349-8669**
New York, NY ... **212-333-2551**
url: www.shannonassociates.com
Bates, Betty: 1060 Malone Rd, San Jose, CA 95125 ... 408-266-1972
Bates, George: 208 Montrose Ave #2, Brooklyn, NY 11206 ... 718-456-4817
Bates, Harry 52 Upper West Ohayo Mountain Rd, Bearsville, NY 12409 ... 914-679-4695
Batten, John: 286 Spring St #301, New York, NY 10013 ... 212-229-0073
Battuz, Christine: 4312 rue Saint-André, Montréal, QU H2J 2Z2 ... 514-522-3675
Bauder, Adam: 224 Highridge Dr, Belleville, IL 62223 ... 618-398-6530
Bauer, Ann: 29580 Northwestern Hwy, Southfield, MI 48034 ... 248-353-7722
• **Bauer, Carla: pg 796** New York, NY ... **212-807-8305**
e-mail: carlabauer@earthlink.net / fax: 212-727-8094
Bauer, Stephen: 731 N 24th St, Philadelphia, PA 19130 ... 215-232-6666
Baughman III, Murray: PO Box 365, Bluffton, SC 29910 ... 919-918-3965
Baughman, Christi: 467 Clearfield, Garland, TX 75043 ... 214-270-5925
Bauman, Jill: PO Box 152, Jamaica, NY 11415 ... 718-886-5616
Bautista, David R: 50 Lillian Rd, Nesconset, NY 11767 ... 516-981-4092
Baxter, Daniel: RR3 Box 159, Feller Newmark Rd, Red Hook, NY 12571 ... 914-758-0766
Bay-Mathis, Melissa: 1341 California St, Berkeley, CA 94703 ... 510-526-3848
Bayouth, Michael: 22429 Friar St, Woodland Hills, CA 91367 ... 818-340-1415
Be, Jamie: 2160 W 2nd Ave #8, Durango, CO 81301 ... 800-876-6955
Beach Illus, Peter: 83 Moseley Ave, Newburyport, MA 01950 ... 978-462-4275
Beach, Lou: 7118 Upper River Rd, Prospect, KY 40059 ... 502-228-9427
Beach, Pearl: 5723 Benner St, Los Angeles, CA 90042 ... 323-256-2170
Beachy, Tim: 204 Virgin Run Rd, Vanderbilt, PA 15486 ... 724-736-0123
Beard, Edward Jr: 39 Niantic Trl, W Greenwich, RI 02817 ... 401-739-1511
Beatty, Tim: 1011 Limerick Ln, Durham, NC 27713 ... 919-806-8068
Beauchamp, Jaime: 99-12 62nd Rd, Rego Park, NY 11374 ... 212-512-2230
Beauchemin, Marie-France: 4651 rue de Salaberry, Carignin, QU J3L 3P9 ... 514-447-4956
Beaulieu, Jean Pierre: 5116-A av.Casgrain, Montréal, QU H2T 1W7 ... 514-272-3682
Beaupre, Richard: 200 Newcastle Ave, Portsmouth, NH 03801 ... 603-431-0177
Beauregard, Christiane: 2324 St. Cunegonde St, Montréal, QU H3J 2Y6 ... 514-935-6794
Beavers, Sean: 60 E 42nd St #1146, New York, NY 10165 ... 212-953-7088
Beck Comm, Joan: 2525 E Franklin Ave #301, Minneapolis, MN 55406 ... 612-338-8642
Beck, David: 68 E Franklin St, Dayton, OH 45459 ... 937-433-8383
Beck, Melinda: 536 5th St #2, Brooklyn, NY 11215 ... 718-499-0985
Becker, Neesa N: 241 Monroe St, Philadelphia, PA 19147 ... 215-925-5363
Becker, Pamela: PO Box 4491, Arcata, CA 95518 ... 707-822-1080
Becker, Polly: 608 York St, San Francisco, CA 94110 ... 415-641-1285
Becker, Ron: 265 E 78th St, New York, NY 10021 ... 212-535-8052
Beckerman, Richard: 137 E 28th St #7B, New York, NY 10016 ... 212-685-7045
Bedrick, Jeffrey: 490 Rockside Rd, Cleveland, OH 44131 ... 216-661-4222
Bedrosian, Wesley: 302 Metropolitan Ave #2, Brooklyn, NY 11211 ... 718-782-5018
Bedwell, Clem: 968 Watkins St NW, Atlanta, GA 30318 ... 404-881-1101
• **Bee, Johnee: pg 897** Costa Mesa, CA ... **949-642-2789**
e-mail: jb@johneebee.com / url: www.johneebee.com / fax: 949-642-1400
Beecham, Greg: 420 Lexington Ave #2760, New York, NY 10170 ... 212-697-8525
Beecham, Tom: 420 Lexington Ave #2760, New York, NY 10170 ... 212-697-8525
Beegle, Sandy: 1002 W 5th St, Loveland, CO 80537 ... 970-663-3574
Beekman, Doug: 24 Pearl St #3, Brattleboro, VT 05301 ... 802-254-8430
Beelen Jr, Frank: 3404 Emerson Ave S #103, Minneapolis, MN 55408 ... 612-560-3629
Beerworth, Roger: 1723 S Crescent Heights Blvd, Los Angeles, CA 90035 ... 323-933-9692
Begany, Jim: 650 Long Lane, Gettysburg, PA 17325 ... 717-337-0698
Begin, Maryjane: 3 Hidden St, Providence, RI 02906 ... 401-421-2344
Bego, Delores: 1601 Third Ave #22A, New York, NY 10128 ... 212-289-7467
Behm, Kim: 1225 W 4th St, Waterloo, IA 50702 ... 319-234-2089
Behrle Jr, Richard: 576 Ridgewood Rd, Maplewood, NJ 07040 ... 201-762-1693
Behum, Cliff: 26384 Aaron Ave, Euclid, OH 44132 ... 216-261-9266
Beilfuss, Kevin: 420 Lexington Ave, New York, NY 10170 ... 212-986-5680
Beisel, Dan: 4713 Ribble Ct, Ellicott City, MD 21043 ... 410-461-6377
Belcastro, Mario: 2946 Sebolt Rd, Library, PA 15129 ... 412-835-8470
Belchér, Steven: 4462 Thunder Vista Ln, Lake Oswego, OR 97035 ... 503-699-8981
Belding, Pam: 235 Byrondale Ave N, Wayzata, MN 55391 ... 612-476-1338
Belford, Kevin: 546 Rosewood Ln, St Louis, MO 63122 ... 314-822-2424
Bell, Charles: 2491 W 22nd Ave, Vancouver, BC V62 1M3 ... 604-684-6826
Bell, Fred: 212 N 77th St, Milwaukee, WI 53213 ... 414-771-0472
Bell, Karen: 1872 N Clybourn #404, Chicago, IL 60614 ... 773-935-8840
Bell, Ron: 7118 Upper River Rd, Prospect, KY 40059 ... 502-228-9427
Bell, Tom: 1831 W Roscoe #2, Chicago, IL 60657 ... 708-445-7159
Bella, Joset: 280 Madison Ave #1110, New York, NY 10016 ... 212-545-9155
Bellamy, Chris: 18 Taylor St East Brighton, 3187 Melbourne, AUSTR ... 61395769716
Bellamy, Gordon: 41 John St, New York, NY 10038 ... 212-571-0090

Bellamy, John Ashley: 2200 N Haskell Ave, Dallas, TX 75204 214-827-2032
Bellamy, Mike: 70 Willow Ave, Hackensack, NJ 07601 201-487-2342
Bellis, M A: 20685 Hillside Dr, Topanga, CA 90290 310-455-2627
Bellora, James: 7021 Haycock Rd #N, Falls Church, VA 22043 703-271-1251
Bellospirito, Robyn: PO Box 302, Locust Valley, NY 11560. 516-759-5560
Bellucci, Patty: 532 La Guardia Pl, New York, NY 10012. 212-924-8654
Belman, Vickie: 376 Edgewood Ave, Teaneck, NJ 07666 718-367-2688
Belmar, Inc: 16780 Oakomat Ave, Gaithersburg, MD 20877. 301-990-2130
Belmont, John: 2106 N 88th St, Seattle, WA 98103 206-523-4684
Belove, Janice: 46 Carolin Rd, Montclair, NJ 07043 201-744-3760
Belser, Burkey: 1818 N St NW #110, Washington, DC 20036 202-775-0333
Bemus, Bart: 353 W 53rd St #1W, New York, NY 10019 212-682-2462
Ben-Ami, Doron: 232 Madison Ave #512, New York, NY 10016 212-889-8777
Ben-Ami, Doron: 25 Arapaho, Brookfield, CT 06804 203-797-8847
Ben-Nahum, Dovrat: 36 Wellington St, London, England, UK WC 2E. 1712-408925
Benallack, John: 325 B North Clippert St, Lansing, MI 48912 517-332-6291
Benas, Jeanne: 54 Alpine Dr, Latham, NY 12110 518-783-9556
• **Bendall-Brunello, John: pg 504** 666 Greenwich St #860, New York, NY 10014 **212-675-5719**
e-mail: harriet@hkportfolio.com / url: www.hkportfolio.com / fax: 212-675-6341
• **Bendell, Norm: pg 499** 41 Union Square W #918, New York, NY 10003. . . . . . **212-807-6627**
e-mail: dgagency@idt.com / url: www.davidgoldmanagency.com
fax: 212-463-8175
• **Bender, Cherie: pg 529** 1431 35th Ave S, Seattle, WA 98144. . . . . **206-325-8595**
url: ldabneyinc@aol.com / fax: 206-325-8594
Boca Raton, FL **561-368-5722**
Bender, Greg: 21 N Main St #209, Port Chester, NY 10573. 914-934-7778
Bender, Howard: 515 Buxton Rd, Toms Rivers, NJ 08755 908-286-1512
Bender, Jon: 4089 San Felipe Rd, San Jose, CA 95135. 408-238-8730
Bendis, Keith: 1423 County Route 7, Ancram, NY 12502 518-329-1986
• **Benfanti, Russell: pg 132,133** 420 Lexington Ave, New York, NY 10170. . . . . . **212-986-5680**
e-mail: mendolaart@aol.com / url: www.mendolaart.com or www.benfanti.com
fax: 212-818-1246
Benger, Brent: 420 Lexington Ave, New York, NY 10170 212-986-5680
Bengivenga, Ron: 92 Mercer Ave #2, N Plainfield, NJ 07060. 908-757-4325
Benjamin, Vincent: 6001 Velasco, Dallas, TX 75206 214-871-0080
Benn, Nathan: 913 E Capitol St SE, Washington, DC 20003 202-546-6182
Bennallack-Hart, Michael: 455 W 23rd St #8D, New York, NY 10011. 212-366-1893
Bennett, Bruce: 432 N Canal St #12, S San Francisco, CA 94080 415-583-8236
Bennett, Carol: 11365 W 72nd Pl, Arvada, CO 80005 303-420-8604
Bennett, Charles A: 547 E Villanova Rd, Ojai, CA 93023 805-646-0494
Bennett, Dianne: 200 W 15th St, New York, NY 10011. 212-243-4209
Bennett, Gary: 7118 Upper River Rd, Prospect, KY 40059. 502-228-9427
• **Bennett, James: pg 16,17** 305 E 50th St #1, New York, NY 10022 . . . . **212-223-9545**
url: www.richardsolomon.com / fax: 212-223-9633
Bennett, Martin: 2617 N Lovegrove St, Baltimore, MD 21218 410-338-0785
Bennett, Mike: 20 Cornwall Dr, Windsor Locks, CT 06096 860-627-9772
Bennett, Peter: 1340 El Prado Ave #37, Torrance, CA 90501. 310-782-7801
Bennett, Tom: 84 Withers St 5th Fl, Brooklyn, NY 11211 718-386-5067
Benney, Robert: 50 W 96th St, New York, NY 10025 212-222-6605
• **Benny, Mike: pg 572,573** 11703 Uplands Ridge Dr, Austin, TX 78733 . . . . . . **512-263-5490**
Benoit: 155 W 15th St #4C, New York, NY 10011 212-989-8770
Bensen, Ben: 800 Montrose Ave, S Pasadena, CA 91030. 626-441-1009
Benson, John D: 9273 Bellbeck Rd, Parkville, MD 21234 410-665-3395
Benson, Linda: 455 W 23rd St #8D, New York, NY 10011 212-366-1893
Benson, Melissa A: PO Box 119, Stratford, CT 06614 . . . .
Bensusen, Sally: 932 S Walter Reed Dr CPAS 2nd Fl, Arlington, VA 22204 703-979-3931
Bentley, James: 4874 Parkinson St, Pierrefonds, QU H8Y 2Z3 514-894-0547
Berasi, Barbara: 30 Village Gate Wy, Nyack, NY 10960 914-353-7317
Berendt, Eric : PMB 351/1989-A Santa Rita Rd #351, Pleasanton, CA 94566 . . . 925-462-6809
• **Berg, John: pg 624,625** 110 Cottage St, Buffalo, NY 14201 . . . . **716-884-8003**
fax: 716-885-4281
•**Berg, Ron: pg 178** 420 Lexington Ave New York, NY **212-986-5680**
e-mail mendolart@aol.com / url: www.mendolaart.com
Bergendorff, Roger: 7429 Orien Ave, La Mesa, CA 91941 619-461-9807
Berger, Scott: 24 Millfarm Rd, Stoughton, MA 02072 . . . .
Berger, Vernon: 5300 Turnabout Ln, Austin, TX 78731 512-452-8866
Bergin, Kieran: 28 Windmere Rd #PH, Upper Montclair, NJ 07043. 212-459-5244
Bergstein, David: 219 Westchester Ave, Port Chester, NY 10573. 914-935-9314
• **Berkeley, Jon: pg 530** 7 Washington St, Beverly, MA 01915 . . . . **978-921-0887**
e-mail: leighton@leightonreps.com / url: www.leightonreps.com
fax: 978-921-0223
Berkey, John: 217 E 86th St #212, New York, NY 10028. 212-427-5632
Berkheiser, Megan: 30 Charles St #42, New York, NY 10014. 212-255-5539
• **Berkson, Nina: pg 533** **416-530-1500**
url: www.linkartists.com / fax: 416-530-1401
Berley, Brian: 227 Godfrey Rd, Weston, CT 06883 203-222-8777
Berlin, Jeff: 238A Summit Dr, Corte Madera, CA 94925. 415-979-8488
Berlin, Rick & Rose: 870 Lock Lane Rd, Yorktown Hts, NY 10598. 914-962-0174
Berman, Craig: 16 Taylor St, Dover, NJ 07801 201-366-4407
Berman, Simi: PO Box 58, Chesterfield, NH 03443. 603-256-8477
Bernal Computer Graphics: 10510 Ridgeland Ave #7, Chicago, IL 60415 708-424-7312
Bernal, Richard: 6239 Elizabeth Ave, St Louis, MO 63139. 314-781-8851
Bernard, Charles: 38 Balsam Dr, Medford, NY 11763 212-596-2610
• **Bernardin, James: pg 193** Chicago, IL. **312-364-0244**
London. **011-44-207-636-1064**
Los Angeles, CA. **323-874-5700**
Washington, DC. **410-349-8669**
New York, NY **212-333-2551**
url: www.shannonassociates.com
Bernatchez, Patrick: 4398 Garnier, Montreal, QU H2J 3S2 514-523-0689
Bernstein, Darryl: 165 Western Ave W, Seattle, WA 98119. 206-285-3440
Bernstein, Linda A: 10-11 50th Ave, Long Island City, NY 11101 718-784-1599
Berran, Bob: 60 E 42nd St, New York, NY 10165 212-867-8092
Berrett, Randy: 15 W 72nd St, New York, NY 10023 212-799-2231
Berry, Bob: 38 Deerview Ln, Poughaug, NY 12570. 914-223-7925
Berry, Fanny Mellet: 155 E 38th St, New York, NY 10016 212-697-6170
Berry, John: 905 E Main St, Wellsville, UT 84339 800-478-0362
Berry, Rick: 93 Warren St, Arlington, MA 02174. 617-648-6375
Berryhill, Thomas: 1317 Maple St, Vancouver, BC V6J3S1 604-733-2492

Bersani, Shennen: 14 Rockwell Ave, Brockton, MA 02402 508-583-1648
Berthiaume, Pierre: 5-A Wood St PO Box 40, Melbourne, QU J0B 2B0 819-826-1633
Beshwaty, Steve: 4425 Messier St, Montréal, QU H2H 2H8 514-525-9687
Besser, Doug: 432 N Cuyler Ave, Oak Park, IL 60302 708-660-9720
Besteman, Jackie: 468 Queen St E #104, Toronto, ON M5A 1T7 416-367-2446
Betcher, Mark: 7118 Upper River Rd, Prospect, KY 40059. 502-228-9427
Bettag, Susannah: 960 Howard St, San Francisco, CA 94103. 415-957-1854
Bevenour, Jay: 123 Java St, Brooklyn, NY 11222 718-383-1277
Bevill, Jennifer: 106 Prospect Park W #2, Brooklyn, NY 11215 718-369-2758
Beyl, Charles: 793 Hershey Mill Rd, Mountville, PA 17554 717-285-2905
Beylon, Cathy: 201 E 28th St, New York, NY 10016. 212-532-0928
Bharadwaj, Hema: 345 Prospect Ave, Hackensack, NJ 07601 201-487-5727
Bianco, Gerard: 1040 82nd St, Brooklyn, NY 11228. 718-836-8637
Bianco, Peter: 201 Manning St, Needham, MA 02131. 617-444-9077
Biber, Hugh: 666 Greenwich St #860, New York, NY 10014 212-675-5719
Bice Jr, Paul: 317 W 64th St, Inglewood, CA 90302. 310-677-2606
Biebl, Jim: 94 Arlian Ln, Carbondale, CO 81623 303-963-3309
Bieck, Kathy: 5855 Green Valley Cir #308, Culver City, CA 90230 310-642-2721
Biedny, David: PO Box 151498, San Rafael, CA 94915. 415-721-0638
• **Biedrzycki, David: pg 327** 217 E 86th St #212, New York, NY 10028 . . . . **212-427-5632**
e-mail: jeff@lavatyart.com / url: www.lavatyart.com / fax: 212-427-6372
Biegel, Michael David: PO Box 428, Allendale, NJ 07401 201-612-1324
• **Biers, Nanette: pg 389** 194 Third Ave, New York, NY 10003. . . . . **212-475-0440**
url: www.morgangaynin.com / fax: 212-353-8538
Biever, Richard: 117 N Frederick, Evansville, IN 47711. 812-426-7761
Big Pixel, The: 3108 Sumatra Pl, Costa Mesa, CA 92626 714-979-8001
• **Bigda, Diane: pg 400** 6 Parker Rd, Arlington, MA 02474. . . . . **781-641-2787**
e-mail: info@lillarogers.com / url: www.lillarogers.com / fax: 781-641-2244
Biggs, Dan: PO Box 565, Bonita, CA 91908 619-421-2107
Bikkers, Anouk: 2 St Leonard's Ave, Toronto, ON M4N 1J9. 416-545-1685
• **Bild, Linda: pg 868** **310-444-9962**
e-mail: lbild16658@aol.com
Billin-Frye, Paige: 216 Walnut St NW, Washington, DC 20012 202-291-3105
• **Billout, Guy: pg 553,570,571** 380 Rector Pl #4M, New York, NY 10280 . . . . . **212-786-4352**
e-mail: billout@rcn.com / url: www.citeweb.net/billout / fax: 212-786-4180
Bills, Mitchell: 53 Hamilton Dr, Bethany, CT 06524 203-393-2183
Billups, Ted: 1435 Addison, Chicago, IL 60613 773-248-2347
Billustrations: 1704 Willow Mound Pl, Ft Wayne, IN 46818. 219-497-9600
Bilotti, Jerry: 5900 Naples Plz #3, Long Beach, CA 90803 310-930-0192
Bilter, Lori: 208 Providence Rd, Annapolis, MD 21401 410-349-8669
Binder, Amy: 58 W 15th St, New York, NY 10011 212-741-2539
Binder, Eric: 1200 Hazel St, Charlottesville, VA 22902 888-374-2278
• **Binfield, Julia: pg 410** 6 Parker Rd, Arlington, MA 02474 . . . . **781-641-2787**
e-mail: info@lillarogers.com / url: www.lillarogers.com / fax: 781-641-2244
Bing Design: 457 State St #2A, Brooklyn, NY 11217 718-522-2335
• **Bingham, Edith L: pg 858** 482 South St, Hollister, CA 95023 . . . . **831-636-8397**
e-mail: edithbing@yahoo.com
Bingham, Sid: 2550 Kemper Ave, La Crescenta, CA 91214 818-957-0163
Binkley, Gina: 209 10th Ave S #214, Nashville, TN 37203 615-354-0211
Biomedical Illustrations: 804 Columbia St, Seattle, WA 98104 206-682-8197
Birchman, Fred: 2561 E Madison Ave, Seattle, WA 98112. 206-325-8312
Bird, Paula: 4 Aldersey St #1, Somerville, MA 02143 617-666-4611
Birdsall Designs, Mike: 106 Linden St #201, Oakland, CA 94607. 510-433-8900
Birdsall, Scott: 441 Old Newport Blvd #306, Newport Beach, CA 92663. 714-645-4536
Birdsong, Keith: 32 W40th St #2 South, New York, NY 10018 212-575-6887
Birdsong, Stephanie K: 2009 Canal St, Venice, CA 90291 310-822-3509
Birdy, Dan: 280 Madison Ave #1110, New York, NY 10016 212-545-9155
Birkey, Randal: 635 S Home, Oak Park, IL 60304. 708-386-5150
Birling, Paul: PO Box 257, Pleasantville, NY 10570 914-747-2220
Birmingham, Barbara: 133 Barrow St #4A, New York, NY 10014. 212-691-5587
• **Birmingham, Christian: pg 490** 455 W 23rd St #8D, New York, NY 10011. . . . **212-366-1893**
e-mail: sally@theartworksinc.com / url: www.theartworksinc.com / fax: 212-604-9643
Birmingham, Lloyd P: 500 Peekskill Hollow Rd, Putnam Valley, NY 10579 914-528-3207
Birnbaum, Dianne: 17301 Elsinore Cir, Huntington Beach, CA 92647 714-847-7631
Birnbaum, Meg: 331 Harvard St #14, Cambridge, MA 02139 617-491-7826
Birtola, Theresa: 6155 Dunn Ave, San Jose, CA 95123 408-629-6517
Bischel, Mark: 228 E 85th St #10D, New York, NY 10028 212-717-9811
Bishop, Brian: 1120 E 1500 S, Bountiful, UT 84010 801-296-6904
• **Bishop, David: pg 731** 610 22nd St #311, San Francisco, CA 94107 . . . . **415-558-9532**
url: www.dbsf.com
Bishop, Don: 17104 NW Countryridge Dr, Portland, OR 97229 888-577-5747
Bishop, Ken: 342 Wymount Terr, Provo, UT 84604. 801-375-7220
Bishop, Lyn: 928 Mackenzie Dr, Sunnyvale, CA 94087. 408-773-1363
Bishop, Randy Mack: 6640 Lakewood Blvd, Dallas, TX 75214 214-977-8206
Bishop, Rich: 55 Botany Dr, Asheville, NC 28806. 704-299-4898
Biskup, Tim: 3214 Ledgewood Dr, Los Angeles, CA 90068 323-467-1288
• **Bissett, Annie: pg 890** 156 Crescent St, Northampton, MA 01060 . . . . **800-515-1060**
e-mail: annie@anniebissett.com / url: www.anniebissett.com / fax: 413-584-6185
Bixby, Mark: 925 Elm Grove Rd, Elm Grove, WI 53122. 414-785-1940
Bjelland, Thomas: 2822 Newport Blvd #A, Newport Beach, CA 92663 949-673-2855
• **Bjorkman, Steve: pg 568,569** 2402 Michelson #200, Irvine, CA 92612. . . . . . **949-261-1411**
url: www.stevebjorkman.com / fax: 949-261-7528
260 E Chestnut #3005, Chicago, IL 60611 . . . . **312-787-8834**
e-mail: vincekamin@worldnet.att.net / url: www.vincekamin.com
fax: 312-787-8172
• **Black, Dave: pg 524** 333 E 49th St, New York, NY 10017 . . . . **212-980-8061**
url: www.bruckandmoss.com / fax: 212-832-8778
100 Bleecker St, New York, NY 10012 . . . . **212-982-6533**
url: www.bruckandmoss.com / fax: 212-358-1586
Black, Fran: 853 Broadway #606, New York, NY 10003. 212-777-6777
Black, Steve: 518 E. Town St #311, Columbus, OH 43215. 614-463-9206
• **Blackard, Rob: pg 518** Dayton, OH **937-433-8383**
New York, NY **212-966-3604**
San Francisco, CA **415-285-3808**
url: www.scotthull.com / fax: 937-433-0434
• **Blackbird Studio/Marc Stolfi: pg 845** 34 Flagler Ave, Cheshire, CT 06410 . . . . . . **203-439-0674**
url: www.marcstolfi.com
Blackdog: 330 Sir Francis Drake Blvd #A, San Anselmo, CA 94960 415-258-9663
Blackford, John: 201 W 21st St #10G, New York, NY 10001 212-807-0840

ILLUSTRATORS

Blackmun, Kathryn: 6166 Outlook Ave, Los Angeles, CA 90042 ... 213-500-5511
Blackshear, Ami: 220 Elm Ct, Colorado Springs, CO 80906 ... 719-636-5009
Blackshear, Thomas: 220 Elm Circle, Colorado Springs, CO 80906 ... 719-636-5009
Blackwell, Grey: 300 E 46th St #4G, New York, NY 10017 ... 212-687-6463
Blackwell, Patrick: 135 Oakwood Rd, Eastham, MA 02642 ... 508-247-9290
Blae, Ken: 1089 Central Ave, Plainfield, NJ 07060 ... 212-869-3488
Blair, David: PO Box 174 Cooper Sta, New York, NY 10276 ... 212-228-1514
• **Blair, Dru: pg 523** 32 W 40th St #2 South, New York, NY 10018 ... **212-575-6887**
url: www.patfosterartrep.com
Blais, Richard: 8777 rue Albanel, Saint-léonard, QU H1P 2X9 ... 514-324-2774
Blake, Alecia: 310 Chelsea Manor, Park Ridge, NJ 07656 ... 201-263-0191
Blake, Marty: PO Box 266, Jamesville, NY 13078 ... 315-492-1332
Blakey, Paul: 137 Fifth Ave 11th Fl, New York, NY 10010 ... 212-529-3556
Blalock, Ron: 5019 Swinton Dr, Fairfax, VA 22032 ... 703-764-2071
Blanchette, Dan: 428 Charleston Dr, Bollingbrook, IL 60440 ... 630-972-0092
Blanchette, G: 108 Patchen Rd, Burlington, VT 05403 ... 802-862-1583
• **Blandino, Carmelo: pg 811** 3465 Cotes des Neiges #603, Montreal, QU H3H 1T7 ... **514-934-5583**
e-mail: blandino@videotron.ca / fax: 514-934-0267
Blankenship, Sandy: 36431 32nd Ave, Auburn, WA 98001 ... 253-838-7155
Blaski, Cathy: 908 E Auer Ave, Milwaukee, WI 53212 ... 414-264-2556
Blasutta, Mary Lynn: 420 Hill St, Southampton, NY 11968 ... 631-204-1805
Blauers, Nancy: 50 Walnut St, Stratford, CT 06497 ... 203-377-6109
Blauweiss, Stephen: 32-15 41st St, Long Island City, NY 11103 ... 718-204-8335
Blavatt, Kathleen: 743 Sunset Cliffs Blvd, San Diego, CA 92107 ... 619-222-0057
Blechman, Laurel: 7853 Mammoth Ave, Panorama City, CA 91402 ... 818-785-7904
Bleck, Cathie: 58 W 15th St, New York, NY 10011 ... 212-741-2539
Bleck, Cathie: 2270 Chatfield Dr, Cleveland Heights, OH 44106 ... 216-932-4910
Bleck, John: 3636 N Bosworth,Chicago, IL 60613 ... 773-975-8232
• **Bleck, Linda: pg 729** ... **877-607-0599**
url: www.lindableck.com
Blessen, Karen: 194 Third Ave, New York, NY 10003 ... 212-475-0440
Blink Studio Inc: 54 Points of View, Warwick, NY 10990 ... 914-986-8040
Bliok, Leo: 25 Old Colony Ln, Great Neck, NY 11023 ... 516-466-8879
Bliss, Anna Campbell: 27 University St, Salt Lake City, UT 84102 ... 801-364-5835
Bliss, Harry : 7 Hawthorne Crl, S Burlington, VT 05403 ... 802-652-5951
Bliss, Jill: 38 St Mark's Pl #3, Brooklyn, NY 11217 ... 718-222-4889
Bliss, Phil: 22 Briggs Ave, Fairport, NY 14450 ... 716-377-9771
Blitt, Barry: 34 Lincoln Ave, Greenwich, CT 06830 ... 203-622-2988
Bloch, Alex: 1712 E Butler Cir, Chandler, AZ 85225 ... 602-899-0600
• **Bloch, Anthony pg 922** 23-39 33rd St. Astoria, NY 11105 ... **718-274-6064**
e-mail abld@mindspring.com / url: 222.anthonybloch.com
Blonder, Ellen: 91 Woodbine Dr, Mill Valley, CA 94941 ... 415-388-9158
Bloom, Tom: 46 Caterson Terr, Hartsdale, NY 10530 ... 914-761-1877
Bloomfield, A Scott: 1972 Golden Ave, Long Beach, CA 90806 ... 310-334-7315
Blower, Gale Holiday: 420 Lexington Ave #220, New York, NY 10170 ... 212-687-3460
Blowtorch Studios Inc: 319 Peck St #36N, New Haven, CT 06513 ... 203-497-8832
Blubaugh, Susan: 2182 Clove Rd, Staten Island, NY 10305 ... 212-570-6731
Blumen, John: 60 S 15th St, Pittsburgh, PA 15203 ... 412-381-1030
Bluming, Joel: 328 E 19th St, New York, NY 10003 ... 212-673-0558
Blumrich, Christoph: 149 Broadway, Greenlawn, NY 11740 ... 631-757-0524
Blumstein, Paul: 60 E 42nd St, New York, NY 10165 ... 212-867-8092
Boatman, Thomas: 1843 NE 177th, Seattle, WA 98155 ... 206-361-0627
Boatwright, Phil: 2342 Stillwater Dr, Mesquite, TX 75181 ... 214-222-7571
Bobnick, Dick: 3412 Barbara Ln, Burnsville, MN 55337 ... 952-890-7833
Bocci, Michael: 672 Talbert Ave, Simi Valley, CA 93065 ... 805-581-4936
Bock, Christian: 276 Lansdowne Ave, Carle Pl, NY 11514 ... 516-997-9887
Boddy, Joe: 5375 Skyway Dr, Missoula, MT 59804 ... 406-251-3587
Boddy, William: 609 N 10th St, Sacramento, CA 95814 ... 916-443-5001
Bodell, Scott: 9617 Vinewood Dr, Dallas, TX 75228 ... 214-320-8433
Bodily, Michael: 1671 Cabrosa, Mission Viejo, CA 92691 ... 714-457-1228
Boehm, Roger: Pier 33 North, San Francisco, CA 94111 ... 415-956-4750
Boelke, David: 827 N Niagara St, Burbank, CA 91505 ... 818-566-8495
• **Boer, Jan-willem: pg 678,679** 2654 Rodea Dr, Blaine, NM 55449 ... **763-786-1200**
e-mail: nbacher@visi.com / url: www.nancybacher.com / fax: 763-786-1200
Europe ... **31206449011**
url: www.artconnection.nl
Boge, Garrett: 6606 Soundview Dr, Gig Harbor, WA 98335 ... 206-851-5158
Boger, Claire: 2000 Madison Ave, Memphis, TN 38104 ... 901-725-0855
Boguslav, Raphael: 200 E 78th St, New York, NY 10021 ... 212-570-9069
Bohbot, Michel: 3823 Harrison St, Oakland, CA 94611 ... 510-547-0667
Bohn, Rex: 14 N First Ave #1410, St Charles, IL 60174 ... 630-513-1269
Bohn, Richard: 595 W Wilson St, Costa Mesa, CA 92627 ... 949-548-6669
Boie, Chuck: 925 Elm Grove Rd, Elm Grove, WI 53122 ... 414-785-1940
Boies, Alex: 1945 Kenwood Pkwy, Minneapolis, MN 55405 ... 612-374-2771
Boileau, Lowell: 45 Colorado, Highland Park, MI 48203 ... 313-865-3084
• **Boise, Kathyjean: pg 791** ... **415-285-3014**
url: www.kathyjean.planeteria.net or www.theispot.com/artist/boise
Boisselle, Allison: 18 Garfield Ave, E Providence, RI 02916 ... 401-438-4840
Boldman, Craig: PO Box 18128, Fairfield, OH 45018 ... 513-868-2874
Boles, Terry: 8145 Hearthside Rd S, Cottage Grove, MN 55016 ... 651-459-0165
Bolesky, John: 2491 W 22nd Ave, Vancouver, BC V62 1M3 ... 604-684-6826
Bolinsky, David: 350 Center St #207, Wallingford, CT 06492 ... 203-284-1224
Boll, Maxine: 2134 Aquetong Rd, New Hope, PA 18938 ... 215-862-2091
Boll, Thomas: 9500 Wyoming Ave South, Bloomington, MN 55438 ... 642-942-6119
Bolling, Bob: 2395 NE 185th St, N Miami Beach, FL 33180 ... 305-931-0104
Bolling, Vickey: 3530 Old Ivy Lane NE, Atlanta, GA 30342 ... 404-846-0254
• **Bollinger, Peter: pg 196-199** Chicago, IL ... **312-364-0244**
London ... **011-44-207-636-1064**
Los Angeles, CA ... **323-874-5700**
Washington, DC ... **410-349-8669**
New York, NY ... **212-333-2551**
url: www.shannonassociates.com
Bolourchian, Flora: 12485 Rubens Ave, Los Angeles, CA 90066 ... 213-827-8457
• **Bolster, Rob: pg 530** 7 Washington St, Beverly, MA 01915 ... **978-921-0887**
e-mail: leighton@leightonreps.com / url: www.leightonreps.com / fax: 978-921-0223
• **Bolton, Jennifer: pg 418** 7118 Upper River Rd, Prospect, KY 40059 ... **502-228-9427**
url: www.jettreps.com / fax: 502-228-8857
Bolz, Wolf: 3518 Eden Croft Dr, Raleigh, NC 27612 ... 919-571-0123
Bomba, Ron: 1900 W Emerson Pl #106, Seattle, WA 98119 ... 206-286-1277

Bomeisl, James: 70 Madison Ave, Demarest, NJ 07627 ... 201-784-3480
Bonauro, Tom: 601 Minnesota St #216, San Francisco, CA 94107 ... 415-648-5233
Bond, Denny: 6481 Miriam Circle, E Petersburg, PA 17520 ... 717-569-5823
Bond, Paul: 1421 N Dearborn #302, Chicago, IL 60610 ... 312-280-5488
Bondante, Chris: 3015 W Speedway, Tucson, AZ 85745 ... 520-624-5994
Bondurant, Steve: 277 Alexander St Ste 400, Rochester, NY 14607 ... 716-325-1530
Bonforte, Lisa: 201 E 28th St, New York, NY 10016 ... 212-532-0928
Bonham, Liz: 509 San Juan Dr, Southlake, TX 76092 ... 817-354-1399
Bonham, Patti: 10006 Cedar Creek, Houston, TX 77042 ... 713-977-6522
Bonilla, MIchael: 2233 Kemper Ln, Cincinnati, OH 45206 ... 513-861-1400
Bonin, Diana Rice: 2405 NW Thurman St, Portland, OR 97210 ... 503-203-8300
Bonk, Chris: 1400 N Elmhurst Rd #308, Mt Prospect, IL 60056 ... 847-577-5157
Bonner, Hannah: 125 Palfrey St, Watertown, MA 02472 ... 617-924-2620
Bono, Mary M: 288 Graham Ave, Brooklyn, NY 11211 ... 718-387-3774
Bono, Peter: 63 Stark Rd, Columbia, NJ 07832 ... 908-496-8524
Booker, Brian: PO Box 17833, Boulder, CO 80308 ... 303-948-7581
Bookwalter, Tom: 14025 Booth Creek Rd, Olsburg, KS 66520 ... 913-468-3556
Bookwalter, Tom: PO Box 174 11440 Oak Dr, Shelbyville, MI 49344 ... 616-672-5756
Boonechai, Paul: 405 E 72nd St #6A, New York, NY 10021 ... 212-288-3765
Booth, Josie: 415 NE 28th, Portland, OR 97232 ... 503-768-1092
Booth, Martha Anne: 310 W 97th St #902, New York, NY 10025 ... 212-243-5888
Borda, Juliette: 280 Madison Ave #1110, New York, NY 10016 ... 212-545-9155
Bordei, Marcel: 99 Park Ave #210A, New York, NY 10016 ... 800-398-9544
Borg, Rich: 459 W 49th St #4W, New York, NY 10019 ... 212-262-9823
Borge, Rich: PO Box 470818, San Francisco, CA 94147 ... 415-383-9026
Borge, Rich: 459 W 49th St #4W, New York, NY 10019 ... 212-262-9823
Borgman, Harry: 39 Hamilton Terr, New York, NY 10031 ... 212-283-3401
Borhi, Michael: 28 7th St, Roxboro, QU HY LE8 ... 514-684-4188
Bornstein, Peter: 474 Fifth Street #4, Brooklyn, NY 11215 ... 718-768-0443
Bornstein-Fahrer, Marguerita: 7 E 17th St #8, New York, NY 10003 ... 212-677-6100
Borowski, Diane: 675 30th Ave North, St Petersburg, FL 33704 ... 813-822-7836
Borrero, Joanna: PO Box 442, Bearsville, NY 12409 ... 914-679-9656
Bortner, Jody: 1495 Alanwood Rd, Conshohocken, PA 19428 ... 800-544-1543
Borum Illustration: 20131 Pinehurst Trail Dr, Humble, TX 77346 ... 713-328-6757
Bory Assoc, Lou: 108 E 35th St, New York, NY 10016 ... 212-889-3337
Borzotta, Joseph: 315 Willow Ave, Hoboken, NJ 07030 ... 201-420-0293
Bosco, Cathi: 109 Boston Post Rd, Madison, CT 06443 ... 203-245-8549
Bossence, David: 48 Glendon Rd, Stratford, ON N5A 5B3 ... 519-273-1495
Bostic: 9629 Dove Hollow Lane, Glen Allen, VA 23060 ... 804-755-7455
Bostick, Blair: 1819 Drury Ln, Alexandria, VA 22307 ... 703-768-2240
Boswick, Steven: 331 Oak Cir, Wilmette, IL 60091 ... 847-251-1430
Botana, Federico: 51 Camden St, Toronto, ON M5V 1V2 ... 416-703-1913
Bote, Tivadar: 280 Madison Ave #1110, New York, NY 10016 ... 212-545-9155
Botelho, Clemente: 16 Phaedra, Laguna Niguel, CA 92677 ... 949-495-3664
Botero, Kirk: 847A Second Ave #150, New York, NY 10017 ... 212-486-0177
Bothelo, Gary: 12203 Sundale Ave, Hawthorne, CA 90250 ... 310-615-1277
Botsis, Peter: 2467 Culver Rd, Rochester, NY 14609 ... 716-544-1928
Botzis, Ka: 9 Babbling Brook Ln, Suffern, NY 10901 ... 845-368-8606
Bouchard, Jocelyne: 1245 boul Saint-Joseph, Montréal, QU H2J 1L7 ... 514-272-4959
Bouck, Brandon: 336 South 450 West, Ceder City, UT 84720 ... 435-586-6678
Bouliane, Héléne: 8353 av de Gaspé, Montréal, QU H2P 2K2 ... 514-858-5344
Bourelle, Edward: 2000 2nd Ave #801, Seattle, WA 98121 ... 206-256-6303
Bourin, Coni: 5737 N 4th St, Phoenix, AZ 85012 ... 602-230-8182
Bouwman, Jason: 3157 Palmer Dr, Burlington, ON L7M 1L3 ... 905-331-1850
Bovy, Deb: 1225 W 4th St, Waterloo, IA 50702 ... 319-234-2089
Bowdren, John: 212 Hodsdon Rd, Pownal, ME 04069 ... 207-688-3320
Bowen Studio, Robert: 137 W 25th St, New York, NY 10001 ... 212-206-0848
• **Bowen, Eddie: pg 200** Chicago, IL ... **312-364-0244**
London ... **011-44-207-636-1064**
Los Angeles, CA ... **323-874-5700**
Washington, DC ... **410-349-8669**
New York, NY ... **212-333-2551**
url: www.shannonassociates.com
Bower, Adele: 2319 ParkDale Dr, Humble, TX 77339 ... 281-358-6802
Bower, Joel: 853 Broadway #1201, New York, NY 10003 ... 212-677-9100
Bower, Theresa: 409 N Main St, Lakeport, CA 95453 ... 707-263-0679
Bower, Tim: 61 Pearl St #306, Brooklyn, NY 11201 ... 718-834-8974
• **Bowers, David: pg 518**, Dayton, OH ... **937-433-8383**
New York, NY ... **212-966-3604**
San Francisco, CA ... **415-285-3808**
url: www.scotthull.com / fax: 937-433-0434
• **Bowers, Mark: pg 756** 5695 Renneberger Rd, Peyton, CO 80831 ... **719-683-2729**
e-mail: mlbowers@earthlink.net / fax: 719-683-2729
Bowler, Jean: PO Box 1854, Orinda, CA 94563 ... 925-256-9923
• **Bowles, Bruce: pg 424** 227 Godfrey Rd, Weston, CT 06883 ... **203-222-8777**
e-mail: jp@artcoreps.com / url: www.artcoreps.com / fax: 203-454-9940
232 Madison Ave #512, New York, NY 10016 ... **212-889-8777**
e-mail: gt@artcoreps.com / url: www.artcoreps.com / fax: 212-447-1475
Bowles, Doug: 4645 Colfax Ave S, Minneapolis, MN 55409 ... 612-825-7564
• **Bowman, Eric: pg 425** 227 Godfrey Rd, Weston, CT 06883 ... **203-222-8777**
e-mail: jp@artcoreps.com / url: www.artcoreps.com / fax: 203-454-9940
232 Madison Ave #512, New York, NY 10016 ... **212-889-8777**
e-mail: gt@artcoreps.com / url: www.artcoreps.com / fax: 212-447-1475
Bowman, Jason: 3157 Palmer Dr, Burlington, ON L7M 1L3 ... 905-331-1850
Bowman, Rich: 709 W 90th Terr, Kansas City, MO 64114 ... 816-822-2024
Bowman, Rich: 6432 Oak, Kansas City, MO 64113 ... 816-363-2474
Bowser, Ken: 922 Camellia St, Winter Park, FL 32789 ... 407-644-9888
Box, Daniel: 118 E Kingwood Dr #G2, Murfreesboro, TN 37130 ... 615-895-2758
• **Boyajian, Ann: pg 408** 6 Parker Rd, Arlington, MA 02474 ... **781-641-2787**
e-mail: info@lillarogers.com / url: www.lillarogers.com / fax: 781-641-2244
Boyd, William H: 300 Burning Oaks Rd, North Huntingdon, PA 15642 ... 724-863-3464
Boyer, Gene: 232 Madison Ave #512, New York, NY 10016 ... 212-889-8777
Boyer, Rebekah: 178 Eighth St, Brooklyn, NY 11215 ... 718-832-1738
Boyer-Nelles, Lyn: PO Box 174 11440 Oak Dr, Shelbyville, MI 49344 ... 616-672-5756
Boyko, Bill: 16 Conrad Ave, Toronto, ON M6G 3G5 ... 416-656-6616
Boyle, Beverly: 19547 Hill Dr, Morrison, CO 80465 ... 303-697-7936
Bozzini, James: 335 Wharton St, Philadelphia, PA 19147 ... 888-269-9464
Bozzini, James: 501 Fifth Ave, New York, NY 10017 ... 212-490-2450
Bozzo, Frank: 400 E 85th St #5J, New York, NY 10028 ... 212-535-9182

Bracco, Anthony: 214 65th St, W New York, NJ 07093 ... 201-861-9098
Bracey, Geraldine: 286 Spring St #301, New York, NY 10013 ... 212-229-0073
Bracken, Carolyn: 43 E 19th St, New York, NY 10003 ... 212-254-4996
Braddick, Wayne: 7132 Edgerton, Dallas, TX 75231 ... 214-343-8655
Bradford, Stuart: 608 York St, San Francisco, CA 94110 ... 415-641-1285
Bradley, Barbara: 750 Wildcat Canyon Rd, Berkeley, CA 94708 ... 510-525-5496
Bradley, John: PO Box 1251, New York, NY 10023 ... 212-774-4271
Bradshaw, Bart: 10721 Smetana Rd #306, Minnetonka, MN 55343 ... 612-935-1771
• **Bradshaw, Jim: pg 775** ... **856-459-3990**
Brady, Chris: 59 W 28th St #3, New York, NY 10001 ... 212-251-0390
Brady, Elizabeth: 461 Broome St 5th Fl, New York, NY 10013 ... 212-966-9897
Brady, Patrick: 19 Riverview Dr, Plains, PA 18705 ... 570-822-6009
Braffet, Cathleen: 2807 Rindge Ln, Redondo Beach, CA 90278 ... 626-792-9257
Braganza, Alan J: 108 Kirk Dr, Thornhill, ON L3T 3L2 ... 905-642-0671
Bragg, Shokie: 234 Philadelphia Pike, Wilmington, DE 19809 ... 302-762-2285
Brak, Syd: PO Box 1251, New York, NY 10023 ... 212-774-4271
Bralds, Braldt: 13 Herrada Court, Santa Fe, NM 87505 ... 505-466-3603
Bralds, Braldt: 115 West 23rd St, New York, NY 10011 ... 212-989-4600
Bramhall, William: 155 W 15th St #4C, New York, NY 10011 ... 212-989-8770
Bramman, Michael: 104 Dudley Court Upper Berkeley St, London, UK WIH7PJ . 441717233564
Bramsen, Dave: 644 N Hope Ave, Santa Barbara, CA 93110 ... 805-687-6864
Brand, Alfred L.: 83-19 116th St #4A, Kew Gardens, NY 11418 ... 718-805-3585
Brandes, Robin: 130 Meadowcroft Dr, San Anselmo, CA 94960 ... 415-454-0787
Brandon, Bill: 137 Fifth Ave 11th Fl, New York, NY 10010 ... 212-529-3556
Brandstetter, Hugo: 1800 N Clark St, Chicago, IL 60614 ... 312-337-5123
Brandt, Elizabeth: 35 1/2 W 8th St, Holland, MI 49423 ... 616-394-4240
Brandt, Joan: 15 Gramercy Park S, New York, NY 10003 ... 212-473-7874
Brandt, Kim Wilson: 219 Crescent Ave, San Francisco, CA 94110 ... 415-824-2055
Brandtner, Allan: 3739 N Sacramento Ave, Chicago, IL 60618 ... 773-588-1860
Brasfield, Shawn: 3087 Majestic Circle, Avondale Estates, GA 30002 ... 404-292-3824
Brassard, France: 4052 rue Cartier, Montréal, QU H2K 4G4 ... 514-529-6183
Brauckmann-Towns, Krista: 6 N 777 Palomino Dr, St Charles, IL 60175 ... 630-513-9525
Brauer, Fred: 700 John Ringling Blvd, Sarasota, FL 34236 ... 813-361-7523
• **Braun, Marty: pg 699** 7 Washington St, Beverly, MA 01915 ... **978-921-0887**
e-mail: leighton@leightonreps.com / url: www.leightonreps.com
fax: 978-921-0223
Braund, Stephen: Treslake, 1 Chytroon Villas, Cornwall, UK TR3 7PS ... 441872862061
Brautigam, Don: 15 Clearfield Rd, Succasunna, NJ 07876 ... 973-584-4772
Brawner, Dan: 7118 Upper River Rd, Prospect, KY 40059 ... 502-228-9427
Brawner, Rebecca: 732 Richfield Dr, Nashville, TN 37205 ... 615-356-1244
Bray, Ed: 697 N Wheeler St #2, St Paul, MN 55104 ... 651-917-7496
Bray, Mark: RD1 Box 694 Huffs Church Rd, Alburtis, PA 18011 ... 215-845-3229
Bray, Robin: 603 Oak Haven Dr, Falls Church, VA 22046 ... 703-237-8653
Brazeal, Lee Lee: 3525 Mockingbird Ln, Dallas, TX 75205 ... 214-521-5156
Bredemeier, Bob: 5002 92nd Ave SE, Mercer Island, WA 98040 ... 206-232-7873
Breeden, Paul M: PO Box 40A, Sullivan Harbor, ME 04689 ... 207-422-3007
Breen, Stanley: 7000 Pelican Bay Blvd, Naples, FL 34108 ... 941-594-8156
Breiger, Elaine: 112 Greene St, New York, NY 10012 ... 212-966-3004
Brejcha, Tom: 3208 El trebol Ct, Santa Fe, NM 87505 ... 505-438-7779
Bremer-Smith, Cornelia: 10 W Garfield St #10, Seattle, WA 98119 ... 206-378-6970
Bremmer & Goris Comm Inc: 1908 Mount Vernon Ave, Alexandria, VA 22301 ... 703-739-0088
• **Bremmer, Mark/Group Five Creative: pg 646** 4600 S Syracuse 9th Fl, Denver, CO 80237 . **303-256-6335**
Brenard, Craig: 3334 Long Beach Rd #168, Oceanside, NY 11572 ... 516-766-2980
Brendler, Matthias: 165 Christopher St #4N, New York, NY 10014 ... 212-633-2159
Brennan, John: 7156 Marlborough Terr, Berkeley, CA 94705 ... 510-704-4469
Brennan, Kristen: 119 School St, Bala Cynwyd, PA 19004 ... 610-771-0655
• **Brennan, Neil: pg 564,565** 983 Heathland Dr, Newport News, VA 23602 ... **757-875-0148**
url: www.neilbrennan.com
Brennan, Steve: 124 Eagle St, New Haven, CT 06511 ... 203-777-5775
Brenner, Tom: 217 E 86th St #212, New York, NY 10028 ... 212-427-5632
Brenno, Vonnie: 5855 Green Valley Cir #308, Culver City, CA 90230 ... 310-642-2721
Brent, Mike: 597 Riverside Ave, Westport, CT 06888 ... 203-226-4724
Breuer, Lee: 307 Harrow Dr, Columbia, SC 29210 ... 803-798-2235
Brevoort, Dick L: 265 LaQuilla Ln, Mission Viejo, CA 92692 ... 949-347-8177
Briant, Ed: 58 W 15th St, New York, NY 10011 ... 212-741-2539
• **Brice, Jeff: pg 444** 7205 28th Ave NW, Seattle, WA 98117 ... **206-784-1136**
e-mail: kolea@kolea.com / url: www.kolea.com or www.jeffbrice.com
fax: 206-784-1171
Brickley Productions, David: 3318 NE Peerless Pl, Portland, OR 97232 ... 503-236-4883
Brickman, Bruce Lee: 619 Marquis Dr NE, Albuequerque, NM 87123 ... 505-271-8635
Brickman, Robin: 165 E 32nd St, New York, NY 10016 ... 212-686-3514
Brickman, Robin: 32 Fort Hoosac Pl, Williamstown, MA 01267 ... 413-458-9853
Brickner, Alice: 4720 Grosvenor Ave, Bronx, NY 10471 ... 718-549-5909
Bridges, Gregory: 58 W 40th St 6th Fl, New York, NY 10018 ... 212-682-1490
Bridy, Dan: 280 Madison Ave #1110, New York, NY 10016 ... 212-545-9155
• **Briers, Stuart: pg 52,53** 108 E 35th St, New York, NY 10016 ... **212-889-3337**
e-mail: gerald@rappart.com / url: www.theispot.com/rep/rapp / fax: 212-889-3341
• **Briggs, Harry: pg 769** PO Box 51266, Pacific Grove, CA 93950 ... **831-393-9433**
e-mail: harry@hairballdesign.com / url: www.hairballdesign.com or
www.theispot.com / fax: 831-393-9433
Brigham, Derek: 4512 Harriet Ave S, Minneapolis, MN 55409 ... 612-827-3431
Brignaud, Pierre: 8301 rue Foucher, Montréal, QU H2P 2B9 ... 514-388-7771
Brignell, Ian: 686 Richmond St W, Toronto, ON M6J 1C3 ... 416-364-4474
Brill, Jackie: 29 Clifton St, Cambridge, MA 02140 ... 617-868-9697
Brillhart, Ralph: 60 E 42nd St, New York, NY 10165 ... 212-867-8092
Brinkman, John & Wendy: 385 Graham Ave #4A, Brooklyn, NY 11211 ... 718-349-9638
Brinkman, Paula: 341 W 48th St #1, New York, NY 10036 ... 212-757-9497
Brion, David: 58 Glenville St, Greenwich, CT 06831 ... 203-531-9381
Brissette, Andre: 417 St. Pierre St #301, Montreal, QU H2Y 2M4 ... 514-282-2019
• **Britt, Tracy: pg 518,519** Dayton, OH ... **937-433-8383**
New York ... **212-966-3604**
San Francisco ... **415-285-3808**
url: www.scotthull.com / fax: 937-433-0434
Britten, Patrick: 377 Douglas Dr, State College, PA 16803 ... 814-237-8879
Britton, Elizabeth: 29351 Smithville Rd, Sheridan, OR 97378 ... 503-843-5055
Broad, David: 100 Golden Hinde Blvd, San Rafael, CA 94903 ... 415-479-5505
Brock, Irwin: 118 Edgewood Ave, Toronto, ON M4L 3H1 ... 416-778-0440
Brocke, Robert: 425 30th St #25, Newport Beach, CA 92663 ... 949-673-4281
Broda, Ron: 420 Lexington Ave #2760, New York, NY 10170 ... 212-697-8525
Broderick, Joe: 6079 9th St N, Arlington, VA 22205 ... 703-960-6051
• **Brodner, Steve: pg 195** Chicago, IL ... **312-364-0244**
London ... **011-44-207-636-1064**
Los Angeles, CA ... **323-874-5700**
Washington, DC ... **410-349-8669**
New York, NY ... **212-333-2551**
url: www.shannonassociates.com
Brody, Bill: PO Box 82533, Fairbanks, AK 99708 ... 907-479-4139
Brody, Rebecca: 1325 Ferry, Lafayette, IN 47901 ... 317-742-7587
• **Brokaw, Tanya: pg 735** 633 Ocean Ave #13 Santa Monica, CA 90402 ... **310-394-8456**
Bronikowski, Ken: 925 Elm Grove Rd, Elm Grove, WI 53122 ... 414-785-1940
• **Bronson, Linda: pg 530** 7 Washington St, Beverly, MA 01915 ... **978-921-0887**
e-mail: leighton@leightonreps.com / url: www.leightonreps.com
fax: 978-921-0223
Brook Trout Studio: 439 Loveman Ave, Columbus, OH 43085 ... 614-885-4889
Brook, Elvis: 133 N Montclair Ave, Dallas, TX 75208 ... 214-943-2569
Brooker, Kyrsten: 9756 88th Ave, Edmonton, AB T6E 2P9 ... 780-433-1410
• **Brooker, Philip: pg 352** 58 W 15th St, New York, NY 10011 ... **212-741-2539**
url: www.jdedell.com or www.theispot.com / fax: 212-741-4660
Brooks, Andrea: Pier 33 North, San Francisco, CA 94111 ... 415-956-4750
Brooks, Andrea: 481 Eighth Ave #1556, New York, NY 10001 ... 212-736-9038
Brooks, Dick: 11712 N Michigan Rd #100, Zionsville, IN 46077 ... 317-873-1117
• **Brooks, Hal: pg 730** , New York, NY ... **212-889-2040**
Brooks, Harold: 2 Marvin Pl, Westport, CT 06880 ... 212-531-0255
Brooks, Karen: 2507 King Arthur Cir, Atlanta, GA 30345 ... 281-334-7770
• **Brooks, Lou: pg 594,595** Redwood Valley, CA ... **707-485-0800**
New York, NY ... **212-245-3632**
url: www.loubrooks.com
• **Brooks, Nan: pg 504** 666 Greenwich St #860, New York, NY 10014 ... **212-675-5719**
e-mail: harriet@hkportfolio.com / url: www.hkportfolio.com / fax: 212-675-6341
Brooks, Rob: 15 E Balfour Ln, Chatham, MA 02633 ... 508-945-4841
Brooks, Rob: 501 Fifth Ave, New York, NY 10017 ... 212-490-2450
• **Brother, Kelly: pg 355** 58 W 15th St, New York, NY 10011 ... **212-741-2539**
url: www.jdedell.com or www.theispot.com or www.kellybrother.com
fax: 212-741-4660
Brothers, Barry: 1920 E 17th St, Brooklyn, NY 11229 ... 718-336-7540
Brower, Robert: 1831 E 19th St, Santa Ana, CA 92705 ... 714-973-0906
Brown Illustration Inc, Rick: 16635 Howard Cir, Omaha, NE 68118 ... 402-697-1962
Brown, Bill: 2029 Oakstone Way, Los Angeles, CA 90046 ... 323-848-9623
Brown, Bob: 223 William St, Englewood, NJ 07631 ... 201-541-7101
Brown, Bradford: 174 S Harrison #2B, E Orange, NJ 07079 ... 973-403-0607
Brown, Carolyn: 27 Edward St, St Albans, VT 05478 ... 802-527-1911
Brown, Charley: 3450 Third St #1D, San Francisco, CA 94124 ... 415-648-9430
Brown, Charlie: 9444 Old Katy Rd #108, Houston, TX 77055 ... 713-468-8161
Brown, Christina: 3999 Brae Burn Dr, Eugene, OR 97405 ... 541-344-0598
Brown, Colin: 23 Ganton St, London, England, UK WIV 1LA ... 71-287-9191
• **Brown, Dan: pg 375** 89 Fifth Ave #901, New York, NY 10003 ... **212-627-1554**
fax: 212-627-1719
Brown, Ellen C: 21007 Topochico Dr, Woodland Hills, CA 91364 ... 818-713-8015
Brown, John Peter: 235 E 22nd St #16R, New York, NY 10010 ... 212-684-7080
Brown, Judith Gwyn: 522 E 85th St, New York, NY 10028 ... 212-288-1599
Brown, Kathi: PO Box 711820, Salt Lake City, UT 84171 ... 404-296-9666
Brown, Marc: 865 Delaware St, Denver, CO 80204 ... 303-820-2599
Brown, Matthew: 720 Jonathon Pl, Escondido, CA 92027 ... 760-738-4643
Brown, Michael David: 108 E 35th St, New York, NY 10016 ... 212-889-3337
Brown, Peter D: 235 E 22nd St #16R, New York, NY 10010 ... 212-684-7080
Brown, Rick: 58 W 40th St 6th Fl, New York, NY 10018 ... 212-682-1490
Brown, Thomas: 244 S Merrimack Rd, Hollis, NH 03049 ... 603-465-3882
Brown, William L: 6704 Westmoreland Ave, Takoma Park, MD 20912 ... 301-270-2014
Browne, Rob: 75 Arbor Rd, Menlo Park, CA 94025 ... 650-325-6832
Browning, Vivian Wu: 2925 Griffith St, San Francisco, CA 94124 ... 800-755-3380
Brownson, Matt: 419 Athena Rd, Golden, CO 80403 ... 303-582-0787
Brownwood, Bruce: 13418 A Sunset Dr, Whittier, CA 90602 ... 562-693-5888
Broxon, Janet: 1156 Sanchez, San Francisco, CA 94114 ... 415-641-9947
Bru, Salvador: 5130 Bradley Blvd, Chevy Chase, MD 20815 ... 301-654-4420
Bruce, Sandra: 13997 Emerald Ct, Grass Valley, CA 95945 ... 530-477-1909
• **Bruce, Taylor: pg 790** 755 Tzabaco Creek Rd, Geyserville, CA 95441 ... **707-857-3373**
Bruemmer, Betsy: Box 1743, Edgartown, MA 02539 ... 508-627-9264
Brugger, Bob: 1930 Robinson St, Redondo Beach, CA 90278 ... 310-372-0135
Bruner, Rick Ernest: PO Box 1469, Shepherdstown, WV 25443 ... 304-876-0945
Brunettin, Alan: 1031 Wesley Ave, Evanston, IL 60202 ... 847-492-0979
Bruning, Bill: 315 Silver Meadow Dr, Orono, MN 55356 ... 612-475-0877
Brunkus, Denise: 111 Perryville Rd, Pittstown, NJ 08867 ... 908-735-2671
Bruno, Peggy: 51 Grove St Cranberry Cove, Marshfield, MA 02050 ... 617-837-6896
Brunz, Robert: PO Box 98059, Las Vegas, NV 89193 ... 702-263-5709
Brünz, Robert: 600 Seventh Ave #523, Seattle, WA 98104 ... 800-750-5809
Bruvel, Gil: 50 Briar Hollow Ln 7th Fl, Houston, TX 77027 ... 713-881-8948
Bryan, Diana: PO Box 391, Saugerties, NY 12477 ... 914-246-3182
Bryan, Mike: PO Box 1760, Highland Park, IL 60035 ... 312-222-0337
Bryant Illus, Web: 9310 Coronado Terr, Fairfax, VA 22031 ... 703-359-1039
Bryant, Eric: 40 S Moulton St, Perryville, MO 63775 ... 573-547-8008
Bryant, Rick J: 18 W 37th St #301, New York, NY 10018 ... 212-594-6718
Bryant, Wallace E: 9310 Coronado Terr, Fairfax, VA 22031 ... 703-276-6499
Bsales, David A: 166 Hillcrest Dr, Wayne, NJ 07470 ... 201-473-1101
Bua: 2044 Dracena Dr, Los Angeles, CA 90027 ... 213-661-2510
Bucci, Richard A: 20 Narragansett Ave, Narragansett, RI 02882 ... 401-783-6903
Buchanan, Nigel: 133 N Montclair Ave, Dallas, TX 75208 ... 214-943-2569
Buchanan, Steve: 317 Colebrook Rd, Winsted, CT 06098 ... 203-379-5668
Buchanan, Thomas: 41 S Rainbow Crest Dr, Golden, CO 80204 ... 303-526-0413
Buchanan, Yvonne: 18 Lincoln Pl #2L, Brooklyn, NY 11217 ... 718-783-6682
Buchart, Greta: 2512 E Thomas Rd #2, Phoenix, AZ 85016 ... 602-381-1332
Buchart, Greta: 839 N Marshall St #61, Milwaukee, WI 53202 ... 888-999-0280
Buchberger, Brian: 610 Water St #310, Milwaukee, WI 53202 ... 414-273-8194
• **Buchman, Doug /The Big Pixel: pg 894** 3183 Airway Ave #G, Costa Mesa, CA 92626 . **714-979-8001**
e-mail: bigpixels@aol.com / url: www.thebigpixelstudios.com
Buchs, Thomas: 925 Elm Grove Rd, Elm Grove, WI 53122 ... 262-785-1940
Buckley, Marjory: 3850 Eddingham Ave, Calabasas, CA 91302 ... 818-222-5445
Buckley, Paul: 177 Amity St #3, Brooklyn, NY 11201 ... 212-243-1696
Buckner, Derek: 133 Spring St 2nd Fl, New York, NY 10012 ... 212-925-4340

Budd, Ken: 30 Ipswich St #107, Boston, MA 02215 ... 617-424-0279
• **Buelow, Alicia: pg 338,339** 58 W 15th St, New York, NY 10011 ... **212-741-2539**
url: www.jdedell.com or www.theispot.com or www.aliciabuelow.com
fax: 212-741-4660
Bueno, Gomez: 1033 Doreen Pl #4, Venice, CA 90291 ... 310-392-8151
Bueno, Luz: 548 Cragmont, Berkeley, CA 94708 ... 510-524-2163
Buerge, Bill: 20421 Callen Dr, Topanga, CA 90290 ... 310-455-3181
Buffington, Beth: 3507 Falkner Dr, Naperville, IL 60564 ... 630-904-1407
Buffington, Hank: 26 W Rt 70 #233, Marlton, NJ 08053 ... 609-770-0868
Bugzester, Ruth: 302 W 56th St, New York, NY 10019 ... 212-757-2964
Buhler, Ray Varn: Blue Mountain Rd, Wilseyville, CA 95257 ... 209-293-4169
Bui, Quinn: 3625 W Mcarther # 303, Santa Ana, CA 92704 ... 714-437-1891
Buket: 270 5th St #1H, Brooklyn, NY 11215 ... 718-832-0665
Bull, Michael: 505 Woodland Rd, Kentfield, CA 94904 ... 415-461-3282
Bull, Mike: 2925 Griffith St, San Francisco, CA 94124 ... 800-755-3380
Bulleit, Dan: 865 Delaware St, Denver, CO 80204 ... 303-820-2599
Bulleit, Dan: 4025 Weatherby Way, New Albany, IN 47150 ... 812-944-2686
Bullerin, David: 32-25 58th St, Woodside, NY 11377 ... 718-777-2665
Bulthuis, Jenny: 10123 La Rosa Dr, Temple City, CA 91780 ... 626-279-1682
Bumas, Jonathan: 99-34 67th Rd #6A, Forest Hills, NY 11375 ... 718-459-5903
Bunk, Richard S: 616 W Healey St #3, Champaign, IL 61820 ... 217-398-5943
Bunn, Darian: 114-81 178th St, St Albans, NY 11434 ... 718-523-6757
Burch, Allan M: 404 Red Maple, Kirbyville, MO 65679 ... 417-335-2410
Burckhardt, Marc: 112 W 41st St, Austin, TX 78751 ... 512-458-1690
Burgard, WC: 2785 Heather Way, Ann Arbor, MI 48104 ... 734-971-3014
Burger, Robert: 145 Kingwood Stockton Rd, Stockton, NJ 08559 ... 609-397-3737
Burgess, Lucy: 3878 Mary Ann Ln, Lake Almanor, CA 96137 ... 408-438-3659
Burgio, Trish: 227 Godfrey Rd, Weston, CT 06883 ... 203-222-8777
• **Burgoyne, John: pg 781** 26 Statler Rd, Belmont, MA 02478 ... **617-489-4960**
e-mail: level9@thecia.net / url: www.theispot.com/artist/burgoyne or
www.johnburgoyne.com / fax: 617-489-0629
Burke, Jim: 647 Walnut St Ext, Manchester, NH 03104 ... 603-668-0103
Burke, Kelly: 2443 Filmore St #280, San Francisco, CA 94115 ... 415-332-2882
Burke, Kevin: 4501 Lyons Rd, Miamisburg, OH 45342 ... 513-866-4013
Burke, Leland: 215 W 83rd St #15A, New York, NY 10024 ... 212-721-4271
Burke, Philip: 1948 Juron Dr, Niagara Falls, NY 14304 ... 716-297-0345
Burleson, Joe: 60 E 42nd St, New York, NY 10165 ... 212-867-8092
• **Burman, Harry: pg 378** 89 Fifth Ave #901, New York, NY 10003 ... **212-627-1554**
fax: 212-627-1719
Burman, Rob: 29580 Northwestern Hwy, Southfield, MI 48034 ... 248-353-7722
Burn, Ted: 5134 Timber Trail NE, Atlanta, GA 30342 ... 888-255-1490
Burn, Ted: 1405 Captain O'Neal Dr, Daphne, AL 36526 ... 334-626-4285
Burnett, Bob: 237 Lowell St, Wakefield, MA 01880 ... 781-245-3474
• **Burnett, Lindy: pg 504** 666 Greenwich St #860, New York, NY 10014 ... **212-675-5719**
e-mail: harriet@hkportfolio.com / url: www.hkportfolio.com / fax: 212-675-6341
Burns, Brad: 11287 Rolling Hills Dr, Dublin, CA 94568 ... 925-829-7939
Burns, Brigette: 3333 Mentone Ave #17, Los Angeles, CA 90034 ... 310-712-5495
Burns, Charles: 210 Brown St, Philadelphia, PA 19123 ... 215-925-7618
Burns, Dan: 647 Allison Dr, Cleveland, OH 44143 ... 216-382-9633
Burns, Jim: 11 Kings Ridge Rd, Long Valley, NJ 07853 ... 908-813-8718
Burns, John: 1593 Parkway Dr, Rohnert Park, CA 94928 ... 707-585-7604
Burns, Regan: 5301 Aspen Dr, W Vancouver, BC V7W 3C8 ... 604-922-2875
Burns, Rhonda: 847A Second Ave #150, New York, NY 10017 ... 212-486-0177
Burnside, John E: 4214 Los Feliz Blvd, Los Angeles, CA 90027 ... 213-665-8913
Burr, Dan: 60 E 42nd St, New York, NY 10165 ... 212-867-8092
Burris, Jon: 125 Concord St, Brooklyn, NY 11201 ... 718-625-6261
Burris, Priscilla: 110 Rising Ridge Rd, Ridgefield, CT 06877 ... 203-438-7307
Burrows & Assoc, Bill: 3100 Elm Ave West, Baltimore, MD 21211 ... 410-889-3288
• **Burward-Hoy, Andrew: pg 194** Chicago, IL ... **312-364-0244**
London ... **011-44-207-636-1064**
Los Angeles, CA ... **323-874-5700**
Washington, DC ... **410-349-8669**
New York, NY ... **212-333-2551**
url: www.shannonassociates.com
Busacca, Mark: 2150 Hyde St #1, San Francisco, CA 94109 ... 415-776-4247
Busch, Lee F: 1 Fitchburg St #C503, Somerville, MA 02143 ... 617-488-3614
• **Busch, Lon: pg 54,55** 108 E 35th St, New York, NY 10016 ... **212-889-3337**
e-mail: gerald@rappart.com / url: www.theispot.com/rep/rapp / fax: 212-889-3341
Bush, George: 22 Seminary Ln, Granite Springs, NY 10527 ... 914-248-4870
Bush, Lorraine: 570A Church Lane Rd, Reading, PA 19606 ... 610-779-8565
Buske, Gregory A: 2031 Holly Dr, Prescott, AZ 86305 ... 520-708-9446
Bustamante, Gerald: PO Box 470818, San Francisco, CA 94147 ... 415-383-9026
Bustamente, Orlando: 1310 Worstead Dr, Fayetteville, NC 28314 ... 910-868-9767
Butcher, Jim: 1357 E MacPhail Rd, Bel Air, MD 21014 ... 410-879-6380
Butkovich, Anthony: 812 Branard #3, Houston, TX 77006 ... 713-523-0388
Butler, Amy: 29 Public Sq, Mt Vernon, OH 43050 ... 740-397-1236
Butler, Callie: 4307 Alder Dr, San Diego, CA 92116 ... 619-280-2343
• **Butler, Chris pg 690, 691**: 7018 Redwing Pl, Longmont, CO 80503 ... **303-494-4118**
Butler, David: 29 Public Sq, Mt Vernon, OH 43050 ... 614-397-1236
Butler, Steve: 407 Indiana Ave, Lynn Haven, FL 32444 ... 904-271-0452
Butterfield, Ned: 278 Cedar Ave, Islip, NY 11751 ... 631-277-3151
• **Buttram, Andy: pg 518** Dayton, OH ... **937-433-8383**
New York, NY ... **212-966-3604**
San Francisco, CA ... **415-285-3808**
url: www.scotthull.com / fax: 937-433-0434
Butts, Christopher C: 919 St Andrews Dr, Malvern, PA 19355 ... 610-993-2395
Buxton, John: 4584 Sylvan Dr, Allison Park, PA 15101 ... 412-486-6588
Buzelli, Christopher: 2149 Lyon St #5, San Francisco, CA 94115 ... 415-921-7140
Buzzworks Studio: 231 Mayatt Rd, Barrington, RI 02806 ... 401-245-8438
Byer, Lou: 1449 N Pennsylvania, Indianapolis, IN 46202 ... 317-264-0843
Bynum, Janie: 4394 Hemmingway Dr, Kalamazoo, MI 49009 ... 616-385-3448
Byram, Stephen: 52 68th St #1, Guttenberg, NJ 07093 ... 201-869-7493
Byrd, Bob: 280 Madison Ave #1110, New York, NY 10016 ... 212-545-9155
Byrd, Robert J: 409 Warwick Rd, Haddonfield, NJ 08033 ... 856-428-9627
Byrne, Tom: 6 Annamoe Rd, Dublin, IE 7 ... 35318389440
Byrnes, Patrick: 3622 N Hamilton, Chicago, IL 60618 ... 773-472-3649
Byrnside, Lora: 46 Christianburg Rd, Shelbyville, KY 40065 ... 502-419-4050

C

Cabarga, Leslie: 253 S Orange Dr, Los Angeles, CA 90036 ... 323-549-0700
Cabib, Leila: 8601 Buckhannon Dr, Potomac, MD 20854 ... 301-299-4158
• **Cable, Annette: pg 416** 7118 Upper River Rd, Prospect, KY 40059 ... **502-228-9427**
url: www.jettreps.com / fax: 502-228-8857
Cable, Jerry: 133 Kuhl Rd, Flemington, NJ 08822 ... 908-788-6750
Cable, Mark: 7118 Upper River Rd, Prospect, KY 40059 ... 502-228-9427
Cabossel, Jannine: 56 Coyote Crossing, Santa Fe, NM 87505 ... 505-983-4099
Caceres, Francisco: 1790 Fell St, San Francisco, CA 94117 ... 415-776-6413
Cacy, Michael: 537 SE Ash St, Portland, OR 97214 ... 503-233-7715
Cadman, Joel: 41-15 50th Ave #1J, Long Island City, NY 11104 ... 718-784-1267
Cage, Gary: 34 Flamingo Rd, Levittown, NY 11756 ... 516-735-1983
Caggiano, Tom: 83-25 Dongan Ave, Elmhurst, NY 11373 ... 718-651-8993
Cain, David H: 200 W 20th St #607, New York, NY 10011 ... 212-633-0258
Cairns, Brian: 58 W 15th St, New York, NY 10011 ... 212-741-2539
Caito, Mike: 7414 Foxfield Dr, Hazelwood, MO 63042 ... 314-839-1714
Calabrese, Vincent: 6357 Sharon Hills Rd, Charlotte, NC 28210 ... 704-553-9677
Calabria, Jo: 316 Independence Ave #4, Washington, DC 20003 ... 202-546-8780
Calabro, Carol: 20 Brucewood Rd, Acton, MA 01720 ... 978-266-1360
Calanché, Magué: 545 Belvedere St, San Francisco, CA 94117 ... 415-664-9541
Caldicott, Karen: 40 S 6th St, Brooklyn, NY 11211 ... 718-486-7704
Caldwell, Kirk: 137 Fifth Ave 11th Fl, New York, NY 10010 ... 212-529-3556
Caldwell, Kirk: 414 Jackson St, San Francisco, CA 94111 ... 415-398-7553
Caldwell, Tony: PO Box 5901, Breckenridge, CO 80424 ... 970-547-9612
Calhoun, Dia: 2712 N 10th, Tacoma, WA 98406 ... 206-383-9111
Callahan, Donna: 15 Connie Dr, Foxboro, MA 02035 ... 508-543-2705
Callanan, Brian: 420 Lexington Ave #2760, New York, NY 10170 ... 212-697-8525
Callanan, Maryjane: 218 Elm Court, Rhinelander, WI 54501 ... 715-369-2130
Callaway, Nicholas: 70 Bedford St, New York, NY 10014 ... 212-929-5212
Calle, Celia: 134 E 22nd St #402, New York, NY 10010 ... 212-979-0525
Calleja, Bob: 490 Elm Ave, Bogota, NJ 07603 ... 201-488-3028
Callies, Timothy J: N6441 906th St, Elk Mound, WI 54739 ... 715-879-5899
• **Callow, Barbara: pg 927** 1839 9th St, Alemeda, CA 94501 ... **510-769-1421**
e-mail: ldmreps@prodigy.net / fax: 510-521-1674
• **Calomino, Rick: pg 751** 4837 W Hayward Pl, Denver, CO 80212 ... **303-455-6561**
e-mail: calominostudio@compuserve.com / url: www.theispot.com/artist/rcalomino /
fax: 303-455-1162
Calooy, Sonya: 3889 Clover Ln, Dallas, TX 75220 ... 214-902-0466
Calsbeek, Craig: 710 Wilshire Blvd #510, Santa Monica, CA 90401 ... 310-394-6037
Calver, Dave: 194 Third Ave, New York, NY 10003 ... 212-475-0440
Calver, Dave: 70 Stoneham Dr, Rochester, NY 14625 ... 716-383-8996
Calvert, Jeff: 9518 Whiskey Bottom Rd, Laurel, MD 20723 ... 301-236-4139
Calvert, Trudy L: PO Box 7272, Bloomington, IN 47407 ... 812-876-9969
Calviello & Cohen Multimedia: 133 Cedar Rd, E Northport, NY 11731 ... 516-368-2031
Calviello, Joe: 23-35 Bell Blvd #6J, Bayside, NY 11360 ... 718-423-3797
Cam's Happy Pencil Studio: 1819 Fiske Ave, Pasadena, CA 91104 ... 626-797-8890
Cameron, Chad: 1705 Oak St, San Francisco, CA 94117 ... 415-255-1598
Cameron, Chad: 5134 Timber Trail NE, Atlanta, GA 30342 ... 888-255-1490
Camp, Barbara: 58 W 40th St 6th Fl, New York, NY 10018 ... 212-682-1490
Camp, Janeane: 2746 Castle Rock Rd, Diamond Bar, CA 91765 ... 909-598-8747
Campbell, Annie: 5650 Fitzgerald Rd, Trumansburg, NY 14886 ... 607-387-9086
Campbell, Deborah: 1310 Coronado Terr, Los Angeles, CA 90026 ... 213-483-1374
Campbell, Denise Hilton: 824 Edwards PO Box 41, Trinidad, CA 95570 ... 707-677-0241
• **Campbell, Harry: pg 833** Baltimore, MD ... **410-889-1100**
e-mail: harry@hspot.com / url: www.hspot.com
Campbell, Jenny: 731 N 24th St, Philadelphia, PA 19130 ... 215-232-6666
Campbell, Jim: 420 Lexington Ave, New York, NY 10170 ... 212-986-5680
Campbell, Karen Albanese: 155 Oakland Park Ave, Columbus, OH 43214 ... 614-268-2175
Campbell, Mark: 91 Ocean Pkwy #1D, Brooklyn, NY 11318 ... 718-854-5162
Campbell, Michael: 4275-29 Rosewood Dr #106, Pleasanton, CA 94588 ... 925-462-0587
Campofiori, Peter: 59 Frank Ct, Monroe, NY 10950 ... 914-782-0838
Cane, Eleni: 2163 Walnut St #200, Baldwin, NY 11510 ... 516-378-3203
Cane, Linda: 731 N 24th St, Philadelphia, PA 19130 ... 215-232-6666
Cane, Linda: 6863 Paxson Rd, New Hope, PA 18938 ... 215-297-5618
• **Cangemi, Antonio: pg 421** 7118 Upper River Rd, Prospect, KY 40059 ... **502-228-9427**
Caniglia, Carmine: 295 Macintosh Rd, Westchester, PA 19382 ... 610-436-1545
Cannizzaro, Gregory, J: 107 York Rd, Towson, MD 21204 ... 410-296-2402
• **Cannoy, Lynne: pg 220,221** Chicago, IL ... **312-364-0244**
London ... **011-44-207-636-1064**
Los Angeles, CA ... **323-874-5700**
Washington, DC ... **410-349-8669**
New York, NY ... **212-333-2551**
url: www.shannonassociates.com
Cantarella, Virginia Hoyt: PO Box 54, S Westerlo, NY 12163 ... 518-966-4419
Cantin, Charles: 809 Cartier, Quebec, QU G1R 2R8 ... 418-524-1931
Canty, Ray: 1512 W Marlene Ave, Peoria, IL 61614 ... 309-682-7941
Canty, Thomas: 178 Old Country Way, Braintree, MA 02185 ... 617-843-7262
Cap Productions/Comp Art Plus: 311 W 34th St 8th Fl, New York, NY 10001 ... 212-279-0800
Capaldi, Gina: 1563 Calle Ciervos, San Dimas, CA 91773 ... 818-967-6483
Capalungan, David: 2340 Renfrew, Sylvan Lake, MI 48320 ... 248-706-0040
Capelle, Yves: 171/22 Co Bac Co Giang District One, Ho Chi Minh City, VIETNAM 848-8360089
Caplanis, Michael: 211 Vaucluse Spring Ln, Stephens City, VA 22655 ... 703-875-2193
Caponigro, John Paul: Rte 1 Box 1055, Cushing, ME 04563 ... 207-354-8578
Caporale, Wende: 3850 Eddingham Ave, Calabasas, CA 91302 ... 818-222-5445
Caporale, Wende: Studio Hill Farm Rte 116, N Salem, NY 10560 ... 914-669-5653
Capshaw, Stan: 41959 County Rd #652, Mattawan, MI 49071 ... 616-668-5556
Capstone Studios, Inc: 2820 Westshire Dr, Los Angeles, CA 90068 ... 213-464-2787
Caputo, Vince: PO Box 257, Pleasantville, NY 10570 ... 914-747-2220
Caradonna, Robert: 19830 25th Ave NE, Seattle, WA 98155 ... 206-364-4073
Carambat, David: 21339 Wilson, Covington, LA 70433 ... 504-893-2432
Caras, George: 5154 Woodstone Cir E, Lake Worth, FL 33463 ... 561-276-3924
Carbone, Lou: 805 Clinton St, Hoboken, NJ 07030 ... 201-656-6008
Carboni, Ron: RR #1 Box 94, Millerton, NY 12546 ... 914-373-9228
Cardarelli, Mike: 4298 5th Ave, San Diego, CA 92103 ... 619-291-6995
Cardella, Elaine: 24 Elizabeth St, Port Jervis, NY 12771 ... 914-856-8889
• **Cardelli, Maria: pg 364** 280 Madison Ave #1110, New York, NY 10016 ... **212-545-9155**
url: www.irmeliholmberg.com / fax: 212-545-9462
Carden, Vince: 2308 E Glenoaks Blvd, Glendale, CA 91206 ... 818-956-0807

Cardinal, Alain: 4611 rue Boyer, Montréal, QU H2J 3E5 . . . 514-527-2262
Cardona Studio: 43 E 19th St, New York, NY 10003 . . . 212-254-4996
Carey, Mark: 3109 Pelham St, Chesapeake, VA 23324 . . . 804-396-5768
Carey, Sue: 1700 Bush St #9, San Francisco, CA 94109 . . . 415-441-7046
Carleton, Kim: 20 Yarmouth Rd, Norwood, MA 02062 . . . 617-762-3228
Carlson Illus, Frederick H: 118 Monticello, Monroeville, PA 15146 . . . 412-856-0982
Carlson, Gary: 227 Godfrey Rd, Weston, CT 06883 . . . 203-222-8777
• **Carlson, Jonathan: pg 56,57** 108 E 35th St, New York, NY 10016 . . . **212-889-3337**
e-mail: gerald@rappart.com / url: www.theispot.com/rep/rapp / fax: 212-889-3341
Carlson, Leslie: 6184 Temple Hill Dr, Los Angeles, CA 90068 . . . 213-237-6634
Carlson, Sue: 859 Sunrise Blvd, Forked River, NJ 08731 . . . 609-971-6828
Carlton, Ashley: 10900 Ventura Blvd, Studio City, CA 91604 . . . 818-761-6644
• **Carluccio, Maria: pg 402** 6 Parker Rd, Arlington, MA 02474 . . . **781-641-2787**
e-mail: info@lillarogers.com / url: www.lillarogers.com / fax: 781-641-2244
Carmi, Gioro: 121 Dodgingtown Rd Box 266, Bethel, CT 06801 . . . 203-748-4823
Carmichael, Dennis J: 19355 Pacific Coast Hwy, Malibu, CA 90265 . . . 310-456-5915
• **Carnabuci, Anthony: pg 504-507** 666 Greenwich St #860, New York, NY 10014 **212-675-5719**
e-mail: harriet@hkportfolio.com / url: www.hkportfolio.com / fax: 212-675-6341
Carnes, Bruce: 4 Emeraude Way, Aliso Viejo, CA 92656 . . . 949-425-1228
Carnes, Bruce: 16 Phaedra, Laguna Niguel, CA 92677 . . . 949-495-3664
Caroline S: 608 York St, San Francisco, CA 94110 . . . 415-641-1285
Caron, Dominique: 2730 Sacramento St #1, San Francisco, CA 94115 . . . 415-929-0864
Caron, Mona: 1218 Page St, San Francisco, CA 94117 . . . 415-255-8488
Carpenter, Carolyn: 99 Park Ave #210A, New York, NY 10016 . . . 800-398-9544
Carpenter, Joe & Polly: 72 Spring St #1003, New York, NY 10012 . . . 212-431-6666
Carr, Alan K: 51 Dean St #2, Brooklyn, NY 11201 . . . 718-596-8850
Carr, Barbara: 245 E 40th S #19D, New York, NY 10016 . . . 212-370-1663
Carr, Ted: 21865 Rainbow Rd, Barrington, IL 60010 . . . 847-381-6976
Carradine, Mary: 2056 Robin Hill Ln, Carrollton, TX 75007 . . . 972-578-8666
Carranza, Steve: 1525 Second St, Manhattan Beach, CA 90266 . . . 310-318-0194
Carreiro, Ron: 6 Hillside Dr, Plymouth, MA 02360 . . . 508-224-9290
Carrier, Alan: 1521 Bidwell Dr, Chico, CA 95926 . . . 916-894-5911
Carroll, Brynn: 4750 Castana Dr, Cameron Park, CA 95682 . . . 530-677-0529
Carroll, Jim: 2456 RT9, East Chatham, NY 12060 . . . 518-392-5234
Carroll, Justin: 612 N 2nd St, St Louis, MO 63102 . . . 314-781-7377
Carroll, Mark Scott: 3301A S Jefferson Ave, St Louis, MO 63118 . . . 314-773-2600
Carroll, Michael: 538 Bellefort, Oak Park, IL 60302 . . . 708-386-6125
Carroll, Tim: 1337 California St #5, San Francisco, CA 94109 . . . 415-929-7050
Carrozza, John: 310 W 97th St #902, New York, NY 10025 . . . 212-243-5888
Carruthers, Roy: 115 West 23rd St, New York, NY 10011 . . . 212-989-4600
Carsello, Margaret: 516 N Vine, Hinsdale, IL 60521 . . . 630-794-9120
Carson, Jim: 11 Foch St, Cambridge, MA 02140 . . . 617-661-3321
Carson, Rene: PO Box 6638, Jersey City, NJ 07306 . . . 201-946-0028
• **Carter, Abby: pg 504** 666 Greenwich St #860, New York, NY 10014 . . . **212-675-5719**
e-mail: harriet@hkportfolio.com / url: www.hkportfolio.com / fax: 212-675-6341
Carter, Alice: 828 Pine Hill Rd, Stanford, CA 94305 . . . 415-424-9886
Carter, Anne: 13 School St, Milton, MA 02186 . . . 617-696-2496
Carter, Bunny: 200 E 78th St, New York, NY 10021 . . . 212-570-9069
Carter, Greg: 6020 Beardsley Ct, Raleigh, NC 27609 . . . 919-676-0238
Carter, Jane: 460 W 42nd St 2nd Fl, New York, NY 10036 . . . 212-967-6655
Carter, Kip: 213 Elderberry Cir, Athens, GA 30605 . . . 706-542-5384
Carter, Lucille: 7323 Clearhaven Dr, Dallas, TX 75248 . . . 972-991-5035
Carter, Randy: 2415 E 37th St, Savannah, GA 31404 . . . 912-234-2504
Carter, Stephanie: 5002 92nd Ave SE, Mercer Island, WA 98040 . . . 206-232-7873
Carter, Stephanie: 3589 Arbutus St, Vancouver, BC V6C 1A1 . . . 604-687-8477
Cartography, Eureka: 1796 University Ave, Berkeley, CA 94703 . . . 510-845-6277
Cartwright, Reg: PO Box 1251, New York, NY 10023 . . . 212-774-4271
Carver, Charles: 72 Monarch Dr, Newburgh, NY 12550 . . . 914-566-8257
Carverletchermiller: 3940 Spring Dr #11, Reno, NV 89502 . . . 702-828-4700
Casals, Pepe: 758 Brookridge Dr NE, Atlanta, GA 30306 . . . 404-872-7980
Casanas, Cristina: 779 Riverside Dr #B12, New York, NY 10032 . . . 212-362-5738
Casanova, Hector: 1229 Union Ave, Kansas City, MO 60101 . . . 816-931-3736
Case, Robert: 635 W Desert Broom Dr, Chandler, AZ 85248 . . . 602-855-1959
Casey, Kathy: 3202 NE 13th, Portland, OR 97212 . . . 503-282-7063
• **Cash, Megan Montague: pg 876** Brooklyn, NY . . . **718-388-3473**
e-mail: megan@megancash.com / url: www.megancash.com / fax: 718-388-0043
Cash, Tina: 170 Tamal Vista Dr, San Rafael, CA 94901 . . . 415-457-0698
Cash, Wayne: 11777 Foothill Blvd #F2, Lakeview Terrace, CA 91342 . . . 310-473-7503
Casilla, Robert: 866 United Nations Plaza, New York, NY 10017 . . . 212-644-2020
Casmer, Tom: 597 Pascal St S, St Paul, MN 55116 . . . 612-696-1664
Casper, Daniel S: One Devon Way, Hastings-on-Hudson, NY 10706 . . . 914-478-7548
Cassano, Rose A: 253 Marcy Loop, Grants Pass, OR 97527 . . . 541-476-9074
Cassidy, Nancy: 1 Beardsley Rd, New Milford, CT 06776 . . . 860-350-3426
Cassler, Carl: 2774 S Bannock, Englewood, CO 80110 . . . 301-789-0528
Cassler, Carl: 420 Lexington Ave, New York, NY 10170 . . . 212-986-5680
Casson, Sophie: 597 av Desjardins, Montréal, QU H1V 2G2 . . . 514-899-7761
Castaneda, Teresa: 53 Pennsylvania St, Denver, CO 80203 . . . 303-744-8110
Castellanos, Carlos: 131-74 80th Ln N, West Palm Beach, FL 33412 . . . 407-791-7993
Castillon, Carly: 3805 Los Feliz #9, Los Angeles, CA 90027 . . . 323-663-4161
Castleman, Doug: 14629 Hilltree Rd, Santa Monica, CA 90402 . . . 310-454-6178
Castleman, Valerie: 60 Gramercy Park #9A, New York, NY 10010 . . . 212-254-5430
Catalano, Dominic: 68 W 5th St #8, Oswego, NY 13126 . . . 315-342-8596
Catalano, Sal: 217 E 86th St #212, New York, NY 10028 . . . 212-427-5632
Catalano, Sal: 114 Boyce Pl, Ridgewood, NJ 07450 . . . 201-447-5318
Cathcart, Marilyn: 6933 Columbia Ave, St Louis, MO 63130 . . . 314-862-2644
Caty, Bartholomew: 198 Seventh Ave #4R, Brooklyn, NY 11215 . . . 718-965-0790
Cavanagh, Tom: 119 NW 93rd Terr, Coral Springs, FL 33071 . . . 305-753-1874
• **Cave Art Studios, Inc: pg 830** 602 Leaning Oaks Dr, Savannah, GA 31410 . . . **912-898-1501**
e-mail mn@caveartstudios.com / url: www.caveartstudios.com / fax: 801-888-6615
Cavey, Bob: 710 Canterbury Cir, Chanhassen, MN 55317 . . . 612-949-2902
• **Ceballos, John: pg 518** Dayton, OH . . . **937-433-8383**
New York, NY . . . **212-966-3604**
San Francisco, CA . . . **415-285-3808**
url: www.scotthull.com / fax: 937-433-0434
Cedergren, Carl: 225 Gramsie Rd, St Paul, MN 55126 . . . 612-481-1429
Celis, Sal: 3712 NE 150th St, Seattle, WA 98155 . . . 206-366-0412
Cellini, Joseph: 501 Fifth Ave, New York, NY 10017 . . . 212-490-2450
Celmer, Steve: 353 W 53rd St #1W, New York, NY 10019 . . . 212-682-2462
Celusniak, Chris: 99 Park Ave #210A, New York, NY 10016 . . . 800-398-9544

Cepeda, Joe: 6737 Bright Ave, Whittier, CA 90601 . . . 562-693-6980
Cerebio, Carlos: 2177 Qualicum Dr, Vancouver, BC V5P 2M3 . . . 604-325-8861
Cericola, Anthony: 731 N 24th St, Philadelphia, PA 19130 . . . 215-232-6666
Cerulli, Frank: 281 Mercer St, Stirling, NJ 07980 . . . 908-580-1198
• **Chabrian, Deborah: pg 377** 89 Fifth Ave #901, New York, NY 10003 . . . **212-627-1554**
fax: 212-627-1719
Chaffee, Doug: 2233 Kemper Ln, Cincinnati, OH 45206 . . . 513-861-1400
Chaffee, James: 5400 Colusa Way, Sacramento, CA 95841 . . . 415-442-1822
Chakkour, Mario Henri: 4319 Gingham Ct, Alexandria, VA 22310 . . . 703-317-1184
Chambers, Clayton: 4900 Kesler Rd NW, Cedar Rapids, IA 52405 . . . 319-390-8881
Chambers, Gregory: 7925 W Washington Blvd, River Forest, IL 60305 . . . 708-771-3515
Chambers, Jill: 36 E 12th St, Holland, MI 49423 . . . 616-392-7274
Chambers, Lindy: RR 1 Box 7, Hockley, TX 77447 . . . 713-467-6819
Chambless-Wright, Jane: 9 Babbling Brook Ln, Suffern, NY 10901 . . . 845-368-8606
Chameleon Artworks: 1100 Fife St, Winnipeg, MB R2X 3A5 . . . 204-982-0623
Champie, Zhon: 4251 Bridger, Kansas City, MO 64111 . . . 816-936-2000
Champlin, Dale: 2405 NW Thurman St, Portland, OR 97210 . . . 503-203-8300
Chan, David: 8 Debden Rd, Markham, ON L3R 6Y6 . . . 416-513-8741
Chan, Harvey: 90 Sumach St #617, Toronto, ON M5A 4R4 . . . 416-863-5115
Chan, Pak Sing: 10219 Caminito Pitaya, San Diego, CA 92131 . . . 619-571-3361
• **Chan, Ron: pg 448,449** San Francisco, CA . . . **415-441-4384**
. . . **415-389-6549**
e-mail: ron@ronchan.com / url: www.ronchan.com
Chandler, Fay: 444 Western Ave-Engine Hs Std, Brighton, MA 02135 . . . 617-254-0428
Chandler, Jean: 385 Oakwood Dr, Wyckoff, NJ 07481 . . . 201-891-2381
Chandler, Karen: 5 Serenity Pl, South Salem, NY 10590 . . . 914-533-1177
Chandler, Karen: 1159 Green St #1, San Francisco, CA 94109 . . . 415-776-2972
Chandler, Mary: 247 Grovers Ave, Black Rock, CT 06605 . . . 203-367-6636
Chandler, Roger: 8302 Orchard Ave, La Mesa, CA 91941 . . . 619-644-9121
Chang, Alain: 232 Madison Ave #512, New York, NY 10016 . . . 212-889-8777
Chang, Charles: 227 Godfrey Rd, Weston, CT 06883 . . . 203-222-8777
Chang, Dr Rodney: 2119 N King #206, Honolulu, HI 96819 . . . 808-845-6216
Chang, George: 67 E 11th St #403, New York, NY 10003 . . . 212-388-0633
Chang, Gloria: 3739 Cogswell Rd, El Monte, CA 91732 . . . 818-579-2007
• **Chang, Michelle: pg 58,,59** 108 E 35th St, New York, NY 10016 . . . **212-889-3337**
e-mail: gerald@rappart.com / url: www.theispot.com/rep/rapp / fax: 212-889-3341
Chapell, Ellis: 89 Fifth Ave #901, New York, NY 10003 . . . 212-627-1554
Chapin, Patrick O: 5740 Eastwood Ct, Kansas City, MO 64129 . . . 816-421-7470
Chapman, CM: 411 1/2 E Huntingdon, Savannah, GA 31401 . . . 912-236-7804
2823 27th St NW 1, Washington, DC 20008 . . . 888-422-0320
Chapman, Scott: 4739 Belleview, Kansas City, MO 64112 . . . 816-531-1992
Chapmanworks: 420 Lexington Ave, New York, NY 10170 . . . 212-986-5680
Chappell, Ellis: 89 Fifth Ave #901, New York, NY 10003 . . . 212-627-1554
Charamonte, Vince: 920 19th St, Rockford, IL 61104 . . . 815-398-6657
Charlier, Mark: 117 S Morgan St #300, Chicago, IL 60607 . . . 312-421-2668
Charmatz, Bill: 25 W 68th St, New York, NY 10023 . . . 212-595-3907
Charpentier, Russ: 51 Oakwood St, San Francisco, CA 94110 . . . 415-553-8943
Chau, Tungwai: 666 Greenwich St #860, New York, NY 10014 . . . 212-675-5719
Chaussé, Monique: 4580 av Coloniale, Montréal, QU H2T 1W2 . . . 514-687-8907
Chausse, Norbert: 1709 Blue Spruce Dr, Sykesville, MD 21784 . . . 410-549-1506
Chauvin, Lynn: 344 Rosewood Ave SE, E Grand Rapids, MI 49506 . . . 616-458-5634
Chawla, Neena: 2813 Carroll Park S, Long Beach, CA 90814 . . . 562-433-4429
Chayka, Douglas: 2515 Emerson Rd, Weedsport, NY 13166 . . . 315-834-6902
Cheek, Kelly: 1243 Adams St, Denver, CO 80206 . . . 303-322-2236
Chen, David: 2149 Lyon St #5, San Francisco, CA 94115 . . . 415-921-7140
Chen, Judy: 800 S Grand Ave #A12, Diamond Bar, CA 91765 . . . 909-861-6289
Chen, Paul: 1000 John R Rd #201, Troy, MI 48083 . . . 248-583-6070
Chen, Rick: 3289 George Cir, Pasadena, CA 91107 . . . 818-578-1718
Chen, Tini: 69 Greenway Terr, Forest Hills, NY 11375 . . . 718-263-5969
Chen, Tony: 241 Bixley Heath, Lynbrook, NY 11563 . . . 516-596-9158
Cheney, George: 5002 92nd Ave SE, Mercer Island, WA 98040 . . . 206-232-7873
Cheney, Rob: 280 Madison Ave #1110, New York, NY 10016 . . . 212-545-9155
Cheng, Kevin: 10 Kelvinway Dr, Scarborough, ON M1W 194 . . . 416-495-7312
Chenoweth, Gloria: 10333 Valmay Ave NW, Seattle, WA 98177 . . . 206-789-7633
Cherington, Nina: 4347 Leach Ave #1, Oakland, CA 94602 . . . 510-482-2046
Cherkasskaya, Maria: 5620 Hempstead Rd #6, Pittsburgh, PA 15217 . . . 412-421-4399
Chermayeff, Ivan: 58 W 15th St, New York, NY 10011 . . . 212-741-2539
Chernin, Donna: 169 Central St, Acton, MA 01720 . . . 508-266-1000
• **Chernishov, Anatoly: pg 832** 4 Willowbank Ct, Mahwah, NJ 07430 . . . **201-327-2377**
e-mail: chern@usa.com / fax: 201-236-9469
Cherry, Eric: 99 Park Ave #210A, New York, NY 10016 . . . 800-398-9544
Cherry, Jim: 902 E Palm Ln #6, Phoenix, AZ 85006 . . . 602-340-0715
Chesire, Benjamin: 12166 Holly Knoll Cir, Great Falls, VA 22066 . . . 703-444-2266
Chessare, Michele: 210 Dartmouth Pl W, Peachtree City, GA 30269 . . . 770-487-8246
Chesser, Preston: 3831 Cherry Laurel Dr, Pensacola, FL 32504 . . . 904-476-4311
Chester, Harry: 20 W 20th St #404, New York, NY 10011 . . . 212-627-8888
• **Chesterman, Adrian: pg 380,381** 89 Fifth Ave #901, New York, NY 10003 . . . **212-627-1554**
fax: 212-627-1719
Chestnut, David: 2233 Kemper Ln, Cincinnati, OH 45206 . . . 513-861-1400
Chesworth, Michael: PO Box 417, Amherst, MA 01004 . . . 413-548-9393
Cheung, Phil: 2149 Lyon St #5, San Francisco, CA 94115 . . . 415-921-7140
Chevrier, Andrée: 176 Du Pinacle Rd, Frelighsburg, QU JOJ 1C0 . . . 450-298-5393
• **Chewning, Randy: pg 504** 666 Greenwich St #860, New York, NY 10014 . . . **212-675-5719**
e-mail: harriet@hkportfolio.com / url: www.hkportfolio.com / fax: 212-675-6341
• **Chezem, Doug: pg 188** , Fairfax, VA . . . **703-591-5424**
e-mail: chezemstudio@acmepixel.com / url: www.acmepixel.com
420 Lexington Ave, New York, NY 10170 . . . **212-986-5680**
e-mail: mendolaart@aol.com / url: www.mendolaart.com / fax: 212-818-1246
Chiang, George: 280 Riverside Dr #10H, New York, NY 10025 . . . 212-663-7907
Chiaramonte, Vince: 4300 N Narragansett, Chicago, IL 60634 . . . 847-670-0912
Chiba, Lisa: 4141 NE 63rd Ave, Portland, OR 97218 . . . 503-282-5816
Chickinelli, Mark: 6348 Pierce St, Omaha, NE 68106 . . . 402-551-6829
Chickinelli, Mark: 332 Bleecker St PMBK56, New York, NY 10014 . . . 212-691-2667
Chickinelli, Mark: 4 E Ohio Studio B, Chicago, IL 60611 . . . 312-321-1336
Chickinelli, Mark: 6348 Pierce St, Omaha, NE 68106 . . . 402-551-6829
Chid Studios: 115 Rumsey Rd, Yonkers, NY 10705 . . . 914-963-6997
Chinchar, Alan: PO Box 891448, Houston, TX 77289 . . . 713-922-7151
Ching, Darren: 312 E 6th St #C-3, New York, NY 10003 . . . 212-254-0963
Chipman, Annette: 8603 NE Burton, Vancouver, WA 98662 . . . 360-256-1492

ILLUSTRATORS

• **Colón, Raúl: pg 390-391** 194 Third Ave, New York, NY 10003 ... **212-475-0440**
url: www.morgangaynin.com / fax: 212-353-8538
Colon, Terry: 2200 Crooks Rd #28, Troy, MI 48084 ... 248-244-0352
Colono, Lynn: 4015 E 53rd St, Tulsa, OK 74135 ... 918-749-9424
Color Forms: 24200 Woodward Ave, Pleasant Ridge, MI 48069 ... 248-399-0060
Colorio, Lynn: 501 E Mansur, Guthrie, OK 73044 ... 405-282-1844
Colozza, Chris: 60 E 42nd St, New York, NY 10165 ... 212-867-8092
Colquhoun, John: 172 Midland Ave, Bronxville, NY 10708 ... 914-779-6965
Colvin, Rob: 1109 N Quail Cir, Farmington, UT 84025 ... 801-451-6858
• **Combs, Jonathan: pg 309** 716 Montgomery St, San Francisco, CA 94111 ... **415-433-1222**
fax: 415-433-9560
Comitini, Peter: 40 Harrison St #4M, New York, NY 10013 ... 212-683-5120
• **Commander, Bob: pg 708** 1565 W Village Round Dr, Park City, UT 84098 ... **435-649-4356**
url: www.bobcommander.com or www.theispot.com
• **Command i: pg 789** 73 Harrison St Verona, NJ 07044 ... **973-857-8110**
e-mail: smclean@command-i.com / url: www.command-i.com / fax: 973-857-8109
Commerford, Bill: 55 Delle Ave on Mission Hill, Boston, MA 02120 ... 617-445-5406
Communication Arts/Bordeaux: 129 E Pasagoula St, Jackson, MS 39201 ... 601-354-7955
Communigrafix: 1119 W Touhy Ave, Park Ridge, IL 60068 ... 773-774-3012
Comport, Allan: 208 Providence Rd, Annapolis, MD 21401 ... 410-349-8669
• **Comport, Sally Wern: pg 242,243** Chicago, IL ... **312-364-0244**
London ... **011-44-207-636-1064**
Los Angeles, CA ... **323-874-5700**
Washington, DC ... **410-349-8669**
New York, NY ... **212-333-2551**
url: www.shannonassociates.com
Computer Illus: 324 Pearl St #1K, New York, NY 10038 ... 212-571-4444
Comstock, Jacqueline: 248 Twin Lakes Village, Bloomingburg, NY 12721 ... 914-733-6781
Conahan, Jim: 822 Charles Ave, Naperville, IL 60540 ... 630-961-1478
Condon, Ken: 126C Ashfield Mountain Rd, Ashfield, MA 01330 ... 413-628-4042
Condrick, Maura: 110 Sullivan St #1H, New York, NY 10012 ... 212-966-5595
Condron, Andrew: 353 W 53rd St #1W, New York, NY 10019 ... 212-682-2462
Confer, Mitchell: PO Box 470818, San Francisco, CA 94147 ... 415-383-9026
Conge, Bob: 8600 Giles Rd, Wayland, NY 14572 ... 716-728-3424
Connelly, Gwen: 666 Greenwich St #860, New York, NY 10014 ... 212-675-5714
Connelly, Gwen: 3470 N Lakeshore Dr, Chicago, IL 60657 ... 312-943-4477
Connelly, Jim: 8964 Bosworth Dr, Jenison, MI 49428 ... 616-457-1284
Conner, Mona: 1 Montgomery Pl #8, Brooklyn, NY 11215 ... 718-636-1527
Conner, Todd: 5338 7th Ave NE, Seattle, WA 98105 ... 206-729-3460
Conner, Tom: 912 President St, Brooklyn, NY 11215 ... 718-230-0391
Connolly, Jim: 25 Cedar St, Hingham, MA 02043 ... 617-749-0825
Connolly, Karl S: 217 W College Ave, Salisbury, MD 21801 ... 410-749-5698
Connor, Todd: 5338 7th Ave NE, Seattle, WA 98105 ... 206-633-3445
Connor, Todd: 810 NE 102nd, Seattle, WA 98125 ... 206-633-3445
Connor, Tom: 912 President St, Brooklyn, NY 11215 ... 718-230-0391
Conrad, James: 2149 Lyon #5, San Francisco, CA 94115 ... 415-921-7140
• **Conrad, Jon: pg 705** Pier 33 North, San Francisco, CA 94111 ... **415-956-4750**
e-mail: cgr@slip.net / url: www.coreygrahamreps.com
60 E Magnolia Blvd, Burbank, CA 91502 ... **818-526-0075**
url: www.jonconrad.com / fax: 818-526-0080
Conrad, Liz: PO Box 257, Pleasantville, NY 10570 ... 914-747-2220
Conrad, Melvin: 655 E Market St 1st Fl, York, PA 17403 ... 717-852-3254
Conran, Kevin: 16426 Moorpark St, Encino, CA 91436 ... 818-990-0611
Consani, Chris: PO Box 1760, Highland Park, IL 60035 ... 312-222-0337
Console, Carmen: 8 Gettysburg Dr, Voorhees, NJ 08043 ... 609-424-8735
Constable, Mike: 2 Silver Ave #205, Toronto, ON M6R3A2 ... 416-530-1500
Constantin, Pascale: 5611 rue Clark #307, Montreal, QU H2T 2V5 ... 514-948-1284
Constantino, Valerie: 2037 New Hyde Park Rd, New Hyde Park, NY 11040 ... 516-358-9121
Constantino, Valerie: 165 E 32nd St, New York, NY 10016 ... 212-686-3514
Contestabile, Greg: 205-B S Haskell Ave, Dallas, TX 75226 ... 214-823-7103
Continuity Studios: 4710 W Magnolia Blvd, Burbank, CA 91505 ... 818-980-8852
Continuity Studios: 62 W 45th St 10th Fl, New York, NY 10036 ... 212-869-4170
Conway, Stephen: 140 W 15th St #2E, New York, NY 10011 ... 212-929-1986
Conway, Will: PO Box 106, Mongaup Valley, NY 12762 ... 914-583-4077
Cook, A.D.: 1700 NW Marshall, Portland, OR 97209 ... 503-241-9693
Cook, Anne: 96 Rollingwood Dr, San Rafael, CA 94901 ... 415-454-5799
Cook, Lynette: 371 Willits St, Daly City, CA 94014 ... 650-991-7106
• **Cook, Matthew: pg 491** 455 W 23rd St #8D, New York, NY 10011 ... **212-366-1893**
e-mail: sally@theartworksinc.com / url: www.theartworksinc.com
fax: 212-604-9643
Cook, Peter Simpson: 5902 Lindenhurst Ave, Los Angeles, CA 90036 ... 323-930-0889
Cook, Traherne: 1907 Eagle St, Murfreesboro, TN 37130 ... 615-895-9484
Cook, William: 3804 E Northern Pkwy, Baltimore, MD 21206 ... 410-426-1130
Cooley, Gary: 29580 Northwestern Hwy, Southfield, MI 48034 ... 248-353-7722
Coon, Jim: Pier 33 North, San Francisco, CA 94111 ... 415-956-4750
Coons, Sean: 12222 Moorpark St #205, Studio City, CA 91604 ... 818-755-9058
Cooper MD, James: 99 Park Ave #210A, New York, NY 10016 ... 800-398-9544
Cooper, Cheryl: 883 Virginia Dr, Sarasota, FL 34234 ... 941-358-9393
Cooper, Dan: 610 S Lincoln, Bloomington, IN 47401 ... 812-334-1266
Cooper, Dave: 1061 Fari Birch Dr, Mississauga, ON L5H 1M4 ... 905-271-4460
Cooper, James: 5277 Pacific Grove Pl, San Diego, CA 92130 ... 828-259-6229
Cooper, Joe: 9423 Haddington Ct, Cincinnati, OH 45251 ... 513-923-3131
Cooper, Martin: 8 Woodcroft Ave, London, England, UK NW7 2AG ... 441819062288
• **Cooper, Matthew: pg 201**Chicago, IL ... **312-364-0244**
London ... **011-44-207-636-1064**
Los Angeles, CA ... **323-874-5700**
Washington, DC ... **410-349-8669**
New York, NY ... **212-333-2551**
url: www.shannonassociates.com
Cooper, Perry: 597 Riverside Ave, Westport, CT 06880 ... 203-226-4724
Cooper, Robert T: 42 Burgundy Dr, Marlton, NJ 08053 ... 609-596-0647
Cooper, Scott: 11 High St, Cold Spring, NY 10516 ... 914-265-3228
Cooperstein, Sam: 677 West End Ave, New York, NY 10025 ... 212-864-4064
Copans, Stuart A.: 202 Putney Rd, Brattleboro, VT 05301 ... 802-257-0811
Copeland, Eric: RR #4, Cobourg, ON K9A 4J7 ... 416-342-3899
Copeland, Greg: 401 Second Ave #800, Minneapolis, MN 55401 ... 612-338-9138
Copie: 286 Oakwood Dr, Paramus, NJ 07652 ... 201-265-3405
Corben, Richard: 43 E 19th St, New York, NY 10003 ... 212-254-4996
Corbitt, John: 5688 Rushmere Dr, Virginia Beach, VA 23464 ... 757-479-1296
Cordano, Marty: PO Box BW, Bisbee, AZ 85603 ... 602-432-4634
Cordes, Kathy: 3714 Rexmere Rd, Baltimore, MD 21218 ... 410-467-8140
Corey, Brian: 18 Craigville Rd Apt10-6, Goshen, NY 10924 ... 888-287-9880
• **Corinne/Kielty, Tracey: pg 908** PO Box 6696, Beverly Hills, CA 90212 ... **800-848-9364**
e-mail: traceyart@go.com / url: www.traceyart.com
Corio, Paul: 263 First Ave #3, New York, NY 10003 ... 212-228-4630
Cork, Richard: 4848 N Clark St #3E, Chicago, IL 60640 ... 773-878-9205
Corkery, John: 1606 Dublin Dr, Silver Spring, MD 20902 ... 301-681-1641
Cormier, Wil: 918 N Pass Ave, Burbank, CA 91505 ... 818-841-8876
Cornelius, Ray-Mel: 1526 Elmwood Blvd, Dallas, TX 75224 ... 214-946-9405
Cornelius-Karp: 26 E Maple Rd, Greenlawn, NY 11740 ... 516-466-4093
Cornell, Laura: 118 E 93rd St #1A, New York, NY 10128 ... 212-534-0596
Cornner, Haydn: 58 W 40th St 6th Fl, New York, NY 10018 ... 212-682-1490
Cornu, Alain: 757A Ave Champangneur, Outremont, QU H2V 3P9 ... 514-948-5888
Corr, Christopher: 58 W 15th St, New York, NY 10011 ... 212-741-2539
Correll, Cory: 11511 Sullnick Way, Gaithersburg, MD 20878 ... 301-977-7254
Corrigan, Paul: 4015 E 53rd St, Tulsa, OK 74135 ... 918-749-9424
Corvi, Donna: 1591 Second Ave #3, New York, NY 10028 ... 212-628-3102
Cory, Larry: 1000 John R Rd #201, Troy, MI 48083 ... 248-583-6070
Cosentino, Carlo: 10752 Vianney, Montreal, QU H2B 1K1 ... 514-384-9596
Cosentino, Cira: 2277 SW Olympic Club, Palm City, FL 34990 ... 561-287-1660
• **Cosgrove, Dan: pg 538** 200 W 15th St, New York, NY 10011 ... **212-243-4209**
url: www.daniellecollignon-reps.com
Cosgrove, Dan: 203 N Wabash Ave #1102, Chicago, IL 60601 ... 312-609-0050
Cosner, Christopher: 44897 Canvasback Dr, Callaway, MD 20620 ... 301-994-9848
Costantino, Frank M: 13B Pauline St, Winthrop, MA 02152 ... 617-846-4766
Costantino, Valerie: 2037 New Hyde Park Rd, New Hyde Park, NY 11040 ... 516-358-9121
• **Costanza, Stephen: pg 530** 7 Washington St Beverly, MA 01915 ... **978-921-0887**
e-mail: leighton@leightonreps.com / url: www.leightonreps.com / fax: 978-921-0887
Cote, Danny: 31 Googin St, Lewiston, ME 04240 ... 207-783-3056
Coto, Bob: 13 Cloverhill Place, Montclair, NJ 07042 ... 201-509-8301
Cottone, Carol: 16 Phaedra, Laguna Niguel, CA 92677 ... 949-495-3664
Couch, Anna Partch: 538 Redlands Ave, Newport Beach, CA 92663 ... 714-631-3946
Couch, Greg: PO Box 77644, San Francisco, CA 94107 ... 415-381-4728
Coulas, Mick: 99 Coleman Ave, Toronto, ON M4C 1P8 ... 416-698-3304
• **Couling, Cindy: pg 879** 645 Cheshire Wy, Sunnyvale, CA 94087 ... **408-431-0675**
e-mail: info@couling.com / url: www.couling.com / fax: 408-524-5389
Coulson, David: 1107 Goodman St, Pittsburgh, PA 15218 ... 412-243-7064
Coulter, Marty: 10129 Conway Rd, St Louis, MO 63124 ... 314-432-2721
Counts, Clinton: 399 Sunset Rd, Skillman, NJ 08558 ... 908-359-5936
Cournoyer, Jacques: 6924 rue de Saint-Vallier, Montréal, QU H2S 2P9 ... 514-490-1412
Cournoyer, Jacques: 278 Hamilton Ave, Princeton, NJ 08540 ... 609-252-9405
Court, Rob: 31815 Camino Capistrano #18, San Juan Capistrano, CA 92675 ... 949-496-1406
Courtin, Thierry: 350 Central Park West, New York, NY 10025 ... 212-749-4907
Courtney Studios: 43 E 19th St, New York, NY 10003 ... 212-254-4996
• **Courtney, John: pg 755** ... **201-599-7340**
779 11th Ave #5D, Paterson, NJ 07514 ... **973-345-7652**
Courtney, Richard: 43 E 19th St, New York, NY 10003 ... 212-254-4996
Cousineau, Normand: 870 av Oak, Saint-Lambert, QU J4P 1Z7 ... 514-672-6940
Cove, Tony: 60 E 42nd St #1146, New York, NY 10165 ... 212-953-7088
Covell, Mark: 950 Farmington Ave #27, New Britain, CT 06053 ... 860-348-0699
Covert, Susan: 1134 Mendon Center Rd, Honeoye Falls, NY 14472 ... 716-624-9682
• **Covey, Traci O'Very: pg 531** 7 Washington St, Beverly, MA 01915 ... **978-921-0887**
Covington, Neverne: 208 Providence Rd, Annapolis, MD 21401 ... 410-349-8669
• **Cowan, Stephanie Dalton: pg 875** 10864 Big Canoe, Jasper, GA 30143 ... **877-792-7096**
e-mail: daltoncowan@earthlink.net / url: www.theispot.com/artist/scowan
Cowles, David: 775 Landing Rd N, Rochester, NY 14625 ... 716-381-0910
Cox, Craig: 2305 Ashland St #C, Ashland, OR 97520 ... 800-435-6509
Cox, Ed: 1147 S Salisbury Blvd #5, Salisbury, MD 21801 ... 410-548-9106
Cox, Graham: The Studio 106 Ballmeade, Ballmeade, DE 19810 ... 302-529-7177
Cox, Mari: 107 Berkeley Pl #4F, Brooklyn, NY 11217 ... 718-783-2247
Cox, Michael: 254 Sherri Dr, Universal City, TX 78148 ... 210-945-4454
• **Cox, Paul: pg 20,21** 305 E 50th St #1, New York, NY 10022 ... **212-223-9545**
url: www.richardsolomon.com / fax: 212-223-9633
Cox, Stephen: 299 Miller Rd #69, Mauldin, SC 29662 ... 864-458-8289
• **Cox, Steve: pg 504** 666 Greenwich St #860, New York, NY 10014 ... **212-675-5719**
e-mail: harriet@hkportfolio.com / url: www.hkportfolio.com / fax: 212-675-6341
Cox, Theresa: 1503 Briar Knoll Dr, Arden Hills, MN 55112 ... 651-631-8480
Cox, Tracy: 1700 Bush St #2, San Francisco, CA 94109 ... 415-673-6461
Coy, Shelley: 2108 Braewick Circle, Akron, OH 44313 ... 888-963-3278
Coyle, Laura: PO Box 5715, Atlanta, GA 31107 ... 404-370-0680
Cozzolino, Paul: PO Box 134, Rockville Centre, NY 11571 ... 212-969-8680
Crackers World: 192 Spadina Ave #510, Toronto, ON M5T 2C2 ... 416-504-4424
Cracknell, Alan: 32 Shelton St, Covent Garden, London, England, UK WC2H ... 442072402077
Craft, Diana: PO Box 831892, Richardson, TX 75083 ... 972-235-1700
Craft, Kinuko Y: 83 Litchfield Rd, Norfolk, CT 06058 ... 203-542-5018
Crague Richardson, James: 7806 Seaglen Dr, Huntington Beach, CA 92648 ... 714-969-7367
Craig, Dan: 58 W 40th St 6th Fl, New York, NY 10018 ... 212-682-1490
Craig, David: 5940 Glen Erin #7A, Mississauga, ON L5M 5W9 ... 905-826-9133
Craig, John: Rt 2 Box 2224 Tower Rd, Soldiers Grove, WI 54655 ... 608-872-2371
Craig, Mitch: 810 NE 102nd St, Seattle, WA 98125 ... 206-526-7171
Craig, Patricia: 16320 SE 15th Street, Bellevue, WA 98008 ... 425-644-5676
Craig, Robert: 612 N 2nd St, St Louis, MO 63102 ... 314-781-7377
Craig, Robert: 179 Massingale Rd, Brooks, GA 30066 ... 770-460-8438
Craig, Robert: 56 South Dr, Saugerties, NY 12477 ... 845-383-3638
Craighead, Ray: 4251 Bridger, Kansas City, MO 64111 ... 816-936-2000
Cramer, DL: 10 Beechwood Dr, Wayne, NJ 07470 ... 201-628-8793
Cramer, George: 6000 Highway TT, Marshall, WI 53559 ... 608-655-4654
Cramp, Cliff: 9620 Downey Ave, Downey, CA 90240 ... 562-862-6919
• **Crampton, Michael: pg 146,147** 420 Lexington Ave, New York, NY 10170 ... **212-986-5680**
e-mail: mendolaart@aol.com / url: www.mendolaart.com / fax: 212-818-1246
Crane, Gary: 1511 W Little Creek Rd, Norfolk, VA 23505 ... 804-423-2664
Crane, John B: PO Box 9413, Santa Fe, NM 87501 ... 505-988-5282
Crane, John B: 60 E 42nd St, New York, NY 10165 ... 212-867-8092
Craner, Ben: 165 E 32nd St, New York, NY 10016 ... 212-686-3514
Cranmer, Thomas F: 826 Bloomfield St, Hoboken, NJ 07030 ... 201-795-9734
Crawford, Allen: 25 Locust Lane, New Egypt, NJ 08533 ... 609-758-8734
Crawford, Denise: 420 Lexington Ave #2760, New York, NY 10170 ... 212-697-8525
Crawford, Emma: 110 Holly St, Cranford, NJ 07016 ... 908-497-1073

DaVinci, Ushana: 14523 Westlake Dr, Lake Oswego, OR 97035 . . . 503-973-2305
Davis Group, Michael: 420 Lexington Ave, New York, NY 10170 . . . 212-986-5680
Davis, Allen: 43 E 19th St, New York, NY 10003 . . . 212-254-4996
Davis, Bill: 50259 Barcus Cir, Coarsegold, CA 93614 . . . 559-642-3177
Davis, Carla: 674 10th St#G-F, Brooklyn, NY 11215 . . . 212-924-6464
Davis, Dennas: 109 Chapelwood Ln, Franklin, TN 37069 . . . 615-595-5580
Davis, Eric: 357 W 37th St #4A, New York, NY 10018 . . . 212-563-7626
Davis, Harry R: RR1 Box 1738, Shohola, PA 18458 . . . 717-559-7919
• **Davis, Jack: pg 62,63** 108 E 35th St, New York, NY 10016 . . . **212-889-3337**
e-mail: gerald@rappart.com / url: www.theispot.com/rep/rapp / fax: 212-889-3341
• **Davis, Jack E: pg 504** 666 Greenwich St #860, New York, NY 10014 . . . **212-675-5719**
e-mail: harriet@hkportfolio.com / url: www.hkportfolio.com / fax: 212-675-6341
Davis, James: 114 Evelyn Ave, Hamilton, NJ 08619 . . . 609-586-1169
Davis, John: 2918 Ferguson #A, Tumwater, WA 98512 . . . 206-753-8728
Davis, John: 604 Ninth St, Carlstadt, NJ 07072 . . . 201-460-7358
Davis, Lambert: 4378 Clayford St, San Diego, CA 92117 . . . 800-344-8034
Davis, Michael: 420 Lexington Ave, New York, NY 10170 . . . 212-986-5680
• **Davis, Nancy: pg 346,347** 58 W 15th St, New York, NY 10011 . . . **212-741-2539**
url: www.jdedell.com or www.theispot.com or www.nancydavis.org
fax: 212-741-4660
Davis, Nancy: 112 S Anasazi Dr, Las Vegas, NV 89144 . . . 702-228-1349
Davis, Nina: 91-B Lordship Park, Stoke Newington, London, England, UK N16 5UP . . . 1818-091872
Davis, Paul: 14 E 4th St, New York, NY 10012 . . . 212-420-8789
Davis, Peter: 59 Summit St, Arlington, MA 02474 . . . 781-646-8514
Davis, Robert: 72 Belcher St, San Francisco, CA 94114 . . . 415-621-0865
Davis, Roz: PO Box 777, Booth Bay Harbor, ME 04538 . . . 207-633-7037
Davis, Sally: 702 W Halladay, Seattle, WA 98119 . . . 206-283-3800
Davis, Scott: 19 W 21st Street #301, New York, NY 10010 . . . 212-989-6446
Davis, Stephen: 365 NE 156th St, Miami, FL 33162 . . . 305-940-9832
Davis, Susan: 1107 Notley Dr, Silver Spring, MD 20904 . . . 301-384-9426
Davison, Bill: 179 Main St, Winooski, VT 05404 . . . 802-655-0407
Dawdy, Sean: 73 Bruce St, Cambridge, ON N1R 2E6 . . . 519-623-5296
• **Dawson, Henk: pg 650,651** 3519 170th Pl NE, Bellevue, WA 98008 . . . **425-882-3303**
url: d3d.com
Dawson, Jennifer: 22 Wyandott St, Chatham, ON N7M 2T3 . . . 519-351-2323
• **Dawson, John: pg 22,23** 305 E 50th St # 1, New York, NY 10022 . . . **212-223-9545**
url: www.richardsolomon.com / fax: 212-223-9633
Dawson, John: 116 Bedford Rd #1, Toronto, ON M5R 2K2 . . . 416-926-0730
Dawson, Will: 11004 E 11th Pl, Tulsa, OK 74128 . . . 918-234-1362
Dawson, William: 9 Fieldcrest Ct, Peekskill, NY 10566 . . . 914-739-2404
• **Day, Brant: pg 445** 7205 28th Ave NW, Seattle, WA 98117 . . . **206-784-1136**
e-mail: kolea@kolea.com / url: www.kolea.com / fax: 206-784-1171
Day, Bruce: 6080 Arney Ln, Boise, ID 83703 . . . 208-853-8336
Day, Douglas: 240 Ocho Rios Way, Oak Park, CA 91377 . . . 818-879-1431
Day, Larry: 110 Rising Ridge Rd, Ridgefield, CT 06877 . . . 203-438-7307
• **Day, Rob: pg 747** 6095 Ralston Ave, Indianapolis, IN 46220 . . . **317-253-9000**
e-mail: r@robday.com / url: www.robday.com
• **Day, Sam: pg 862** PO Box 4425, Seattle, WA 98104 . . . **206-382-7413**
url: www.samday.com
Dayton, Warren: 3850 Meyers Rd/PO Box 717, Camino, CA 95709 . . . 916-644-7044
DBIMAGE: 17104 NW Countryridge Dr, Portland, OR 97229 . . . 888-577-5747
De Anda, Ruben: 890 Entrada Pl, Chula Vista, CA 91910 . . . 619-421-2845
De Blois, Danièle: 6341 rue Chambord, Montréal, QU H2G 3B8 . . . 514-274-6477
De Castro, Marion: 21 W Van Buren St, Phoenix, AZ 85003 . . . 602-252-1462
De Cerchio, Joe: 143 Hearthstone Ln, Marlton, NJ 08053 . . . 609-596-0598
De Freitas, Peter: 280 Madison Ave #1110, New York, NY 10016 . . . 212-545-9155
de Graffenried, Jack: 323 Unity Rd, Trumbull, CT 06611 . . . 203-372-6453
de la Houssaye, Jeanne: 950 Poydras St, New Orleans, LA 70113 . . . 504-581-2167
De La Hoz, D'Ann: 6995 NW 82nd Ave #32, Miami, FL 33166 . . . 305-592-6887
De Martini, Kelly E: 7124 Hemlock St, Oakland, CA 94611 . . . 510-339-7237
De Musée, Christina: 4224 Glencoe Ave, Marina Del Rey, CA 90292 . . .
de Ruiter, Eline: Het Hoogst, Amsterdam, NL, 45610 . . . 020-636-4381
de Sève, Peter: 25 Park Pl, Brooklyn, NY 11217 . . . 718-398-8099
Deacon, Jim: 373 Benefit St 1st Fl, Providence, RI 02903 . . . 401-331-8742
Deal, David: 1651 Monte Vista Dr, Vista, CA 92084 . . . 619-758-2655
Deal, Jim: 1431 35th Ave S, Seattle, WA 98144 . . . 206-325-8595
DeAlmada, Paulo: 3450 Andrew's Dr #313, Pleasanton, CA 94588 . . . 510-734-0738
DeAmicus, John: 35 S Durst Dr, Milltown, NJ 08850 . . . 732-249-4937
Dean, Bruce: 23211 Leonora Dr, Woodland Hills, CA 91367 . . . 818-716-5632
Dean, Michael: 10 E Ontario #4708, Chicago, IL 60611 . . . 312-573-1370
Dean, Mike: 2001 Sul Ross, Houston, TX 77098 . . . 713-527-0295
Deardorff, Patricia: 729 W Valerio St, Santa Barbara, CA 93101 . . . 805-682-3507
Dearstyne, John: 22820 SE Trillium Ct, Gresham, OR 97080 . . . 503-674-5386
• **Dearth, Greg: pg 519** , Dayton, OH . . . **937-433-8383**
e-mail: NY-212-966-3604 or SF-415-285-3808 / url: www.scotthull.com
fax: 937-433-0434
Dearwater, Andy: 5650 Kirby Dr #255, Houston, TX 7705 . . . 713-807-8070
• **Deas, Michael J: pg 721** Brooklyn, NY . . . **718-852-5630**
New Orleans, LA . . . **504-524-3957**
Deaver, Georgia: 1045 Sansome St #306, San Francisco, CA 94122 . . . 415-217-3301
Deaver, Lucas: 10 E 23rd St #300, New York, NY 10010 . . . 212-477-5610
DeBiasso, Thomas A: Media Arts/2501 Stevens Ave S, Minneapolis, MN 55404 . 612-874-3638
DeBro, James: 2245 Godby Rd, Atlanta, GA 30349 . . . 404-212-0155
DeCarlo, Dan: 1570 First Ave #6C, New York, NY 10028 . . . 212-879-8660
Deckado, Marshall: 99 Park Ave #210A, New York, NY 10016 . . . 800-398-9544
Decker, George: 273 E 10th St #8, New York, NY 10009 . . . 212-673-3263
• **Decoster, Jeffrey: pg 492** 455 W 23rd St #8D, New York, NY 10011 . . . **212-366-1893**
e-mail: sally@theartworksinc.com / url: www.theartworksinc.com / fax: 212-604-9643
Dedman, David J: 345 Ridge Rd, Orange, CT 06477 . . . 203-795-9009
Deel, Guy: 60 E 42nd St #1940, New York, NY 10165 . . . 212-867-8092
Deen, Georganne: 3834 Aloha St, Los Angeles, CA 90027 . . . 213-665-2700
Deeter, Catherine: 160 West End Ave #23-S, New York, NY 10023 . . . 212-486-9644
Defiebe Jr, Matthew: 940 Salem Rd, Union, NJ 07083 . . . 908-688-2536
Defino Jr, Frank: 2917 N Latoria Ln, Franklin Park, IL 60131 . . . 800-633-7887
DeFranco, Gerard R: 64 Whitestone Ln, Rochester, NY 14618 . . . 716-271-0413
Degen, Paul: 155 W 15th St #4C, New York, NY 10011 . . . 212-989-8770
DeGrandpre, Patty: 233 Hale St, Beverly, MA 01915 . . . 508-921-0410
DeGray, Joan: 3 Thyra Ave, Toronto, ON M4C 5G4 . . . 416-698-9854
DeGroat, Diane: 134 Flat Hills Rd, Amherst, MA 01002 . . . 413-253-1463
Deigan, Jim: 309 Walnut Rd, Pittsburgh, PA 15202 . . . 412-761-5666
Dekle, Merritt: 11 Kings Ridge Rd, Long Valley, NJ 07853 . . . 908-813-8718
Dekle, Merritt: 4318 Lafayette St, Marianna, FL 32446 . . . 904-526-3319
Del Rossi, Ken: 174 Sprucewood Dr, Levittown, NY 11756 . . . 516-796-7252
Del Rossi, Ric: 1133 Broadway Ste 825, New York, NY 10010 . . . 212-243-1333
Del Rossi, Richard: 8 Washington St, Hicksville, NY 11801 . . . 516-939-0256
del Valle, Ellen: 83 Walnut Ave, Corte Madera, CA 94925 . . . 415-924-7881
Delago, Ken: 6 Crest Rd, Norwalk, CT 06853 . . . 203-661-6547
DeLancey, Alison: 4610 Cloverlawn Dr, Grants Pass, OR 97527 . . . 541-471-1340
Delaney, John: 14 Castle St, Saugus, MA 01906 . . . 617-233-1409
Delano, Art: 923 Greenhills Dr, Ann Arbor, MI 48105 . . . 313-741-1370
Delany, Mary Ann: 29A Borthwick Ave, Delmar, NY 12054 . . . 518-475-0515
Delapine, Jim: 99 Park Ave #210A, New York, NY 10016 . . . 800-398-9544
DeLeon, Cam: 1819 Fisk Ave, Pasadena, CA 91104 . . . 626-797-8890
Delessert, Etienne: PO Box 1689, Lakeville, CT 06039 . . . 860-435-0061
Delezenne, Christine: 4354 Berri St, Montréal, QU H2J 2R1 . . . 514-849-2597
Delhomme, Jean Philippe: 225 Lafayette St #902, New York, NY 10012 . . . 212-941-1777
Deliantoni, Ric: 136 Freelon St, San Francisco, CA 94107 . . . 415-495-1115
• **Delich, Donna: pg 368** 280 Madison Ave #1110, New York, NY 10016 . . . **212-545-9155**
url: www.irmeliholmberg.com / fax: 212-545-9462
Delich, Donna: 889 Williams Pl, Hartsville, PA 18974 . . . 215-674-2506
Dell'Aquila, Mei Ying: 2820 Cozumel Cir, Santa Clara, CA 95051 . . . 408-246-8875
Dellicolli, Ronald E: 1 Argilla Rd, Methuen, MA 01844 . . . 508-437-9459
• **Dellorco, Chris: pg 164** 420 Lexington Ave, New York, NY 10170 . . . **212-986-5680**
e-mail: mendolaart@aol.com / url: www.mendolaart.com or www.dellorcoart.com /
fax: 212-818-1246
Delmirenburg, Barry: 301 E 38th St, New York, NY 10016 . . . 212-573-9200
Delmonte, Steve: 328 W Delavan Ave, Buffalo, NY 14213 . . . 716-883-6086
DeLong, Carol: PO Box 1936, Durango, CO 81302 . . . 970-247-8538
Delorme, Guy: 4481 rue Gatineau, Laval, QU H7T 1GB . . . 514-687-0700
DeLouise, Dan: 15 Youngs Rd, Gloucester, MA 01930 . . . 978-282-1540
DeLoy, Dee: 8166 Jellison St, Orlando, FL 32825 . . . 407-273-8365
Deloy, Dee: 217 E 86th St #212, New York, NY 10028 . . . 212-427-5632
Delton, Julie: 669 Summit Ave, St Paul, MN 55105 . . . 651-227-3848
DeMarco, Kim: 85 E 10th St, New York, NY 10003 . . . 212-253-8020
• **Demaree, Joseph: pg 861** 2538 La Miranda Dr, San Jose, CA 95125 . . . **408-297-8332**
e-mail: joe@nothingenterprises.com / url: www.nothingenterprises.com
Demarest, Robert: 87 Highview Terr, Hawthorne, NJ 07506 . . . 201-427-9639
• **Demers, Don: pg 315** 217 E 86th St #212, New York, NY 10028 . . . **212-427-5632**
e-mail: jeff@lavatyart.com / url: www.lavatyart.com / fax: 212-427-6372
• **deMichiell, Robert: pg 64,65** 108 E 35th St, New York, NY 10016 . . . **212-889-3337**
e-mail: gerald@rappart.com / url: www.theispot.com/rep/rapp / fax: 212-889-3341
Demorat, Charles J: 2621 S 376th Pl, Federal Way, WA 98003 . . . 253-874-6026
Dempsey, Diane: 675 30th Ave N, St Petersburg, FL 33704 . . . 727-822-7836
848 Greenwood Ave NE, Atlanta, GA 30306 . . . 404-875-1363
Dempsey, Kristin: 1804 Illinois St, Lawrence, KS 66044 . . . 785-749-3368
Dempsey, Paul: 731 N 24th St, Philadelphia, PA 19130 . . . 215-232-6666
DeMuth, Roger: 59 Chenango St, Cazenovia, NY 13035 . . . 315-655-8599
DeNicola, Robert: 45-49 165th St, Flushing, NY 11358 . . . 718-359-5336
Denise & Fernando: 420 Lexington Ave, New York, NY 10170 . . . 212-986-5680
Denise, Christopher: 329 Wickenden St, Providence, RI 02903 . . . 401-273-3145
Denn, Walter: 13332 Slope Crest Dr, Oakland, CA 94619 . . . 415-476-1152
Dennet, Derek: 515-A 21st Ave SW, Calgary, AB T2S 0G9 . . . 403-228-1895
Dennewill, Jim: 5823 Autry Ave, Lakewood, CA 90712 . . . 562-920-3895
Dennis, Drift: 9403 Marilla Dr, El Cajon, CA 92019 . . . 619-441-9095
Denny, Barbara: 8071 Ainsworth Ln, La Plama, CA 90623 . . . 714-527-8503
Dente, Phil: RRL Box 343, Canadensis, PA 18325 . . . 570-595-3585
DePalma, Mary Newell: 45 Bradfield Ave, Boston, MA 02131 . . . 617-327-6241
Depew, Bob: 353 W 53rd St #1W, New York, NY 10019 . . . 212-682-2462
Deponte, Fabio & Sara: PO Box 393/N Main St, Petersham, MA 01366 . . . 508-724-8823
Deronzier, Sylvie: 604 3 Rang Est app 2, Le Bic, QU G0L 1B0 . . . 418-736-8312
deRosa, Dee: 3409 Pleasant Valley Rd, Syracuse, NY 13215 . . . 315-673-2308
Dervaux, Isabelle: 155 W 15th St #4C, New York, NY 10011 . . . 212-989-8770
Desaix, Deborah: 866 United Nations Plaza, New York, NY 10017 . . . 212-644-2020
• **DeSantis, Laura: pg 531** 7 Washington St, Beverly, MA 01915 . . . **978-921-0887**
e-mail: leighton@leightonreps.com / url: www.leightonreps.com / fax: 978-921-0223
Desbiens, Dominique: 5813 Third Ave, Montréal, QU H1Y 2X2 . . . 514-712-9263
Deschamps, Bob: 108 E 35th St, New York, NY 10016 . . . 212-889-3337
DeSeta, Maxine: 202 W 107th St #6E, New York, NY 10025 . . . 212-316-3563
Deshetler, Steve: 4533 Southridge Meadows Dr, St Louis, MO 63128 . . . 314-892-6880
Design DTI/Capital Automation: 6120 Harris Technology, Charlotte, NC 28269 . . 800-BEST-CAD
Design International: 430 E 63rd St, New York, NY 10021 . . . 212-755-2321
Design Loiminchay: 390 Broadway 3rd Fl, New York, NY 10013 . . . 212-941-7488
Design Plus: PO Box 1140, Aquebogue, NY 11931 . . . 631-722-4384
Designation, Inc: 53 Spring St 5th Fl, New York, NY 10012 . . . 212-226-6024
Desimini, Lisa: 131 Avenue B #1C, New York, NY 10009 . . . 212-645-2932
Desola Group: 477 Madison Ave, New York, NY 10022 . . . 212 832-4770
DeSpain, Pamela: #10 West Side Apts, Burgaw, NC 28425 . . . 910-259-9097
Després, Geneviève: 4452 av des Érables, Montréal, QU H2H 2C8 . . . 514-527-8363
Desrocher, Jack: Rt 7 Box 611, Eureka Springs, AR 72632 . . . 501-253-6615
Detrich, Susan: 28 Carroll St, Brooklyn, NY 11231 . . . 718-237-9174
Detwiller, Darius: 22727 Cielo Visto, San Antonio, TX 78255 . . . 210-698-1409
Devaney, John: 421 Broadway, Cambridge, MA 02138 . . . 617-876-4046
DeVaney, Richard: 460 W 42nd St 2nd Fl, New York, NY 10036 . . . 212-967-6655
Devarieux, Wendy: 2105 Evergreen, Tallahassee, FL 32303 . . . 904-386-7683
Devarj Associates: 1324 Park Dr, Munster, IL 46321 . . . 312-266-1358
Devaud, Jacques: 865 Delaware St, Denver, CO 80204 . . . 303-820-2599
Dever, Eric: 2134 Aquetong Rd, New Hope, PA 18938 . . . 215-862-2091
Dever, Jeff: 1056 West St, Laurel, MD 20707 . . . 301-776-2812
DeVito, Grace: 58 W 40th St 6th Fl, New York, NY 10018 . . . 212-682-1490
DeVito, Grace: 281 Elm St, New Canaan, CT 06840 . . . 203-967-2198
Devlin, Bill: 108 E 35th St, New York, NY 10016 . . . 212-889-3337
Devries, Dave: 1352 N Formosa Ave Ste 2, Los Angeles, CA 90046 . . . 323-874-5700
Dewar, Nick: 80 Nassau St #202E, New York, NY 10038 . . . 212-964-9141
DeWolf, Holly: 137 E 18th St, Hamilton, ON L9A 4P2 . . . 905-920-8999
Dexter, Cliff: PO Box 2023, Ocean Bluff, MA 02065 . . . 781-834-0211
Dey, Lorraine: 45 Johnson Ln N, Jackson, NJ 08527 . . . 732-928-5510
DeYoung, Sheralyn: 55 North Griggs, St Paul, MN 55104 . . . 651-645-3861
Dhand, Mark: 7075 Redwood Blvd Ste G, Novato, CA 94945 . . . 415-892-7341

Di Fate, Vincent: 227 Godfrey Rd, Weston, CT 06883 203-222-8777
Di Mare, Paul: 217 E 86th St #212, New York, NY 10028 212-427-5632
Di Rubbio, Jennifer: 1500 Richard Ave, Merrick, NY 11566 516-8680212
Di Vincenzo, Mark: 61 Fordham Dr, Buffalo, NY 14216 716-873-3566
Diamond, Donna: 420 Lexington Ave #2760, New York, NY 10170 212-697-8525
Diana Sutherland Art Direction: 1061 Gate Lane, Pilot Hill, CA 95664 . . 916-933-1513
Diatz-Schlaifer, Dianna: 421 Mt Vernon Ave, Alexandria, VA 22301 . . . 703-751-4064
• **Diaz, David: pg 770** **800-474-ICON**
   1697 Robin Pl, Carlsbad, CA 92009 . . . . **760-438-0070**
   url: www.diazicon.com / fax: 760-438-0315
Diaz, Jose: 37-15 191st St #156, Flushing, NY 11358 718-886-9506
Diaz, Octavio: 235 Spoonbill Lane, Melbourne Beach, FL 32951 407-951-2900
DiBlasio, Nicholas: 207 Commonwealth Ave, Boston, MA 02116 617-266-2650
• **Dibley, Glin: pg 204** Chicago, IL **312-364-0244**
   London **011-44-207-636-1064**
   Los Angeles, CA **323-874-5700**
   Washington, DC **410-349-8669**
   New York, NY **212-333-2551**
   url: www.shannonassociates.com
DiCarlo, Chid: 115 Rumsey Rd, Yonkers, NY 10705 914-793-5220
DiCesare, Joe: 27 Sterling Pl, Brooklyn, NY 11217 718-622-4157
DiCianni, Ron: 340 Thompson Blvd, Buffalo Grove, IL 60089 847-634-1848
Diciolo, Jeff: 866 N Hilldale Ave #7, Los Angeles, CA 90069 310-854-4432
• **Dickens, Holly: pg 933** 50 E Bellevue #406 Chicago, IL 60611 . . . . **312-280-0777**
   e-mail: holly hollydickens.com / www.hollydickens.com
Dickert, Sheryl: 4603 Russell St, Salt Lake City, UT 84117 801-359-4636
Dickey, Burrell: 4975 Elmwood Dr, San Jose, CA 95130 408-866-0820
Dickinson, Chuck: 17 Hilburn Rd, Scarsdale, NY 10583 914-472-1730
DiComo, Charles: 311 W 34th St 8th Fl, New York, NY 10001 212-279-0800
Didia, Doug: PO Box 396, Bloomfield Hills, MI 48303 313-460-2451
Didier, Paul: 5855 Green Valley Cir #308, Culver City, CA 90230 310-642-2721
Diefendorf, Cathy: 420 Lexington Ave, New York, NY 10170 212-986-5680
   e-mail: mendolaart@aol.com / url: www.mendolaart.com / fax: 212-818-1246
Diercksmeier, Bob: 2512 E Thomas Rd #2, Phoenix, AZ 85016 602-381-1332
Diercksmeier, Robert: 550 E McKellips Rd #2072, Mesa, AZ 85203 . . . 602-962-4864
Dietz, Jim: 165 E 32nd St, New York, NY 10016 212-686-3514
Diez-Luckie, Cathy: 62728 Clive, Oakland, CA 94611 510-482-5600
DiFabio, Jessica: 301 E 75th St #20B, New York, NY 10021 212-988-9623
Diffenderfer, Ed: 32 Cabernet Ct, Lafayette, CA 94549 925-284-8235
DiGennaro, Robert: 10 Godfrey Rd W, Weston, CT 06883 203-454-9658
Diggory, Nick: 23 Ganton St, London, England, UK WIV 1LA 71-287-9191
• **Digital Art : pg 710** 3166 E Palmdale Blvd Ste 120, Palmdale, CA 93550 . . . **661-265-8092**
   url: www.digitalart1.com / fax: 661-265-8095
• **Digital Dimensions: pg 156,157** 420 Lexington Ave, New York, NY 10170 . . . . **212-986-5680**
   e-mail: mendolaart@aol.com / url: www.mendolaart.com / fax: 212-818-1246
Dildine, Jim: 1989 W 5th Ave #7, Columbus, OH 43212 614-486-5679
Dillon, Kathryn: 10848 Morning View Ct, Riverside, CA 92505 909-359-1481
Dillon, Leo & Diane: 221 Kane St, Brooklyn, NY 11231 718-624-0023
DiMartino, Paul: 560 Mountain Ave, Washington Twnshp, NJ 07675 . . . 212-764-5591
Dimensional Illustrators: 362 2nd St Pike #112, Southampton, PA 18966 . . 215-953-1415
Dimino Assoc, Frank: 72 Grecian Garden Dr, Rochester, NY 14626 716-225-3510
Dinamation Int'l: 9560 Jeronimo Rd, Irvine, CA 92618 714-753-9630
Dineen, Tom: 8025 McGee Ave, St Louis, MO 63123 314-827-2937
Dingler & Associates, Fred: 1805 Raleigh Dr, Burnsville, MN 55337 . . . 612-890-3122
• **Dingman, Alan : pg 457, 464** 300 E 46th St #4G, New York, NY 10017 . . . . . **212-687-6463**
   e-mail: Sari@LevyCreative.com / url: www.levycreative.com / fax: 212-661-4839
Dini, Alejandro: Via Togliatti 11, Borgo San Dalmazzo, IT 017-126-0780
• **Dininno, Steve: pg 497** 41 Union Square W #918, New York, NY 10003 . . . . . **212-807-6627**
   e-mail: dgagency@idt.com / url: www.davidgoldmanagency.com / fax: 212-463-8175
Dinnerstein, Harvey: 933 President St, Brooklyn, NY 11215 718-783-6879
Dinnerstein, Matt: 1918 W Foster Ave, Chicago, IL 60640 773-769-2989
Dinser, John: 9308 Merrill Rd, Whitmore Lake, MI 48189 734-449-5969
Dinyer, Eric: 3301A S Jefferson Ave, St Louis, MO 63118 314-773-2600
Dior, Jerry: 9 Old Hickory Ln, Edison, NJ 08820 908-561-6536
Dippietro, Hugo: 2480 Irbine Blvd #219, Tustin Ranch, CA 92782 714-832-7674
Dircks, David: 16 Dunford St, Melville, NY 11747 516-427-9377
Dirkes-Costanzo, Jessica: 2614 Bigelow Dr, Sarasota, FL 34239 941-924-7255
DiRubbio, Jennifer: 1500 Richard Ave, Merrick, NY 11566 516-868-0212
• **Dismukes, John Taylor: pg 165** 420 Lexington Ave, New York, NY 10170 . . . . **212-986-5680**
   e-mail: mendolaart@aol.com / url: www.mendolaart.com or www.dismukes.com /
   fax: 212-818-1246
Dispoto, Tony: 524 W 23rd St #4035, New York, NY 10011 973-472-4004
Ditko, Steve: 3333 E Camelback #200, Phoenix, AZ 85018 602-955-2707
Dittmer, Mark: PO Box 308, Tumacacori, AZ 85640 520-287-0160
Dittrich, Dennis: 395 Broadway #10A, New York, NY 10013 212-343-0096
• **Diven, Bob: pg 859** **505-527-4727**
   url: www.divenart.com
Dixon, David: 8 Gentry Carson Dr, Gray, TN 37615 615-283-0484
• **Dixon, Debra Spina: pg 293** 731 N 24th St, Philadelphia, PA 19130 . . . . . **215-232-6666**
   url: www.deborahwolfeltd.com / fax: 215-232-6585
Dixon, Don: 2519 Cedar Ave, Long Beach, CA 90806 562-235-1338
Dixon, Susan: 7512 218th St SW #6, Edmonds, WA 98026 425-313-8537
Dixon, Ted: 594 Broadway #902, New York, NY 10012 212-226-5686
Dobbs, Bill: 3152 Elliot Ave S, Minneapolis, MN 55407 612-823-2880
Dodds, Glenn: 392 Central Park W #9M, New York, NY 10025 212-866-7327
Dodeles, Elise: 425 Huff Rd, North Brunswick, NJ 08902 908-821-5299
Dodge, Bill: 60 E 42nd St, New York, NY 10165 212-867-8092
Dodge, Larry: 29580 Northwestern Hwy, Southfield, MI 48034 248-353-7722
Dodson, Bert: RR1 Box 1660, Bradford, VT 05033 802-222-9384
Dodson, Dale: 1255 Richfield Dr, Roswell, GA 30075 404-582-7002
Dodson, Lisa: 3028 Commerce St, Dallas, TX 75226 214-855-1264
Dodson, Liz: 1920 S First St #2002, Minneapolis, MN 55454 612-333-8150
Doe, Don: 706 DeGraw St, Brooklyn, NY 11217 718-622-0124
Doerner, Dan: 1645 Waller St, San Francisco, CA 94117 415-831-1480
Doggett, Kirk: 138 Mountain Rd, Salmouth, ME 04105 781-235-6004
• **Doglight Studios: pg 907** 600 Moulton Ave #302, Los Angeles, CA 90031 . . . . **323-222-1928**
   e-mail: dogboys@doglight.com / url: www.doglight.com / fax: 323-222-8151
Dogstar: 626 54th St, Birmingham, AL 35212 205-591-2275
Doheny, Dennis: 3772 Lincoln Rd, Santa Barbara, CA 93110 805-569-0925

Doheny, Donald: 266 Woolston Dr, Morrisville, PA 19067 215-295-7306
Dohlen, Greg: 14 68th Place, Long Beach, CA 90803 562-439-7635
Doktor, Patricia: 4118 Beck Ave, Studio City, CA 91604 818-769-7321
Dolack, Monte: 139 W Front St, Missoula, MT 59802 406-549-3248
Dolan, Paul: 3810 N Leavitt, Chicago, IL 60605 773-528-8159
Dollekamp, Ron: 33 Bendale Blvd, Scarborough, ON M1J 2B1 416-289-7155
Dolobowsky, Mena: 121 Dodgingtown Rd Box 266, Bethel, CT 06801 . . 203-748-4823
Dolphens, Tom: 3525 Mockingbird Ln, Dallas, TX 75205 214-521-5156
Dolphin-Kingsley, Kamala: 2503 NE 100th St #A, Seattle, WA 98125 . . 206-529-8377
• **Dombrowski, Bob: pg 374** 89 Fifth Ave #901, New York, NY 10003 . . . . . . **212-627-1554**
   fax: 212-627-1719
Domin, Jacqueline: 26 Monroe St, Honeoye Falls, NY 14472 716-624-3318
Dominguez, Miguel: 600 W 174th St #33, New York, NY 10033 212-928-2451
Dommermuth, Travis: 52 Railroad Ave, Yonkers, NY 10710 914-769-1487
Donahue, James: 43-11 58th St 3rd Fl, Woodside, NY 11377 718-639-8867
Donahue, Michael: PO Box 26090, Colorado Springs, CO 80936 719-591-1958
Donaldson, Phil: 702 Saw Creek, Bushkill, PA 18324 717-588-9583
Donally, Cindy: 1190 Tobler Terr, Austin, TX 78753 512-339-4607
Donato: 397 Pacific St, Brooklyn, NY 11217 718-797-2438
Donato, Michael A: 93 Navesink Ave, Highlands, NJ 07732 908-291-3119
Donelan, Eric: 919 N Howard St, Wheaton, IL 60187 630-260-1712
Doney, Todd: PO Box 1760, Highland Park, IL 60035 312-222-0337
Doney, Todd: 26 Elm St #1B, Morristown, NJ 07960 201-292-7572
Doniger, Nancy: 109 Eighth Ave #1, Brooklyn, NY 11215 718-399-8666
Donley, Scott: 2734 Rothgeb Dr, Raleigh, NC 27609 919-781-4695
Donnarumma, Dom: 81 Parkway Blvd, Ronkonkoma, NY 11779 516-588-2705
Donnelly, Martha: 434 10th St NW, Corvalis, OR 97330 541-753-3148
Donner, Carol: 501 Fifth Ave, New York, NY 10017 212-490-2450
Donovan, D B: 437 Engel Ave, Henderson, NV 89015 702-564-3598
Donovan, John: 1456 N Dayton #301, Chicago, IL 60622 312-649-9144
Donovan, Thomas: 791 Tremont St #E202, Boston, MA 02118 617-247-3237
Doody, Jim: 1010 S Robertson Blvd, Los Angeles, CA 90035 213-962-2500
Doolin, Charlie: 23 Seaview Rd, Buckie, Banffshire, England, UK AB56 . . 1542832550
Dooling, Michael: 161 Wyoming Ave, Audubon, NJ 08106 856-546-6507
Doolittle, Troy: 3925 54th St, Des Moines, IA 50310 515-276-8421
Doquilo, Jesse James: 557 Roy St #150, Seattle, WA 98109 206-282-8945
• **Doret, Michael: pg 931** New York, NY **212-929-1688**
   . . . . **323-467-1900**
   url: www.michaeldoret.com
Dorrien, John: 30065 San Martinez Rd, Val Verde, CA 91384 805-257-3905
Dorsey, Bob: 165 E 32nd St, New York, NY 10016 212-686-3514
Dos Santos, Daniel: 19 Meadowbridge Rd, Shalton, CT 06484 203-924-1652
Dothan, Uri: 37 W 20th St #1209-10, New York, NY 10011 212-255-5399
• **Doty, Eldon: pg 505** 666 Greenwich St #860, New York, NY 10014 . . . . . . **212-675-5719**
Dougan, Michael: 6207 Maridian Ave N, Seattle, WA 98103 206-527-4695
Dougherty, Mike: 110 E Sharon Rd, Glendale, OH 45246 513-772-0650
Doughman, Terry: 810 N 48th Ave #B, Omaha, NE 68132 402-551-6930
Douglas Studios, Keith: 520 N Andrews Ave, Ft Lauderdale, FL 33301 . . 954-763-5883
Douglas, Allen G: 309 Sixth St, Brooklyn, NY 11215 718-499-4101
Douglas, Dave: 6251 Ridgebury Dr, Mayfield Village, OH 44124 440-442-3283
Douglas, Steve: 52 Ashford Ct, Brampton, ON L6V 2Z1 905-452-7231
Douglas, Timothy: 1500 South Butler Ave, Compton, CA 90221 310-608-0829
Dovaston & Assoc: 51 Broadview Ave, Mississauga, ON L5H 2S8 416-278-1401
Dove Design Studio: 2025 Rockledge Rd NE, Atlanta, GA 30324 404-873-2209
Dove, Helen Greene: 335 S El Molino #9, Pasadena, CA 91101 818-449-7967
Dow, Brian W: 115 N. Marshall St, N. Revere, MA 02151 781-321-1315
Dowalo, John: 4574 Tam O'Shanter Dr, West Lake Village, CA 91362 . . 805-494-3822
Dowd, Douglas: 165 E 32nd St, New York, NY 10016 212-686-3514
Dowd, Jason: 420 Lexington Ave, New York, NY 10170 212-986-5680
Dowd, Kenneth L: 9322 Olive St Rd, Olivette, MO 63132 314-997-2655
Dowdalls, Jim: 12750 E Centralia St #128, Lakewood, CA 90715 941-865-9550
Dowlen, James: 2129 Grahn Dr, Santa Rosa, CA 95404 707-579-1535
Dowling, Mike:1729 South Wayland Ave, Sioux Falls, SD 57105 605-332-5150
Downing, Ray: 227 Godfrey Rd, Weston, CT 06883 203-222-8777
Downs, Mare: 278 Burtis Ave, Hamilton Square, NJ 08690 609-586-8890
Downs, Richard: 108 E 35th St, New York, NY 10016 212-889-3337
Doyle, Beverly: 19547 Hill Dr, Morrison, CO 80465 303-697-7936
Doyle, Mary Miller: 838 Ash St, Lake Oswego, OR 97034 503-636-5522
Doyle, Matthew: 16 Littleton Street, London, UK SW18 441819474002
Doyle, Pat: 15344 Treetop St, Orland Park, IL 60462 708-460-3059
Drake, Patti: 657 Meadow Rd, Bridgewater, NJ 088007 908-725-4254
Drayton, Richard: PO Box 20053, Sedona, AZ 86341 520-284-1566
Dreamer, Sue: 153 Clapp Rd, Scituate, MA 02066 617-545-2236
Drechsler, Debbie: 605 Wright St, Santa Rosa, CA 95404 707-579-2548
Dreher, Neil: 462 S Pennsylvania St, Denver, CO 80209 303-871-0419
• **Dreier, Kyle: pg 531** 7 Washington St, Beverly, MA 01915 . . . . **978-921-0887**
Drescher, Henrik: 108 E 35th St, New York, NY 10016 212-889-3337
Drescher, Joan: 23 Cedar, Hingham, MA 02043 617-749-5179
Dressel, Peggy: 99 Park Ave #210A, New York, NY 10016 800-398-9544
Dressel, Peggy: 11 Rockaway Ave, Oakland, NJ 07436 201-337-2143
Drew, Kim: 810 NE 102nd, Seattle, WA 98125 206-633-3445
Drew, Lionel: 199 Rouge Hills Dr, Scarborough, ON M1C 2Y9 416-281-6032
Drew-Brook-Cormack Assoc: 9 Babbling Brook Ln, Suffern, NY 10901 . . 845-368-8606
Drops Everything: 106 Cummings Ct, Antioch, TN 37013 615-333-0401
Drorack, Philip: 632 Steiner St, San Francisco, CA 94117 415-487-1923
• **Drucker, Mort: pg 426** Los Angeles, CA **323-934-3395**
   url: www.reets.com
   PO Box 1760, Highland Park, IL 60035 . . . . **313-222-0337**
   232 Madison Ave #512, New York, NY 10016 . . . . **212-889-8777**
   e-mail: gt@artcoreps.com / url: www.artcoreps.com / fax: 212-447-1475
   227 Godfrey Rd, Weston, CT 06883 . . . . **203-222-8777**
   e-mail: jp@artcoreps.com / url: www.artcoreps.com / fax: 203-454-9940
Drummey, Jack: 8 Ninth St #313, Medford, MA 02155 617-395-2778
Drummond, Deborah: 67 Concord Rd, Sudbury, MA 01776 508-443-3160
Drury, Christian Potter: 44 Spencer St, Litchfield, CT 06759 203-567-2075
Drury-Wattenmaker, Pamela: 17 S Palomar Dr, Redwood City, CA 94062 . . 650-368-7878
Dryden, Jim: 1503 Briarknoll Dr, Arden Hills, MN 55112 651-631-8480
Dryden, Jim: 1757 Fairview Ave N, Falcon Heights, MN 55113 651-631-8480
Dryden, Rod: 5855 Green Valley Cir #308, Culver City, CA 90230 310-642-2721

Dubin, Jill: 2070 Abby Ln, Atlanta, GA 30345 404-634-1650
Dubois, Gerard: 17 Pl. DuSoleil #302, Montreal, QU H3E 1P7. 514-762-5043
Dubrowski, Ken: 845 Moraine St, Marshfield, MA 02050. 781-837-3457
Ducak, Danilo: 60 E 42nd St, New York, NY 10165 212-867-8092
Duckworth, Thomas C: 10109 Rain Drop Cir, Granger, IN 46530 219-674-6226
Duckworth,Susie: 2912 Kings Chapel Rd #7, Falls Church, VA 22042. 877-815-4248
Dudash, Michael C: RR #1 Box 2803 Loop Rd, Moretown, VT 05660. 802-496-6400
Duddridge, Linsey: 1116 Church Ln, Carpinteria, CA 93013. 805-684-6258
Dudley, Don: 2029 Custer Pkwy, Richardson, TX 75080 972-761-0500
Dudzinski, Andrzej: 52 E 81st St, New York, NY 10028. 212-772-3098
Duerrstein, Dick: 22261 Kenzie St, Chatsworth, CA 91311 818-407-1379
Duffus, Bill: 1745 Wagner, Pasadena, CA 91106 818-577-7531
Duffy, Amanda: 135 Presley Ave, Toronto, ON M1L 3P9. 416-755-4447
Duffy, Bevely: 4120 Black Tail Dr, Sacramento, CA 95823 916-393-6133
Duffy, Dan: 89 Fifth Ave #901, New York, NY 10003 212-627-1554
Duffy, Ricardo: 20431 Sun Valley Dr, Laguna Beach, CA 92651 714-494-7185
Dugan, Bill: 620 S Lakewood Ave, Baltimore, MD 21224. 410-276-5307
Dugan, Brian: 24 Arlington Rd, Cranford, NJ 07016 908-497-0936
Dugan, Louise: 5046 MacArthur Blvd, Washington, DC 20016 202-966-7549
Duggan, Lee: 108 E 35th St, New York, NY 10016. 212-889-3337
Duke, W E: 26 Washington St, Newburyport, MA 01950 978-499-9280
• **Duke, Chris: pg 311** 217 E 86th St #212, New York, NY 10028. . . . . **212-427-5632**
e-mail: jeff@lavatyart.com / url: www.lavatyart.com / fax: 212-427-6372
Duke, Lawrence: PO Box 421443, San Francisco, CA 94142 415-647-5660
Dulak, Danilo: 60 E 42nd St, New York, NY 10165 212-867-8092
Dumville, Fritz: 22 Edison Ave, Providence, RI 02906 401-861-7629
Dunaway, Suzanne Shimek: 10211 Chrysanthemum Ln, Los Angeles, CA 90077. 310-470-1914
Dunbar, Fiona: 666 Greenwich St #860, New York, NY 10014. 212-675-5719
Dundee, Angela: 250 W 57th St #521, New York, NY 10107 212-397-7330
Dunlap, Leslie: 510 Robinson Court, Alexandria, VA 22302 703-836-9067
Dunlap, Philip: 332 Bleecker St PMBK56, New York, NY 10014 212-691-2667
Dunlap, Philip: 4 E Ohio Studio B, Chicago, IL 60611. 312-321-1336
Dunlap, Ronald: 600 Moulton Ave #302, Los Angeles, CA 90031. 213-222-1928
Dunlavey, Rob: 8 Front St, South Natick, MA 01760 508-651-7503
Dunn, Carl: 104 Island Rd, Dayville, CT 06241 860-779-0616
Dunn, Frank: #5 Academy St, Pine Hill, NY 12465. 914-254-6079
Dunn, Katherine: PO Box 470818, San Francisco, CA 94147 415-383-9026
Dunne, Kathleen: 3850 Eddingham Ave, Calabasas, CA 91302. 818-222-5445
Dunne, Tom: 6539 New Sharon Church Rd, Rougemont, NC 27572 919-644-1087
Dunnelly, Carol: 430 20th Ave, San Francisco, CA 94121 415-751-2889
• **Dunnick, Regan: pg 275** 250 W 57th St #521, New York, NY 10107 . . . . **212-397-7330**
San Francisco: **415-788-8552**
url: www.lindgrensmith.com
• **Dunton, Trevor: pg 764** London, UK **442077035552**
. . . . **800-379-1251**
e-mail: info@trevordunton.com / url: www.trevordunton.com
Dunville, Diane: 15309 Moysonike Ct, Lenexa, VA 23809 804-966-5756
Duquette, Benoit: 6610 rue de Lanaudière, Montréal, QU H2G 3A9. 514-270-9075
Duquette, Steven: 99 Park Ave #210A, New York, NY 10016 800-398-9544
Duranceau, Suzanne: 232 Madison Ave #512, New York, NY 10016. 212-889-8777
Durbin, Mike: 401 Janisch Rd, Houston, TX 77018. 713-694-0909
Durfee, Tom: 414 Jackson St, San Francisco, CA 94111 415-781-0527
Durham, Bob: 15 Warrenton Ave, Hartford, CT 06105. 860-523-4562
Durham, Elaine: 6027 42nd Ave SW, Seattle, WA 98136 206-966-9772
Durham, Sarah: 143 W 29th St, New York, NY 10001 212-594-0878
Durk, Jim: 43 E 19th St, New York, NY 10003 212-254-4996
Durke, Stephen: 134 North Dr, San Antonio, TX 78201 210-737-2209
Dussinger, Bill: 11 Penny Ln, Lititz, PA 17543 717-627-0257
Dutko, Deborah: 245 Roselle St, Fairfield, CT 06432. 203-579-1751
DuVal, Janee: 5009 Stanley Dr, The Colony, TX 75056 972-625-6761
Dverin, Anatoly: 9 Oak Dr, Plainville, MA 02762. 508-695-2931
Dverin, Anatoly: 58 W 40th St 6th Fl, New York, NY 10018. 212-682-1490
Dvorak, Phillip: 632 Steiner St, San Francisco, CA 94117 415-487-1923
Dweck, Michael: 22 W 19th St 5th Fl, New York, NY 10011 212-219-0600
Dye Illustration, Gregory: 7952 W Quarto Dr, Littleton, CO 80123 303-933-0340
Dye, Gregory: 307 N Michigan Ave #1006, Chicago, IL 60601 312-704-0500
Dyen, Don: 410 Parkview Way, Newtown, PA 18940. 215-968-9083
Dyess, John: 1133 Broadway Ste 825, New York, NY 10010. 212-243-1333
• **Dykes, John S: pg 618,619** PO Box 85, Fairfield, CT 06430 . . . . **203-254-7180**
e-mail: jsdart@freewwweb.com / url: www.theispot.com/artist/dykes
fax: 203-254-7436
• **Dynamic Duo Studio Inc, The: pg 130** 108 E 35th St, New York, NY 10016 . . . **212-889-3337**
e-mail: gerald@rappart.com / url: www.theispot.com/rep/rapp / fax: 212-889-3341
Dypold, Pat: 332 Bleecker St PMBK56, New York, NY 10014 212-691-2667
Dypold, Pat: 4 E Ohio Studio B, Chicago, IL 60611. 312-321-1336
Dyson, Ed: 74 Greendale Dr, St Louis, MO 63121. 314-721-5360
Dywelska, Michael: 1287 Tredmore Dr, Mississauga, ON L5J 3V5 905-823-6771
Dzedzy, John: 60 E 42nd St, New York, NY 10165. 212-867-8092
Dzialo, Joe: 410 Central Pk W #6D, New York, NY 10025 212-678-7741
Dzielak, Dennis: 350 W Ontario St #600, Chicago, IL 60610. 312-642-1241

E

EA Illustration & Design: 15544 SE 175th CT, Renton, WA 98058 425-204-9400
EADE Creative Service, Inc: 7905 Byrchmont Pl, Charlotte, NC 28210. 301-963-7335
Eagle, Cameron: 7118 Upper River Rd, Prospect, KY 40059 502-228-9427
Eagle, Joseph: 262 Miner St, Malvern, PA 19355. 610-647-5823
Eagle, Mike: 7 Captains Ln, Old Saybrook, CT 06475 860-388-5654
Earl, James: 17 Parkview Dr, Hingham, MA 02043. 617-749-7982
• **Earle, Cathleen: pg 906** 233 Mackenzie St N, Sarnia, ON N7T 6L2 . . . . **519-383-1668**
fax: 519-383-8835
Eastman, Bryant: 60 E 42nd St, New York, NY 10165 212-867-8092
Eastman, Jody: 1079 E 5290 S, Salt Lake City, UT 84117 801-685-2918
Eastside Illustration: 737 SE Sandy Blvd, Portland, OR 97214 503-235-6878
Eastwood, Matt: 32 Shelton St, Covent Garden, London, England, UK WC2H . . 442072402077
Eaton, James: 5241 N Magnolia, Chicago, IL 60640. 773-784-9697
Ebel, Alex: 30 Newport Rd, Yonkers, NY 10710. 914-961-4058
• **Eberbach, Andrea: pg 519** , Dayton, OH **937-433-8383**
e-mail: NY-212-966-3604 or SF-415-285-3808 / url: www.scotthull.com
fax: 937-433-0434
Ebersol, Rob: 734 Clairemont Ave, Decatur, GA 30030 404-687-8889
Ebert, Laura: 2705 Alexander Ave, Escondido, CA 92026 858-663-8809
Ebert, Len: 408 Levengood Rd, Douglassville, PA 19518 215-689-9872
Ebon Ursine Productions, Christopher Taylor: 344 Wayne Ave, Lansdowne, PA 19050. . . 610-259-8345
Echevarria, Abe: 153 Chestnut Land Rd, New Milford, CT 06776 860-355-1254
• **Echevarria, Felipe: pg 285** 731 N 24th St, Philadelphia, PA 19130. . . . . **215-232-6666**
url: www.deborahwolfeltd.com / fax: 215-232-6585
Eckart, Chuck: PO Box 1090, Point Reyes Sta, CA 94956 415-663-9016
Eckerman, Brian: 1410 Boundary Blvd NW, Suwanee, GA 30174 770-813-1715
Eckes, Sacha: 836 Alvarado St, San Francisco, CA 94114 415-282-7971
Ecklund, Rae: PO Box 470818, San Francisco, CA 94147 415-383-9026
Ecklund, Rae: 3 Roxanne Ln, Lafayette, CA 94549 925-283-6648
Eckstein, Bob: 680 Ft Washington Ave #8G, New York, NY 10040 212-740-8799
Eddins, George: 1249 East Blvd, Charlotte, NC 28203 704-334-4543
Edelman, Richard: 203 W 81st St, New York, NY 10024. 212-595-3654
Edelson, Wendy: 5002 92nd Ave SE, Mercer Island, WA 98040 206-232-7873
Eden, Terry: 1812 Sand Hill Rd #312, Palo Alto, CA 94304 415-328-7724
Edens, John: 99 Park Ave #210A, New York, NY 10016 800-398-9544
Edgar, Sarah: 6265 Saunders St, Rego Park, NY 11374. 718-896-2812
Edge Studio: 958 Chiswick Cir, Newport News, VA 23608 757-890-9982
Edgerton, Tom: 911 Elizabethan Dr, Greensboro, NC 27410. 910-854-2816
Edholm, Michael: 227 Godfrey Rd, Weston, CT 06883 203-222-8777
Edholm, Michael: 232 Madison Ave #512, New York, NY 10016 212-889-8777
Edholm, Michael: 4201 Teri Ln, Lincoln, NE 68502 402-489-4314
Edinjiklian, Teddy: 3850 Eddingham Ave, Calabasas, CA 91302 818-222-5445
Edison, Susan: 2768 County Rd #334, Decatur, TX 76234 940-768-2272
Edlund, Bård: 1111 Park Ave/Sutton Pl #1018, Baltimore, MD 21201 410-728-3059
Edmon, Jim: 133 Walton Ave, Lexington, KY 40508 800-530-5678
Edmonds, Laurie: 210 E 21st St, New York, NY 10010. 212-477-5693
Edmunds, David: 1312 Monmouth Dr, Burlington, ON L7P 3N4 905-332-6047
Edsey, Michael: 401 N Wabash, Chicago, IL 60611 312-527-0351
Edwards, Karl: 1109 Ripple Ave, Pacific Grove, CA 93950. 831-647-9100
Edwards, Kathleen: 1045 Sansome St #345, San Francisco, CA 94111. 888-406-0400
Edwards, Tom: 2933 W Cary St, Richmond, VA 23221 804-355-6463
Effler, Jim: 353 W 53rd St #1W, New York, NY 10019. 212-682-2462
Egan, Shawn: 201 County Creek, Ballwin, MO 63011 314-227-7770
Egan, Tim: 7453 Jordan Ave, Canoga Park, CA 91303 818-347-1473
Egas, Eric: Box 600, Greenville, NY 12083 518-966-8421
Eggert, John: 420 Lexington Ave, New York, NY 10170. 212-986-5680
Eggleston-Wirtz, Kate: 810 NE 102nd, Seattle, WA 98125. 206-633-3445
Ehlers, Gary: 20703 G Cristal Hill Cir, German Town, MD 20874 301-924-0173
Ehlert, Lois: 218 Elm Court, Rhinelander, WI 54501. 715-369-2130
Ehrenfeld, Howard: 1250 Key Hwy, Baltimore, MD 21230. 410-685-3686
Ehrenfeld, Jane: 645 Jasonway Ave, Columbus, OH 43214 614-442-8936
Eibner, Frederic: 515 rue Osborne, Saint-Lambert, QU J4R 1C1 514-672-8630
Eid, Jean-Paul: 6659 rue de Normanville, Montréal, QU H2S 2B8. 514-270-4708
Eiko, Joni: 1317 12th St #6, Santa Monica, CA 90401 310-395-1761
Einsel, Naiad & Walter: 26 Morningside Dr S, Westport, CT 06880 203-226-0709
Eisenach, Barry: 7508 Queen Circle, Arvada, CO 80005 303-424-1161
Eiser, Eric: 67 Morton St #4F, New York, NY 10014 212-206-9183
Eisler, Sarah: 16 Phaedra, Laguna Niguel, CA 92677 949-495-3664
Eisler, Sarah: 71 Atwood, Sausalito, CA 94965. 415-331-2031
Eisner, Gil: 310 W 86th St #11A, New York, NY 10024 212-595-2023
• **Eisner, Viv: pg 682,683** 157 Joseph Ct, Warwick, RI 02886. . . . . **401-884-3424**
e-mail: vivinc1@home.com
Eklund, Pamela: 384 N Windridge Dr, Round Lake Park, IL 60073 847-740-9429
El-Diery, Maged: 506 Old Post Rd, Port Jefferson, NY 11777 516-474-1094
Elberg, Eve: 60 Plaza St E #6E, Brooklyn, NY 11238 718-398-0950
Eldredge, Ernie: 2683 Vesclub Cir, Birmingham, AL 35216 205-822-3879
Eldridge, Gary: 163 South Center St, Lowell, MI 49331. 616-897-6668
Eldridgevicius, Stasys: 211 E 89th St #A-1, New York, NY 10128 212-289-5514
Electric Soup: 232 Madison Ave #512, New York, NY 10016 212-889-8777
Electric Soup: 227 Godfrey Rd, Weston, CT 06883 203-222-8777
Electro Entertainment Group: 4037 E Independence Blvd #245, Charlotte, NC 28205. 704-567-1145
Electron Spin Productions: 1244 Jackson St, San Francisco, CA 94109 415-563-3377
ElektraPress: 1320 Main St, Venice, CA 90291 310-399-4985
Eli, Michael J: 8224 La Bajada Ave, Whittier, CA 90605 626-398-3625
Elins, Michael: 353 W 53rd St #1W, New York, NY 10019 212-682-2462
Elkin, Irvin: 572 Grand St #1804, New York, NY 10002. 212-982-1804
Elle Studio: 3719 Gilbert Ave, Dallas, TX 75219. 214-526-6712
Ellescas, Richard: 321 N Martel, Hollywood, CA 90036. 213-939-7396
Elliot, David: 165 E 32nd St, New York, NY 10016 212-686-3514
Elliot, Gloria: 866 United Nations Plaza, New York, NY 10017 212-644-2020
Elliott, Elizabeth: 532 20th St NW #809, Washington, DC 20006 202-638-6009
• **Elliott, Mark: pg 205** Chicago, IL **312-364-0244**
London **011-44-207-636-1064**
Los Angeles, CA. **323-874-5700**
Washington, DC. **410-349-8669**
New York, NY **212-333-2551**
url: www.shannonassociates.com
Ellis Design, Inc, Steve: 10843 SE Mather Rd, Clackamas, OR 97015. 503-698-3142
Ellis, Brad: 11026 Tibbs St, Dallas, TX 75230. 214-692-7047
Ellis, Carl: 18 The Homing, Teversham, Cambridge, UK CB5 8SD 441223294924
Ellis, Jon: 420 Lexington Ave, New York, NY 10170 212-986-5680
Ellis, Steve: 12480 SE Wiess Rd, Boring, OR 97009. 503-658-7070
Ellis, Steve: 2031 Holly Dr, Prescott, AZ 86305 520-708-9446
Ellison, Jake: 2233 Kemper Lane, Cincinnati, OH 45206. 513-861-1400
Ellison, Pauline: 58 W 40th St 6th Fl, New York, NY 10018. 212-682-1490
Ellmore, Dennis: 3245 Orange Ave, Long Beach, CA 90807 562-424-9379
Ellsworth, Holly: 9548 Linda Rio Dr, Sacramento, CA 95827 916-364-1058
Ellsworth, Kevin: 2224 N 38th Ave, Hollywood, FL 33021. 954-967-0409
Elmer, Richard: 504 E 11th St , New York, NY 10009 212-598-4024
Elmore Illustration & Design, Inc, Jim: 13182 Trails End Ct, Manassas, VA 20112 703-590-4074
Elmore, Larry: 490 Rockside Rd, Cleveland, OH 44131 800-486-1248
Eloqui: 100 G Street, Mt Lake Park, MD 21550. 301-334-4086
Elson, Matt: 11901 Sunset Blvd #207, Los Angeles, CA 90049. 310-471-4511

Elstrott, Patty: 9604 Robin Ln, River Ridge, LA 70123 ... 504-738-0833
Elvidge, Ed: PO Box 709, SW Harbor, ME 04679 ... 207-244-5048
Elwell, Tristan: ... 212-333-2551
1352 N Formosa Ave Ste 2, Los Angeles, CA 90046 ... 323-874-5700
41 Main St, Dobbs Ferry, NY 10522 ... 914-674-9235
Elwood, Don: 24205 E First, Liberty Lake, WA 99019 ... 509-255-6670
Elwood, Paul: 334 Dunellen Ave, Dunellen, NJ 08812 ... 732-752-4315
• **Ely, Richard: pg 666,667** 207 W 86th St, New York, NY 10024 ... **212-874-4816**
eM2: 4625 Drew Ave S, Minneapolis, MN 55410 ... 612-926-0594
• **Ember, Dave: pg 477** 865 Delaware St, Denver, CO 80204 ... **303-820-2599**
... 800-417-5120
url: www.artagent.com / fax: 303-820-2598
• **Ember, Kathi: pg 505** 666 Greenwich St #860, New York, NY 10014 ... **212-675-5719**
e-mail: harriet@hkportfolio.com / url: www.hkportfolio.com / fax: 212-675-6341
Emerson, Carmela: 99 Park Ave #210A, New York, NY 10016 ... 800-398-9544
Emerson/Wajdowicz Studios, Inc: 1123 Broadway, New York, NY 10010 ... 212-807-8144
Emlen, Kate: 12 Elm St, Norwich, VT 05055 ... 802-649-2523
Emmart, Weston: 39 Hamilton Terr, New York, NY 10031 ... 212-283-3401
Emmert, Eva Ashley: 3026 Richmond Blvd #4, Oakland, CA 94611 ... 310-392-4877
Emmett, Bruce: 11 Browns Ln, Bellport, NY 11713 ... 516-286-7087
Emmett, Bruce: 217 E 86th St #212, New York, NY 10028 ... 212-427-5632
Emmons, Barbara: 504 Hilldale Dr, Decatur, GA 30030 ... 404-377-8950
Emmons, Jean: 15648 94th Ave SW, Vashon, WA 98070 ... 206-567-5458
Emmott, Gail: 3870 Easton St, Sarasota, FL 34238 ... 914-921-3842
Endewelt, Jack: 50 Riverside Dr, New York, NY 10024 ... 212-877-0575
Endicott, James: 2149 Lyon St #5, San Francisco, CA 94115 ... 415-921-7140
Endle, Katy: 609 N 48th St, Seattle, WA 98103 ... 206-625-0711
Endres, Helen E: 2506 Sixth St, Monroe, WI 53566 ... 608-328-4535
Enfield, Fred: 4 Hudson Lane, Great Meadows, NJ 07838 ... 908-637-8325
Engineering Arts: 7941 Crestway Ft #7051, Indianapois, IN 46236 ... 317-595-9955
Engleman, Jeremy: 5929 Troost Ave, N Hollywood, CA 91601 ... 818-753-9052
English, M John: 5844 Fontana Dr, Fairway, KS 66205 ... 913-831-4830
English, Mark: 539 Ridgeway, Liberty, MO 64068 ... 816-781-0056
English, Sarah Jane: 46 Chester Crescent, Georgetown, ON L7G 5W5 ... 905-702-9790
Enik, Ted: 43 E 19th St, New York, NY 10003 ... 212-254-4996
Ennis, John: 1203 Evergreen Rd, Yardley, PA 80231 ... 215-428-9094
• **Enos, Randall: pg 66,67** 108 E 35th St, New York, NY 10016 ... **212-889-3337**
e-mail: gerald@rappart.com / url: www.theispot.com/rep/rapp / fax: 212-889-3341
Ensign, Jean: 1001 Green Bay Rd, Winnetka, IL 60093 ... 847-501-5328
Ensrud, Wayne: 420 Lexington Ave #2760, New York, NY 10170 ... 212-697-8525
Enthoven, Antonia: 23 Ganton St, London, England, UK WIV 1LA ... 1712-879191
Entwisle, Mark: 42 Delavan St, Brooklyn, NY 11231 ... 718-624-1906
• **Epic Studios, Inc: pg 794** ... **908-879-6583**
e-mail: mark@epicstudios / url: www.epicstudios.com / fax: 908-879-6579
Epkes, Greg: 1001 Northway Dr, Anchorage, AK 99508 ...
Epperly's Art Studio: 308 N Maple St, Graham, NC 27253 ... 910-227-2117
Epstein, Aaron: 2015 Aspen Dr, Plainsboro, NJ 08536 ... 609-275-1034
Epstein, Edward: PO Box 1089, Montpelier, VT 05602 ... 802-229-5123
Epstein, Jason: 401 Fifth Ave 4th Fl, New York, NY 10016 ... 212-951-7220
Epstein, Len: 230 Windsor Ave, Narbeth, PA 19072 ... 215-664-4700
Epstein, Lorraine: 21 Marianne Rd, Darien, CT 06820 ... 203-656-1185
Epstein, Steve: 530 Bush St 5th Fl, San Francisco, CA 94108 ... 415-438-6014
Epting, Thomas: 330 Haven Ave #4E, New York, NY 10033 ... 212-740-4158
Epton, Amy: 1110 N Lake Shore Dr, Chicago, IL 60611 ... 312-337-4170
Epure, Serban: 60-11 Broadway #5L, Woodside, NY 11377 ... 718-335-7685
Erdmann, Dan: 3301A S Jefferson Ave, St Louis, MO 63118 ... 314-773-2600
Ericksen, Marc: 1045 Sansome St #306, San Francisco, CA 94111 ... 415-362-1214
Erickson, Kerne: PO Box 2175, Mission Viejo, CA 92690 ... 714-364-1141
• **Ericksen, Marc: pg 309** 716 Montgomery St, San Francisco, CA 94111 ... **415-433-1222**
... **800-417-5120**
url: www.sweetreps.com / fax: 415-433-9560
Erickson, Mary Anne: 1203 Glasco Tpke, Saugerties, NY 12477 ... 914-246-3804
Erickson, Richard: 666 Greenwich St #860, New York, NY 10014 ... 212-675-5719
Ericson, Nick: 612 N 2nd St, St Louis, MO 63102 ... 314-781-7377
Ericson, Paul: 3 Winnisimette Ave, Wakefield, MA 01080 ...
• **Eriksson, Christer: pg 475** 865 Delaware St, Denver, CO 80204 ... **303-820-2599**
... **800-417-5120**
url: www.artagent.com / fax: 303-820-2598
Erkeneff, Rick: 33566 Seawind Ct, Dana Point, CA 92629 ... 949-493-5019
Ernster, Scott: 853 Broadway #1201, New York, NY 10003 ... 212-677-9100
• **Ersland, William: pg 366** 280 Madison Ave #1110, New York, NY 10016 ... **212-545-9155**
url: www.irmeliholmberg.com / fax: 212-545-9462
Escobedo, Jacob: 200 Franklin Rd #V3, Atlanta, GA 30342 ... 404-303-0873
Eslinger, Kevin: 232 Madison Ave #512, New York, NY 10016 ... 212-889-8777
Esparza, Ruben: 1308 N Havenhurst Dr, West Hollywood, CA 90046 ... 323-656-5449
• **Espinosa, Leo: pg 68,69** 108 E 35th St, New York, NY 10016 ... **212-889-3337**
e-mail: gerald@rappart.com / url: www.theispot.com/rep/rapp / fax: 212-889-3341
Estioko, Mario: 5416 Havenhurst Cir, Rocklin, CA 95677 ... 916-624-3845
Estraordinaire Art, Inc.: 4316 Squire Green, Richmond, IL 60071 ... 815-678-0038
Etheridge, John: 4246 Trellis Crescent, Mississauga, ON L5L 2M2 ... 416-828-2879
Etheridge, Randy: PO Box 450173, Garland, TX 75045 ... 972-205-4666
Etheridge, Tim: Brookside, Plaistow Rd, Kirdford, West Essex, UK RH14 ... 441403820458
ETIC Studios Inc: 121 South Rd, Chester, NJ 07930 ... 908-879-6583
Etow, Carole: 18224 Herbold St, Northridge, CA 91325 ... 818-772-7501
Ettlinger, Doris: 10 Imlaydale Rd, Hampton, NJ 08827 ... 908-537-6322
Eucalyptus Tree Studio: 1745 Circle Rd, Dowlson, MD 21204 ... 410-243-0211
Evans, Bill: 7012 Iaverary Ct, W Chester, OH 45069 ... 513-755-9489
Evans, Brian: ... 800-417-5120
865 Delaware St, Denver, CO 80204 ... 303-820-2599
Evans, Jan: 5015 Clinton St #306, Los Angeles, CA 90004 ... 323-957-2327
Evans, Jonathan: 612 N 2nd St, St Louis, MO 63102 ... 314-781-7377
Evans, Leslie: 15 Bay St, Watertown, MA 02472 ... 617-924-3058
Evans, Patricia Peacock: 454 Queen St S, Hamilton, ON L8P 3V1 ... 905-529-6363
• **Evans, Robert: pg 309** 716 Montgomery St, San Francisco, CA 94111 ... **415-433-1222**
url: www.sweetreps.com / fax: 415-433-9560
Evans, Shane: 4032 Holmes St, Kansas City, MO 64110 ... 816-545-0208
• **Evans, Shane W: pg 457, 463** 300 E 46th St #4G, New York, NY 10017 ... **212-687-6463**
e-mail: Sari@LevyCreative.com / url: www.levycreative.com / fax: 212-661-4839
Evans, Sharron: 5810 Mission St #405, San Francisco, CA 94112 ... 415-239-7024
Evans, Virginia: 10 State St #214, Newburyport, MA 01950 ... 508-465-1386
Evcimen, Al: 305 Lexington Ave #6D, New York, NY 10016 ... 212-889-2995
Eve Design: 60 Plaza St E #6E, Brooklyn, NY 11238 ... 718-398-0950
Eveland, Russ: 1103 Ralph Rd, Newark, DE 19713 ... 302-737-9102
Everitt Illustration, Betsy: 582 Santa Rosa Ave, Berkeley, CA 94707 ... 510-527-3239
Everitt, Paul: 2120 S Ervay, Dallas, TX 75215 ... 214-426-6806
• **Evernden, Graham: pg 490** 455 W 23rd St #8D, New York, NY 10011 ... **212-366-1893**
e-mail: sally@theartworksinc.com / url: www.theartworksinc.com / fax: 212-604-9643
Everndern, Graham: 455 W 23rd St #8D, New York, NY 10011 ... 212-366-1893
Evraets, David: 3215 Cherrywood Ave, Bellingham, WA 98225 ... 360-734-5725
Ewers, Joseph: 1820 Old Harrisburg Rd, Gettysburg, PA 17325 ... 717-337-3785
Ewing, Carolyn: 201 E 28th St, New York, NY 10016 ... 212-532-0928
Ewing, Julie: 1818 County Rd #526, Bayfield, CO 81122 ... 303-884-4265
• **Ewing, Richard P: pg 759** 3966 Gaviota Ave, Long Beach, CA 90807 ... **888-403-1004**
e-mail: carickature@aol.com / url: www.theispot.com/artist/rewing
fax: 562-989-9539
Eyolfson, Norman: 30 Waller Ave, Toronto, ON M6S 1B9 ... 416-604-7620

F

Fabian, Limbert: 61 Marble Hill, New York, NY 10463 ... 941-350-3497
Fabian, Natalie: 5 Brookside Pk, Westport, CT 06880 ... 203-226-2398
Fabre, Jacques: 353 W 53rd St #1W, New York, NY 10019 ... 212-682-2462
Fabricatore, Carol: 16 Watson Ave, Ossining, NY 10562 ... 914-762-0376
Fahey, Gilbert: 60 Ridgewood St, Manchester, CT 06040 ... 203-647-8955
Fain, Nick: 300 Broadway #32, San Francisco, CA 94133 ... 415-398-3434
Fairman, Dolores: 58 W 15th St, New York, NY 10011 ... 212-741-2539
Falcott, Julia: 74 Elmhurst Rd, Newton, MA 02158 ... 617-964-6556
Falkenstern, Lisa: 232 Madison Ave #512, New York, NY 10016 ... 212-889-8777
Falkowski, Daniel: 38 N Landon Ave, Kingston, PA 18704 ... 215-529-0259
Falliers, Zoe Danae: 369 Montezuma Ave #387, Santa Fe, NM 87501 ... 505-989-5061
Fallin, Ken: 220 E 57th St #5J, New York, NY 10022 ... 212-832-8116
Fallon, Douglas: 50 Twin Brooks Ave, Middletown, NJ 07748 ... 201-671-6064
Fallon, Mary: 2327 30th Ave S, Minneapolis, MN 55406 ... 612-728-0908
Falquet, Joan: 763 Ninth Ave #3S, New York, NY 10019 ... 212-247-3854
Fancher, Lou: 440 Sheridan Ave S, Minneapolis, MN 55405 ... 612-377-8728
Fanelli, Carolyn: 19 Stuyvesant Oval, New York, NY 10009 ... 212-533-9829
Fanelli, Sara: Howitt Close Howitt Rd #11, London, UK NW3 4LX ... 441714832544
Fanning, Jim: 10 E 66th St, Kansas City, MO 64113 ... 816-361-5191
Faragher-Gomez, Patsy: 1198 Santa Ynez Ave, Los Osos, CA 93402 ... 805-528-4542
Farber, Joan: 630 Fifth Ave 20th Fl, Rockefeller Ctr, New York, NY 10111 ... 212-332-3460
Faria, Jeff: 937 Garden St, Hoboken, NJ 07030 ... 201-656-3063
• **Faricy, Patrick: pg 206,207** Chicago, IL ... **312-364-0244**
London ... **011-44-207-636-1064**
Los Angeles, CA ... **323-874-5700**
Washington, DC ... **410-349-8669**
New York, NY ... **212-333-2551**
url: www.shannonassociates.com
Farkas, David: PO Box 23, Amherst, MA 01004 ... 800-809-0958
Farkas, Gabriella: 841 N Kenter Ave, Los Angeles, CA 90049 ... 310-471-0990
Farley, Andrew: 32 Shelton St, Covent Garden, London, England, UK WC2H ... 442072402077
Farley, David M: 353 W 53rd St #1W, New York, NY 10019 ... 212-682-2462
Farley, Malcolm: 13061 W 29th Ave, Golden, CO 80401 ... 303-278-7890
Farley, Malcolm: 4 E Ohio Studio B, Chicago, IL 60611 ... 312-321-1336
Farley, Malcolm: 332 Bleecker St, New York, NY 10014 ... 212-691-2667
San Francisco, CA ... 415-543-6056
Farmer, Tom: 2505 Kennedy St NE, Minneapolis, MN 55413 ... 800-659-2001
Farnham, Joe: The Hall-Haskell House/ 36 S Main St, Ipswich, MA 01938 ... 978-356-2350
Farr, Laura: 96 Ballardvale Rd, Andover, MA 01810 ... 978-475-5738
Farrell, Anne: 131 Huddleson, Santa Fe, NM 87501 ... 505-983-5126
Farrell, Marybeth: 320 Highwood Ave, Tenafly, NJ 07670 ... 201-569-1299
Farrell, Richard: 3918 N Stevens, Tacoma, WA 98407 ... 253-752-8814
Farrell, Rick:, PO Box 1760, Highland Park, IL 60035 ... 312-222-0337
Los Angeles, CA ... 213-934-3395
Farrell, Russell: 353 W 53rd St #1W, New York, NY 10019 ... 212-682-2462
Farrell, Sean: 5030 Stevens Ave, Minneapolis, MN 55419 ... 612-822-6865
• **Farrington, Susan: pg 409** 6 Parker Rd, Arlington, MA 02474 ... **781-641-2787**
e-mail: lilla@rcn.com / url: www.lillarogers.com / fax: 781-641-2244
Farris, Dan: 2233 Kemper Ln, Cincinnati, OH 45206 ... 513-861-1400
• **Farris, Jason: pg 427, Front Flap Representatives' Book** 227 Godfrey Rd, Weston, CT 06883 **203-222-8777**
e-mail: jp@artcoreps.com / url: www.artcoreps.com / fax: 203-454-9940
232 Madison Ave #512, New York, NY 10016 ... **212-889-8777**
e-mail: gt@artcoreps.com / url: www.artcoreps.com / fax: 212-447-1475
Fasen, Gary: 4316 Squire Green Dr, Richmond, IL 60071 ... 815-678-0038
Fasolino, Peter: 100 President St, Brooklyn, NY 11231 ... 718-834-6276
• **Fast, Ingo: pg 713** 25 Broadway, Brooklyn, NY 11211 ... **718-387-9570**
e-mail: ingo@ingofast.com / url: www.ingofast.com / fax: 718-387-5970
Fast, Judith: 33-68 21st St, Long Island City, NY 11106 ... 718-721-5426
Fath, Carolyn: 221 N Hillside Terr, Madison, WI 53705 ... 608-233-8521
Faucher, Virginie: 4667 rue Hutchinson, Montréal, QU H2V 4A2 ... 514-271-8105
Faulk, Claudia: 1445 Fern Pl, Vista, CA 92083 ... 619-945-6576
• **Faulkner, Andrew: pg 823** 1207 Bridgeway #B1, Sausalito, CA 94965 ... **415-332-3521**
e-mail: andrew@afstudio.com / url: www.afstudio.com
Faulkner, BJ: 63 Hawthorne St, Lenox St, MA 01240 ... 413-637-4951
Faulkner, David: 6209 Academy Ridge Dr, Albuquerque, NM 87111 ... 505-296-5944
Faulkner, Martin: 22 Highgate Grove, Sawbridgeworth, Hartfordshire, UK CM21 ... 01279726755
Faulkner, Matt: PO Box 61, Birmingham, MI 48012 ... 248-549-7010
Faure, Renee: 600 Second St, Neptune Beach, FL 32233 ... 904-246-2781
Faust, Clifford: 322 W 57th St #42P, New York, NY 10019 ... 212-581-9461
Faust, Leslie A: 49 North Gore, St Louis, MO 63119 ... 314-918-0464
Fauver, Chris: 601 Oak Haven Dr, Falls Church, VA 22046 ... 703-538-4291
Favreau, Marie-Claude: 7779 rue Drolet, Montréal, QU H2R 2C8 ... 514-274-9644
Favreau, Mark: PO Box 131, East Middlebury, VT 05740 ... 802-388-0041
Faw, Andrew M: 29 W 19th St 4th Fl, New York, NY 10011 ... 212-260-5602
Faw, Jenny: 29 W 19th St 4th Fl, New York, NY 10011 ... 212-633-9063
Fay, Jon-Paul: 3235 S Park Rd, Aurora, CO 80014 ... 303-750-2045
Fay, Michael: 8 Thomas Rd, Lynnfield, MA 01940 ... 617-334-2784

FeBland, David: 670 West End Ave #11B, New York, NY 10025 ... 212-580-9299
Feeney, Betsy: PO Box 257, Pleasantville, NY 10570 ... 914-747-2220
Fehlau, Dagmar: PO Box 288, Westport, NY 12993 ... 518-962-2348
Fei, Xing: 402 E 90th St, New York, NY 10128 ... 212-828-7427
Feigenbaum, Joseph: 1 Bridge St, Irvington, NY 10533 ... 914-591-5911
Feigus, Jan: Box 207, Hatboro, PA 19040 ... 215-957-9395
Feild, Ann Rebecca: 714 E 33rd St, Baltimore, MD 21218 ... 410-235-0240
Feinen, Jeff: 4702 Sawmill Rd, Clarence, NY 14031 ... 716-759-8406
Feingold, Ken: 140 Fifth Ave, New York, NY 10011 ... 212-645-9485
Feininger: 5 E 22nd St, New York, NY 10010 ... 212-533-4984
Feldhaus, Anne Leuck: 2156 N Oakley, Chicago, IL 60647 ... 773-772-1085
• **Feldman, Daniel: pg 878** 11911 Magnolia Blvd #39, N Hollywood, CA 91607 ... **818-760-1759**
e-mail: daniel@ogdemlifeldman.com / url: www.ogdemlifeldman.com / fax: 818-760-1582
Feldman, Joey: 1139 Titan St, Philadelphia, PA 19147 ... 215-551-1960
• **Felker, Robert: pg 414** 7118 Upper River Rd, Prospect, KY 40059 ... **502-228-9427**
url: www.jettreps.com / fax: 502-228-8857
Fell, Dan: 420 Lexington Ave, New York, NY 10170 ... 212-986-5680
Toronto, ON ... **416-699-1525**
• **Fellman, Lynn/Fellman Studio Inc: pg 680,681** 7958 Island Rd, Eden Prairie, MN 55347 ... **952-975-0296**
e-mail: lynn@fellmanstudio.com / url: www.fellmanstudio.com or www.theispot.com/artist/fellman / fax: 952-975-0297
Fellows, Kara: 901 Rider St, Iowa City, IA 52246 ... 319-337-9571
Fellows, Stan Olson: 756 8th Ave S, Naples, FL 34102 ... 941-403-4393
Feltenstein, Keith: 144-10 38th Ave, Flushing, NY 11354 ... 718-359-5140
• **Fennimore, Linda: pg 634,635** 808 West End Ave #801, New York, NY 10025 **212-866-0279**
• **Fenster, Diane: pg 676,677** 1015-B Battery St, San Francisco, CA 94111 ... **415-398-9121**
e-mail: fredarep@earthlink.net / url: www.dianefenster.com / fax: 415-398-6136
Fequire, Paul-Emile: 555 Monica Rd Crl #725, Apopka, FL 32703 ... 407-772-0081
Ferguson, Heleman: 10512 Pilla Terra Ct/Warfld Fr, Laurel, MD 20723 ... 301-604-4270
Ferlic, Lisa Marie: 102 N 62nd St #B, Seattle, WA 98103 ... 206-784-7141
Fernandes, Stanislaw: 874 Broadway #305, New York, NY 10003 ... 212-533-2648
Fernandez, Jacobson: 141-10 28th St, Flushing, NY 11354 ... 212-206-0066
Fernandez, Luis: 731 Stovall Blvd NE, Atlanta, GA 30342 ... 800-791-1189
Ferran, Raul: 700 Victory Blvd #11A, Staten Island, NY 10301 ... 718-556-2300
Ferrato, Donna: 25 Lenard St, New York, NY 10013 ... 212-367-7004
Ferreira, Melissa: 231 Nayatt Rd, Barrington, RI 02806 ... 401-245-8438
Ferretti, James: 401 Oak Dr, Harleysville, PA 19438 ... 215-513-0355
Ferris, Keith: 50 Moraine Rd, Morris Plains, NJ 07950 ... 201-539-3363
Ferro, Sam: 700 North Illinois St, Arlington, VA 22205 ... 703-527-2503
Ferrulli, Dan: 7953 Kimlough Dr, Indianapolis, IN 46240 ... 317-257-5438
Ferry, John: 3002 N Calvert, Baltimore, MD 21218 ... 410-467-3725
Fervoy, John: 1331 Monroe St, Evanston, IL 60202 ... 847-869-9886
Feuereisen, Fernando: 885 Tenth Ave #2G, New York, NY 10019 ... 212-399-3269
Field, Ann: 53 W Jackson Blvd, Chicago, IL 60604 ... 312-435-0055
Field, Ann: 325 Wilson Way, Larkspur, CA 94939 ... 415-927-4500
Field, Ann: 137 W 14th St #204, New York, NY 10011 ... 212-337-0055
Field, Ann: 2910 16th St, Santa Monica, CA 90405 ... 310-450-6413
Field, Bob: 17 Cranston St, Jamaica Plains, MA 02130 ... 617-983-3230
Field, Lori Nelson: 8 Garden St, Montclair, NJ 07042 ... 201-783-1321
• **Fielder, Joseph: pg 256** 250 W 57th St #521, New York, NY 10107 ... **212-397-7330**
San Francisco: ... **415-788-8552**
url: www.lindgrensmith.com
Fields, Cathy: 5111 So Orcas St, Seattle, WA 98118 ... 206-725-9192
Fields, Gary: 30 Allen Dr, Wayne, NJ 07470 ... 973-633-8060
Fifield, Lew: 1300 W Mt Royal-Visual Comms, Baltimore, MD 21217 ... 410-225-2239
Fijal, Ted: 121 Carriage Rd, Chicopee, MA 01013 ... 413-532-7334
Fike, Scott: 1200 E Colorado Blvd Studio B, Pasadena, CA 91106 ... 818-405-9219
Filanovsky, Serge: 275 Clinton Ave #3-6, Brooklyn, NY 11205 ... 718-789-1747
Filipas, Mark: 3439 NE Sandy Blvd PMB 363, Portland, OR 97232 ... 503-281-7385
Filippone, Danny: 62 W 39th St #803, New York, NY 10018 ... 212-730-4898
Filippucci, Sandra: 455 W 23rd St #8D, New York, NY 10011 ... 212-366-1893
Filippucci, Sandra: 433 Kent Cornwall Rd #29, Kent, CT 06757 ... 860-927-1101
Fillbach, Jeff: 22 Morning Breeze, Irvine, CA 92612 ... 949-854-6322
Filler Scott, Jeanne: 8641 County Rd #159, Kaufman, TX 75142 ... 972-962-5923
Film Roman Animation: 420 Lexington Ave, New York, NY 10170 ... 212-986-5680
Findley, John: 500 Stanyan St #105, San Francisco, CA 94117 ... 415-386-7292
Finewood, Bill: 109 Highland Ave, Newark, NY 14513 ... 315-331-2905
Finger, John: 1241 Mountain View Blvd, Walnut Creek, CA 94596 ... 925-945-0612
Finger, Matthew: 107 Elmgrove Ave #2, Providence, RI 02906 ... 401-421-0581
Finger, Ronald: 58 W 40th St 6th Fl, New York, NY 10018 ... 212-682-1490
Finkbeiner, Robert: 733 Brafferton Dr, Pittsburgh, PA 15228 ...
Finlay, Steve: 1059 Fairfax Circle W, Lantana, FL 33462 ... 561-965-4728
Finley, Traci: 915 S Bedford St #6, Los Angeles, CA 90035 ... 310-652-6421
Finocchi, Ilena: PO Box 670, N. Lima, OH 44452 ... 330-549-2466
Fiore, Mark: 972 Guerrero St, San Francisco, CA 94110 ... 415-824-5192
• **Fiore, Peter: pg 379** 89 Fifth Ave #901, New York, NY 10003 ... **212-627-1554**
fax: 212-627-1719
Fiorentino, James: 39 Treetop Rd, Middlesex, NJ 08846 ... 888-788-3664
Firchow, Steve: 1410 Wellesley Ave #107, Los Angeles, CA 90025 ... 310-826-9858
Fire, Richard: 1708 Linden Ave, Venice, CA 90291 ... 213-848-8041
Firestone, Bill: 14027 Memorial #125, Houston, TX 77079 ... 281-579-3220
Firestone, Bill: 4810 Bradford Dr, Annandale, VA 22003 ... 703-354-0247
Fisari, Frank: 240 W 38th St, Ny, NY 10018 ... 212-840-3211
Fisch, Amy: 718 Broadway, New York, NY 10003 ... 212-677-3509
Fisch, Nora: 140 5th Ave #5A, New York, NY 10011 ... 212-645-9485
Fisch, Paul: 5111 Coffee Tree Ln, N Syracuse, NY 13212 ... 315-451-8147
Fischer, Gini Frank: 129 Chestnut Ridge Rd, Bethel, CT 06801 ... 203-798-8696
Fischer, Hannelore: 25 Plane Ave, Woodland, CA 95695 ... 916-666-6957
• **Fishauf, Louis: pg 353** 58 W 15th St, New York, NY 10011 ... **212-741-2539**
url: www.jdedell.com or www.theispot.com or www.fishauf.com / fax: 212-741-4660
Fisher, Bob: 6703 Woodcrest Dr, Austin, TX 78759 ... 512-918-0636
Fisher, Cynthia: RFD Box 87B, Charlemont, MA 01339 ... 413-625-8204
Fisher, Debby: 597 Palo Verde Way, Central Point, OR 97502 ... 541-665-2034
Fisher, Hyman W: 121 E Northfield Rd, Livingston, NJ 07039 ... 201-994-9480
Fisher, Jeanne: 70 Ash St, Piermont, NY 10968 ... 914-398-1739
Fisher, Jeffrey: 155 W 15th St #4C, New York, NY 10011 ... 212-989-8770
Fisher, Mark S: 474 Beacon St, Lowell, MA 01850 ... 978-459-2736
• **Fisher, Michael: pg 474** 865 Delaware St, Denver, CO 80204 ... **303-820-2599**
e-mail: 800-417-5120 / url: www.artagent.com / fax: 303-820-2598
Fisher, Reed: 2866 Via Bellota, San Clemente, CA 92673 ... 714-498-0634
Fisher, Shell: PO Box 152, Carmel, CA 93921 ... 831-659-8272
Fishman, Ben: 1492 Jackson St, San Francisco, CA 94109 ... 415-673-2731
Fiske, ML: 181 Baltic St, Brooklyn, NY 11201 ... 718-855-1650
Fitch, Tony: 3620 Queen Mary Dr, Olney, MD 20832 ... 301-924-0642
Fitting, Cynthia: 1015-B Battery St, San Francisco, CA 94111 ... 415-398-9121
Fitting, Cynthia: PO Box 695, Ross, CA 94957 ... 415-454-0937
Fitz-Maurice, Jeff: 217 E 86th St #212, New York, NY 10028 ... 212-427-5632
Fitz-Maurice, Jeff: 1098 Cooper Rd, Newtown, PA 18940 ... 215-493-4755
Fitzgerald, Barry: 1334 N 1750 Rd, Lawrence, KS 66044 ... 785-841-2983
Fitzgerald, Patrick: 45 Rivercourt Blvd, Toronto, ON M4J 3A3 ... 416-429-2512
Fitzgerald, Royce: 11936 W Jefferson Blvd #C, Culver City, CA 90230 ... 310-390-8663
Fitzgerrell-Smith, Lee: 1815 Woodsman Ct, Placerville, CA 95667 ... 530-626-8113
Fitzpatrick Pinkman, Ellen: 22 Elm Ave, Hackensack, NJ 07601 ... 201-342-4034
Fjelstrom, Gustaf: 5094 Moorpark Ave, San Jose, CA 95129 ... 408-253-6680
Flagg, Holley: 103 E 84th St #5A, New York, NY 10028 ... 212-734-5790
Flaherty, David: 1 Union Square W #712, New York, NY 10003 ... 212-675-2038
Flakenham, Debi: 27 Pershing Ave, Seymour, CT 06483 ... 203-888-5051
Flaming, Jon: 3922 Gilbert Ave #106, Dallas, TX 75219 ... 214-526-2020
Flanagan, Sean: 608 York St, San Francisco, CA 94110 ... 415-641-1285
Flanders, Phil: 948 Straphinge Trail, Stone Mountain, GA 30083 ... 404-292-1806
Flatland: 1128 Ocean Park Blvd #314, Santa Monica, CA 90405 ... 310-394-0322
Flax, Carol: 5555 W Lazy C Dr, Tucson, AZ 85745 ... 520-743-8599
Fleischer, Pat: 223 Katherine St, Scotch Plains, NJ 07076 ... 908-889-9059
Fleisher, Audrey: 430 W 24th St, New York, NY 10011 ... 212-463-3722
Fleishman, Michael: 247 Whitehall Dr, Yellow Springs, OH 45387 ... 937-767-7955
Fleming, Brian: 229-48 129th Ave, Laurelton, NY 11413 ... 718-276-5533
Fleming, Dean: 3262 N Raymond Ave, Altadena, CA 91001 ... 626-791-1830
Fleming, Joe: 52 Stewart St, Toronto, ON M5V 1H6 ... 416-504-9488
Fleming, Ron: 58 W 40th St 6th Fl, New York, NY 10018 ... 212-682-1490
Fleming, Thomas: 10 E Sixth Ave, Conshocken, PA 19428 ... 610-940-2300
Flesher, Vivienne: 71 Atwood Ave, Sausalito, CA 94965 ... 415-921-2440
Flett, David: 23 R Atlantic Ave, Toronto, ON M6C 3E7 ... 416-516-4649
Flewellen, Neal: 247 Manhattan Ave, Brooklyn, NY 11211 ... 718-486-5133
• **Flint, Mike: pg 850** 20 Levesque Ln, Mount Vernon, NH 03057 ... **603-673-6234**
e-mail: maflint@mindspring.com / fax: 603-673-6234
Flock-Lempa, Mary: 612 N 2nd St, St Louis, MO 63102 ... 314-781-7377
Flood, Richard: 1603 Sheridan Rd, Champaign, IL 61821 ... 217-352-8356
Florczak, Robert: 2510G Las Posas Rd #431, Camarillo, CA 93010 ... 805-529-8111
Florentina: 20 New Port Way, Thornhill, ON L3T 5G4 ... 905-707-7629
• **Fluharty, Thomas: pg 457, 462:** 300 E 46th St #4G, New York, NY 10017 ... **212-687-6463**
url: www.levycreative.com / fax: 212-661-4839
Flynn, Bob: 131 Barrow #4A, New York, NY 10003 ... 212-741-2419
Flynn, Heather: 2 Ferdinand St, Stoneham, MA 02180 ... 617-665-8644
Flynn, Maura C: 242-09 43rd Ave, Douglaston, NY 11363 ... 718-279-1659
Foerster, John: 419 Hastings Pl, Martinez, GA 30907 ... 706-651-0774
Fog, Michael: 285 Place Youville #55, Montreal, QU H2Y 2A4 ... 514-845-9555
Foge, Kurt: 8422 Singapore Ct, Orlando, FL 32817 ... 407-657-0595
Fogle, David W: 2372 Wooster Rd #4, Cleveland, OH 44116 ... 216-521-2854
• **Fogle, Jamie: pg 531** 7 Washington St, Beverly, MA 01915 ... **978-921-0887**
e-mail: leighton@leightonreps.com / url: www.leightonreps.com / fax: 978-921-0223
Foley, Don: 720 Compton Crl, Cummings, GA 30040 ... 770-205-4121
Fondersmith, Mark: 3070 Lindsey Ct, Ijamsville, MD 21754 ... 410-290-8127
Fong, Linda: PO Box 37394, Honolulu, HI 96837 ... 808-526-0836
Fong, Tina: 5104 26th Ave NE, Seattle, WA 98105 ... 206-526-6147
Foran, Bob: 401 Columbus Ave, Valhalla, NY 10595 ... 914-747-1500
Forbes, Bart: 5510 Nakoma Dr, Dallas, TX 75209 ... 214-357-8077
Ford, Andrew: 57 Mountfort St, Portland, ME 04101 ... 207-774-9386
Ford, Cindy: PO Box 521180, Tulsa, OK 74152 ... 918-743-3673
Ford, Dan: 225 N Gay Ave, Clayton, MO 63105 ... 314-862-3005
Forder, Nicholas: "Delphi," Albert Rd, Hedge End, Southhampton, ENG, UK SO30 ... 441489798435
Fordesign Marketing: Bridgeport, CT ... 203-336-3999
Foreman, Michael: PO Box 1062, Bayonne, NJ 07002 ... 201-436-4362
Forest, Crista: 60 E 42nd St, New York, NY 10165 ... 212-867-8092
Forgus, Rick: 8120 E Montebello Ave, Scottsdale, AZ 85250 ... 520-483-7609
• **Forkish, Karen: pg 706** ... **888-686-8863**
e-mail: karen@forkish.com / url: www.forkish.com
• **Forney, Steve : pg 724** 3830 Harrison St #101, Oakland, CA 94611 ... **510-653-4523**
url: www.steveforney.com / fax: 510-653-6506
Forrest, William: 1027 12th St #A, Santa Monica, CA 90403 ... 310-458-9114
Forslund, Kathy: 400 First Ave N #218, Minneapolis, MN 55401 ... 612-375-9598
Forte, Joseph: 17 Parsonage Rd, E Setauket, NY 11733 ... 516-941-3641
Fortune, John: 3033 13th Ave W, Seattle, WA 98119 ... 206-284-4701
Foss/Camp Graphics, Patrick: 3826 Martha Ln., Dallas, TX 75229 ... 214-352-7894
Foster Inc, Stephen: 894 Grove St, Glencoe, IL 60022 ... 847-835-2741
Foster, B Lynn: 309 W 100th St #1, New York, NY 10025 ... 212-866-1895
Foster, Jack: 835 Birch Ave, Downers Grove, IL 60515 ... 630-769-1232
• **Foster, Jeff: pg 889** 652 B Ave, Lake Oswego, OR 97034 ... **503-636-4980**
e-mail: artstuff@aracnet.com / url: www.jefffoster.com
Foster, Matt: 200 W 15th St, New York, NY 10011 ... 212-243-4209
Foster, Matt: PO Box 5366, Carefree, AZ 85377 ... 480-595-7950
Foster, Patricia: 32 W 40th St #2J, New York, NY 10018 ... 212-575-6887
• **Foster, Phil: pg 70,71** 108 E 35th St, New York, NY 10016 ... **212-889-3337**
e-mail: gerald@rappart.com / url: www.theispot.com/rep/rapp / fax: 212-889-3341
Foster, Stephen: 894 Grove St, Glencoe, IL 60022 ... 847-835-2741
Foster, Susan: 4800 Chevy Chase Dr #500, Chevy Chase, MD 20815 ... 301-652-3848
Foster, Travis: PO Box 470818, San Francisco, CA 94147 ... 415-383-9026
Foster, Travis: 2420 Crocker Springs Rd, Goodlettsville, TN 37072 ... 615-227-0895
Fotheringham, Ed: 1809 7th Ave #1710, Seattle, WA 98101 ... 206-447-1600
Fotis, Evan: 59 Themistocleous St Alimos 17455, Athens, GR ... 30-1-9810884
Foty, Tom: 3836 Shady Oak Rd, Minnetonka, MN 55305 ... 952-933-5570
Foulke, Nancy Pelham: 4243 Sucia Dr, Ferndale, WA 980248 ... 360-312-0248
• **Fountain, Linda: pg 725** 8 Windham Hill, Mendon, NY 14506 ... **716-624-1405**
fax: 716-624-2624
Fournier, Jeff: 170 N Ridgeland, Oak Park, IL 60302 ... 708-848-2756
Fournier, Joe: 170 N Ridgeland, Oak Park, IL 60302 ... 708-848-2756
Fowler, Ann: 475 Candler St NE, Atlanta, GA 30307 ... 404-688-4730
Fowler, Geoffrey Stewart: 234 E 14th St #4A, New York, NY 10003 ... 212-387-0885
Fowler, M Farkas: PO Box 230486, Anchorage, AK 99523 ... 907-563-4175

Gardner, Mike: 37 Buckmaster Rd, Westwood, MA 02090 617-762-0906
Gardner, Stephen: 89 Fifth Ave #901, New York, NY 10003 212-627-1554
Gardner, Terry: 431 E Dakota Ave, Denver, CO 80209 303-744-6730
Gardos, Susan: 469 Queen St #102, Toronto, ON M5A 1T7 416-867-9345
Garland, Bill: 353 W 53rd St #1W, New York, NY 10019 212-682-2462
• **Garland, Michael: pg 806** 79 Manor Rd , Patterson, NY 12563 . . . . **845-878-4347**
e-mail: garlandmp@aol.com / url: www.bestweb.net/~artmtn/ / fax: 845-878-4349
Garner, David: 311 W 97th St #7E, New York, NY 10025 212-663-9548
Garner, Hjordis: 1834 Lincoln Park W, Chicago, IL 60614 312-664-8673
• **Garns, Allen: pg 576,577** 611 S Loma Vista Cir, Mesa, AZ 85204 . . . . **480-854-3121**
url: www.theispot.com/artist/agarns / fax: 480-218-9084
Garon, David: 409 W Maryland St, Duluth, MN 55803 218-724-3020
Garramone, Richard: 49 Ridgedale Ave #201, East Hanover, NJ 07936. 201-887-7234
Garret, Inc, The: 9322 Olive Blvd, St Louis, MO 63132 314-997-2655
Garrett, John: 8529 N 62nd St, Brown Deer, WI 53223 414-355-8319
Garrett, Tom: 623 3rd Ave SE, Minneapolis, MN 55414 612-331-3123
Garrett, Tom: 756 8th Ave S, Naples, FL 34102 941-403-4393
Garrick, Jacqueline: 333 E 75th St, New York, NY 10021 212-628-1018
Garrido, Hector: 420 Lexington Ave, New York, NY 10170 212-986-5680
Garrison, Barbara: 12 E 87th St, New York, NY 10128 212-348-6382
• **Garrity, Bruce: pg 291** 731 N 24th St, Philadelphia, PA 19130 . . . . **215-232-6666**
url: www.deborahwolfeltd.com / fax: 215-232-6585
Garrity, Dennis: 8443 Michael Dr, Boynton Beach, FL 33437 407-734-9414
Garro, Mark: 20 Kent Pl, Cos Cob, CT 06807 203-661-6922
• **Garrow, Dan: pg 656,657** 2013 W 17th St, Wilmington, DE 19806 . . . . **302-651-0179**
Garson, Michael: 1129 Branywine St, Philadelphia, PA 19123 215-769-6838
Gartel, Laurence: 19650 Black Olive Ln, Boca Raton, FL 33498 407-477-2526
Gartner, Stephanie: 28950 Fountainwood St, Agoura Hills, CA 91301 818-889-0891
Gartrell, Pamela: 31-33 W 129th St #18, New York, NY 10027. 212-828-2036
• **Garvie, Ben: pg 309** 716 Montgomery St, San Francisco, CA 94111 . . . . **415-433-1222**
url: www.sweetreps.com / fax: 415-433-9560
Garvin, Elaine: 2045 S McLintock Dr #153, Tempe, AZ 85282 480-967-9479
Garvin, Vance: 2509 W Woodlyn Way, Greensboro, NC 27410 910-684-7447
Garza, Roy: 302 Berlin Ave, San Antonio, TX 78211 210-922-7282
Gasowski, Igor: 1220 Colusa Ave, Berkeley, CA 94707 510-524-3777
Gast, Jane: 1417 Township Line Rd, Gwynedd Valley, PA 19437. 610-296-2555
Gast, Josef: 68 E Franklin St, Dayton, OH 45459 937-433-8383
Gates Design, Jeff: 2000 Hermitage Ave, Silver Spring, MD 20902 301-949-0436
Gates, Donald: 7915 1/4 Norton Ave, West Hollywood, CA 90046 323-822-9291
Gates, Kathleen: 1901 Felix, Memphis, TN 38114 901-725-4667
Gatto, Chris: PO Box 4041, Stamford, CT 06907 203-264-2400
Gaudette, Christine: 630 rue Mott, Saint-jean-sur-ric, QU J3B 4Z2 514-349-1818
Gauthier, Corbert: 4350 Mackey Ave, St Louis Park, MN 55424 612-926-1096
Gavin, Bill: 268 Orchard St, Millis, MA 02054 508-376-5727
Gavin, Kerry: 154 E Canaan Rd, East Canaan, CT 06024. 860-824-4839
Gay-Kassel, Doreen: 17 Seminary Ave, Hopewell, NJ 08525 609-466-0267
Gayler, Anne: 148 Prospect Rd, Monroe, NY 10950 914-496-4425
Gaz, Stan: 58 W 15th St, New York, NY 10011 212-741-2539
Gazzo, Peppi: 42 Tamaques Way, Westfield, NJ 07090 201-798-6389
Geary, Rick: 99 Park Ave #210A, New York, NY 10016 800-398-9544
Geerinck, Manuel: Pier 33 North, San Francisco, CA 94111 415-956-4750
Gefen, Harry: 49 Spadina Ave #4, Toronto, ON M5V 2J1 888-829-7834
Gehm, Charles: 13 Buckingham Lane, Gaylordsville, CT 06755. 800-354-1459
Geiser, Janie: 1938 Commonwealth Ave, Los Angeles, CA 90027 212-353-5015
Gelb Illustration, Jacki: 3921 N Greenview Ave, Chicago, IL 60613 773-281-5276
Gelb, Jacki: 108 E 35th St, New York, NY 10016. 212-889-3337
Gelen, Michael: 68 Dorchester Rd, Buffalo, NY 14222. 716-882-0102
Gelfer, Regina: 115 Jonathan Dr, Mahopac, NY 10541 914-621-5821
Gelhardt, Rob: 902 Brookwood Dr, Tallahassee, FL 32308 850-877-6185
Gellman, Rachel: 192 Bleecker St, New York, NY 10012 212-473-7502
Gellman, Sim: 475 N Prince Rd, St Louis, MO 63132 314-994-3045
Gellos, Nancy: 3634 W Lawton St, Seattle, WA 98199 206-285-5838
Gencarelli, Elizabeth: 235 W 22nd St #7K, New York, NY 10011. 212-353-9073
Genco, Chuck: 423 Edgar Rd, Westfield, NJ 07090 212-677-4588
• **Genn, R: pg 739** 1810 Hardison Pl #10, S Pasadena, CA 91030 . . . . **626-441-5691**
url: www.rgenn.com or www.theispot.com/artist/rgenn / fax: 626-441-5691
Genova, Joe: 58 W 40th St 6th Fl, New York, NY 10018. 212-682-1490
• **Genovese, Janell: pg 406** 6 Parker Rd, Arlington, MA 02474 . . . . **781-641-2787**
e-mail: info@lillarogers.com / url: www.lillarogers.com / fax: 781-641-2244
Gensheimer, Frank: 5 Lawrence St Bldg 15, Bloomfield, NJ 07003 201-743-4305
Gentile, John & Anthony: 244 W 54th St 9th Fl, New York, NY 10019 212-757-1966
Gentry, John Edward: 2617 Mendocino Dr, Pinole, CA 94564. 510-758-8456
Genzo, John Paul: 217 E 86th St #212, New York, NY 10028. 212-427-5632
Geogriann, Margaret: 3314 Oberon St, Kensington, MD 20895 301-496-5566
George, Jeff: 853 Broadway #1201, New York, NY 10003 212-677-9100
George, Maureen Radcliffe: 1034 Clinton ave, Alameda, CA 94501 510-523-8170
George, Robert J: 366 Sterling Pl, Brooklyn, NY 11238 718-783-8514
Georgiann, Margaret G: 3314 Oberon St, Kensington, MD 20895 301-933-4912
Gerace, Patrick: 116 Park Ave #8, Morrison, CO 80465 303-697-1732
• **Geras, Audra: pg 262,263** 250 W 57th St #521, New York, NY 10107 . . . . . . **212-397-7330**
e-mail: San Francisco: 415-788-8552 / url: www.lindgrensmith.com
Gerber Studio: 18 Oak Grove Rd, Brookfield, CT 06804 203-775-3658
Gerber, John: 3537 Aldrich Ave South, Minneapolis, MN 55408 612-825-1227
Gergely, Peter: 24 Roe Park, Highland Falls, NY 10928 914-446-2367
Gerlach, Carmeron: 7215 Lanark Rd, Baltimore, MD 21212. 410-821-8625
99 Park Ave #210A, New York, NY 10016 800-398-9544
Germain, Phillipe: 27 chemin ile de Mai, Boisbriand, QU J7G 1R7 514-434-2116
Germon, Roy: 647 Warren St, Brooklyn, NY 11217 212-807-9728
Gerns, Laurie: 7108 Allot Ave, Van Nuys, CA 91405. 818-785-8253
Gerro, Mark: 20 Kent Pl, Cos Cob, CT 06807. 203-661-6922
Gersch, Wolfgang: PO Box 698, Point Reyes Station, CA 94956 415-633-9150
Gerstein, Mordicai: 186 Crescent St, Northampton, MA 01060 413-268-7549
Gersten, Gerry: 177 Newtown Turnpike, Weston, CT 06883 203-222-1608
Gervais, Stephen: 183 Riverside Ave, Warwick, RI 02889 401-737-8526
Gerwitz, Rick: 228 E 10th St, New York, NY 10003 212-353-9838
Getchell, Scott: 322 Windsor St, Cambridge, MA 02141 617-661-0658
Geter, Tyrone: 218 Elm Court, Rhinelander, WI 54501. 715-369-2130
Geyer, Jackie: 607 Penn Ave #212, Pittsburgh, PA 15222. 412-261-1111
Ghaboussi, Sina: 666 Greenwich St #860, New York, NY 10014 212-675-5719
Gherardi, Bob: 721 Stony Brook Way, North Brunswick, NJ 08902. . . . .
Ghiglione, Kevin: 90 Sumach St #617, Toronto, ON M5A 4R4 416-863-5115
Ghirardo, Claudio: 146 Geoffrey St, Toronto, ON M6R 1P5. 416-530-0702
• **Giacobbe, Beppe: pg 392** 194 Third Ave, New York, NY 10003. . . . . **212-475-0440**
url: www.morgangaynin.com / fax: 212-353-8538
Giana, Alan D: 17 Colonial Dr, Simsbury, CT 06089 860-658-2938
Giancola, Debby: 112 Old English Rd, Pittsburgh, PA 15237 412-369-0366
Giancola, Donato: 397 Pacific St, Brooklyn, NY 11217 718-797-2438
Giangregorio, Laurie: 6847 La Pasada, Hereford, AZ 85615 520-378-3183
Giannetti, Francesco: 31 Amity Pl, Amherst, MA 01002. 888-339-3172
Giannini-Hurtley, Gay: 645 Sierra Dr, Dixon, CA 95620 916-678-3645
Giardina, Laura: 12 Buckingham Ct, Pomona, NY 10970. 914-354-0871
Giarnella, Andy: 259 Main St, E Berlin, CT 06023 860-828-8410
Gibb, Caroline: 50-602 Governors Rd, Dundas, ON L9H 5M3. 905-628-3280
• **Gibb, Sarah: pg 491** 455 W 23rd St #8D, New York, NY 10011 . . . . **212-366-1893**
e-mail: sally@theartworksinc.com / url: www.theartworksinc.com / fax: 212-604-9643
Gibbon, Rebecca: 155 W 15th St #4C, New York, NY 10011 212-989-8770
Gibbons, Bill: 368 Broadway #203, New York, NY 10013. 212-227-0039
Gibbs, Michael: 2149 Lyon St #5, San Francisco, CA 94115 415-921-7140
• **Gibson-Nash, Nancy: pg 883** 88 Welch St, Peaks Island, ME 04108 . . . . **207-766-5761**
url: www.nancygibsonnash.com / fax: 207-766-4472
Gibson, Barbara: 3501 Toddsbury Ln, Onley, MD 20832 301-570-9480
Gibson, Clancy: 231 Humbercrest Blvd, Toronto, ON M6S 4L5 416-530-1500
Giedd, Richard: 28 Emerson Rd, Watertown, MA 02172 617-924-4350
Gieseke, Thomas A: 7909 W 61st St, Merriam, KS 66202. 913-677-4593
Giglio, Richard: 2231 Broadway #17, New York, NY 10024 212-724-8118
Gignilliat, Elaine: 5409 Beau Reve Pk, Marietta, GA 30068 770-998-0727
Gignilliat, Elaine: 420 Lexington Ave, New York, NY 10170 212-986-5680
Giguere, Ralph: 230 Cliveden Ave, Glenside, PA 19038 215-885-8434
Gil, Ramon: 87-10 51st Ave #5-0, Elmhurst, NY 11373. 800-874-7442
Gilbert, Adam: 1524 E 8th St, Tucson, AZ 85719. 520-884-8078
Gilbert, Douglas R: 4 Whittier Meadows Dr, Amesbury, MA 01913. 978-388-0029
Gilbert, Yvonne: 666 Greenwich St #860, New York, NY 10014. 212-675-5719
Gilbride, Eileen: 310 W 97th St #902, New York, NY 10025. 212-243-5888
Giles, Dorothy: 1751 E Whittier Blvd, La Habra, CA 90631 310-694-1424
Gilfoy, Bruce: 568 Washington St, Wellesley, MA 02181 . . . . 617 235 8977
Gill, Tim: PO Box 1251, New York, NY 10023. 212-774-4271
Gillies, Chuck: 420 Lexington Ave, New York, NY 10170 212-986-5680
Gilligan, Paul: 65 Burnaby Blvd, Toronto, ON M5N 1G3. 416-651-2556
Gilligan, Sheila: 185 Highland Ave, Somerville, MA 02143. 617-628-5144
Gillot, Carol: 30-80 33rd St #3L, Long Island City, NY 11102 718-204-8791
Gilman, Mary: Star Rte 13-A, Wendell Depot, MA 01380. 508-544-7425
Gimbrone, Joanne: 24 DeWitt St, Buffalo, NY 14213 716-881-2850
Gin, Byron: 1872 N Clybourn #404, Chicago, IL 60614 773-935-8840
Gino: 134 Christian St, New Preston, CT 06777. 860-868-1011
Ginsburg, Max: 40 W 77th Street #14B, New York, NY 10024 212-787-0628
Ginzinger, Karla: 20 W Hubbard St #3E, Chicago, IL 60610 312-222-1361
Giordano, Edward: PO Box 226, Clifton, NJ 07011. 201-772-1401
Giorgio, Nate: 481 8th Ave #E24, New York, NY 10001 212-631-0009
• **Giovannina Illustrations: pg 870** 19 East Dr, Toronto, ON M6N 2N8 . . . . **416-604-0057**
Giovanopoulos, Paul: 119 Prince St, New York, NY 10013. 212-677-5919
Girden, JM: 2125 Cerrada Nopal E, Tucson, AZ 85718 520-628-2740
Girvin Design, Tim: 501 Fifth Ave, New York, NY 10017 212-490-2450
Gisko, Max: 2629 Wakefield Dr, Belmont, CA 94002. 415-595-1893
Gist, Linda E: 224 Madison Ave, Fort Washington, PA 19034. 215-643-3757
Giusti, Robert: 115 West 23rd St, New York, NY 10011 212-989-4600
Glad, Deanna: PO Box 1962, San Pedro, CA 90733 310-831-0274
Gladstone, Dale: 32 Havermeyer St #2A, Brooklyn, NY 11211 718-782-2250
Glasbergen, Randy J: PO Box 611, Sherburne, NY 13460 607-674-9492
Glasgow, Dale: 448 Hartwood Rd, Fredericksburg, VA 22406 540-286-2539
Glass, Damian: 102 Cooks Bay Dr, Keswick, ON L4P 1M3. 905-476-7985
• **Glass, Randy: pg 309** 716 Montgomery St, San Francisco, CA 94111 . . . . **415-433-1222**
fax: 415-433-9560
Glassman, Judy: 120A E 23rd St, New York, NY 10010 212-512-7800
Glazer & Kalayjian, Inc: 301 E 45th St #18F, New York, NY 10017 212-687-3099
Glazer, Art: 2 James Rd, Mt Kisco, NY 10549 914-666-4554
Glazer, Ted: 28 West View Rd, Spring Valley, NY 10977. 914-354-1524
Glazier, Garth: 353 W 53rd St #1W, New York, NY 10019 212-682-2462
Gleeson, Tony: 2525 Hyperion Ave #4, Los Angeles, CA 90027 213-668-2704
Glenn, Mary Jane: 2 Thorne Ln, Oakdale, NY 11769. 516-589-8065
Glessner, Marc: 81 Hidden Lake Dr, North Brunswick, NJ 08902 908-249-5038
Gletkin: 23 W 88th St #GR, New York, NY 10024 212-875-8583
Glick, Judith: 301 E 79th St #26C, New York, NY 10021 212-734-5268
Glick, Tracey: 3118 18th St #8, San Francisco, CA 94110 415-861-7409
Glidden, Althea: 2 Butler Rd, Reiserstown, MD 21136. 301-523-5903
• **Gnan, Patrick: pg 299** 731 N 24th St, Philadelphia, PA 19130 . . . . **215-232-6666**
url: www.deborahwolfeltd.com / fax: 215-232-6585
Godfrey, Linda: N7347 Nine Indians Trail, Elkhorn, WI 53121 262-742-4448
Goehring, Steven: 25456 Bull Run, Alpine, OR 97456 541-424-5443
Goethals, Raphaelle: 3235 Barham Blvd, Los Angeles, CA 90068. 323-662-0020
Goettemoeller, Cheryl: 4319 Wilkinson Ave, Studio City, CA 91604 818-766-4929
Goines, David Lance: 1703 MLK Way, Berkeley, CA 94709 510-549-1405
Gojanovic, Zivana: 1807 Lasuen Rd, Santa Barbara, CA 93103 508-965-0629
Gok, Diana: 1522 Innes Ave, San Francisco, CA 94124. 415-826-2846
Golan, Ari: 1501 N Magnolia Ave, Chicago, IL 60622 312-649-1800
Golan, Doron: 10 Warren St #2, New York, NY 10007 212-571-1824
Gold, Eva: 87 Barrow St #6E, New York, NY 10014. 212-337-0977
Gold, Sandi: 18 High St, Westerly, RI 02891 401-348-9571
Goldammer, Ken: 844 W Gunnison #2E, Chicago, IL 60640 773-878-6806
Goldberg, Amy: PO Box 1669, Tahoe City, CA 96145 916-581-3401
Goldberg, Richard: 2149 Lyon St #5, San Francisco, CA 94115 415-921-7140
Golden Design, John W: 201 N Front St #912, Wilmington, NC 28402 910-254-1300
Golden, Gary: 300 N Schiller, Little Rock, AR 72205. 501-376-4500
• **Golden, Harriet: pg 905** 217 E 85th St #11, New York, NY 10028 . . . . **212-249-4194**
e-mail: goldenhr@earthlink.net / url: www.harrietgolden.com
Golden, Helen: 460 El Capitan Pl, Palo Alto, CA 94306. 415-494-3461
Golden, Jan: 2305 Ashland St #C, Ashland, OR 97520. 800-435-6509
Golden, Kenneth Sean: 696 10th Ave, New York, NY 10019 212-246-3875
Golden, Peg: 822 Grand Terrace Ave, Baldwin, NY 11510 516-868-1858

Grimwood, Brian: 58 W 40th St 6th Fl, New York, NY 10018 212-682-1490
Griner, Larry: 1 North St #2W, Hastings-on-Hudson, NY 10706 914-478-5074
Grinnell, Derek: 621 42nd Ave #A, San Francisco, CA 94121 415-221-2820
Griswold, Theophilus Britt: 823 Holly Dr E, Annapolis, MD 21401 410-757-8379
Groff Illustration, David W: 2149 Lyon St #5, San Francisco, CA 94115. 415-921-7140
Groff Illustration, David W: 420 N Liberty St, Delaware, OH 43015 614-363-2131
Groham, Chad: 188 Heritage Rd, Tonawanda, NY 14150. 716-694-4763
Gross, Alex: 1727 La Senda Pl, S Pasadena, CA 91030. 626-799-4014
Gross, John: 30 N First St, Minneapolis, MN 55401 612-339-5181
• **Gross, Susan: pg 766** 532 Cabrillo St, San Francisco, CA 94118 . . . . **415-751-5879**
url: www.susangross.com
Grossman Illus, Larry: 5309 Coldwater Canyon Ave #C, Sherman Oaks, CA 91401818-907-8626
Grossman, Rhoda: 216 4th St, Sausalito, CA 94965 415-331-0328
Grossman, Robert: 19 Crosby St, New York, NY 10013 212-925-1965
• **Grossman, Wendy: pg 340,341** 58 W 15th St, New York, NY 10011 . . . . **212-741-2539**
url: www.jdedell.com or www.theispot.com or www.rosebudstudios.com / fax: 212-741-4660
Grote, Rich: 22 Seminary Ln, Granite Springs, NY 10527. 914-248-4870
Grotenhuis, Eric: 3044 34th Ave S, Minneapolis, MN 55406. 612-729-4689
Grothman, Lisa: 137 Fifth Ave 11th Fl, New York, NY 10010. 212-529-3556
Grotsky: 21-16 28th St, Long Island City, NY 11105. 718-204-6184
Grounard, Mark: 1150 Fairview Ave, Wyomissing, PA 19610 215-372-7482
• **Group Five Creative: pg 646,647** 4600 S Syracuse 9th Fl, Denver, CO 80237 . . **303-932-8759**
Grove, David: 382 Union St, San Francisco, CA 94133 415-433-2100
Grove, Keith: 9801 DuPont Ave S #168, Minneapolis, MN 55431 612-884-4045
Grover Sopin, Nan: 9 Bradley Dr, Freehold, NJ 07728 732-462-7154
Grubb, Lisa: PO Box 388, Sparkill, NY 10976 914-921-4526
Gruel, George: 759 Charles St, Moorpark, CA 93021. 805-529-2727
• **Grunewald Digital Illustration, Jeff: pg 814** **773-281-5284**
url: www.jeffgrunewald.com
Grychczynski, Mark: 3116 Chapman St, Oakland, CA 94601 510-436-7865
Guancione, Karen: 262 DeWitt Ave, Belleville, NJ 07109. 201-450-9490
Guarnaccia, Steven: 31 Fairfield St, Monclair, NJ 07042 973-746-9785
Gubenko, Alex: 1 Calvo Pl, Hawthorne, NJ 07506 201-871-1076
Gude, Karl: 15 Possom Lane, Norwalk, CT 08854 212-445-4000
Gudynas, Peter: 11 Kings Ridge Rd, Long Valley, NJ 07853 908-813-8718
Guell, Fernando: 43 E 19th St, New York, NY 10003 212-254-4996
Guerin, Kirsten: 438 Howard Ave, Franklin Square, NY 11010 516-483-0407
Guevara, Susan: PO Box 980, Soda Springs, CA 95728. 530-426-0235
• **Guida Chauncy, Lisa: pg 776** **970-845-0771**
url: www.theispot.com/artist/guida / fax: 970-949-0633
Guidice, Rick: 9 Park Ave, Los Gatos, CA 95050 408-354-7787
Guilded Imagery Prdctns: 2995 Woodside Rd #400, Woodside, CA 94062 415-324-0323
Guion, Tamara: 556 S Fair Oaks Ave #101-175, Pasadena, CA 91105 626-798-8878
• **Guitteau, Jud: pg 342,343** 58 W 15th St, New York, NY 10011 . . . . **212-741-2539**
url: www.jdedell.com or www.theispot.com / fax: 212-741-4660
Gulick, Dorothy: 6822 N Lotus Ave, San Gabriel, CA 91775. 818-287-5104
Gullickson, Vicki: 1035 A Cherokee St, Denver, CO 80204 303-592-9811
Gullo, Tom: 391 Clinton St, Brooklyn, NY 11231 718-625-2708
Gully, Bethany: 512 Central Ave, Needham, MA 02494. 617-350-3089
Guluk, Steve: 33802 Copper Lantern, Dana Point, CA 92629. 949-661-7222
Gumble, Gary: 1316 102nd Ave NE, Bellevue, WA 98004. 425-688-1961
Gunn, Robert: PO Box 1760, Highland Park, IL 60035 312-222-0337
Gunn, Toni: 5182 E Cherokee Dr, Canton, GA 30115 770-345-9576
Gunning, Kevin: 3 Huckleberry Acres, East Hampton, CT 06424 860-347-0688
Gunsaullus, Marty: 824 Edwards PO Box 41, Trinidad, CA 95570. 707-677-0241
Gura, Catherine: 200 E 71st St #3F, New York, NY 10021 . . . .
Gurak, Ellen: 4416 Canal St, New Orleans, LA 70119. 504-486-7255
Gurche, John: 1304 Olive St, Denver, CO 80220 303-370-8365
Gurney, James: PO Box 693, Rhinebeck, NY 12572 914-876-7746
• **Gurney, John Steven: pg 812** 710 Western Ave, Brattleboro, VT 05301 . . . . **802-258-2654**
e-mail: jsgurney@cheshire.net / url: atom.cheshire.net/~jsgurney / fax: 802-258-9154
Gurth, Per: 215 Marguaretta St, Toronto, ON M6H 3S4 416-531-5856
Gurvin Festive Illustrations, Abe: 31341 Holly Dr, Laguna Beach, CA 92651 . . . 949-499-2001
Gushock, Mike: 4450 N 12th st #106, Phoenix, AZ 85014. 602-650-1810
Gusman, Annie: 15 King St, Putnam, CT 06260. 860-928-1042
Gussin, Jane E: 90 Riverside Dr #2B, New York, NY 10024. 212-873-3584
Gustafson, Dale: 420 Lexington Ave, New York, NY 10170. 212-986-5680
Gustafson, Jon: 621 East F St, Moscow, ID 83843 208-882-3672
Gustafson, Mats: 130 W 17th St, New York, NY 10011. 212-627-4665
Gutermuth, Stefan: 608 York St, San Francisco, CA 94110. 415-641-1285
Gutierrez, Rudy: 330 Haven Ave #4N, New York, NY 10033 212-568-2848
Guy, Edmond: 309 Race Track Rd, Hohokus, NJ 07423 201-251-7660
Guy, Robert: 80 E Hartsdale Ave, Hartsdale, NY 10530. 914-682-3723
Guyer, Terry: 1139 San Carlos Ave #301, San Carlos, CA 94070. 650-596-0363
Guzman, Christine: 22605 SW 65th Terr, Boca Raton, FL 33428 561-883-3210
Guzzi, George: 11 Randlett Pk, W Newton, MA 02165 617-244-2932
• **Gwilliams, Scott: pg 869** 213 Glen Rd, Toronto, ON M4W 2X2 . . . . **416-929-8432**
e-mail: scottgwilliams@home.com / fax: 416-926-8875
GXCENTRIKS, Gabrielle Lasporte: 2350 W Dundas St, Toronto, ON M6P 4B1 . . . 416-533-5746
Gygi, Darren: 259 E 760 N #12, Orem, UT 84057 801-372-4606
Gyson, Mitch: 4603 Simms Ave, Baltimore, MD 21206. 410-485-0207
Gyurcsak, Joe: 133 Eaton Ave, Mercerville, NJ 08619. 609-586-7007

H

Ha, Inae: 333 E 66th St #11D, New York, NY 10021 212-452-1487
Haake, Martin: 250 W 57th St #521, New York, NY 10107 212-397-7330
Haaland, Ann: 85 Maple Ave Ste S, Dover, NJ 07801 973-989-0630
Haas, Bill: 415 South Main St, Hutchinson, MN 55350. 320-587-5016
Haas, Irene: 133 E 80th St #10A, New York, NY 10021. 212-628-2444
Haas, Shelley: 207 W Sherlock St/PO Box 333, Harrington, WA 99134 509-253-4752
Haas, Susan: 1481 Bristol Dr, Pittsburgh, PA 15129. 412-650-4446
Haasis, Michael: 504 N California, Burbank, CA 91505. 818-559-6309
Haber-Schaim, Tamar: 1870 Beacon St Bldg #6-B1, Brookline, MA 02146 617-738-8883
Hackworth, Alex: 1523 W Jackson Blvd, Chicago, IL 60681. 312-563-9476
Hadam Kemly, Kathleen: 7543 13th NW, Seattle, WA 98117. 206-782-8647
Haddon, Julie: One South Rd, Harrison, NY 10528 914-381-8400
Hadlock, David: 2632 E 1st St, Long Beach, CA 90803 562-433-4429
Haedrich, Todd: 10 Byron Dr, Basking Ridge, NJ 07920 908-204-0624
Hafner, Marylin: 33 Richdale Ave #105, Cambridge, MA 02140. 617-625-6944
Hagel, Mike: 15910 Jones Cir, Omaha, NE 68118 402-691-8682
Hagen, David: 14637 Stone Range Dr, Centreville, VA 22020. 703-830-4208
Hager, Sherrie: 4338 Taylorsville Hwy, Statesville, NC 28677 704-838-1894
Haggerty, Tim: 380 Shamrock Dr, Ventura, CA 93003 805-653-5611
Haggland, Martin: 2345 Broadway #638, New York, NY 10024. 212-787-0500
Hagio, Cunio: 2510G Las Posas Rd #431, Camarillo, CA 93010 805-529-8111
1352 N Formosa Ave Ste 2, Los Angeles, CA 90046. 323-874-5700
Hagner, Dirk: 824 Edwards PO Box 41, Trinidad, CA 95570. 707-677-0241
Hahn, Eileen: 8 Hillwood Rd, East Brunswick, NJ 08816. 908-390-4188
Hahn, Marika: 679 Oak Tree Rd PO Box 670, Palisades, NY 10964 914-365-3317
• **Haight, Sandy: pg 596,597** 911 Western Ave # 525, Seattle, WA 98104 . . . . . **206-343-0656**
url: www.showcase.com/artist/sandyhaight / fax: 206-343-5697
Haiman, Kurt: 384 Blanch Ave, Closter, NJ 07624 201-767-1383
Haimowitz, Steve: 67-40 Yellowstone Blvd #5D, Forest Hills, NY 11375 718-520-1461
Haines-Hall Design, Stephen: 405 Ash St, Mill Valley, CA 94941. 415-388-3970
Hajek, Olaf: 80 Nassau St #202E, New York, NY 10038. 212-964-9141
Halbert, Michael: 2419 Big Bend Rd, St Louis, MO 63143 314-645-6480
• **Hale, Brent: pg 762** 3505 Melanie Ct, Tyler, TX 75707 . . . . **903-565-4900**
e-mail: artog@tyler.net / fax: 903-566-4958
Hale, Bruce: 1201 NW Blakely Ct, Seattle, WA 98177 206-440-9036
Haleen, Brentano: PO Box 148, Tesuque, NM 87574 505-986-1799
Haley, David: 1400 S Highway Dr, Fenton, MO 63099 314-827-2840
Halfacre, Elizabeth: 9530A 45th NE, Seattle, WA 98115. 206-529-1669
Hall Design, Stephen: 405 Ash St, Mill Valley, CA 94941. 415-388-3970
Hall, Bill: 1235-B Colorado Ln, Arlington, TX 76015 817-467-1013
Hall, Brian: 7118 Upper River Rd, Prospect, KY 40059. 502-228-9427
Hall, David: 2785 Westshire Dr, Los Angeles, CA 90068 213-464-2495
Hall, Eric: 2146 Spring St, Philadelphia, PA 19103 215-564-0712
Hall, Jane Allen: 2138 Higdon Ferry Rd, Hot Springs, AR 71903 501-525-2098
Hall, Jeffrie: 174 Hollyglen Ln, San Dimas, CA 91773. 909-599-3802
Hall, Joan: 155 Bank St, Studio H954, New York, NY 10014. 212-243-6059
Hall, Kate Brennan: 1900 Hawthorne Dr, Cedar Falls, IA 50613 319-266-9734
Hall, Melanie: 22 Krom Rd, Olivebridge, NY 12461 845-657-8242
Hall, Scott: 4129 Ginger Creek Dr, Meridian, ID 83642 208-376-5352
Hall, Stephen: 11 Kings Ridge Rd, Long Valley, NJ 07853 908-813-8718
Hall, Susan: 7500 NW First Ct #110, Plantation, FL 33317 305-923-5111
Hallgren, Gary: 98 Laurelton Dr, Mastic Beach, NY 11951 631-399-5531
Halliday, Caroline: 350 Central Park West, New York, NY 10025 212-865-4349
Hallman, Tom: 2553 Mill House Rd, Macungie, PA 18062. 610-395-5656
Hally, Greg: 248 Edison St, Salt Lake City, UT 84111 801-355-5510
Halsey, Megan: 225 Church St #3F, Philadelphia, PA 19106 215-925-2090
Halstead, Virginia: 4336 Gayle Dr, Tarzana, CA 91356 818-705-4353
• **Haltom, Sam: pg 841** PO Box 775909, Steamboat Springs, CO 80477 . . . . . . **970-871-0151**
e-mail: sam@anothercolor.com / url: www.anothercolor.com / fax: 970-871-0150
Halverson, Lydia: PO Box 1086, Taos, NM 87571 505-776-5435
Hamagami Carroll & Assocs: 1316 Third St #305, Santa Monica, CA 90401 . . . 310-458-7600
Hamagami, John: 1316 3rd St Promenade, Santa Monica, CA 90401 310-458-7600
Hamann, Brad: 80 Yerry Hill Rd, Woodstock, NY 12498 914-679-4748
Hamblin, George: 12283 N Ledges Dr, Roscoe, IL 61073 815-389-1250
Hamblin, Randy: 731 N 24th St, Philadelphia, PA 19130 215-232-6666
• **Hambly, Bob: pg 258** 250 W 57th St #521, New York, NY 10107 . . . . **212-397-7330**
e-mail: San Francisco: 415-788-8552 / url: www.lindgrensmith.com
Hamers, Michael: 2259 Mt Sherman Rd, Nywot, CO 80503. 303-527-1222
Hamil, Doug: PO Box 762, Rome, GA 30162. 706-232-3684
Hamill, Paul: 16167 Oxford Cir, Truckee, CA 96161 530-582-7497
Hamill, Valerie: 686 Mandana Blvd, Oakland, CA 94610. 510-465-7940
Hamilton, Bruce & Susan: Rt 1 Box 5C, Glorieta, NM 87535 505-757-6603
Hamilton, Carolyn: 7380 South Eastern #124-216, Las Vegas, NV 89123. 702-798-6000
Hamilton, Ken: 16 Helen Ave, West Orange, NJ 07052 973-736-6532
Hamilton, Laurie: 1255 N Sandburg #2703, Chicago, IL 60610. 312-944-3970
Hamilton, Marcus: 12225 Ranburne Rd, Charlotte, NC 28212 704-545-3121
Hamilton, Meredith: 128 State St #2, Brooklyn, NY 11201. 800-963-7896
Hamilton, Pamela: 353 W 53rd St #1W, New York, NY 10019 212-682-2462
• **Hamlin, Janet: pg 773** 164 9th Street #1, Brooklyn, NY 11215 . . . . **718-768-3647**
e-mail: hamchat@earthlink.net / url: www.janethamlin.com / fax: 718-768-3675
Hamlin, Peter: 166 Ninth St #1, Brooklyn, NY 11215. 718-832-8817
• **Hamlin, Peter/Secret Sauce Studio: pg 687** ,, ... **718-832-8817**
url: www.secretsaucestudio.com
Hammer, Claudia: 7118 Upper River Rd, Prospect, KY 40059 502-228-9427
Hammes, Alan: 200 W 93rd St #6D, New York, NY 10025 212-691-6387
Hammond, Cris: 410 Johnson St, Sausalito, CA 94965 415-332-7556
• **Hammond, Franklin: pg 620** 142 W Winter St, Delaware, OH 43015 . . . . **740-369-9702**
fax: 740-369-0547
Hammond, Ted: 370 Rathburn Rd #55, Mississauga, ON L4Z 1H7. 905-803-9698
Hampshire, Michael: 134 Christian St, New Preston, CT 06777 860-868-1011
Hampton, Gerry: 27892 Cummins Dr, Laguna Niguel, CA 92677 949-831-5910
Hamrick, Chuck: 420 Lexington Ave #2760, New York, NY 10170. 212-697-8525
Hancock, Roberta: 156 W Lynwood St, Phoenix, AZ 85007 602-252-6368
Haney, William: 674 S Branch River Rd, Somerville, NJ 08876 908-369-8792
Hanley, John: 4803 Wyoming Way, Crystal Lake, IL 60012 815-459-1123
Hanley, John: 847A Second Ave #150, New York, NY 10017 212-486-0177
Hanley, Katherine: 1831 E 61st St, Indianapolis, IN 46220 317-251-7989
• **Hanley/Daisy Art Studio, Debbie: pg 886** 500 Aurora Ave N #405, Seattle, WA 98109 **206-621-0410**
e-mail: daiseyart@aol.com / fax: 206-621-0410
Hanna, B Scott: 1352 N Formosa Ave Ste 2, Los Angeles, CA 90046 323-874-5700
Hanna, Renie: 314 Locust St, W Hempstead, NY 11552 516-292-3166
Hanna, Tony: Insta Grafix/ 500 State St, Glendale, CA 91203 818-551-0747
Hannah, Halstead: 1250 Addison St Stu 211B, Berkeley, CA 94705 510-644-2241
Hannah, Johnny: 455 W 23rd St #8D, New York, NY 10011 212-366-1893
Hannan, Michel: 20 Tower Rd, Plymouth, MA 02360 508-747-0089
Hannon, Holly: 43 E 19th St, New York, NY 10003 212-254-4996
• **Hannum/Creative Conspiracy, Neil: pg 895** 679 E 2nd Ave #11, Durango, OR 81301 **970-247-2262**
url: www.creativeconspiracy.com
Hansen, Biruta Akerbergs: RD1 Box 39G Sun Hill, Liverpool, PA 17045 717-444-3682

Heinly, John: 5939 Ridge Ford Dr, Burke, VA 22015 ... 703-451-7263
Heinz, Joel M: 1127 S Highland Ave, Oak Park, IL 60304 ... 708-386-1949
Heinz, Laure: 2405 NW Thurman St, Portland, OR 97210 ... 503-203-8300
Heinze, Mitchell: 165 E 32nd St, New York, NY 10016 ... 212-686-3514
Heinze, Mitchell: 721 E Maxwell Ln, Lathrop, CA 95330 ... 209-858-1131
Hejja, Attila: 420 Lexington Ave, New York, NY 10170 ... 212-986-5680
Helander, Bruce: 513 Clematis St #C, West Palm Beach, FL 33401 ... 561-655-0504
Helgeson-Moen, Connie: 278 Hwy 105, Lake Mills, IA 50450 ... 515-592-5900
Hellard, Susan: 42 Delavan St, Brooklyn, NY 11231 ... 718-624-1906
Heller, Debbie: 601 West End Ave #11B, New York, NY 10024 ... 212-580-0917
Hellmann, Margaret: 1007 Lewis Cir, Santa Cruz, CA 95062 ... 831-462-9337
Helmintoller, Tom: 14840 Sunset Blvd, Pacific Palisades, CA 90272 ... 310-230-4230
Helms, John: 4255 Arrowhead, Memphis, TN 38118 ... 901-363-6589
• **Helquist, Brett: pg 212,213** Chicago, IL ... **312-364-0244**
London ... **011-44-207-636-1064**
Los Angeles, CA ... **323-874-5700**
Washington, DC ... **410-349-8669**
New York, NY ... **212-333-2551**
url: www.shannonassociates.com
Helton, Linda: 7000 Meadow Lk, Dallas, TX 75214 ... 214-319-7877
• **Henderling, Lisa: pg 428** 227 Godfrey Rd, Weston, CT 06883 ... **203-222-8777**
e-mail: jp@artcoreps.com / url: www.artcoreps.com / fax: 203-454-9940
232 Madison Ave #512, New York, NY 10016 ... **212-889-8777**
e-mail: gt@artcoreps.com / url: www.artcoreps.com / fax: 212-447-1475
Hendershott, Karen: 1801 Pulaski Dr, Blue Bell, PA 19422 ... 215-272-2716
Henderson, Alan: 31 Jane St #10B, New York, NY 10014 ... 212-243-0693
• **Henderson, Dave: pg 175** 420 Lexington Ave, New York, NY 10170 ... **212-986-5680**
e-mail: mendolaart@aol.com / url: www.mendolaart.com / fax: 212-818-1246
Henderson, Garnet: 309 Racetrack Rd, HoHoKus, NJ 07423 ... 201-251-7660
Henderson, Hayes: 58 W 15th St, New York, NY 10011 ... 212-741-2539
Henderson, Lael: 1665 W 1000 N, Provo, UT 84604 ... 801-377-3304
Henderson, Louis: 4520 Rising Hill Rd, Altadena, CA 91001 ... 626-797-6754
Henderson, Louis: 32 w 40th St #2 South, New York, NY 10018 ... 212-575-6887
Henderson, Meryl: 1712 E Butler Cir, Chandler, AZ 85225 ... 602-899-0600
Henderson, Stephanie: 24 E Lawrence, Pontiac, MI 48324 ... 810-334-5134
Hendler, Sandra: 1823 Spruce St, Philadelphia, PA 19103 ... 215-735-7380
Hendricks, Sharie: 3038 Mountain View Dr, Laguna Beach, CA 92651 ... 714-494-8186
Hendricks, Steve: 1050 Elsie May Dr, Boulder Creek, CA 95006 ... 831-338-6639
Hendrickson, Andrew: 1225 S 23rd St, Philadelphia, PA 19146 ... 215-462-7834
Hendrickson, Kathy: PO Box 883, New Providence, NJ 07974 ... 908-665-2192
Hendrix, Bryan: 777 Ponce De Leon Terr, Atlanta, GA 30306 ... 404-875-4290
Hendrix-Townley, Gina: 1966 California Rd, Pomona, KS 66076 ... 913-746-5465
• **Hennessy, Tom: pg 485** 83 Walnut Ave, Corte Madera, CA 94925 ... **415-924-7881**
... **800-924-7881**
e-mail: gatlin@ritareps.com / url: www.ritareps.com / fax: 415-924-7891
Hennings, Darwen & Vally: 15623 Jim Creek Rd, Arlington, WA 98223 ... 360-435-3763
• **Henrie, Cary: pg 696,697** 1659 E Maple Hills Dr, Bountiful, UT 84010 ... **801-298-2044**
fax: 801-299-1919
Henrie, Kip: 610 E 250 North, Centerville, UT 84014 ... 801-299-1567
Henriquez, Celeste June: 310 NE 45th St #6, Seattle, WA 98105 ... 206-547-8384
Henriquez, Scott: 2223 W Roscoe St, Chicago, IL 60618 ... 773-883-9747
Henry, Doug: 353 W 53rd St #1W, New York, NY 10019 ... 212-682-2462
Henry, James: 1839 Ninth St, Alameda, CA 94501 ... 510-769-1421
Henry, Mike: 3400 Aurora Ave, Des Moines, IA 50310 ... 515-279-9478
Henry, Paul: 15 W 72nd St, New York, NY 10023 ... 212-799-2231
Henry, Roger: 1030 N Laurel Ave, Los Angeles, CA 90046 ... 213-654-2629
Henry, Steve: 7 Park Ave, New York, NY 10016 ... 212-532-2487
Henry-May, Rosemary: 2625 Garfield St NW, Washington, DC 20008 ... 202-667-0455
Hensarling, Dale: 5 Russet In, Petal, MS 39465 ... 601-582-5559
• **Herbert, Jennifer: pg 279** 250 W 57th St #521, New York, NY 10107 ... **212-397-7330**
San Francisco, CA ... **415-788-8552**
url: www.lindgrensmith.com
Herbert, Tom: 302 Hillside Ave, Jenkintown, PA 19046 ... 215-884-7348
Herbst, Susan: 8 July Ave #2, Bayville, NY 11709 ... 516-628-2633
Herder, Edwin: 60 E 42nd St, New York, NY 10165 ... 212-867-8092
Hering, Alan: 16 Lown Ct, Poughkeepsie, NY 12603 ... 914-471-7326
Herman, Barbara: 474 W 238th St, Riverdale, NY 10463 ... 718-549-5778
Herman, Joseph: 54 E 8th St #2E, New York, NY 10003 ... 212-473-3043
Herman, Mark: 853 Broadway #1201, New York, NY 10003 ... 212-677-9100
Herman, Michael: 1627 13th Ave SW, Calgary, AB T3C 0T8 ... 403-228-3495
Herman, Terry: 925 Elm Grove Rd, Elm Grove, WI 53122 ... 414-785-1940
Hermine Design Group: 3 Lockwood Ave, Old Greenwich, CT 06870 ... 203-698-1732
Hernandez Smith, Elaine : 1079 Syracuse Ln, Westerville, OH 43081 ... 614-985-3257
Hernandez, Erasmo: 34-21 78th St, Jackson Heights, NY 11372 ... 718-651-7052
Herr, Tad: 141 W Market St, Marietta, PA 17547 ... 717-426-2939
Herranen, K: 4114 E Union Hills Dr #1011, Phoenix, AZ 85024 ... 602-569-6209
Herrera, Yayo Diego: 5605 Davies Ave, Cote-Saint-Luc, QU H4W 2P9 ... 514-485-2962
Herrero, Lowell: 433 Bryant St, San Francisco, CA 94107 ... 415-543-6400
Herrick, David: 2425 Musselwhite Ave, Orlando, FL 32804 ... 407-898-8921
Herrmann, Robert: Gordon Rd RD#2, Carmel, NY 10512 ... 914-228-4972
Hersey Illustration, John: 546 Magnolia, Larkspur, CA 94939 ... 415-927-2091
Hersey, John: 58 W 15th St, New York, NY 10011 ... 212-741-2539
Hertel, Matthew: 725 Sydney St, Greensburg, PA 15601 ... 724-532-2945
Hertling, Heiner: 1000 John R Rd #201, Troy, MI 48083 ... 248-583-6070
Hertz Media Arts, Paul: 2215 W Fletcher St, Chicago, IL 60618 ... 773-975-9153
Herzberg, Tom: 4128 W Eddy St, Chicago, IL 60641 ... 773-736-1089
Heslop, Michael: 232 Madison Ave #512, New York, NY 10016 ... 212-889-8777
Hess, Derek: 1300 W 78th St 2nd Fl, Cleveland, OH 44102 ... 216-281-4868
Hess, Lydia: 100 Bleecker St, New York, NY 10012 ... 212-982-6533
Hess, Mark: 115 West 23rd St, New York, NY 10011 ... 212-989-4600
Hess, Paul: 23 Ganton St, London, England, UK WIV 1LA ... 71-287-9191
Hess, Robert: 63 Littlefield Rd, E Greenwich, RI 02818 ... 401-885-0331
Hesselberg, Brenda: 554 Cherbourg Ct S, Buffalo Grove, IL 60089 ... 847-634-2388
Hevron-Mahoney, Kit: 2682 S Newport St, Denver, CO 80224 ... 303-757-0689
• **Hewgill, Jody: pg 490** 455 W 23rd St #8D, New York, NY 10011 ... **212-366-1893**
e-mail: sally@theartworksinc.com / url: www.theartworksinc.com / fax: 212-604-9643
• **Hewitson, Jennifer: pg 782** 1145 Wotan Dr, Encinitas, CA 92024 ... **760-944-6154**
url: www.theispot.com/artist/jhewitson / fax: 760-943-0322
Hewitt, Margaret: 16 Phaedra, Laguna Niguel, CA 92677 ... 949-495-3664
Hewitt/Low Studios: 144 Soundview Rd, Huntington, NY 11743 ... 516-427-1404
Heyboer, Bryan: 4622 New Brunswick Ave, Piscataway, NJ 08854 ... 732-752-7262
Heyer, Marilee: 1619 Sixth St, Los Osos, CA 93402 ... 805-528-0161
Heyr, Carol: 925 Avenue Arbolis, Thousand Oaks, CA 91360 ... 805-492-3683
• **Hickcox/Creative Conspiracy, Kris: pg 895** 679 E 2nd Ave #11, Durango, OR 81301 ... **970-247-2262**
url: www.creativeconspiracy.com
Hickes, Andrew: 303 W 29th St #B, New York, NY 10001 ... 212-564-7034
Hickey, Christopher: 70 Dartmouth Ave, Avondale Estates, GA 30002 ... 404-534-1117
Hickey, John: 3821 Abingdon Cir, Norfolk, VA 23513 ... 804-853-2956
Hickman, Stephen: 10 Elm St, Red Hook, NY 12571 ... 914-758-3930
Hicks, Mark A: PO Box 83383, Phoenix, AZ 85071 ... 602-789-0964
Hicks, Robin: 153 Caselli Ave, San Francisco, CA 94114 ... 415-252-0277
Hicks, Ron: 4065 E 11th Ave, Denver, CO 80220 ... 303-366-6862
Hidy, Lance: 2 Summer St, Merrimac, MA 01860 ... 978-346-0075
• **HieroGraphix Productions: pg 871** 424 Macon St #1, Brooklyn, NY 11233 ... **718-919-8925**
... **917-719-0498**
e-mail: true@HGX.com / url: www.HGX.com / fax: 718-919-8223
Hierro, George: 396 Morningside Ave, Fairview, NJ 07022 ... 201-941-5639
Higgins, Chris: 1620 Central, Evanston, IL 60201 ... 847-866-9570
Higgins, Dave: 29580 Northwestern Hwy, Southfield, MI 48034 ... 248-353-7722
High Priority Consulting: 45 First Ave #5-O, New York, NY 10003 ... 212-673-1145
High, Philip: 329 Hightower Rd, Lexington, KY 40517 ... 606-272-3060
High, Richard: 420 Lexington Ave #2760, New York, NY 10170 ... 212-697-8525
High, Richard: 6311 Grovewood Ln, Houston, TX 77008 ... 713-861-7779
Hilber, Nelson: 7205 28th Ave NW, Seattle, WA 98117 ... 206-784-1136
Hildebrandt, Tim: 217 E 86th St #212, New York, NY 10028 ... 212-427-5632
Hill, Dave: 189-07 120th Ave, St Albans, NY 11412 ... 718-525-1178
Hill, Brad: PO Box 96, Queensville, ON LOG 1R0 ... 905-478-4861
• **Hill, Charlie: pg 150,151** 420 Lexington Ave, New York, NY 10170 ... **212-986-5680**
e-mail: mendolaart@aol.com / url: www.mendolaart.com or www.charliehill.com
fax: 212-818-1246
Hill, Drew: 14568 Fancher Ave, Fair Haven, NY 13064 ... 315-947-6016
Hill, Ed: 309 W 100th St #1, New York, NY 10025 ... 212-866-1895
Hill, Henry: 2356 E Broadway, Tucson, AZ 85719 ... 520-623-4325
Hill, John J: 12 John St #10, New York, NY 10038 ... 212-766-8035
Hill, John K: 18 Brompton Ln, Cincinnati, OH 45218 ... 513-851-4266
Hill, Julie: 1405 N Myrtle #5, Myrtle Creek, OR 97457 ... 541-863-4429
Hill, Michael: 80 Nassau St #202E, New York, NY 10038 ... 212-964-9141
• **Hill, Roger: pg 309** 716 Montgomery St, San Francisco, CA 94111 ... **415-433-1222**
url: www.sweetreps.com / fax: 415-433-9560
Hill, Tina: 83 Walnut Ave, Corte Madera, CA 94925 ... 415-924-7881
Hill, Tina Lee: 837 W Gregory Blvd, Kansas City, MO 64114 ... 816-361-9827
Hillam, Corbin: 1340 Big Valley Dr, Colorado Springs, CO 80919 ... 719-528-1229
Hillard-Barry, Pat: 2119 5th St, Berkeley, CA 94710 ... 510-704-4044
Hilliard, Fred: PO Box 421443, San Francisco, CA 94142 ... 415-647-5660
Hilliard-Barry, Pat: Pier 33 North, San Francisco, CA 94111 ... 415-956-4750
Hillier, Diane: 170 Corte Madera Rd, Portola Valley, CA 94028 ... 650-851-9715
Hillier, Karen: 2301 Bristol, Bryan, TX 77802 ... 409-822-5528
Hillios, Sonia: PO Box 90, Southampton, MA 01073 ... 413-527-4059
Hillis, Craig F: 550 Thomas St, Woodland, CA 95776 ... 916-668-5848
Hilscher, Anthony: 1503 Washington Ave S, Minneapolis, MN 55454 ... 612-332-8634
Hilton Campbell, Denise: 824 Edwards PO Box 41, Trinidad, CA 95570 ... 707-677-0241
Himsworth III, Jim: 731 N 24th St, Philadelphia, PA 19130 ... 215-232-6666
Hineline, Aaron: 112 Shawnee Ct, Franklin, OH 45005 ... 513-746-8297
Hines, Carol F: 1102 Buckingham Ave, Norfolk, VA 23508 ... 804-423-1028
Hines, Joel: 1127 S Highland, Oak Park, IL 60304 ... 708-386-1949
Hines, Laura Freedman: 1641 Third Ave, New York, NY 10028 ... 212-423-0091
Hinlicky, Gregg: PO Box 1521, Toms River, NJ 08754 ... 732-270-4300
Hinrichs, Ashton: 12552 Mandarin Rd, Jacksonville, FL 32223 ... 904-262-6596
Hinrichs, Chris: 5002 92nd Ave SE, Mercer Island, WA 98040 ... 206-232-7873
Hinton, Hank: 6118 W 6th St, Los Angeles, CA 90048 ... 213-938-9893
Hinton, Patricia Gural: 313 Sunset Ave, Louisburg, NC 27549 ... 919-496-6486
Hirashima, Jean: 310 W 97th St #902, New York, NY 10025 ... 212-243-5888
Hires, Bob: 100 Park Blvd #64B, Cherry Hill, NJ 08034 ... 609-428-5624
Hirokawa, Masami: 3144 W 26th Ave, Denver, CO 80211 ... 303-455-9613
Hiroko: 67-12 Yellowstone Blvd #E2, Forest Hills, NY 11375 ... 718-896-2712
• **Hitch, David: pg 131** 11 Kings Ridge Rd, Long Valley, NJ 07853 ... **908-813-8718**
e-mail: alartists@aol.com / url: www.arenaworks.com / fax: 908-813-0076
Hitch, Jeffery: 4500 Campus Dr #521, Newport Beach, CA 92660 ... 714-250-8640
• **Hite, Michael/Grp Five Creative: pg 647** 4600 S Syracuse 9th Fl, Denver, CO 80237 ... **303-256-6335**
Hitz, Christopher: 77 Hudson St #5, New York, NY 10013 ... 212-227-6670
Hladin, Brian: 109 Niagara St Box 71, Toronto, ON M5V 1C3 ... 416-504-2114
Ho, David: 3586 Dickenson Common, Fremont, CA 94538 ... 510-656-2468
Hoar, Randy: 10 Westport Rd, Wilton, CT 06897 ...
Hobbs, Dan: 164 Colbeck St, Toronto, ON M6S 1V9 ... 416-767-6035
Hobbs, Francis: PO Box 1510, Big Bear City, CA 92314 ... 909-585-8495
Hobbs, Michael A: 1035 Washington Ave #2K, Brooklyn, NY 11225 ... 718-287-7807
Hobbs, Pamela: 608 York St, San Francisco, CA 94110 ... 415-641-1285
Hobeler, Allan: PO Box 483, Kenmore, NY 14223 ... 716-838-3129
Hobrath, Jeff: 40 Yarrow Ct, Perkasie, PA 18944 ... 215-258-6393
Hobson, Ken: 3 Pineburr Ct, Greensboro, NC 27455 ... 910-282-7789
Hoch, Doug: 95 GH Carter Dr, Danville, NH 03819 ...
Hochgertel, Robert: PO Box 1491, Lancaster, PA 17608 ... 717-291-6544
Hockerman, Dennis: 6024 W Chapel Hill Rd, Mequon, WI 53092 ... 414-242-4103
Hocking, Philip: 1615 Manchester Ln NW, Washington, DC 20011 ... 202-882-8237
Hodde, Julie: 68 E Franklin St, Dayton, OH 45459 ... 513-433-8383
Hodgdon, Scott H: 77 Kellogg St, Farmingham, MA 01701 ... 617-742-7111
Hodge, Gerald: 1241 Bending Rd, Ann Arbor, MI 48103 ... 313-998-6270
Hodges, John: 8 Sycamore Circle, Grenada, MS 38901 ... 601-226-7527
Hodges, Ken: 12401 Bellwood Rd, Los Alamitos, CA 90720 ... 562-431-4343
Hodges, Mike: PO Box 711820, Salt Lake City, UT 84171 ... 404-296-9666
Hodges, Mike: 420 Lexington Ave #2760, New York, NY 10170 ... 212-697-8525
Hodgins, Glen: 424 N Midland Ave #D2, Saddle Brook, NJ 07663 ... 770-963-1991
Hodgkins, Rosalind: 720 Greenwich St #7R, New York, NY 10014 ... 212-675-3904
Hoeffner, Deb: 37 Cherry Tree Ln, Kinnelon, NJ 07405 ... 973-838-5490
Hoellman-Kahn, Jane: 241 Central Park W #14D, New York, NY 10024 ... 212-787-4421
Hoerr, Fred: 500 Molino St #315, Los Angeles, CA 90013 ... 213-680-4188
• **Hoey, Peter: pg 574,575** 1534 Waller St, San Francisco, CA 94117 ... **415-431-1069**
e-mail: hoeyart@earthlink.net / url: www.peterhoey.com / fax: 415-431-1719

Kanzburg, Yury: 1539 W Altgeld, Chicago, IL 60614 . . . 773-348-0715
Kapdia, Phiroza: 1515 Cedar Place, Los Altos, CA 94024 . . . 415-988-1163
Kapitain, Sean:, Toronto, ON . . . 416-923-8215
• **Kapitain, Sean: pg 752** 404-340 Avenue Rd, Toronto, ON M4V 2H4 . . . **416-923-8215**
Kaplan, Frederic C: 524 Spruce Ave, Upper Darby, PA 19082 . . . 610-734-1231
Kaplan, Kari: 110 Lovato Ln, Santa Fe, NM 87505 . . . 505-989-8483
Kaplan, Lawrence: 46 Mercer St, New York, NY 10013 . . . 212-925-3010
Karaberis, Char: 130 W 12th Ave, Denver, CO 80204 . . . 303-446-9116
Karetnikov, Dimitri: 7 Tennyson Dr, Plainsboro, NJ 08536 . . . 609-275-6491
Kargus, Jo Ann: 5300 Old Lemay Ferry Rd, Imperial, MO 63052 . . . 314-942-4159
Kari, Morgan: 22853 Mariano #226, Woodland Hills, CA 91367 . . . 818-346-9167
Karl Studio, Kevin: 12437 Court Dr, St Louis, MO 63127 . . . 888-802-8111
Karl, Jason: 5704 SE 22nd Ave, Portland, OR 97207 . . . 503-768-1413
Karlic, Anthony: 160-30 25th Ave, Whitestone, NY 11357 . . . 718-747-2274
Karloff, Katia: 2122 Yosemite Dr, Los Angeles, CA 90041 . . . 213-340-1960
Karn, Murray: 120 E 86th St, New York, NY 10028 . . . 212-289-9124
Kars, Norman: 13827 Olive St Rd, Chesterfield, MO 63017 . . . 314-878-1780
Kasahara, Margaret: 3100 Carlisle #210, Dallas, TX 75204 . . . 214-969-0026
• **Kascht, John: pg 90,91** 108 E 35th St, New York, NY 10016 . . . **212-889-3337**
e-mail: gerald@rappart.com / url: www.theispot.com/rep/rapp / fax: 212-889-3341
Kase, Merri Ellen: 3109 Royal Sydney Court, Plano, TX 75093 . . . 972-306-5122
Kasid, Leo: 2272 Holyoke, Superior, CO 80027 . . . 303-499-2515
Kasnot, Keith: 612 N 2nd St, St Louis, MO 63102 . . . 314-781-7377
Kasperski, Tom: 1400 South Highway Dr, Fenton, MO 63099 . . . 314-827-4000
Kassan, David Jon: 7101 4th Ave #E6, Brooklyn, NY 11209 . . . 718-836-1280
Kassler, Elizabeth: 128 Prospect Ave, Dumont, NJ 07628 . . . 201-385-3551
Kasso, Larry: PO Box 40461, Baton Rouge, LA 70835 . . . 504-295-1644
Kastaris, Rip: 3301A S Jefferson Ave, St Louis, MO 63118 . . . 314-773-2600
Kastner, John: 158 Burwell Rd, Rochester, NY 14617 . . . 716-461-4701
Kasun Illustration, Mike: 301 N Water St 6th Fl, Milwaukee, WI 53202 . . . 414-347-1992
Kasun, Mike: 332 Bleecker St PMBK56, New York, NY 10014 . . . 212-691-2667
Kasun, Mike: 4 E Ohio Studio B, Chicago, IL 60611 . . . 312-321-1336
Katayama, Mits: 1904 Third Ave #630, Seattle, WA 98101 . . . 206-625-6946
Kato, RM: 710 Wildrose Ave, Monrovia, CA 91016 . . . 818-303-7229
Katrencik, Jeff: 632 W Grant St, Houston, PA 15342 . . . 724-745-4577
Katz, Aliona: 6 Parker Rd, Arlington, MA 02474 . . . 781-641-2787
Katz, Ivan: 198 19th Ave, San Francisco, CA 94121 . . . 718-668-8996
Katz, Les: 451 Westminster Rd, Brooklyn, NY 11218 . . . 718-284-4779
Katz, Louis: 2256 Ewing St, Los Angeles, CA 90039 . . . 323-661-3890
Katzowitz, Joel: 2570 Chimney Springs Dr, Marietta, GA 30331 . . . 770-641-9718
Kaufman, Donna: 3044 Orange Ave, La Crescenta, CA 91214 . . . 818-248-7022
Kaufman, Judith H: 1326 La Playa St, San Francisco, CA 94122 . . . 415-564-7291
Kaufman, Luana: 2635 St Paul St, Baltimore, MD 21218 . . . 410-366-4674
Kaufman, Mark: 5123 Reeder St, Elmhurst, NY 11373 . . . 718-672-3257
Kaufman, Shirona: 20 Chestnut St #9, Rye, NY 10580 . . . 914-967-4338
Kauftheil, Henry: 220 W 19th St #1200, New York, NY 10011 . . . 212-633-0222
• **Kay Design, Laura: pg 930** 105 Nutley St, Ashland, OR 97520 . . . **800-497-1752**
Kay, Michael: 4232 N Francisco Ave, Chicago, IL 60618 . . . 773-463-8565
• **Kay, Stanford: pg 785** Nyack, NY . . . **845-358-0798**
e-mail: skay@spyral.net / url: www.spyral.net/para
• **Kayganich, Bob: pg 305** 731 N 24th St, Philadelphia, PA 19130 . . . **215-232-6666**
url: www.deborahwolfeltd.com / fax: 215-232-6585
Kazi, Pat: 2813 Rocks Rd, Jarrettsville, MD 21084 . . . 410-838-9584
Kearin, Alan: 69 Engert Ave #2L, Brooklyn, NY 11222 . . . 718-388-6037
Kearney, Andrea Gay: 605 Mentone Ave #B, Grover Beach, CA 93433 . . . 805-481-3439
Kearney, Rob: 332 East 18th St, New York, NY 10003 . . . 212-388-0107
Kearney, Victoria: 7832 Toland Ave, Los Angeles, CA 90045 . . . 310-410-0292
Keating, Andrew: 1386 Holman Rd, Oakland, CA 94610 . . . 510-465-5192
Keating, Cameron: 548 N Wilson Ave, Pasadena, CA 91106 . . . 626-683-1159
Keats, Deborah: PO Box 6027, Schenectady, NY 12301 . . . 518-725-2664
Kecman, Milan: 7643 Montello Rd, Independence, OH 44134 . . . 216-520-3662
Kedar Designs, Ruth: 433 College Ave, Palo Alto, CA 94306 . . . 650-566-1900
Keegan, Jonathan: 711 Carroll St #3L, Brooklyn, NY 11215 . . . 718-399-7123
Keeling, Gregg Bernard: 5955 Harbor Dr, Oakland, CA 94611 . . . 510-653-8518
Keen, Katy: 163 Withers St, Brooklyn, NY 11211 . . . 718-389-7665
Keenan, Rob: 100 Van Dam St 2nd Fl, New York, NY 10013 . . . 212-255-7700
Keene, Donald: 3100 Carlisle #210, Dallas, TX 75204 . . . 214-969-0026
Keene, Donald: 519 Main St 2nd Fl, New Rochelle, NY 10801 . . . 914-636-2128
• **Keeter, Susan: pg 505** 666 Greenwich St #860, New York, NY 10014 . . . **212-675-5719**
e-mail: harriet@hkportfolio.com / url: www.hkportfolio.com / fax: 212-675-6341
Keeton, Sharon: 30 Tenney Dr, Rogue River, OR 97537 . . . 541-582-2165
Keeton, Sharon: 8202 Sorenson Ave, Santa Fe Springs, CA 90670 . . . 310-696-8085
Kehl, Richard: 8622 17th NE, Seattle, WA 98115 . . . 206-634-1162
Keim, Barbara: 161 Llewellyn Dr, Westfield, MA 01084 . . . 413-572-0688
Keith, Doug: 909 N 78th St, Seattle, WA 98103 . . . 206-783-3912
Keith, Gary: 1419 Parrott Dr, San Mateo, CA 94402 . . . 415-350-0307
Keitly, Laurence: Viewswood House, Uckfield, UK TN22 . . . 441825733746
Kelemen, Stephen: 161 Henry St, Brooklyn, NY 11201 . . . 718-855-7005
Kelen: 1922 W Newport, Chicago, IL 60657 . . . 773-975-9696
Keleny, Earl: 4202 Bagley Pkwy, Madison, WI 53705 . . . 608-236-0022
Keller, Katie: 100 Bleecker St, New York, NY 10012 . . . 212-982-6533
Keller, Laurie: 280 Madison Ave #1110, New York, NY 10016 . . . 212-545-9155
Keller, Merle: 5855 Green Valley Cir #308, Culver City, CA 90230 . . . 310-642-2721
• **Keller, Steve: pg 92,93** 108 E 35th St, New York, NY 10016 . . . **212-889-3337**
e-mail: gerald@rappart.com / url: www.theispot.com/rep/rapp / fax: 212-889-3341
Keller, Thomas K: 1095 Market St #41, San Francisco, CA 94103 . . . 415-558-8000
Kellerson, Cory: 913 Lancaster Ave, Syracuse, NY 13210 . . . 315-474-8160
Kelley, Barbara: 280 Madison Ave #1110, New York, NY 10016 . . . 212-545-9155
• **Kelley, Gary: pg 28,29** 305 E 50th St Ste 1, New York, NY 10022 . . . **212-223-9545**
url: www.richardsolomon.com / fax: 212-223-9633
Kelley, Kris: 11956 Gorham Ave #1, Los Angeles, CA 90049 . . . 310-826-5757
Kelley, Shane: 3417 University Blvd W #201, Kensington, MD 20895 . . . 800-222-0753
Kelley, Steve: 3501 Windom Rd, Brentwood, MD 20722 . . . 301-699-1766
Kelliher, Ralph: 406 Marine St, Richmond, CA 94801 . . . 510-237-9885
Kelly, Blair: 4 Hargate Ct, Etobicoke, ON M9R 3H5 . . . 416-249-4547
Kelly, Don: 69 Ocean St, New Bedford, MA 02740 . . . 508-993-5688
Kelly, Eileen: 813 Lincoln Ave, Falls Church, VA 22046 . . . 703-241-2727
Kelly, Gregory: 1815 S Lane St, Seattle, WA 98144 . . . 206-329-4010
Kelter, Joseph: 4 Village Row/Logan Sq, New Hope, PA 18938 . . . 215-862-4860
Kemp, Dan: 9543 Dublin Rd, Walkersville, MD 21793 . . . 301-845-6107
Kenarov, Miro: 317 Paseo de Peralta, Santa Fe, NM 87501 . . . 505-992-6740
Kendall, Brad: 217 Slater Ave, Providence, RI 02906 . . . 401-351-8017
Kendall, Dawn: 3 Harvard Dr, Brookfield, CT 06804 . . . 203-740-2535
Kendall, Gideon: 408 Seventh St #4, Brooklyn, NY 11215 . . . 718-788-8993
Kendrick, Dennis: 99 Bank St #3G, New York, NY 10014 . . . 212-594-5563
• **Kennedy, Anne: pg 505** 666 Greenwich St #860, New York, NY 10014 . . . **212-675-5719**
e-mail: harriet@hkportfolio.com / url: www.hkportfolio.com / fax: 212-675-6341
Kennedy, Dean: 865 Delaware St, Denver, CO 80204 . . . 303-820-2599
Kennedy, Kelly: 1025 Idaho Ave, Santa Monica, CA 90403 . . . 310-394-2239
Kennedy, Victor: 514 Meadowfield Ct, Lawrenceville, GA 30243 . . . 770-339-0345
Kennefick, Ed: 6039 N 17th Ave, Phoenix, AZ 85015 . . . 602-277-2975
Kenny, Mike: 43 E 19th St, New York, NY 10003 . . . 212-254-4996
Kenny, Steven: 130 Fodderstack Rd, Washington, VA 22747 . . . 540-675-2355
Kent, Nicholas: 138 W Olive, Long Beach, NY 11561 . . . 516-431-4258
Kent, William: 12424 Wilshire Blvd #1400, Los Angeles, CA 90025 . . . 310-207-6507
Kenyon, Kathleen: 59 Tinker St, Woodstock, NY 12498 . . . 914-679-2589
Kenyon, Liz: 4225 N 36th St #3, Phoenix, AZ 85018 . . . 602-224-6103
Keppler, Margaret: 350 W 57 St #4F, New York, NY 10019 . . . 212-315-5266
Kern, Michael: 2320 La Paz, Oceanside, CA 92054 . . . 760-752-3336
Kernan, Patrick: 26 NE 76th Ave, Portland, OR 97213 . . . 503-251-1839
Kerr, Bruce: 2530 Crawford #208, Evanston, IL 60201 . . . 847-328-0855
• **Kerr, Michael: pg 292** 731 N 24th St, Philadelphia, PA 19130 . . . **215-232-6666**
url: www.deborahwolfeltd.com / fax: 215-232-6585
Kesaji, Natasha: 1347 N Dearborn St #305, Chicago, IL 60610 . . . 312-482-8032
• **Kest, Kristin: pg 506** 666 Greenwich St #860, New York, NY 10014 . . . **212-675-5719**
e-mail: harriet@hkportfolio.com / url: www.hkportfolio.com / fax: 212-675-6341
Keswick Hamilton, Kimberlee: 3519 W 6th St, Los Angeles, CA 90020 . . . 213-380-3933
Keswick, Lauren: 425 14th St #C2, Brooklyn, NY 11215 . . . 718-965-6762
Ketchum, Charles Ray: 420 Lexington Ave #220, New York, NY 10170 . . . 212-687-3460
• **Ketelhut, Linda: pg 898** 23 Christopher St, New York, NY 10014 . . . **212-929-0922**
e-mail: farfetch@aol.com / url: www.theispot.com/artist/ketelhut
fax: 212-941-1514
Ketler, Ruth Sofair: 101 Bluff Terr, Silver Spring, MD 20902 . . . 301-593-6059
Kettler, Al: 3301 Mt Vernon Ave, Alexandria, VA 22305 . . . 703-548-8040
Key, Pamela: 18821 Kirkcolm Ln, Northridge, CA 91326 . . . 818-360-6295
Keyes, Steven: 481 8th Ave #E24, New York, NY 10001 . . . 212-631-0009
Keys, Watt: 612 E Tremont Ave, Charlotte, NC 28203 . . . 704-332-6576
Khalsi, Viviana Diaz: 36-25 30th St, Astoria, NY 11106 . . . 718-482-0682
Khromina, Ekaterina: RD #1 Box 361, Gilboa, NY 12076 . . . 607-588-8909
Kianersi, Nadir: 309 E Harrison #206, Seattle, WA 98102 . . . 206-329-3461
Kibiuk, Lydia V: 8 F Cross Keys Rd, Baltimore, MD 21210 . . . 410-433-1107
Kidd, Jason: 220 Kavanaugh Way, Pacifica, CA 94044 . . . 800-466-4060
Kidd, Jeremy: 615 Victoria Ave, Venice, CA 90291 . . . 310-827-6862
Kidd, Tom: 59 Cross Brook Rd, New Milford, CT 06776 . . . 203-355-1781
Kiefer, Alfons: 420 Lexington Ave, New York, NY 10170 . . . 212-986-5680
Kiel, Ronaldo: 661 Metroplitan Ave #3L, Brooklyn, NY 11211 . . . 718-782-4963
• **Kielty/Corinne, Tracey: pg 908** PO Box 6696, Beverly Hills, CA 90212 . . . **800-848-9364**
e-mail: traceyart@go.com / url: www.traceyart.com
• **Kiernan, Kenny: pg 177** 420 Lexington Ave, New York, NY 10170 . . . **212-986-5680**
e-mail: mendolaart@aol.com / url: www.mendolaart.com / fax: 212-818-1246
Kikuchi, Alan: 999 16th St #9, San Francisco, CA 94107 . . . 415-255-4594
Kilby, Don: 181 Carlaw Ave #226, Toronto, ON M4M 2S1 . . . 416-778-0106
Kilfoy Design: 3301A S Jefferson Ave, St Louis, MO 63118 . . . 314-773-2600
Kilgore, Susi: 2804 W Averill Ave, Tampa, FL 33611 . . . 813-837-9759
Kilgore, Tony: PO Box 882, Bloomington, IN 47401 . . . 812-331-7920
Killen, Michael: 112 Stratford Dr, McMurray, PA 15317 . . . 724-942-2977
Kilmer, Melinda: 35 Wooster St #4F, New York, NY 10013 . . . 212-226-6581
Kilroy, John: 28 Fairmount Way, Nantasket, MA 02045 . . . 617-925-0582
Kim, Joung Un: 866 United Nations Plaza, New York, NY 10017 . . . 212-644-2020
Kim, Soo Sa: 691 Post St #203, San Francisco, CA 94109 . . . 415-673-1567
Kim-Jin-Hwa, Saerom: 118 Horace Harding Blvd, Great Neck, NY 11020 . . . 212-880-3577
Kimak, James: 151 Kings Hwy, Orangeburg, NY 10962 . . . 914-359-1158
Kimball, Joel Michael: PO Box 506, Tekoa, WA 99033 . . . 509-284-3002
Kimball, Kathleen: 6207 29th Ave NE, Seattle, WA 98115 . . . 206-522-2710
• **Kimber, Murray: pg 30,31** 305 E 50th St Ste 1, New York, NY 10022 . . . **212-223-9545**
url: www.richardsolomon.com / fax: 212-223-9633
• **Kimble, David: pg 541** 4541 Highway 47 N, Rhinelander, WI 54501 . . . **715-369-2130**
Marfa, TX . . . **915-729-4802**
Kincade, John Orin: 27 Clove Brook Rd, Valhalla, NY 10595 . . . 914-773-0504
Kincaid, Samuel J: 242 E 38th St #1A, New York, NY 10016 . . . 212-697-2263
• **King, Alan: pg 284** 731 N 24th St, Philadelphia, PA 19130 . . . **215-232-6666**
url: www.deborahwolfeltd.com / fax: 215-232-6585
King, Fiona: PO Box 232722, Encinitas, CA 92023 . . . 888-522-3745
King, Greg: 2134 Aquetong Rd, New Hope, PA 18938 . . . 215-862-2091
• **King, JD: pg 94,95** 108 E 35th St, New York, NY 10016 . . . **212-889-3337**
e-mail: gerald@rappart.com / url: www.theispot.com/rep/rapp / fax: 212-889-3341
King, Manuel: 118 Congress St, Orange, MA 01364 . . . 978-544-7124
King, Stephen: 11645 SE 208th St Ste 6, Kent, WA 98031 . . . 253-856-1874
King-Judge, Cynthia: PO Box 4644, Montebello, CA 90640 . . . 213-721-3826
Kingfish Studios: PO Box 1491, Lancaster, PA 17608 . . . 717-291-6544
Kingham, David: 42 Blue Spruce Cir, Weston, CT 06883 . . . 203-226-3106
Kingsbery, Guy: 305 High St, Milford, CT 06460 . . . 203-878-8939
Kingsley, D: 525 W 22nd Street #3-E, New York City, NY 10011 . . . 212-645-7379
Kinkopf, Kathleen: 420 Lexington Ave, New York, NY 10170 . . . 212-986-5680
Kinnick, Liza: PO Box 1280/12053 Dove Terr, Truckee, CA 96160 . . . 530-587-0794
Kinstrey, Jim: 1036 Broadway, W Longbranch, NJ 07764 . . . 908-229-0312
Kirby, Jeffrey: 318 Ethan Allen Ave, Takoma Park, MD 20912 . . . 301-270-3462
Kirby, Jill: 1559 S 16th St, Milwaukee, WI 53204 . . . 414-672-1272
Kirk Noll, Cheryl: 19 Hooker St, Providence, RI 02908 . . . 401-861-5869
Kirk, Betsy: 216 Blenheim Rd, Baltimore, MD 21212 . . . 410-377-7530
Kirk, Bev: 5815 Sovereign Dr, Cincinnati, OH 45241 . . . 513-530-5353
Kirk, Daniel: 58 W 40th St 6th Fl, New York, NY 10018 . . . 212-682-1490
Kirk, Rainey: PO Box 174 11440 Oak Dr, Shelbyville, MI 49344 . . . 616-672-5756
• **Kirkbride, Michael: pg 847** ,, . . . **415-924-3839**
url: www.theispot.com / fax: 415-924-3839
Kirkland Studios: 232 Madison Ave #512, New York, NY 10016 . . . 212-889-8777
Kirkland, Cynthia: 10428 County Rd, 2332, Terrell, TX 75160 . . . 972-524-8578
Kirkland, Guy: 100 Jackson #302, Houston, TX 77002 . . . 713-228-7874

Kurman, Miriam: 422 Amsterdam #2A, New York, NY 10024 212-580-1649
Kurrasch, Toni: 420 Lexington Ave, New York, NY 10170. 212-986-5680
Kurrasch, Toni: 664 Old Quarry Rd N, Larkspur, CA 94939 415-464-0744
Kursar, Ray: 1 Lincoln Plaza #43R, New York, NY 10023 212-873-5605
Kurtz, John: 43 E 19th St, New York, NY 10003 212-254-4996
Kurtz-Schoettel, Nancy: W2705 County Rd NN, Neosho, WI 53059 414-476-1587
Kurtzman, Ed: 60 E 42nd St #1146, New York, NY 10165 212-953-7088
Kurtzman, Harvey: 481 8th Ave #E24, New York, NY 10001. 212-631-0009
Kurylonek, Adam: 5483 Palmerston Crl, Mississauga, ON L5M5Z8 416-889-8502
Kushner, Leslie: PO Box 660, Mill Valley, CA 94941 415-389-9576
Kusmierski, Janet: 9 Murray St Loft 6SE, New York, NY 10007. 212-233-5458
Kutakoff, Lauren: 47 Cobblewood Rd, Livingston, NJ 07039. 201-994-3569
Kutsch, Patricia: 32 N Fifth Ave, Des Plaines, IL 60016. 847-803-8728
Kutz, Carol: RFD #1 Box 58, Lagrange, ME 02143. 207-943-7974
Kuyath, John: 500 Wyoming, Cincinnatti, OH 45215 513-761-7773
Kwong, Michael: 391 Oak St #A1, Columbus, OH 43215 614-221-1326
Kyhos, Brian: 1885 Baird Rd, Penfield, NY 14526 716-385-8998
Kylberg, Virginia: PO Box 186, Clio, CA 96106. 530-836-4312

L

L'Abbe, Mary Beth: 4790 E Belleview Ave, Littleton, CO 80121 303-741-4391
La Haye, Barney: 611 Broadway #610, New York, NY 10012 212-505-6802
• **La Pine, Julia: pg 872** **206-284-4701**
Chicago **888-546-7688**
San Francisco **415-440-1990**
fax: 206-282-3499
La Rocca, Isabella: 1155 Fifth St #304, Oakland, CA 94607. 510-839-4652
Labadie, Ed: 3720 Stone Creek Wy, Boise, ID 83703 208-388-0411
Labaff, Tom: 714 Saxbury Ave, Orlando, FL 32835 407-290-1552
Labatt, Diane D: 515 Roselawn Ave, Toronto, ON M5N 1K2 416-485-9829
Labbe, Jeff: 311 Avenue H #D, Redondo Beach, CA 90277. 310-540-5958
Labbe, John: 97 Third Ave #2E, New York, NY 10003 212-529-2831
LaBonty, GJ: 1138 West Glen Springs Wy, West Jordan, UT 84088. 801-565-8212
Labrasca, Judy: 7 Walcott Ave, Falmouth, ME 04105 207-781-3858
Lacano, Frank: 336 Sherwood Rd, Union, NJ 07083. 908-688-9251
Lacek, Joe: 51 Lyons Run Rd, Glenmoore, PA 19343 610-458-1511
Lacey, Joe: 6115 Vista Terr, Orefield, PA 18069 610-336-4460
Lacey, Lucille: 45 Carmine St, New York, NY 10014 212-366-1682
Lachance, Patti: 4 Pelham Park, Fairport, NY 14450. 716-388-9332
Lackner, Paul: 332 Bleecker St PMBK56, New York, NY 10014. 212-691-2667
Lackner, Paul: 4 E Ohio Studio B, Chicago, IL 60611 312-321-1336
Lackner, Paul: 1225 W 4th St, Waterloo, IA 50702. 319-234-2089
Lackow, Andy: 7004 Boulevard East #29C, Guttenberg, NJ 07093 201-868-9585
LaCourse, Carol: Six Steppingstone Rd W, Lee, NH 03824 603-659-6149
Lacz, John: 2840 Somerset Dr, Ft Lauderdale, FL 33311. 305-735-0752
• **Lada, Elizabeth: pg 525** 100 Bleecker St, New York, NY 10012 . . . . **212-982-6533**
url: www.bruckandmoss.com / fax: 212-358-1586
333 E 49th St, New York, NY 10017. . . . . **212-980-8061**
url: www.bruckandmoss.com / fax: 212-832-8778
Lada, Mir: 280 Madison Ave #1110, New York, NY 10016 212-545-9155
Ladas, George: 165 E 32nd St, New York, NY 10016 212-686-3514
Ladden, Randee: 7445 N Rockwell St, Chicago, IL 60645 773-761-6288
Laden, Nina: 5002 92nd Ave SE, Mercer Island, WA 98040 206-232-7873
Lafebvre, Yolaine: 4282-C rue Fullum, Montréal, QU H2H 2J5 514-434-6620
• **Lafleur, Dave: pg 221** Chicago, IL. **312-364-0244**
London. **011-44-207-636-1064**
Los Angeles, CA. **323-874-5700**
Washington, DC. **410-349-8669**
New York, NY **212-333-2551**
url: www.shannonassociates.com
Lafrance, Laurie: 90 Sumach St #617, Toronto, ON M5A 4R4 416-863-5115
Lafrance, Marie: 4030 St Ambroise #400, Montréal, QU H4C 2C7 514-397-2363
Lagano, Alex: 1555 W 7th St, Brooklyn, NY 11204 718-331-1143
LaGrossa, Anthony: 223m Hendrickson Mill Rd, Swedesboro, NJ 08085 856-467-7930
Lahdesmaki, Markku: 8950 Ellis Ave, Los Angeles, CA 90034 310-838-9833
• **Laidlaw, Ken: pg 361** 280 Madison Ave #1110, New York, NY 10016 . . . . **212-545-9155**
url: www.irmeliholmberg.com / fax: 212-545-9462
Laipnitz, Joan: 405 Menge Rd, Marengo, IL 60152. 815-943-5490
Laird, Campbell: 100 Hudson St #3D, New York, NY 10013 212-219-3767
Laird, Thomas L: 706 Scott St, Philipsburg, PA 16866 814-342-2935
Laish, James: 55 Charles St W #2604, Toronto, ON M5S 2W9 416-921-1709
Laizure, Nichole: PO Box 434, Cave Creek, AZ 85331. 520-488-9012
Lajos, Andre: 124 Renny Cresent, London, ON N6E 2C5 519-686-2969
LaLiberté, Louise-Andrée: 1111 Rue De Gustave-Langelier, Cap-rouge, PQ G1Y 2J3 418-658-0523
LaLiberté, Richard: 5610 N Kenmore #1N, Chicago, IL 60660. 773-271-0380
Lallky-Seibert, Bonnie: 1675 NE 36th St, Ft Lauderdale, FL 33334. 954-564-3259
Lally, Michele: 345 California Dr #196, Burlingame, CA 94010 415-344-2100
Lam, Chris: 57 Corning Rd, North York, ON M25 2L9 416-756-0206
Lamb, Greg: 58 School St, Holliston, MA 01746. 508-429-4778
Lambase, Barbara: 137 W 14th St #204, New York, NY 10011. 212-337-0055
2705 Via Anita, Palos Verdes Estates, CA 90274 310-373-4993
3100 Carlisle #210, Dallas, TX 75204. 214-969-0026
• **Lambert, Anne: pg 530** 7 Washington St, Beverly, MA 01915 . . . . **978-921-0887**
e-mail: leighton@leightonreps.com / url: www.leightonreps.com
fax: 978-921-0223
Lambert, John: 1727 N Warren Ave, Milwaukee, WI 53202. 414-643-5205
Lambrenos, Jim: 803 Salem Ct, Atco, NJ 08004 856-768-0580
Lammle, Leslie A: 687 E 2nd Ave #7, Salt Lake City, UT 84103 801-539-5065
LaMont, Susan: 1025 Union Church Rd, McLean, VA 22102 703-759-0246
Lampe, Alan: 1331 47th St, Des Moines, IA 50311 515-274-6567
Lamut, Sonja: 201 E 87th St #19K, New York, NY 10128 212-831-4634
Lamut, Sonja : 350 Central Park West, New York, NY 10025 212-749-4907
Lanaux, Thomas: 1224 Taylor St #4, San Francisco, CA 94108 415-776-9296
Landerman, Art: 9458 Dunloggin Rd, Ellicott City, MD 21042 410-461-7926
Landis, Jeff: 318 Fairside Ct, Sun City Cntr, FL 33573. 813-229-2300
Landis, Joan: 6 Jane St, New York, NY 10014 212-989-7074
Landman, Mark: 365 Maple Ave, Cotati, CA 94931 707-792-1326
Landon, Carolyne: 41 Union Square W #937, New York, NY 10003 212-414-1942
Landry, Marie-France: 6652 rue de Saint-Vallier, Montréal, QU H2S 2P7. 514-270-2108
Lane, Edmund: 25 Lexington Ln, Millis, MA 02054. 508-376-8752
Lane, Nancy: 10 Glendale Rd, Ossing, NY 10562 914-944-0565
Lane, Robert: 6711 East Ave, Chevy Chase, MD 20815. 301-215-7974
Lane, Sherry: 155 Bank St #404, New York, NY 10014 212-675-6224
Lane, Tammie: 431 W Colfax Ave #540, Denver, CO 80204 303-446-2611
Lane, Tammie: 413 Independence Pl, Aspen, CO 81611 970-925-9213
Lang, Cecily: 336 West End Ave #18C, New York, NY 10023 212-580-3424
Lang, Donna: 564 Madrone Ave, Sunnyvale, CA 94085 408-739-4731
Lang, Gary: 420 Lexington Ave #2760, New York, NY 10170 212-697-8525
Lang, Glenna: 42 Stearns St, Cambridge, MA 02138 617-661-7591
Lange, Andrew: 9 Thoma Ave, Maywood, NJ 07607 201-646-9210
Lange, Denis K: 1545 Country Rd #995, Ashland, OH 44805 419-289-0181
Lange, Jim: 203 N Wabash #1312, Chicago, IL 60601 312-606-9313
Lange, Poul Hans: 156 Ludlow St 3rd Fl, New York, NY 10002 646-654-6760
Langeder, Helmut: 6700 Park Ave #400, Montreal, QU H2V 4H9. 514-495-6700
Langelier-Lebeda, Suzanne: 63 Bay Rd, S Colton, NY 13687 315-262-3150
Langenderfer, Tim: 10 E Ontario #4708, Chicago, IL 60611 312-573-1370
Langenderfer, Tim: 135 W Dorothy Lane #116, Dayton, OH 45429 937-298-5133
Langeneckert, Donald: 4939 Ringer Rd, St Louis, MO 63129. 314-487-2042
Langenstein, Michael: 56 Thomas St 2nd Fl, New York, NY 10013 212-964-9637
Langer, DC: 1800 Sunset Harbour #2201, Miami Beach, FL 33139 305-604-0444
Langer, Jean-Claude: 2117 5th St, Berkeley, CA 94710. 510-883-0513
Langevin, Isabelle: 1091 Rang 1 CP 37, Bernierville, QU G0N 1N0. 418-428-9835
Langille, Lori: 31 Morris St, Ottawa, ON K1S 4A6. 613-226-5898
• **Langley, Stephanie: pg 486** 83 Walnut Ave, Corte Madera, CA 94925 . . . . . . **415-924-7881**
e-mail: gatlin@ritareps.com / url: www.ritareps.com / fax: 415-924-7891
. . . . **800-924-7881**
Langlios, Suzane: 2164 rue Amherst, Montréal, QU H2L 3L8 514-526-2600
Langsdorf, Henrik: 636 Broadway #1218, New York, NY 10012 212-982-5222
• **Languedoc, Patricia: pg 422** 7118 Upper River Rd, Prospect, KY 40059 . . . . . **502-228-9427**
url: www.jettreps.com / fax: 502-228-8857
Lanino, Deborah: 6735 Ridge Blvd #6B, Brooklyn, NY 11220 718-491-0085
Lansaw, J Lea: 7018 Braeburn Pl, Bethesda, MD 20817. 301-320-9169
Lantz, David: 280 Madison Ave #1110, New York, NY 10016 212-545-9155
Lanza, Barbara: 134 Christian St, New Preston, CT 06777. 860-868-1011
Laoang, Alfred: 13416 Justice Rd, Rockville, MD 20853 301-946-2530
Lapadula, Tom: 43 E 19th St, New York, NY 10003 212-254-4996
Lapinski, Joe: 853 Broadway #1201, New York, NY 10003. 212-677-9100
Laplante, Jacques: 4068 St Christophe, Montreal, QU H2L 2Y2. 514-983-9020
Laporte, Michele: 579 Tenth St, Brooklyn, NY 11215 718-499-2178
Lapsley, Bob: 2430 Glen Haven Blvd, Houston, TX 77030. 713-667-4393
Lara, Carlos: 300 Broadway #14, San Francisco, CA 94133 415-957-1369
Lara, Mabel: 182 W 960 N #B, Provo, UT 84604 801-373-4199
Laramie, Jason: 25 Cornell Rd, Nashua, NH 03060 603-886-5857
Lardy, Philippe: 225 Lafayette St #613, New York, NY 10012 212-219-0324
Larocca, Isabelle: 1155 5th Street #304, Oakland, CA 94607 510-839-4652
LaRocco, Richard: 8 Parnell Dr, Smithtown, NY 11787 516-360-7796
LaRoche, Giles: 41 Dearborn St, Salem, MA 01970 978-745-4629
Larochelle, Yvon: CP 1284 Étang-du-Nord, Iles de la madele, QU G0B 1E0 418-986-6165
LaRose, Lou: 11768 Monte Leon Wy, Northridge, CA 91326 818-360-1200
LaRotonda, Craig: PMB 275 1072 Folsom St, San Francisco, CA 94103 415-557-1023
Larrivee, Steven: 1430 Pippin Orchard Rd, Cranston, RI 02921 401-821-8417
Larsen, Eric: 710 SE Grand Ave #10, Portland, OR 97214 503-234-1913
Larson, Keith: 99 Park Ave #210A, New York, NY 10016 800-398-9544
Larson, Lynne: 121 Corona Way, Portola Valley, CA 94028 . . . . 415-854 6485
Larson, Paul: 1125 6th St #9, Santa Monica, CA 90403. 310-458-9140
• **Lascaro, Rita: pg 827** 75 E 7th St, New York, NY 10003. . . . . **212-677-6494**
e-mail: britonia@aol.com / fax: 212-260-6076
Lasher, Mary Ann: 58 W 40th St 6th Fl, New York, NY 10018 212-682-1490
Laslo, Rudy: 89 Fifth Ave #901, New York, NY 10003 212-627-1554
Latronica, Lisa Joy: 16955 Oak Ridge Ln, Morgan Hill, CA 95037. 408-778-1229
Latta Art Services, Bill: 536 Wilson Dr, Mt Juliet, TN 37122 615-758-8369
Lattimer, Evan: 4203 Holly, Kansas City, MO 64111 816-561-0103
Latto, Sophia: 723 President St, Brooklyn, NY 11215 718-789-1980
Latulippe, Luc: 404-5 Benlamond Ave, Toronto, ON M4E 1Y8. 416-924-2431
Lau, Bernadette: 50 Perthshire St, Scarborough, ON M1V 3A9 416-291-0524
Laub, Rolf: 4101 Greenbriar #320, Houston, TX 77098 713-522-9873
Laubach, Rainer: 4948 St Elmo Ave, Bethesda, MD 20814 301-718-7955
Laubengayer, Karen: 6012 Essex St, Millington, TN 38053. 901-872-2593
Laughing Stock: 192 Southville Rd, Southborough, MA 01772 508-460-6058
Laughlin, David: 1210 Virginia St, Key West, FL 33040. 305-292-5607
Laughlin, Stephen: 11 River Park Dr, New Paltz, NY 12561 914-255-2017
• **Laumann, Scott: pg 98,99** 108 E 35th St, New York, NY 10016. . . . . **212-889-3337**
e-mail: gerald@rappart.com / url: www.theispot.com/rep/rapp / fax: 212-889-3341
Lauren The Cartoon Goddess: PO Box 2283, Edison, NJ 08818 732-549-1455
Laurence, Karen: 531 Main St #1002, Roosevelt Island, NY 10044 212-751-8215
Laureys, Cecilia M: 463 W 24th St #3R, New York, NY 10011 212-727-1894
Laven, John: 1231 W 12th Ave, Escondido, CA 92025 619-547-4114
Lavendel, Larry: PO Box 1418, Aptos, CA 95001 831-662-9634
Lavenstein, Victor: 119 Massasoit Ave, Cranston, RI 02905 401-461-9611
Laverdiere, Benoit: 5230 av Papineau, Montreal, QU H2H 1W2 514-522-2510
Lavigne, Dan: 11936 W Jefferson Blvd #C, Culver City, CA 90230 310-390-8663
Lavin, Arnie: 23 Glenlawn Ave, Seacliff, NY 11579 516-676-1228
Law, Polly: 15 Clint Finger Rd, Saugerties, NY 12477 914-247-9026
Law, Rebecca: 12590 Wardell Ct, Saratoga, CA 95070 510-873-3764
Lawerence, John: 44-10 Ketchum St, Elmhurst, NY 11373 718-426-3320
Lawhead, Elizabeth: 6233 SE 40th Ave, Portland, OR 97202. 503-242-0034
Lawler, Elizabeth: 2918 English Ave, Louisville, KY 40206 502-895-0515
Lawrence, John: 455 W 23rd St #8D, New York, NY 10011 212-366-1893
Lawrence, Juliet : 174 Summit Ave #306, Summit, NJ 07901 908-273-1934
Lawson, Gregory M.: 14325 Wrangler Ln, Dale City, VA 22193. 703-878-1785
Lawson, Paula: 101 LaCosta Ct, Garland, TX 75044 972-414-4035
Lawson, Rob: 99 Park Ave #210A, New York, NY 10016 800-398-9544
Lawson, Rob: 4005 Grand Prarie Rd, Kalamazoo, MI 49006 616-345-7607
Lawton, April: 31 Hampshire Dr, Farmingdale, NY 11735 516-454-0868
Lay, Toby: 7118 Upper River Rd, Prospect, KY 40059 502-228-9427
Layman, Linda J: 9 Alan Rd, South Hamilton, MA 01982 508-468-4297

Lazansky, Aaron: 60 Amsterdam Ave #5A, New York, NY 10023 212-586-8747
• **Lazar, Zohar: pg 749** 102 Luquer St #1L, Brooklyn, NY 11231 . . . . **718-852-2293**
e-mail: zlazar@earthlink.net / url: www.zoharlazar.com
Lazerus: PO Box 13249, Oakland, CA 94661 510-339-6263
Lazure, Catherine: 593 Riverside Dr #6D, New York, NY 10031 212-690-1867
Le Masurier, James: 165 E 32nd St, New York, NY 10016 212-686-3514
Le Pautremat, Bertrand: 420 Lexington Ave #2760, New York, NY 10170 212-697-8525
Le Van Studio, Susan: 30 Ipswich St #211, Boston, MA 02215 617-536-6828
Le-Tan, Pierre: 155 W 15th St #4C, New York, NY 10011 212-989-8770
Lea, Derek: 692 Sammon Ave, Toronto, ON M4C 2E4 416-429-4020
Leaders, Marsha: 20117 Laurel Hill Way, Germantown, MD 20874 301-540-1652
Leahy, Joe: 4730 Latona Ave NE, Seattle, WA 98105 206-547-1001
Leary, Catherine: 11672 Missouri Ave, Los Angeles, CA 90025 310-473-2775
Leary, T Pat: 883 E 11150 S, Sandy, UT 84094 801-572-2753
Leathers, Bob: 1285 Old River Rd, Cleveland, OH 44113 216-621-6933
Leavitt, Brian: 309 W Oak Hill Rd, Porter, IN 46304 219-395-8646
• **LeBarre, Erika: pg 495** PO Box 174 11440 Oak Dr, Shelbyville, MI 49344 . . . . **616-672-5756**
e-mail: neisgroup@wmis.net / url: www.neisgroup.com / fax: 616-672-5757
• **LeBarre, Matt: pg 494** PO Box 174 11440 Oak Dr, Shelbyville, MI 49344 . . . . . **616-672-5756**
e-mail: neisgroup@wmis.net / url: www.neisgroup.com / fax: 616-672-5757
Lebbad, James: 24 Independence Way, Titusville, NJ 08560 609-737-3458
LeBlanc, Rebecca: 363 Dunbar Knoll, Mahtomedi, MN 55115 651-779-0202
LeBlond, Jason: 11 Crestwood Ln, Clark, NJ 07066 732-388-9650
Lebo, Narda: 1004 N Montclair, Dallas, TX 75208 214-941-2156
Lederman, Marsha: 4 Alpine Ct, East Brunswick, NJ 08816 908-257-9324
Ledger, Richard: 7 Heath House, Main Rd, Sidcup Kent, London, England, UK DA14 1813-023930
Leduc, Huguette: 825 Av. Dollard, Outremont, QU H2V 3G8 514-279-7675
Ledwidge, Natacha: 42 Delavan St, Brooklyn, NY 11231 718-624-1906
Lee, Bill: 792 Columbus Ave #1-O, New York, NY 10025 212-866-5664
Lee, Bryce: 38 W 21st St 3rd Fl, New York, NY 10010 212-268-9400
Lee, Charmain: 752 Manning Ave, Toronto, ON M6G 2W4 416-534-1461
Lee, Daniel: 200 Mercer St, New York, NY 10012 212-677-2989
Lee, Fran: 7225 N Vincent Ave, Portland, OR 97217 503-286-4767
Lee, Hector Viveros: 355 Head St, San Francisco, CA 94132 415-641-8041
• **Lee, Jared: pg 602,603** 2942 Hamilton Rd, Lebanon, OH 45036 . . . . **513-932-2154**
e-mail: jleestudio@aol.com / url: www.theispot.com/artist/jaredlee or www.workbook.com/portfolios/lee_j / fax: 513-932-9389
Lee, Jee Hee: 58 Kensington Ave #303, Toronto, ON M5T 2K1 416-351-1196
Lee, Jennifer: 398 Third Ave #3C, New York, NY 10016 212-686-4558
Lee, Jim: 346 C Pleasent St, Pasadena, CA 91101 626-396-9465
Lee, Kelly: 3511 N 22nd St, Arlington, VA 22207 703-527-4089
• **Lee, Lilly: pg 880** Pittsburgh, PA **412-802-0800**
www.jrille@earthlink.net
Lee, Michael: 5855 Green Valley Cir #308, Culver City, CA 90230 310-642-2721
Lee, Michele Dina: 12306 7th Helena Drive, Los Angeles, CA 90049 310-472-0980
Lee, Rick: 2645 Osceola St, Denver, CO 80212 303-561-1370
Lee, Robert J: PO Box 257, Pleasantville, NY 10570 914-747-2220
Lee, Steve: 709 W 90th Terr, Kansas City, MO 64114 816-822-2024
• **Lee, Tim: pg 138** 420 Lexington Ave, New York, NY 10170 . . . . **212-986-5680**
e-mail: mendolaart@aol.com / url: www.mendolaart.com / fax: 212-818-1246
Lee, Victoria: D8 Holiday Estates, Jessup, MD 20794 301-596-3532
Lee, Walter: 85 N Chester Ave, Pasadena, CA 91106 626-792-8770
Lee, Warren: 88 Meadow Valley Rd, Corte Madera, CA 94925 415-924-0261
• **Lee, Yuan: pg 320, 321** 217 E 86th St #212, New York, NY 10028 . . . . **212-427-5632**
e-mail: jeff@lavatyart.com / url: www.lavatyart.com / fax: 212-427-6372
Leech, Dorothy: 1024 Ave of Americas 4th Fl, New York, NY 10018 212-354-6641
• **Leech, Kent: pg 309** 716 Montgomery St, San Francisco, CA 94111 . . . . **415-433-1222**
www.sweetreps.com / fax: 415-433-9560
Leeds, Beth Whybrow: 990 Filbert St, San Francisco, CA 94133 415-928-0457
Leedy, Jeff: 607 Bridgeway, Sausalito, CA 94965 415-331-9091
Leer, Rebecca J: 294 Bellair Rd, Ridgewood, NJ 07450 201-612-7728
Leete, William W: 202 Silver Lake Ave, Wakefield, RI 02879 401-783-8055
Lefkowitz, Mark: 132 Oak Hill Dr, Sharon, MA 02067 617-784-5293
Legaspi, Randy: 1311 E Harvard, Glendale, CA 91205 818-244-4786
Legnami, Susan: 389 Clementina St, San Francisco, CA 94103 415-777-9569
Lehar, Carol: 9 Lawnwood Pl, Charlestown, MA 02129 781-449-1714
Lehar, Cecil: 27 Bleecker St, New York, NY 10012 212-533-0466
Lehew, Ron: 17 Chestnut St, Salem, NJ 08079 609-935-1422
Lehman, Connie: PO Box 281, Elizabeth, CO 80107 303-646-4638
Lehner & Whyte Digital Design/Illustration: 8-10 S Fullerton Ave, Montclair, NJ 07042 . 973-746-1335
Leifheit, Diane: Hunt Bldg Rt 86, Gabriels, NY 12939 518-327-3473
Leigh, Tom: RR1 Box 224A Swain's Cove Rd, Little Deer Isle, ME 04650 207-348-9382
• **Leighton, Aaron: pg 532** **416-530-1500**
url: www.linkartists.com or www.aaronleighton.com / fax: 416-530-1401
Leiner, Alan: 353 W 53rd St #1W, New York, NY 10019 212-682-2462
• **Leister, Bryan: pg 336,337** 58 W 15th St, New York, NY 10011 . . . . **212-741-2539**
url: www.jdedell.com or www.theispot.com or www.bryanleister.com
fax: 212-741-4660
Lekander, Lance: 2149 Lyon St #5, San Francisco, CA 94115 415-921-7140
Lelup, Carol: 2134 Aquetong Rd, New Hope, PA 18938 215-862-2091
Lemay, Katy: 962 Davaar St #5, Montral, QU H2V 3B6 514-495-8387
Lemelman, Martin: 1286 Country Club Rd, Allentown, PA 18106 215-395-4536
Lemieux, Margo: 22 Highland Ave, Mansfield, MA 02048 508-339-7487
Lemieux, Marie-Andrée: 857 Ste Anne Rd, Stukely Sud, QU J0E 2J0 450-539-3930
LeMonnier, Joe: 9 Babbling Brook Ln, Suffern, NY 10901 845-368-8606
LeMoult, Dolph: 597 Riverside Ave, Westport, CT 06880 203-226-4724
Lenar, Loci B: 17 Central Ave, Mine Hill, NJ 07801 201-989-0934
Lengyel, Kathy: poBox 2621, Dunedin, FL 34698 727-736-8421
Lengyel, Kathy: 848 Greenwood Ave NE, Atlanta, GA 30306 404-875-1363
Lennon, Jim: 2603 W Fairmont #204, Fresno, CA 93705 559-227-7648
Lensch, Chris: 16 Phaedra, Laguna Niguel, CA 92677 949-495-3664
Lentz, Jon Warren: 3213 Via Pescado, Carlsbad, CA 92009 760-476-0022
Lentz/PSI, Jon Warren: 2718 Socorro Ln, Carlsbad, CA 92009 760-730-3554
Leon, Anthony: 1350 Winstead Ct, St Charles, MO 63304 314-939-5290
Leon, Karen: 154-01 Barclay Ave, Flushing, NY 11355 718-461-2050
Leon, Thomas: 314 N Mission Dr, San Gabriel, CA 91775 818-458-7699
Leonard, Jenkins: 1712 2nd Ave #5N, New York, NY 10128 212-876-3858
Leonard, Joann: 2525 Thames St, Los Angeles, CA 90046 323-656-3899
Leonard, Richard: 212 W 17th St #2B, New York, NY 10011 212-243-6613
Leonard, Tom: 866 United Nations Plaza, New York, NY 10017 212-644-2020
Leonard-Gibson, Barbara: 3501 Toddsbury Ln, Olney, MD 20832 301-570-9480
Leonard-Stock, Lois: 3 Stratton Pl, Portland, ME 04101 207-761-0038
Leonardo, Curtis: 4308 Omega Ave, Castro Valley, CA 94546 510-886-1669
• **Leonardo: pg 733** 95 Weldrick Rd E #10 Richmond Hills, Ont L4C0H6 . . . . **905-770-2199**
fax: 905-770-9798
• **Leonardo, Todd: pg 900** 19110 Almond Rd, Castro Valley, CA 94546 . . . . **510-728-1076**
fax: 510-728-1076
Leone, Renee: 220 W Willow, Chicago, IL 60614 312-944-9733
• **Leopold, Susan: pg 270** 250 W 57th St #521, New York, NY 10107 . . . . **212-397-7330**
e-mail: San Francisco: 415-788-8552 / url: www.lindgrensmith.com
Lepine, Philip W: 31 Brighton Rd, Tonawanda, NY 14150 716-875-5490
Lerwigsky, Leon: 95 Weldrick Rd E Ste 10, Richmond Hill, ON L4C 0H6 905-770-2199
Lesh, David: 18 McKinley St, Rowayton, CT 06853 203-866-3734
Lesh, David: 5693 N Meridian St, Indianapolis, IN 46208 317-253-3141
Leslie, Carolanne: 138 Cleveland Ave, Rockville Centre, NY 11570 516-594-9297
Lesnick, H Robert: 1001 City Ave #EE821, Wynnewood, PA 19096 610-642-8948
Lessard, Marie: 4641 rue Hutchinson, Montréal, QU H2V 4A2 514-272-5696
Lesser, Ron: 420 Lexington Ave #2760, New York, NY 10170 212-697-8525
• **Lester, Mike: pg 503** 597 Riverside Ave, Westport, CT 06880 . . . . **203-226-4724**
e-mail: creative.svcs@snet.net / url: www.brewstercreative.com / fax: 203-454-9904
. . . . **706-234-7733**
url: www.mikelester.com / fax: 706-234-0084
Leszczynski, Tomas: 350 Central Park West, New York, NY 10025 212-749-4907
Letostak, John: 933 N Church Dr #106, Cleveland, OH 44130 216-885-1753
Letter Perfect: PO Box 785, Gig Harbor, WA 98335 206-956-9422
LeuckFeldhaus, Anne: 2156 N Oakley, Chicago, IL 60647 773-772-1085
LeVan, Jeff: 731 N 24th St, Philadelphia, PA 19130 215-232-6666
Levan, Lon: 13060 Otsego St, Sherman Oaks, CA 91423 323-791-5030
• **LeVan, Susan: pg 524,525** 333 E 49th St, New York, NY 10017 . . . . **212-980-8061**
url: www.bruckandmoss.com / fax: 212-832-8778
100 Bleecker St, New York, NY 10012 . . . . **212-982-6533**
url: www.bruckandmoss.com / fax: 212-358-1586
LeVan/Barbee Studio: 30 Ipswich St #211, Boston, MA 02215 617-536-6828
Levee, Gayle: 51 Century St, Medford, MA 02155 617-396-9656
Levenson, Wendy: 19 Flintlock Dr, Warren Town, NJ 07059 908-647-0900
Leveque, Lyne: 34 av des Saules, Saint Basile le gr, QU J3N 1G8 514-461-2935
Levin, Arnie: 23 Glenlawn Ave, Sea Cliff, NY 11579 516-676-1228
Levin, Bill: 4903 N Winthrop Ave, Indianapolis, IN 46205 317-335-6023
Levin, Keith: 16512 Blackbeard Ln #103, Huntington Beach, CA 92649 714-840-7381
Levin, Lynne: 175 W 93rd St, New York, NY 10025 212-932-0042
Levin, Mara: 23 Water St, Holliston, MA 01746 508-429-0762
Levine, Andy: 23-30 24th St, Long Island City, NY 11105 718-956-8539
Levine, Bette: 639 S Highland, Los Angeles, CA 90036 323-935-9199
Levine, Faye: 4609 Shoreline Dr #210, Spring Park, MN 55384 612-471-8441
Levine, John: 8897 S Zephya St, Littleton, CO 80128 303-233-3348
Levine, Lucinda: 2613 Blain Dr, Chevy Chase, MD 20815 202-667-5365
Levine, Ned: 301 Frankel Blvd, Merrick, NY 11566 516-378-8122
Levine, Polar: 86 Thomas St, New York, NY 10013 212-732-2449
Levinson, David: 65 Arthur St, Ridgefield Park, NJ 07660 201-994-1585
Levinson, Jason: 11625 Sun Circle Way, Columbia, MD 21044 410-720-1004
Levona, Avner: 11 Davies Ave #202, Toronto, ON M4M 2A9 416-461-4847
Levstek, Ljuba: 4 Normandy Blvd, Toronto, ON M4L 3K2 416-867-9345
Levy, Aimee: 527 San Vicente Blvd #301, Santa Monica, CA 90402 310-319-3788
Levy, Pamela R: 7 Trapelo St, Brighton, MA 02135 617-254-5779
Levy, Robert S: 1023 Fairway Rd, Franklin Square, NY 11010 516-872-3713
Lew, Kent: 452 Washington Mtn Rd, Washington, MA 01223 413-623-0212
Lewin, Laurie: 206 Sir Geoffrey Ct, Blakeslee, PA 18610 570-643-1519
Lewin, Ted: 152 Willoughby Ave, Brooklyn, NY 11205 718-622-3882
LeWinter, Renee: 41 Sewall St, Somerville, MA 02145 617-628-5695
• **Lewis, Anthony: pg 506** 666 Greenwich St #860, New York, NY 10014 . . . . . . **212-675-5719**
e-mail: harriet@hkportfolio.com / url: www.hkportfolio.com / fax: 212-675-6341
Lewis, Buck: 150 Chestnut St 4th Fl, Providence, RI 02930 800-522-1377
Lewis, EB: 1425 Mays Landing Rd, Folsom, NJ 08037 609-561-8469
Lewis, H B: 16 Canoncuet Rd, Hope Valley, RI 02832 800-522-1377
Lewis, Maurice: 353 W 53rd St #1W, New York, NY 10019 212-682-2462
Lewis, Polly Krumbhaar: 125 McClenaghan Mill Rd, Wynnewood, PA 19096 . . . 215-649-1989
Lewis, Ray: 1424 Hacienda Dr, El Cajon, CA 92020 619-596-0793
Lewis, Stacey: 225 S 18th St #1017, Philadelphia, PA 19103 215-545-5614
• **Lewis, Stephen: pg 506** 666 Greenwich St #860, New York, NY 10014 . . . . . . **212-675-5719**
e-mail: harriet@hkportfolio.com / url: www.hkportfolio.com / fax: 212-675-6341
Lewis, Tim: 184 St Johns Pl, Brooklyn, NY 11217 718-857-3406
Lewis, Tim: 192 Southville Rd, Southborough, MA 01772 508-872-4549
• **Leyonmark, Roger: pg 371** 280 Madison Ave #1110, New York, NY 10016 . . . **212-545-9155**
url: www.irmeliholmberg.com / fax: 212-545-9462
Leyshon, Judy: 5606 Sonoma Rd, Bethesda, MD 20817 301-530-5070
• **LeZinsky, Jon: pg 518** Dayton, OH **937-433-8383**
New York **212-966-3604**
San Francisco **415-285-3808**
url: www.scotthull.com / fax: 937-433-0434
Li, Tommy: 232 Austin Dr, Markham, ON L3R 6N6 905-475-7747
Liao Inc, Sharmen: 314 N Mission Dr, San Gabriel, CA 91775 818-458-7699
Liaw, Anson: 80 Sherbourne St #106, Toronto, ON M5A 2R1 416-944-3164
90 Sumach St #617, Toronto, ON M5A 4R4 416-863-5115
Liberman, Joni Levy: 99 Taylor St, Needham, MA 02194 617-986-4657
Libetti, Thomas: 49 Briggs Ave, Yonkers, NY 10701 914-376-7611
Licht, Lisa: 4915 Tyrone #207, Sherman Oaks, CA 91423 818-995-5724
Licht, Max: 25 Thorne Lane, Toronto, ON L3T 5K6 905-886-3984
Lichtenfels, Lisa: PO Box 90537, Springfield, MA 01139 413-781-1359
Lichty, Patrick: 8211 E Wadora NW, N Canton, OH 44720 330-494-5593
Lick, Nancy: 1400 Winston Rd, South Euclid, OH 44121 216-291-3158
Liddy, Mike: 30 Charles St #42, New York, NY 10014 212-255-5539
Lieberman, Ron: 109 W 28th St, New York, NY 10001 212-947-0653
Liebler, John: 40 Putzel Ave, Guilford, CT 06437 203-457-0114
Liebman, Ruth: 1565 Chestnut St #31, San Francisco, CA 94123 415-637-1582
Lieder, Rick: 60 E 42nd St, New York, NY 10165 212-867-8092
Lien, Tuan: 1300 Pennsylvania #203, Denver, CO 80203 303-863-9879
Liepke, Skip: 30 W 72nd St #2B, New York, NY 14304 212-724-5593
Lies, Brian: 108 King Phillips Path, Duxbury, MA 02332 781-319-0456

Life, Kay: 419 Southwick Rd B7, Westfield, MA 01085 ... 413-562-6418
Ligasan, Darryl: 422 E 77th St #5W, New York, NY 10021 ... 212-737-4393
Lightbown, Meredith: 27 Old Rd, Weston, MA 02193 ... 781-647-5258
Lightburn, Ron: PO Box 667, Kentville, NS B4N 3X9 ... 902-678-3383
Lightfield, Jaqueline: 319 Peck St, New Haven, CT 06513 ... 203-497-8832
Lillard, Jill M: 32 Westgate, Luguna Niguel, CA 92677 ... 949-661-2270
• **Lillash, Rich: pg 621** 142 W Winter St, Delaware, OH 43015 ... **740-369-9702**
fax: 740-369-0547
Lim, Deborah: 505 N Lake Shore Dr #5606, Chicago, IL 60611 ... 312-527-3271
• **Limer, Tina Bela: pg 370** 280 Madison Ave #1110, New York, NY 10016 ... **212-545-9155**
url: www.irmeliholmberg.com / fax: 212-545-9462
Limnidis, Larry: 75 Heaslip Terr, Scarborough, ON M1T 1W8 ... 416-292-6144
Lin, Grace: PO Box 1036, North Cambridge, MA 02140 ... 617-629-7735
Lin, John: 17738 Plummer St, Northridge, CA 91325 ... 818-886-6182
Lincey, Michael: 1504 W 1st Ave #301, Columbus, OH 43212 ... 614-486-2921
Lincoln, Jay: 265 Elmwood Ave, East Aurora, NY 14052 ... 716-884-8010
Lind, Monica: 636 Broadway, Ste 708, New York, NY 10012 ... 212-253-9991
Lindberg, Dean: 5335 39th Ave S, Minneapolis, MN 55417 ... 612-721-4993
Lindberg, Jeffrey: 207 Garfield Pl, S Orange, NJ 07079 ... 973-761-5195
Lindbloom, Bruce: 7370 Walnut Ct, Eden Prairie, MN 55346 ... 612-937-9627
Lindgren, Cindy: 5236 W 56th St, Minneapolis, MN 55436 ... 612-926-5585
Lindgren, Malin: 100 Bleecker St, New York, NY 10012 ... 212-982-6533
Lindley, Eric: 46 N Sheffield Rd, Indianapolis, IN 46222 ... 317-636-5696
Lindlof, Ed: 603 Carolyn Ave, Austin, TX 78705 ... 512-472-0195
Lindner, Verne: 2277 Canyon Dr, Los Angeles, CA 90068 ... 213-667-2758
Lindroth, David: 85 Broadway, W Milford, NJ 07480 ... 201-697-1965
Lindstrom, Jack: PO Box 21189, Minneapolis, MN 55421 ... 612-586-9160
Lindt, Peggy: 1627 Calle Canon, Santa Barbara, CA 93101 ... 805-569-1002
Lingta, Kung: 420 Lexington Ave #2760, New York, NY 10170 ... 212-697-8525
Linley, Michael: 1504 W First Ave, Columbus, OH 43212 ... 614-486-2921
Linn, Warren: 155 W 15th St #4C, New York, NY 10011 ... 212-989-8770
Linnett, Charles: 99 High St, Canton, MA 02021 ... 617-828-4972
Linstromberg, Ruth: 35 Summer St, Nashua, NH 03060 ... 603-882-5021
Lionel Tepper Design, Inc: 449 E 14th St, New York, NY 10009 ... 212-505-0029
Lipczenko, S Dimitri: 3901 Tunlaw Rd NW #402, Washington, DC 20007 ... 202-338-1318
Lipman, Michael: 310 Rydal Ave, Mill Valley, CA 94941 ... 415-383-1927
Lipner, Robin: 220 W 21st St #2F, New York, NY 10011 ... 212-929-5807
Lipowec, Alex: 304 Mulberry St #GLB, New York, NY 10012 ... 212-925-7663
Lippman, Peter: 410 Riverside Dr #134, New York, NY 10025 ... 212-865-1823
Lipstein, Morissa: 1712 E Butler Cir, Chandler, AZ 85225 ... 602-899-0600
Lisi, Johanna: 115 E 9th St, New York, NY 10003 ... 212-228-0657
Lisker, Emily: 139 Rathburn St, Woonsocket, RI 02895 ... 401-762-2503
Liss, Julius: 446 Lawrence Ave W, Toronto, ON M5M 1C2 ... 416-784-1416
Litchfield, Linda: 8 Mountain View Rd, Cape Elizabeth, ME 04107 ... 207-774-4750
Little Apple Art: 409 Sixth Ave, Brooklyn, NY 11215 ... 718-499-7045
Little Bear Graphics: 4236 Brookside Ave, Cincinnati, OH 45223 ... 513-542-5722
Little, Chad: 4206 N Central Ave, Phoenix, AZ 85012 ... 602-265-9030
Little, Ed: 232 Madison Ave #512, New York, NY 10016 ... 212-889-8777
Little, Rod: 712 10th St NE, Washington, DC 10002 ... 202-955-2120
Littmann, Rosemary: 299 Rutland Ave, Teaneck, NJ 07666 ... 201-833-2417
Liu, Davy: 108 E 35th St, New York, NY 10016 ... 212-889-3337
1 Belvedere, Aliso Viejo, CA 92656 ... 949-448-0592
• **Livingston, Francis: pg 246,247** 250 W 57th St #521, New York, NY 10107 ... **212-397-7330**
e-mail: San Francisco: 415-788-8552 / url: www.lindgrensmith.com
Livingston, Randy: 4132 Faithway Dr, Murfreesboro, TN 37129 ... 615-896-9390
Liwske, Renata: #6 1605 28th Ave SW, Calgary, AB T2T 1J5 ... 403-541-1103
Lizarraga, Sergio: 2759 N Hampton St, Orange, CA 92667 ... 714-778-5692
Lizzul, Karmen: 120 Bedford Ave #2L, Brooklyn, NY 11211 ... 718-387-7568
Lloyd, Gregory: 5534 Red River Dr, San Diego, CA 92120 ... 619-582-3487
Lloyd, Mary Anne: 7 Washington St, Beverly, MA 01915 ... 978-921-0887
Lobo, Gerard: 805 College St, Toronto, ON M6G 1C9 ... 416-538-3625
Loccisano, Karen: 121 Dodgingtown Rd Box 266, Bethel, CT 06801 ... 203-748-4823
Lochray Inc., Tom: 5645 10th Ave S, Minneapolis, MN 55417 ... 612-823-7630
• **Locke, Gary: pg 521** 4015 E 53rd St, Tulsa, OK 74135 ... **918-749-9424**
url: www.suzannecraig.com / fax: 918-749-5165
Locke, Helen: 33 Lower Maidstone Rd New Southgate, London, UK N11 2RU ... 442083610842
Locke, Keith: 4015 E 53rd St, Tulsa, OK 74135 ... 918-749-9424
Locke, Keith: 3823 W State, Springfield, MO 65802 ... 417-866-2885
Lockwood, Chris: 1009 West 6th St #207, Austin, TX 78703 ... 512-481-0907
Lockwood, Todd: 58 W 40th St 6th Fl, New York, NY 10018 ... 212-682-1490
Lockyear, Doug: 158 W 29th Street 11th Floor, New York, NY 10001 ... 212-268-9400
Lodge, Bernard: 455 W 23rd St #8D, New York, NY 10011 ... 212-366-1893
• **Lodge, Katherine: pg 506** 666 Greenwich St #860, New York, NY 10014 ... **212-675-5719**
e-mail: harriet@hkportfolio.com / url: www.hkportfolio.com / fax: 212-675-6341
Lodrick, Karen: PO Box 641492, San Francisco, CA 94164 ... 415-885-0228
Loehle, Don: 9075 Gullatt Rd, Palmetto, GA 30268 ... 770-306-1336
Loehle, Richard: 2608 River Oak Dr, Decatur, GA 30033 ... 404-633-5639
Loehr, Hope F: 8804 W 95th Terr, Overland Park, KS 66212 ... 913-642-3038
Loew, David: 227 Godfrey Rd, Weston, CT 06883 ... 203-222-8777
Loew, David: 232 Madison Ave #512, New York, NY 10016 ... 212-889-8777
Lofaro, Jerry: 58 Gulf Rd, Henniker, NH 03242 ... 603-428-6135
Lofaro, Jerry: 353 W 53rd St #1W, New York, NY 10019 ... 212-682-2462
Loffel, Hans: 1038 B Queen St, Honolulu, HI 96814 ... 808-593-2205
Lofficier, Jean-Marc: PO Box 17270, Encino, CA 91416 ... 818-343-7942
Loftus, David: 31 Prothero Rd, Fulham, London, UK SW6 7LY ... 171-381-9145
Loftus, David: 58 W 15th St, New York, NY 10011 ... 212-741-2539
Logan, Patrick: 112 Winged Foot Pl, San Ramon, CA 94583 ... 925-828-0262
Logan, Ron: PO Box 306, Brentwood, NY 11717 ... 516-273-4693
• **LoGrippo, Robert: pg 326** 217 E 86th St #212, New York, NY 10028 ... **212-427-5632**
e-mail: jeff@lavatyart.com / url: www.lavatyart.com / fax: 212-427-6372
• **Lohstoeter, Lori: pg 261** 250 W 57th St #521, New York, NY 10107 ... **212-397-7330**
e-mail: San Francisco: 415-788-8552 / url: www.lindgrensmith.com
Loken, Stein: 231 E 76th St #5D, New York, NY 10021 ... 212-535-0438
Lomax, Liz: 320 8th Ave, Brooklyn, NY 11215 ... 718-965-4570
Lombardo, William: 491 Broadway 12th Fl, New York, NY 10012 ... 212-226-3471
LoMele, Bachrun: 16 Phaedra, Laguna Niguel, CA 92677 ... 949-495-3664
Lomprey, Steve: 5474 Boyd Ave, Oakland, CA 94618 ... 888-LOMPREY
London, Sherry: 1523 Pleasant Dr, Cherry Hill, NJ 08003 ... 609-795-1710
Long Illustration, Jim: 4415 Briarwood Court N #16, Annandale, VA 22003 ... 703-256-1718
Long, Bill: 514 Boulder Dr, Delaware, OH 43015 ... 740-369-2918
Long, Ethan: PO Box 561608, Orlando, FL 32856 ... 407-425-1818
Long, John: 666 West End Ave #16E, New York, NY 10025 ... 212-724-0428
Long, Lennie: 100 Jenkins St, Providence, RI 02906 ... 401-274-6314
• **Long, Loren: pg 32,33** 305 E 50th St Ste 1, New York, NY 10022 ... **212-223-9545**
url: www.richardsolomon.com / fax: 212-223-9633
Long, Suzanne: 1076 Jackson St, Benicia, CA 94510 ... 707-745-6123
Lono, Erik: 1142 W 1390 St, Orem, UT 84058 ... 801-671-7100
Lonsdale, Ashley: 420 Lexington Ave, New York, NY 10170 ... 212-986-5680
Lopez Assocs, Stewart: 550 W Kentucky St, Louisville, KY 40203 ... 502-583-5502
Lopez, Emmanuel: 192 Spadina Ave #510, Toronto, ON M5T 2C2 ... 416-504-4424
Lopez, Rafael: 2149 Lyon St #5, San Francisco, CA 94115 ... 415-921-7140
Lopez, Rafael: 843 10th Ave #C, San Diego, CA 92101 ... 619-237-8061
Lord Motorsport Art & Design, David: 2100 Cord St, Speedway, IN 46224 ... 317-634-1992
Lord, Rosalind: 1330 Funston Ave #A, San Francisco, CA 94122 ... 415-664-8971
Lord, Tim: 7205 28th Ave NW, Seattle, WA 98117 ... 206-784-1136
Lorenz, Albert: 49 Pine Ave, Floral Park, NY 11001 ... 516-354-5530
Lorenz, Lee: 108 E 35th St, New York, NY 10016 ... 212-889-3337
Lorick, Blake: Manitou Rd RR2 Box 414, Garrison, NY 10524 ... 914-424-3549
Lorimer, Cindy: 268 E 9th St, Brooklyn, NY 11218 ... 718-853-7831
Lorincz, James: 1321 Hastings Crescent SE, Calgary, AB T2G 4C8 ... 604-684-6826
Lorusso, Joseph: 4600 JC Nichols Pkwy, Kansas City, MO 64112 ... 816-756-5723
Loschiavo, Doree: 2714 S Marvine St, Philadelphia, PA 19148 ... 215-336-1724
Lose, Hal: 533 W Hortter St Toad Hall, Philadelphia, PA 19119 ... 215-849-7635
• **Lotenero, Michael: pg 530** 7 Washington St, Beverly, MA 01915 ... **978-921-0887**
e-mail: leighton@leightonreps.com / url: www.leightonreps.com
fax: 978-921-0223
Lott, Eric JW: 60 E 42nd St #1146, New York, NY 10165 ... 212-953-7088
Loudon, Greg: 1804 Pine Rd, Homewood, IL 60430 ... 708-799-4339
Lougee, Michelle: 2 Lothian Rd #3, Brighton, MA 02135 ... 617-254-7252
• **Loughran, PJ: pg 100,101** 108 E 35th St, New York, NY 10016 ... **212-889-3337**
e-mail: gerald@rappart.com / url: www.theispot.com/rep/rapp or www.pjloughran.com / fax: 212-889-3341
Lourdes, Candace: 99 Coleman Ave #208, Toronto, ON M4C1P8 ... 416-698-3304
Lovato, Rich: 4864 Valley Hi Dr, Sacramento, CA 95823 ... 916-429-2655
Love, Judith DuFour: 68 Agassiz Ave, Belmont, MA 02178 ... 617-484-8023
Love, Nan: PO Box 5004, Santa Rosa, CA 95402 ... 707-527-5683
Love, Sara: 720 E 73rd St, Indianapolis, IN 46240 ... 317-255-1197
Loveless, Jim: 4137 San Francisco Ave, St Louis, MO 63115 ... 314-533-7914
Loveless, Roger: 22 Seminary Ln, Granite Springs, NY 10527 ... 914-248-4870
• **Lovell, Rick: pg 383** 89 Fifth Ave #901, New York, NY 10003 ... **212-627-1554**
fax: 212-627-1719
Lovitt, Anita: 308 E 78th St, New York, NY 10021 ... 212-628-8171
Low, William: 194 Third Ave, New York, NY 10003 ... 212-475-0440
Lowenbein, Adam: 397 W 12th St, New York, NY 10014 ... 212-645-4280
Lowery, Denise C: 35 Flatt Rd #102, Rochester, NY 14623 ... 716-292-5435
Lowry Graphics, David: PO Box 158262, Nashville, TN 37215 ... 615-298-5841
Lowry, Rose: 41 Cutter Rd, Temple, NH 03084 ... 603-878-3955
Lox, Graham: 106 Ballymeade Dr, Wilmington, DE 19810 ... 302-529-7177
• **Lozano, Armandina: pg 514** 728 Castro St, San Francisco, CA 94114 ... **415-441-4384**
e-mail: jimlilie@aol.com / url: www.planetpoint.com/jim_lilie ... **213-385-1970**
fax: 213-380-1980
Lozano, Henry Jr: 3205 Belle River Dr, Hacienda, CA 91745 ... 818-330-2095
Lozner, Ruth: 133 Spring St 2nd Fl, New York, NY 10012 ... 212-925-4340
• **Lu, Kong: pg 528** 1431 35th Ave S, Seattle, WA 98144 ... **206-325-8595**
url: ldabneyinc@aol.com / fax: 206-325-8594
Lubert, Randall: 17767 Mitchell, Irvine, CA 92714 ... 714-660-9396
Lubey, Dick: 726 Harvard, Rochester, NY 14610 ... 716-442-6075
Lubinsky, D Adolph: 7301 Argentina, Buena Park, CA 90620 ... 714-523-8189
Lucas, Cedric: 866 United Nations Plaza, New York, NY 10017 ... 212-644-2020
• **Lucas, Margeaux: pg 506** 666 Greenwich St #860, New York, NY 10014 ... **212-675-5719**
e-mail: harriet@hkportfolio.com / url: www.hkportfolio.com / fax: 212-675-6341
Luce, Ben: 4 E Ohio Studio B, Chicago, IL 60611 ... 312-321-1336
Luce, Ben: 332 Bleecker St PMBK56, New York, NY 10014 ... 212-691-2667
Luce, Craig: P2052 Buford Rd #1A, Richmond, VA 23235 ... 804-823-2745
Lucero, Andre: 100 Bleecker St, New York, NY 10012 ... 212-982-6533
Lucero, Anita: 96 Maple Ave, Barre, VT 05641 ... 802-878-9205
Lucero, Rebecca: Box 3603, Citrus Hgts, CA 95672 ... 916-723-5155
Lucier, Brian: 45 Constitution Dr, Leominster, MA 01453 ... 978-534-9900
Luckom, Lawrence: 117 Prescott St, North Andover, MA 01845 ... 508-557-5530
Luckwitz, Matthew: 3500 Osceola St, Denver, CO 80212 ... 303-839-8442
Luczak, Laurie B: 223 E 35th St #2WR, New York, NY 10016 ... 212-251-9694
Ludwig, Ira: 2353 N 61st St, Wauwatosa, WI 53213 ... 414-258-2319
Lueck, Craig: 9811 W 124th St, Overland Park, KS 66213 ... 913-851-3957
Lui, David: Regency Pk 3 Wah King Hill Rd, Hong Kong ... 212-925-0491
Luikart, Erika: 1550 9th Avenue #7, San Francisco, CA 94122 ... 415-242-1770
Luke, Scott: 1657 N California Blvd, Walnut Creek, CA 94596 ... 925-930-7576
Lukens, Jan: 2354 Chaucer Ln, Winston-Salem, NC 27107 ... 910-788-5451
Lukova, Luba: 315 W 14th St, New York, NY 10014 ... 212-645-1485
Lulevitch, Tom: 205 6th Ave, Brooklyn, NY 11217 ... 718-623-9536
Lum, Bernice: 205 Howland Ave, Toronto, ON M5R 3B7 ... 416-923-4961
Lumley, Diane: 11 Kings Ridge Rd, Long Valley, NJ 07853 ... 908-813-8718
Lund, Hal: 15 Sweetbriar Ln, St Louis, MO 63122 ... 314-966-8507
Lund, John: 134 Christian St, New Preston, CT 06777 ... 860-868-1011
Lund, Jon C: 124 E Streetsboro St, Hudson, OH 44236 ... 330-655-0784
Lundgren, Alvalyn: 274 Mariposa Dr, Newbury Park, CA 91320 ... 805-480-9600
Lundgren, Tim: 165 E 32nd St, New York, NY 10016 ... 212-686-3514
Lundman, Julia: 2697 S Embers Ln, Arlington Heights, IL 60005 ... 708-386-2608
Lundquist, Roger: 1503 Washington Ave S, Minneapolis, MN 55454 ... 612-332-8634
Lung, YW: 3300 Don Mills Rd #2404, Willowdale, ON M2J 4X7 ... 416-497-4359
Lunsford, Annie: 515 N Hudson St, Arlington, VA 22201 ... 703-527-7696
Lussier, Robert: 18 Pleasant Cir, Methuen, MA 01844 ... 508-670-6734
Lustig, Loretta: 330 Clinton Ave, Brooklyn, NY 11205 ... 718-789-2496
Lutts, Heidi: 12 Rand Rd, Salem, MA 01970 ... 508-741-1878
Lutz, Dan: 456 Lincoln Blvd, Santa Monica, CA 90402 ... 310-393-9747
Lutzen, Michelle: 696 Westbrook St #12K, S Portland, ME 04106 ... 207-879-1190
Lutzow, Jack A: 906-A Noe St, San Francisco, CA 94114 ... 415-641-5800
Luzuriaga, Denis: 39 Hamilton Terr, New York, NY 10031 ... 212-283-3401

- **Lyall, Dennis: pg 382** 89 Fifth Ave #901, New York, NY 10003 . . . . **212-627-1554**
  fax: 212-627-1719

Lyle, Pamela S: 1600 Cecil Dr, Carrollton, TX 75006. 972-323-0753
Lyles, L Kelly: 5029 26th Ave SW, Seattle, WA 98106 206-937-2058
Lynaugh, Matt: 110 Academy Dr, Austin, TX 78704 512-416-7772
Lynch, Alan: 11 Kings Ridge Rd, Long Valley, NJ 07053 908-813-8718
Lynch, Bob: 1829 Prindell Dr, Bel Air, MD 21015. 410-893-9175
Lynch, Cheryl: 1365 Leonard Dr, Moneta, VA 24121. 540-297-2190

- **Lynch, Fred: pg. 531** 7 Washington St Beverly, MA 01915 . . . . **978-921-0223**
  e-mail: leighton@leightonreps.com / url: www.leightonreps.com

Lynch, Jeffrey: 420 Lexington Ave, New York, NY 10170 212-986-5680
Lynch, Tiffiny: 286 Spring St #301, New York, NY 10013 212-229-0073
Lynn, Jeffery: 1554 Stagecoach Rd, Stowe, VT 05672. 802-253-4767
Lynn, Jenny: 18 S Letitia St, Philadelphia, PA 19106 215-925-8967
Lynn, Nicholas: 305 E 86th St, New York, NY 10028 212-503-3969
Lyon, Aaron: 1351 Woodland Ave, Chico, CA 95973. 530-899-0922

- **Lyon, Rebecca: pg 738** 414 Lake St #6, San Francisco, CA 94118 . . . . **415-751-7343**
  e-mail: reblyon@earthlink.net / url: www.rebeccalyon.com / fax: 415-751-7343

Lyons, Claudia: 2891 Wyndham Ln, Redding, CA 96001 530-335-3225
Lyons, Jonathan Lee: 2302 W Indianhead Dr, Tallahassee, FL 32301 850-942-9442
Lyons, Linda: 787 Schaefer Ave, Oradell, NJ 07649 201-262-5020
Lyons, Sam: 731 Stovall Blvd NE, Atlanta, GA 30342 800-791-1189
Lyons, Steven: 136 Scenic Rd, Fairfax, CA 94930. 415-459-7560
Lyte, Mason: 610 Anacapa St, Santa Barbara, CA 93101. 805-683-4884
Lytle, John: 17301 Fitch Ranch Rd, Sonora, CA 95370. 209-928-4849
Lyubner, Boris: 9015 Flint Way, Park City, UT 84098 435-649-2129

M

Ma, Tom: 8 Wells Hill Ave, Toronto, ON M5R 3A6. 416-535-9178
Mac, Kenny: 63 Kendrick St #201, Needham, MA 02494 617-235-6800
Macanga, Steve: 20 Morgantine Rd, Roseland, NJ 07068 201-403-8967
Maccio, Tristana: 509 W 23rd St #3, New York, NY 10011 212-647-1042
MacCombie, Turi: 201 E 28th St, New York, NY 10016. 212-532-0928
MacDonald, Brad: 788 Amsterdam #4N, New York, NY 10025 212-222-5646
MacDonald, Greg: PO Box 19412, Seattle, WA 98109 206-634-1880
MacDonald, John: 501 Fifth Ave, New York, NY 10017. 212-490-2450

- **MacDonald, John: pg 604,605** 1021 Hancock Rd, Williamstown, MA 01267 . . **413-458-0056**
  e-mail: john@jmacdonald.com / url: www.jmacdonald.com / fax: 413-458-5379

MacDonald, Ross: 56 Castle Meadow Rd, Newton, CT 06470 203-270-6438
MacDougall, Rob: 420 Lexington Ave, New York, NY 10170. 212-986-5680
MacDouglas Home Press: 861 SW Webster, Topeka, KS 66606 913-234-0336
MacEachern, Stephen: 1024 Enola Ave, Mississauga, ON L5G 4A9. 905-271-7410
Maceren, Jude: PO Box 4112, Montebello, CA 90640. 213-887-8958
92 Kossuth St, Piscataway, NJ 08854. 732-752-5931
MacFarland, Diana: 958 Chiswick Crl, Newport News, VA 23608 757-875-2296
MacFarland, Jean: 2300 W Alameda #A6, Santa Fe, NM 87501 505-471-2867
Mach, Steven: 87 E Elm St #3, Chicago, IL 60611. 312-280-0071
Machalek, Jan: 3355/108 Queen Mary Rd, Montreal, QU H3V1A5 514-341-1592
Machat, Mike: 4426 Deseret Dr, Woodland Hills, CA 91364. 818-702-9433
Machlis, Gail: 1 Arcade Ave, Berkeley, CA 94708 510-845-5284
Maciejewski, Roman: 1609 Huran St, London, ON N5V 3A4 519-451-4028
MacIntosh, Guy: 714 Enright Ave, Cincinnati, OH 45205. 513-244-7160
MacKenzie, Vic: 1913A Ruhland Ave, Redondo Beach, CA 90278. 310-372-2216
Mackey, Melissa: 7376 Clifton Rd, Clifton, VA 20124 703-815-7570
Mackie, Clare: PO Box 1062, Bayonne, NJ 07002 201-436-4362
Maclachian, Neil: 45 Earswick Dr, Toronto, ON M1E 1C7. 416-269-8141
MacLeod, Ainslie: 29 East Pier, Kappas Marina, Sausalito, CA 94965 415-331-2588
MacLeod, Andi: 536 S Rios Ave, Solana Beach, CA 92075 619-481-3537
MacLeod, Lee: 58 W 40th St 6th Fl, New York, NY 10018 212-682-1490
MacNair, Greg: 612 N 2nd St, St Louis, MO 63102 314-781-7377
MacNeill, Scott A: 74 York St, Lambertville, NJ 08530 609-397-4631
MacNicol, Gregory: 2557 Branciforte Dr, Santa Cruz, CA 95065 831-459-0880
MacPherson, Kevin: 10415 N 38th St, Phoenix, AZ 85028 602-257-0097
Macrae, Jock: 74 E Lynn Ave, Toronto, ON M4C FX2. 416-690-0401
Macrino Design, Janeen: 656 N 56th St, Omaha, NE 68132 402-551-9105
Macy, Sarah: 76 High St, E Rutherford, NJ 07073 201-896-0637
Maday, Jane: 134 Christian St, New Preston, CT 06777 860-868-1011
Maddalone, John: 81 Lindberg Blvd, Bloomfield, NJ 07003 201-338-1674
Madden, Don: 866 United Nations Plaza, New York, NY 10017 212-644-2020
Maddocks, Bruce: 39 Holman Rd, Auburndale, MA 02166. 617-332-7218
Maddox, Kelly: 420 Lexington Ave #2760, New York, NY 10170 212-697-8525
Madrid, Carlos: 502 W 55th St #5W, New York, NY 10019. 212-541-5797
Madrid, Katya S: 2026 A Parker St, Berkeley, CA 94704 510-649-7435
Maffia, Daniel: 236 S Dwight Pl, Englewood, NJ 07631 201-871-0435
Magalos, Christopher: 3308 Church Rd, Cherry Hill, NJ 08002. 609-667-7433
Magdich, Dennis: 420 Lexington Ave #2760, New York, NY 10170 212-697-8525
Magee, Alan: 476 Pleasant Point Rd, Cushing, ME 04563 207-354-8838

- **Maggard, John: pg 518** Dayton, OH **937-433-8383**
  New York, NY **212-966-3604**
  San Francisco, CA **415-285-3808**
  url: www.scotthull.com fax: 937-433-0434
- **Magiera, Rob: pg 457** 9636 Ruskin Circle, Sandy, UT 84092. . . . . **801-943-3650**

Magill, Doug: 3712 S Cabrillo Ave, San Pedro, CA 90731 310-547-5257
Magistry, Louise: 3280 av Ridgewood app, Montréal, QU H3V 1B8 514-733-5591
Magnes, Ron: 139 Edgewood Ave #203, Pittsburgh, PA 15218 412-241-2603
Magnuson, Diana: 234 Fifth Ave 4th Fl, New York, NY 10001 212-696-4680
Magovern, Peg: 853 Broadway #1201, New York, NY 10003 212-677-9100
Magsig, Stephen: 29580 Northwestern Hwy, Southfield, MI 48034 248-353-7722
Maguire, Bob: 60 E 42nd St, New York, NY 10165. 212-867-8092
Magyar, Fred: 200 Leslie Dr #531, Hallandale, FL 33009 954-455-3076
Mahan, Benton: PO Box 66, Chesterville, OH 43317. 419-768-2204
Maharry, Carol: 11 Chenin Run, Fairport, NY 14450 716-223-8996
Mahler, Russ: 306 NE Thompson St, Portland, OR 97212 503-282-4226
Mahon, Rich: 95-23 Sol Bangla MU 4/Tatong, Kathu, Puket, THAIL. 667-629-2086
Mahon, Rich: 481 8th Ave #E24, New York, NY 10001 212-631-0009
Mahoney, Greg: 5226 Artistic Cir, Colorado Springs, CO 80917. 719-638-0818
Mahoney, Jennifer F: 1640 San Pablo Ave #C, Berkeley, CA 94702. 510-524-9773
Mahoney, John: 61 Dartmouth St, Boston, MA 02116. 617-267-8791
Mahoney, Katherine : 60 Hurd Rd, Belmont, MA 02478 617-868-7877
Mahoney, Kit Hevron: 2682 S Newport St, Denver, CO 80224 303-757-0689
Mahoney, Ron: 353 W 53rd St #1W, New York, NY 10019 212-682-2462
Maile, Richard W: 3232 Valley View St, Powder Springs, GA 30073 770-439-6747

- **Maisner, Bernard: pg 924,925** 108 E 35th st. New York, NY 10016 . . . . **212-889-3337**
  e-mail: gerald@rappart.com

Majewski, Chuck: 10075 Paradise Blvd, Treasure Island, FL 33706. 813-367-3954
Majewski, Dawn: 3116 Addison Ct, Bensalem, PA 19020 215-752-4879
Major, Chris: 1260 Ave of Americas, New York, NY 10020. 212-632-4295
Mak, Kam: 369 Sackett St, Brooklyn, NY 11231 718-624-6173
Makowski, Stan: 208 Providence Rd, Annapolis, MD 21401. 410-349-8669
Malara, Nicholas: 12950 W 86th Ave, Arvada, CO 80005. 303-432-2615
Male, Alan: 353 W 53rd St #1W, New York, NY 10019 212-682-2462
Malek, Kim: 222 SW Harrison GO3, Portland, OR 97205 503-223-4250
Maleki, Dariush C: 205 Second Ave, Murfreesboro, TN 37130 615-895-6213
Maley, Matthew: 5 Enclave Manor Dr, New Paltz, NY 12561 914-255-3072
Malia, James: 1231 Franciscan Ct #6, Carpinteria, CA 93013. 805-684-3124
Mallory, Kristin: 146 Westminster Rd #2, Rochester, NY 14607 716-241-3848
Malone, Peter: 455 W 23rd St #8D, New York, NY 10011 212-366-1893
Maloney, Dave: 1816 Banks St, Houston, TX 77098 713-522-1862
Malonis, Tina: 243 E 83rd St #2D, New York, NY 10028 212-794-5232
Maltese, Jim: 1365 York Ave #8G, New York, NY 10021 212-628-6780
Mammarella, Candace: 931 Fugate, Houston, TX 77009 713-864-5964
Mamrose, Sharon: 9598 Leatherwood Ln, Douglasville, GA 30135 770-949-6349

- **Manchess, Gregory: pg 34,35** 305 E 50th St Ste 1, New York, NY 10022 . . . . . **212-223-9545**
  url: www.richardsolomon.com / fax: 212-223-9633

Manda, Antonia: 6215 SE 22nd St, Portland, OR 97202 503-236-5826
Mandel, Debi Lee: 32860 Main St, Dutch Flat, CA 95714 530-389-8312
Mandel, Saul: 12A Rothwell Dr, Cranbury, NJ 08512 609-655-8531

- **Manders, John: pg 506** 666 Greenwich St #860, New York, NY 10014. . . . . **212-675-5719**
  e-mail: harriet@hkportfolio.com / url: www.hkportfolio.com / fax: 212-675-6341

Mandio, Meridee: 5855 Green Valley Cir #308, Culver City, CA 90230 310-642-2721
Mandrell, Mark: 1810 Summit Dr, Urbana, IL 61802 217-355-3089
Manelis, Jessica: 123 Cypress Ct, Cherry Hill, NJ 08003. 609-489-0134

- **Mangiat, Jeff: pg 154,155** 420 Lexington Ave, New York, NY 10170. . . . . **212-986-5680**
  e-mail: mendolaart@aol.com / url: www.mendolaart.com / fax: 212-818-1246

Manhattan, Maria: 329 W 71st St #3, New York, NY 10023 212-799-6320
Mani, Anand: 1139 Barclay St #205, Vancouver, BC V6E 1K2. 604-669-9507
Manley, Kirk W.: 45 Maple St #4E, Norwalk, CT 06850 203-838-3017
Manley, Matt: Pier 33 North, San Francisco, CA 94111 415-956-4750
Mann, Heidi: 180 Magazine St #3, Cambridge, MA 02139 617-864-3424
Mann, Sarah: 95 Sewall Woods Rd, Melrose, MA 02176 617-979-0191
Mann, Wanchai: 50 Greenwich Ave #4D, New York, NY 10011 212-255-1040
Manna, Connie: 49 Old Stage Coach Rd, Andover, NJ 07821 201-786-7409

- **Mannes, Don: pg 324,325** 217 E 86th St #212, New York, NY 10028. . . . . . . **212-427-5632**
  e-mail: jeff@lavatyart.com / url: www.lavatyart.com / fax: 212-427-6372

Manning, Garrian: 777 N Michigan Ave Ste 706, Chicago, IL 60611 312-337-7770
Manning, Lisa: 7 Washington St, Beverly, MA 01915 978-921-0887
Manning, Michele: PO Box 470818, San Francisco, CA 94147. 415-383-9026
Manojlovic, Branko: 2700 Bathurst St #309, Toronto, ON M6B 2Z7 416-784-0007
Manoli, Georgios: 8 Woodcroft Ave, London, England, UK NW7 2AG 441819062288
Manos, Jim: 53 Apple Way, Evesham Township, NJ 08053 609-596-8843
Mantel, Richard: San Francisco, CA 415-788-8552
250 W 57th St #521, New York, NY 10107. 212-397-7330
Manter, Barry: 46 Eastern Promenade, Portland, ME 04101 207-773-0790

- **Mantha, John: pg 722** 8 Felstead Ave, Toronto, ON M4J 1G2. . . . . **416-778-5089**
  e-mail: jmantha@netcom.ca / fax: 416-778-5089

Mantha, Nancy: 3101 Shoreline Dr #325, Austin, TX 78728. 512-388-0229
Manton, Helen: 99 Pleasant St, Plainville, MA 02762 508-695-5862
Manz, Paul: 420 Lexington Ave, New York, NY 10170. 212-986-5680
Mar Design, William: 220 Montgomery St #942, San Francisco, CA 94104 415-989-3935
March, Laurie: 8 Skyway Dr RR 2, Guelph, ON N1H 6H8 519-766-1651
Marchese, Carole M: 77 Lyons Plain Rd, Weston, CT 06883. 203-226-4535
Marchesi, Steve: 121 Dodgingtown Rd Box 266, Bethel, CT 06801. 203-748-4823
Marciuliano, Frank: 420 Lexington Ave #2760, New York, NY 10170 212-697-8525
Marcolina, Dan: 1100 E Hector St, Conshohocken, PA 19428 610-940-0680
Marconi, Gloria: 2525 Musgrove Rd, Silver Spring, MD 20904 301-890-4615
Marcotte, Bob: 2606 Root St, San Diego, CA 92123. 619-292-1961
Marcotte, Tom: 2233 Kemper Ln, Cincinnati, OH 45206 513-861-1400
Mardaga/TMP, Dana: 3032 Bunker Hill Ln Ste 207, Santa Clara, CA 95054 408-987-3151
Mardarosian, Mark: 43 E 19th St, New York, NY 10003 212-254-4996
Mardon, Allan: 108 E 35th St, New York, NY 10016 212-889-3337
Mardon, John: 27 Colonsay Rd, Thornhill, ON L3T 3E9 416-881-5854
Marek, Mark: 199 Owatonna St, Haworth, NJ 07641 201-384-1791
Marelich, Jeffrey: 3251 County Side Dr, San Mateo, CA 94403 415-578-8635
Margeson, John: 307 N Michigan Ave #1006, Chicago, IL 60601 312-704-0500
Margeson, John: 46-147 Hinapu St, Kaneohe, HI 96744. 808-247-3830
Margolin, Diane: 41 Perry St, New York, NY 10014 212-691-9537
Margolis, Don: 4300 N Narragansett, Chicago, IL 60634 847-670-0912
Margulies, Robert: 1408 Brickell Bay Dr #314, Miami, FL 33131 305-372-1046
Mariano, Simonetta: 2230 av Prud'homme, Montréal, QU H4A 3H2 514-483-6651
Marinelli, Jeff: 74 S Main St 2nd Fl #3B, Canandaigua, NY 14424 716-394-2856
Marinelli, Robert: PO Box 257, Pleasantville, NY 10570 914-747-2220
Marinick Electronic Media, Stephen: 19601 N Harness Ct, Edmond, OK 73003 . 800-445-3652
Marino, Keri Lee: 287 3rd Ave #2F, New York, NY 10010. 212-779-3541
Marinsky, Jane: 63 Cleveland Ave, Buffalo, NY 14222. 716-881-3138
Marion Design, Bruce: 7961 E Solano Dr, Scottsdale, AZ 85250. 480-874-3934
Marion, Harriet Regina: 95 Ave B 4th Fl, New York, NY 10009. 212-475-7410
Marion, Kate: 85 Columbus Ave, Greenfield, MA 01301. 413-774-4862
Maritz Motivation Co: 1400 S Highway Dr, Fenton, MO 63099 314-827-4000
Mark One Visual Communications: 2500 Camino Diablo #202, Walnut Creek, CA 94596. . . 925-945-1414
Mark, Roger: 353 W 53rd St #1W, New York, NY 10019 212-682-2462
Mark, Steve: 3516 Arbor Ln, Minnetonka, MN 55305. 707-745-5228
Markley, Andy: 2432 Capitol Ave, Sacramento, CA 95816 916-444-8877
Marks, David: 726 Hillpine Dr NE, Atlanta, GA 30306 404-872-1824
Marks, Laurie: 315 New St #216, Philadelphia, PA 19106 215-413-1941
Maron, Betsy: 1170 Baker St, Mt Dora, FL 32757 352-383-9166
Marosvolgyi, Istvan: 461 E Providencia Ave #J, Burbank, CA 91501 818-566-8740

Marozsan, Karen: 7491-C5 N Federal Hwy #288, Boca Raton, FL 33487 ... 407-265-2482
Marquis, Paul: 26301 Parkside Dr, Hayward, CA 94542 ... 510-889-8098
Marsella, Valerie: 542 Hopmeadow St #147, Simsbury, CT 06070 ... 860-651-4952
Marsh, Cynthia: PO Box 1760, Highland Park, IL 60035 ... 312-222-0337
Marsh, Cynthia: 4434 Matilija Ave, Sherman Oaks, CA 91423 ... 818-789-5232
Marsh, James: 115 West 23rd St, New York, NY 10011 ... 212-989-4600
Marsh, James: 21 Elms Rd, London, England, UK SW4 9ER ... 1716-229530
Marsh, Roni: 1709 Howell Ave, Medford, OR 97501 ... 541-770-6826
Marshall, Byron: PO Box 4447, Pineville, LA 71361 ... 318-640-6752
Marshall, Dan: 1390 Lexington Ave #3, New York, NY 10128 ... 212-369-0359
Marshall, David S: 32 Brock #4, Brighton, MA 02134 ... 617-254-1345
Marshall, Fred: 435 E 70th St #22K, New York, NY 10021 ... 212-249-7041
Marshall, Pat: 33325 M St NW 3rd Fl, Washington, DC 20007 ... 202-342-0222
Martel, Louise: 4600 rue Parthenais, Montréal, QU H2H 2G7 ... 514-525-3019
Martin, Don: 5110 S W 80th St, Miami, FL 33143 ... 305-665-2376
Martin, Doug: 90 Sumach St #617, Toronto, ON M5A 4R4 ... 416-863-5115
Martin, Gary: 224 Riverside Dr #7C, New York, NY 10025 ... 212-749-3911
Martin, Greg J: 58 W 40th St 6th Fl, New York, NY 10018 ... 212-682-1490
Martin, Greg J: 3495 Heidelberg Dr, Boulder, CO 80303 ... 303-499-8220
Martin, Gregg: 392 Bay Ridge Blvd, Willowick, OH 44095 ... 216-241-3455
Martin, Gregory: 20 W Hubbard St #3E, Chicago, IL 60610 ... 312-222-1361
Martin, Jeff: 68 Page Rd, Bow, NH 03304 ... 603-225-4911
Martin, JF: 7376 Cliffton, Cliffton, VA 20124 ... 800-847-5101
Martin, John: 501 Fifth Ave, New York, NY 10017 ... 212-490-2450
• **Martin, John A: pg 849** 37276 Chelsea Ct, Farmington Hills, MI 48331 ... **248-848-1388**
e-mail: jamartn@flash.net / url: www.flash.net/~jamartn / fax: 248-848-1161
Martin, Kellie L: 13 Brown St, Andover, MA 01810 ... 508-475-3216
• **Martin, Larry: pg 518** Dayton, OH ... **937-433-8383**
New York, NY ... **212-966-3604**
San Francisco, CA ... **415-285-3808**
url: www.scotthull.com / fax: 937-433-0434
Martin, Lyn: 6628 Hickory Trace Cir, Chattanooga, TN 37421 ... 423-899-7756
Martin, Nina: 260 Highfield Ln, Nutley, NJ 07110 ... 973-667-7648
Martin, Richard: 13 Waltuma Ave, Edison, NJ 08837 ... 732-738-4838
Martin, Sean: 4 Normandy Blvd, Toronto, ON M4L 3K2 ... 416-867-9345
Martinetti, Don: 206 Linda Ln, Edison, NJ 08820 ... 908-756-9254
Martinez, Edward: 420 Lexington Ave, New York, NY 10170 ... 212-986-5680
Martinez, Sergio: 43 E 19th St, New York, NY 10003 ... 212-254-4996
Martinot, Claude: 1133 Broadway #1614, New York, NY 10010 ... 212-229-2249
Martis, Michael W: 612 SE Spring, Des Moines, IA 50315 ... 515-285-8122
Martz, John: 200 Melrose Ave, Kitchener, ON N2H 2C1 ... 416-924-8225
Maruca, Francisco Rodriguez: 612 N 2nd St, St Louis, MO 63102 ... 314-781-7377
Maruszewska, Beata: 5207 W Henderson, Chicago, IL 60641 ... 773-202-8375
Marvin, Fred: 43 E 19th St, New York, NY 10003 ... 212-254-4996
Maryanski, Ken: 314 Chelsea St, Everett, MA 02149 ... 617-381-1806
Marzullo, Michael: 307 Greenwood Rd, Ruxton, MD 21204 ... 410-823-2490
Masciovecchio, Marie: 16 W 16th St #8JN, New York, NY 10011 ... 212-698-4246
Masi, Kevin: 309 N Justine, Chicago, IL 60607 ... 312-421-7858
Masla, Robert: 165 E 32nd St, New York, NY 10016 ... 212-686-3514
Maslen, Barbara: 55 Bayview Ave, Sag Harbor, NY 11963 ... 631-725-3121
Mason III, Hatley N: 1101 N Hamilton St #E, Richmond, VA 23221 ... 804-358-1820
Mason Studio, John: PO Box 3973, Carmel, CA 93921 ... 408-625-3868
Mason, Susan: 200 Centre Ave, New Rochelle, NY 10805 ... 914-576-5310
Masse, DD: 81 Seward Ln, Aston, PA 19014 ... 215-494-7525
Masse, Josée: 4030 St Ambroise #4000, Montréal, QU H4C 2C7 ... 514-937-2363
Massé, Pierre: 72 av Laurier Ouest, Montréal, QU H2T 2N4 ... 514-277-7395
Masseau, Jean Carlson: RR 1 Box 303 Silver St, Hinesburg, VT 05461 ... 802-482-2407
Massey, Jane: 25 Cambridge Rd #3, Hove, E Sussex, UK BN3 1DE ... 441273710662
Masuda, Coco: PO Box 470818, San Francisco, CA 94147 ... 415-383-9026
• **Matcho, Mark: pg 472,473** 608 York St, San Francisco, CA 94110 ... **415-641-1285**
url: www.theispot.com/rep/weinberg / fax: 415-641-5500
CA ... **626-796-6906**
fax: 626-796-9640
Mateu, Franc: 43 E 19th St, New York, NY 10003 ... 212-254-4996
Matheis, Shelley: 534 East Passaic Ave, Bloomfield, NJ 07003 ... 201-338-9506
Mathias, John: 520 2nd St #3F, Brooklyn, NY 11215 ... 718-788-2133
Mathias, Krishna: 100 New Road #E10, Somers Point, NJ 08244 ... 609-601-1721
Matsick, Anni: 1000 Bayberry Dr, State College, PA 16801 ... 814-234-4752
• **Matsu: pg 268** 250 W 57th St #521, New York, NY 10107 ... **212-397-7330**
e-mail: San Francisco: 415-788-8552 / url: www.lindgrensmith.com
Matt, Baier: 30 Second Pl #2, Brooklyn, NY 11231 ... 718-802-9483
Mattelson, Marvin: 37 Cary Rd, Great Neck, NY 11021 ... 516-487-1323
Matthews Illustration LLC, Bonnie: 3000 Chestnut Ave #340, Baltimore, MD 21211 ... 410-243-3514
Matthews, Alex: 443 Lexington Ave, El Cerrito, CA 94530 ... 212-984-3149
Matthews, Lu: 280 Madison Ave #1110, New York, NY 10016 ... 212-545-9155
Matthews, Pete: PO Box 18128, Fairfield, OH 45018 ... 513-868-2874
Matthews, Scott: 2925 Griffith St, San Francisco, CA 94124 ... 800-755-3380
Matthews, Scott: 7530 Ethel Ave, St Louis, MO 63117 ... 314-647-9899
Matthieson, Brad: 310 Delaware St #210, Kansas City, MO 64105 ... 816-221-1047
Mattingly, David B: 1112 Bloomfield St, Hoboken, NJ 07030 ... 201-659-7404
Mattingly, Matthew: 55 S Mount Holyoke Dr, Amherst, MA 01002 ... 413-259-1394
Mattioli, Angela: 455 N Deheny Drive #103, Beverley Hills, CA 90210 ... 310-385-1901
Mattioli, Mark: 990 Filbert St, San Francisco, CA 94133 ... 415-928-0457
Mattiucci, Jim: 247 N Goodman St, Rochester, NY 14607 ... 716-271-2280
Mattix, Tom: 1400 Markan Dr #29, Atlanta, GA 30306 ... 404-876-3128
• **Mattos, John: pg 415, 704** 1546 Grant Ave, San Francisco, CA 94133 ... **415-397-2138**
e-mail: mattos@sirius.com / fax: 415-397-1174
7118 Upper River Rd, Prospect, KY 40059 ... **502-228-9427**
url: www.jettreps.com / fax: 502-228-8857
Mattson, Tom: 1814 Cleveland, Santa Barbara, CA 93103 ... 805-569-5751
• **Maughan, Bill: pg 186** 420 Lexington Ave, New York, NY 10170 ... **212-986-5680**
e-mail: mendolaart@aol.com / url: www.mendolaart.com / fax: 212-818-1246
Maun, Patrick: 255 E Kellogg Blvd #509, St Paul, MN 55101 ... 612-227-2780
Maurer, Marsha: 304 Corbin Dr, Newport News, VA 23606 ... 757-595-5921
Mauterer, Erin: 51 Ascot Dr, Ocean City, NJ 07712 ... 800-258-9287
Max, Adam: 21-16 28th St, Long Island City, NY 11105 ... 718-204-6184
Max, Deborah Dudley: 157 Newbrook Ln, Bay Shore, NY 11706 ... 631-968-5918
Max, Louise: 102 Quail Dr, Doylestown, PA 18901 ... 215-345-8547
Maxedon, Terry: 718 Broadway, New York, NY 10003 ... 212-677-3509
Maxson, Greg: 116 W Florida Ave, Urbana, IL 61801 ... 217-359-6835
Maxwell, Misty: 2233 Kemper Ln, Cincinnati, OH 45206 ... 513-861-1400
Maxwell, Sylvie: 171 Marine Parade #4, Santa Cruz, CA 95062 ... 408-426-6452
May, Anthony: 382 Day St, San Francisco, CA 94131 ... 415-648-2690
May, Danny: 3535 Newton St, Denver, CO 80211 ... 303-433-4880
May, Darcy: 201 E 28th St, New York, NY 10016 ... 212-532-0928
May, Jeff: 7368 Ahern Ave, St Louis, MO 63130 ... 314-727-1476
May, Jody: 5413 Willowmere Way, Baltimore, MD 21212 ... 410-435-8864
Mayabb, Darrell: 10180 W 73rd Pl, Arvada, CO 80005 ... 303-420-7200
Mayberry, Douglas: 1315 Oakhill Ave, Gulfport, MS 39507 ... 601-688-1884
Maydak, Michael: 2780 Wild West Trail, Cool, CA 95614 ... 530-889-8118
Maydak, Michael: 2149 Lyon St #5, San Francisco, CA 94115 ... 415-921-7140
Mayeda, Kaz: 243 Bickwell #A, Santa Monica, CA 90405 ... 310-452-0054
• **Mayer, Bill: pg 281,590,591** 250 W 57th St #521, New York, NY 10107 ... **212-397-7330**
San Francisco ... 415-788-8552
url: www.lindgrensmith.com
240 Forkner Dr, Decatur, GA 30030 ... **404-378-0686**
fax: 404-373-1759
Mayer, Jason: 240 Forkner Dr, Decatur, GA 30030 ... 404-378-0686
Mayes, Kevin: 3002 Timberlane Circle, Wichita, KS 67216 ... 316-522-6742
• **Mayforth, Hal: pg 102,103** 108 E 35th St, New York, NY 10016 ... **212-889-3337**
e-mail: gerald@rappart.com / url: www.theispot.com/rep/rapp / fax: 212-889-3341
Mayo, Frank: 25000 Creekside Dr, Farmington Hills, MI 48336 ... 810-661-8498
Mayo, Martin: 285 Manor Ave, Woodbridge, NJ 07095 ... 732-750-1669
Mayse, Bert: 4404 Mildren, Bellaire, TX 77401 ... 713-432-7542
Mayse, Steve: 7515 Allman, Lenexa, KS 66217 ... 913-599-5440
Mazellan, Ron: 704 W Spencer, Marion, IN 46952 ... 765-668-7140
Mazer, Carl: 4030 21st St, San Francisco, CA 94114 ... 415-648-1159
Maziacyzk, Claire: 834 River Rd, Schodack Landing, NY 12156 ... 518-732-2779
Mazoujian, Charles: 20 Brook Rd, Tenafly, NJ 07670 ... 201-569-8057
Mazut, Mark: 218 Oak St, Weehawken, NJ 07087 ... 201-656-0657
Mazzella, Mary Jo: 98 Youngblood Rd, Montgomery, NY 12549 ... 914-361-1765
Mazzetti, Alan: 834 Moultrie St, San Francisco, CA 94110 ... 415-647-7677
Mazzini, John: 68 Grey Ln, Levittown, NY 11756 ... 516-579-6518
Mazzucchelli, David: 123 W 93rd St, New York, NY 10025 ... 212-666-7050
McAdams, Barbara: 731 N 24th St, Philadelphia, PA 19130 ... 215-232-6666
McAdoo, Pam: 12670 Palisade St, Truckee, CA 96162 ... 530-587-2388
McAfee, Steve: PO Box 54272, Atlanta, GA 30308 ... 770-925-2481
McAlick, Michael: 209 Louis Ave #2L, South Bound Brook, NJ 08880 ... 732-271-9329
McAllen, Bob: 3268 Military Ave, Los Angeles, CA 90034 ... 310-477-8374
• **McAllister, Chris: pg 668,669** 3080 Highland Scenic Dr S, Baxter, MN 56425 ... **218-828-8786**
url: www.theispot.com/artist/mcallister
McAllister, Kit: 21 River St #7, Toronto, ON M5A 3P1 ... 416-363-3573
McArthur, Dennis: 170-44 130th Ave #8D, Jamaica, NY 11434 ... 718-987-3946
McBee, Scott: 39 Hamilton Terr, New York, NY 10031 ... 212-283-3401
McBride, David: 6319 Jackie Ave, Woodland Hills, CA 91367 ... 818-884-8149
McBrine, Mike: 61 Bickford Rd, Braintree, MA 02184 ... 617-843-2285
McCabe, Trish: 4908 FM 165, Dripping Springs, TX 78620 ... 830-833-5936
McCain, Kevin: 1420 N Kenneth Ave, Kuna, ID 83634 ... 208-922-5143
McCampbell, Rachael: 311 Ave H #D, Redondo Beach, CA 90277 ... 310-540-5958
McCampbell, Rachael: 716 Montgomery St, San Francisco, CA 94111 ... 415-433-1222
McCampbell, Rachael: 2815 Grayson Ave, Venice, CA 90291 ... 310-306-0469
McCandlish, Mark: 2205 Hilltop Dr #158, Redding, CA 96002 ... 530-223-3849
McCann, Stephanie: 2417 Foothill Ln, Santa Barbara, CA 93105 ... 805-966-1877
McCannon, Desdemona: 455 W 23rd St #8D, New York, NY 10011 ... 212-366-1893
McCarthy, Emmett: 123 Elizabeth St, New York, NY 10013 ... 212-431-4134
McCarthy, Errol: 3918 Pacific Avenue, Long Beach, CA 90807 ... 310-424-9014
• **McCauley, Adam: pg 468,469** 608 York St, San Francisco, CA 94110 ... **415-641-1285**
Oakland, CA ... **510-832-0860**
url: www.atomicalley.com
url: www.theispot.com/rep/weinberg / fax: 415-641-5500
McClintock, Wendell: 60 E 42nd St #1146, New York, NY 10165 ... 212-953-7088
McCloskey, Kevin: 140 E Main, Kutztown, PA 19530 ... 215-683-6546
McClure, Nancee: 2755 B Road, Grand Junction, CO 81503 ... 970-242-4744
McCollum, Rick: 232 Madison Ave #512, New York, NY 10016 ... 212-889 8777
McCollum, Sudi: 83 Walnut Ave, Corte Madera, CA 94925 ... 415-924-7881
3244 Cornwall Dr, Glendale, CA 91206 ... 818-243-1345
McConnell, Gerald: 10 E 23rd St, New York, NY 10010 ... 212-505-0950
• **McConnell, Mike: pg 626,627** 6 Seven Springs Ct, Phoenix, MD 21131 ... **410-527-0055**
e-mail: mike@wetinc.com / url: www.wetinc.com
McCord, Kathleen: PO Box 1086, Taos, NM 87571 ... 505-776-5435
McCormack, Daphne: 14027 Memorial #125, Houston, TX 77079 ... 281-579-3220
McCormack, Geoffrey: 420 Lexington Ave, New York, NY 10170 ... 212-986-5680
McCormack, Jeffrey J: 6408 Elmarge Dr, Independence, OH 44131 ... 216-524-0369
McCormick, Peter: 13726 Aleppo Dr, Sun City West, AZ 85375 ... 520-584-8403
McCoy, David: 28 Hilltop Terr, Bloomingdale, NJ 07403 ... 973-283-4323
McCracken, Steve: 500 3rd St SE, Washington, DC 20003 ... 202-332-5857
McCurdy, Michael: 66 Lake Buel Rd, Great Barrington, MA 01230 ... 413-528-2749
McDaniel, Jerry: 155 E 38th St, New York, NY 10016 ... 212-697-6170
McDaniel, Jerry: 20 Brookside Dr, Greenwich, CT 06830 ... 203-661-0490
McDermond, Patricia: 9 Gracie Square #1RW, New York, NY 10028 ... 212-737-1982
• **McDermott, Joe: pg 478** 865 Delaware St, Denver, CO 80204 ... **303-820-2599**
e-mail: 800-417-5120 / url: www.artagent.com / fax: 303-820-2598
McDermott, Teri: 38W563 Koshare Trail, Elgin, IL 60123 ... 847-888-2206
McDonald Design, Jim: 5703 E Evans Dr, Scottsdale, AZ 85254 ... 602-464-0747
McDonald, Janice: 2212 Ash St, Denver, CO 80207 ... 303-316-0987
McDonald, Mercedes: 325 Wilson Way, Larkspur, CA 94939 ... 415-927-4500
McDonnell, Patrick: 3420 Westmore, Montreal, QU H4B 1Z8 ... 514-483-5489
• **McDonnell, Peter: pg 466** 1839 Ninth St, Alameda, CA 94501 ... **510-769-1421**
e-mail: ldmreps@prodigy.net
McDougall, David: 5403 104th Pl SW, Mukilteo, WA 98275 ... 206-787-9766
McDougall, Scott: 712 N 62nd St, Seattle, WA 98103 ... 206-783-1403
McEachron, CJ: 1306 S. 19th St, Milwaukee, WI 53204 ... 414-647-2403
McElhaney, Gary: 8104 Peaceful Hill Ln, Austin, TX 78748 ... 512-282-5743
McElligot, Matt: 132 Morton Ave, Albany, NY 12202 ... 518-427-6880
McElligott, Matt: 279 Jericho Rd, Selkirk, NY 12158 ... 518-767-0915
McEntire, Larry: 612 N 2nd St, St Louis, MO 63102 ... 314-781-7377
McEvoy, Greg: PO Box 701/Adelaide, Toronto, ON M5C 2J8 ... 416-214-2752
McFarland, Diana: 958 Chiswick Cir, Newport News, VA 23608 ... 757-890-9981

ILLUSTRATORS

Mihaesteanu, Lucian: 39 Hamilton Terr, New York, NY 10031 212-283-3401
Mikec, Larry: 925 Elm Grove Rd, Elm Grove, WI 53122 414-785-1940
Mikolaycak, Charles: 64 E 91st St #2, New York, NY 10128 212-427-9628
Mikos, Mike: 420 Lexington Ave, New York, NY 10170 212-986-5680
Mikovon, Michael: 41175 Southwind Dr, Canton, MI 48188 734-394-0810
Mikros, Nikita: 58-31 44th Ave, Woodside, NY 11377 718-458-6456
Milam, Larry: 3530 SE Hawthorne #3, Portland, OR 97214 503-236-9121
810 NE 102nd St, Seattle, WA 98125 206-526-7171
Milbourn, Patrick D: 327 W 22nd St #2F, New York, NY 10011 212-989-4594
89 Fifth Ave #901, New York, NY 10003 212-627-1554
Milburn, Ken: 2934 Ford St Studio #38, Oakland, CA 94601 510-436-6601
Milec, Larry: 925 Elm Grove Rd, Elm Grove, WI 53122 414-785-1940
• **Milelli, Pascal: pg 640,641** 609-402 W Pender St, Vancouver, BC V6B 1T6 . . . **604-608-2708**
e-mail: pascal@pascalmilelli.com / url: www.pascalmilelli.com
fax: 604-682-6086
Miles, Chris: 385 Douglas, Brooklyn, NY 11217 718-622-6907
Milgrim, David: 53 Christopher St, Wakefield, RI 02879 877-283-9747
Miliano, Ed: Cullellen/Lowr Glenageary Rd/Dunlaoghaire, Dublin, Ireland 31-280-1513
Mille, Mark: 133 W Pittsburgh Ave #502, Milwaukee, WI 53204 414-278-8400
Miller, Charlie: 11 Hartack Ct, Baltimore, MD 21236 410-668-4131
Miller, Cindy: PO Box 7917, Ann Arbor, MI 48107 313-663-2144
Miller, Cliff: 60 E 42nd St, New York, NY 10165 212-867-8092
Miller, Dave: 246 W 4th St #3, New York, NY 10014 917-568-5318
• **Miller, Dave: pg 901** 11318 Forrestville Ave, Chicago, IL 60628 . . . . **773-264-1152**
fax: 773-264-0916
Miller, David: 353 W 53rd St #1W, New York, NY 10019 212-682-2462
Miller, David: 231 E 76th St #5D, New York, NY 10021 212-535-0438
Miller, Doug: 420 Lexington Ave #3020, New York, NY 10170 212-692-9200
Miller, Edward: 379 First Ave #2, New York, NY 10010 212-254-0182
Miller, Frank: 58 W 15th St, New York, NY 10011 212-741-2539
Miller, Frank: 500 Coventry Ln, Edina, MN 55435 612-935-8888
Miller, Gregory: 7317 Loch Aleme Ave, Pico Rivera, CA 90660 310-948-2915
Miller, Jack Paul: 1331 N Lincoln St, Burbank, CA 91506 818-841-4668
Miller, Jane: 1260 Day Valley, Aptos, CA 95003 408-684-1593
Miller, Jeff: 111 E Hull St #D, Savannah, GA 31401 912-447-0474
Miller, Judy: 6638 N 13th St, Phoenix, AZ 85014 602-263-8990
Miller, Judy: 801 N Shepherd Hills, Tucson, AZ 85710 520-296-5323
Miller, Kathleen: 2149 E Norma Ave, W Covina, CA 91791 818-966-4978
Miller, Lyle: 124 Cedar Valley Ln-Cedar Hill, Dallas, TX 75104 214-291-1577
Miller, Mark: 5855 Green Valley Cir #308, Culver City, CA 90230 310-558-3325
Miller, Max: 58 W 15th St, New York, NY 10011 212-741-2539
Miller, Maxine: 3148 Atwater Ave, Los Angeles, CA 90039 323-660-5796
Miller, Melissa: 317 High St, Milford, CT 06460 203-389-6988
Miller, Paul: 2233 Kemper Ln, Cincinnati, OH 45206 513-861-1400
Miller, Roger E: 3520 W 21st St, Minneapolis, MN 55416 612-925-0781
Miller, Steve: 2586 Majella Rd, Vista, CA 92084 619-758-0804
Miller, Thomas O: 2233 Kemper Ln, Cincinnati, OH 45206 513-861-1400
Miller, Victoria: 695 West 810 North, Pleasant, UT 84062 801-796-9575
Miller-Mann, Sheila: 5 Arrow Path, S Natick, MA 01760 508-650-0998
Milligan, Dan: 33 Yonge St 12th Fl, Toronto, ON M53 1X6 416-363-3772
Mills, Elise: 4 Bloomer Rd, North Salem, NY 10021 914-669-5948
Millsap, Darrel: 5996 Bounty St, San Diego, CA 92120 619-286-8668
Milne, Jonathan: 420 Lexington Ave, New York, NY 10170 212-986-5680
e-mail: mendolaart@aol.com / url: www.mendolaart.com / fax: 212-818-1246
• **Milot, René: pg 586,587** 49 Thorncliffe Pk Dr #1604, Toronto, ON M4H 1J6 . . **416-425-7726**
501 Fifth Ave, New York, NY 10017 . . . . **212-490-2450**
url: www.renardrepresents.com / fax: 212-697-6828
Mina, Val: 28031 Blandings, Mission Viejo, CA 92692 949-855-9388
Minardy, Michael: 5009 Cloister Dr, Rockville, MD 20852 301-493-8799
Minkin, Yishai: 232 Madison Ave #512, New York, NY 10016 212-889-8777
Minnick, Jay: 13367 Shirley, Omaha, NE 68144 402-334-5238
Minnix, Gary: 201 S Cuyler, Oak Park, IL 60302 708-386-4484
Minor, Wendell: 15 Old North Rd, Washington, CT 06793 203-868-9101
Minot, Karen: 26 Deuce Ct, Fairfax, CA 94930 415-457-7559
Mintz, Margery: 108 Albermare Rd, Newton, MA 02460 617-332-8858
Mirabella, Tony: 1127 Shannon St, Upland, CA 91784 909-949-2238
Miracle, Michael: 1 Wall Street, Arlington, MA 02476 888-393-3779
Miralles, Jose-Maria: 43 E 19th St, New York, NY 10003 212-254-4996
Mires Design Inc: 2345 Kettner Blvd, San Diego, CA 92101 619-234-6631
Mirkin, Ekaterina S: 2026A Parker St, Berkley, CA 94704 510-644-3969
Mirocha, Paul: 425 E 17th St, Tucson, AZ 85701 520-623-1515
Mironchuk, Greg: 409 Central Ave, Saugus, MA 01906 617-941-8030
Miserendino, Peter: 33 Stonegate Dr, Southbury, CT 06488 203-264-0908
Miskell, Jack: 47 Walker St #2B, New York, NY 10013 212-226-0462
Mistretta, Andrea: 135 E Prospect St, Waldwick, NJ 07463 201-652-7531
Mistretta, Tony: 223 W Erie St #5EC, Chicago, IL 60610 312-751-1005
Mitchell Design, Dean: 10219 Caminito Pitaya, San Diego, CA 92131 858-566-1032
Mitchell, Bill: 7517 Meadowshire Ln, Crystal Lake, NY 60012 815-477-1455
Mitchell, Bono: 2118 N Oakland St, Arlington, VA 22207 703-276-0612
Mitchell, Briar Lee: 11552 Hartsook St, N Hollywood, CA 91601 818-752-6809
Mitchell, Celia: 22-29 19th St, Long Island City, NY 11105 718-626-4095
Mitchell, Charlie: 865 Mountainbrooke Dr, Stone Mountain, GA 30087 770-381-9929
Mitchell, Charlie: PO Box 711820, Salt Lake City, UT 84171 404-296-9666
Mitchell, Dean: 64 Orlon Cr, Thornhill, ON L4J 1J1 905-881-6062
Mitchell, JoBeth: 4611 Talisman St, Torrance, CA 90503 310-370-1728
Mitchell, Kurt: 3004 W 66th St, Chicago, IL 60629 773-476-4429
Mitchell, Lori: 10219 Camito Pitaya, San Diego, CA 92131 858-566-1033
Mitchell, Mark: 7 W 34th St, New York, NY 10001 212-576-5916
Mitchell, Sean: 2701 Newkirk Ave #3B, Brooklyn, NY 11226 718-462-2782
Mitchell, Sharon Augusta: 2735 Elmwood Ave, Berkeley, CA 94705 510-548-6101
Mitchell, Tim: 7718 Kingman St, Panama Beach City, FL 32408 904-230-9030
Mitchell, Tucker: 42 Tooker Ave, Oyster Bay, NY 11771 516-922-3373
• **Mitsui, Glenn: pg 446,447** 557 Roy St #150, Seattle, WA 98109 . . . . **206-283-5901**
e-mail: glenn@glennmitsui.com / url: www.glennmitsui.com / fax: 425-687-0113
San Francisco, CA **415-441-4384**
. . . . **206-619-9403**
Mitta, Eugene: 5015 Clinton St #306, Los Angeles, CA 90004 323-957-2327
Miura, Terry: 1300 Miners Way, Roseville, CA 95661 916-780-5872
Mix, Garth: PO Box 5752, Bellingham, WA 98227 360-738-3496
Miyake, Yoshi: 121 Dodgingtown Rd Box 266, Bethel, CT 06801 203-748-4823
Mize, Charles: 633 Battery St #200, San Francisco, CA 94111 415-421-1548
• **Mjolsness, Jane: pg 716** 101 Kitty Hawk Bay Dr, Kill Devil Hills, NC 27948 . . . . **252-480-0165**
e-mail: janem@pinn.net / url: www.janemjolsness.com / fax: 252-480-0401
Mladinich, Charles: 7 Maspeth Dr, Melville, NY 11747 516-271-8525
MLH Communications Group: 51 Madison Ave #1201, New York, NY 10010 . . . 212-576-5916
Mockensturm, Steve: 2660 Letchworth, Toledo, OH 43606 419-474-0484
Mocri, Joe: 241 New York Ave, Massapequa Pk, NY 11762 516-797-0941
Modaff, Linda: 6620 W 81st St, Los Angeles, CA 90045 310-641-6916
Modny, Marilyn: 180 Chaplin Rd, Bernardsville, NJ 07924 908-630-9797
Moerder, Lynn: 284 7th Ave #2E, Brooklyn, NY 11215 718-832-6508
Moffatt, Judith: 13 Charles St, Medway, MA 02053 508-533-4496
Moffet, Maureen: 121 Lyall Ave, Toronto, ON M4E 1W6 416-691-3242
Mohr, Mark: 5106 Reinhardt Pkwy, Roeland Park, KS 66205 913-631-0943
Moire Studio: 3152 Elliot Ave S, Minneapolis, MN 55407 612-823-2880
Mojhr, Michael: 781 Mojave Trail, Maitland, FL 32751 407-644-9615
Moldenhauer, Egon: 2228 N Moisertown Rd, Sagertown, PA 16433 814-763-4197
Molina, Luis: 238 Reed St, Covina, CA 91723 626-966-4852
Moline, Robin: 2149 Lyon St #5, San Francisco, CA 94115 415-921-7140
Mollica, Gene: 1269 Prospect Ave, Brooklyn, NY 11218 718-686-6764
Mollica, Pat: 319 E 50th St, New York, NY 10022 212-355-4020
Molloy, Jack A: 756 8th Ave S, Naples, FL 34102 941-403-4393
Molnar, Albert: 1875 Hialeah Dr, Orleans, ON K4A 3S7 613-841-7901
Monahan, Frank: 28 Cornwall Dr, New Milford, CT 06776 860-354-8962
Monahan, Leo: 654 Pier Ave #C, Santa Monica, CA 90405 310-392-4877
Monahan, Leo: 1809 7th Ave #1710, Seattle, WA 98101 206-447-1600
Moncrieff, Judi: 4543 SW Water Ave, Portland, OR 97201 503-294-9947
Mondok, Wayne: 27 Renault Crescent, Weston, ON M9P 1J2 416-249-2676
Mones, Isdre: 43 E 19th St, New York, NY 10003 212-254-4996
Monet, André: 460 rue Saint-Catherine W #300, Montréal, QU HB3 1A7 514-393-0844
Monge, Mary T: 78 Allenwood Ln, Aliso Viejo, CA 92656 949-831-2762
Mongeau, Marc: 278 Hamilton Ave, Princeton, NJ 08540 609-252-9405
Monley, Jerry: 29580 Northwestern Hwy, Southfield, MI 48034 248-353-7722
Monlux, Mark: 7622 S Yakima Ave, Tacoma, WA 98408 206-471-0820
• **Monroy, Bert: pg 911** 11 Latham Ln, Berkeley, CA 94708 . . . . **510-524-9412**
e-mail: bert@bertmonroy.com / url: www.bertmonroy.com / fax: 510-524-2514
Montagne: 1405 Bishop St #302, Montréal, QU H3G 2E4 514-288-7414
Montague, Desmond: 4185 Wheelwright Crescent, Mississauga, ON L5L 2X4 . . . 416-820-4921
Montana, Leslie: 6 S Fullerton St, Montclair, NJ 07042 973-744-3407
Monte, Joy: 103 Walnut St, Walden, NY 12586 914-778-5303
Montecalvo, Janet: 10 Cavotorta Dr, Framingham, MA 01701 508-875-4209
Monteiro, Marcus: 32 W 40th St #2 South, New York, NY 10018 212-575-6887
Monteiro, Mary: 29 Medeiros Ln, N Dartmouth, MA 02747 508-999-2880
Montero, Carmen: PO Box 02-5635, Miami, FL 33102 506-253-1800
Montgomery, Jay: 4836 Royal Dr, Duluth, GA 30096 770-447-4622
Montgomery, Linda: 280 Madison Ave #1110, New York, NY 10016 212-545-9155
Monti, Jean Restivo: 50 Greenfield Rd, Cumberland, RI 02864 401-333-4797
Montiel, David: 453 Fourth St, Brooklyn, NY 11215 718-456-1369
Montoliu, Raphael: 800-652-1785
PO Box 470818, San Francisco, CA 94147 415-383-9026
Montoya, Andy: 1800 Lear #5, Dallas, TX 75215 214-421-3993
Montoya, Ricardo: 7203 Raintree Cir, Culver City, CA 90230 310-837-5957
Mooers, R Craig: 1075 Seco St, Pasadena, CA 91103 818-449-0975
Mooney, Gerry: 2 Main St #3N, Dobbs Ferry, NY 10522 914-693-8076
Mooney, Scott: 5 Douglas St Top Fl, Guelph, ON N1H 2S8 519-767-2948
• **Moonlight Press Studio: pg 636,637** 362 Cromwell Ave, Ocean Breeze, NY 10305 . **718-979-9695**
e-mail: cjspollen@aol.com / url: www.inch.com/~cspollen/ / fax: 718-979-8919
Moore, Angela: 450 W 46th St #5FW, New York, NY 10036 212-315-1540
Moore, Chris: 58 W 40th St 6th Fl, New York, NY 10018 212-682-1490
Moore, Connie: 107 Fahnestock Rd, Pittsburgh, PA 15215 412-784-8439
Moore, Cyd: 280 Madison Ave #1110, New York, NY 10016 212-545-9155
Moore, Gustav: 9 Twin Knolls Ln, Portland, ME 04102 207-773-4708
• **Moore, Harry: pg 290** 731 N 24th St, Philadelphia, PA 19130 . . . . **215-232-6666**
url: www.deborahwolfeltd.com / fax: 215-232-6585
Moore, Jack: 131 Cedar Lake West, Denville, NJ 07834 201-627-6931
Moore, Jo: 1314 Kearney St NE, Washington, DC 20017 202-526-2356
Moore, John Blair: 3204 Longfellow Rd, St Louis, MO 63104 314-664-9687
• **Moore, Larry: pg 518** Dayton, OH **937-433-8383**
Moore, Marlene: 300 E 34th St #10D, New York, NY 10016 212-481-0124
Moore, Monte: 5360 N Franklin St, Denver, CO 80216 303-294-0146
Moore, Sam: 920 Eighth Ave, Brooklyn, NY 11215 718-768-1337
Moore, Scott: 1203 Harris St, Eden, NC 27288 910-627-1559
Moore, Stephen: 1077 Country Creek Dr, Lebanon, OH 45036 859-292-5532
Moore, Tim: 23 Summer Rd #3, Brookilne, MA 02146 617-731-7783
• **Moores, Jeff: pg 578,579** 5187 County Rd 36, Honeoye, NY 14471 . . . . **716-229-4603**
e-mail: jmoores1@rochester.rr.com / url: www.jeffmoores.com / fax: 716-229-4604
Moors, Steve: 77 Gordon St, Tel Aviv, Israel, 64388 3-5225372
Mora, Tony: 11037 Paddison Ave, Norwalk, CA 90650 562-929-2481
Moraes, Greg Studio: 4760 Columbus Ave, Sherman Oaks, CA 91403 818-905-5267
Morale, D.C.: 18949 Marsh Ln, Dallas, TX 75287 972-307-6934
Morales, Manuel: 146 Mountain Ave, Pompton Plains, NJ 07444 201-676-8187
Morales, Rosemary: 5775 Foothill Dr, Los Angeles, CA 90068 213-467-4674
Moran, Edna: 2104 A San Antonio Ave, Altameda, CA 94501 510-769-7936
Moran, Michael: 39 Elmwood Rd, Florham Park, NJ 07932 201-966-6229
Moran, Robert: 759 N Park Ave, W Redding, CT 06896 203-452-1116
Mordan, CB: 4908 Sycamore Dr, Roeland Park, KS 66205 913-677-4976
Morecraft, Ron: 97 Morris Ave, Denville, NJ 07834 201-625-5752
Moreiro, Enrique: 3612 Ditmars Blvd, Astoria, NY 11105 718-626-1228
Morena, Alain: 325 Idaho Ave #11, Santa Monica, CA 90403 310-319-9506
Moreschi, Alfred: 750 Zorn Ave #31, Louisville, KY 40206 502-894-0937
Moreua, Alain: 325 Idaho Ave #11, Santa Monica, CA 90403 310-319-9506
Morgan, Jacqui: 1637 N Las Palmas Ave, Hollywood, CA 90046 213-933-2500
Morgan, Jacqui: 176 E 77th St, New York, NY 10021 212-772-0627
Morgan, Leonard: 730 Victoria Ct, Bolingbrook, IL 60440 630-739-7705
Morgenstern, Michael: 429 E 73rd St #5FE, New York, NY 10021 212-861-7391
Morozko, Bruce: 111 First St, Jersey City, NJ 07203 201-792-5974
Morpheus Technologies: 58 Fore St, Portland, ME 04101 207-772-3900
Morra, Janet: 19 Stanley Ave, Crotonville, NY 10562 914-762-7250

ILLUSTRATORS

Neider, Alan: 66 Center St, Shelton, CT 06484 ... 203-924-8088

Neidigh, Sherry: 325 W Huron, Chicago, IL 60610 ... 312-787-6826

Nellis, Ryan: 1101 S Tremaine Ave, Los Angeles, CA 90019 ... 213-934-7118

Nelms-Byrne, Cynthia: 12468 Oak Brook Pl, Dubuque, IA 52001 ... 319-557-8970

Nelsen, Randy: 865 Delaware St, Denver, CO 80204 ... 303-820-2599

Nelson, Annika: 455 W 23rd St #8D, New York, NY 10011 ... 212-366-1893

• **Nelson, Bill: pg 36,37** 305 E 50th St Ste 1, New York, NY 10022 ... **212-223-9545**
url: www.richardsolomon.com / fax: 212-223-9633

Nelson, Craig: 58 W 40th St 6th Fl, New York, NY 10018 ... 212-682-1490

Nelson, Dave: PO Box 768, Nassau, NY 11123 ... 518-766-2607

Nelson, Dave: RR2 Box 125A, Peterborough, NH 03458 ... 603-563-8267

Nelson, Diane: 2 Northfield Plz #100, Northfield, IL 60093 ... 847-501-5560

Nelson, Gerald: 500 Aurora N #403, Seattle, WA 98109 ... 206-292-9186

Nelson, Gregory T: 1525 Parkway St, Dubuque, IA 52001 ... 319-582-1573

Nelson, Hilber: 7205 28th Ave NW, Seattle, WA 98117 ... 206-784-1136

Nelson, Jerry: 500 Aurora Ave North #403, Seattle, WA 98109 ... 206-292-9186

Nelson, John: 7205 28th Ave NW, Seattle, WA 98117 ... 206-784-1136

Nelson, John: 36 W Palmdale, Tempe, AZ 85282 ... 480-829-8992

Nelson, Kadir: Chicago, IL ... 312-364-0244

Nelson, Linda: 25 Commerce SW #400, Grand Rapids, MI 49503 ... 616-774-0510

Nelson, Pamela: 7700 Bailey Cove Rd, Huntsville, AL 35802 ... 205-881-3623

Nelson, R Kenton: 3100 Carlisle #210, Dallas, TX 75204 ... 214-969-0026

Nelson, R Kenton: 12 South Fair Oaks Ave, Pasadena, CA 91105 ... 818-792-5252

Nelson, R Kenton: 18 E 16th St 7th Fl, New York, NY 10003 ... 212-255-6456

Nelson, Randy: 865 Delaware St, Denver, CO 80204 ... 303-820-2599

Nelson, Rich: 236 Midland Blvd, Royal Oak, MI 48073 ... 248-545-5242

Nelson, Scott: 22 Rayburn Dr, Millbury, MA 01527 ... 508-865-5045

Nelson, Susan: 322 NW 7th, Pendleton, OR 97801 ... 541-278-2511

• **Nelson, Will: pg 309** 716 Montgomery St, San Francisco, CA 94111 ... **415-433-1222**
fax: 415-433-9560 / url: www.sweetreps.com

Nemec, Gregory: 37 Martling Ave, Pleasantville, NY 10570 ... 914-747-6125

Nessim & Assocs, Barbara: 63 Greene St #503, New York, NY 10012 ... 212-219-1111

• **Neubecker, Robert: pg 190, 191, 544** Salt Lake City, UT ... **801-531-6999**
New York, NY ... **212-219-8435**
e-mail: robert@neubecker.com / url: www.neubecker.com

Neufeld, Josh: 24 Pearl St, Provincetown, MA 02657 ... 508-487-7409

Neuhaus, David: PO Box 1086, Taos, NM 87571 ... 505-776-5435

Neumann, Ann: 78 Franklin St, Jersey City, NJ 07307 ... 201-420-1137

Neuwirth, Alan: 310 E 75th St, New York, NY 10021 ... 212-879-8162

Nevfeld, Josh: 175 Eastern Pkwy, Brooklyn, NY 11238 ... 718-625-1663

Newbold, Greg: Chicago, IL ... 312-364-0244

Newcomer, David: 1413 Highland Ave, Plainfield, NJ 07060 ... 908-561-5305

Newell, Claudia: 34 Benefit St #24, Providence, RI 02904 ... 401-861-1167

Newfangled Graphics: 12 Thomas St, Providence, RI 02903 ... 401-861-3300

Newgarden, Mark: 18 Havemeyer St, Brooklyn, NY 11211 ... 718-387-2286

Newman, Barbara Johansen: 45 South St, Needham, MA 02192 ... 781-449-2767

Newman, Dave: 13844 N Thunderbird Rd, Prescott, AZ 86305 ... 520-708-0623

Newman, Kathleen: 12325 S 90th Ave, Palos Park, IL 60464 ... 708-448-0607

Newman, Kevin: 1128 Ocean Park Blvd, Santa Monica, CA 90405 ... 310-394-0322

Newman, Leslie: 810 NE 102nd, Seattle, WA 98125 ... 206-633-3445

Newman, Leslie: 1904 3rd Ave #635, Seattle, WA 98101 ... 206-622-3025

Newman, Paula: 14540 Biola Ave, La Mirada, CA 90638 ... 714-994-3535

Newman, Robert: 420 Springbrook Ln, Hatboro, PA 19040 ... 215-672-8079

Newport, Jim: 22448 SW 126th Ave, Goulds, FL 33170 ... 305-258-2482

Newsom, Carol: 420 Lexington Ave, New York, NY 10170 ... 212-986-5680

• **Newsom, Tom: pg 168** 420 Lexington Ave, New York, NY 10170 ... **212-986-5680**
e-mail: mendolaart@aol.com / url: www.mendolaart.com / fax: 212-818-1246

• **Newton, David: pg 225** Chicago, IL ... **312-364-0244**
London ... **011-44-207-636-1064**
Los Angeles, CA ... **323-874-5700**
Washington, DC ... **410-349-8669**
New York, NY ... **212-333-2551**
url: www.shannonassociates.com

Newton, Jill: 350 Central Park West, New York, NY 10025 ... 212-749-4907

• **Newton, Richard: pg 169** 420 Lexington Ave, New York, NY 10170 ... **212-986-5680**
e-mail: mendolaart@aol.com / url: www.mendolaart.com / fax: 212-818-1246

Newton-King, Laurie: 5910 Grand Ave, Kansas City, MO 64113 ... 816-444-8159

Ng, Michael: 58-35 155th St, Flushing, NY 11355 ... 718-461-8264

Ng, Simon: 51 Camden St, Toronto, ON M5V 1V2 ... 416-703-1913

Nguyen, Richard Quan: 728 Castro St, San Francisco, CA 94114 ... 415-441-4384

Nicastre, Michael: 420 Lexington Ave #2760, New York, NY 10170 ... 212-697-8525

Nicato, James: 1219 W Lewis St, San Diego, CA 92103 ... 619-491-0433

Nicholason, Brant: 700 W 48th Ave #A, Denver, CO 80216 ... 303-293-9215

Nicholls, Calvin: 48 Bond St, Lindsay, ON K9V 3R2 ... 705-878-1640

Nicholls, Chris: 276 Carlaw Ave #305, Toronto, ON M4M 3L1 ... 416-469-0812

Nichols, Ann Marie: 58 Harloff Rd, Honeoye Falls, NY 14472 ... 716-624-6860

Nichols, Garry: 3094 W 200 South, Greenfield, IN 46140 ... 317-861-6550

Nichols, Iris: 1509 45th Ave SW, Seattle, WA 98116 ... 206-932-3398

Nicholson, Norman: 132 Leona Ct, Alamo, CA 94507 ... 510-837-0695

Nicholson, Trudy: 7400 Arden Rd, Cabin John, MD 20818 ... 301-229-0195

Nick, Christopher: 4305 NW 16th St, Oklahoma City, OK 73107 ... 405-943-5245

Nickel, Spencer: 457 Quakie Way, Bailey, CO 80421 ... 303-838-7690

Nickle, John: 306 14th St, Brooklyn, NY 11215 ... 718-788-7310

Nickum, Jan: 7118 Upper River Rd, Prospect, KY 40059 ... 502-228-9427

Nicodemus, Stephen: 23424 Aetna St, Woodland Hills, CA 91367 ... 818-716-7172

Nicol, Brock: 850 Canterbury Ave #714, Ottawa, ON K1G 3B1 ... 613-526-0381

Nicol, Robert: 206 Linda Ln, Edison, NJ 08820 ... 908-756-9254

Nicotra, Rosanne: 420 Lexington Ave #2760, New York, NY 10170 ... 212-697-8525

Nicotra, Tom: 420 Gates Ave, East Meadow, NY 11554 ... 516-292-8540

Nidenoff, Michelle: 100 Rosehampton Ave #1215, Toronto, ON M4P 1R3 ... 416-482-5348

Niehaus, Dave: 6239 Elizabeth Ave, St Louis, MO 63139 ... 314-781-8851

• **Nielsen, Cliff: pg 227** Chicago, IL ... **312-364-0244**
London ... **011-44-207-636-1064**
Los Angeles, CA ... **323-874-5700**
Washington, DC ... **410-349-8669**
New York, NY ... **212-333-2551**
url: www.shannonassociates.com

Nielsen, Jim: 120 King Hill Rd, Golden Valley, MN 55416 ... 763-595-0201

Nielsen, Terese: 6049 Kauffman Ave, Temple City, CA 91780 ... 626-451-0454

Niemann, Andrew: 1290 Astoria St, Victoria, BC V8P1W1 ... 604-383-9367

Nieves Design: 1528 Holcomb's Pond Ct, Alpharetta, GA 30022 ... 770-650-7391

Nieves, Meredith: 280 Madison Ave #1110, New York, NY 10016 ... 212-545-9155

Niffenegger, Bill: 1 St Francis Pl #6201, San Francisco, CA 94107 ... 415-243-8710

Nigash, Chuck: 2259 El Empino Dr, La Habra Heights, CA 90631 ... 310-697-7626

Nigrelli, Charles: 10928 Audelia Rd #227, Dallas, TX 75243 ... 214-349-0609

• **Nihoff, Tim: pg 531** 7 Washington St, Beverly, MA 01915 ... **978-921-0887**
e-mail: leighton@leightonreps.com /url: www.leightonreps.com / fax: 978-921-0223

• **Niklewicz, Adam: pg 524,** 333 E 49th St, New York, NY 10017 ... **212-980-8061**
fax: 212-832-8778
100 Bleecker St, New York, NY 10012 ... **212-982-6533**
url: www.bruckandmoss.com / fax: 212-358-1586

Nila Barja, Guadalupe: 4440 Old Redwood Hwy #25, Santa Rosa, CA 95403 ... 805-563-1572

Niland, Brian: 12 Columbine Rd, Paramus, NJ 07652 ... 201-265-6419

Nimoy, Nancy: 10534 Clarkson Rd, Los Angeles, CA 90064 ... 310-202-0773

Nine, Carlos: 43 E 19th St, New York, NY 10003 ... 212-254-4996

Ning, Amy: 16 Phaedra, Laguna Niguel, CA 92677 ... 949-495-3664

Nishi: 18 E 16th St 7th Fl, New York, NY 10003 ... 212-255-6456

Nishinaka, Jeff: 654 Pier Ave #C, Santa Monica, CA 90405 ... 310-392-4877

Nishinaka, Jeff: 58 W 40th St 6th Fl, New York, NY 10018 ... 212-682-1490

Nishino, Gen: 270 Park Ave S #7A, New York, NY 10010 ... 212-674-3308

Nisinson, Dorian: 16 E 71st St, New York, NY 10021 ... 212-595-6823

Nitta, Kazushige: 41 Union Square W #918, New York, NY 10003 ... 212-807-6627

Nix, Thomas: 39201 Carmel Valley Rd, Carmel Valley, CA 93924 ... 408-659-3351

• **Nixon, Marian: pg 835** 2867 W Leland Ave #3, Chicago, IL 60625 ... **773-588-8640**
e-mail: nixonm@enteract.com / fax: 773-588-7640

Nixon, Sean: 1369 S Pine Creek Rd #1, Fairfield, CT 06430 ... 203-319-0579

Nixon, Tony: 7210 Robinson St, Overland Park, KS 66204 ... 913-384-5444

Nobens, CA: 709 W 90th Terr, Kansas City, MO 64114 ... 816-822-2024

• **Noble, Steven: pg 309,672,673** 47 Andreas Circle Novato, CA 94945 ... **415-433-1222**
... **415-897-6961**
e-mail: nobleart@earthlink.net / url: www.blackbook.com / fax: 415-892-4449

Noche, Mario: 7118 Upper River Rd, Prospect, KY 40059 ... 502-228-9427

Nocito, James M: 1219 W.Lewis St, San Diego, CA 92103 ... 619-491-0433

Noel, Chris: 1010 Rockville Pike #400, Rockville, MD 20852 ... 301-838-9001

Noftsinger, Pamela: 600 W 111th St #6A, New York, NY 10025 ... 212-316-4241

Noi Viva Design: 34 Old Mill Rd, Chappaqua, NY 10514 ... 914-238-3708

Noiset, Michele: 279 Twin Lakes Dr, Halifax, MA 02338 ... 781-294-0206

Nolan, Dennis: 106 Nash Hill Rd, Williamsburg, MA 01096 ... 413-586-0381

Nolte, Larry: 2901 Meramec St, St Louis, MO 63118 ... 314-481-6983

• **Noma: pg 518** Dayton, OH ... **937-433-8383**
New York, NY ... 212-966-3604
San Francisco ... 415-285-3808
url: www.scotthull.com / fax: 937-433-0434

Nonnenmacher, Mark: 2261 Williams St, Palo Alto, CA 94306 ... 415-688-3461

Noonan, Julia: 2031 Holly Dr, Prescott, AZ 86305 ... 520-708-9446

Norby, Carol H: 112 S Main, Alpine, UT 84004 ... 801-756-1096

Norcia, Ernie: 60 E 42nd St, New York, NY 10165 ... 212-867-8092

Nordell, Dale: 8615 26th Ave NE, Seattle, WA 98115 ... 206-527-8223

• **Nordling, Todd: pg 309** 716 Montgomery St, San Francisco, CA 94111 ... **415-433-1222**
url: www.sweetreps.com / fax: 415-433-9560

Nordling, Tom: 810 NE 102nd, Seattle, WA 98125 ... 206-633-3445

Nordmann, Suzanne: 1100 Meredith Ln #913, Plano, TX 75093 ... 972-930-7302

Noreika, Bob: PO Box 1594, Avon, CT 06001 ... 860-678-0681

Norman, Marty: 5 Radcliff Blvd, Glen Head, NY 11545 ... 516-671-4482

Normand, Jean-Pierre: 8608 av Henri-Julien, Montréal, QU H2P 2J7 ... 514-381-4162

Normandin, Luc: 4030 St Ambroise #400, Montréal, QU H4C 2C7 ... 514-937-2363

Norouzi, Arash: 18700 Walker's Choice Rd #412, Gaithersburg, MD 20886 ... 301-527-0103

Norris, Bruce W: 1725 17th St #103 NW, Washington, DC 20009 ... 202-387-5771

North, Ashby: 6748 Brigadoon Dr, Bethesda, MD 20817 ... 301-320-4325

North, Jan: 99 Park Ave #210A, New York, NY 10016 ... 800-398-9544

North, Russ: 5 Gramercy Park W, New York, NY 10003 ... 212-228-8639

Northeast, Christian: 108 E 35th St, New York, NY 10016 ... 212-889-3337

Norton, Jennifer: 3102 Cyrus Ave, San Jose, CA 95124 ... 408-626-8701

Norton, Lorence: 22633 NE 169th St, Woodenville, WA 98072 ... 425-788-2925

Norton, Tom: 177 Magazine St, Cambridge, MA 02139 ... 617-492-2609

Norvell, Jill: 2123 Cabots Point Ln, Reston, VA 22091 ... 703-264-0600

Norwell, Jeff: 1077 N Service Rd #207, Mississauga, ON L4Y 1A6 ... 905-615-9191

Notarile, Chris: 420 Lexington Ave, New York, NY 10170 ... 212-986-5680

Notmot, Nik: 353 W 53rd St #1W, New York, NY 10019 ... 212-682-2462

Nottoli, Joseph: 1823 Tree Top Way, Marietta, GA 30062 ... 770-977-0982

Nourse, Bill: 301 N Water St 6th Fl, Milwaukee, WI 53202 ... 414-278-7717

Novak, Justin: 156 Fifth Ave #617, New York, NY 10010 ... 212-243-1333

Novak, Tony: 4645 Colfax Ave S, Minneapolis, MN 55409 ... 612-825-7564

Noyce Jr, John Douglas: 5426 E 25th St, Tucson, AZ 85711 ... 520-571-0981

Noyes, Cecilia: 472 Schooner Wy, Seal Beach, CA 90740 ... 562-493-1471

Noyes, David: 1945 Scottsville Rd #B-2, Bowling Green, KY 42104 ... 502-781-9181

Noyse, Janet: 216 Maple Ave, Wyncote, PA 19095 ... 215-572-6975

Nozska, Marilyn: 1326 S Negley Ave, Pittsburgh, PA 15217 ... 412-422-7960

Nunnelly, Dana: 11020 127th Pl NE, Kirkland, WA 98033 ... 206-822-0397

• **Nurse, Chris: pg 189** Chicago, IL ... **312-364-0244**
London ... **011-44-207-636-1064**
Los Angeles, CA ... **323-874-5700**
Washington, DC ... **410-349-8669**
New York, NY ... **212-333-2551**
url: www.shannonassociates.com

Nuttle, Jim: 14904 Wellwood Rd, Silver Spring, MD 20905 ... 301-989-0942

Nyberg, Tim: 3307 N Victoria, Shoreview, MN 55126 ... 651-493-0694

Nye, Linda S: 307 S Trooper Rd, Norristown, PA 19403 ... 610-539-1130

Nyman, Steven: 10 Maywood Ct, Fairlawn, NJ 07410 ... 201-797-1003

O

O'Brien, Ann Sibley: Maple St, Peaks Island, ME 04108 ... 207-766-5555

O'Brien, Dennis: 17 Nauyaug Point Rd, Mystic, CT 06355 ... 860-536-1684

ILLUSTRATORS

• **Paraskevas, Michael: pg 276** 250 W 57th St #521, New York, NY 10107 .... **212-397-7330**
San Francisco: **415-788-8552**
url: www.lindgrensmith.com
Pardini, Patricia: 1133 Midland Ave #1C, Bronxville, NY 10708 914-793-0977
Pardo, Jackie: 853 Broadway #606, New York, NY 10003 212-777-6777
Pardue Studio, Jack: 2307 Sherwood Hall Ln, Alexandria, VA 22306 703-765-2622
• **Parett, Lisa: pg 808** Clinton, CT **860-669-4045**
e-mail: lisa@itsalooloo.com
Pariseau, Pierre-Paul: 3997 St Dominique 2, Montreal, QU H2W 2A4 514-849-2964
Pariseau, Pierre-Paul: 16 Phaedra, Laguna Niguel, CA 92677 949-495-3664
Parisi, Mark: 16 Slayton Rd, Melrose, MD 02176 781-665-4442
Park, Charlie: 7120 Lexington Ave #3, W Hollywood, CA 90046 323-845-4540
Park, Chang: 58 W 15th St, New York, NY 10011 212-741-2539
Park, Chang: 154-16 Beech Ave 1st Fl, Flushing, NY 11355 718-939-0998
Park, Darcie: 2461 Roswell Ave, Long Beach, CA 90815 310-985-0506
Park, Elliot: 8325 Cr 462, Baird, TX 79504 888-324-4428
• **Park, Jun: pg 638,639** 15 Cassidy Pl, Toronto, ON M3B 2S3 .... **416-441-9422**
e-mail: junpark@home.com / url: www.junpark.com / fax: 416-441-1328
Parke, Steven: 3233 O'Donnel St #34, Baltimore, MD 21224 410-327-9363
• **Parker, Curtis: pg 518** Dayton, OH **937-433-8383**
New York, NY **212-966-3604**
San Francisco, CA **415-285-3808**
url: www.scotthull.com / fax: 937-433-0434
• **Parker, Ed: pg 348** 58 W 15th St, New York, NY 10011 .... **212-741-2539**
url: www.jdedell.com or www.theispot.com / fax: 212-741-4660
Parker, Geoffrey: 285 Fishcreek Rd, Saugerties, NY 12477 914-246-2166
Parker, Robert Andrew: 155 W 15th St #4C, New York, NY 10011 212-989-8770
Parkinson, Jim: 6170 Broadway Terr, Oakland, CA 94618 510-547-3100
Parkinson, Keith: 1681 W Geranium Pl, Tucson, AZ 85737 520-229-1621
Parks, John: 5 Broadview Ln, Red Hook, NY 12571 914-758-0656
Parks, Kevin: 1156 Ventura Ave, Oak View, CA 93022 805-649-4059
Parks, Melanie Marder: 5 Broadview Ln, Red Hook, NY 12571 914-758-0656
Parks, Phil: 806 Woodcrest, Royal Oaks, MI 48067 810-545-6477
• **Parks, Rick: pg 515** 94 Natoma St #233, San Francisco, CA 94105 .... **415-442-1822**
url: www.wileyreps.com / fax: 415-442-1823
Parks, Tricia: 247 E 57th St 2nd Fl, New York, NY 10022 212-980-7979
Parmenter, Wayne: 10439 Parmento Rd NE, Erie, PA 16428 814-725-8566
Parnell, John: 2121 Albenarle Terr, Brooklyn, NY 11226 212-226-7682
Parnell, Miles: 98 Wallace Rd, North Salem, NY 10560 203-226-4724
e-mail: creative.svcs@snet.net / url: www.brewstercreative.com / fax: 203-454-9904
• **Parr, Catherine: pg 817** Los Angeles, CA **213-622-2921**
1308 Factory Pl #401, Los Angeles, CA 90013 .... **888-288-2794**
url: www.theispot.com/artist/parr
Parrish, Bruce: 22910 NW Pink Hill Rd, Blue Springs, MO 64015 816-229-2250
Parsekian, John: 5 Lawrence St Bldg 15, Bloomfield, NJ 07003 201-748-9717
Parson, Stephen: 2330 Bedford St #2, Durham, NC 27707 919-490-0608
Parsons Design, Glenn: 8522 National Blvd #108, Culver City, CA 90232 310-559-6571
Parsons, John: 420 Lexington Ave #2760, New York, NY 10170 212-697-8525
Partington, Michael: PO Box 20391, Indianapolis, IN 46220 317-577-9444
Parton, Steve: 400 W 43rd St #37S, New York, NY 10036 212-766-2285
Partridge, Todd: 227 Godfrey Rd, Weston, CT 06883 203-222-8777
Paschkis, Julie: 309 NE 94th St, Seattle, WA 98115 206-525-5205
Pasqua, Lou: 309 Walnut Rd, Pittsburgh, PA 15202 412-761-5666
Passalacqua, David: 325 Versa Pl, Sayville, NY 11782 516-589-1663
Passarelli, Chuck: 353 W 53rd St #1W, New York, NY 10019 212-682-2462
Passey, Kim: 115 Hurlbut #17, Pasadena, CA 91105 626-441-4384
Passow, Faye: 1503 Briar Knoll Dr, Arden Hills, MN 55112 651-631-8480
Pasternak, Robert: 114 W 27th St #55, New York, NY 10001 212-675-0002
Paston, Herbert: 28 S Silver Ln, Sunderland, MA 01375 413-665-3366
Pastoreck, Robert Jr: 33 Lawndale St, Springfield, MA 01108 413-734-8816
• **Pastrana, Robert: pg 800** 473A Riverdale Dr, Glendale, CA 91204 .... **818-548-6083**
e-mail: robertp4@idt.net / url: www.robertpastrana.com / fax: 818-548-6083
Pastucha, Ron: 336 McNeans Ave, Winnipeg, MB R2C 2J7 204-222-3178
Pastucha, Ron: 1011 Pico Blvd #9, Santa Monica, CA 90405 310-392-7660
Pate, Martin: 2460 Peachtree Rd NW, Atlanta, GA 30305 404-881-6627
Patelis, Dimitrios: 232 Madison Ave #512, New York, NY 10016 212-889-8777
Patrick, Cyndy: 5 Dresden St #1, Jamaica Plain, MA 02130 617-522-4433
• **Patrick, John: pg 519** Dayton, OH **937-433-8383**
New York, NY **212-966-3604**
San Francisco, CA **415-285-3808**
url: www.scotthull.com / fax: 937-433-0434
Patrick, Pamela: 100 Bleecker St, New York, NY 10012 212-982-6533
Patrick, Tom: 731 Stovall Blvd NE, Atlanta, GA 30342 800-791-1189
Patrick, Tom: 4726 Fairmont Ave, Kansas City, MO 64112 816-531-4853
Patterson, James: 4312 Mt Olney Ln, Olney, MD 20832 301-774-8329
Patterson, Tom: 2233 Kemper Ln, Cincinnati, OH 45206 513-201-0095
• **Patti, Joyce: pg 387** 194 Third Ave, New York, NY 10003 .... **212-475-0440**
url: www.morgangaynin.com / fax: 212-353-8538
• **Patton Brothers Illustration: pg 807** 3768 Miles Ct, Spring Valley, CA 91977 ... **619-463-4562**
url: www.pattonbros.com / fax: 619-463-4763
Patton, Edd: 295 19th Ave #6, San Francisco, CA 94121 415-387-3126
807A Baylor St, Austin, TX 78703 512-478-3338
Patton, Henry: 1570-D Dekalb Ave, Atlanta, GA 30307 404-377-6504
Paul Illust, Peter: PO Box 639, Bellflower, CA 90707 310-876-3880
Paul, David: 120 Jackson St #1R, Hoboken, NJ 07030 201-933-7157
Paul, Edie: 859 Hollywood #136, Burbank, CA 91505 818-505-1874
Paul, Jon: 60 E 42nd St, New York, NY 10165 212-867-8092
Paul, Keith: 165 E 32nd St, New York, NY 10016 212-686-3514
Pauling, Galen T: PO Box 3150, Southfield, MI 48037 313-533-7674
Paulos, Martha: 5941 MacCall St, Oakland, CA 94609 510-601-1813
Paulsen, Larry: 58 W 40th St 6th Fl, New York, NY 10018 212-682-1490
Pauly, Thomas Allen: 4224 N Hermitage Ave, Chicago, IL 60613 773-477-0440
Pavey, Jerry: 232 Madison Ave #512, New York, NY 10016 212-889-8777
Pavia, Cathy: 332 Loma Ave, Long Beach, CA 90814 562-434-5285
Pavlov, Elana: 377 W 11th #1F, New York, NY 10014 212-243-0939
Pavlovich, Paul: 562 43rd Ave NE, St Petersburg, FL 33703 813-824-5620
Pavlovsky, Dawn: 5419 S Nordica, Chicago, IL 60638 773-586-0631
Pawelka, Rick: 2005 Carl Williamson Rd, Raleigh, NC 27610 919-878-7883
Payea, Heather: 609 Harper Ln, Midland, MI 48640 734-678-4424
• **Payne, Adair: pg 717** 1824 N Somerset, Mesa, AZ 85205 .... **480-641-7345**
e-mail: adairpayne@aol.com / fax: 480-641-7779
• **Payne, CF: pg 38,39** 305 E 50th St Ste 1, New York, NY 10022 .... **212-223-9545**
url: www.richardsolomon.com / fax: 212-223-9633
Payne, Kevin: 3338 Copper Ave, Broomfield, CO 80020 303-464-9222
Payne, Lawrence: 13265 SW Aragon St, Beaverton, OR 97005 541-644-7158
Payne, Tom: 2031 Holly Dr, Prescott, AZ 86305 520-708-9446
Peacock, Matthew: 403 Acorn St, Lansdale, PA 19446 215-412-8210
Peake, Kevin: 133 N Montclair Ave, Dallas, TX 75208 214-943-2569
4205 Clawson Rd, Austin, TX 78704 512-443-3907
Peal, Michael: 903 Rebud Trail, Austin, TX 78746 512-892-1798
Peale, Charles: 108 2nd St SW #36, Charlottesville, VA 22902 804-293-3394
Pearce, Juliette: 286 Spring St #301, New York, NY 10013 212-229-0073
Pearson, Jim: 218 Elm Court, Rhinelander, WI 54501 715-369-2130
Pechanec, Vladimir: 34-43 Crescent St #4C, Long Island City, NY 11106 718-729-3973
Peck, Virginia: 34 Erie Ave, Newton, MA 02161 617-558-7014
Peck, Byron: 1857 Lamont St NW, Washington, DC 20010 202-331-1966
Peck, Everett: 716 Sanchez St, San Francisco, CA 94114 415-285-8267
Peck, Marshall: 10 Larch Ln, Londonderry, NH 03053 603-432-2108
Peck, Michael: 731 N 24th St, Philadelphia, PA 19130 215-232-6666
Peck, Scott: 2701 Thorndale Crl, Plano, TX 75074 972-422-7438
Peck, Suzanne: 420 Lexington Ave, New York, NY 10170 212-986-5680
Pedersen, Dennis: 5105 Shady Ave, San Jose, CA 95129 408-873-9531
Pederson, Judy: 16 McEwen St., Warwick, NY 10990 914-987-1090
• **Peebles, Peter: pg 378** 89 Fifth Ave #901, New York, NY 10003 .... **212-627-1554**
e-mail: artworksillustration@earthlink.net / url: www.artworksillustration.com / fax: 212-627-1719
Peele, Lynwood: 344 W 88th St #1A, New York, NY 10024 212-799-3305
• **Peen, Bud: pg 454,455** **510-482-8302**
e-mail: studio@budpeen.com / url: www.budpeen.com
San Francisco, CA **415-441-4384**
Pegasus, Telesis: 2525 Thames St, Los Angeles, CA 90046 323-656-3899
Peji, Bennett: 1110-B Torrey Pines Rd, La Jolla, CA 92037 619-456-8071
Pelaez, Joan: 43 E 19th St, New York, NY 10003 212-254-4996
• **Pelavin, Daniel: pg 926** 80 Varrick St 3B New York, NY 10013 .... **212-941-7418**
e-mail daniel@pelavin.com / url: www.pelavin.com / fax: 212-431-7138
Pelham-Foulke, Nancy Alliger: 4243 Sucia Dr, Ferndale, WA 98248 360-312-0248
Pelicano, Chris: 1400 S Highway Dr, Fenton, MO 63099 314-827-2840
Pelikan, Judy: 200 E 78th St, New York, NY 10021 212-570-9069
Pell, Alan: 4728 King Rd, Loomis, CA 95650 916-632-7877
Pellaton, Karen: PO Box 1086, Taos, NM 87571 505-776-5435
Pelletier, Joel: Box 1842, Hollywood, CA 90078 818-980-8304
• **Pelo, Jeffrey: pg 452,453** , San Francisco, CA **415-441-4384**
Mill Valley, CA **415-388-2076**
url: www.jeffreypelo.com
Pelo, Lisa: 516 Brookline Ave, Mill Valley, CA 94941 415-381-2079
Peltier Designs, Pam: 330 Silver Springs Crl, Colorado Springs, CO 80919 719-598-1791
Pembroke, Richard: 353 W 53rd St #1W, New York, NY 10019 212-682-2462
Penalva, Jordi: 43 E 19th St, New York, NY 10003 212-254-4996
Penberthy, Mark: 47 Greene St, New York, NY 10013 212-219-2664
Penca, Gary: 8335 NW 20th St, Coral Springs, FL 33071 305-752-4699
Pendleton, Nancy: 10415 N 38th St, Phoenix, AZ 85028 602-257-0097
Pendola, Joanne: 414 E 11th St #2E, New York, NY 10009 212-353-1834
• **Peng, Leif: pg 302** 731 N 24th St, Philadelphia, PA 19130 .... **215-232-6666**
url: www.deborahwolfeltd.com / fax: 215-232-6585
Pennington, Jack: 8882 Woodsman Dr, Washington, MI 48094 810-781-0805
Pennington, Jack: 2233 Kemper Ln, Cincinnati, OH 45206 513-861-1400
Pentelovitch, Robert Alan: 340 W 55th St #2D, New York, NY 10019 .... 212 397 0209
Pentleton, Carol: 685 Chestnut Hill Rd, Chepachet, RI 02814 401-568-0275
Pepera, Fred: 1344 State Park Rd., Ortonville, MI 48462 248-627-6493
Pepler, Susan Elizabeth: 1206 av Seymour, Montréal, QU H3H 2A5 514-862-0420
Pepper, Bob: 157 Clinton St, Brooklyn, NY 11201 718-875-3236
Pepper, Brenda: 157 Clinton St, Brooklyn, NY 11201 718-875-3236
Peralta, Bella: PO Box 1093, Weaverville, CA 96093 916-623-4872
Percivalle, Rosanne: 450 W 31st St Gr Fl, New York, NY 10001 212-295-7763
Percy, Graham: 455 W 23rd St #8D, New York, NY 10011 212-366-1893
Peregoy, Chris: 1201 W Ostend St, Baltimore, MD 21230 410-539-8460
Pereiro, Pablo: Julio Herrera y Reissig 738/301, 11200 Montevideo, URUGUAY . 59827112474
Perevra, Greg: 18734 Kenya St, Northridge, CA 91326 818-832-9364
Perez, Gerardo: 100 Blue Ravine Rd, Folsom, CA 95630 916-363-5000
Perez, German: 69 W 106th St #5A, New York, NY 10025 212-932-8639
Perez, Vincent: 1279 Weber St, Alameda, CA 94501 510-521-2262
Pergament Graphics: 38 E 30th St, New York, NY 10016 212-213-8310
Peringer, Stephen: 5002 92nd Ave SE, Mercer Island, WA 98040 206-232-7873
17808 184th Ave NE, Woodinville, WA 98072 425-788-5767
Perini, Ben: PO Box 421443, San Francisco, CA 94142 415-647-5660
Perini, Ben: 1607 Lancelot Ln, Winston Salem, NC 27103 910-724-2260
Perkins, Gary Reid: 117 Leola, Hot Springs, AR 71913 501-767-1683
Perkins, Ken: 1415 Garden St, Glendale, CA 91201 818-244-0110
Perkins, Ken: 235 Agate Way, Broomfield, CO 80020 303-465-4346
Perle, Quimetta: 265 12th St, Brooklyn, NY 11215 718-965-1858
Perlman, David: 59 Stoneham Dr, Rochester, NY 14625 716-381-3543
Perlow, Paul: 123 E 54th St #6E, New York, NY 10022 212-758-4358
Perna, Jess: 52-41 Douglaston Pkwy, Douglaston, NY 11362 718-224-5652
Perrin-Falquet, Joan: 763 Ninth Ave #3S, New York, NY 10019
Perrone, Donna: 53 Second Ave, New York, NY 10003 212-254-9453
Perry, Phil: 1913 Hudson Crossing Rd Apt 3, Tucker, GA 30084 404-325-2930
Perry, Rebecca: 15532 Antioch St #510, Pacific Palisades, CA 90272 310-459-0071
• **Persiani, Tony: pg 510** 310 W 97th St #25, New York, NY 10025 .... **212-243-5888**
e-mail: lori@lorinowicki.com / url: www.lorinowicki.com / fax: 212-243-5955
Persky, Lisa Jane: 419 N. Larchmont Blvd #161, Los Angeles, CA 90004 213-461-9738
Perspectiva: 66 W 77th St #45, New York, NY 10024 212-875-1380
Pertile, Paula: 419 22nd Ave, San Francisco, CA 94121 415-668-7156
Perugi, Deborah: 19 Church St, Newton, MA 02158 617-569-5822
Pérusse-Bell, Anouk: 5190 rue Rivard, Montréal, QU H2J 2P1 514-277-7098
Perzell, Bob: 1577 Antler Point, Eagan, MN 55122 651-686-0877
Pesek, Marjorie E: 1235 Lyman Ave, Wayzata, MN 55391 612-476-2800
Petan, Greg: 58 W 40th St 6th Fl, New York, NY 10018 212-682-1490
Peterka, Cheryl: 10 Beach St, New York, NY 10013 212-334-5091
Peters Design, David: 2141 Walnut Ave, Venice, CA 90291 310-390-3528

Pranica, John: 2004 W Walton St, Chicago, IL 60622 773-276-7606
Prato, Rodica: 154 W 57th St, New York, NY 10019 212-245-5854
Pratt, Christine Joy: 1050 Queen St #200, Honolulu, HI 96814 808-591-8879
Pratt, Pierre: 231 Humbercrest Blvd, Toronto, ON M6S 4L5 416-530-1500
Pratt, Wayne: PO Box 1421, Wilmington, VT 05363 802-368-7207
Pravato, Victor: 14 Emily Ave, Weston, ON M9L 2R1 416-742-4764
Pravda, Kit Monroe: 2148 Sand Hill Rd, Menlo Park, CA 94025 415-854-1050
Preising, David J: PO Box 3952, Brewer, ME 04412 207-991-9672
Premru, Greg: 348 Congress St 3rd Fl, Boston, MA 02210 617-451-7770
Prendergast, Michael: 12 Merrill St, Newburyport, MA 01950 508-465-8598
Prescott, Carl: 887 35th Ave, Santa Cruz, CA 95062 831-464-2176
Presley, Greg: 12532 Timber Hollow Pl, Germantown, MD 20874 301-601-4999
Preslicka, Greg: 5000 Edgewater Dr, Savage, MN 55378 612-432-2166
Presnall, Terry: 50 Fuller Brook Rd, Wellesley, MA 02482 781-235-8658
Preston, Heather: 20 Savannah Ave, San Anselmo, CA 94960 415-454-4099
Preston, Jeff: 6182 Sydney Dr, Huntington Beach, CA 92647 714-898-7288
Preuitt, Clayton: 420 S Detroit St #4, Los Angeles, CA 90036 323-965-8285
Previn, Stacey: 1415 Garden St, Glendale, CA 91201 818-244-0110
Pribanic, Chris: 2340 Cleveland Rd, Sandusky, OH 44870 419-624-9023
Price, Amy: 213 Antisdel Pl NE, Grand Rapids, MI 49503 616-459-7595
Price, David: 6101 Bel-Air Dr, Texarcana, TX 75503 903-832-5552
Price, Jim: 401 N. Wabash #532, Chicago, IL 60611 312-222-1361
Price, Joan: 1469 Canyon Rd, Sante Fe, NM 87501 505-986-3823
Price, Kimberly : 822 Wildgrove Dr, Garland, TX 75041 972-278-8085
• **Price, Paul: pg 224** Chicago, IL **312-364-0244**
London **011-44-207-636-1064**
Los Angeles, CA **323-874-5700**
Washington, DC **410-349-8669**
New York, NY **212-333-2551**
url: www.shannonassociates.com
Priesing, David: PO Box 3952, Brewer, ME 04412 888-991-9672
Priester, Gary: 353 Laurel Ave, Novato, CA 94945 415-331-4531
• **Prince, Robert: pg 501** 597 Riverside Ave, Westport, CT 06880 . . . . **203-226-4724**
e-mail: creative.svcs@snet.net / url: www.brewstercreative.com / fax: 203-454-9904
Principato, Salvatore: 220 Sullivan St #4H, New York, NY 10012 212-477-8161
Pritchett, Karen: 309 Walnut Rd, Pittsburgh, PA 15202 412-761-5666
Pritty, Mandy: 7 Abbots Pl, W Hampstead, London, UK NW6 4NP 442076254835
Probert, Jean: 612 N 2nd St, St Louis, MO 63102 314-781-7377
Prochnow, Bill: 3855 Greenwood Ave, Oakland, CA 94602 415-777-8745
Proffer, Arabella: 24721 EL Camino Capistrano, Dana Point, CA 92629 949-443-3945
• **Proffitt, Paine: pg 289** 731 N 24th St, Philadelphia, PA 19130 . . . . **215-232-6666**
url: www.deborahwolfeltd.com / fax: 215-232-6585
Prokell, Jim: 26 Marylee Ave #300, Pittsburgh, PA 15227 412-232-3636
Prosser, Les: 3501 Windom Rd, Brentwood, MD 20722 301-927-8867
Proulx, Art: 1316 Third St #305, Santa Monica, CA 90401 310-458-7600
Prout, Michael: 3725 Plymouth-Laporte Trail, Walkerton, IN 46574 219-656-8333
Provenzano, Anthony: 6980 W Touhy Ave #201, Niles, IL 60648 847-647-6418
Prud'homme, Jon: 4611 Talisman St, Torrance, CA 90503 310-370-1728
Prud'Homme, Jules: 4853 av Melrose, Montréal, QU H3X 3P4 514-485-2641
Prusinski, John: 65 Main St #300, Warwick, NY 10990 914-986-6522
Pryor, Robert: PO Box 1760, Highland Park, IL 60035 312-222-0337
Przewodek, Camille: 108 E 35th St, New York, NY 10016 212-889-3337
Psychic Dog Illustration: 6620 W 81st St, Los Angeles, CA 90045 310-641-6916
Puchalski, John: 7 Sage Hill Ln, Laguna Hills, CA 92653 310-828-0841
Puckett Design, David: 248 Irvine Blvd #342, Tustin, CA 92782 714-966-5896
Puente, Lyle: 296 E 4th St, Brooklyn, NY 11218 718-436-4447
Pugh, Lorena: 323 Harrison St, N Kingstown, RI 02852 401-885-9438
Pulitzer, Carol: 3311 Mandeville Canyon Rd, Los Angeles, CA 90049 310-471-1805
Pullen, Lucy: PO Box 461, Halifax Central, NS B3J 2P8 902-425-4654
Pullen, Zachary: PO Box 276 296 Main St #1, Rosendale, NY 12472 914-658-5399
Pulver Jr, Harry: 105 Meadow Ln N, Minneapolis, MN 55422 612-377-1797
Punchatz, Don Ivan: 2605 Westgate Dr, Arlington, TX 76015 817-469-8151
Pundyk, Anne: 30 Waterside Plz #31d, New York, NY 10010 212-889-6833
Punin, Nikolai: 311 Greenwich #9B, New York, NY 10013 212-227-7863
Purcell, Chris: PO Box 692000, Houston, TX 77269 713-374-4679
Purdom, Bill: 2805 Oleander Dr, Wilmington, NC 28403 910-763-1208
Putka, Doron: 310 W 97th St #902, New York, NY 10025 212-243-5888
• **Pyle, Charles: pg 265** 250 W 57th St #521, New York, NY 10107 . . . . **212-397-7330**
San Francisco: **415-788-8552**
url: www.lindgrensmith.com
Pyle, Liz: 155 W 15th St #4C, New York, NY 10011 212-989-8770
Pyner, Marcia: 455 W 23rd St #8D, New York, NY 10011 212-366-1893
Python, Tifenn: 485 Central Park West #6F, New York, NY 10025 212-635-0272

Q

Quarles, Oscar: 1478 Beach Channel Dr #3C, Far Rockaway, NY 11691 718-327-6907
Quartuccio, Dom: 410 W 24th St #9M, New York, NY 10011 212-727-7329
Quillen, Mike: 954 Delaware Ave, Columbus, OH 43201 614-299-8216
Quinlan, Stephen: 3602 Silverthorn Dr, Oakville, ON LCL 5N7 905-469-0525
Quinn, Colleen: 307 N Michigan Ave #1006, Chicago, IL 60601 312-704-0500
Quinn, Ger & Barbara: 7405 Arden Rd, Cabin John, MD 20818 301-229-8030
Quint, Chuck: 4539 N Paulina, Chicago, IL 60640 773-271-8056
Quirion, Daniel: 10131 rue Cartier, Montréal, QU H23 2B3 514-389-8974
Quon Design Office, Mike: 53 Spring St 5th Fl, New York, NY 10012 212-226-6024

R

Raabin, Victoria L: 22 Schlichter Rd, Fishkill, NY 12524 914-897-5066
Rabagliati, Michel: 5505 Saint Laurent Blvd #3009, Montral, QU H2T 1S6 514-271-5606
Rabi, Lorraine: 629 Glenwood Ave, Teaneck, NJ 07666 201-836-4283
Rabin, Bill: 30 E Huron St, Chicago, IL 60611 312-944-6655
Rabinovitch, William: PO Box 403 Canal St Sta, New York, NY 10013 212-226-2873
Rabinowich, Leonid: 19560 S Rancho Way, Dominguez Hills, CA 90220 310-884-3492
Rabinowicz, Vicky: 301 Elizabeth St #8T, New York, NY 10012 212-603-9900
Rabinowitz, Lauren: PO Box 2283, Edison, NJ 08820 732-549-1455
Rabinowitz, Stephanie: PO Box 3612, Bellevue, WA 98009 425-467-0444
Racer, Tim: 3059 Richmond Blvd, Oakland, CA 94611 510-451-0303
• **Racoon Illustration: pg 684,685** 1 Beechwood Rd, Bedford Hills, NY 10507 . . **212-691-5841**
e-mail: roldancarl@aol.com / fax: 212-206-8519
Radencich, Mike: 420 Lexington Ave, New York, NY 10170 212-986-5680
Radigan, Bob: 280 Madison Ave #1110, New York, NY 10016 212-545-9155
Radionov, Gregory: 17830 Suerman Way #303, Reseda, CA 91335 818-881-1864
Radmilovich, Joanne: 2405 NW Thurman St, Portland, OR 97210 503-203-8300
Radulovic, Milos: Batajnickih ilegalaca 14/15, Belgrade, Serbia, YUGOS 381118480882
Rae, William: 662 Warren St, Brooklyn, NY 11217 718-398-4423
Raetz, Kyle: 612 N 2nd St, St Louis, MO 63102 314-781-7377
Rafei, Bob: 11730 W Sunset Blvd #309, Los Angeles, CA 90049 818-777-6889
Raff, Lyne: 9501 Rolling Oaks Trail, Austin, TX 78750 512-219-1208
Rafferty, Jim: 1518 139th Ln NW, Andover, MN 55304 612-755-8488
Raffetto, Teresa: 241 E 14th St #2A, New York, NY 10003 212-375-9432
Raffi, Alex: 1142 Sierra Laurel Ct, Henderson, NV 89014 702-434-3534
Ragland, Wynne: One Meca Way #600, Norcross, GA 30093 770-564-5606
• **Raglin, Tim: pg 274** 250 W 57th St #521, New York, NY 10107 . . . . **212-397-7330**
San Francisco: **415-788-8552**
url: www.lindgrensmith.com
Rainey, Kirk: 478 Craighead St #105, Nashville, TN 37204 615-463-0203
Rainock, Norman: 2921 Sentry Station Rd, Mechanicsville, VA 23111 804-559-8703
Rall, Ted: PO Box 2092/Times, New York, NY 10108 212-932-3407
Ramage, Alfred: 5 Irwin St, Winthrop, MA 02152 617-846-5955
• **Ramazan, Seid: pg 848** Queens, NY **718-261-7243**
url: www.seidramazan.com
Ramey, Ken: 435 S Ridge Rd, Hesston, KS 67062 316-327-2669
Rammer, Anthony: 950 Woodlake Rd, Kohler, WI 53044 414-459-6800
Ramos, Ruben: 4300 N Narragansett, Chicago, IL 60634 847-670-0912
Ramsey, Heather: 1411 La Salina St, Oceanside, CA 92054 760-967-5977
Ramsey, Ted: 11039A Villaridge St, Reston, VA 20191 703-481-9424
Ramune: 210 Hillside Ave #27, Needham, MA 02194 781-444-1185
Rancorn, Chuck: 208 Providence Rd, Annapolis, MD 21401 410-349-8669
Randall, Gail Greenfield: 1912 Comstock Ave, Los Angeles, CA 90025 310-556-9770
Randazzo, Tony: 353 W 53rd St #1W, New York, NY 10019 212-682-2462
Rane, Walter: 60 E 42nd St, New York, NY 10165 212-867-8092
Raneri, Marci: 2035 Richmond St, Philadelphia, PA 19125 800-522-0888
Raney, Ken: 433 S Ridge Rd, Hesston, KS 67062 316-327-2669
Ranger, Christin: 500 Aurora Ave N #406C, Seattle, WA 98109 206-818-0879
• **Rangne, Monica: pg 420** 7118 Upper River Rd, Prospect, KY 40059 . . . . **502-228-9427**
url: www.jettreps.com / fax: 502-228-8857
Rangner, Mike: 1647 NE 142nd, Portland, OR 97230 503-262-7313
• **Rankin, David: pg 457,459** 300 E 46th St #4G, New York, NY 10017 . . . . . . **212-687-6463**
url: www.levycreative.com / fax: 212-661-4839
Ransley, Rich: 39 Hamilton Terr, New York, NY 10031 212-283-3401
Ransome, James: 71 Hooker Ave, Poughkeepsie, NY 12601 914-473-8281
Rapalee, Susan: 342 Seventh Ave #4, Brooklyn, NY 11215 718-499-2301
Raphael & Bolognese: 53 Irving Pl, New York, NY 10003 212-228-5219
Raschella, Carole: 8607 Bothwell Rd, Northridge, CA 91324 818-349-6742
Raschka, Chris: 310 Riverside Dr #418, New York, NY 10025 212-865-0864
Rasema, Scott: 1844 McIlwirth, Muskegon, MI 49442 616-728-2435
Rashid, Mai Gebara: 93 86th St, Brooklyn, NY 11209 718-833-1982
Rashid, Sarah: 10 Grenoble Dr #202, North York, ON M3C 1CS 416-429-0410
Rasmussen, Bonnie: 8828 Pendleton, St Louis, MO 63144 314-962-1842
Rasmussen, Wendy: PO Box 131/950 Durham Rd, Durham, PA 18039 610-346-8117
Raszka, Brian: 2475 Robb Dr #837, Reno, NV 89523 775-624-6145
Rattin, Mark: 2300 W Wabansia Ave #105, Chicago, IL 60647 312-642-0359
Ratz de Tagyos, Paul: 30 Eastchester Rd #6A, New Rochelle, NY 10801 914-636-2313
Rauchman, Robert: 5210 SW 60th Pl, Miami, FL 33155 305-663-9432
Rauffenbart, Bruce: 170 W 23rd St #4E, New York, NY 10011 212-924-2771
39 Hamilton Terr, New York, NY 10031 212-283-3401
Rauffenbart, Bruce: 170 W 23rd St #4E, New York, NY 10011 212-924-2771
Raulick, ML: 219 Glenwood Dr, Houston, TX 77007 713-864-9041
Rausch, Robert: PO Box 847, Savannah, TN 38372 901-925-9158
Ravanelli, Terry: 3301A S Jefferson Ave, St Louis, MO 63118 314-773-2600
Ravel, Ken: 226 Arlington St, Reading, PA 19611 215-378-9313
Ravenwolf, Patricia Randall: 1 Gilmore Rd, Trenton, NJ 08628 609-882-3066
Rawley, Don: 7520 Blaisdell Ave S, Richfield, MN 55423 612-866-1023
Rawlings, Andrea: 1140 Hermosa Ave #6, Hermosa Beach, CA 90254 310-670-5042
• **Rawlings, Steve: pg 230,231** Chicago, IL **312-364-0244**
London **011-44-207-636-1064**
Los Angeles, CA **323-874-5700**
Washington, DC **410-349-8669**
New York, NY **212-333-2551**
url: www.shannonassociates.com
Rawson, Jon: 1368 Waterside Dr, Bolingbrook, IL 60440 630-226-9320
Rayevsky, Robert: 76 Marian St, Northhampton, MA 01060 413-586-3375
Rea, Tracy: 9969 Southwind Dr, Indianapolis, IN 46256 317-570-0700
Read, Elizabeth: 431 W Colfax Ave #540, Denver, CO 80204 303-446-2611
Read, Elizabeth: 1809 7th Ave #1710, Seattle, WA 98101 206-447-1600
Ready, Lee: 927 164th Ave SE, Bellevue, WA 98008 425-747-8783
Reagan, Mike: 303 Fern Valley Ln, Apex, NC 27502 919-387-8230
Reagan, Mike: 2134 Aquetong Rd, New Hope, PA 18938 215-862-2091
Reamer, Tim: PO Box 551, San Diego, CA 92112 619-260-0021
Rearick, Kevin: 293 Goldenwood Cir, Simi Valley, CA 93065 805-584-9259
Reas, Anne: 12646 Alcacer Del Sol, San Diego, CA 92198 858-592-4184
Réault, Patrick: One Captain Dr #D358, Emeryville, CA 94608 510-653-3996
Reay, Richard: 6010 Liebig Ave #2, Bronx, NY 10471 718-884-2317
Rebelo, Tanya: 1133 Broadway Ste 825, New York, NY 10010 212-243-1333
• **Rechin, Kevin: pg 158,159** 420 Lexington Ave, New York, NY 10170 . . . . **212-986-5680**
e-mail: mendolaart@aol.com / url: www.mendolaart.com / fax: 212-818-1246
Recio, Marta: 664 S Lake Ave, Pasadena, CA 91106 818-793-3088
Redding, Harvey: 240 Elizabeth St, New York, NY 10012 212-966-5062
Rediger, Deborah: 612 N 2nd St, St Louis, MO 63102 314-781-7377
Redl, Dave: 45 Surrey Dr, Wayne, NJ 07470 201-696-4748
Redner, Todd: 121 Little Brook Dr, Woodstock, GA 30188 770-516-4255

Rodericks, Mike: 129 Lounsbury Rd, Trumbull, CT 06611 ... 203-268-1551
Rodgers, Joel: 44 Milland Dr, Northport, NY 11768 ... 800-439-9217
Rodin, Christine: 38 Morton St #5A, New York, NY 10014 ... 212-242-3260
Rodney, Gail: 500 E 83rd St, New York, NY 10028 ... 212-249-9572
Rodorigo, Sandro: 23-17 33rd St #7, Astoria, NY 11105 ... 718-274-2764
Rodrigues, Teco: 48 Lakeshore Dr, Etobicoke, ON M8V 1Z6 ... 416-253-5992
Rodriguez, Claudio: 304 Mulberry St #4B, New York, NY 10012 ... 212-941-0573
Rodriguez, Doris: 255 Powers St #3-LR, Brooklyn, NY 11211 ... 212-388-7336
Rodriguez, Edel: 16 Ridgewood Ave #102, Mt Tabor, NJ 07878 ... 973-983-7776
Rodriguez, Francisco: 612 N 2nd St, St Louis, MO 63102 ... 314-781-7377
Rodriguez, Gisela: 695 Talcottville Rd #17-6, Vernon, CT 06066 ... 413-782-6870
Rodriguez, Lisandro: 86 Fort Washington Blvd #4F, New York, NY 10032 ... 212-781-5175
• **Rodriguez, Robert: pg 266,267** 250 W 57th St #521, New York, NY 10107 ... **212-397-7330**
San Francisco, CA: ... **415-788-8552**
url: www.lindgrensmith.com
Rodriguez, Syl: 11516 Sixth Ave, Seattle, WA 98117 ... 206-364-9077
Rodriguez, Teco: 48 Lakeshore Dr, Toronto, ON M8V 1Z6 ... 416-253-5992
Rodriquez, Jose: 14521 Cullen St, Whittier, CA 90603 ... 310-693-1031
Roe, Dale: PO Box 291, Round Rock, TX 78760 ... 512-733-1414
Roeger, Daniel T: 21 Elm St, Methuen, MA 01844 ... 603-898-1087
Roffo, Sergio: 222 Thomas Clapp Rd, Scituate, MA 02066 ... 617-787-5861
Rofheart-Piggot, Irene: PO Box 420, Garrison, NY 10524 ... 914-424-8304
Rogala, Miroslaw: 329 W 18th Street #900, Chicago, IL 60616 ... 312-243-2952
Rogers, Adam: 2491 W 22nd Ave, Vancouver, BC V62 1M3 ... 604-684-6826
Rogers, Buc: 1025 W. Madison, Chicago, IL 60607 ... 312-421-4132
Rogers, Gerald: 1296 E Lakeview Dr, Bountiful, UT 84010 ... 888-388-3729
Rogers, Glenda: 4049 Marlton Cir, Liverpool, NY 13090 ... 315-451-3220
Rogers, Mark: 3535 Oakwood Ct, Morgan Hill, CA 95037 ... 408-776-5168
Rogers, Mike: PO Box 16311, Encino, CA 91416 ... 818-344-8609
Rogers, Nip: 212 S Front St, Philipsburg, PA 16866 ... 814-342-6572
Rogers, Nip: 848 Greenwood Ave NE, Atlanta, GA 30306 ... 404-875-1363
• **Rogers, Paul: pg 492** 455 W 23rd St #8D, New York, NY 10011 ... **212-366-1893**
e-mail: sally@theartworksinc.com / url: www.theartworksinc.com
fax: 212-604-9643
Rogers, Randy: 2233 Kemper Ln, Cincinnati, OH 45206 ... 513-861-1400
Rogers, RS: 212 S Front St, Philipsburg, PA 16866 ... 814-342-6572
Rogers, Stephanie Morgan: 3033 13th Ave W, Seattle, WA 98119 ... 206-284-4701
Rohani, Michael Sours: 9229 215th St SW, Edmonds, WA 98020 ... 425-771-2905
Rohr, Dixon: 372 Central Park W#6K, New York, NY 10025 ... 212-280-7423
Rohrbacher, Patricia: 1374 Midland Ave #308, Bronxville, NY 10708 ... 914-776-1185
Roland, George S: 435 Sunset Dr, Meadville, PA 16335 ... 814-333-2006
• **Roldan, Ismael: pg 684** 1 Beechwood Rd, Bedford Hills, NY 10507 ... **877-RACOON1**
e-mail: roldancari@aol.com
Roldan, Jim: 141 E Main St, E Hampstead, NH 03826 ... 603-382-1686
Rollins, Kent: 690 Clearview Rd, Nashville, TN 37205 ... 615-665-0411
Rom, Holly Meeker: 4 Stanley Keys Ct, Rye, NY 10580 ... 914-921-3155
Roma, Ursula: 4236 Brookside Ave, Cincinnati, OH 45223 ... 513-542-5722
Roman, Barbara J: 814 Kaipii St, Kailua, HI 96734 ... 808-262-4708
Roman, Greg: 22 Seminary Ln, Granite Springs, NY 10527 ... 914-248-4870
• **Roman, Irena: pg 296** 731 N 24th St, Philadelphia, PA 19130 ... **215-232-6666**
url: www.deborahwolfeltd.com / fax: 215-232-6585
Romano, Al: 10 Millinocket Trl, Guilford, CT 06437 ... 203-245-2952
Romas: 389 Cako Ave, Keene, NH 03431 ... 603-357-7306
Romeo Empire Design, Donna: 108 E 35th St, New York, NY 10016 ... 212-889-3337
Romer, Dan: 176 5th Ave #4R, Brooklyn, NY 11217 ... 718-789-8442
Romney, Jordan: 1301 Henry St, Berkley, CA 94709 ... 510-548-5614
Romney, Michael: 201 E 77th St PH-C, New York, NY 10021 ... 212-288-0618
Ronald, Lawrence: 17 Chapel Ln, Buffalo, NY 14224 ... 716-892-5152
Roper, Marty: 6115 Brookside Blvd, Kansas City, MO 64113 ... 816-361-8589
Roraback, Robin: 121 Dodgingtown Rd Box 266, Bethel, CT 06801 ... 203-748-4823
Rosa, Tony: 4 Holly Ave, West Keansburg, NJ 07734 ... 908-787-0786
Rosandich, Dan: Box 410, Chassell, MI 49916 ... 906-482-6234
Rosario, Rudolph: 360 Atlantic Ave #151, Brooklyn, NY 11217 ... 718-875-7465
Rosas, Willie: 60-63 Street, West New York, NJ 07093 ... 201-854-8142
Rosborough, Tom: 325 51st St, Des Moines, IA 50312 ... 515-277-1785
Rosch, Brucie: 61 Thoroughbred Dr, Saratoga Springs, NY 12866 ... 518-581-0288
Rosco, Delro: 455 W 23rd St #8D, New York, NY 10011 ... 212-366-1893
Rosco, Delro: 91-822B Pohakupuna Rd, Ewa Beach, HI 96706 ... 808-689-4635
Rose, David: 1623 N Curson Ave, Los Angeles, CA 90046 ... 323-876-0038
Rose, Jim: 55 E 8th Ave, Clarion, PA 16214 ... 814-226-0801
Rose, Lee: 4250 TC Jester Blvd, Houston, TX 77018 ... 713-686-4799
Rose, Robert: 2915 Pinon Ct, Highland, CA 92346 ... 909-425-3639
Rose, Terry: PO Box 3053, Venice, CA 90294 ... 310-314-0060
Rose, William: PO Box 2159, Hanover, MA 02339 ... 781-871-3944
Rosebush, Judson: 154 W 57th St #826, New York, NY 10019 ... 212-956-6020
Rosefelt, Mitch: 6006 Hawser Rd, Middleton, WI 53705 ... 608-831-1892
Rosen, Eileen: 412 Anglesey Terr, West Chester, PA 19380 ... 215-524-8455
• **Rosen, Elizabeth: pg 398,399** 194 Third Ave, New York, NY 10003 ... **212-475-0440**
url: www.morgangaynin.com / fax: 212-353-8538
Rosen, Judith H.: 5451 Bartlett St, Pittsburgh, PA 15217 ... 412-422-0863
Rosen, Terry: 35 W 81st St, New York, NY 10024 ... 212-580-4784
• **Rosenbaum, Jonathan & Georgina: pg 500, Back Flap, Representatives Book**
597 Riverside Ave, Westport, CT 06880 ... **203-226-4724**
e-mail: creative.svcs@snet.net / url: www.brewstercreative.com / fax: 203-454-9904
Rosenbaum, Saul: 731 N 24th St, Philadelphia, PA 19130 ... 215-232-6666
Rosenberg, Ben: 3734 SE Stephens, Portland, OR 97214 ... 503-230-7735
Rosenberg, Ken: 60 E 42nd St, New York, NY 10165 ... 212-867-8092
Roseneck, Paul: Box 1717, Schenectady, NY 12301 ... 518-381-6570
Rosenfeld, Eileen: 33-52 Crescent St #7B, Astoria, NY 11106 ... 718-956-3930
Rosenheim, Cindy Salans: 15 Westgate Dr, San Francisco, CA 94127 ... 415-334-2723
• **Rosenthal, Marc: pg 110,111** 108 E 35th St, New York, NY 10016 ... **212-889-3337**
e-mail: gerald@rappart.com / url: www.theispot.com/rep/rapp
or www.marc-rosenthal.com / fax: 212-889-3341
Rosenwald, Laurie: 1809 7th Ave #1710, Seattle, WA 98101 ... 206-447-1600
Rosier, Bruce: 62 Indian Church Rd, Buffalo, NY 14210 ... 716-823-4690
Rosolek, Mick: 804 N Van Buren #7, Milwaukee, WI 53202 ... 414-290-4313
Ross, Shannon: 70 Heathdale Rd, Toronto, ON M6C 1M8 ... 416-789-4707
Ross Culbert & Lavery: 15 W 20th St 9th Fl, New York, NY 10011 ... 212-206-0044
Ross Design, Marlene: PO Box 1501, Brockville, ON K6V 5Y6 ... 613-345-2673

Ross, Barry: 51 E Broadway Ave #303, Fairfield, IA 52556 ... 413-585-8993
Ross, Bill: 602 Davidson Rd, Nashville, TN 37205 ... 615-352-3729
Ross, Dave: 833 Clinton Ave, Des Moines, IA 50313 ... 515-243-7833
Ross, Doug: 610 Eighth Ave, E Northport, NY 11731 ... 516-754-0387
Ross, Doug: 310 W 97th St #902, New York, NY 10025 ... 212-243-5888
Ross, Eileen: 6736 N 11th St, Phoenix, AZ 85014 ... 602-234-1598
Ross, Ian: 205 E 95th St #34K, New York, NY 10128 ... 212-828-0284
Ross, Larry: 53 Fairview Ave, Madison, NJ 07940 ... 201-377-6859
• **Ross, Mary: pg 487** 83 Walnut Ave, Corte Madera, CA 94925 ... **415-924-7881**
... **800-924-7881**
e-mail: gatlin@ritareps.com / url: www.ritareps.com / fax: 415-924-7891
Ross, Rhoda: 473 West End Ave #7B, New York, NY 10024 ... 212-724-7253
Ross, Scott: 731 N 24th St, Philadelphia, PA 19130 ... 215-232-6666
Ross, Shannon: 70 Heathdale Rd, Toronto, ON M6C 1MB ... 416-789-4707
Rossi, Joseph: 45 Lockwood Dr, Clifton, NJ 07013 ... 201-278-5716
Rossi, Pamela: 908 Main St #3, Evanston, IL 60202 ... 847-475-2533
Rossiter, Nan: 14 Pleasant St, New Milford, CT 06776 ... 203-354-3065
Rotblatt, Steven: 1106A 22nd St, Santa Monica, CA 90403 ... 310-828-1109
Roth, Dan J: 3124 Oregon Ave, St Louis, MO 63118 ... 314-773-0219
Roth, Hy: 1300 Ashland St, Evanston, IL 60201 ... 847-491-1937
• **Roth, Marci: pg 893** 2025 NE 50th Ave, Portland, OR 97213 ... **503-284-2978**
url: www.theispot.com/artist/marciroth
Roth, Roger: 7227 Brent Rd, Upper Darby, PA 19082 ... 610-352-3235
Rother, Sue: 865 Delaware St, Denver, CO 80204 ... 303-820-2599
Rothman, Mike: 62 E Ridge St, Ridgefield, CT 06877 ... 203-438-4954
• **Rotondo, Nick: pg 295** 731 N 24th St, Philadelphia, PA 19130 ... **215-232-6666**
url: www.deborahwolfeltd.com / fax: 215-232-6585
Rotunda, Matthew: 89 Fifth Ave #901, New York, NY 10003 ... 212-627-1554
Roundy, Laine: 98 Quassuk Rd, Woodbury, CT 06798 ... 203-263-7531
Rounthwaite, Graham: Riversdale Rd 52, London, UK N5 2JT ... 441717041410
Roure, Rebecca Migdal: 77 Lefferts Pl, Brooklyn, NY 11238 ... 718-622-9554
Rouya, Es: 30 Winthrop Dr, Woodbury, NY 11797 ... 516-367-1359
Rowe, Charles: 133 Aronimink Dr, Newark, DE 19711 ... 302-738-0641
• **Rowe, John: pg 616,617** 420 Lexington Ave, New York, NY 10170 ... **212-986-5680**
e-mail: mendolaart@aol.com / url: www.mendolaart.com / fax: 212-818-1246
Rowley, Carter: 201 Linden St #301, Fort Collins, CO 80524 ... 970-407-7240
Rownd, Jim: 1503 Washington Ave S, Minneapolis, MN 55454 ... 612-332-8634
Roy, Joanna: 549 W 123rd St, New York, NY 10027 ... 212-663-7876
Roy, Lyse-Anne: 783 Shefford St, Bromont, QU J2L 1C4 ... 450-534-4963
Roy, Martin: 4667 rue Hutchinson, Montréal, QU H2V 4A2 ... 514-271-8105
Royce, Johnathan: 350 7th St #8-1, Brooklyn, NY 11215 ... 212-337-0077
Royo, Luis: 11 Kings Ridge Rd, Long Valley, NJ 07853 ... 908-813-8718
Royse, Gary: 7254 Beef Branch Rd, Joplin, MO 64804 ... 417-623-1342
Rozasy, Frank: 2228 3rd St #12, Santa Monica, CA 90405 ... 310-399-1891
Rubalcava, Alejandro: 16 Technology #115, Irvine, CA 92618 ... 949-727-3126
• **Rubel, Sasha: pg 801** 3421 N Marshfield, Chicago, IL 60657 ... **773-525-3075**
e-mail: sasha@sasharubel.com / url: www.sasharubel.com / fax: 773-525-3075
Rubess, Balvis: 260 Brunswick Ave, Toronto, ON M5S 2M7 ... 416-927-7071
Rubin, Terry: 1404 W Mount Royal Ave, Baltimore, MD 21217 ... 410-383-8100
• **Rubino, Cornel: pg 344** 58 W 15th St, New York, NY 10011 ... **212-741-2539**
url: www.jdedell.com or www.theispot.com or www.handandeyesstudio.com
fax: 212-741-4660
Rubinstein, Josef: 320 Seventh Ave #1, Brooklyn, NY 11215 ... 718-369-1527
Rudd, Michael Gregory: 220 Hoydens Ln, Fairfield, CT 06430 ... 203-261-4462
Ruddell, Gary: 405 N Wabash #2709, Chicago, IL 60611 ... 312-222-0337
Rudinsky, Joyce: 7311 Chamberlain Ave, St Louis, MO 63130 ... 314-721-1114
Rudnak, Theo: 549-6 Amsterdam Ave NE, Atlanta, GA 30308 ... 404-876-4058
• **Rüegger, Rebecca: pg 525** 333 E 49th St, New York, NY 10017 ... **212-980-8061**
url: www.bruckandmoss.com / fax: 212-832-8778
100 Bleecker St, New York, NY 10012 ... **212-982-6533**
fax: 212-358-1586
Ruf, Joseph: 36 Franklin Ave, Deerpark, NY 11729 ... 516-586-5633
Ruff, Donna: 12 Top Sail Rd, Rowayton, CT 06853 ... 203-866-8626
Ruffing, Eric: 620 Rosencrans Ave, Manhattan Bch, CA 90266 ... 310-546-7135
Ruffins, Reynold: 51 Hampton St, Sag Harbor, NY 11963 ... 516-725-3480
Ruggerl, John: 245 E 19th St, New York, NY 10003 ... 212-979-6029
Rugh, Doug: 604 Country Rd, Pocasset, MA 02559 ... 508-759-6910
Ruhl, Greg: 40 Alexander St PH 9, Toronto, ON M4Y 1B5 ... 416-928-1997
Ruiz, Aristides: 39 Hamilton Terr, New York, NY 10031 ... 212-283-3401
Runnion Design, Jeff: 93 River Rd, Topsfield, MA 01983 ... 508-887-2418
Runt Illustrations: 72 Lippincott St, Toronto, ON M5S 2P1 ... 416-504-7089
Rupp Art & Design, Katherine: 8511 Cheltenham Cir, Louisville, KY 40222 ... 502-425-9266
Ruppert, Larry: 1503 Washington Ave S, Minneapolis, MN 55454 ... 612-332-8634
Rush, John: 123 Kedzie St, Evanston, IL 60202 ... 847-869-2078
Rushing, Alan: 503 1st Ave W #208, Seattle, WA 98119 ... 206-284-6976
Russ, Mary: 327 Hugo St, San Francisco, CA 94122 ... 415-661-2930
Russell, Bill: 608 York St, San Francisco, CA 94110 ... 415-641-1285
Russell, Bill: 2074 Huckleberry Rd, San Rafael, CA 94903 ... 415-491-9734
Russell, Doug: 1452 NW 185th, Seattle, WA 98177 ... 206-542-1452
Russell, Gerald R.: Gleason Ctr 314 2nd St #10, Liverpool, NY 13088 ... 315-453-2242
Russell, Mike: 12 Gordon Rd, Bergenfield, NJ 07621 ...
• **Russo, Anthony: pg 489** 455 W 23rd St #8D, New York, NY 10011 ... **212-366-1893**
e-mail: sally@theartworksinc.com / url: www.theartworksinc.com
fax: 212-604-9643
Russo, David Anson: 41 Union Square W #918, New York, NY 10003 ... 212-807-6627
Rusynyk, Kathy: 2309 Twp Rd 257, Jeromesville, OH 44840 ... 419-368-3664
Ruth, Julie: PO Box 398, sugarcreek, OH 44681 ... 330-852-8060
Rutherford, John: 44859 Meadow Cir, Mendocina, CA 95460 ... 707-937-2114
Rutten, Nicole: 866 United Nations Plaza, New York, NY 10017 ... 212-644-2020
Ruzich, Denise: 120 Bishop's Gate, Grand Island, NY 14072 ... 716-774-2700
Ryabinky, Maria: 10012 Stonemill Rd, Richmond, VA 23233 ... 804-273-6505
Ryan, Cheri: PO Box 19412, Seattle, WA 98109 ... 206-634-1880
Ryan, Glenn: 116 Spadina Ave Ste 400, Toronto, ON M5V 2K6 ... 416-505-9522
Ryan, Jason: 83 Helen St #4, Hamden, CT 06514 ... 203-248-7950
Ryan, Joyce: 275 Marchand Ct, Atlanta, GA 30328 ... 404-252-3837
Rybka, Steve: 3119 W 83rd St, Chicago, IL 60614 ... 773-737-1981
Rydberg, Steven: 1204 Harmon Pl #25, Minneapolis, MN 55403 ... 612-340-1212
Ryden, Mark: 542 San Gabriel St, Sierra Madre, CA 91024 ... 626-355-1750
Ryder, Jennifer: Berkshire Hills Motel #RT7, Williamstown, MA 01267 ... 617-479-4774

Ryersen, Leslee: 3395 Edella Ave, Central Point, OR 97502 541-664-4905
Ryus, Michael: 4 Waverly Rd, Cape Elizabeth, ME 04107 207-767-2228

S

S & V Enterprises: 4600 Kings Crossings Dr, Kennesaw, GA 30144 770-928-8050
S, Caroline: 608 York St, San Francisco, CA 94110 415-641-1285
S. I. International: 43 E 19th St, New York, NY 10003 212-254-4996
Saas, Susan: 80 Nassau St #202E, New York, NY 10038 212-964-9141
Sabanosh, Michael: 433 W 34th St #18-B, New York, NY 10001 212-947-8161
Sachs, Jenny: 157 E 32nd St, New York, NY 10016 212-684-0565
Sachs, Jim: 28971 Banoff Dr Box 1182, Lake Arrowhead, CA 92352 909-337-5838
Sacks, Ron: 1189 Rosebank Dr, Worthington, OH 43235 614-846-1921
• **Sadowski, Wiktor: pg 525** 333 E 49th St, New York, NY 10017 . . . . **212-980-8061**
url: www.bruckandmoss.com / fax: 212-832-8778
100 Bleecker St, New York, NY 10012 . . . . **212-982-6533**
url: www.bruckandmoss.com / fax: 212-358-1586
Saecker, Tom: 225 North 170 West, Centerville, UT 84014 801-294-6812
Saffold, Joe: 490B Beaulieu Ave, Savannah, GA 31406 912-352-2472
Safier-Kerzner, Sonia: 9413 Locust Hill Rd, Bethesda, MD 20814 301-530-5167
Safr, Paul: 295 Queen St, Blyth, ON N0M 1H0 519-523-9114
Sagasti, Miriam: 2441 Sedgefield Dr, Chapel Hill, NC 27514 919-942-9839
Sagona, Marina: 155 W 15th St #4C, New York, NY 10011 212-989-8770
Sahli, Barbara: 115 Indian Spring Dr, Silver Spring, MD 20901 301-585-5122
Saint-John, Bob: PO Box1412, Portsmouth, NH 03802 207-363-1249
Sakahara, Dick: 28826 Cedarbluff Dr, Rancho Palos Verdes, CA 90275 310-541-8187
• **Sakai, Miyuki: pg 517** 94 Natoma St #233, San Francisco, CA 94105 . . . . **415-442-1822**
url: www.wileyreps.com / fax: 415-442-1823
Sakimoto, Wayne: 3505 Cadillac Ave #B1, Costa Mesa, CA 92626 714-513-9250
Sakno, Theresa: PO Box 13 Station Q, Toronto, ON M4T 2L7 415-925-5499
Saksa, Cathy: 10 Hidden Hollow Dr, Hamilton Township, NJ 08620 609-259-7792
Sala, Richard: 3130 College Ave, Berkeley, CA 94705 510-658-0259
Salans Rosenheim, Cindy: 15 Westgate Dr, San Francisco, CA 94127 415-334-2723
Salas, Felipe: Felix Para 134, San Jose Insurgentes, Mexico, 03900 525-593-3900
Salazar, Miro: PO Box 421443, San Francisco, CA 94142 415-647-5660
Salem, Kay: 13418 Splintered Oak, Houston, TX 77065 713-469-0996
Salentine, Katherine: 990 Filbert St, San Francisco, CA 94133 415-928-0457
Salerno, John: 2033 Ainsley Rd, San Diego, CA 92123 858-571-3333
• **Salerno, Steven: pg 283** 250 W 57th St #521, New York, NY 10107 . . . . **212-397-7330**
San Francisco: **415-788-8552**
url: www.lindgrensmith.com
Salerno, Vincent: 1825 E 2nd St, Brooklyn, NY 11223 718-645-6739
Salgian, Mitzura: 60 E 42nd St, New York, NY 10165 212-867-8092
Salicrup, Fernando: 1685 Lexington Ave, New York, NY 10029 212-831-4333
Salina, Joseph: 2255B Queen St E, Toronto, ON M4E 1G3 416-699-4859
Salinger, Joan: 2701 Fairview Rd/Box 5005, Costa Mesa, CA 92628 714-432-5691
Salk, Larry: 19029 Sprague St, Tarzana, CA 91356 818-776-1992
Salmela, Don: 24262 E Typo Dr NE, Stacy, MN 55079 651-462-1456
Salmon, Paul: 5826 Jackson's Oak Ct, Burke, VA 22015 703-250-4943
Salvati, Jim: 1400 N Hayworth Ave #36, Los Angeles, CA 90046 323-851-7737
Salvatore, Rosemary McGuirk: Box 273, New London, NH 03257 603-526-6798
Samanich, Barbara: 211 E Ohio Suite 2404, Chicago, IL 60611 312-661-1717
Samanick, Barbara: 188 E Vista Del Cerro, Tempe, AZ 85281 480-966-3070
Samatis, Karin: 74 Prescott St, Reading, MA 01867 781-944-0024
Saminski, Melinda: 45 Cowart Ave, Manasquan, NJ 08738 732-223-5937
Sammel, Chelsea: PO Box 30132, Oakland, CA 94604 510-628-8474
Samonte, Ayvin: 24 Rumson Rd, Goose Creek, SC 29445 843-553-1724
Sample, Paul: 32 Shelton St, Covent Garden, London, England, UK WC2H 442072402077
Sampson, Heather: 1067 Wothington St #5, Sherbrooke, QC J1H 3V1 819-562-9066
Sampson, Maren: 12725 Gilmore Ave, Los Angeles, CA 90066 310-821-9491
Sampson, Ronnie: 268 Ninth Ave, San Francisco, CA 94118 415-979-4980
Sams, BB: PO Box A, Social Circle, GA 30025 770-464-2956
Samson, Heather: PO Box 642, Derby, VT 05829 401-822-2537
Samuels, Barbara: 299 Riverside Dr #8D, New York, NY 10025 212-666-5533
Samul, Cynthia: 165 E 32nd St, New York, NY 10016 212-686-3514
Samul, Cynthia: 15 Pacific St, New London, CT 06320 860-444-7060
San Juan, Jose: 200 Varick St Ste 902, New York, NY 10014 212-924-8944
Sancha, Jeremy: 58 W 40th St 6th Fl, New York, NY 10018 212-682-1490
Sanchez, Carlos: 2149 Lyon St #5, San Francisco, CA 94115 415-921-7140
Sanchez, Carlos: 3301A S Jefferson Ave, St Louis, MO 63118 314-773-2600
Sanchez, Daniel: 3233 Pheasant Hollow, Denton, TX 76207 940-383-0882
Sanchez, Michael: 457 Nevada St, San Francisco, CA 94110 415-641-1791
Sanchez, Pat: 8603 Baumgarten, Dallas, TX 75228 214-328-2942
Sanchez, Santiago: 215 40th St Dr SE #304, Cedar Rapids, IA 52403 319-364-8308
• **Sanchez, Wilma: pg 685** 1 Beechwood Rd, Bedford Hills, NY 10507 . . . . **877-RACOON1**
e-mail: sanchezwj@aol.com
Sand, Ethan: 332 E 18th St, New York, NY 10003 212-475-2681
Sandbox Digital Playground: 854 N Milwaukee Ave, Chicago, IL 60622 312-733-5644
• **Sanders, Bruce: pg 530** 7 Washington St, Beverly, MA 01915 . . . . **978-921-0887**
e-mail: leighton@leightonreps.com / url: www.leightonreps.com / fax:978-921-0223
Sanders, Hiroko: 3516 Jasmine Ave #209, Los Angeles, CA 90034 310-837-4066
Sanders, Jane: 47-51 40th St #6D, Sunnyside, NY 11104 718-786-3505
Sanders, Lauren: 2558 Cochran St, Simi Valley, CA 93065 805-522-9121
Sanders, Rosanne: 23 Ganton St, London, England, UK WIV 1LA 71-287-9191
• **Sanders, Terry W.: pg 923** New York, NY **212-980-1893**
e-mail: lonesaser@aol.com
Sanderson, Bill: Famleigh, Huntindon Rd Houghton, Huntindon, Cambs, England, UK PE17 . . . 1480-461506
Sandford, Ron: 455 W 23rd St #8D, New York, NY 10011 212-366-1893
Sanford, Steve: 41 Union Sq W #615, New York, NY 10003 212-243-6119
Sanford, Susan: 608 York St, San Francisco, CA 94110 415-641-1285
• **Sano, Kazuhiko: pg 726** 105 Stadium Ave, Mill Valley, CA 94941 . . . . **415-381-6377**
fax: 415-381-3847
Sansevero, Tony: 501 W Fayette St #270, Syracuse, NY 13204 315-428-8585
• **Santalucia, Francesco: pg 167** 420 Lexington Ave, New York, NY 10170 . . . . . . **212-986-5680**
e-mail: mendolaart@aol.com / url: www.mendolaart.com or www.picturegrill.com /
fax: 212-818-1246
Santana, Miguel: 251 Seaman Ave#4B, New York, NY 10034 212-369-8405
Santiago, Rafael: 306 E 6th St #16, New York, NY 10003 212-505-6296
Santo, Vincent: 2 Skibo Ln, Mamaroneck, NY 10543 914-698-4667
Santoleri, Ray: 153 Courtelyous, Somerset, NJ 08873 908-297-9116
Santora, Robert: 90 Abinet Ct, Selden, NY 11784 212-922-0344
Santore, Charles: 138 S 20th St, Philadelphia, PA 19103 215-563-0430
Santos, Ellen: 111 Vreeland Ave, Nutley, NJ 07110 201-748-0384
Santry, Karen: 463 West St #1025, New York, NY 10014 212-645-9595
Sapulich, Joe: 8454 W 161st Pl, Tinley Park, IL 60477 708-532-8766
• **Saputo, Joe: pg 163** 420 Lexington Ave, New York, NY 10170 . . . . **212-986-5680**
e-mail: mendolaart@aol.com / url: www.mendolaart.com or jillustration.com / fax: 212-818-1246
Sardinha, Anthony: 16 Sparta Rd, Toronto, ON M6L 2M5 416-249-0285
Sargent, Claudia Karabaic: 15-38 126th St, College Point, NY 11356 718-461-8280
Sarrazin, Marisol: 1507 rue des Bécassines, St Margurite, QU J0T 2K0 514-228-2855
Sasaki, Goro: 58 W 40th St 6th Fl, New York, NY 10018 212-682-1490
Sass Illustration, Cindy: 15 Torne Rd, Sloatsburg, NY 10974 914-753-5119
• **Sasso, Marc: pg 917** 27 General Health Ave, N White Plains, NY 10603 . . . . . . **914-949-1949**
e-mail: blkmetal1@aol.com / url: www.marcsasso.com / fax: 914-949-1966
• **Sassouni Illustration, Maral: pg 795** 1416 Queens Rd, W Hollywood, CA 90069 **213-650-5865**
e-mail: marals@starnet.fr / url: www.theispot.com/artist/msassouni
• **Sauber, Robert: pg 394,395** 194 Third Ave, New York, NY 10003 . . . . **212-475-0440**
url: www.morgangaynin.com / fax: 212-353-8538
Sauer & Assocs, Christian: 1800 Olive St, St Louis, MO 63103 314-664-4646
Sauer, April: 4105 159th St 2nd Fl, Flushing, NY 11358 800-411-5454
Sauer, Kristie: 615 Cheryl Ln, Phoenix, OR 97535 541-535-1810
Saulsberry, Demitrius: 621 Clinton St, Gary, IN 46406 219-944-7598
Saunders, Fred: 810 NE 102nd, Seattle, WA 98125 206-633-3445
• **Saunders, Robert: pg 744** 45 Bartlett Crescent, Brookline, MA 02446 . . . . **617-566-4464**
e-mail: rob@robertsaunders.com / url: www.robertsaunders.com or
www.theispot.com/artist/rsaunders / fax: 617-739-0040
Saurda, Tomas: 875 Third Ave 4th Fl, New York, NY 10022 212-303-8326
Sauriol, Brian: PO Box 396, Bloomfield Hills, MI 48303 313-460-2451
Sauvageau, Daniel: 760 Av Lacombe, Laval, QU H7E 3A6 450-664-4380
Savadier, Elivia: 45 Walnut Hill Rd, Chestnut Hill, MA 02167 617-661-0951
Savage, David: PO Box 1422, Boca Raton, FL 33429 407-394-4644
• **Savage, Stephen: pg 748** 444 Sackett St, Brooklyn, NY 11231 . . . . **718-624-5435**
e-mail: stephensavage@earthlink.net / fax: 718-624-5435
Savard, Sister Judith: 250 Riverside Dr #24A, New York, NY 10025 212-663-6273
Savas, Michael: 23591 Torero Crl, Mission Viejo, CA 92691 949-597-0500
• **Savely, Rod: pg 530** 7 Washington St, Beverly, MA 01915 . . . . **978-921-0887**
e-mail: leighton@leightonreps.com / url: www.leightonreps.com / fax: 978-921-0223
Savidge, Robert T: 1006 Lilac Ln, Lebanon, PA 17042 202-547-5186
Sawaya, Linda Dalal: PO Box 91024, Portland, OR 97291 503-297-4777
Sawka, Jan: 353 W 53rd St #1W, New York, NY 10019 212-682-2462
Sawyer, Arnie: 115 W 27th St 8th Fl, New York, NY 10001 212-645-4455
Sawyer, David: 2471 Franklin Avenue, Louisville, CO 80027 303-666-5581
Sawyer, Peter A: 7768 Clifton Rd, Fairfax, VA 22039 703-250-3117
• **Sawyer, Scott: pg 309** 716 Montgomery St, San Francisco, CA 94111 . . . . **415-433-1222**
url: www.sweetreps.com / fax: 415-433-9560
Saxe, Joe: 920 McLellan Dr, San Jose, CA 95110 408-287-7273
Sayers, Walter: 682 Huron St, London, ON N5Y 4J8 519-434-2499
Sayles, Elizabeth: 318 Fulle Dr, Valley Cottage, NY 10989 845-267-4127
Sayles, John: 420 Lexington Ave #2760, New York, NY 10170 212-697-8525
Sayles, John: 3701 Beaver Ave, Des Moines, IA 50310 515-243-2922
• **Scanlan, David: pg 804** 1601 N Sepulveda #156, Manhattan Beach, CA 90266 . . . . . **310-721-8016**
e-mail: davidscanl@aol.com / url: www.theispot.com / fax: 310-376-8740
Scanlan, Peter: 22 Seminary Ln, Granite Springs, NY 10527 914-248-4870
Scanlon, Susan: 417 E 87th St #1A, New York, NY 10128 212-996-0591
Scantland, Chris: 6509 Old Railroad Bed Rd, Toney, AL 35773 205-420-3821
• **Scarabottolo, Guido: pg 397** 194 Third Ave, New York, NY 10003 . . . . **212-475-0440**
url: www.morgangaynin.com / fax: 212-353-8538
Scaramozzino, Michael: 50 Clifford St, Providence, RI 02903 401-861-8002
Scardova, Jaclyne: 17 Redwood Rd, Fairfax, CA 94930 415-721-0707
Scarisbrick, Ed: 853 Broadway #1201, New York, NY 10003 212-677-9100
Scarola, Vito-Leonardo: 24671 Sutton Ln, Laguna Niguel, CA 92677 714-831-1270
Schaare, Harry: 60 E 42nd St, New York, NY 10165 212-867-8092
Schact, Michael: 145 15th St NE #805, Atlanta, GA 30361 404-607-9489
Schader/Eagleye, Steve: 10817 Snow Cloud Trail, Littleton, CO 80125 720-981-8655
Schaffer, Amanda: 445 Hanson Ln, Ramona, CA 92065 760-788-0388
Schaffer, Kristen: 412 W 10th #3, Lawrence, KS 66044 785-331-2025
Schall, Rene: 5 Field Green Dr, Colchester, VT 05446 802-878-1086
Schaller, Tom: 2112 Broadway #407, New York, NY 10023 212-362-5524
Schamber, Kim: 8231 Russell Ave South, Bloomington, MN 55431 612-886-0436
Schamber, Kim: PO Box 30245 Port Authority Station, New York, NY 10011 . . . 612-887-2125
Schanzer, Roz: 234 Fifth Ave 4th Fl, New York, NY 10001 212-696-4680
Schap, Sandra: 291 Henry St #3, Brooklyn, NY 11201 718-834-9631
Scharf, Linda: PO Box 1562, Boston, MA 02146 617-738-9294
Schattner, Gillie: 420 Lexington Ave, New York, NY 10170 212-986-5680
Schauman, Clare: 280 Madison Ave #1110, New York, NY 10016 212-545-9155
Scheckel, Eric: 6432 E Freeport Dr, Highlands Ranch, CO 80126 303-470-5658
Scheff, Adam: 219 E 30th St, Kansas City, MO 64108 816-931-5758
Scheffer Studios: 1027 Berkshire Ln, Tarpon Springs, FL 34689 813-938-8388
Scheld, Betsy: PO Box 257, Wading River, NY 11792 212-876-5281
Schell, Paul: 1608 E 51st St, Brooklyn, NY 11234 718-951-8976
Schellhorn, Jill: 465 Prospect Ave, Piscataway, NJ 08854 908-424-1243
Schermer-Gramm, Kathy: 2655 Shieldale Dr, Winston Salem, NC 27107 909-247-6220
Scheuer, Lauren: 2 Fowler Rd, Upton, MA 01568 508-529-9053
Scheuer, Phil: 126 Fifth Ave, New York, NY 10011 212-620-0728
Schey, Pattie: 6837 Aetna Ct, Wauwatosa, WI 53213 414-257-1115
Schieffer, John: PO Box 7114, Prospect, CT 06712 203-758-3176
Schields, Gretchen: 4556 19th St, San Francisco, CA 94114 415-558-8851
Schier, Jeffrey: 3928 Shafter, Oakland, CA 94609 510-653-5825
Schildbach, Stephen: 1521 15th Ave #R, Seattle, WA 98122 206-720-6486
Schill, George: 309 Walnut Rd, Pittsburgh, PA 15202 412-761-5666
Schill, Nancy: 235 Channing Ave, Malvern, PA 19355 610-644-3426
Schilling, John: 3033 13th Ave W, Seattle, WA 98119 206-284-4701
Schilt, Audrey: 310 E 75th St #5G, New York, NY 10021 212-861-4730
Schindler, Max: 42 Delavan St, Brooklyn, NY 11231 718-624-1906
Schiwall, Linda: 280 Madison Ave #1110, New York, NY 10016 212-545-9155
Schleh, Joy: 49 Pine Ave, Floral Park, NY 11001 516-354-5530
Schleinkofer, David: 420 Lexington Ave, New York, NY 10170 212-986-5680

Schlemme, Roy: 585 Centre St, Oradell, NJ 07649 ... 212-921-9732
Schlowsky Digital Studios: 73 Old Rd, Weston, MA 02493 ... 781-899-5110
Schmelzer, J P: 1002 S Wesley Ave, Oak Park, IL 60304 ... 708-386-4005
Schmid, Paul: 4645 Colfax Ave S, Minneapolis, MN 55409 ... 612-825-7564
Schmid, Paul: 2702 Walnut Ave SW, Seattle, WA 98116 ... 206-938-4516
Schmidt, Aaron: 730 N Glasgow Dr, Dallas, TX 75214 ... 214-828-9389
Schmidt, Bill: 60 E 42nd St, New York, NY 10165 ... 212-867-8092
Schmidt, Chuck: 311 Avenue H #D, Redondo Beach, CA 90277 ... 310-540-5958
Schmidt, Chuck: 853 Broadway #1201, New York, NY 10003 ... 212-677-9100
Schmidt, George: 183 Steuben St, Brooklyn, NY 11205 ... 718-857-1837
• **Schmidt, Heidi: pg 176** 420 Lexington Ave, New York, NY 10170 ... **212-986-5680**
e-mail: mendolaart@aol.com / url: www.mendolaart.com or www.heidischmidt.com / fax: 212-818-1246
Schmidt, John F: 7308 Leesville Blvd, Springfield, VA 22151 ... 703-750-0927
Schmidt, Lori: PO Box 4101, Chatsworth, CA 91313 ... 805-527-4902
Schmidt, Urs: 1 Ch De Boston 1004,Lusanne, Switzerland, ... 121-625-2274
Schmidtmann, Eddie: 315 Laskin Rd, Virginia Beach, VA 23451 ...
Schminke, Karin: 5803 NE 181st St, Kenmore, WA 98028 ... 206-402-8606
Schmitt, Erik: 3 Acton Cir, Berkeley, CA 94702 ... 510-540-8055
Schneegass, Martinu: 241 Eldridge St #2R, New York, NY 10002 ... 212-529-7445
Schneider, Christine M: 5429 Foxridge Dr #303, Mission, KS 66202 ... 913-677-5465
Schneider, Douglas: 9016 Danube Ln, San Diego, CA 92126 ... 858-695-6796
Schneider, Leila: PO Box 2341, Maple Grove, MN 55311 ... 612-325-4100
Schneider, Roy: 1813 Killdeer Dr, Naperville, IL 60565 ... 630-357-8732
• **Schneider, Tim: pg 864** 148 S Oakland Ave #2, Pasadena, CA 91101 ... **626-683-0648**
e-mail: timsch@pacbell.net / url: www.timschneiderillustration.com
fax: 626-683-0648
Schneider, William: 6 Windsor Pl, Athens, OH 45701 ... 740-594-3205
Schneidman, Jared: 155 Katonah Ave, Katonah, NY 10536 ... 914-232-1499
Schnurr, Edward: 775 St Clair Ave W #18, Toronto, ON M6C 1B7 ... 416-652-8931
Schoenberger, Carl: 1925 16th St NW #701, Washington, DC 20009 ... 202-483-3117
Schoenfliess, Rebecca Butcher: 3811 Pleasant Pl, Baltimore, MD 21211 ... 410-467-8307
Schofield, Glen: 99 Park Ave #210A, New York, NY 10016 ... 800-398-9544
Schofield, Russ: 5313 Waneta Rd, Bethesda, MD 20816 ... 301-320-5008
Scholberg, Barbara: 35 Buckboard Rd, Duxbury, MA 02332 ... 508-934-7896
Schonbach Graphics, Friedrich: 1851 Columbia Rd NW #603, Washington, DC 20009 ... 202-265-2240
Schongut, Emanuel: 728 Castro St, San Francisco, CA 94114 ... 415-441-4384
Schoolcraft, Robert : 125 Prospect Park W, Brooklyn, NY 11215 ... 718-369-1781
Schooley, Greg: 207 Bellwood Circle, Cranberry, PA 16066 ... 724-776-4156
Schopper, Bernie: 2415 Windbreak Dr, Alexandria, VA 22306 ... 703-765-4652
Schorr, Kathy Staico: PO Box 142, Roxbury, CT 06783 ... 203-266-4084
Schorr, Todd: PO Box 142, Roxbury, CT 06783 ... 203-266-4084
Schott, Robert & Cathleen: 831 40th Ave N, St Petersburg, FL 33703 ... 813-525-4944
Schotte, Marilyn: 7205 15th Ave, Takoma Park, MD 20912 ... 301-357-4993
Schottland, Miriam: 2201 Massachusetts Ave NW, Washington, DC 20008 ... 202-328-3825
Schreck, John: 101 Spring Hill Rd, Fairfield, CT 06430 ... 203-259-6824
Schreiber, Dana: 36 Center St, Collinsville, CT 06022 ... 203-693-6688
Schreiber, Laszlo: 39 Hamilton Terr, New York, NY 10031 ... 212-283-3401
Schreier, Joshua: 466 Washington St, New York, NY 10013 ... 212-925-0472
• **Schreiner, John: pg 542** 1503 Washington Ave S, Minneapolis, MN 55454 ... **612-332-8634**
e-mail: erep@spectrumstudio.net / url: www.spectrumstudio.net / fax: 612-332-2364
Schroder, Mark: 133 N Montclair Ave, Dallas, TX 75208 ... 214-943-2569
Schroeder, Mark: 1021 Sherman St, Alameda, CA 94501 ... 510-814-7382
Schuchman, Bob: 1914 Pacific Hwy #200, Redondo Beach, CA 90277 ... 310-376-1448
• **Schudlich, Stephen: pg 820** 1376 Pearl St #110, Denver, CO 80203 ... **303-861-1820**
e-mail: stephen@ssid.com / url: www.ssid.com / fax: 303-861-1618
Schuett, Stacey: 110 Rising Ridge Rd, Ridgefield, CT 06877 ... 203-438-7307
Schuh, Chris: 414 Winter St, Holliston, MA 01746 ... 508-429-6928
• **Schulenburg, Paul: pg 778** 500 Depot, Harwich, MA 02645 ... **508-432-0994**
url: www.elbowpond.com
Schuler, Mark E: 5113 W 70 Terr, Prairie Village, KS 66208 ... 913-384-0646
Schultz, CG: 1140 West Street Rd, West Chester, PA 19382 ... 215-793-3622
Schultz, Eileen Hedy: 430 E 63rd St, New York, NY 10021 ... 212-755-2321
Schultz, Robert C: 656 West Knoll Dr #102, West Hollywood, CA 90069 ... 310-360-7557
Schumacher, Kurt: 320 W. Ohio #100, Chicago, IL 60610 ... 312-944-3000
Schumacher, Michael: 2025 NE 123rd St, Seattle, WA 98125 ... 206-364-7150
Schumaker, Ward: 466 Green #203, San Francisco, CA 94133 ... 415-398-1060
Schumer, Arlen: 95 Kings Hwy S, Westport, CT 06880 ... 203-454-4518
Schuster, David: 1 Wood St, Southborough, MA 01772 ... 508-460-6831
Schuster, Elle: 3719 Gilbert Ave, Dallas, TX 75219 ... 214-526-6712
Schuster, Rob: 2233 Kemper Ln, Cincinnati, OH 45206 ... 513-861-1400
Schuster, Robert: 60 E 42nd St, New York, NY 10165 ... 212-867-8092
Schwab, Michael: 108 Tamalpais Ave, San Anselmo, CA 94960 ... 415-257-5792
Schwartz, Carol: 2515 Hunters Run Way, Weston, FL 33327 ... 954-385-0121
Schwartz, Joanna H: 51 Woodland St #4, Newburyport, MA 01950 ... 508-465-9635
Schwartz, Judith: 231 E 5th St, New York, NY 10003 ... 212-777-7533
Schwartz, Lisa: 102-25 67th Dr #6M, Forest Hills, NY 11375 ... 718-896-8943
Schwartz, Marty: 18 Winfield Ct, East Norwalk, CT 06855 ... 203-838-9935
Schwartz, Sara: 130 W 67th St #22G, New York, NY 10023 ... 212-877-4162
Schwartze, Evan: 104 S Home Ave #1, Oak Park, IL 60302 ... 708-445-0154
• **Schwarz, Joanie: pg 393** 194 Third Ave, New York, NY 10003 ... **212-475-0440**
url: www.morgangaynin.com / fax: 212-353-8538
Schwarz, Terri: 7362 La Veta, St Louis, MO 63117 ... 314-644-0091
Schwarze, Evan: 104 S Home Ave, Oak Park, IL 60302 ... 708-445-0154
Schweigert, Carol: 9 Lawnwood Pl, Boston, MA 02129 ... 617-242-3901
Schweitzer, David: 332 Bleecker St PMBK56, New York, NY 10014 ... 212-691-2667
Schweitzer, David: 4 E Ohio Studio B, Chicago, IL 60611 ... 312-321-1336
Schwinger, Larry: 89 Fifth Ave #901, New York, NY 10003 ... 212-627-1554
Sciacca, Thomas: 405 N Wabash Ave #4410, Chicago, IL 60611 ... 312-234-7055
Sciacca, Tom: 77-39 66th Dr, Middle Village, NY 11379 ... 718-326-9124
Scialla, Stefano: Centro Direzionale di Napoli/Pal. Esedra Is.F.11, Napoli, Italy, ... 81-734-5397
Scibilia, Dom: 8277 Broadview Rd, Broadview, OH 44147 ... 216-526-2036
Scoggins, Tim: 27552 Dandelion Ct, Temecula, CA 92591 ... 909-699-6150
Scogins, Charles: 656 Dover St, Marietta, GA 30066 ... 770-924-7264
Scopinich, Robert: 28952 Selfridge Dr, Malibu, CA 90265 ... 310-589-9109
Scott, Bill: 925 Elm Grove Rd, Elm Grove, WI 53122 ... 414-785-1940
Scott, Bill: 405 N Wabash Ave #1712, Chicago, IL 60611 ... 312-321-0848
• **Scott, Bob: pg 910** 3838 Cheverly Rd, Richmond, VA 23225 ... **804-320-0007**
e-mail: bob@bscott.com / url: www.bscott.com / fax: 804-320-1297
Scott, Davis: 19 W 21st St #301, New York, NY 10010 ... 212-989-6446
Scott, Elizabeth B: 54 Lee St #1, Cambridge, MA 02139 ... 617-354-2423
Scott, Jerry: 225 E Michigan St #300, Milwaukee, WI 53202 ... 414-271-5210
Scott, Margaret: 1525 31st St NW, Washington, DC 20007 ... 202-965-0523
Scott, Martin: 1045 Sansome St #221, San Francisco, CA 94111 ... 415-487-2160
Scott, Roy: 731 N 24th St, Philadelphia, PA 19130 ... 215-232-6666
Scratchmann, Max: Finstown, Orkney Islands, UK KW17 ... 448707879342
Scribner, Joanne: N 3314 Lee, Spokane, WA 99207 ... 509-484-3208
Scrofani, Joseph: 353 W 53rd St #1W, New York, NY 10019 ... 212-682-2462
Scroggs, Phil: 624 Linwood Ave NE #2, Atlanta, GA 30306 ... 404-885-1762
• **Scruton, Clive: pg 507** 666 Greenwich St #860, New York, NY 10014 ... **212-675-5719**
e-mail: harriet@hkportfolio.com / url: www.hkportfolio.com / fax: 212-675-6341
Scudder, Brooke: 2064 Wisard Ct, San Jose, CA 95131 ... 408-929-0907
Scullin, Maureen A: 109 W Hanover Ave, Randolph, NJ 07869 ... 201-907-0394
Seabaugh, Max: 2149 Lyon St #5, San Francisco, CA 94115 ... 415-921-7140
Seabrook, Alexis: 330 E 33rd St #5G, New York, NY 10016 ... 212-679-9320
Sealock, Rick: 420 Lexington Ave, New York, NY 10170 ... 212-986-5680
Searle, Ronald: PO Box 1062, Bayonne, NJ 07002 ... 201-436-4362
Seaver, Jeff: 14 Maple Ave S, Westport, CT 06880 ... 203-254-1900
Seckler, Judy: 4548 Irvine Ave, Studio City, CA 91602 ... 818-508-8778
• **Secret Sauce Studio/Peter Hamlin: pg 687** ... **718-832-8817**
url: www.secretsaucestudio.com
• **Secret Sauce Studios/Joe Rocco: pg 686, 687** ... **718-965-4852**
e-mail: roccoplanet@earthlink.net / url: www.secretsaucestudio.com
Sedelmaier, JJ: 199 Main St 10FL, White Plains, NY 10601 ... 914-949-7979
Seder, Jason: 134 E 40th St 4th Fl, New York, NY 10016 ... 212-490-9300
See, Henry: Art Dept/Williams Hall, Burlington, VT 05405 ... 802-656-2014
Seed, Susan: 3 Windigo Ln, N Truro, MA 02652 ... 508-487-6426
• **Seeley, Dave: pg 229** Chicago, IL ... **312-364-0244**
London ... **011-44-207-636-1064**
Los Angeles, CA ... **323-874-5700**
Washington, DC ... **410-349-8669**
New York, NY ... **212-333-2551**
url: www.shannonassociates.com
Segal, John: 165 W 91st St #5A, New York, NY 10024 ... 212-662-3278
Sehmi, Gagan: 95-14 120th St, Richmond Hill, NY 11419 ... 718-849-3882
Seibert, Dave: 488 Curtis Corner Rd, S Kingston, RI 02879 ... 401-782-2103
Seibert, Sinclair: 347 W 22nd St #4, New York, NY 10011 ... 212-741-1652
• **Seiffer, Alison: pg 112,113** 108 E 35th St, New York, NY 10016 ... **212-889-3337**
e-mail: gerald@rappart.com / url: www.thespot.com/rep/rapp / fax: 212-889-3341
Seigel, Matthew: 33 Vandewater St #302, San Francisco, CA 94133 ... 415-433-5817
Sekeris, Pim: 570 Milton St #10, Montreal, QU H2X 1W4 ... 514-844-0510
Sekine, Hisashi: 630 Fifth Ave 20th Fl, Rockefeller Ctr, New York, NY 10111 ... 212-332-3460
Sela, Eliot: 220 W 21st St #7E, New York, NY 10011 ... 212-627-2450
Selby, Andréa: 194 Third Ave, New York, NY 10003 ... 212-475-0440
Selewacz, Mark: 24 French St, Watertown, MA 02172 ... 617-926-6331
Selfridge, MC: 817 Desplaines St, Plainfield, IL 60544 ... 815-436-7197
Selgin, Peter: 2465 Palisade Ave #6J, Spuyten Devil, NY 10463 ... 718-549-9029
Sellars, Joseph: 2423 W 22nd St, Minneapolis, MN 55405 ... 612-377-8766
Selman, Jan: 79 Pinecrest Bch Dr, E Falmouth, MA 02536 ... 508-540-4586
Selto, Michael: 7231 E 6th Ave, Denver, CO 80220 ... 303-509-1929
Seltzer Design & Illus, Meyer: 744 W Buckingham Pl, Chicago, IL 60657 ... 773-883-0964
Seltzer, Isadore: 285 Riverside Dr #2B, New York, NY 10025 ... 212-666-1561
Selvage, Roger: 2148 Cartwright Pl, Reston, VA 22091 ... 703-264-5325
Selwyn, Paul: 68 Whiting Ln, W Hartford, CT 06119 ... 203-523-5752
Semler, Robert: 3308 56th Ter E, Bradenton, NJ 34203 ... 941-751-0183
Sempe, Jean Jacques: 155 W 15th St #4C, New York, NY 10011 ... 212-989-8770
Sena, Miyuki: 5403 Clearsite St, Torrance, CA 90505 ... 310-316-0027
Senn, Oscar: 1532 Riverside Ave, Jacksonville, FL 32204 ... 904-358-1445
Serafin, Marsha: PO Box 1086, Taos, NM 87571 ... 505-776-5435
Sereta, Bruce: 1118 Morning Sun Pkwy, Las Vegas, NV 89110 ... 702-452-0991
Serra, Mary C: 6033 Hoover Ave, Whittier, CA 90601 ... 562-463-6367
Serrat-Sans: 43 E 19th St, New York, NY 10003 ... 212-254-4996
Serratt, Ron: PO Box 1510, Laytonville, CA 95454 ... 707-984-6462
Servin, Karyn: 5327 SW Illinois, Portland, OR 97221 ... 503-620-8080
Sese, Maria: 7501 Holiday Terr, Bethesda, MD 20817 ... 301-405-4619
Sesto, Carl: 10 Rolfe's Ln, Newbury, MA 01951 ... 508-462-3783
• **Seth: pg 114,115** 108 E 35th St, New York, NY 10016 ... **212-889-3337**
e-mail: gerald@rappart.com / url: www.theispot.com/rep/rapp / fax: 212-889-3341
Settimi Creative & Co: 334 Cobblesprings Ct, Avon, IN 46168 ... 317-272-0882
Seun, Won Hwa: 1224 Kinnear Rd, Columbus, OH 43212 ... 614-292-3416
Sevalrud, Thom: 280 Madison Ave #1110, New York, NY 10016 ... 212-545-9155
Sexton, Brenda: 5027 Greenbush Ave, Sherman Oaks, CA 91423 ... 818-995-8140
Sexton, Rob: 151 Kalmus #A203, Costa Mesa, CA 92626 ... 714-966-2581
SFSI: 493 8th Ave, San Francisco, CA 94118 ... 415-221-4022
SG Design: 33802 Copper Lantern, Dana Point, CA 92629 ... 949-661-7772
Shaff, Tom: 1862 Selby Ave, St Paul, MN 55104 ... 612-645-3822
Shaffer, Allen: 955 Duvall Highway, Pasadena, MD 21122 ... 410-437-9042
Shafie, Taher: 1 Nordica Dr, Croton on Hudson, NY 10520 ... 914-271-6822
Shah, Shaheen: 9 Begonia Ct, Sayerville, NJ 08872 ... 908-238-8458
Shahan, David: 854 Virginia Dr, Sarasota, FL 34234 ... 941-351-2568
Shahsovar, Antonina: 141 Grove St, Ramsey, NJ 07446 ... 201-934-1750
Shamburger, Steve: 5315 Lamar, Mission, KS 66202 ... 913-384-6060
Shanahan, Danny: 155 W 15th St #4C, New York, NY 10011 ... 212-989-8770
Shannon, Bill: 10837 Trailwood Ct, Cincinnati, OH 45240 ... 513-777-5418
Shannon, David: 1328 W Morningside Dr, Burbank, CA 91506 ... 818-563-6763
Shansky Works: 334 County Rd #B, Barrington, RI 02806 ... 401-247-2248
Shap, Sandra: 291 Henry St #3, Brooklyn, NY 11201 ... 718-834-9631
Shap, Sandra: 58 W 40th St 6th Fl, New York, NY 10018 ... 212-682-1490
Shapiro, Neil: 3639 N Harding, Chicago, IL 60618 ... 312-729-6474
Shapter, Andrew: 213 W 4th St #201, Austin, TX 78701 ... 512-499-8877
Shapton, Leanne: 777 Queen St W #2, Toronto, ON M6J 1G1 ... 416-383-2358
Share Reeves Active Media: 1133 6th St, Santa Monica, CA 90403 ... 310-451-9695
Sharp, Ann: PO Box 1251, New York, NY 10023 ... 212-774-4271
Sharp, Bruce: 15808 SE 47th St, Bellevue, WA 98006 ... 425-703-2255
Sharp, Chris: 231 E 76th St #5D, New York, NY 10021 ... 212-535-0438
Sharp, Paul: 7498 Shady Side Dr, Bloomington, IN 47401 ... 812-824-3680
Sharp, William M: 197 E 3rd St #11, New York, NY 10009 ... 212-260-7185
Shasky, Jane: PO Box 354, Hansville, WA 98340 ... 360-638-1276

Shaul, Wendy: 7556 Rio Mondego Dr, Sacramento, CA 95831 ... 916-429-0288
Shaver, Mark: 16 Phaedra, Laguna Niguel, CA 92677 ... 949-495-3664
Shaw, Kurt: 206 W Prospect Ave, Pittsburgh, PA 15205 ... 412-922-5818
• **Shaw, Ned: pg 772** 4950 Bethel Ln, Bloomington, IN 47408 ... **812-333-2181**
e-mail: nshaw@kiva.net / url: www.nedshaw.com / fax: 812-331-0420
Shaw, Patti: 192 Spadina Ave #312, Toronto, ON M5T 2C2 ... 416-504-3184
Shaw, Paul: 785 West End Ave #16A, New York, NY 10025 ... 212-666-3738
• **Shaw, Simon: pg 287** 731 N 24th St, Philadelphia, PA 19130 ... **215-232-6666**
url: www.deborahwolfeltd.com / fax: 215-232-6585
Shawl, Tim: 671 Pinnacle Hill Rd, Kingston Springs, TN 37082 ... 615-952-5725
Shawver, Natasha: 2750 Adeline, Berkeley, CA 94703 ... 510-548-5349
Shay, RJ: 2029 Custer Pkwy, Richardson, TX 75080 ... 972-761-0500
Shea, Michael: 47 Maple St, Burlington, VT 05403 ... 802-864-5884
Shea, Naomi: 35 Hyde Hill Rd, Williamsburg, MA 01096 ... 413-268-3407
Sheban, Chris: 300 N State St #3302, Chicago, IL 60610 ... 773-792-9169
Shed, Greg: 824 Edwards PO Box 41, Trinidad, CA 95570 ... 707-677-0241
Sheean, Hugh: 1935 S Bentley, Los Angeles, CA 90025 ... 310-268-1137
Sheehan, Tom: 31 Marmion Rd, Melrose, MA 02176 ... 617-734-6038
Sheehy, Michael: 58 W 40th St 6th Fl, New York, NY 10018 ... 212-682-1490
Sheerin, Sean: 13 Edmunds Pl, Wakefield, MA 01880 ... 617-245-6984
Sheffield, David: 655 W Irving Park Rd #3602, Chicago, IL 60613 ... 616-954-9921
Shega, Marla: 58 W 40th St 6th Fl, New York, NY 10018 ... 212-682-1490
Sheild, Lori: 13 Seneca St, E Northport, NY 11731 ... 516-261-2919
Shek, WE: 1315 Ebener St #4, Redwood City, CA 94061 ... 415-363-0687
Sheldon, David: 350 Central Park West, New York, NY 10025 ... 212-749-4907
Shelley Brown Associates: 155 Lippincott Street, Toronto, ON M5S 2P3 ... 416-505-9522
Shelley, Ronald: 6790 Sunset Dr, South Miami, FL 33143 ... 305-667-0154
• **Shelly, Jeff: pg 757** 2330 San Marco Dr, Los Angeles, CA 90068 ... **323-460-4604**
... **800-318-3244**
url: ww.jeffshelly.com / fax: 323-464-6630
Shelton, Darryl: 1325 Cameo Dr, Campbell, CA 95008 ... 408-559-6752
Shelton, Dean: 7632 Crow Cut Rd SW, Fairview, TN 37062 ... 615-799-0409
Shelton, Joyce: 525-121 Oak Terr, Altamonte Springs, FL 32701 ... 407-644-5294
Shepard, Steven T: 3661 Carambola Circle N, Pompano Beach, FL 33066 ... 800-603-AXIS
Shephard, James R: 108 W.Wells St #2-D, Milwaukee, WI 53203 ... 414-291-9817
Shephard, Tom: 401 Bounty Way #245, Avon Lake, OH 44012 ... 216-930-2811
Shepherd, James R: 108 W Wells St #2D, Milwaukee, WI 53203 ... 414-291-9817
• **Shepherd, Mike: pg 232** Chicago, IL ... **312-364-0244**
London ... **011-44-207-636-1064**
Los Angeles, CA ... **323-874-5700**
Washington, DC ... **410-349-8669**
New York, NY ... **212-333-2551**
url: www.shannonassociates.com
• **Sheppard, Richard: pg 786** San Francisco, CA ... **707-433-9641**
url: www.artstudios.com
Sherbo, Dan: 4208 38th St NW, Washington, DC 20016 ... 202-244-0474
Sheridan, Brian: 145 Main St, Ossining, NY 10562 ... 914-941-1738
Sheridan, Todd: 399 East State Rd, Pleasant Grove, UT 84062 ... 801-796-9777
Sherman, Gene: PO Box 35, Williamson, NY 14589 ... 315-589-8939
Sherman, Irwin: 5515 Westcreek Dr, Ft Worth, TX 76133 ... 817-370-7891
Sherman, John: Dept of Art-Art Hist & Des, Notre Dame, IN 46556 ... 219-631-5000
Sherman, Linda: 9825 Canal Rd, Gaithersburg, MD 20879 ... 301-590-0604
• **Sherman, Oren: pg 457** 300 E 46th St #4G, New York, NY 10017 ... **212-687-6463**
e-mail: Sari@LevyCreative.com / url: www.levycreative.com / fax: 212-661-4839
Sherman, Paul: 1915 Storm Dr, Falls Church, VA 22043 ... 703-790-1105
• **Sherman, Whitney: pg 116,117** 108 E 35th St, New York, NY 10016 ... **212-889-3337**
e-mail: gerald@rappart.com / url: www.theispot.com/rep/rapp / fax: 212-889-3341
Sherrill, Robert: 3207 1/2 Foothill Blvd, Pasadena, CA 91107 ... 818-769-1468
Sherwood, Stewart: 625 Yonge St #303, Toronto, ON M4Y 1Z5 ... 416-925-8528
Shieldhouse, Stephanie: 1468 Edgewood Cir, Jacksonville, FL 32205 ... 904-384-9475
Shields, Bill: 14 Wilmot, San Francisco, CA 94115 ... 415-346-0376
Shields, Sandra: 62 Burton St, Bristol, RI 02809 ... 401-253-1922
Shiff, Andrew Z: 153 Clinton St, Hopkinton, MA 01748 ... 508-435-3607
Shigley, Neil: 920 E St #204, San Diego, CA 92101 ... 619-232-7444
Shilda, Joy Massen: 6037 11th Ave So, Minneapolis, MN 55417 ... 612-866-0358
Shilstone, Arthur: 42 Picketts Ridge Rd, W Redding, CT 06896 ... 203-438-2727
Shim, Jae: 105 Nonesuch Pl, Irving, TX 75061 ... 972-986-0947
Shin, Young: 162-11 9th Ave #5C, Whitestone, NY 11357 ... 718-767-5668
Shinnick, Margie: 220 12th Ave, San Francisco, CA 94118 ... 415-221-4208
Shipman, Anna: 9-28 Steeplebush Rd, Essex Junctn, VT 05452 ... 802-878-5073
Shipper, Beth: 5001 Green Oak Dr, Lilburn, GA 30047 ... 770-381-5167
Shoates, Jon: 225 Lafayette St #1003, New York, NY 10012 ... 212-965-9890
Shock, Steve: 441 Allen St #4, Waterloo, IA 50701 ... 319-236-0340
Shoemaker, Doug: 5780 Lincoln Dr #107, Edina, MN 55436 ... 952-944-5324
• **Shoffner Illustrator Inc., Terry: pg 844** 11 Irwin Ave, Toronto, ON M4Y 1L1 ... **416-967-6717**
Shohet, Marti: 250 W 57th St #521, New York, NY 10107 ... 212-397-7330
Shohet, Marti: 32 W 83rd St #6, New York, NY 10024 ... 212-362-9082
Short, Kevin: 666 Greenwich St #860, New York, NY 10014 ... 212-675-5719
Short, Kevin: PO Box 2888, Capistrano Beach, CA 92624 ... 949-240-6979
Short, Kevin: PO Box 7544, Phoenix, AZ 85011 ... 602-265-4389
Short, Robbie: 2903 Bentwood Dr, Marietta, GA 30062 ... 770-565-7811
Shoshana Rama, Susan: PO Box 393, East Windsor Hill, CT 06028 ... 860-289-4248
• **Shovel, Martin: pg 913** 13 Lancaster Rd, Brighton, UK BN15DG ... **441273552950**
e-mail: info@shovel.co.uk / url: www.shovel.co.uk
Shtern, Adele: 11-21 47th Rd #3L, Long Island City, NY 11101 ... 718-937-6363
Shukan, Luis: 123 Hummingbird, Livingston, TX 77351 ... 409-327-2666
Shumate, Michael: 198 Chelsea Rd, Kingston, ON K7M 3Y8 ... 613-384-5019
Sibayan, Noel: 362 Cromwell Ave, Staten Island, NY 10305 ... 718-595-0812
• **Siboldi, Carla: pg 419** 7118 Upper River Rd, Prospect, KY 40059 ... **502-228-9427**
url: www.jettreps.com / fax: 502-228-8857
Sibthorp, Fletcher: 58 W 15th St, New York, NY 10011 ... 212-741-2539
Siciliano, Gerald: 9 Garfield Pl, Brooklyn, NY 11215 ... 718-636-4561
Sicuro, Amiee: pg 518,519 Dayton, OH ... 937-433-8383
Sieber, Balind: 96 Gerrard St E. #16b4, Toronto, ON M5B 1G7 ... 416-873-6858
Siebers, Tom: 10182 Whitnall Ct, Hales Corner, WI 53130 ... 414-425-6405
Siebert, Lori: 7118 Upper River Rd, Prospect, KY 40059 ... 502-228-9427
Siegal, Jennifer: 2006 Hyde St, San Francisco, CA 94109 ... 415-441-1443
Siegel Creative Graphics, Mark: 8 Perabo Terr, Boston, MA 02132 ... 617-923-9021
Siegel, Dink: 100 W 57th St #10G, New York, NY 10019 ... 212-246-9757
Siegel, Mark: 9 Babbling Brook Ln, Suffern, NY 10901 ... 845-368-8606
Siegel, Stuart: 106 High Plain St, Walpole, MA 02081 ... 508-668-5392
Siemer, Patrick: 1809 W Division St, Chicago, IL 60622 ... 773-862-4244
Sienkowski, Laurie: 199 Deer Run, Ada, MI 49301 ... 616-676-3040
Sigberman, Rich: 600 Second Ave, San Francisco, CA 94118 ... 415-668-8832
Signorino, Slug: 3587 N Cross Trail, LaPort, IN 46350 ... 219-879-5221
Sillman, Mary: 2015 MW Flanders St, Portland, OR 97209 ... 541-344-1266
Silver Graphics: PO Box 51, Weedsport, NY 13166 ... 315-834-6738
• **Silver Kid: pg 234,235** Chicago, IL ... **312-364-0244**
London ... **011-44-207-636-1064**
Los Angeles, CA ... **323-874-5700**
Washington, DC ... **410-349-8669**
New York, NY ... **212-333-2551**
url: www.shannonassociates.com
Silver Moon Graphics: 57 S Monroe Ave, Columbus, OH 43205 ... 614-469-0847
Silver, Judy Reed: 7536 Ogelsby Ave, Los Angeles, CA 90045 ... 310-641-8556
Silver, Stanley: 701 N.Arden Dr, Beverley Hills, CA 90210 ... 310-285-0800
Silverberg-Kiss, Esti: 132-H Edison Ct, Monsey, NY 10952 ... 914-356-8875
Silveria, Gordon: 284 Juanita Way, San Francisco, CA 94127 ... 415-731-8789
Silverman, Burt: 324 W 71st St, New York, NY 10023 ... 212-799-3399
Silverman, Marc: 62 W 70th St, New York, NY 10023 ... 212-595-5464
Silvers, Bill: 11128 Katherine Crl, Clermont, FL 34711 ... 407-854-2192
Silvers, Bill: 420 Lexington Ave, New York, NY 10170 ... 212-986-5680
Silvestri, Lorraine: 122 Plimpton St, Walpole, MA 02081 ... 508-668-0111
Simanson, Greg: 5002 92nd Ave SE, Mercer Island, WA 98040 ... 206-232-7873
• **Simard, Remy: pg 507** 666 Greenwich St #860, New York, NY 10014 ... **212-675-5719**
e-mail: harriet@hkportfolio.com / url: www.hkportfolio.com / fax: 212-675-6341
Simmons, Elaine: 4628 W Browning Ave, Tampa, FL 33629 ... 813-831-9575
Simmons, JuLee: 1562 S Parker Rd, Aurora, CO 80231 ... 303-337-4070
Simmons, Suzanne: 39 Hamilton Terr, New York, NY 10031 ... 212-283-3401
• **Simms, Kelley Allan: pg 839** 75 Helen St, Hamden, CT 06514 ... **203-288-3115**
Simnacher, Kevin: 951 32nd Ave SW, Cedar Rapids, IA 52406 ... 319-365-8025
Simon, Angela: 2512 E Thomas Rd #2, Phoenix, AZ 85016 ... 602-381-1332
Simon, Dennis: 16312 Yeoho Rd, Sparks, MD 21152 ... 410-329-3983
Simon, Joel: 344 Mt View Lane, Colorado Springs, CO 80907 ... 719-594-0490
• **Simon, Jonathan: pg 914** 30 Cheever Pl #2RR, Brooklyn, NY 11231 ... **718-246-1172**
... **800-945-266**
e-mail: simon74@gte.net / url: www.theispot.com/artist/jsimon
Simon, Susan: 962 E State St, Ithaca, NY 14850 ... 607-277-5903
Simon, William: 9431 Bonhomme Woods, St Louis, MO 63132 ... 314-993-3522
Simonetti, Lucille: 14 Edgemere Rd, Livingston, NJ 07039 ... 973-535-6453
Simons, Stuart: 24 Westchester Ave, Pound Ridge, NY 10576 ... 914-764-9424
Simonsen, Ken: PO Box 88295, Carol Stream, IL 60188 ... 630-665-6609
Simpson, Craig: 1546 Powell St, Norristown, PA 19401 ... 215-279-0991
Simpson, Elizabeth: 2491 W 22nd Ave, Vancouver, BC B6L 1M3 ... 604-684-6826
Simpson, Elizabeth: 5 Adelaide St, Ottawa, ON K1S 3R9 ... 613-237-0196
Simpson, Gretchen Dow: 155 W 15th St #4C, New York, NY 10011 ... 212-989-8770
Sims, Ronald Bennett: 10609 Sandpiper Dr, Houston, TX 77096 ... 713-271-3703
• **Sinclair, Valerie: pg 254,255** 250 W 57th St #521, New York, NY 10107 ... **212-397-7330**
e-mail: San Francisco: 415-788-8552 / url: www.lindgrensmith.com
Singer Design, Paul: 494 14th St, Brooklyn, NY 11215 ... 718-499-8172
Singer, Phill: 37 Cary Rd, Great Neck, NY 11021 ... 516-487-1323
Singletary, Julie: 3678 Barham Blvd #K-204, Los Angeles, CA 90068 ... 323-876-0827
Singleton, Bill: 809 W Wedwick St, Tucson, AZ 85706 ... 520-294-1667
Sinnen, Cherie: 2217 Canyon Dr, Los Angeles, CA 90068 ... 213-463-0868
Sinovcic, Miro: 60 E 42nd St, New York, NY 10165 ... 212-867-8092
Sintz, Jim: 151 N Chase, Columbus, OH 43204 ... 614-278-9330
Sipp, Geo: 4170 S Arbor Cir, Marietta, GA 30066 ... 770-924-4793
Sipple, Dan: 219 S Second Ave #B, Arcadia, CA 91006 ... 626-447-0197
Sir Real Labs: 16745 Maple St, S Holland, IL 60473 ... 312-409-3160
Sirko, Robert: 707 Fox Point Dr, Chesterton, IN 46304 ... 219-926-8759
Sirrell, Terry: 768 Red Oak Dr, Bartlett, IL 60103 ... 630-213-9003
Sis, Peter: 252 Lafayette St #5E, New York, NY 10012 ... 212-226-2203
• **Sisco, Sam: pg 658,659** 1561 Narva Rd, Mississauga, ON L5H 3H4 ... **905-278-2716**
fax: 905-278-2716
Sisk, Graham: 31-21 29th St #1E, Astoria, NY 11106 ... 718-626-0306
Sisti, Jerald: 422 Bay Berry Pl, Encinitas, CA 92024 ... 619-944-7836
• **Siu, Peter: pg 588,589** ,, ... **650-692-1839**
url: www.theispot.com/artist/petersiu / fax: 650-697-3306
Sivavec, Diane: 60 E 42nd St, New York, NY 10165 ... 212-867-8092
Sizemore, Ted: 60 E 42nd St, New York, NY 10165 ... 212-867-8092
Skeen, Keith: 3228 Prairie Dr, Deerfield, WI 53531 ... 608-423-3020
Skelton, Steve: 1215 W 67th St, Kansas City, MO 64108 ... 816-333-0744
Skelton, Steve: 3205 Fifth St, Boulder, CO 80304 ... 303-546-0117
Skidmore, John: 1112 Morefield Rd, Philadelphia, PA 19115 ... 215-698-9114
Skiles, Jacqueline: 236 W 27th St, New York, NY 10001 ... 212-675-7932
Skiles, Jamie: 305 Second Ave #305, New York, NY 10003 ... 212-253-8585
Skillicorn, Mark: 844 N Humphrey Ave, Oak Park, IL 60302 ... 773-549-9548
Skinner, Cortney: 32 Churchill Ave, Arlington, MA 02174 ... 617-648-2875
Sklar, Andy: 4574 N FInley Ave #2, Los Angeles, CA 90027 ... 323-913-1446
Sklar, Herb: 4 Broadway #5, Valhalla, NY 10595 ... 914-328-8880
Skok, Przemyslaw: 763 Leonard St, New York, NY 11222 ... 718-349-1625
Skolsky, Mark: 257 12th St, Brooklyn, NY 11215 ... 718-499-1148
Skopp, Jennifer: 1625 Emmons Ave #6H, Brooklyn, NY 11235 ... 718-646-2344
Skrzydlewski, Carolyn: 2140 Vallejo St #10, San Francisco, CA 94123 ... 415-931-0940
• **Skutnik, Andy: pg 728** ... **212-343-1727**
Skutz, Peter: 50 W 34th St #21C10, New York, NY 10001 ... 212-581-6579
Skwish, A: 556 W Aldine #3E, Chicago, IL 60657 ... 773-755-7101
Skygh, Michael: 38 Fresh River Ave, Hingham, MA 02043 ... 617-749-3937
Skypeck, George: 15407 Overlea Ct, Accokeek, MD 20607 ... 301-203-9136
Slabbers, Ronald: 32 W 31st St 5th Fl, New York, NY 10001 ... 212-239-4283
Slack, Chuck: 58 W 40th St 6th Fl, New York, NY 10018 ... 212-682-1490
Slack, Chuck: 9 Cambridge Ln, Lincolnshire, IL 60069 ... 847-948-9226
Slagle, Krystal: 166 St Joseph, Long Beach, CA 90803 ... 310-433-8459
Slatky, Tom: 60 E 42nd St, New York, NY 10165 ... 212-867-8092
Slattery, Jack: 12850 Whittington #1402, Houston, TX 77077 ... 281-558-2246
Slave, Neil: 312 S Lombard, Oak Park, IL 60302 ... 708-358-0018
Sledd, John W: 60 E 42nd St, New York, NY 10165 ... 212-867-8092
Sledd, John W: 561 Harris Dr, Front Royal, VA 22630 ... 540-635-8012

Slemons, Jeff: 2555 Walnut St #LF, Denver, CO 80205 ... 303-298-0807
Slezak, Will: 4820 E Creek Ridge Trl, Reno, NV 89509 ... 775-826-3858
Sloan, Lois: 21 Tennis Ct NW, Albuquerque, NM 87120 ... 505-899-2262
• **Sloan, Michael: pg 648, 649, 944** 32 Gramercy Park S #13K, New York, NY 10003 ... **212-253-2047**
e-mail: michaelsloan@earthlink.net
Sloan, Rick: 9432 Appalachian Dr, Sacramento, CA 95827 ... 916-364-5844
Sloan, William: 236 W 26th St #805, New York, NY 10001 ... 212-463-7025
Sloane, Sarah: 37 Schiller St, Pawtucket, RI 02860 ... 401-727-3385
Slone Illustration: 833 W Main St, Louisville, KY 40202 ... 502-585-4670
Slonim, David: 232 South St, Chesterfield, IN 46017 ... 317-378-6511
Sloss, Tinka Anjali: 1424 Las Positas Place, Santa Barbara, CA 93105 ... 805-682-6775
Slygh, Michael: 38 Fresh River Ave, Hingham, MA 02043 ... 781-749-3937
Small, David: 155 W 15th St #4C, New York, NY 10011 ... 212-989-8770
• **Smalley, Guy: pg 760** 146 Chestnut Walk, Waynesville, NC 28786 ... **828-456-4930**
url: www.guysmalley.com
Smallish, Craig: 777 N Michigan Ave #706, Chicago, IL 60611 ... 312-337-7770
Smallish, Craig: 5448 Cigrand Ave, Fredonia, WI 53021 ... 414-692-9594
Smallwood, Bud: 6 Lamplighter's Way, Saugus, MA 01906 ... 617-231-2075
Smallwood, Steve: 4702 Summer Creek Ln SE, Grand Rapids, MI 49508 ... 616-249-2845
Smart, Randy: 357 Hillandale Rd #253, Greenville, NC 29609 ... 716-359-4797
Smart Art: 28 Aubrey Rd, Upper Montclair, NJ 07043 ... 973-783-1171
Smiglowski, Michal: 1 Melissa Dr, Pembroke, NH 03275 ... 603-485-4032
Smith, Alison: 19 Bowers Ave, Tyngsboro, MA 01879 ... 978-957-4273
• **Smith, Anne: pg 401** 6 Parker Rd, Arlington, MA 02474 ... **781-641-2787**
e-mail: info@lillarogers.com / url: www.lillarogers.com / fax: 781-641-2244
Smith, Brett: 353 W 53rd St #1W, New York, NY 10019 ... 212-682-2462
Smith, Christina M: PO Box 701/ Adelaide, Toronto, ON M5C 2J8 ... 416-214-2752
Smith, Christopher: 7954 Queens Rd, Glen Burnie, MD 21061 ... 410-766-8743
Smith, Dan & Tracey: 353 W 53rd St #1W, New York, NY 10019 ... 212-682-2462
Smith, Daniel: 1157 N 185 W, Orem, UT 84057 ... 801-368-9816
Smith, Debbie: 4604 River Oak Dr, Knoxville, TN 37920 ... 423-579-6530
Smith, Don: 21850 Poppy Ln, Nuevo, CA 92567 ... 909-928-1577
Smith, Donald: PO Box 391, Athens, GA 30603 ... 706-543-5555
• **Smith, Douglas: pg 40,41** 305 E 50th St #1, New York, NY 10022 ... **212-223-9545**
url: www.richardsolomon.com / fax: 212-223-9633
Smith, E Fitz: 112 Burr, Easton, CT 06612 ... 203-255-5468
Smith, Eileen: 809 E 41st St, Savannah, GA 31401 ... 912-233-3786
Smith, Ellen: 185 South Rd, Marlborough, CT 06447 ... 203-295-0004
• **Smith, Elwood H: pg 707** 41 Locust Grove Rd, Rhinebeck, NY 12572 ... **845-876-2358**
e-mail: elwood@infi.net / url: www.theispot.com/artist/esmith or
www.elwoodsmith.com / fax: 845-876-5931
Smith, Fred: 760 E Naomi Ave Unit C, Arcadia, CA 91007 ... 626-447-8333
Smith, Gary D: 5646 E Dixileta Dr, Cave Creek, AZ 85331 ... 480-585-1634
Smith, Genine: 606 Montana Ave, Santa Monica, CA 90403 ... 310-451-1039
• **Smith, Geoffrey P: pg 519** Dayton, OH ... **937-433-8383**
e-mail: NY-212-966-3604 or SF-415-285-3808 / url: www.scotthull.com
fax: 937-433-0434
Smith, Graham: 3510 Front St #3D, San Diego, CA 92103 ... 619-296-9323
Smith, J Randall: 8240 Laurelridge Rd, San Diego, CA 92120 ... 619-229-8746
Smith, James Noel: 137 W 14th St #204, New York, NY 10011 ... 212-337-0055
• **Smith, Jamie: pg 507** 666 Greenwich St #860, New York, NY 10014 ... **212-675-5719**
e-mail: harriet@hkportfolio.com / url: www.hkportfolio.com / fax: 212-675-6341
Smith, Jeffrey: 108 E 35th St, New York, NY 10016 ... 212-889-3337
Smith, Jere: 7205 28th Ave NW, Seattle, WA 98117 ... 206-784-1136
Smith, Joseph A: 169 John St 6th Fl, New York, NY 10038 ... 212-825-1475
Smith, Kenneth C: 239 W 46th St, Chicago, IL 60609 ... 773-373-3015
Smith, Keri: PO Box 411, Flesherton, ON N0C 1E0 ... 519-924-3535
• **Smith, Laura: pg 732** 6545 Cahuenga Terr, Hollywood, CA 90068 ... **323-467-1700**
url: www.laurasmithart.com
New York, NY ... **212-206-9162**
Smith, Lee Fitzgerrell: 1815 Woodsman Ct, Placerville, CA 95677 ... 916-626-8113
Smith, Leigh Ann: RR 1 Box 77, Coxsackie, NY 12051 ... 518-731-6924
Smith, Marcia: 112 Linden St, Rochester, NY 14620 ... 716-461-9348
Smith, Mark: 319 W Northfield Rd, Livingston, NJ 07039 ... 201-992-4213
Smith, Mark T: 235 E 22nd St #13V, New York, NY 10010 ... 212-679-9485
Smith, Marty: PO Box 421443, San Francisco, CA 94142 ... 415-647-5660
Smith, Mary Anne: 43 W 21st St 3rd Fl, New York, NY 10010 ... 212-691-3570
Smith, Meg: 3144 Bryant Ave S, Minneapolis, MN 55408 ... 612-822-4461
Smith, Owen: 1608 Fernside Blvd, Alameda, CA 94501 ... 510-865-1911
Smith, Pamela: 4434 Corinth Ave, Culver City, CA 90230 ... 310-391-3637
Smith, Patrick: 60 Calvin Dr, McKees Rocks, PA 15136 ... 412-787-0241
Smith, Randy: 577 S200 East #200, Salt Lake City, UT 84111 ... 801-355-9541
Smith, Raymond: 602 Willow Ave, Hoboken, NJ 07030 ... 201-653-6638
Smith, Rick E: 1280 Civic Dr Ste 306, Walnut Creek, CA 94596 ... 510-938-8866
Smith, Samantha Carol: 3818 Greenmount Ave, Baltimore, MD 21218 ... 301-243-6184
Smith, Sean C: 295 S Broadway #1W, Yonkers, NY 10705 ... 914-376-0715
Smith, Shelly: 1311 Cascade Ave, Hood River, OR 97031 ... 541-386-9232
Smith, Tad: 2512 E Thomas Rd #2, Phoenix, AZ 85016 ... 602-381-1332
• **Smith, Tammy: pg 519** Dayton, OH ... **937-433-8383**
New York, NY ... **212-966-3604**
San Francisco, CA ... **415-285-3808**
url: www.scotthull.com / fax: 937-433-0434
Smith, Terry: 14333 Tyler St, Sylmar, CA 93402 ... 818-362-3599
Smith, Terry E: 1713 Dryden Way, Crofton, MD 21114 ... 301-858-0734
Smith, Terry L: 425 Black Mountain Dr, Antioch, TN 37013 ... 615-361-5839
Smith, Theresa: 666 Greenwich St #860, New York, NY 10014 ... 212-675-5719
Smith, Tim: 150 E 79th St #3, New York, NY 10021 ... 212-472-8702
Smith, Winston: PO Box 410990 #426, San Francisco, CA 94141 ... 415-487-1336
Smith-Griswold, Wendy: 9 Babbling Brook Ln, Suffern, NY 10901 ... 845-368-8606
Smithem, Shari: 5793 Dowling St, Montague, MI 49437 ... 231-894-2253
Smock, Doug: 3105 Dekalb Blvd, Norristown, PA 19401 ... 610-272-3182
Smola, Jim: 165 E 32nd St, New York, NY 10016 ... 212-686-3514
Smolenski, Peter: 55 Olive St, Northampton, MA 01060 ... 413-584-5105
Smolinski, Dick: PO Box 1086, Taos, NM 87571 ... 505-776-5435
Smolla, Jim: 165 E 32nd St, New York, NY 10016 ... 212-686-3514
Smollin, Mark: 232 Madison Ave #512, New York, NY 10016 ... 212-889-8777
Smollin, Michael: 420 Lexington Ave, New York, NY 10170 ... 212-986-5680
Smool, Carl: 812 26th Ave S, Seattle, WA 98144 ... 206-322-3423
Smyth, Amy: 10 Thrush Way, Medford, NJ 08055 ... 609-953-5952
Smyth, Fiona: 51 Camden St, Toronto, ON M5V 1V2 ... 416-703-1913
Smyth, Richard F: 1235 Glenview Rd, Glenview, IL 60025 ... 847-998-8345
Smythe, Danny: PO Box 1760, Highland Park, IL 60035 ... 312-222-0337
Sneed, Brad: 709 W 90th Terr, Kansas City, MO 64114 ... 816-822-2024
Snelson, Kenneth: 140 Sullivan St, New York, NY 10012 ... 212-777-0356
Snider, Jackie: Concession 2 West #800, RR1, Warkworth, ON K0K 3K0 ... 705-924-1487
Snider, Stephen: Concession 2 West #800, RR 1, Warkworth, ON K0K 1H0 ... 705-924-1487
Snodgrass, Steve: 837 W Grand Ave 3rd Fl, Chicago, IL 60622 ... 312 633-0500
Snow, Lizzie: 9275 Troon Ct, St Paul, MN 55125 ... 612-578-3579
Snow, Scott: 99 Park Ave #210A, New York, NY 10016 ... 800-398-9544
Snow, Scott: 1537 S Main St, Salt Lake City, UT 84115 ... 801-484-0419
Snure, Roger: Box 1294, Orleans, MA 02653 ... 508-255-8667
Snyder, David: 3455 Elm Swamp Rd, Lebanon, IN 46052 ... 317-482-2770
Snyder, David: 4812 Burris Dr, Louisville, KY 40291 ... 502-239-2075
Snyder, Teresa & Wayne: 25727 Mountain Dr, Arlington, WA 98223 ... 206-435-8998
Snyder, Zachary: 2199 NW Everett St #107, Portland, OR 97210 ... 503-690-7004
• **So, Meilo: pg 489** 455 W 23rd St #8D, New York, NY 10011 ... **212-366-1893**
e-mail: sally@theartworksinc.com / url: www.theartworksinc.com
fax: 212-604-9643
So, Pak: 126 Bedford Ave, Brooklyn, NY 11211 ... 718-388-5540
Sobel, June: 2131 Lindengrove St, Westlake Village, CA 91361 ... 805-495-0626
Sobel, Phillip Eric: 80-15 41st Ave #128, Elmhurst, NY 11373 ... 718-476-3841
Sobieski, Jean: 514 West End Ave #7C, New York, NY 10024 ... 212-749-9691
Society of Illustrators / San Diego: PO Box 704, Cardiff, CA 92007 ... 649-297-8675
Soderlind, Kirsten: 13500 SE 43rd St, Bellevue, WA 98006 ... 425-603-9455
Sofo, Frank: 32C Stratton Sq, E Hampton, NY 11937 ... 516-324-6119
• **Sokolova, Valerie: pg 272** 250 W 57th St #521, New York, NY 10107 ... **212-397-7330**
e-mail: San Francisco: 415-788-8552 / url: www.lindgrensmith.com
Sokolowski Illustraton: RR #2 Box 408, Lake Ariel, PA 18436 ... 570-937-4527
Solem, Robert: 3370 N 55th St, Milwaukee, WI 53216 ... 414-445-7698
Solevad, Paul: 3273 NE Mason St, Portland, OR 97211 ... 503-284-3965
Solie, John: PO Box 249, Seal Rock, OR 97376 ... 541-454-8147
Solomon, Alana: 2123 Belmont Dr, Reidsville, NC 27320 ... 910-342-1095
Solomon, Debra: 1 Hudson St 3rd Fl, New York, NY 10013 ... 212-619-7900
Solomon, Kristy: 1694 Cherrywood Pl, Seaford, NY 11783 ... 516-826-5214
Solotoff, Susan AM: 61 Terrace Ave, Floral Park, NY 11001 ... 516-328-2393
Soltis, Linda DeVito: 137 Barn Hill Rd, Woodbury, CT 06798 ... 203-263-4019
Soma, Matthew: 12657 Elkwood St, N Hollywood, CA 91605 ... 818-701-9845
Somers, Paul: 333 N Michigan Ave #1105, Chicago, IL 60601 ... 312-263-6593
Somerville, Kevin: 85 High St, Jamestown, RI 02835 ... 401-423-1263
Sommerfield, Heather: 115 W 16th St, New York, NY 10011 ... 212-337-0881
Songero, Jay: 17858 Rose St, Lansing, IL 60438 ... 708-849-5676
Soper, Patrick: 214 Stephens, Lafayette, LA 70506 ... 318-233-1635
Sorel, Edward: 156 Franklin St, New York, NY 10013 ... 212-966-3949
Sorel, Madeline: 140 Jaffray St, Brooklyn, NY 11235 ... 718-646-8404
• **Sorensen Illustrates, Marcos: pg 470,471** ... **415-282-5796**
url: www.astrocat.com or www.theispot.com / fax: 415-282-5681
608 York St, San Francisco, CA 94110 ... **415-641-1285**
url: www.theispot.com/rep/weinberg / fax: 415-641-5500
Sorensen, Robert: 22 Strathmore Ave, Milford, CT 06460 ... 203-874-6381
Sorensen, Tom: 5808 S Pacific Coast Hwy #4, Redondo Beach, CA 90277 ... 310-540-5511
Sorensen, Vibeke: 708 Barbara Ave, Solana Beach, CA 92075 ... 619-350-4567
Sorren, Joe: 906 W Summit #B, Flagstaff, AZ 86001 ... 520-214-9980
Sosa, Yvette: 7119 Halray Ave, Whittier, CA 90606 ... 562-698-8635
• **Sosnovsky, John: pg 237** Chicago, IL ... **312-364-0244**
London ... **011-44-207-636-1064**
Los Angeles, CA ... **323-874-5700**
Washington, DC ... **410-349-8669**
New York, NY ... **212-333-2551**
url: www.shannonassociates.com
Sotnick, Stephen J: 220 W Santa Fe Ave, Placentia, CA 92870 ... 714-993-9099
Soto, Penny: 2586 Shadow Mtn Dr, San Ramon, CA 94583 ... 925-820-0708
Sou Sou, Samar: 280 Riverside Dr #14H, New York, NY 10025 ... 212-496-7335
Souitanian, Denise: PO Box 981, Redwood City, CA 94064 ... 650-701-0632
Soukup, James: Route 1, Seward, NE 68434 ... 402-643-2339
Soule, Robert Alan: 15229 Baughman Dr, Silver Spring, MD 20906 ... 301-598-8883
Soultanian, Denise: PO Box 981, Redwood City, CA 94064 ... 650-794-7749
Sours, Michael: 9229 215th St SW, Edmonds, WA 98020 ... 206-771-2905
Sowash, Randy: 550 Sunset Blvd, Mansfield, OH 44907 ... 419-756-7139
Soyka, Ed: 231 Lafayette Ave, Peekskill, NY 10566 ... 914-737-2230
Spacek, Peter: 7 Deforest Rd, Montauk, NY 11954 ... 631-668-9092
Spain, Valerie: 152 Winsor Ave #1, Watertown, MA 02472 ... 617-923-1989
Spalenka, Greg: 21303 San Miguel St, Woodland Hills, CA 91364 ... 888-295-5828
• **Spalenka: pg 226** Chicago, IL ... **312-364-0244**
London ... **011-44-207-636-1064**
Los Angeles, CA ... **323 874 5700**
Washington, DC ... **410-349-8669**
New York, NY ... **212-333-2551**
url: www.shannonassociates.com
Sparacio, Mark & Erin: 30 Rover Ln, Hicksville, NY 11801 ... 516-579-6679
Sparks, Jesse: 220 Kavanaugh Way, Pacifica, CA 94044 ... 800-466-4060
Sparks, Richard: 7 Parkhill Ave, Norwalk, CT 06851 ... 203-866-2002
• **Sparky: pg 855** ... **44139871358**
e-mail: mail@spark-y.co.uk / url: www.spark-y.co.uk
Spataro, Tery: 665 Broadway 6th Fl, New York, NY 10012 ... 212-358-8080
Spaulding, Kevin: 38 Mountain View Ln, Vergennes, VT 05491 ... 802-877-3291
Spear, Charles: 456 9th St #2, Hoboken, NJ 07030 ... 201-798-6466
Spearing, Craig: 866 United Nations Plaza, New York, NY 10017 ... 212-644-2020
Spears, Brent: 1422 N Sierra Bonita Ave, Pasadena, CA 91104 ... 626-564-1255
Speckels, Jenny: PO Box 12421, San Francisco, CA 94112 ... 415-585-4861
• **Spector, Joel: pg 386** 194 Third Ave, New York, NY 10003 ... **212-475-0440**
url: www.morgangaynin.com / fax: 212-353-8538
Speer, Marla: 74-45 260th St, Glen Oaks, NY 11004 ... 718-343-3589
Speer, Stephan: 6105 81st St, Middle Village, NY 11379 ... 718-457-7641
Speer, Terry: 181 Forest St, Oberlin, OH 44074 ... 216-774-8319
Speers, Pauline Cilmi: 133 N Montclair Ave, Dallas, TX 75208 ... 214-943-2569
Speidel, Sandra: 2150 Western Ave, Petaluma, CA 94952 ... 707-765-1151
Spellman, Susan: 50 Fuller Brook Rd, Wellesley, MA 02482 ... 781-235-8658
Spencer Studios, Mary: 7816 Connie Dr, Huntington Beach, CA 92648 ... 714-848-4954

Stone, Petula: 23 Ganton St, London, UK WIV 1LA 71-287-9191
Stonesifer, Sue: 1918 Bank St, Baltimore, MD 21231 410-276-3727
Stong, Michel: 655 Cherry St, Santa Rosa, CA 95404 707-575-0749
Storey, Lee: 6565 Green Valley Cir #306, Culver City, CA 90230 310-670-3477
Storozuk, Walter: 99 Park Ave #210A, New York, NY 10016 800-398-9544
Story, Karl: 3104 Mercer University Dr #100, Atlanta, GA 30341 770-986-0453
Stott, Dorothy: 666 Greenwich St #860, New York, NY 10014 212-675-5719
Stouffer, Stephanie: RR 1 Box 196, Belmont, VT 05730 802-259-2686
Stout, Tim: 135 W Dorothy Ln #205, Dayton, OH 45429 513-298-5133
Strachan, Bruce: 999 Lorimer St, Brooklyn, NY 11222 718-383-1264
Stranovsky, John: 253 Montpelier Ct, Westminster, MD 21157 410-876-0103
Strassburg, Brian: 111 S Hamilton St, Madison, WI 53703 608-255-6244
Stratton, Thalia: 680 W Sunnyoaks Ave, Campbell, CA 95008 408-395-1463
Straub, Matt: 48 Eldridge St #4W, New York, NY 10002 212-995-9359
Straub, Philip: 1355 Boulevard #4, W Hartford, CT 06119 203-261-4334
Strauss, Matthew: 9818 Jellison Way, Westminster, CO 80021 303-467-3744
Strauss, Pamela: 160 W Brookline St, Boston, MA 02118 617-859-8766
Strauss, Ron: 212 3rd Ave N #415, Minneapolis, MN 55401 612-339-6214
Strawn, Susan: 1216 W Olive St, Ft Collins, CO 80521 970-493-0679
Strebel Illustration, Carol: 2930 Hackberry St, Cincinnati, OH 45206 513-281-6837
Street, Janet: 15 Warrenton Ave, Hartford, CT 06105 860-523-4562
Streeter, Eric: 2 Chrysanthy Ct, Johnston, RI 02919 401-231-0433
Streeter, Katherine: 17 Little West 12th St #310, New York, NY 10014 212-924-7966
Streff, Michael: 3735 S Berkley, Cincinnati, OH 45236 513-985-0568
Strelecki, Karen: 848 Greenwood Ave NE, Atlanta, GA 30306 404-875-1363
Stribling-Sutherland, Kelly: 1208 San Gabriel Dr, Denton, TX 76205 817-382-1253
Strizek, Jan: 333 E Ontario St, Chicago, IL 60611 312-266-4900
Strode, Brad: 778 Tree Ln, West Chester, PA 19380 215-358-5088
Stromoski, Rick: 2031 Holly Dr, Prescott, AZ 86305 520-708-9446
Stroster, Maria: 200 W 15th St, New York, NY 10011 212-243-4209
Stroud, Steven: 1031 Howe Ave, Shelton, CT 06484 203-924-2460
• **Struthers, Doug: pg 457** 300 E 46th St #4G, New York, NY 10017 . . . . . . **212-687-6463**
e-mail: Sari@LevyCreative.com / url: www.levycreative.com / fax: 212-661-4839
Struve-Dencher, Goesta: #303 750 E 7th Ave, Vancouver, BC V5T 4H5 604-872-3439
• **Struzan, Drew: pg 120,121** 108 E 35th St, New York, NY 10016 . . . . . . **212-889-3337**
e-mail: gerald@rappart.com / url: www.theispot.com/rep/rapp / fax: 212-889-3341
Stuart, Marina : 65 Hurlbutt St, Wilton, CT 06897 203-762-0453
Stuart, Walter: 824 Edwards PO Box 41, Trinidad, CA 95570 707-677-0241
Stubbs, Charles: 638 Cordelia Dr #1, Santa Rosa, CA 95405 707-544-8358
Stubbs, Diane N: 8855 Mia Moore Ave, Las Vegas, NV 89117 702-871-2711
Stubbs, Elizabeth: 27 Wyman St, Arlington, MA 02174 617-646-0785
Stubbs, Tommy: 5134 Timber Trail NE, Atlanta, GA 30342 888-255-1490
Stuck, Marion: 1088 Diamond Ct, Mississauga, ON L5Y1J5 416-567-1493
• **Studer, Gordon: pg 450,451** **510-655-4256**
San Francisco, CA **415-441-4384**
e-mail: gstuder@dnai.com / url: www.gordonstuder.com
Studholme, Hal: PO Box 50063, Minneapolis, MN 55405 . . . . . .
Studio 202: 215 W 10th St #4B, New York, NY 10014 212-741-1610
Studio 212: 232 Madison Ave #512, New York, NY 10016 212-889-8777
• **Studio Arts / Brian Jenson: pg 793** 420 N Fifth St #920, Minneapolis, MN 55401 . . . . **612-339-7055**
url: www.studio-arts.com / fax: 612-339-8689
Studio Liddell: 217 E 86th St #212, New York, NY 10028 212-427-5632
Studio M: 3591 Long Beach Blvd, Long Beach, CA 90807 562-426-1888
Studio Macbeth: 130 W 42nd St, New York, NY 10036 212-921-8922
Studio Productions, Inc: 650 N Bronson Ave #223, Los Angeles, CA 90004 213-856-8048
• **Studio Y/ Sandy Young: pg 877** 17503 Sonoma Highway, Sonoma, CA 95476 . . . **707-939-1131**
e-mail: Ideas@studio-y.com / url: www.studio-y.com
Studt, Alan: 8575 Broadview Rd, Broadview Heights, OH 44147 216-546-1274
Stuhmer, Robert: 26 W 17th St 6th Fl, New York, NY 10011 212-366-9776
Sturm, Linda: 1763 Dogwood Dr, Yorktown Heights, NY 10598 914-245-7981
Sturman, Sally Mara: 853 Broadway #606, New York, NY 10003 212-777-6777
Stutesman, Deborah Howard: 14378 Country Rd, Lyons, OH 43533 419-335-3340
Stutzman, Mark: 100 G St, Mountain Lake Park, MD 21550 301-334-4086
Stymest, Brian: 39 Hamilton Terr, New York, NY 10031 212-283-3401
Su, Hui-Ching: 1616 Kings Wy, Vista, CA 92084 619-945-9166
Sucher, Laurie: 6718 N Newgard, Chicago, IL 60626 773-764-2692
Suchit, Stu: 117 Jayne Ave, Port Jefferson, NY 11777 516-928-6775
Suh, Ellen: 500 S Lake St #411, Los Angeles, CA 90057 213-483-8683
Suh, John: 165 E 32nd St, New York, NY 10016 212-686-3514
Suhre, James: 17 Greenwich Ave #11, New York, NY 10014 212-647-9734
Sullivan, Dan: 250 W Center St, Orem, UT 84057 801-235-9191
Sullivan, Don: 865 Delaware St, Denver, CO 80204 303-820-2599
Sullivan, Jem: 3734 Mackey Cove Dr, Pensacola, FL 32514 850-479-9117
Sullivan, Melinda May: 834 Moultrie St, San Francisco, CA 94110 415-648-2376
• **Sullivan, Michael: pg 433** 227 Godfrey Rd, Weston, Ct 06883 . . . . . . **203-222-8777**
e-mail: jp@atcoreps.com / www.artcoreps.com / fax: 203-454-9940
232 Madison Ave, #512 New York, NY 10016 . . . . . . **212-889-8777**
e-mail gt@artcoreps.com / url: www.artcoreps.com / fax: 212-477-1475
Sullivan, Pat: 29 Elmstead, Trumbull, CT 06611 203-628-1623
Sullivan, Robert M: 227 Godfrey Rd, Weston, CT 06883 203-222-8777
Sullivan, Rose: 150 Grove Ave, Woodbridge, NJ 07095 908-750-8747
Sullivan, Steve: 99 Park Ave #210A, New York, NY 10016 800-398-9544
Sully, Tom: 73 Moultrie St #A, Charleston, SC 29403 843-723-2734
Sulski, Victoria: PO Box 7709, Santa Cruz, CA 95061 408-426-4247
Sume, Debbie: 1936 S Lake St, Salt Lake City, UT 84105 801-487-8270
Sumichrast, Jözef: 501 Fifth Ave, New York, NY 10017 212-490-2450
• **Summers, Mark: pg 42,43** 305 E 50th St #1, New York, NY 10022 . . . . . . **212-223-9545**
url: www.richardsolomon.com / fax: 212-223-9633
Sumption, Brian F: 712 Concord St NW, Massillon, OH 44646 216-832-8453
Surah, Laurie: 68475 S La Pasada Pl, Hereford, AZ 85635 520-378-3183
Surman, Thomas: 446 Old Newport Blvd #201, Newport Beach, CA 92663 . . . 714-650-3884
Sussman, Rob: 163 Amsterdam Ave #112, New York, NY 10023 212-874-0441
Susynski, Ken: 316 N 45th St, Seattle, WA 98103 206-650-1016
Suteski, Monika: 1030 Falgarwood Dr #58, Oakville, ON L6H 2P5 905-339-3782
Sutherland, Emma: 22 Wakefield Rd, Brighton, England, UK N2 3FP 1273-673980
Sutliff, Joe: 14600 Farming Way, Centreville, VA 20120 703-968-6852
Sutton, Eva: 158 Spring St #3, New York, NY 10012 212-343-0952
Sutton, Jason: 227 Godfrey Rd, Weston, CT 06883 203-222-8777
Sutton, Jeremy: 245 Everett Ave, Palo Alto, CA 94301 415-325-3493
Sutton, Judith: 41 W Ferry St, New Hope, PA 18938 215-862-9771
Sutton, Ward: 799 Greenwich St #4S, New York, NY 10014 212-924-4992
Suvityasiri, Sarn: 2419 Bonar St, Berkeley, CA 94702 510-548-8218
Suzdaltseva, Jenny: 5932 Nora Lynn Dr, Woodland Hills, CA 91367 818-888-2414
Suzuki, Bob: 192 Spadina Ave #502, Toronto, ON M5T 2C2 416-504-8739
Svolos, Maria: 1635 W Chase Ave, Chicago, IL 60626 773-338-4675
Swaine, Mike: 6735 N 10th Pl, Phoenix, AZ 85014 602-264-5400
Swales, Scott: 245 Parkside Ave #A, Buffalo, NY 14214 716-836-2360
Swaminathan, S: PO Box 1547, Captola, CA 95010 408-722-3301
Swan, Joan: 133 N Montclair Ave, Dallas, TX 75208 214-943-2569
Swan, Sara: 2466 Moreno Dr, Los Angeles, CA 90039 213-661-4707
Swan, Susan: 1300 Ravenwood Dr, Arlington, TX 76013 817-265-1928
Swanson, Barbara: 380 W 12th St #5B, New York, NY 10014 212-924-0559
Swanson, Chris E: 4309 BE Antelope Dr, USAF Academy, CO 80840 719-472-6335
Swanson, James: 15 Richmond Ave, La Grange Park, IL 60526 708-352-3081
Swanson, Robert: 60 E 42nd St, New York, NY 10165 212-867-8092
Swarner, Kristina: 1415 W Jonquil, Chicago, IL 60626 773-338-2772
Swarts, Jeff: PO Box 289 308 S Cedar St, Danville, OH 43014 740-599-6516
Swartzback, Michael: 214 5th St NE, Washington, DC 20002 202-547-6217
Swasey, Scott: 1234 Earlham St, Pittsburgh, PA 15205 412-922-8560
• **Swearington, Greg: pg 233** Chicago, IL **312-364-0244**
London **011-44-207-636-1064**
Los Angeles, CA **323-874-5700**
Washington, DC **410-349-8669**
New York, NY **212-333-2551**
url: www.shannonassociates.com
Sweeney, Jerry: 1644 Beryl Dr, Pittsburgh, PA 15227 412-391-4471
Sweeney, Robert: 3925 Dolphin Cir, Colorado Springs, CO 80918 719-594-8857
Sweeny, Glynis: 612 N 2nd St, St Louis, MO 63102 314-781-7377
Sweet, Brian: 145 E Palatine Rd, Palatine, IL 60067 847-359-2608
• **Sweet, Melissa: pg 779** **207-236-0348**
url: www.melissasweet.net / fax: 207-236-0350
Sweetland, James: 16 Burnham Rd, Toronto, ON M4G 1C1 416-424-2101
Sweetland, Sally: PO Box 334, Waitsfield, VT 05673 802-496-5759
Sweetlight Creative Partners: 11516 Sixth Ave NW, Seattle, WA 98177 206-364-9077
Sweitzer, Randy: 4729 N Artesian Ave, Chicago, IL 60625 773-728-3759
Swendsen, Paul: 4630 Fulton St, San Francisco, CA 94121 415-668-1077
Sweny, Stephen: 3121 Hollywood Dr, Decatur, GA 30033 404-299-7535
Swift, Elvis: 756 8th Ave S, Naples, FL 34102 941-403-4393
Swift, Gary: 8 Hague Park Ln, S Kirkby, Pontefract, W Yorkshire, UK WF9 3SS . . . 1977-646431
Syme, Alec: 5051 Drew Ave S, Minneapolis, MN 55410 612-827-4510
Syme, Hugh: 420 Lexington Ave, New York, NY 10170 212-986-5680
Symington, Gary: 2652 Volley Ln, Meadow Vista, CA 95722 916-878-6876
Synarski, Susan: 565 57th St, Oakland, CA 94609 510-594-1242
Syntax: 19 Los Amigos Ct, Orinda, CA 94563 510-253-3131
Syska, Richard: 1830 W Foster, Chicago, IL 60640 773-728-2738
Sysko, Ray: 300 E 33rd St #20L, New York, NY 10016 212-598-9710
Szabo, Gustav: 380 Riverside Dr #5H, New York, NY 10025 212-663-1106
Szotak, Matt: 19 Niles Ave, Middletown, NJ 07748 908-671-3274
Szpura, Beata: 48-02 69th St, Woodside, NY 11377 718-424-8440
Szpura, Beata: 3033 13th Ave W, Seattle, WA 98119 206-284-4701
Szumowski, Tom: 13 Florence Rd, Easthampton, MA 01027 413-529-0572

T

Taback, Simms: 98 Hickory Rd, Willow, NY 12495 914-688-2605
Tabler, Marie: 17717 Hidden Valley, Independence, MO 64057 . . . . . . 816 795 0820
Tachiera, Andrea: 7416 Fairmount Ave, El Cerrito, CA 94530 510-525-3484
• **Tagel, Peggy: pg 507** 666 Greenwich St #860, New York, NY 10014 . . . . . . **212-675-5719**
e-mail: HKPfolio@aol.com / url: www.spar.com / fax: 212-675-6341
Taggart, Sean: 450 Broadway, Hastings-on-Hudson, NY 10706 914-478-8221
Taglianetti Illus, Clare: 256 Iven Ave #3A, Saint Davids, PA 19087 610-429-3774
Taglianetti, Clare: 280 Madison Ave #1110, New York, NY 10016 212-545-9155
Takagi, Michael: 60920 Larsen Rd, Bend, OR 97702 541-385-3263
Takahashi, Hideko: 637 S Cloverdale Ave #10, Los Angeles, CA 90036 213-938-8587
Takai, John: 3623 Clarington Ave #2, Los Angeles, CA 90034 310-838-8234
Talamini, Marie: 3922 Gilbert Ave #106, Dallas, TX 75219 214-526-2020
Talaro, Lionel: 716 W Chase Ave, El Cajon, CA 92020 619-441-8545
Talaro, Lionel: 32 W 40th St #2 South, New York, NY 10018 212-575-6887
• **Talbot, Jim: pg 134** 420 Lexington Ave, New York, NY 10170 . . . . . . **212-986-5680**
e-mail: mendolaart@aol.com / url: www.mendolaart.com / fax: 212-818-1246
Talcott, Julia: 7 Washington St, Beverly, MA 01915 978-921-0887
Taleporos, Plato: 333 E 23rd St #2EE, New York, NY 10010 212-689-3138
Tallant, Judy: 17528 Tester Rd, Snohomish, WA 98290 425-865-4759
Tallon, Revelle: 26 W Pine St, Plaistow, NH 03865 603-382-3397
Tanabe, Hiroshi: 80 Nassau St #202E, New York, NY 10038 212-964-9141
Tanaka, Lynn: 4018 W 44th St, Edina, MN 55424 612-926-8923
• **Tanaka, Yasuo: pg 280** 250 W 57th St #521, New York, NY 10107 . . . . . . **212-397-7330**
San Francisco: 415-788-8552 / url: www.lindgrensmith.com
• **Tanenbaum, Robert: pg 174** 420 Lexington Ave, New York, NY 10170 . . . . . . **212-986-5680**
e-mail: mendolaart@aol.com / url: www.mendolaart.com / fax: 212-818-1246
Tank, Darrel: 716 Montgomery St, San Francisco, CA 94111 415-433-1222
Tankersly, Paul: 420 Lexington Ave, New York, NY 10170 212-986-5680
Tannehill, Terry: 838 West End Ave #2B1, New York, NY 10025 212-316-1470
Tanner, Sharon: 1766 Mandeville Cyn Rd, Los Angeles, CA 90049 310-496-1501
Tanovitz, Ron: 2149 Lyon St #5, San Francisco, CA 94115 415-921-7140
Tanovitz, Ron: 6300 Estates Dr, Oakland, CA 94611 510-339-0182
Tanzey, Pam: 2763 College Blvd, Oceanside, CA 92056 760-724-3566
Tapscott, Linda: 35212 Cand Ct, Freemont, CA 94536 510-792-6362
Tarabay, Sharif: 4398 St Laurent St #305, Montreal, QU H2W 1Z5 514-842-4530
• **Taranovic, Lydia: pg 369** 280 Madison Ave #1110, New York, NY 10016 . . . . . **212-545-9155**
url: www.irmeliholmberg.com / fax: 212-545-9462
Tarantolla, Daniel: 3 Ernest Ct, Kings Park, NY 11754 516-544-4387
Targete: 60 E 42nd St, New York, NY 10165 212-867-8092
Tarleton, Suzanne: 1740 Stanford St, Santa Monica, CA 90404 310-859-7563
Tarlow, Phyllis: 131 Lawrence Pl, New Rochelle, NY 10801 914-235-9473
Tarner, J: 2638 49th Ave SW, Seattle, WA 98116 206-938-2347
Taroete, Jean: 60 E 42nd St, New York, NY 10165 212-867-8092

Tarr-Memmons, Tina: 145 Newbury St, Portland, ME 04104 ... 207-828-9454
- **Tarrish, Laura: pg 916** 11 S Lodge, Circus Rd, St John's Wood, London, UK NW8 9ER . **44207266585**
  e-mail: lauratarrish@earthlink.net / fax: 442072665485

Tasha Illustration & Design: 4855 Sisson Rd, Titusville, FL 32780 ... 407-843-7000
Tatum, Keith: 285 Alexander Alley, Columbus, OH 43206 ... 614-444-2845
Taugher, Larry: 227 Godfrey Rd, Weston, CT 06883 ... 203-222-8777
Taus, Sasha: 111 Kentucky Ave, San Luis Opispo_, CA 93401 ... 805-541-3155
Tauss, Herbert: South Mountain Pass, Garrison, NY 10524 ... 914-424-3765
Tauss, Marc: 484 W 43rd St #40H, New York, NY 10036 ... 212-410-2827
Tave, Sara: 28 Leigh Dr, Lakewood, NJ 08701 ... 908-367-7723
Tavonatti, Mia: 440 Bolero Way, Newport Beach, CA 92663 ... 949-673-0861
Tavshunsky, Alex: 765 Steeles Ave W #1406, Toronto, ON M2R 2S7 ... 416-663-8588
Taxali, Gary: 41 Union Square W #918, New York, NY 10003 ... 212-807-6627
Taylor, Alastair: 24 Watling St, Thaxted, Essex, UK CM6 2PJ ... 441371831126
Taylor, Barry: 17 Lascelles Blvd, Toronto, ON M4V 2B6 ... 416-481-9766
Taylor, BK: 24940 S Cromwell, Franklin, MI 48025 ... 248-414-5387
Taylor, Brian: 4753 S Park Ct, Woodbridge, VA 22193 ... 703-580-8221
Taylor, Bridget Starr: 9 Babbling Brook Ln, Suffern, NY 10901 ... 845-368-8606
Taylor, Bridget Starr: 675 Hudson St, New York, NY 10014 ... 212-924-9468
Taylor, C Winston: 17008 Lisette St, Granada Hills, CA 91344 ... 818-363-5761
- **Taylor, Dahl: pg 396** 194 Third Ave, New York, NY 10003 ... **212-475-0440**
  url: www.morgangaynin.com / fax: 212-353-8538

Taylor, Doug: PO Box 169, Guilford, NY 13780 ... 607-895-6062
Taylor, Jay: 21-16 28th St, Long Island City, NY 11105 ... 718-204-6184
- **Taylor, Joseph: pg 179** 420 Lexington Ave, New York, NY 10170 ... **212-986-5680**
  e-mail: mendolaart@aol.com / url: www.mendolaart.com / fax: 212-818-1246

Taylor, Karen: 4577 Apple Way, Boulder, CO 80301 ... 303-447-8737
Taylor, Katherine Lynn: 702 Albert St, Ottawa, ON K1R 6L4 ... 613-233-0655
Taylor, Ken: 1000 John R Rd #201, Troy, MI 48083 ... 248-583-6070
Taylor, Peter: 1559 Carletta Dr, Mississauga, ON L4X 1E2 ... 905-896-7307
Taylor, Terry: 24 Eldridge St, Port Chester, NY 10573 ... 914-937-7730
Tchalcovsky, Beny: 92 Piper Ln, Fairfax, CA 94930 ... 415-459-3414
Teach, Buzz Walker: 4848 Thor Way, Carmichael, CA 95608 ... 916-488-4392
Teague, Tom: 617 Hillcrest Drive SW, Vienna, VA 22180 ... 703-281-7036
Teare, Brad: 89 Fifth Ave #901, New York, NY 10003 ... 212-627-1554
Tedesco, Bob: 8 Payne Rd, Bethel, CT 06801 ... 203-531-8484
Tedesco, Michael: 120 Boerum Pl #1E, Brooklyn, NY 11201 ... 718-398-1770
Tedesco, Thomas: 24 Elizabeth St, Port Jervis, NY 12771 ... 914-856-8889
Tedford, Karla J: 125 CityCentre Drive, Cincinnati, OH 45216 ... 513-761-8200
Teich, David: 41 Tamara Dr, Roosevelt, NJ 08555 ... 609-448-5036
Teisher, Anne: 977 Via Del Monte, Palos Verdes, CA 90274 ... 310-375-0575
Tekarts-Technical Art Service: PO Box 2023, Ocean Bluff, MA 02065 ... 720-570-9106
Ten, Arnie: 37 Forbus St, Poughkeepsie, NY 12601 ... 914-485-8419
- **Tenenbaum, Karen: pg 356** 58 W 15th St, New York, NY 10011 ... **212-741-2539**
  url: www.jdedell.com or www.theispot.com or www.karentenenbaum.com
  fax: 212-741-4660

Tenga, Kathlyn: 25-05 Ditmars Blvd, Long Island City, NY 11105 ... 718-626-4344
Tenud, Tish: 447 Amhurst Circle, Folsom, CA 95630 ... 916-355-8511
Terezakis, Peter: 50 W 22nd St, New York, NY 10010 ... 212-929-8978
Ternay, Bill: 119 Birch Ave, Bala Cynwyd, PA 19004 ... 215-667-8626
Terreson, Jeffrey: 420 Lexington Ave, New York, NY 10170 ... 212-986-5680
Terreson, Jeffrey: 38 Westchester Ave, Pound Ridge, NY 10576 ... 914-764-5001
Terry, Will: 392 E 1075 N, Springville, UT 84663 ... 801-489-0879
- **Thacker, Kat: pg 365** 280 Madison Ave #1110, New York, NY 10016 ... **212-545-9155**
  url: www.irmeliholmberg.com / fax: 212-545-9462

Tharler, Gary: 1131 S Burnside Ave, Los Angeles, CA 90019 ... 213-857-0981
Tharp, Pepper: 6638 N 13th St, Phoenix, AZ 85014 ... 602-263-8990
Thatcher, Charles: 2820 Westshire Dr, Los Angeles, CA 90068 ... 323-467-3522
Thayer, Brett: 1983 Lake St Salt Lake City, UT 84105 ... 801-486-6954
The Big Pixel/Dougals Buchman: 3183 Airway Ave, Costa Mesa, CA 92626 ... 714-979-8001
- **Thelen, Mary: pg 282** 250 W 57th St #521, New York, NY 10107 ... **212-397-7330**
  San Francisco, CA: ... **415-788-8552**
  url: www.lindgrensmith.com

Thelen, Nick: 335 1/2 N Heliotrope, Los Angeles, CA 90004 ... 213-953-4707
Theodore, Jim: 5 W Main St, Westerville, OH 43081 ... 614-898-5316
- **Thermes, Jennifer: pg 531** 7 Washington St, Beverly, MA 01915 ... **978-921-0887**
  e-mail: leighton@leightonreps.com / url: www.leightonreps.com
  fax: 978-921-0223

Thewes Jr., Thomas: 1229 E Lincoln, Royal Oaks, MI 48067 ... 248-545-4053
Thewlis, Diana: 5755 San Juan Way, Pleasanton, CA 94566 ... 925-484-9777
Thiel, Libby: Rte 2 Box 181C Fenwick, Bryan's Road, MD 20616 ... 301-283-6347
Thien Do: 510 Stockton St #101, San Francisco, CA 94108 ... 415-982-4624
Thisdale, Francois: 4651 rue de Salaberry, Carignan, QU J3L 3P9 ... 514-477-4956
Thole, Cathleen: 353 W 53rd St #1W, New York, NY 10019 ... 212-682-2462
Thomas Harper Design: 9192 Russell Ave, Garden Grove, CA 92644 ... 714-721-4732
Thomas, Chris: 102 Sara Ave N, Spanish Fort, AL 36527 ... 334-626-9031
Thomas, Chris: 1101 Mill Hill Rd, Southport, CT 06490 ... 203-255-9620
Thomas, Fred W.: 2128 NW 197th, Shoreline, WA 98177 ... 206-546-5249
Thomas, George: 42 Merrell Ave #C14, Stamford, CT 06902 ... 203-359-9132
Thomas, Pat: 711 Carpenter, Oak Park, IL 60304 ... 708-383-8505
Thomas, Rene Tina: 708 Old Colony Rd, Midwest City, OK 73130 ... 405-733-4315
Thomas, Rod: 16 Grasmere Rd, Needham, MA 20194 ... 617-449-0480
Thomas, Scott: 20A Pimentel Ct #B, Novato, CA 94949 ... 415-382-3388
Thomas, Terrill: 4932 Charlene Circle #4, Huntington Beach, CA 92649 ... 714-840-2798
Thomas, Troy: 1247 Portage Ln, Woodstock, IL 60098 ... 815-338-9455
Thompson Brothers: 43 E 19th St, New York, NY 10003 ... 212-254-4996
Thompson Illustration, M Kathryn: 333 Cascade Dr, Fairfax, CA 94930 ... 415-459-8835
Thompson, Arthur: 39 Prospect Ave, Pompton Plains, NJ 07444 ... 914-928-5333
Thompson, Bill: 66 Fox Run, Southington, CT 06489 ... 860-621-5501
Thompson, Brian: 183 E Palm, Altadena, CA 91001 ... 818-798-5901
Thompson, Bryce: 14 Forrest Park Crescent, Thornhill, ON L3T 2M6 ... 416-419-9917
Thompson, Bryon: 6132 Bellingham Ln, Ft Wayne, IN 46835 ... 219-486-5941
Thompson, Darren: 130 Fodderstack Rd, Washington, VA 22747 ... 540-675-2355
Thompson, Ellen: 2149 Lyon St #5, San Francisco, CA 94115 ... 415-921-7140
Thompson, Emily: 5440 Old Easton Rd, Doylestown, PA 18901 ... 215-766-3892
Thompson, George: 5440 Old Easton Rd, Doylestown, PA 18901 ... 215-766-3892
Thompson, Jim: PO Box 388, Talent, UT 97540 ... 541-488-9360
Thompson, John: 1225 W 4th St, Waterloo, IA 50702 ... 319-234-2089
Thompson, John M: 206 Haddonfield Dr, Dewitt, NY 13214 ... 315-449-1241
Thompson, L C: 9629 Dove Hollow Ln, Glen Allen, VA 23060 ... 804-755-7455
Thompson, M Kathryn: PO Box 307, Ross, CA 94957 ... 415-456-7711
- **Thompson, Marina: pg 819** ... **781-581-1725**
  e-mail: marinath@aol.com / url: www.marinathompson.com / fax: 781-581-5808

Thompson, Nick: PO Box 465, Belmont, MA 02178 ... 617-623-4366
Thompson, Richard: 9309 Judge Pl, Gaithersburg, MD 20879 ... 301-948-3732
Thompson, Stephen: 612 N 2nd St, St Louis, MO 63102 ... 314-781-7377
Thompson, Thierry: 420 Lexington Ave, New York, NY 10170 ... 212-986-5680
Thomson, Bill: 66 Fox Run Dr, Southington, CT 06489 ... 860-621-2764
Thomson, Pamela: 2915 Redhill Ave B-201A, Costa Mesa, CA 92626 ... 714-557-6274
Thomssen, Kate: 2532 Kipling Ave S, Minneapolis, MN 55416 ... 612-926-5585
Thon, Bud: 410 View Park Ct, Mill Valley, CA 94941 ... 415-389-9220
Thoner, Dan: 3485 Copley Ave, San Diego, CA 92116 ... 619-282-0031
Thonnessen, Sabina: 141 Wooster St #3B, New York, NY 10012 ... 212-254-7436
Thor, Leifur: 1020 Aoloa Pl #106B, Kailua, HI 96734 ... 877-333-3742
Thorn, Dick: 353 W 53rd St #1W, New York, NY 10019 ... 212-682-2462
Thornburgh, Bethann: 250 W 57th St #521, New York, NY 10107 ... 212-397-7330
- **Thornley, Blair: pg 2,3,526,527** 192 Southville Rd, Southborough, MA 01772 . **508-872-4549**
  e-mail: laughstoc@aol.com / url: www.laughing-stock.com or www.blairthornley.com
  fax: 508-480-9221

Thornton, Brek: 15433 Country Club Dr Apt A306, Mill Creek, WA 98012 ... 206-338-2513
Thornton, Jeremy: 389 Ethel Ave, Mill Valley, CA 94941 ... 415-388-7240
Thornton, Michael: 7844 Starward Dr, Dublin, CA 94568 ... 510-828-5032
Thornton, Sandra: 3129 Root Ave, Carmichael, CA 95608 ... 916-489-2877
Thorpe, Eric: 106 N Chester Ave, Pasadena, CA 91106 ... 818-792-5708
Threinen, Cher: 4646 Narragansett Ave, San Diego, CA 92107 ... 619-226-6050
Thurston, Ron: 211 Ft Pitt Blvd, Pittsburgh, PA 15222 ... 412-766-3810
- **Thurston, Russell: pg 539** 300 N State St #3302, Chicago, IL 60610 ... **773-792-9169**
  e-mail: ewinman@aol.com / fax: 773-792-9189

Tiani, Alex: 227 Godfrey Rd, Weston, CT 06883 ... 203-222-8777
Tibbetts, Christopher: 1704 Bush Ave, St Paul, MN 55106 ... 651-776-5300
Tibbles, Jean Paul: 58 W 40th St 6th Fl, New York, NY 10018 ... 212-682-1490
Ticker Dèsign, Shane: 8510 23rd Ave NE #4, Seattle, WA 98115 ... 206-301-0575
Tieber, Simone: 161 Hudson St #550, New York, NY 10013 ... 212-503-5074
Tien, Chung Ming: 1 Pocahontas Dr, Middletown, RI 02840 ... 401-849-7608
Tierney, John P: 659 Churchill St, Pittsfield, MA 01201 ... 413-442-8428
Tiessen, Ken: 1643 W Swallow Rd, Ft Collins, CO 80526 ... 970-223-3027
Tilden, David Anders: End of Wirt Way Box 2191, Duxbury, MA 02332 ... 617-934-0345
Tillander, Michelle: 3530 Bapaume Ave, Norfolk, VA 23509 ... 804-857-7269
Tillery, Angelo: 1449 Longfellow Ave, Bronx, NY 10459 ... 718-617-2907
- **Tillinghast, David: pg 480,481** 3238 Griffith Park Blvd, Los Angeles, CA 90027 **323-664-0997**
  url: www.davidtillinghast.com / fax: 323-664-0999
  Pier 33 North, San Francisco, CA 94111 ... **415-956-4750**
  e-mail: cgr@slip.net / url: www.coreygrahamreps.com

Tillofson, Katherine: 1407 Cole St, San Francisco, CA 94117 ... 415-664-0331
Tilney, Barnes: 473 4th St #2L, Brooklyn, NY 11215 ... 718-768-8312
Timmes, Patrick: 5 Oakmere Dr, Baldwin, NY 11510 ... 516-377-8907
Timmons, Bonnie: 18 McKinley St, Rowayton, CT 06853 ... 203-866-3734
Ting, Bob: 3301 Bay Ct, Belmont, CA 94002 ... 415-592-5247
Tink a Sloss: 1424 La Positas Plaza, Santa Barbara, CA 93105 ... 805-682-6775
Tinkelman, Murray: 728 Castro St, San Francisco, CA 94114 ... 415-441-4384
Tinney, Robert: PO Box 778, 331 E Carriere St, Washington, LA 70589 ... 337-826-3003
Tinoco, Roberto: 36738 Munyan St, Newark, CA 94560 ... 510-797-4574
Tinsley, Larry: 226 Goldengate Dr, Verona, PA 15147 ... 412-795-3047
Tipton, Beth: 6164 Westminster Pl, St Louis, MO 63112 ... 314-727-5657
Tiritilli, Jerry: 3939 N Hamlin Ave, Chicago, IL 60618 ... 773-267-4955
Tirolese, Ana: 268 Grosvenor St #F128, London, ON N6A 4V2 ... 519-646-6170
Tischenkov, Oleg: Gazetniy pereulok h3 sroenie 2, Moscow, RU 103 009 ... 7-0952298833
Tishman, Jill Rosean: PO Box 1592, Sante Fe, NM 87504 ... 505-986-9987
Tito, Marina: 8213 Severn Dr #A, Boca Raton, FL 33433 ...
Titonis, George: 217 Dan Dr, Pittsburgh, PA 15216 ... 412-343-4529
- **Titus Illustration, Dave: pg 628,629** PO Box 7395, Mammoth Lakes, CA 93546 ... **760-935-4455**
  e-mail: dtitus@qnet.com / url: www.davetitus.com

Tivadar, Bote: New York, NY ... 212-643-0896
Toal, Mark: 138 Stanford Shopping Ctr, Palo Alto, CA 94303 ... 415-326-7687
Tobiassen, Kris: 132 Thompson St #37, New York, NY 10012 ... 212-388-0870
Tocchet, Mark: 225 Weldy Ave, Oreland, PA 19075 ... 215-885-1292
Tod-Kat Studios: 353 W 53rd St #1W, New York, NY 10019 ... 212-682-2462
Todd, Barbara: 231 Judd Rd, Easton, CT 06612 ... 203-445-1511
- **Todd, Chuck: pg 867** 4031 Susanwood Dr, Concord, CA 94521 ... **925-691-8541**
  url: www.chucktodd.com
- **Todd, Mark: pg 670** 123 Prospect Pl #1, Brooklyn, NY 11217 ... **718-783-1488**
  e-mail: funchicken@earthlink.net / url: www.mtodd.net / fax: 718-783-9590
- **Toelke, Cathleen: pg 600,601** PO Box 487, Rhinebeck, NY 12572 ... **845-876-8776**
  url: www.cathleentoelke.com / fax: 845-758-2784

Tofanelli, Mike: 9514 Village Tree Dr, Elk Grove, CA 95758 ... 916-683-8224
Tokach, Michele: PO Box 1241, Conyngham, PA 18219 ... 717-455-2144
Tokyo Design Center: 703 Market St #252, San Francisco, CA 94103 ... 415-543-4886
Tokyo, Max: 236 W 26th St #805, New York, NY 10001 ... 212-463-7025
Tollison, Ray: 2820 Paddington Rd, Ft Collins, CO 80525 ... 970-482-5540
Tom, Jack: 135 Lazy Brook Rd, Monroe, CT 06468 ... 203-452-0889
Tom-Conway, Ket: 607 Maple St, Aptos, CA 95003 ... 831-684-2378
Tomasulo, Patrick: 76 Howard St, Dumont, NJ 07628 ... 201-385-4350
Tomek, Tom: 943 N Winchester Ave, Chicago, IL 60622 ... 773-227-7845
Tomine, Adrian: PO Box 4025, Berkeley, CA 94704 ...
Tomlin, Lara: 108 E 35th St, New York, NY 10016 ... 212-889-3337
Tomlinson, Richard: 319 E 24th St, New York, NY 10010 ... 212-685-0552
Toney, Allen: 3064 Wallace Cir, Huntington, WV 25705 ... 304-523-7744
Tong, Paul: 2312 Roosevelt Ave, Berkeley, CA 94703 ... 510-644-0596
Tonkin, Thomas: 353 W 53rd St #1W, New York, NY 10019 ... 212-682-2462
Toolbox: 420 Lexington Ave, New York, NY 10170 ... 212-986-5680
- **Toomer, George: pg 632,633** 3923 Cole Ave, Dallas, TX 75204 ... **214-522-1171**
  fax: 214-528-3588

Tooney, Ellen: 1111 Talbot Ave, Albany, CA 94708 ... 510-526-0737
Torline, Kevin: 2233 Kemper Ln, Cincinnati, OH 45206 ... 513-861-1400
Torluemke, Tom: 3319 Orchard Dr, Hammond, IN 46323 ... 312-939-3883
Torp, Cynthia: 7118 Upper River Rd, Prospect, KY 40059 ... 502-228-9427
Torque: 309 N Justine, Chicago, IL 60607 ... 312-421-7858
Torres, Carlos: 60 Hagen Ave, N Tonawanda, NY 14120 ... 716-695-9440

Torres, Daniel: 11 Kings Ridge Rd, Long Valley, NJ 07853 908-813-8718
Torres, Jordy: 43 E 19th St, New York, NY 10003 212-254-4996
Torres, Leyla: 14 N Henry St, Brooklyn, NY 11222 718-389-6101
Torrisi, Gary: 50 Fuller Brook Rd, Wellesley, MA 02482 781-235-8658
Torroll, Cynthia Lund: 3920 S Greenlawn Terr, New Berlin, WI 53151 414-221-4540
Torzecka, Marlena: 278 Hamilton Ave, Princeton, NJ 08540. 609-252-9405
Tosch, Jamie R: 2801 Manlove Rd #76, Sacramento, CA 95826 916-369-2106
Tosh, Katrina: 6240 Ardis Dr, Winnemucca, NV 89445 775-625-1954
Touzie, Miriam: 9 E 32nd St #6A, New York, NY 10016 212-532-6956
Tow, David: 851 Thompson St, Glastonbury, CT 06033 860-659-1147
Towle, Wendy: 15318 Mack Ave, Grosspoint Park, MI 48230. 313-884-3332
Towler, Martha: 34-30 78 St #1J, Jackson Heights, NY 11372 718-651-1549
Towler, Matthew: 277 Lake Ave, Worcester, MA 01604 508-791-2416
Towner, Bob: 5855 Green Valley Cir #308, Culver City, CA 90230 310-642-2721
Townswick, Gary: 7339 S 71 Avenue, Omaha, NE 68157 402-593-7115
Toyama, Ken: 94 Natoma St #233, San Francisco, CA 94105 415-442-1822
Trachok, Cathryne: 2080 Coombsville, Napa, CA 9458 707-252-0728
Tracy, Donna: 2011 Vista Cerro Gordo St, Los Angeles, CA 90039. 213-666-4087
Tracy, Joe: 1320 Alessandro Dr, Newberry Park, CA 91320 805-375-0905
Tracy, Stan: 484 W 43rd St #32K, New York, NY 10036 212-967-1665
Trainor, Sandra: 33 Montvale Ave #4, Woburn, MA 01801. 617-933-6196
Tran, Vi: 2957 Ribillard Crescent, Windsor, ON N8W 5L2 519-969-0787
Traub, Paul: PO Box 38173, Greensboro, NC 27438. 910-288-0527
Travis-Keene, Gayle: 334 Swinton Way, Severne Park, MD 21146 410-647-7220
• **Traynor, Elizabeth: pg 122,123** 108 E 35th St, New York, NY 10016 . . . . . **212-889-3337**
e-mail: gerald@rappart.com / url: www.theispot.com/rep/rapp / fax: 212-889-3341
Treadway, Todd: 1225 W 4th St, Waterloo, IA 50702 319-234-2089
Treatner, Meryl: 239 Monroe St, Philadelphia, PA 19147 215-627-2297
Trefry, Charlie: 5220 E Colonial Dr, Orlando, FL 32807 407-249-7949
Tremblay, Sylvain: 460 Saint Catherine West St bur 300, Montréal, QU H3B 1A7 514-393-0844
Tremlett, Mark: 133 N Montclair Ave, Dallas, TX 75208 214-943-2569
Trenc, Milan: 99 Perry St, New York, NY 10014 212-924-6768
Trenholm, Zach: 1466 40th Ave, San Francisco, CA 94122 415-753-6020
Trillion Inc/Anderson: 5989 Tahor Dr SE, Grand Rapids, MI 49546 616-940-9944
Trinh, John: 9221 E Longden Ave, Temple City, CA 91780 626-287-5989
Troll, Ray: 5 Creek St, Ketchikan, AK 99901 907-225-5954
Troller, Michael Design: 201 Gates St., San Francisco, CA 94110 415-206-0326
• **Tronc, Jo: pg 286** 731 N 24th St, Philadelphia, PA 19130 . . . . . **215-232-6666**
url: www.deborahwolfeltd.com / fax: 215-232-6585
Trook, Jim: 17 White St #5C, New York, NY 10013 212-219-3854
Trostli, Elisabeth: 19 Lafayette St, Pawtucket, RI 02860 401-351-3429
Trow Bridge, David: 918 NW Market St, Seattle, WA 98107. 206-706-9204
• **TRUE: pg 871** 424 Macon St #1, Brooklyn, NY 11233. . . . . **718-919-8925**
e-mail: true@hgx.com / url: www.hgx.com / fax: 718-919-8223
Trusilo, Jim: 309 Walnut Rd, Pittsburgh, PA 15202. 412-761-5666
Truxaw, Dick: 6404 W 125th St, Shawnee Mission, KS 66209. 913-383-1555
Tsinganos, Jim: 58 W 15th St, New York, NY 10011 212-741-2539
Tsuchiya Sloneker Comms: 423 Washington #500, San Francisco, CA 94111. . . . 415-986-5365
Tsui, George & Selena: 1772 Hendrickson Ave, N Merrick, NY 11566 516-223-8474
• **Tsukushi: pg 662,663** 60 E 42nd St #1146, New York, NY 10165. . . . . **212-953-7088**
Tucci, Dominick: 31 Valley Dr W, Glenwood, NJ 07418 973-764-5583
Tuchman, Mark: 145 Luquer St, Brooklyn, NY 11231 718-222-1281
Tuchman, Michael A: 1742 Lerner Ln, Santa Ana, CA 92705 949-721-3334
Tucker, Ezra: PO Box 1611, Monument, CO 80132. 719-487-0648
Tucker, Ezra: 728 Castro St, San Francisco, CA 94114. 415-441-4384
• **Tucker, Greg: pg 784** 1915 Lakeview SW, Albuquerque, NM 87105 . . . . . **505-873-3727**
e-mail: gregtuckerillus@aol.com
Tucker, Tom: 421 Nevada Dr, Erie, PA 16505. 814-459-5053
Tuke, Scott W: 1657 N California Blvd #207, Walnut Creek, CA 94596. 510-930-7576
Tull, Bobbi: 6103 Beachway Dr, Falls Church, VA 22041. 703-998-9292
Tull, Jeff: 3301A S Jefferson Ave, St Louis, MO 63118 314-773-2600
Tunstull, Glenn: 201 Clinton Ave #14G, Brooklyn, NY 11205. 718-834-8529
Turchette, Peggy: 17 Follen St #2F, Boston, MA 02116 617-536-3372
Turchyn, Sandie: 156 N Hamel Dr, Beverly Hills, CA 90211 310-275-8877
Turgeon, Jim: 2031 Holly Dr, Prescott, AZ 86305 520-708-9446
Turgeon, Pol: 250 W 57th St #521, New York, NY 10107 212-397-7330
Turk, Stephen: 927 Westbourne Dr, Los Angeles, CA 90069 310-788-0682
Turk, Stephen: 3525 Mockingbird Ln, Dallas, TX 75205 214-521-5156
Turk, Tasha: 3737 E Turney #126, Phoenix, AZ 85018. 602-954-8116
Turner, Clay: 58 W 40th St 6th Fl, New York, NY 10018 212-682-1490
Turner, Cynthia: 3 Old Miller Pl, Santa Rosa Bch, FL 32459. 904-231-4112
Turner, Dave: 800 Clearview Dr, Nashville, TN 37205 423-297-5377
Turner, Dona: 5139 Coronado Avenue, Oakland, CA 94618 510-547-8832
Turner, Jeanne: 809 Fulton Ave, Falls Church, VA 22046 703-237-1108
Turner, John: 201 Forest Dr, Graham, NC 27253 910-227-1035
Turner, Patrick: 117-1720 Southmore Crescent, South Surrey, BC V4A 6E3. 604-536-9776
Turner, Ray: 221 W Maple, Monrovia, CA 91016 818-303-4784
Turner, Ray: Pier 33 North, San Francisco, CA 94111 415-956-4750
Turner, Shawn: 3220 Somerset Rd, Sacramento, CA 95864 916-481-8923
Turner, Tracy: 918 Sheridan Rd, Glencoe, IL 60022. 312-663-5300
Turtel, Jason: 574 Leheigh Ln, Woodmere, NY 11598. 516-569-5437
Tusa, Tricia: 619 Asbury St, Houston, TX 77007. 713-864-8864
Tuscan, Christopher: 2144 W Concord Pl, Chicago, IL 60647 773-278-3320
• **Tuschman, Richard: pg 334** 58 W 15th St, New York, NY 10011 . . . . . **212-741-2539**
url: www.richardtuschman.com or www.jdedell.com or www.theispot.com / fax: 212-741-4660
• **Tuson, Lorraine: pg 519** Dayton, OH **937-433-8383**
New York **212-966-3604**
San Francisco **415-285-3808**
url: www.scotthull.com / fax: 937-433-0434
Tuttle, Jean: 78 Harlan St, Manchester, CT 06040 800-816-0460
Tuveson, Christine: 1119 Hi- Point St, Los Angeles, CA 90035. 323-936-5851
Twinem, Neecy: 9 Babbling Brook Ln, Suffern, NY 10901 845-368-8606
Twohy, Tom: 1980 Park Ave #23, San Jose, CA 95126. 408-261-8431
Tylden-Wright, Jenny: 11 Kings Ridge Rd, Long Valley, NJ 07853 908-813-8718
Tyler, Barbara: 60 E 42nd St #1146, New York, NY 10165. 212-953-7088
Tyler, Craig: 163 Bard Ln, Ventura, CA 93001 805-653-0384
Tyler, Wayne R: 3035 E Middleton Way, Salt Lake City, UT 84124. 801-272-9320
Tyminski, Lori: 830 N Niagra St, Burbank, CA 91505 818-846-1613
Tyrrell, Susan: 124 Mica Ln, Wellesley, MA 02181 617-431-8686
Tysko, Lisa: 361 Nassau, Princeton, NJ 08540. 609-921-3610
Tyson, Abbey: 27 Laurel Mountain Dr, Whately, MA 01093. 413-665-9268
Tzur, Zahava: 24 E 23rd St 3rd Fl, New York, NY 10010. 212-420-0656

U

Uceda, Santiago: 1010 W MacArthur Blvd #140, Santiago, CA 92707 714-545-7816
Udave, Consuelo: 3203 19th St, Bremerton, WA 98312 360-792-1017
Ugodnikova, Natalya: 5802 Spring Rock Cir, Columbus, OH 43229. 614-895-9637
• **Uhl Studios/David Uhl: pg 851** 1261 Delaware St, Denver, CO 80204. . . . . **303-534-2054**
e-mail: daviduhl@sni.net / url: www.uhlstudios.com or www.theispot.com/artist/duhl
fax: 303-534-2056
Uiss, Troy: 343 4th Ave #201, San Diego, CA 92101. 619-233-9633
Ulan, Helen Cerra: 4227 San Juan Dr, Fairfax, VA 22030 703-691-0474
• **Ulrich, George: pg 507** 666 Greenwich St #860, New York, NY 10014. . . . . **212-675-5719**
e-mail: harriet@hkportfolio.com / url: www.hkportfolio.com / fax: 212-675-6341
Ulrich, Mike: 1541 Bitterroot Dr, Twin Falls, ID 83301 208-734-2120
Ulrich, Robert: 300 Congress St, Neenah, WI 54956. 920-722-8809
Ulriksen, Mark: 455 W 23rd St #8D, New York, NY 10011. 212-366-1893
Ulriksen, Mark: 608 York St, San Francisco, CA 94110 415-641-1285
Ulve, Kirsten: 611 Broadway #426, New York, NY 10012. 212-533-1105
Ulve, Kirsten: 837 W Grand Ave 3rd Fl, Chicago, IL 60622 . . . . . 312 633-0500
Uman, Michael: 1781 Riverside Dr #4C, New York, NY 10034 212-304-0756
Undemehr, Linda: 12199 S Zion Rd, Lowell, AR 72745 501-751-6269
Underhill, Gary R: 24-26 Church St, Montclair, NJ 07042 201-783-1155
Unger, Elaine: 23650 Via Beguine, Valencia, CA 91355. 661-259-2174
Unger, Joe: 17120 NE 96th St, Redmond, WA 98052 206-883-1419
Unger, Judy: PO Box 421443, San Francisco, CA 94142 415-647-5660
Unger, Judy: 19600 Ballinger, Northridge, CA 91324 818-701-9030
United Illustrators: 636 Broadway #1218, New York, NY 10012 212-505-8713
• **Unruh, Rick: pg 909** 395 Broadway #3A, New York, NY 10013 . . . . . **212-966-5569**
e-mail: rickunruh@aol.com / fax: 212-966-3117
Uram, Lauren: 194 Third Ave, New York, NY 10003 212-475-0440
Urbanovic, Jackie: 450 E Foothill Blvd, Glendora, CA 91741. . . . .
Uriss, Mike: 1421 Old Ballard Rd, Charlottesville, VA 22901 804-296-5719
Ursino, John: 2 Corcoran Rd, Burlington, MA 01803. 781-272-1540
Ursyn-Czarnecka, Anna: 1117 Cranford Pl, Greeley, CO 80631. 303-353-4887
Utley, Tom: 490 Rockside Rd, Cleveland, OH 44131. 216-661-4222
Utterback, Bill: 6105 Kingston Ave, Lisle, IL 60532 630-852-9764
Uyehara, Elizabeth: 1020 Westchester Pl, Los Angeles, CA 90019 213-731-4168
Uzilevsky, Marcus: 23 Park St, Woodacre, CA 94973. 415-488-9194

V

Vacanti, Sam: 352 Oakvale Blvd, Tonawanda, NY 14223. 716-837-0989
Vaccaro, Lou: 99 Park Ave #210A, New York, NY 10016 800-398-9544
• **Vaccaro, Victor: pg 434** 227 Godfrey Rd, Weston, CT 06883. . . . . **203-222-8777**
e-mail: jp@artcoreps.com / url: www.artcoreps.com / fax: 203-454-9940
232 Madison Ave #512, New York, NY 10016. . . . . **212-889-8777**
e-mail: gt@artcoreps.com / url: www.artcoreps.com / fax: 212-447-1475
Vahrameev, Vadim: 570 26th Ave #3, San Francisco, CA 94121 415-751-5471
Vail, Baker: 1749 Narrowa Hill Rd, Upper Black Eddy, PA 18972 610-982-9405
Vainisi, Jenny: 58 Middagh St #16, Brooklyn, NY 11201. 718-858-4914
Vakser, Julia: 1150 Harvard Pl, Fort Lee, NJ 07024 201-886-7140
Valenti, Lisa: 964 PelhamDale Ave, Pelham, NY 10803. 914-738-1995
• **Valero, Art: pg 531** 7 Washington St, Beverly, MA 01915 . . . . . **978-921-0887**
e-mail: leighton@leightonreps.com / url: www.leightonreps.com
fax: 978-921-0223
Valero, Wayne: 11244 Corona Dr, North Glen, CO 80233 970-452-3468
Valesco, Frances: 4701 San Leandro St #38, Oakland, CA 94601 415-647-5607
Valk, Tinam: 280 Madison Ave #1110, New York, NY 10016 212-545-9155
Valla, Victor: 19 Prospect St, Falls Village, CT 06031 860-824-5014
Valle, Robin: 513-1/2 N Spaulding Ave, Los Angeles, CA 90036 213-653-1238
Vallecoccia Illustration, Bart: 164 Manitoba St, Toronto, ON M8Y 1E3. 416-255-7499
Valley, Gregg: 144 Jonathan Dr, McMurray, PA 15317. 724-941-4662
Valley, Gregg: 310 W 97th St #902, New York, NY 10025 212-243-5888
Valtiekunas, Vince M: 5350 W Hill Ave #44, Montreal, QU H4V 2W9. 514-482-2356
Van Der Palen, Erik: 1959 Juanita Ave, Pasadena, CA 91104. 626-797-9804
• **Van Dusen, Chris: pg 692,693** 37 Pearl St, Camden, ME 04843. . . . . **207-236-2961**
e-mail: vandusen@mint.net / url: www.chrisvandusen.com / fax: 207-236-2961
• **Van Es, Chris: pg 307** 731 N 24th St, Philadelphia, PA 19130 . . . . . **215-232-6666**
url: www.deborahwolfeltd.com / fax: 215-232-6585
Van Horn, Michael: 741 Milan Hill Rd, Red Hook, NY 12571. 914-758-8407
Van Kanegan, Jeff: PO Box 60-B RR1, Camp Point, IL 62320. 217-455-4171
Van Nguyen, Quan: 1460 Tully Rd #603, San Jose, CA 95122 408-289-9720
Van Nostrand, Kirk: 7215 37th Ave #2G, Flushing, NY 11372. 718-939-6803
Van Overloop, Chris J: 1 Shoal Ct #75, Sacramento, CA 95813 916-421-2983
Van Ryzin, Peter: 60 E 42nd St, New York, NY 10165. 212-867-8092
Van Schelt, Perry L: 4495 Balsam Ave, Salt Lake City, UT 84123 801-266-7097
van Wyk, Rupert: 455 W 23rd St #8D, New York, NY 10011. 212-366-1893
Vance Wright Adams & Assocs: 930 North Lincoln, Pittsburgh, PA 15233. 412-322-1800
Vander Houwen, Greg: PO Box 498, Issaquah, WA 98027 206-999-2584
Vanderbeek, Don: 68 E Franklin St, Dayton, OH 45459 937-433-8383
VanDerBos, Joe: P.O. Box 2299, Guerneville, CA 95446. 707-869-1414
Vanderkarr, Andrew: 1008 Rotherham Dr, Antioch, CA 94509. 925-691-6280
• **Vanderstelt, Jerry: pg 372,373** 89 Fifth Ave #901, New York, NY 10003 . . . . . **212-627-1554**
e-mail: artworksillustration@earthlink.net / url: www.artworksillustration.com
fax: 212-627-1719
Vandervoort, Gene: 3201 S Ramona Dr, Santa Ana, CA 92707. 714-549-3194
Vandruff, Marshall: 24656 Via Carlos, Laguna Niguel, CA 91103 949-360-9300
• **Vangsgard, Amy: pg 854** 517 N Beachwood Dr, Los Angeles, CA 90004 . . . . . **323-461-3094**
e-mail: amyvangsgard@aol.com@ / url: www.theispot.com/artist/vangsgard
Vanha-Aho, Hannele: 280 Madison Ave #1110, New York, NY 10016. 212-545-9155
VanLeeuwen, Terrel: 14257 Edson Rd, Poplar Grove, IL 61065. 815-765-3834
VanMil, Al: 12 Lang Rd, Thornhil, ON L3T 7E7 905-731-3627
Vann, Bill: 1706 S 8th St, St Louis, MO 63104 314-231-2322
Vann, Bill: 420 Lexington Ave, New York, NY 10170 212-986-5680
Vann, Robert: PO Box 952344, Lake Mary, FL 32795. 407-330-5230

W

ILLUSTRATORS

Warnick, Elsa: 636 NW 20th Ave #7, Portland, OR 97209 503-228-2659
Warren, Jim: 11 Kings Ridge Rd, Long Valley, NJ 07853 908-813-8718
Warren, Kirk: 83 Walnut Ave, Corte Madera, CA 94925 415-924-7881
Warren, Shari: 127 Bonita Ave, Redwood City, CA 94061 650-592-3395
Warren, Valerie: 14 E 4th St #1103, New York, NY 10012 212-505-5366
Warrender, Patrice M: 2685 Burnside Rd, Sebastopol, CA 95472 800-892-3325
Warshaw Blumenthal: 104 E 40th St #201, New York, NY 10016 212-867-4225
Warshaw, Andrea: 104 E 40th St #207, New York, NY 10016 212-867-4225
Washington, Romeo: 368 Bradford, San Francisco, CA 94110 415-821-7826
Wass, Chip: 180 Varick St 8th Fl, New York, NY 10014 212-741-2550
Wasserman, Amy L: 6 Country Ln, Pelham, MA 01002 413-253-4664
Wasserman, Amy L: 420 Lexington Ave, New York, NY 10170 212-986-5680
Wasserman, Randie: 15 Sulky Cir, E Hampton, NY 11937 516-324-7186
Wassink-Ackison, Wendy: 2233 Kemper Ln, Cincinnati, OH 45206 513-861-1400
Wasson, Cameron: 16 Phaedra, Laguna Niguel, CA 92677 949-495-3664
Watanabe, Kaori: 310 E 23rd St, New York, NY 10010 212-353-3197
Watanabe, Tomoko: 1285 Cresthaven Dr, Pasadena, CA 91105 213-344-9612
Waterhouse, Charles: 67 Dartmouth St, Edison, NJ 08837 908-738-1804
Waters Art Studio: 1820 E Garry St #207, Santa Ana, CA 92705 714-250-4466
Waters, Julian: 23707 Woodfield Rd, Gaithersburg, MD 20882 301-253-3422
• **Waters, Susy Pilgrim: pg 407** 6 Parker Road Arlington, MA 02474 **781-641-2787**
e-mail: info@lillarogers.com / url: lillarogers.com
Watford, Wayne: 612 N 2nd St, St Louis, MO 63102 314-781-7377
• **Watkins, Jane: pg 489** 455 W 23rd St #8D, New York, NY 10011 **212-366-1893**
e-mail: sally@theartworksinc.com / url: www.theartworksinc.com
fax: 212-604-9643
Watkins, Leslie: 25 Grove St #3, New York, NY 10014 212-989-2616
Watkins, Scott: 4340 Yorkshire Ct, Loganville, GA 30052 770-466-6510
Watkinson, Brent: 58 W 40th St 6th Fl, New York, NY 10018 212-682-1490
• **Watson, Esther Pearl: pg 671** 123 Prospect Pl #1, Brooklyn, NY 11217 **718-783-1488**
url: www.estherwatson.com / fax: 718-783-9590
Watson, Joseph: 2538 Sundial Dr #E, Chino Hills, CA 91709 909-606-1409
Watson, Karen: 14 Blueberry Ln, Lexington, MA 02173 617-674-1136
Watson, Neil: 32 W 40th St #2 South, New York, NY 10018 212-575-6887
Watson, Paul: 614 Manning Ave, Toronto, ON M6G 2V9 416-535-2648
Watson, Richard Jesse: 2305 Ivy St, Port Townsend, WA 98368 360-385-7805
Watt, Denise: 253 W 72nd St #1706, New York, NY 10023 212-595-4957
Wattenmaker, Pamela Drury: 17 S Palomar Dr, Redwood City, CA 94062 650-368-7878
Watts, David: 465 Northridge Dr, Boone, NC 28607 828-265-1936
Watts, Jeff & Robert: 1906 Avocado Ranch Rd, El Cajon, CA 92019 619-447-1419
Watts, Lee: 656 N 56th St, Omaha, NE 68132 402-551-9105
• **Watts, Mark: pg 761** 2004 Par Dr, Doylestown, PA 18901 **215-343-8490**
e-mail: wattsart@aol.com / url: www.wattsart.com / fax: 215-343-8717
Watts, Sharon: 201 Eastern Pkwy, Brooklyn, NY 11238 718-398-0451
Watts, Stan: 353 W 53rd St #1W, New York, NY 10019 212-682-2462
Wax, Wendy: 322 E 55th St #2A, New York, NY 10022 212-371-6156
• **Waxberg, Cecilia: pg 509** 310 W 97th St #902, New York, NY 10025 **212-243-5888**
e-mail: lori@lorinowicki.com / url: www.lorinowicki.com / fax: 212-243-5955
Waxham, Taunya Tae: 116 S Mason St, Smithfield, VA 23430 757-357-0442
• **Way, James: pg 238,239** Chicago, IL **312-364-0244**
London **011-44-207-636-1064**
Los Angeles, CA **323-874-5700**
Washington, DC **410-349-8669**
New York, NY **212-333-2551**
url: www.shannonassociates.com
Wayman, Leo: PO Box 1214, Gresham, OR 97030 503-267-4215
Weast, Jonathan: 10401 Georgetown Dr, Rancho Cordova, CA 95670 916-638-4119
Weaver, Carol Maria: 70 W 95th St #21C, New York, NY 10025 212-864-2394
Weaver, Michael: 2927 W 43rd Ave, Kansas City, KS 66103 913-432-5078
Weaver, Mike: 1505 Vott Dr, West Bend, WI 53095 262-335-0868
Webb, David: 2100 Morris Ave, Birmingham, AL 35203 205-458-9348
Webb, Lisa: 110 Habersham Dr, Athens, GA 30606 706-549-6711
Webb, Lizanne E: 1374 Midland Ave #610, Bronxville, NY 17008 914-237-3080
Webb, Quentin: 99 Park Ave #210A, New York, NY 10016 800-398-9544
Webber, Helen: 14 Commercial Blvd #101, Novato, CA 94949 415-883-6604
Webber, Warren: 559 Dutch Valley Rd, Atlanta, GA 30324 404-881-6627
Weber, Joan: 1474 Westerly Terrace, Los Angeles, CA 90026 323-662-9300
Weber, John: 3637 Ridgewood Dr, Hilliard, OH 43026 614-777-0631
Weber, Mark: 92 Five Crown Royal, Marlton, NJ 08053 856-985-0008
Weber, Rachel: 3240 Lyndale Ave S, Minneapolis, MN 55408 612-824-1513
Weber, Richard L: 312 Glen Leven Ct, Schaumburg, IL 60194 847-798-7946
Webster & Assocs, John: 1445 Fern Pl, Vista, CA 92083 619-945-6576
Wedman, Belgin: 1611 Lookout Dr, Agoura Hills, CA 91301 818-707-2165
Weeb, Herman: 2372 Rosemont, Montreal, QU H2G 1V1 514-271-4321
Weed, Greg: PO Box 396, Bloomfield Hills, MI 48303 313-460-2451
Weeks, Brenda: 35 Jane St #15, Toronto, ON M6S 3Y3 416-766-2942
• **Weems, Alexandra: pg 354** 58 W 15th St, New York, NY 10011 **212-741-2539**
url: www.jdedell.com or www.theispot.com / fax: 212-741-4660
Wegner, Brad: 333 Briarwood Dr, Winter Park, FL 32789 407-628-9875
Wehrman, Vicki: PO Box 146, East Bloomfield, NY 14443 716-657-7910
Wehrstein, David: 20 W Hubbard St #3E, Chicago, IL 60610 312-222-1361
Weiland, Garison: 19 Barry Place, Falmouth, MA 02540 508-540-2551
Weilbrenner, Johanne: 5158 rue Chabot, Montréal, QU H2H 1Y8 514-525-6967
Weiller, Raoul: 217 Hanover St #8, Annapolis, MD 21401 410-280-2818
Weiman, Jon: 88 Wyckoff St #3C, Brooklyn, NY 11201 718-855-8468
Weiner, Jeffrey: 240 E 27th St #18n, New York, NY 10016 212-564-7548
• **Weiner, Jonathan: pg 457,458, Front Cover, Representatives' Book**
300 E 46th St #4G, New York, NY 10017 **212-687-6463**
e-mail: Sari@LevyCreative.com / url: www.levycreative.com / fax: 212-661-4839
Weiner, Paul S: 14 Cypress St #2, Brookline, MA 02445 617-738-0446
Weingard, Eileen: 2800 28th St #111, Santa Monica, CA 90405 310-452-4445
Weinland, Rick E.: 23110 Kuykendahl Rd, Spring, TX 77375 281-251-1921
Weinman, Brad: 311 Avenue H #D, Redondo Beach, CA 90277 310-540-5958
Weinstein, Ellen: 1 Union Sq W #512, New York, NY 10003 212-675-4360
Weinstein, Jeffrey: 18447 Adrian, Southfield, MI 48075 313-559-4392
Weinstein, Morey: 807 Larkwood Dr, Greensboro, NC 27410 910-854-5161
Weinstock, Bruce: 25-98 36th St #5E, Astoria, NY 11103 718-956-1670
Weintraub, Prof Annette: 138th St & Convent Ave, New York, NY 10031 212-650-7410
Weisbecker, Philippe: 155 W 15th St #4C, New York, NY 10011 212-989-8770
Weisberg, Pamela: 3551 Celinda Dr, Carlsbad, CA 92008 760-720-5328
Weisgerber, Phil: 2116 Curtis Ave, Redondo Beach, CA 90278 310-764-3772
• **Weisman, David: pg 828** 70 E 10th St #8G, New York, NY 10003 **212-387-7805**
e-mail: dudesicl@interport.net
Weismann, Roy: 7118 Upper River Rd, Prospect, KY 40059 502-228-9427
Weiss, Conrad: 40 Mohawk Trail, W Milford, NJ 07480 201-697-7226
Weiss, Conrad: 60 E 42nd St, New York, NY 10165 212-867-8092
Weiss, Kristina: 2817 Whitney Dr, Pleasanton, CA 94566 925-426-8964
Weiss, Richard: 1308A SE 36th Ave, Portland, OR 97214 503-236-2143
Weiss, Theresa: 976 Calle Jazmin, Thousand Oaks, CA 91360 805-379-3583
Weissenburger, Joe: 714 Orlando St, Edison, NJ 08817 908-548-9456
Weisser, Carl: 304 Henry St #1500, Brooklyn, NY 11201 718-834-0952
Weissman, Bari: 41 Atkins St, Brighton, MA 02135 617-783-0230
Weissman, Sam: 2510 Fenton Ave, Bronx, NY 10469 718-654-5381
Weistling, Morgan: 15900 Condor Ridge, Canyon Country, CA 91351 805-250-1129
Weiter, Sharon: 1031 S 4th St, Louisville, KY 40203 502-581-9410
Weithers, Arlington: PO Box 585, Tuskegee, AL 36087 205-727-3514
• **Welch, Jeff: pg 818** **415-337-1640**
Welch, W John: 2020 Santa Clara Ave #204, Alameda, CA 94501 510-523-9054
Weliver, Howard: 5740 Martel Ave #A8, Dallas, TX 75206 214-827-3919
Welkis, Allen: 53 Heights Rd, Fort Salonga, NY 11768 516-261-4160
Wellamn, Charles: 509 University Ave #111, Syracuse, NY 13210 315-471-8824
Weller, Don: 200 W 15th St, New York, NY 10011 212-243-4209
Weller, Don: PO Box 518, Oakley, UT 84055 435-783-5378
Weller, Kathy: 392 Harvard St, Cambridge, MA 02138 617-876-0891
Weller, Linda: 121 Dodgingtown Rd Box 266, Bethel, CT 06801 203-748-4823
Welles, Toby: 1352 N Formosa Ave Ste 2, Los Angeles, CA 90046 323-874-5700
Wells, Carol: 12122 Hooper Ln, Glen Arm, MD 21057 410-592-5072
Wells, Leigh: 17 Little W 12th St #310, New York, NY 10014 212-627-8518
Wells, Pamela: 136 Verdi Ave, Cardiff By the Sea, CA 92007 760-632-8495
Wells, Peter: 332 Bleecker St PMBK56, New York, NY 10014 212-691-2667
• **Wells, Sharon: pg 746** Aspen, CO **970-925-6701**
e-mail: swdesign@aspeninfo.com
Wells, Stephen: 848 Greenwood Ave NE, Atlanta, GA 30306 404-875-1363
Wells, Stephen: 14027 Memorial #125, Houston, TX 77079 281-579-3220
Welsh, Patrick J: 59 Bryant Rd, Turnersville, NJ 08012 856-232-3130
Wennekes, Ron: 2024 S Wabash Ave #201, Chicago, IL 60616 312-829-8853
Wenngren, Anders: 17 Little West 12th St #205, New York, NY 10014 212-645-9592
Wenzel, David: 95-R Maple Ave PO Box 294, Durham, CT 06422 860-349-1319
Wepplo, Michael: 311 Avenue H #D, Redondo Beach, CA 90277 310-540-5958
Werblun, Steve: 5855 Green Valley Cir #308, Culver City, CA 90230 310-642-2721
Werner, Jerry: PO Box 133, Sisters, OR 97759 541-549-9130
Werner, Mike: 7600 Juniper Ave, Miller Beach, IN 46403 219-938-1592
Werner, Tom: PO Box 854, Northfield, NJ 08225 609-383-1596
Werrmayer, Arthur: 15 N Gore, St Louis, MO 63119 314-968-1231
Wertheim, Ann: 4150 Hana Highway, Haiku, HA 96708 808-572-6571
• **Wertz, Michael: pg 888** 483 Capital St, Oakland, CA 94610 **415-824-5542**
e-mail: mykl@wertzateria.com / url: www.wertzateria.com
• **West, Jeff: pg 834** 283 Pine Forest Dr, Aptos, CA 95003 **831-688-6075**
url: www.jwestdesign.com / fax: 831-688-6072
West, Joel: 7000 Cleopatra Pl NW, Seattle, WA 98117 206-706-014
West, Justin: 16 Clark St, Saratoga Springs, NY 12866 518-587-0674
West, Sam: 2468 Runyon Cir, Orlando, FL 32837 407-826-9136
West, Stephen: 21801 Linda Dr, Torrance, CA 90503 310-540-3190
Westbrook, Eric: 2325 42nd St NW #419, Washington, DC 20007 202-328-8593
Westerberg, Rob: 420 Lexington Ave, New York, NY 10170 212-986-5680
Westlight New Media: 2223 S Carmelina Ave, Los Angeles, CA 90064 800-872-7872
Weston, Al: 903 N Main St, Royal Oak, MI 48067 248-548-4500
Westphal, Ken: 9208 Roe Ave, Prairie Village, KS 66207 913-381-8399
Westwood Studios, David: 1230 Stanford St, Santa Monica, CA 90404 310-828-6694
Wet Inc.: pg 626, 627 6 Seven Springs Ct, Phoenix, MD 21131 **410-527-0055**
Wetmore, Barry: 1003 Diamond Ave ste 209, S Pasadena, CA 91030 818-441-4496
Wetterhahn, Kristen: 1314 Kearny St, San Francisco, CA 94133 415-398-1953
Wetzel, Marcia: 758 Brookridge Dr NE, Atlanta, GA 30306 404-872-7980
Wexler, Ed: 4701 Don Pio Dr, Woodland Hills, CA 91364 818-888-3858
Whamond, Dave: 468 Queen St E #104, Toronto, ON M5A 1T7 416-367-2446
Whatley, Bruce: 7-3 Grouse Hollow Rd, Meredith, NH 03253 603-279-5098
Wheatley-Maxwell, Misty: 2233 Kemper Ln, Cincinnati, OH 45206 513-861-1400
Wheaton, Liz: PO Box 307, Ross, CA 94957 415-456-7711
Wheeler, Caley: 2345 Farrington St, Dallas, TX 75207 214-631-1080
Wheeler, David: 20104 48th Ave W #4, Lynnwood, WA 98036 888-454-0800
• **Wheeler, Jody: pg 768** 375 South End Ave #12T, New York, NY 10280 **212-775-1484**
Wheeler, Rick: PO Box 673, Moab, UT 84532 435-259-3012
Wheeler, Ron L: 1147 Crystal Ct, Avon, IN 46123 317-839-5255
Wheeler, Winky: 3647 SE Ogden St, Portland, OR 97202 503-788-8060
• **Whelan, Jeff: pg 792** **877-755-8369**
e-mail: jeff@jeffwhelan.com / url: www.jeffwhelan.com / fax: 877-755-8369
Whelan, Michael: 23 Old Hayrake Rd, Danbury, CT 06811 203-792-8089
Whelan, Patrick: 23821 Hillhurst Dr #45, Laguna Niguel, CA 92677 949-363-7274
Whim Whams Illustration Studio: 3314 Oberon St, Kensington, MD 20895 301-933-4912
Whipple, Rick: 2820 Rainforest Ct, Southlake, TX 76092 817-481-2212
Whitaker, Angela: `Author' 5 Broad Ct, Lnodon, UK WC2B 441713795938
Whitby, Michelle: 173 Carsonage Rd, Greenwich, CT 06830 203-629-2501
White Jr, John: 5109-C Monroe Rd, Charlotte, NC 27410 704-537-7717
White, Caroline: 137 Fifth Ave 11th Fl, New York, NY 10010 212-529-3556
White, Caroline: 126C Ashfield Mountain Rd, Ashfield, MA 01330 413-628-4042
White, Craig: 608 York St, San Francisco, CA 94110 415-641-1285
White, Eric: 608 York St, San Francisco, CA 94110 415-641-1285
White, Janie: 6245 E McDonald Dr, Paradise Valley, AZ 85253 480-905-2628
White, Jeff: 13775 SW 27th St, Beaverton, OR 97008 503-520-1019
White, K.C.: 931 S Mansfield Ave #201, Los Angeles, CA 90036 323-965-0035
White, Richard: 57 Ridge Dr, Berkeley Heights, NJ 07922 908-508-0640
White, Tom: pg 582, 583, 920, 921 750 Columbus Ave, #2E New York, NY 10025 **212-866-7841**
e-mail: tom@twimages.com / url: www.twimages.com
Whitehead, Brian: 286 Spring St #301, New York, NY 10013 212-229-0073
Whitehead, S B: 311 Almshouse Rd, Doylestown, PA 18901 215-230-7412
Whitehead, Sarah: 5220 Gabbert Rd Ste A, Moonpark, CA 93021 805-532-2453
Whitehouse, Debora: New York, NY 212-682-1490
Whitesides, Kim: 1972 S Broadmoor, Salt Lake City, UT 84108 801-466-0209

Wood, Tracey: 51 Camden St, Toronto, ON M5V 1V2. 416-703-1913
Woodend, James: 420 Lexington Ave #2760, New York, NY 10170 212-697-8525
Woodhams, Lezley: 105 Cowan Ave, Toronto, ON M6K 2N1 416-516-7838
• **Woodin, Mary: pg 492** 455 W 23rd St #8D, New York, NY 10011 . . . . . . **212-366-1893**
  e-mail: sally@theartworksinc.com / url: www.theartworksinc.com
  fax: 212-604-9643
Woodle, Arthur: 169 Forest Ave #1, Marietta, GA 30060. 770-429-1432
Woodman, Dave: 750 Kings Rd #224, Los Angeles, CA 90069 213-782-0116
Woods, Alison: 414 Jackson St #304, San Francisco, CA 94111 415-399-1984
• **Woods, Noah: pg 126,127** 108 E 35th St, New York, NY 10016 . . . . **212-889-3337**
  e-mail: gerald@rappart.com / url: www.theispot.com/rep/rapp / fax: 212-889-3341
• **Woods, Paul: Front Flap Illustrators' Book** 414 Jackson St #304, San Francisco, CA 94111 . . **415-399-1984**
Woods, Rosemary: 8403 32nd Ave S.W., Seattle, WA 98126 206-938-0368
Woods, Rosemary: 11 Kings Ridge Rd, Long Valley, NJ 07853 908-813-8718
Woodward, Teresa: 544 Paseo Miramar, Pacific Palisades, CA 90272 213-459-2317
Woolery, Lee: 2233 Kemper Ln, Cincinnati, OH 45206 513-861-1400
Woolf, Anatol: 495 Chestertown St, Gaithersburg, MD 20878 301-527-1757
• **Woolley, Janet: pg 131** 11 Kings Ridge Rd, Long Valley, NJ 07853 . . . . . . **908-813-8718**
  e-mail: alartists@aol.com / url: www.arenaworks.com / fax: 908-813-0076
Woolrey, Lee: 2233 Kemper Ln, Cincinnati, OH 45206 513-861-1400
Wooten, Rick: 67 Ayamonte Ct, San Ramon, CA 94583 925-867-1724
Worcester, Mary: 2670 Marshland Rd, Wayzata, MN 55391 612-449-4850
Workman, Beth: 723 Pierce St, Boise, ID 83712 208-343-1094
Workman, Judy: 2233 Kemper Ln, Cincinnati, OH 45206 513-861-1400
Workplace Technology: 11330 Old Ranch Cir, Chatsworth, CA 91311 818-407-0682
Works, The: 425 E Broadway Blvd, Long Beach, CA 90802 562-436-0343
Worley, Zoe: 2 Kirsten Pl, Weston, CT 10023 203-222-9421
• **Wormell, Christopher: pg 489** 455 W 23rd St #8D, New York, NY 10011 . . . . **212-366-1893**
  e-mail: sally@theartworksinc.com / url: www.theartworksinc.com
  fax: 212-604-9643
Worry, Ed: 305 Market St, Belle Vernon, PA 15012 412-929-2705
Worthington, Nancy: PO Box 2558, Sebastopol, CA 95473 707-823-3581
Woska, Marsha: 203 School Ave, Rochelle, IL 61068 815-562-3702
Wray, Greg: 40681 Via Diamante, Murrieta, CA 92562 909-696-3560
Wray, Lisa: RR1 Box 147, Springville, PA 18844 570-836-2887
Wriedt, Edward E: 12601 Kristy Cir, Raleigh, NC 27613 919-847-3412
Wright Crtv Group, Bob: 247 N Goodman St, Rochester, NY 14607 716-271-2280
Wright, Amy: 202 Cottontail Dr, Portsmouth, RI 02871 401-849-4680
Wright, Candace: 3447 Glenrose Ave, Altadena, CA 91001 818-794-8284
Wright, Carol: 2500 Angie Way, Rancho Cordova, CA 95670 916-635-4705
Wright, Jane Chambless: 9 Babbling Brook Ln, Suffern, NY 10901 845-368-8606
Wright, Jon Q: PO Box 290055, Minneapolis, MN 55429 888-658-5211
Wright, Jonathan: 353 W 53rd St #1W, New York, NY 10019 212-682-2462
Wright, Michael Ragsdale: 2021 S Alameda #10, Los Angeles, CA 90058 . . . 213-748-4022
Wright, Susan L: RD #1 Box 116, Schoharie, NY 12157 518-458-8000
Wright, Ted: 612 N 2nd St, St Louis, MO 63102 314-781-7377
Wrinkle, James: 1141 Calle Pensamiento, Thousand Oaks, CA 91360 805-495-5732
Wrobel, Cindy: 415 Alta Dena, St Louis, MO 63130 314-721-4467
Wrobel, Schuyler: 1669 Hilliard Dr, San Marino, CA 91108 818-286-7126
Wu, Benjamin: 654 Pier Ave #C, Santa Monica, CA 90405 310-392-4877
Wu, Leslie: 1217 Quassey Ave, Lake Bluff, IL 60044 847-615-9891
• **Wummer, Amy: pg 298** 731 N 24th St, Philadelphia, PA 19130 . . . . **215-232-6666**
  url: www.deborahwolfeltd.com / fax: 215-232-6585
Wunderlich, Dirk J: 1802 Lantana Dr, Minden, NV 89423 800-711-1811
Wunsch, Marjory: 78 Washington Ave, Cambridge, MA 02140 617-492-3839
Wyant, Julia: 96 East Ave, Norwalk, CT 06851 203-838-0191
Wyatt, Carol: 1835 Colina Dr, Glendale, CA 91208 818-240-8641
Wyckoff, Diane: 202 Wilson St, Bridgeport, CT 06605 203-368-0392
Wygant, Matthew: 509 W Lake Ave, Guilford, CT 06437 203-453-2078
Wynes, Joyce: 6137 Oxwynn Ln, Charlotte, NC 28270 704-442-9323
Wynne, Patricia: 446 Central Park W, New York, NY 10025 212-865-1059

X

Xavier, Roger: 23200 Los Codona Ave, Torrance, CA 90505 310-373-7049
Xavier, Roger: 16 Phaedra, Laguna Niguel, CA 92677 949-495-3664
Xenakis, Thomas: 523 W 24th St #25, Norfolk, VA 23517 804-622-2061
• **Xplane: pg 630,631** 809 Geyer Ave, St Louis, MO 63104 . . . . **800-750-6467**
  url: www.xplane.com / fax: 314-436-0506

Y

Yablon, Miriam: 229 E 96th St #2FE, New York, NY 10128 212-534-2536
• **Yaccarino, Dan: pg 715** 95 Horatio St #703, New York, NY 10014 . . . . **212-675-5335**
  url: www.danyaccarino.com
Yadin, Hanan: 5709 Hartsdale, Houston, TX 77036 213-936-4790
Yamada, Kenny: 501S Tumbleweed Rd, Anaheim, CA 92807 714-685-1154
• **Yang, Eric: pg 915** 19062 Foxwood Lane Huntington Beach, CA 92648 . . . . **714-969-5314**
  e-mail: etyang@pacbell.net / url: www.eric-yang.com / fax: 714-969-5304
• **Yang, James pg 496, 552:** 41 Union Square W #918, New York, NY 10003 . . . . **212-807-6627**
  e-mail: dgagency@idt.com / url: www.davidgoldmanagency.com or
  www.jamesyang.com / fax: 212-463-8175
Yaniv, Etty: 32 Laurence Ct, Closter, NJ 07624 201-784-8136
Yanson, John Michael: 211 8th St NE/Carriage House, Washington, DC 20002 . . 202-546-0600
Yapp, Kenneth: 2705-A Ostiguy St, Montréal, QU H4R 1N3 514-332-9912
Yarmolinsky, Miriam: 8211 Greenwood Ave #1, Takoma Park, MD 20912 . . . 301-588-2434
Yazzolino, Brad: 6451 SE Morrison Ct, Portland, OR 97215 503-238-3776
Yeager, Alice: 3157 Rolling Rd, Edgewater, MD 21037 301-956-4252
Yealdhall, Gary: 353 W 53rd St #1W, New York, NY 10019 212-682-2462
Yearington, Tim: 4709 Northwoods Dr/Box 811 RR #3, Woodlawn, ON K0A 3M0 613-832-0879
Yee, Josie: 43 E 19th St, New York, NY 10003 212-254-4996
Yee, Vincent: 5927 135th Pl SE, Bellevue, WA 98006 425-653-1534
Yeh, Jeff: 13100 Creek View #103, Garden Grove, CA 92644 714-638-2934
Yemi: 99 Park Ave #210A, New York, NY 10016 800-398-9544
Yemi: 4707 Mt Zion Rd, Frederick, MD 21703 301-865-1434
• **Yeo, Brad: pg 128,129** 108 E 35th St, New York, NY 10016 . . . . **212-889-3337**
  e-mail: gerald@rappart.com / url: www.theispot.com/rep/rapp / fax: 212-889-3341
Yeomans, Jeff: 4691 Orchard Ave, San Diego, CA 92107 619-224-2654

Yerkes, Lane: 200 S Roberts Rd #F6, Bryn Mawr, PA 19010 610-520-3470
Yermal, Bill: 62 Carey Rd, Succasunna, NJ 07876 973-927-8909
Yesko, John: 5131 N Mason Ave, Chicago, IL 60630 773-467-4270
Yezerski, Thomas: 270 Union Ave, Rutherford, NJ 07070 201-939-6093
Yiannias, Vicki: 159 W 4th St, Apt 3, New York, NY 10014 212-675-1457
Yiannias, Vicki: 200 W 15th St, New York, NY 10011 212-243-4209
Yip, Filip: PO Box 320177, San Francisco, CA 94132 415-682-0758
Yip, Jennie: 420 Lexington Ave, New York, NY 10170 212-986-5680
Yip, Jennie: 67-40 Yellowstone Blvd, Forest Hills, NY 11375 718-896-3889
Yoe Studio, Craig: 209 Chateau Rive, Peekskill, NY 10566 914-734-4756
Yoon, Young-Min: 66 S Grant Ave #15, Columbus, OH 43215 614-280-9817
York, Jeff: 1445 N State Pkwy #1902, Chicago, IL 60610 312-664-8849
York, Judy: 13 Buckingham Ln, Gaylordsville, CT 06755 860-354-1459
Yoshikawa, Sachiko pg 780,942,943: 14155 SW Wilson Dr, Beaverton, OR 97008 . **503-626-7271**
  url: www.studiosachiko.com / fax: 503-626-7271
Youll, Paul: 60 E 42nd St, New York, NY 10165 212-867-8092
Young & Laramore: 310 E Vermont, Indianapolis, IN 46204 317-264-8000
Young Assocs, Robert: 78 N Union St, Rochester, NY 14607 716-546-1973
Young, Amy: 14165 Garfield Rd, Spring Lake, MI 49436 616-847-1630
Young, Bruce: 2917 N Fulton Dr NE, Atlanta, GA 30305 404-266-0088
Young, Coulter: Po Box 2644, Peekskill, NY 10566 914-788-0147
• **Young, Eddie: pg 887** Long Beach, CA **562-429-2513**
  e-mail: youngeddie@eddieyoung.com / url: www.eddieyoung.com
  fax: 562-429-1400
Young, Emily: 2173 NE Multnomah, Portland, OR 97232 503-281-3923
Young, Leigh: 1016 Falgarwood Dr #35, Oakville, ON L6H 2P5 905-338-8128
Young, Marjorie: 7010 Ontario St, Vancouver, BC V5X 3B5. 604-324-9222
Young, Mary O'Keefe: 62 Midchester Ave, White Plains, NY 10606 914-949-0147
Young, Michael: 425 Fontana Pl NE, Albuquerque, NM 87108 505-255-0670
Young, Paul: PO Box 344, Champaign, IL 61824 217-398-1923
Young, Ron: 7 Gifford Lane, Medusa, NY 12120 518-239-6551
Young, Sara: 8709 Dorrington Ave, Los Angeles, CA 90048 310-659-5456
Young, Stephanie: 2427 Bay St, San Francisco, CA 94123 415-776-1218
Young, Timothy: 30 Bridgman Rd Chiswick, London, England, UK W4 5BD 1819-950191
Young, Vivian: 330 Arguelio Blvd #3, San Francisco, CA 94118 415-386-0107
Young, Wally: 7 Birch Hill Rd, Weston, CT 06883 203-227-5672
• **Young/Studio Y, Sandy: pg 877** 17503 Sonoma Highway, Sonoma, CA 95476 . . **707-939-1131**
  e-mail: ideas@studio-y.com / url: www.studio-y.com
• **Younger, Heidi: pg 350,351** 58 W 15th St, New York, NY 10011 . . . . **212-741-2539**
  url: www.jdedell.com or www.theispot.com / fax: 212-741-4660
Yourke, Oliver: 525A Sixth Ave, Brooklyn, NY 11215. 718-965-0609
Youssi, John: 60 E 42nd St, New York, NY 10165 212-867-8092
Youtsey, Scott: 1400 Turtle Creek Blvd #209, Dallas, TX 75207 214-739-0898
• **Yücel: pg 240,241** Chicago, IL **312-364-0244**
  London **011-44-207-636-1064**
  Los Angeles, CA **323-874-5700**
  Washington, DC **410-349-8669**
  New York, NY **212-333-2551**
  url: www.shannonassociates.com
Yuen, Allen: 7 Elizabeth St #D1, New York, NY 10013 212-219-9760
Yuh, Jennifer: 4828 Obispo Ave, Lakewood, CA 90712 310-425-6830
Yule, Susan Hunt: 176 Elizabeth St, New York, NY 10012 212-226-0439
Yurkovic, Michael: 5234 N Leamington, Chicago, IL 60630 773-282-7445
Yves, Jean: 60 E 42nd St, New York, NY 10165 212-867-8092

Z

Zabarte, Charlie: 3479 Agate Dr #1, Santa Clara, CA 95051 408-985-4841
Zacharow, Christopher: 115 West 23rd St, New York, NY 10011 212-989-4600
Zador, Lisa: 64 Morton St #3C, New York, NY 10014 212-242-3006
Zagorski, Stanislaw: 142 E 35th St, New York, NY 10016 212-532-2348
Zaharuk, Michael: 61 Alvin Ave, Toronto, ON M4T 2A8 416-538-7410
Zahnd, Mark: 11621 Long Forest Dr, Charlotte, NC 28269. 704-948-9886
Zakari, Chantal: 124 Maplewood St, Watertown, MA 02472. 617-926-3233
Zakashansky, Hannah: 1340 E 9th St #C8, Brooklyn, NY 11230 212-726-4098
Zakrasjsek, Molly: 7009 Madison Ave, Cleveland, OH 44102 216-281-3395
Zale, David: 3529 Highway Ave, Highland, IN 46322 219-838-4254
Zalewski, Todd: 1446 Van Kirk, Philadelphia, PA 19149 215-831-9565
Zaloom, Carol: 302 High Falls Rd, Saugerties, NY 12477 914-246-7441
Zaman, Farida: 18 Norman Rd, Montclair, NJ 07043 973-744-9377
Zamchick, Gary: 56 Hillside Ave, Tenafly, NJ 07670 201-568-3727
• **Zammarchi, Robert: pg 882** 44 Pleasant St, Watertown, MA 02472 . . . . **617-787-9513**
  Watertown, MA **617-924-3737**
  url: www.zamarchi.com
Zappy, Michael: 6606 rue Drolet, Montréal, QU H2S 2S8. 514-948-0477
Zarins, Joyce Audy: 19 Woodland St, Merrimac, MA 01860 508-346-8994
Zaslavsky, Morris: 13763 Fiji way #EU1, Marina Del Rey, CA 90292 213-399-3666
Zastrow, Stuart: 925 Elm Grove Rd, Elm Grove, WI 53122. 414-785-1940
Zavell, Bonnie: 115 Woodcrest St, Elyria, OH 44035. 216-365-3477
Zawacki, Alison: PO Box 278631, Sacramento, CA 95827 916-981-9367
Zebot, George: PO Box 4295, Laguna Beach, CA 92652 714-494-7311
Zeines, Bruce: 643 Vanderbilt St, Brooklyn, NY 11218 718-972-7256
Zeleznik, John: 7307 Kelvin Ave #10, Canoga Park, CA 91306 818-884-4954
Zelinsky, Paul: 54 Orange St #1D, Brooklyn, NY 11201. 718-855-1841
Zellin, Lisa: 236 E 33rd St #D, New York, NY 10016 212-978-2291
Zeltner, Tim: 116 Spadina Ave Ste 400, Toronto, ON M5V 2K6 416-505-9522
• **Zernitsky, Leon: pg 856** 95 Weldrick Rd E #10, Richmond Hill, ON L4C 0H6 . . **905-770-2199**
  url: www.leonzernitsky.com / fax: 905-770-9798
Zero Degrees Kelvin: 324 Pearl St, New York, NY 10038 212-385-8600
• **Zero-Up: pg 932,** PO Box 20828 Baltimore, MD 21209 . . . . **800-570-5204**
  e-mail: Showcase@zero-up.com / url: www.zero-up.com / fax: 877-614-3492
Zgodzinski, Rose: 29 High Park Gardens, Toronto, ON M6R 1S8 416-762-1055
Zhu, Hua: 32 W 40th St #2 South, New York, NY 10018 212-575-6887
Zick, Brian: 250 W 57th St #521, New York, NY 10107 212-397-7330
Zielinski, John: 6239 Elizabeth Ave, St Louis, MO 63139 314-781-8851

ILLUSTRATORS

ILLUSTRATORS

GRAPHIC DESIGNERS

1

1185 Design: 119 University Ave, Palo Alto, CA 94301 ... 415-325-4804

2

289 Design, Inc: 289 Wellington Rd, Buffalo, NY 14216 ... 212-838-2281
2B Design: 15 Myrtle Sconset Sq #10A, Westport, CT 06880 ... 203-227-4789
2H Studio: 54 Old Post Rd, Southport, CT 06490 ... 203-256-1625

3

30-Sixty Design: 2801 Cahuenga Blvd W, Los Angeles, CA 900068 ... 231-850-5312
3DO Co, The: 600 Galveston Dr, Redwood City, CA 94063 ... 415-261-3000

4

4-D-Adv Web Programming: PO Box 1282, Iowa City, IA 52244 ... 319-338-6353

5

555 Design Fabrication: 1238 S Ashland Ave, Chicago, IL 60608 ... 312-733-6777
5D Studio: 20651 Seaboard Rd, Malibu, CA 90265 ... 310-317-0705

9

• **9 Surf Studios: pg 920,921** 750 Columbus Ave #2E, New York, NY 10025 ... **212-866-8778**
e-mail: tom@9surf.com / url: www.9surf.com

A

Aart-Werk Graphic Design, Inc: 1920 E 3rd St #11, Tempe, AZ 85281 ... 602-921-3060
A & S Creative Works: 1677 Tullie Circle #102, Atlanta, GA 30329 ... 404-636-6622
A Creative Group: PO Box 612006, South Lake Tahoe, CA 96152 ... 916-544-4701
A Designing Woman: 4651 E Vernon, Phoenix, AZ 85008 ... 602-840-1117
A La Carte Graphics: 2024 Spring Rd, Smyrna, GA 30080 ... 770-432-7639
A Priori Art & Design: 2722 Kaaha St, Honolulu, HI 96826 ... 808-949-2708
A Solutions Company: 304 1/2 8th St #220, Des Moines, IL 50309 ... 515-247-0003
A Street Design: 1284 Antwerp Ln, San Jose, CA 95118 ... 408-266-5544
A To Z communications: 100 Ross St #212, Pittsburgh, PA 15219 ... 412-471-4160
A-Musing Creative: 114 3rd St #201, Minneapolis, MN 55401 ... 612-341-9333
A1 Brochure & Postcard Production: 17 Cabrillo Dr, Avalon, CA 90704 ... 310-510-3100
A2Z Creative Services: 2020 Arboles Pl, Escondido, CA 92029 ... 619-739-0896
Aardvark Illus & Graphics: 13000 Bel Red Rd #201, Bellevue, WA 98005 ... 206-453-6010
Aardvark/Schill Design: 2749 S Westgate Ave, Los Angeles, CA 90064 ... 310-445-8651
Abacus Graphics: 4701 Morning Canyon Rd, Oceanside, CA 92056 ... 619-724-7750
Abbate Design: 726 Bloomfield Basement, Hoboken, NJ 07030 ... 201-222-9046
Abbott/Barrington & Co: 2217 E Turney Ave, Phoenix, AZ 85016 ... 602-553-8130
ABC Design: 3425 Riverknoll Way, West Lynn, OR 97068 ... 503-699-1886
Abdo, Lynda: 22727 Schoolcraft St, West Hills, CA 91307 ... 818-710-8108
Abrams Creative Services: 2049 Red Coach Ln, Encinitas, CA 92024 ... 619-942-4380
Abrams Design Group: 100 View St #203, Mountain View, CA 94041 ... 415-964-2388
Abrams Design, Kym: 213 W Institute Pl #608, Chicago, IL 60610 ... 312-654-1005
Abrams, Elaine: 112 Fourth Ave, New York, NY 10003 ... 212-254-1688
ABS Graphics: 901 S Rohlwing rd, Addison, IL 60101 ... 630-495-2400
Absolute Graphics: 343 S Dearborn #1111, Chicago, IL 60604 ... 312-427-2120
Accent Marketing: 800 Douglas Rd #100, Coral Gables, FL 33134 ... 305-461-1112
Access Creative Communications: 210 Avenue I #E, Redondo Beach, CA 90277 ... 310-543-9820
Accumind Services, Neil: 462 S Pensylvania St, Denver, CO 80209 ... 303-733-7775
Ace Design: 480 Gate Five Rd #310, Sausilito, CA 94965 ... 415-332-9390
Acme Design Group: 100 North State St, Newtown, PA 18940 ... 215-579-4946
Acorn Interactive: 23 E 10th St #226, New York, NY 10003 ... 212-673-3333
Active 8: 601 N Eutaw St # 704, Baltimore, MD 21201 ... 410-962-0270
ACTV Interactive: 1270 Avenue of the Americas, New York, NY 10020 ... 212-262-2570
Ad Agency, The: 8605 Westwood Center Dr #200, Vienna, VA 22182 ... 703-821-2030
Ad Art Design: 1407 Cross St, Eugene, OR 97402 ... 503-344-8476
Ad Department, The : 6409 Ellis Rd, Ft Worth, TX 76112 ... 817-451-7980
AD Design: 2501 W Zia Rd #2-203, Santa Fe, NM 87505 ... 505-473-5163
Ad Gallery By Capielo: 2465 Campus Dr, Irvine, CA 92715 ... 714-261-0280
Ad Group, The: 927 Lincoln Way, Auburn, CA 95603 ... 916-888-0484
Ad Infinitum: 1414 2nd St #102, Santa Monica, CA 90401 ... 310-395-7531
Ad Med Assocs, Inc: 6 Kingswoods Dr, New Hope, PA 18938 ... 215-862-2316
Ad Media: 111 E Lincoln Rd, Spokane, WA 99208 ... 509-466-1632
Ad Store, Inc, The : 8950 St Ives Dr, Los Angeles, CA 90069 ... 310-276-1865
Ad-hoc Interactive: 80 Liberty Shipway Ste 1, Sausalito, CA 94965 ... 415-332-0180
Ad/Art Studios: 1501 Euclid Ave #830, Cleveland, OH 44115 ... 312-832-4100
Adams Graphic Design, Pam: 5274 E Broadway, Long Beach, CA 90803 ... 310-438-5422
Adams Graphic Design, Wanda: 5098 Springhill Dr NW, Albany, OR 97321 ... 503-926-2709
Adams, Cheryl: 2124 NW 139th St, Des Moines, IA 50325 ... 515-223-7174
Adams, David R: 2105 Commerce St #102, Dallas, TX 75201 ... 214-741-4007
Adams, Deborah S: 440 East 57th St #GC, New York, NY 10022 ... 212-486-1002
Adams, Gaylord: 521 Fifth Ave, New York, NY 10175 ... 212-684-4625
Adams, Nina: 3952 Western Ave, Western Springs, IL 60558 ... 708-246-0766
Adams/Moriokas Double Vision: 9348 Civic Center Dr, Beverly Hills, CA 90201 ... 310-246-5758
Addante Design, Inc: 417 W 43rd St #20, New York, NY 10036 ... 212-957-3769
Adhouse: 4539 N 22nd St #105, Phoenix, AZ 85016 ... 602-468-9877
Adkins/Balchunas: 765 Allens Ave, Providence, RI 02905 ... 401-941-1370
Adler & Schinkel, Inc: 3842 W Peoria Ave, Phoenix, AZ 85029 ... 602-277-9366
Adler Assocs, Stan: 305 Seventh Ave 19th Fl, New York, NY 10001 ... 212-366-4860
Adler Design Group: 9690 Deereco Rd #230, Timonium, MD 21093 ... 410-561-5550
Adler, Shelly: 2647 S Magnolia, Los Angeles, CA 90007 ... 213-749-7347
Adler-Schwartz Graphics: 9690 Deerceo Rd #230, Timonium, MD 21093 ... 410-561-5550
Adlerblum Design: 1133 Broadway #1225, New York, NY 10010 ... 212-807-8429
Admagic Creative Services: 160 W Pomona Ave, Monrovia, CA 91016 ... 818-303-5514
Adnet Communications: 1378 Hilda Ave #203, Glendale, CA 91205 ... 818-243-7802
Adrienne Youngstein & Assocs: 127 W24th St, New York, NY 10011 ... 212-242-7140
Ads Plus: 15112 McRae St, Norwalk, CA 90650 ... 310-929-0984
Adsit, Chuck: 1123 Louise St, San Leandro, CA 94578 ... 510-483-4239
ADT Design For Marketing: 933 Lyford Dr, San Dimas, CA 91773 ... 909-592-4768
Adv Design, Scott: 9411 Headlands Rd, Mentor, OH 44060 ... 305-743-2116
Advance Design Center: 2501 Oak Lawn Ave #200, Dallas, TX 75219 ... 214-526-1420
Advanced Concepts Center: 13500 Reeck Rd, Southgate, MI 48195 ... 313-246-0323
Advertising a la Carte: 11400 W Olympic Blvd #207, Los Angeles, CA 90064 ... 310-551-9237
Advertising Arts: 3730 Stone Creek Wy, Boise, ID 83703 ... 208-388-0411
Advertising Design: 1201 First Ave S #326, Seattle, WA 98134 ... 206-587-6530
Advertising Design Assocs: 1095 Market St #411, San Francisco, CA 94103 ... 415-558-8000
Advertising Designers, Inc: 7087 Snyder Ridge Rd, Mariposa, CA 95338 ... 209-742-6704
Adzema, Diane: 17 Bleecker St, New York, NY 10012 ... 212-982-5657
Aerial: 58 Federal St, San Francisco, CA 94107 ... 415-957-9761
Aerocraft Charter Art Service: 3618 W Voltaire Ave, Phoenix, AZ 85029 ... 602-978-1570
Aeschlima Design, Inc: 307 Fifth Ave 14th Fl, New York, NY 10016 ... 212-685-1585
After Hours: 434 Marieta St NW #404, Atlanta, GA 30313 ... 404-523-9950
After Hours: 1201 Jefferson #100B, Phoenix, AZ 85034 ... 602-256-2648
After Hours Design & Adv: 33309 Santiago Rd #314, Acton, CA 93510 ... 805-251-0197
After Midnight: 51 Melcher St, Boston, MA 02210 ... 617-350-7970
Aga: 2 park ave 4Th Fl, New York, NY 10016 ... 212-726-7000
Agency, The: 402 Friday Creek Rd, Burlington, WA 98233 ... 206-724-3054
Agency.com Ltd.: 665 Broadway 9th Fl, New York, NY 10012 ... 212-358-8220
AGI: 424 Larchmont Blvd, Los Angeles, CA 90004 ... 213-462-0821
Agnew Moyer Smith: 503 Martindale St, Pittsburgh, PA 15212 ... 412-322-6333
Agnew, Scott: 4170 17th St #204, San Francisco, CA 94114 ... 415-864-5233
Agra: 60 Madison Ave 9th Fl, New York, NY 10010 ... 212-545-0510
AHA Creative Solutions: 3300 NE Expressway Bldg 4 #M, Atlanta, GA 30341 ... 770-986-9997
Ahdoot, Samantha: 817 S Westgate Ave #302, Los Angeles, CA 90049 ... 310-826-8716
Ainsworth Design: 2341 Moulton Pkwy #200, Laguna Hills, CA 92653 ... 714-768-8500
Air Castle Productions: 410-40 Alexander St, Toronto, ON M4Y 1B5 ... 416-921-4337
Aizawa & Furuta Advertising: 141 Industrial St, San Francisco, CA 94124 ... 415-695-8700
AJ Buttler & CO: 122 Huntington St, New Brunswick, NJ 08901 ... 908-828-4244
AJ Design & Assocs: PO Box 532, Basalt, CO 81621 ... 970-927-4924
Ajamian, Jeanine: 25 W 45th St #203, New York, NY 10036 ... 212-302-1325
AK Productions: 461 Second St #7558, San Francisco, CA 94107 ... 408-356-1044
AKA Design: 1605 S Ninth St, St. Louis, MO 63104 ... 314-621-6070
AKA Hound Dog Studio: 1710 Hayes St #203, Nashville, TN 37203 ... 615-327-9577
Akagi Design: 632 Commercial St 4th Fl, San Francisco, CA 94111 ... 415-397-4668
Akers Designers, Kevin: 13 Hart St, San Rafael, CA 94901 ... 415-455-0562
Akiyama Design: 16608 E Prentice Ave, Aurora, CO 80015 ... 303-680-8298
Akobian, Hutch: 620 E Angeleno Ave #G, Burbank, CA 91501 ... 818-557-7739
Aktari Design & Comm : 781 Raycliff Pl, Concord, CA 94518 ... 510-686-9610
Aktulun, Kenan: 111 Southwood Rd, Austin, TX 78704 ... 512-447-6522
Alaimo Studio, Terry M: 2233 Martin St #113, Irvine, CA 92715 ... 714-724-8899
Alameda Group, The: 1585 The Alameda #100, San Jose, CA 95126 ... 408-287-9055
Alan Gallery: 36 Park St, Berea, OH 44017 ... 216-243-7794
Alaskan Designs: PO Box 41572, Tucson, AZ 85717 ... 602-323-3282
Album Graphics: 1950 N Ruby St, Melrose Park, IL 60160 ... 708-344-9100
Alden Design, Inc: 2157 India St, San Diego, CA 92101 ... 619-544-9299
Aleida Graphics: 16777 Bernardo Center Dr #E6, San Diego, CA 92128 ... 714-444-3403
Alessi Design, Anthony: 15737 Thomas Ln, Oak Forest, IL 60452 ... 708-535-6542
Alexander Communications: 1000 W MacArthur Blvd #49, Santa Ana, CA 92707 ... 714-641-7522
Alexander Design Assocs: 588 Broadway #202, New York, NY 10012 ... 212-925-7755
Alexander Design, Inc, Jann: 4100 N 23rd St, Arlington, VA 22207 ... 703-528-1200
Alexander Graphic Design, Jeanette: 1055 Nakata Ave, Bainbridge Island, WA 98110 ... 206-842-6368
Alexander, Martha: Box 130144, Houston, TX 77219 ... 713-529-0472
Alfonso Architects, Inc: 1705 N 16th St, Tampa, FL 33605 ... 813-247-3333
Aliman Design, Inc: 134 Spring St 7th Fl, New York, NY 10012 ... 212-925-9621
Alinsangan/Doyle: 2319 6th St #1, Santa Monica, CA 90405 ... 310-392-7705
Aljon Graphics: 1721 E Lambert Rd, La Habra, CA 90631 ... 310-694-3144
Allen & Assocs: 712 Midland Park, Aspen, CO 81611 ... 303-925-5630
Allen & Assocs, William: 87 Wall St 2nd Fl, Seattle, WA 98121 ... 206-443-9933
Allen Creative: 2573 Laurel View Ct, Snellville, GA 30278 ... 770-972-8862
Allen Graphics: 954 Arlington, Redwood City, CA 94062 ... 415-366-4009
Allied Graphic Arts: 2 Park Ave 4th Fl, New York, NY 10036 ... 212-726-7000
Allison & Assocs: 1151 Amherst Ave #12, Los Angeles, CA 90049 ... 310-820-5298
Allison Design: 7645 Jarboe St, Kansas City, MO 64114 ... 816-444-7782
Almazan Graphics: 3136 Camino Graciosa, Thousand Oaka, CA 91360 ... 805-492-0030
AlphaConn Web Design: PO Box 1954, Hartford, CT ... 860-376-9028
Altered Image: 7 Deerpark Dr #D, Monmouth Juncti, NJ 08852 ... 908-274-2220
Altgelt & Korge: 3308 Broadway #203, San Antonio, TX 78209 ... 210-829-0151
Alto Design: 3300 Business Dr, Sacramento, CA 95820 ... 916-732-2068
Altschul, Charles: 356 Riverbank Rd, Stamford, CT 06903 ... 203-329-7251
Alvarez Group: 3171 Cadet Ct, Los Angeles, CA 90068 ... 213-876-3491
Alvey Design, Trent: 307 W 200 South #5000, Salt Lake City, UT 84101 ... 801-363-8001
Amber Enterprises: 11828 Rancho Bernardo Rd #123, San Diego, CA 92128 ... 619-755-0847
Amber W Design: 2791 W Calle de Dalias, Tucson, AZ 85745 ... 602-743-7549
Ambrosi & Assocs: 1100 W Washington Blvd, Chicago, IL 60607 ... 312-666-9200
America Now, Inc: 2101 S Platt River Dr, Denver, CO 80223 ... 303-934-7575
American Express Publishing Co: 1120 Ave of Americas, New York, NY 10036 ... 212-382-5600
American Graphics: 2300 Defoor Hills Rd, Atlanta, GA 30318 ... 404-355-7220
American Greetings: 1 American Rd, Cleveland, OH 44144 ... 216-252-7300
American Model & Design: 496 East Main St, Denville, NJ 07834 ... 201-627-0084
American Tech Systems: 5 Suburban Park Dr, Billerica, MA 01821 ... 508-663-6755
American Visualists: 301 Mesa Dr, Costa Mesa, CA 92627 ... 714-631-3260
American Web Classics: 4 Lincoln St, Baldwin, NY 11510 ... 516-377-4749
AMG Marketing Resources: 2217 E Ninth St #306, Cleveland, OH 44115 ... 216-621-1835
Amoeba Design: 49 Spadina Ave, Toronto, ON M5V 2J1 ... 416-599-2699
Amorosi, Philip R: 1432 E Cedar St, Tempe, AZ 85281 ... 602-968-5530
Amos B Designs: 4073 Gresham #2, San Diego, CA 92109 ... 619-296-8235
Amos Design, Gwen: 4909 Cottage Way #1, Carmichael, CA 95608 ... 916-486-4491
Ampersand Assocs: 1620 S Canal St #3000, Chicago, IL 60616 ... 630-241-2282
Ampersand Graphic Design: 15425 N Greenway Hayden Loop, Scottsdale, AZ 85260 ... 602-998-4200
Ampersand Studios: 1290 S Columbine, Denver, CO 80210 ... 303-733-0846
Amsterdam King Assocs, Inc: 3435 Ocean Pk Blvd #112, Santa Monica, CA 90405 ... 310-393-7263
Amundson, Eric: 1100 W Cambridge Circl Dr #550, Kansas City, KS 66103 ... 913-281-4433

Anagnost Design: 17320 Burbank Blvd #36, Encino, CA 91316 ... 818-784-4642
Anagram Design Group: 48 Lance Drive, Somers, CT 06071 ... 860-749-5095
Anastasion Studio: 563 W 200 S, Salt Lake City, UT 84101 ... 801-355-4400
Ancona & Assocs: 2450 SW Sherwood Dr, Portland, OR 97201 ... 503-532-7363
Ancona 2: 19 W 21st St #1001, New York, NY 10010 ... 212-807-8772
Andersen Design: 308 G St #A, San Rafael, CA 94901 ... 415-883-2004
Andersen, Bill: 27 Minkel Rd, Ossining, NY 10562 ... 914-762-4867
Anderson Jones Partners: 31726 Rancho Viejo Rd #207, San Juan Capistrano, CA 92675 714-240-6802
Anderson, David: 539 North Linden Ave, Oak Park, IL 60302 ... 708-848-1020
Anderson, Hornall: 1008 Western Ave #600, Seattle, WA 98104 ... 206-467-5800
Anderson, Jeri Lyn: 750 Berkshire Ave, Pittsburgh, PA 15226 ... 412-531-0145
Anderson, Lance: 5937 Shasta Ave, Dunsmuir, CA 96025 ... 415-788-5893
Anderson, Lisa: 15750 Crestwick Dr, La Mirada, CA 90638 ... 310-943-7851
Anderson, Mark: 790 High St, Palo Alto, CA 94301 ... 415-328-8864
Anderson, Michael: 28202 Cabot Rd #300, Laguna Niguel, CA 92677 ... 714-831-3501
Anderson, Mike: PO Box 9315, Newport Beach, CA 92658 ... 714-662-6546
Anderson, Russ & Terry: 1054 W Dragoon Ave, Mesa, AZ 85210 ... 602-969-5299
Anderson-Thomas Design, Inc: 110 29th Ave N #301, Nashville, TN 37203 ... 615-327-9894
Anderson/Clark Design: 10999 Riverside Dr #110, N Hollywood, CA 91602 ... 818-760-8881
Andre & Assocs, Brian: 3 Hutton Center #700, Santa Ana, CA 92704 ... 714-957-1314
Andrews Co, Inc, WE: 140 South Rd, Bedford, MA 01730 ... 617-275-0720
Animated Systems & Design: 1900 Embaracero Rd #110, Palo Alto, CA 94303 ... 415-424-8586
Annis, Scott: 26099 McCiver, Conifer, CO 80433 ... 303-674-1151
Annivette Stuido: 802 Belvidere Ave, Plainfield, NJ 07060 ... 908-561-5596
Another Artist: 2601 Thrasher Ln #2, San Jose, CA 95125 ... 408-978-7010
Another Planet: 7430 Milan Ave, St Louis, MO 63130 ... 314-726-5013
Ansbro Design: 1261 Green Acres Ct, Santa Cruz, CA 95062 ... 408-475-4684
Anslow & Spathas Design: 6214 SE Milwaukie Ave, Portland, OR 97202 ... 503-231-0806
Anspach Grossman PORTUGAL: 711 Third Ave 12th Fl, New York, NY 10017 ... 212-692-9000
Anthony Co, Robert: 10 E 23rd St 2nd Fl, New York, NY 10010 ... 212-673-3011
Anthony-Franklin: 342 W 200 South #230, Salt Lake City, UT 84101 ... 801-532-0670
Antisdel Image Group: 2332 Fruitdale Ave, San Jose, CA 95054 ... 408-988-1010
Antista Fairclough Design: 64 Lenox Point NE, Atlanta, GA 30324 ... 404-816-3201
Antokas Graphics, Stacey: 152 W 24th St/3rd Fl, New York, NY 10011 ... 212-675-6006
Antonuccio Design, David: 31-72 41st St 2nd Fl, Long Island City, NY 11103 ... 718-956-7815
Apex Design: 906 Mulberry Ave, Hagerstown, MD 21742 ... 301-791-9312
Aplin, Uno & Chibana: 2685 Marine Way #1415, Mountain View, CA 94043 ... 415-966-8000
Apor Design: 701 Atkins Dr, Glendale, CA 91206 ... 818-549-0822
Appelbaum Company: 220 E 23rd St #507, New York, NY 10010 ... 212-213-1130
Apple Design Source: 58 W 40th St 6th Fl, New York, NY 10018 ... 212-575-6373
Apple Design, Hal: 1112 Ocean Dr #203, Manhattan Beach, CA 90266 ... 310-318-3823
Apple Design/CA: 1309 Milton Ave, Walnut Creek, CA 94596 ... 510-256-6625
Appleton Design: 488 Fern St, West Hartford, CT 06107 ... 860-521-4745
Aramian, Tammy: 663 S Bernardo Ave #7B, Sunnyvale, CA 94087 ... 415-964-3938
Arana, Lupe & Assoc: 11533 Slater Ave #H, Fountain Valley, CA 92708 ... 714-540-6700
Aratar: 220 Downey St, San Francisco, CA 94117 ... 415-753-5855
Arcanna Design Comm: 650 Central Ave, Peekskill, NY 10566 ... 914-736-1760
Arce & Kwan Inc: 10 E 2nd St #1, New York, NY 10003 ... 212-387-9209
Arce, Alex: 10 E 2nd St, New York, NY 10003 ... 212-387-9209
Archambault, Donna: One Scenic Drive, Portland, CT 06480 ... 203-342-1023
Archer Design: 353 Folsom St 2nd Fl, San Francisco, CA 94105 ... 415-777-5788
Archey & Cavala: 1045 San Some St., #201, San Francisco, CA 94111 ... 415-392-9870
Architectural Design Alliance Inc: 1737 Chestnut St, Philadelphia, PA 19103 ... 215-561-9700
Architext: 121 Interpark Blvd #208, San Antonio, TX 78216 ... 210-490-2240
Archuleta Design, Archie: 11200 Hume NE, Albuquerque, NM 87112 ... 505-291-0285
Arena & Assocs: 61 Camino Alto #101, Mill Valley, CA 94941 ... 415-383-9632
Arias Design Group: 502 Waverley, Palo Alto, CA 94301 ... 415-321-8138
Arizona Graphics Network: 1054 W Dragoon Ave, Mesa, AZ 85210 ... 602-969-5299
Arkkit-Forms: 692-A Moulton Ave, Los Angeles, CA 90031 ... 213-227-0191
Arlt Graphics, Bob: 8392 Westlawn Ave, Los Angeles, CA 90045 ... 310-568-0087
Armstrong Assocs: 1330 N Dutton Ave #201, Santa Rosa, CA 95401 ... 707-527-8511
Armstrong Design Consultants: Box 12967, Raleigh, NC 27605 ... 919-233-5786
Arneal, Clark Graphics: 1001 John St, Manhattan Beach, CA 90266 ... 310-376-6666
Arnell Group: 130 Prince St, New York, NY 10011 ... 212-219-8400
Arnold Assocs, Peter: 1 Hollis St #211, Wellesley, MA 02181 ... 617-239-1030
Arnold Design: 105 Fifth Ave S #450, Minneapolis, MN 55401 ... 612-339-2440
Arnott Group Design, Inc, The: 33 Davies Ave, Toronto, ON M4M 2A9 ... 416-778-8990
Aron & Co, Michael: 156 Fifth Ave #500, New York, NY 10010 ... 212-627-4054
Art Assocs: 5450 Louie Ln, Reno, NV 89511 ... 702-828-3500
Art At Work: 4500 N 12th St, Phoenix, AZ 85014 ... 602-274-9833
Art By Christian, Inc: 6343 Waterway Dr, Falls Church, VA 22044 ... 703-642-5429
Art City: 6284 Brookhill Dr, Houston, TX 77087 ... 713-644-1018
Art Department: 2 W 46th St, New York, NY 10036 ... 212-391-1826
Art Department Inc, The: 1 W Market St #205, York, PA 17401 ... 717-845-4344
Art Department, The: 14714 Midship Woods Ct, Chesterfield, VA 23832 ... 804-739-1198
Art Department, The: 2039 Willow Wood Ln, Encinitas, CA 92024 ... 619-944-7606
Art Department, The: 1779 Independence Blvd, Sarasota, FL 34234 ... 813-355-7266
Art Depot Creative Agency, The: 710 13th St #210, San Diego, CA 92101 ... 619-696-6545
Art Direction: 1100 W Lincoln Ave, Anaheim, CA 92805 ... 714-778-6767
Art Direction: 3774 Westside Ave, Los Angeles, CA 90018 ... 213-296-4858
Art Direction Services: 3319 El Dorado Blvd, Missouri City, TX 77749 ... 713-977-0654
Art Directions: 201A Tubac Rd, Tubac, AZ 85646 ... 520-398-9938
Art Directions, Inc: 28558 Lowell Court S, Southfield, MI 48076 ... 810-569-8566
Art Directors Club of Metropolitan Washington: 1620 Greenbrier Ct, Reston, VA 20190 ... 703-742-8055
Art Directors Service: 222 Waukegan Rd, Glenview, IL 60025 ... 847-657-1600
Art Etc: 2600 7th Street Rd, Louisville, KY 40208 ... 502-637-6066
Art Factory: 925 Elm Grove Rd, Elm Grove, WI 53122 ... 414-785-1940
Art Forms, Inc: 5150 Prospect Ave, Cleveland, OH 44103 ... 216-361-3855
Art Group, The: 3100 Smoketree Ct #1004, Raleigh, NC 27604 ... 919-876-6765
Art Hotel: 321 1/2 Huntly Dr, Los Angeles, CA 90048 ... 310-854-6154
Art O Matic: 33951 Calle La Primavera, Dana Point, CA 92629 ... 714-240-1856
Art Only, Inc: 2830 S Bannock St, Englewood, CO 80110 ... 303-762-0422
Art Patrol Graphics Design: 25 W 89th St #4B, New York, NY 10024 ... 212-787-3390
Art Rageous Design Services, Inc: 5904 Funston St, Hollywood, FL 33023 ... 305-961-7997
Art Service: 1135 Spring St NW, Atlanta, GA 30309 ... 404-892-2105
Art Spikol: 751 S Fifth St, Philadelphia, PA 19147 ... 215-627-4545
Art Studio, The: 110 30th Ave N #3, Nashville, TN 37203 ... 615-329-3511
Art Works: 11418 SE 90th Ave #117, Portland, OR 97266 ... 503-659-2103
Art Worx: 155 Teaneck Rd, Teaneck, NJ 07666 ... 201-836-1273
Arteffects, Inc: Midtown Tower #1115, Rochester, NY 14604 ... 716-232-7000
Artemis: 721 Emerson St, Palo Alto, CA 94301 ... 415-325-6596
Artery, The: 12 W Biddle St, Baltimore, MD 21201 ... 301-752-2979
Artful Education: 2913 Fulton St, Berkely, CA 94705 ... 510-843-7421
Arthur Design: 4751 Del Moreno Pl, Woodland Hills, CA 91364 ... 818-884-8748
Arthur Eckstein & Assoc Inc: 47 Pinetree Ln, Roslyn Hts, NY 11577 ... 516-484-0606
Artifakt: 3748 22nd St, San Francisco, CA 94114 ... 415-647-4700
Artists Studios: 850 Euclid Ave Ste 800, Cleveland, OH 44114 ... 216-241-5355
Artmania: 8961 Complex Dr, San Diego, CA 92123 ... 619-277-0071
Artmarks: 11 Rally Ct, Fairfax, CA 94930 ... 415-721-2900
Artmaster Studios: 122-50 Monteque St, Pacoima, CA 91331 ... 818-896-7551
Artmill, The: 2701 N Reserve, Missoula, MT 59802 ... 406-543-7983
Artographix: 436 W Colorado #114, Glendale, CA 91204 ... 818-500-1191
Artrix Interactive Studios: 71 W 23rd St #507, New York, NY 10010 ... 212-633-9695
Arts & Graphics: 4010 Justine Dr, Annandale, VA 22003 ... 703-941-2560
Arts Place: 210 N Higgins #232, Missoula, MT 59802 ... 406-549-3460
Artsake: 900 E First St #307, Los Angeles, CA 90012 ... 213-617-0488
Artscape: 532 El Dorado St, Pasadena, CA 91101 ... 818-584-3997
Artwerks: 303 Potrero St #52, Santa Cruz, CA 95060 ... 408-427-9040
Artworks: 18 Vine St, Lexington, MA 02173 ...
Artworks, Inc: PO Box 11001, Norfolk, VA 23517 ... 757-624-2424
Arunski Assocs, Joe: 10660 NW 17th Pl, Plantation, FL 33322 ... 305-473-4114
Asbury & Assocs: 3450 E Spring St #214, Long Beach, CA 90806 ... 310-595-6481
Ascending Graphics: 1054 W Dragoon Ave, Mesa, AZ 85210 ... 602-969-5299
Ashcraft Design: 11832 W Pico Blvd, Los Angeles, CA 90064 ... 310-479-8330
Asher Studio: 1700 E 17th Ave, Denver, CO 80218 ... 303-321-5599
Asher, Terri: 21800 Schoenborn St #162, Canoga Park, CA 91304 ... 818-348-4278
Ashton & Co, David: 611 Cathedral St, Baltimore, MD 21201 ... 301-727-1151
Askey Design & Illus: PO Box 591, Skaneateles, NY 13152 ... 315-685-3908
Aslan Media: 4801 Woodway #280E, Houston, TX 77057 ... 713-960-9411
Aspect Ratio Design: 1347 Cahuenga Blvd, Hollywood, CA 90028 ... 213-467-2121
Associated Graphics: 3630 W Pioneer Pkwy #131, Arlington, TX 76013 ... 817-459-1409
Associates Design, Inc: 509 19th St, Galveston, TX 77750 ... 489-762-5552
Associates Inc, The : 5319 Lee Hwy, Arlington, VA 22207 ... 703-534-3940
Aster: 136 High Dr, Laguna Beach, CA 92651 ... 714-494-6192
Asylum: 848 W Eastman #206, Chicago, IL 60622 ... 312-482-8877
Atelier 85: PO Box 491413, Los Angeles, CA 90049 ... 310-826-1785
Athanasius Design: 1300 N Damen Ave, Chicago, IL 60622 ... 773-252-7271
Atkins Design, Alexander: 3790 El Camino Real #346, Palo Alto, CA 94306 ... 650-948-6644
Atkins, Martyn: 1655 N Cherokee #300, Hollywood, CA 90028 ... 213-653-8625
Atkins, Sharon: 20 Birch Hill Rd, Weston, CT 06883 ... 203-222-7040
Atlanta Wristworks: 282 Southerland Terr NE, Atlanta, GA 30307 ... 404-373-3001
Atlas Communications: 1312 N Greenview, Chicago, IL 60622 ... 773-772-0177
Atlas Design: 27560 Falling Star Ln, Santa Clarita, CA 91350 ... 805-297-0013
Attenzione Graphics: 191 S Goodman St, Rochester, NY 14607 ... 716-244-8028
Attiliis & Assocs: 9710 Days Farm Dr, Vienna, VA 22182 ... 703-759-4283
Atwood Design, Donna: 1137 W Culver, Phoenix, AZ 85007 ... 602-254-7168
Au Design, Poung: 8550 Katy Freeway #218, Houston, TX 77024 ... 713-468-8288
Auburn Ad Group, The: 927 Lincoln Way, Auburn, CA 95603 ... 916-888-0484
Aucella & Assocs: 132 Woodcliff Dr, Westfield, MA 01085 ... 413-568-7069
Augusta Design Group: 520 Broadway 2nd Fl, New York, NY 10012 ... 212-941-4753
Auras Design: 8435 Georgia Ave, Silver Spring, MD 20910 ... 202-745-0088
Auster, Walter: 18 E 16th St, New York, NY 10003 ... 212-627-8448
Auston Design Group: 651 Main St, St Helena, CA 94574 ... 707-963-4152
Authentic Design: PO Box 310, Malibu, CA 90265 ... 818-880-5015
Auto Graphics: PO Box 1000, San Leandro, CA 94577 ... 510-352-5665
Autographic: 530 W 37th St, San Pedro, CA 90731 ... 310-833-3840
Automated Graphics: 6075 E Molly Rd, Syracuse, NY 13211 ... 315-437-7561
AV Graphics: 757 Bethel School Rd, Coppell, TX 75019 ... 214-393-7700
Avallon Thackwell Design: 1672 Michael Ln, Pacific Palisades, CA 90272 ... 310-459-9991
Avanti Case/Hoyt Advertising: 568 Broadway, New York, NY 10012 ... 212-966-6661
Avatar NuMedia: 2635 Park Blvd, Palo Alto, CA 94306 ... 415-322-3838
Avchen & Assocs: 1645 Hennepin Ave S #308, Minneapolis, MN 55403 ... 612-339-1206
Avenue Creative Group: 10 SE First Ave, Delray Beach, FL 33444 ... 407-274-4663
Avery Design Consultants, Eileen: 211 W Gutierrez St #8, Santa Barbara, CA 93101 ... 805-884-0221
Avit Corp, The: 1355 15th St #100, Fort Lee, NJ 07024 ... 201-886-1100
AVM Graphics: PO Box 386, Tempe, AZ 85280 ... 602-894-9365
AVS, Inc: 2109 Ward Ave, La Crosse, WI 54601 ... 415-322-3838
Award Design: PO Box 82222, Fairbanks, AK 99708 ... 907-455-8000
Aware Media: PO Box 834, Santa Cruz, CA 95061 ... 408-457-2425
Awjm Systems: 224 Pennsylvania Way, North Brunswick, NJ 08902 ... 908-745-9475
Axiom Communications: 36 S Paca St #108, Baltimore, MD 21201 ... 410-727-4222
Axiom Design: 1415 S Church St #H, Charlotte, NC 2802 ... 704-372-1600
Axiom Design & Mktg Comms: 331 S Main St, Salt Lake City, UT 84111 ... 801-532-2442
Axion Design, Inc: 137 Tunstead Ave, San Anselmo, CA 94960 ... 415-258-6800
Axis Design: 5807 N Tobias Ave, Van Nuys, CA 91411 ... 818-781-8848
Axis Design Communications, Inc: 2966 Twin Oaks Dr, Highland Park, IL 60035 ... 847-266-9330
Axo Design Studio: 423 Tehama St, San Francisco, CA 94103 ... 415-543-8712
Ayers Johanek Publication Design: 4750 Rolling Hills Dr, Bozeman, MT 59715 ... 406-585-8826
Ayzenberg Design: 39 E Walnut St, Pasadena, CA 91103 ... 818-584-4070

B

B & A Design Group: 634C W Broadway, Glendale, CA 91204 ... 818-547-4080
B & B Design: 300 Mass Ave Mezz, Boston, MA 02115 ... 617-859-8300
B Amos Designs: 4073 Gresham #2, San Diego, CA 92109 ... 619-296-8235
B Productions: 7741 Alabama Ave #13, Canoga Park, CA 91304 ... 818-347-8738
B Zign Communications, Inc: 3209 W Highland Blvd #205, Milwaukee, WI 53208 ... 414-937-6543
B3 Design: 2822 Kinney Dr, Walnut Creek, CA 94595 ... 510-947-6179
Babcock & Schmid Assocs: 2138 N Cleveland-Massillon Rd, Bath, OH 44210 ... 216-666-8826
Bachman Design Group, Inc: 6001 Memorial Dr, Dublin, OH 43017 ... 614-793-9993
Bachner & Co: 130 W 25th St 10th Fl, New York, NY 10001 ... 212-243-5287
Baer Design Assocs, Kimberly: 620 Hampton Dr, Venice, CA 90291 ... 310-399-3295
Baer, Kimberly Design Assoc: 620 Hampton Dr, Venice, CA 90291 ... 310-399-3295
Baese, Gary: 2229 N Charles St, Baltimore, MD 21218 ... 410-235-2226
Bagby Design: 455 City Front Plz Dr 16th Fl, Chicago, IL 60611 ... 312-755-3100
Bagnell & Socha: 14 Rock Hill Rd, Bala Cynwyd, PA 19004 ... 610-667-2040
Bailey Spiker, Inc: 2250 Hickory Rd #200, Plymouth Meetin, PA 19462 ... 610-940-9030

Bailey, Robert: 0121 SW Bancroft St, Portland, OR 97201 ... 503-228-1381
Bailey-Montague & Assocs: 19 E 200 South 10th Fl, Salt Lake City, UT 84111 ... 801-328-0573
Bailie, Gail: 3 Milwaukee Ave, Bethel, CT 06801 ... 203-790-8487
Bain, S Milo: 3 Shaw Ln, Hartsdale, NY 10530 ... 914-946-0144
Baker & Baker Design: 8422 Valley View Dr SE, Huntsville, AL 35802 ... 205-883-0963
Baker Assocs: 708 E Lake St, Wayzata, MN 55391 ... 612-473-4882
Baker, Arthur: PO Box 29, Germantown, NY 12526 ... 518-537-4438
Baker, Eric: 11 E 22nd St 5th Fl, New York, NY 10010 ... 212-598-9111
Baker, Richard: 4230 W Porter Ave, Fullerton, CA 92633 ... 714-994-0459
Balasas, Cora: 651 Vanderbilt St, Brooklyn, NY 11218 ... 718-633-7753
Balbes, Sydney L: 9740 Sepulveda #17, N Hills, CA 91343 ... 818-891-1370
Baldassini, Paul: 234 Clarendon St, Boston, MA 02116 ... 617-236-0190
Balderman & Assocs: 30191 Avenida de las Banderas, Rancho St Margarita, CA 92688 ... 714-589-7403
Baldino Design, Patt: 305 Madison Ave #956, New York, NY 10165 ... 212-986-5987
Baldwin Assocs Adv & Design: 5205 Ellicott Ct, Centerville, VA 20120 ... 703-222-9686
Baldwin Design: 47 Warren St, Salem, MA 01970 ... 508-745-6462
Baldwin, James: 1467 Jordan Ave, Crofton, MD 21114 ... 301-721-1896
Balin Design, Raquel: 3 Simmons Dr N, Woodstock, NY 12498 ... 914-679-4228
Ball Design Group: 410 W Fallbrook Ave #206, Fresno, CA 93711 ... 209-275-7136
Ballard Design Inc, Carole: 52 Lemoyne Pkwy, Oak Park, IL 60302 ... 708-848-3611
Bally Design: 424 N Craig, Pittsburgh, PA 15213 ... 412-621-9009
Balmer, Dave: 8821 Horn Day Cir #513, Ft Worth, TX 76120 ... 817-656-1925
Balog Group: 742 N Las Palmas Ave, Los Angeles, CA 90038 ... 213-464-4140
Bancer Printing: 401 Osage, Maumee, OH 43537 ... 419-891-1234
Banks & Assocs: 507 Veteran Ave, Los Angeles, CA 90024 ... 310-476-5289
Banks Design Assoc: 6 Bel Aire Dr, Plainville, CT 06062 ... 203-747-0701
Banks Design, Albert: 215 Church St #218, Decatur, GA 30030 ... 404-370-1999
Banks Design, Lynda: 15 Saddlebrook Ct, Novato, CA 94947 ... 415-898-9988
Bant Assocs, T: PO Box 183, Wrightwood, CA 92397 ... 619-249-5897
Bantam Books, Inc: 1540 Broadway, New York, NY 10036 ... 212-354-6500
Baranti Group, Inc: 210 Cochrone Dr Unit 6, Markham, ON L3R 8E6 ... 905-479-0148
Barber Design, Jane: 4343 N Clarendon St #415, Chicago, IL 60613 ... 779-472-5172
Barclay & Assocs: 306 Laurel Ave, Wilmette, IL 60091 ... 847-251-5821
Barfuss Creative Services: 1331 Lake Dr SE, Grand Rapids, MI 49506 ... 616-459-8888
Barhydt-Krall, Anne: 6012 Simpson Ave, North Hollywood, CA 91606 ... 818-762-0213
Barich & Assocs, David: 830 Lake St, San Francisco, CA 94118 ... 415-750-8048
Barker & Lee Graphic Design: 3248 Minnesota Ave, Costa Mesa, CA 92626 ... 714-850-1935
Barker Design: 212 High St, Palo Alto, CA 94301 ... 415 322-7272
Barker Design, Judith: 779 Eighth Ave, San Francisco, CA 94118 ... 415-386-3531
Barnes Design/Chicago: 680 N Lakeshore Dr #625, Chicago, IL 60611 ... 312-337-0495
Barnes Graphics, Herb: 142 W Colorado Blvd, Pasadena, CA 91105 ... 818-682-2420
Barnes, Christopher: 1801 Falls Rd #2A, Baltimore, MD 21201 ... 410-576-0856
Barnes, Kathy: 20231 Orchid St, Newport Beach, CA 92660 ... 714-852-8886
Barnett Design: 270 Lafayette St #801, New York, NY 10012 ... 212-431-7130
Barnett, Gregory: 4869 Topanga Canyon Blvd #8, Woodland Hills, CA 91364 ... 818-340-2123
Barnstorm Design: 2902 W Colorado Ave #200, Colorado Springs, CO 80904 ... 719-630-7200
Baron Graphics: 147 Concress St, Portsmouth, NH 03801 ... 603-436-3153
Barrett Design, Janice: 2154 Golden Ave, Long Beach, CA 90806 ... 310-218-8484
Barrett Laidlaw Gervais: 9260 Sunset Dr #103, Miami, FL 33173 ... 305-596-1379
Barrett, Lisa: 6216 Murietta Ave, Van Nuys, CA 91401 ... 818-989-1016
Barry, Jim: 69 W 68th St, New York, NY 10023 ... 212-873-6787
Barsuhn Design: 420 N 5th St #1186, Minneapolis, MN 55401 ... 612-339-2146
Bart Direction: 850 Battery St, San Francisco, CA 94111 ... 415-421-1434
Bartel Design Group: 2820 Glendale Blvd, Los Angeles, CA 90039 ... 213-662-6869
Bartels & Cartsens: 3286 Ivanhoe, St Louis, MO 63139 ... 314-781-7377
Bartelt Design: 4055 N Downer Ave, Milwaukee, WI 53211 ... 414-332-4031
Barth & Co: 10 Bassett Highway, Dover, NJ 07801 ... 201-328-7776
Barth, Henrietta: 2113 Warwick Ln, Shaumburg, IL 60193 ... 847-582-1063
Bartholomew Assocs: 433C Fourth St, Annapolis, MD 21403 ... 301-261-1422
Barton: 17195 Newhope #110, Fountain Valley, CA 92708 ... 714-434-7465
Barton & Barton: 3027 Broadmoor Dr, Sugar Land, TX 77478 ... 713-626-2246
Barton Design, Gladys: 245 Everit Ave, Hewlett, NY 11557 ... 516-295-4472
Barton-Cotton: 10099 SE White Pelican Way, Jupiter, FL 33469 ... 561-743-4700
Baseline Designs: 445 Bryant St, San Francisco, CA 94107 ... 415-974-1238
Basic Technology, Inc: 7125 Saltsburg Rd, Pittsburgh, PA 15235 ... 412-795-5300
Basika, Lee Reedy: 1542 Williams St, Denver, CO 80218 ... 303-333-2936
Baskin Group, The: 213 Bonifinated Rd, Silver Spring, MD 20905 ... 301-989-0515
Baskin, Hal: 6931 Arlington Rd #301, Bethesda, MD 20814 ... 301-913-2902
Bass Yager & Assocs: 8360 Melrose Ave, Los Angeles, CA 90069 ... 213-466-9701
Bassett Design: 90 East 11th St, Arcata, CA 95521 ... 707-826-2550
Bassinger: Star Route Box 20, Woodside, CA 94062 ... 415-529-1210
Basso & Associates: 3802 Buncombe Dr, Springboro, NC 27407 ... 336-461-3603
Bast Design, Beth: 81 Westwood Dr, San Francisco, CA 94112 ... 415-469-8773
Bates: 8143 Hihn Rd, Ben Lomond, CA 95005 ... 408-336-3661
Bates Design Studio: 207 E Bay St #303, Charleston, SC 29401 ... 803-722-6009
Batley, Glenis: 1811 N Tamarind #108, Los Angeles, CA 90028 ... 213-467-4352
Battles, Kim C: 919 Main St #211, El Segundo, CA 90245 ... 310-322-0637
Bauders Computer Graphics, Don: 1825A Egbert Ave, San Francisco, CA 94124 ... 415-468-5500
Bauer Design, Laura: 2611 Broadway, Redwood City, CA 94063 ... 415-327-3102
Baugh, Larry: 1417 N Irving Hgts, Irving, TX 75061 ... 214-438-5696
Bauman Design, Leslie: 310 W 106th St #8D, New York, NY 10025 ... 212-932-9423
Bausch Design: 1261 Alden Ct, Belmont, CA 94002 ... 415-595-1955
Baxter & Korge, Inc: 8323 Westglen St, Houston, TX 77063 ... 713-972-1600
Bay Graphics: 2030 Fifth St, Berkeley, CA 94710 ... 510-843-0701
Bay Network: 4401 Great American Pkwy, Santa Clara, CA 95054 ... 408-988-2400
Bazata Design, Tara: 9947 Monroe Dr, Thornton, CO 80229 ... 303-252-7712
BBID: 270 E Main Loft, Los Gatos, CA 95032 ... 408-354-3811
BC Studios: 3645 Jeannine Dr, Colorado Springs, CO 80917 ... 719-550-0505
BCA Design: 71 Saddle Rd, Walnut Creek, CA 94595 ... 510-946-1716
BCB Group: 670 Newfield St, Middletown, CT 06457 ... 203-347-7848
BCD Ink Ltd: 108 E 16th St, New York, NY 10003 ... 212-420-1222
Be One Design: 655 Bryant St, San Francisco, CA 94107 ... 415-243-0361
Beach Advertising: 225 S 15th St 23rd Fl, Philadelphia, PA 19102 ... 215-735-4747
Beals Advtg Agency: 5225 N Chartel #201, Oklahoma City, OK 73118 ... 405-848-8513
Bean Graphics, Inc: 310 West Main St, Greenwood, IN 46142 ... 317-882-7222
Bear Brook Design: 69 Helms Hill Rd, Washintonville, NY 10992 ... 914-496-2800
Bear Graphics: 105 E Main St, Mason, OH 45040 ... 513-398-2788
Beauchamp Group: 1743 Wazee St #321, Denver, CO 80202 ... 303-296-1133
Bechtel Design, Bill: 1629 Ogden St, Denver, CO 80218 ... 303-839-1818
Bechtold Studio, Bob: 471 S Fairview St, Burbank, CA 91505 ... 818-563-1405
Beck & Graboski Design Office: 247 16th St, Santa Monica, CA 90402 ... 310-393-9325
Beck/Durell Creative Dept: 1335 Worthington Woods Blvd, Worthington, OH 43085 ... 614-844-5544
Becker Design Assoc: 2715 Western Ave, Seattle, WA 98121 ... 206-448-7990
Beckett Advertising & Design, Edward: 1051 E Altadena Dr, Altadena, CA 91001 ... 818-791-7954
Bedlam Studio: 500 Molino St #310, Los Angeles, CA 90013 ... 213-617-1963
Bee Design, Paula: 182 Costa Mesa St, Costa Mesa, CA 92627 ... 714-548-0366
Beggs Design, Inc, Stephanie Langley : 619 Maybelle Ave, Palo Alto, CA 94506 ... 415-857-9539
Behr, Mario: 2463 Pine Tree Dr #3, Miami Bch, FL 33140 ... 305-674-8406
Behrens Design, Doug: PO Box 1674, Honolulu, HI 96806 ... 808-625-7522
Bel Aire Assocs: 730 Fifth Ave #2000, New York, NY 10019 ... 212-245-5700
Bell Group, The Clark: 339 Kreag Rd, Pittsford, NY 14534 ... 716-586-8848
Bell, Andrea: 11949 Darlington Ave #6, Los Angeles, CA 90049 ... 310-826-3898
Bell, Jill: 521 Indiana St Suite#C, El Segundo, CA 90245 ... 310-322-5542
Bellini Design: 325 W Huron #706, Chicago, IL 60610 ... 312-649-1710
Bellomo, Clea: 11911 Magnolia Blvd #27, N Hollywood, CA 91607 ... 818-509-6756
Belser, Burkey: 1818 N St NW #110, Washington, DC 20036 ... 202-775-0333
Belyea Design: 1809 7th Ave #1007, Seattle, WA 98101 ... 206-682-4895
Benchmark Display Inc: 1001 Woodlands Parkway, Vernon Hills, IL 60061 ... 847-541-2828
Benchmark Group, The: 700 W Pete Rose Way, Cincinnati, OH 45203 ... 513-621-3038
Bender, Diane: 2729 S Cleveland St, Arlington, VA 22206 ... 703-521-1006
Benes Communications, Inc: 1840 Massachusetts Ave 2nd Fl, Lexington, MA 02173 ... 617-647-2327
Benes Communications, Sigrid: 4265 Marina City Dr #317 W, Marina del Rey, CA 90292 310-827-7765
Benhase, Meg: 9541 E Myra Dr, Tucson, AZ 85730 ... 520-721-0330
Bennet Comm Graphics: 387 Bonhill Rd, Los Angeles, CA 90049 ... 310-472-4321
Bennett & Assoc, Ford: 3355 W Alabama #110, Houston, TX 77098 ... 713-871-0833
Bennett & Assocs: 1205 S Dewey #3, Bartlesville, OK 74003 ... 918-337-3773
Bennett Assocs, Ralph: 6361 Nestle Ave, Reseda, CA 91335 ... 818-342-7655
Bennett Design Assocs, Joel: 2606-514 Phoenix Dr, Greensboro, NC 27406 ... 910-547-0009
Bennett Design, Brandon: 1218 Armacost Ave #2, Los Angeles, CA 90025 ... 310-478-8331
Bennett Graphics Design, Martin: 2617 Lovegrove St, Baltimore, MD 21218 ... 410-338-0785
Bennett Peji Design: 1110 Tori Pines Rd #B, La Jolla, CA 92037 ... 619-456-8071
Bennett-Elia: 3304 Cole Ave Ste 171, Dallas, TX 75204 ... 214-855-3740
Benoit Design: 825 18th St, Plano, TX 75074 ... 214-509-7588
Benoit, Diane: 15777 Cleekwood Way, Morrison, CO 80465 ... 303-697-1463
Benton: 4612 Phacher Rd, Ojai, CA 93023 ... 805-646-8118
Berdahl Smith Wilson: 9 SW Pack Sq, Asheville, NC 28801 ... 704-253-8893
Berg Design, Neal: 604 W Third St, Tempe, AZ 85281 ... 602-966-2002
Berger & Assocs, Barry David: 54 King St, New York, NY 10014 ... 212-255-4100
Berger Design, Carin: 215 Berkeley Ol 3rd Fl, Brooklyn, NY 11217 ...
Berglund Advertising Design: 1555 Mesa Verde Dr East #37F, Costa Mesa, CA 92626 ... 714-545-4948
Bergstrom Design: 52 Gilbert St, So Salem, NY 10590 ... 914-533-5553
Berkshire Group: 14 Station St, Simsbury, CT 06070 ... 203-658-0012
Bernhardt/Fudyma: 133 E 36th St, New York, NY 10016 ... 212-889-9337
Berni, Inc: 666 Steamboat Rd, Greenwich, CT 06830 ... 203-661-4747
Berns & Kay Ltd: 7347 Wisconsin Ave 2nd Fl, Bethesda, MD 20814 ... 310-652-2611
Bernstein & Co, Steve: 33 Riverside Dr, New York, NY 10023 ... 212-877-7758
Bernstein Design, Sara: 799 Union St 3rd Fl, Brooklyn, NY 11215 ... 718-783-4156
Bernstein, Harvey: 160 Fifth Ave #804, New York, NY 10010 ... 212-243-4149
Berry Design: 755 Mid Broadwell Rd, Alpharetta, GA 30201 ... 770-664-9531
Berry Design, Patt Mann: 20340 Hebard Rd, Los Gatos, CA 95030 ... 408-353-6403
Berson, Julie: 10 Westfair Dr, Westport, NY 06880 ... 203-255-9431
Berta Graphic Design, Michael: 590 Hull Ave, San Jose, CA 95125 ... 408-293-6779
Bertin Design Group: 44 Harbor Park Dr, Port Washington, NY 11050 ... 516-484-1490
Bertz Design, Ted: 190 Washington St, Middletown, CT 06457 ... 860-347-4332
Berwald Graphic Design Inc, Patty: 1 Shorewood Ln, Centerport, NY 11721 ... 516-754-5646
Berwyn Design: 7670 Opportunity Rd #230, San Diego, CA 92111 ... 619-571-3632
Besalel, Ely: 235 E 49th St, New York, NY 10017 ... 212-759-7820
Besser Design Group: 1004 Santa Monica Blvd, Santa Monica, CA 90401 ... 310-899-1895
Best Design: 815 W Armitage Ave #2, Chicago, IL 60614 ...
Best Road: 26 Palmer Ave, N Tarrytown, NY 10591 ... 914-631-9168
Bestgen Design: 33775 Dianna Dr, Dana Point, CA 92629 ... 714-493-6857
Betro Communications: 345 Hollywood Ave, Akron, OH 44303 ... 330-867-9825
Betz Design: 211 Washington Ave N, Minneapolis, MN 55401 ... 612-340-1514
Beuret, Janis: PO Box 22645, Honolulu, HI 96814 ... 808-537-6647
Beveridge & Assocs, Inc: 2020 N 14th St #444, Arlington, VA 22201 ... 202-243-2888
Beveridge Seay, Inc: 2020 N 14th St #444, Arlington, VA 22201 ... 703-516-9000
Bevilacqua, Joe: 202 E 42nd St, New York, NY 10017 ... 212-490-0355
Beynon Company, The: 10355 Washington Blvd, Culver City, CA 90232 ... 310-836-3363
Beyond Design: 6 Bordeaux Ct, Petaluma, CA 94954 ... 707-763-1678
Beyond Words: PO Box 41645, Santa Barbara, CA 93140 ... 310-841-5807
Bezdek Design: 140 Harrington Rd, Waltham, MA ... 617-894-7119
Bhang Design Assocs, Samuel: 824 S Burnside, Los Angeles, CA 90036 ... 213-382-1126
Bi Design: 2070 Business Ctr Dr #210, Irvine, CA 92715 ... 714-261-1114
Bianco Marchilonis Design: 60 Deham Ave, Needham, MA 02192 ... 617-444-9077
Bieger Assocs, Walter: 1689 W County Rd F, Arden Hills, MN 55112 ... 612-636-8500
Bielenberg Design Group, John: 6020 Pacific View Dr, Los Angeles, CA 90068 ... 213-874-9952
Bielenberg Design, John: 421 Tehana, San Francisco, CA 94103 ... 415-495-3371
Biesek Design: 2829 See Canyon Rd, San Luis Obispo, CA 93405 ... 805-595-2640
Big Bang Graphics: 1300 Micheltorena St, Los Angeles, CA 90026 ... 213-664-6287
Big City Graphics: 8270 SW 116th Terr, Miami, FL 33156 ... 305-235-4700
Big Design: 3733 N Lowell, Chicago, IL 60641 ... 773-205-0083
Big Design Group, The: 1708 Peachtree St NW #100, Atlanta, GA 30309 ... 404-724-4944
Big Time Creative Services: 840 Ogden St #2, Denver, CO 80218 ... 303-837-0689
Biggs Design: 110 Veterans Blvd #121A, Metarie, LA 70005 ... 504-828-3020
Bilcat Company: 815 Harbour Way #6/PO Box 37, Point Richmond, CA 94807 ... 510-233-5358
Bilenker, Susan: PO Box 620, Hastings-on-Hudson, NY 10706 ... 914-478-3514
Billings, Susan: PO Box 629, Norwood, CO 81423 ... 303-327-4378
Binder & Assocs, Andrew Paul: 12812 Landale St, Studio City, CA 91604 ... 818-508-8621
Biner Design: 2208 Crystal Way, Crystal Lake, IL 60012 ... 815-477-1650
Bingenheimer Design Comm: 126 E Ctr College St, Yellow Springs, OH 45387 ... 937-767-2521
Biondo Design Assocs, Charles: 680 5th Ave 20th Fl, New York, NY 10019 ... 212-645-5300
Bios: 216 First Ave S #204, Seattle, WA 98104 ... 206-587-2451
Birchler, Mary: 67 Water St, San Francisco, CA 94133 ... 415-474-2182
Bird & Co, R: 150 E 52nd St, New York, NY 10022 ... 212-317-8300
Bird Advertising Design, John: 212 High St, Palo Alto, CA 94301 ... 415-325-0665
Bird Design: 875 Main St, Cambridge, MA 02192 ... 617-491-7491
Birnbaum Design: 331 Harvard St #14, Cambridge, MA 02139 ... 617-491-7826
Bischoff Design Inc, Phinney : 614 Boyston Ave E, Seattle, WA 98102 ... 206-322-3484

Bizart: 302 W Loraine St #8, Glendale, CA 91202 818-545-1114
BJM Creative Services: 1394 Taylor SW, Jenison, MI 49428 616-457-8790
Bjorck Posson, Liselotte: 8340 San Marcos, Ataskadero, CA 93422 805-461-4171
BK Design: 9 Hawthorne Place #11D, Boston, MA 02114 617-523-8940
Black & White Design: 155 Browenten Pl, Louisville, KY 40222 502-326-0613
Black Advertising Group Inc, Gib: 206 Merchant St, Honolulu, HI 96813 808-531-4277
Black Bean Studios: 35 Kenneth St, West Roxbury, MA 02132 617-338-5444
Black Diamond Design: 948 E 50 North, Lindon, UT 84042 801-785-0963
Black Dog Graphics: 413 Wacouta St #550, St Paul, MN 55101 612-647-0780
Black Graphics: 1050 Franklin St #401, San Francisco, CA 94109 415-563-7345
Black Point Group, The: 353 laurel Ave, Novato, CA 94965 415-331-4531
Black Studio, Roger: 251 Park Ave S 10th Fl, New York, NY 10010 212-293-7200
Black, Roger: 251 Park Ave S 10th Fl, New York, NY 10010 212-293-7200
Blair Communications: 2104 Holly Dr, Los Angeles, CA 90068 213-871-0889
Blair Creative Group: 73A Del Mar St, San Francisco, CA 94117 415-252-1233
Blair Design, Barry: 30100 Town Center Dr #O 155, Laguna Niguel, CA 92677 . . 714-249-1577
Blair Graphics: 1740 Stanford St, Santa Monica, CA 90404 310-829-4621
Blair, Michelle: 1221 Nicollet Mall #230, Minneapolis, MN 55403 612-338-1700
Blake & Barancik Design: 135 S 18th St #403A, Philadelphia, PA 19103 215-977-9540
Blake Graphic Design, SJ: 4437 Ambrose Ave #16, Los Angeles, CA 90027 . . 213-666-5984
Blake, Susan: 750 Eighth Ave #503, New York, NY 10036 212-575-4705
Blankenburg Assocs: 2435 Beltmont Ave, Chicago, IL 60618 773-935-1860
Blankenship, Gaylen: 328 Redwood Ave, Corte Madera, CA 94925 415-927-3730
Blazej Graphics, Rosalie: 50 Laidley St, San Francisco, CA 94131 415-695-0264
Blazing Graphics: 25 Amflex Dr, Cranston, RI 02921 401-946-6100
Bledsoe, Sheila: 324 Timber Loop, Post Falls, ID 83854 208-773-1387
Blevins Design: 111 E First St, Elmhurst, IL 60126 630-530-8343
Blick Benest & Co: 609 N Broadway #200, Wichita, KS 67214. 316-267-4287
Blink: 326 Teresita Blvd, San Francisco, CA 94127 415-775-3617
Blink Studio: 54 Points Of View, Warwick, NY 10990 914-987-1001
Bloch & Coulter Design: 2440 S Sepulveda #152/Bldg #2, Los Angeles, CA 90064 . . 310-445-6550
• Bloch, Anthony: pg 922 23-39 33rd St, Astoria, NY 11105 . . . . **718-274-6064**
   e-mail: abld@mindspring.com / url: www.anthonybloch.com / fax: 718-274-1826
Bloch, Graulich & Whelan Inc: 333 Park Ave S, New York, NY 10010 212-473-7033
Block & Nardizzi: 1 Stamford Landing, Stamford, CT 06902 203-969-1311
Bloom, Mary Ellen: 1222 Eighth St, Hermosa Beach, CA 90254 310-376-2614
Blue Hen Graphics: 3 Great Jones St, New York, NY 10012 212-260-2423
Blue Mammoth Design: 65543 Naper Blvd #11, Naperville, IL 60540 630-579-9036
Blue Moon Graphics: 3910 Bowser Ave, Dallas, TX 75219 214-526-3881
Blue Rock Design: 120 Charles River St, Needham, MA 02192 617-449-5374
Blue Sky: 1912 Spring Croft Dr, Franklin, TN 37067. 615-771-6726
Blue Sky Limited: 15 Kimball Rd, Boxford, MA 01921 508-352-7939
Blumhoff Design, William: 28210 N Avenue Stanford, Valencia, CA 91355 . . . 805-257-0785
Blumlein Assocs: 25 Northern Blvd, Greenvale, NY 11548 516-625-2713
Boardwalk: 116 N Maryland Ave, Glendale, CA 91206 818-566-7007
Bobel, Jane: 7543 Juler Ave, Cincinnati, OH 45243. 513-791-5337
Bober, Marlene: 449 Pleasant St, Framingham, MA 01701 508-872-4165
Bode Design: 1781 Blodgett Rd, Mount Vernon, WA 98273 206-424-0368
Boden Fugate Marketing Design: 511 S Magnolia Ave #14, El Cajon, CA 92020 . . 619-440-0444
Bodenhamer Inc, William S: 7380 SW 121st St, Miami, FL 33156 305-253-9284
Bodkin Design Group: 25 Sylvan Rd S, Westport, CT 06880 203-221-0404
Bodo Communications: 9594 First Ave NE #426, Seattle, WA 98115 206-818-8640
Body Comp: 7101 Hannum Ave, Culver City, CA 90230 310-572-7758
Bodzioch Design, Leon: 30 Robins Farm Rd, Dunstable, MA 01827. 508-251-1308
Boelter, Herbert A: 1014 W Riverside Dr #43, Burbank, CA 91506. 818-846-3134
Boelts Brothers Vis Comms: 345 E University Blvd, Tucson, AZ 85705. 520-792-1026
Bogart Szabodes, Inc: 2828 Upton St NW, Washington, DC 20008 202-363-6699
Bogner Design Communications, Albert: 617 W Chestnut St, Lancaster, PA 17603 . . 717-399-4094
Bohlin, Marshall: 17 W220 22nd St #400, Oakbrook Terr, IL 60181. 630-920-1092
Bohn, Richard: 595 W Wilson St, Costa Mesa, CA 92627. 949-548-6669
Bohnhoff Design: 409 S East Ave, Oak Park, IL 60302 708-848-8009
Boldface Design: 1332 1/2 N McCadden Pl, Los Angeles, CA 90028 213-957-2338
Boller Coates Ltd: 900 N Franklin #800, Chicago, IL 60610 312-787-2783
BonDurant, Steve: 277 Alexander St Ste 400, Rochester, NY 14607 716-325-1530
Bonick Design, Inc: 4811 W Amherst, Dallas, TX 75209 214-902-0977
Bonkers Graphic Design: 4118 Adams Ave #2, San Diego, CA 92116 619-280-5180
Bonnell Design Assocs, Inc: 409 W 44th St, New York, NY 10036 212-757-4420
Bonner Advertising Art: 1315 Washington Ave, New Orleans, LA 70130. 504-895-7938
Bonneville Comms: 179 Social Hall Ave, Salt Lake City, UT 84111 801-237-2600
Book Builders, Inc: 762 Madison Ave 4th Fl, New York, NY 10021 212-737-8210
Bookends: 1920 13th St #8, Boulder, CO 80302 303-443-8277
Boom Graphics: 1402 N Sierra Bonita Ave, Los Angeles, CA 90046. 213-876-3896
Booth Simpson Designers: 14 Arrow St, Cambridge, MA 02138. 617-661-2630
Borchew Design Group: 155 N Pfingsten St #215, Derfield, IL 60015. 947-317-0099
Bordelon, Kathleen: 37 W 72nd St #6A, New York, NY 10023. 212-873-5180
Borden, Emily: 2727 17th St, Santa Monica, CA 90405. 310-392-2746
Borejko Leibler: 124 W 24th St 4th Fl, New York, NY 10011 212-463-9292
Borgheian, Shideh: 24382 Nugget Falls Ln, Laguna Niguel, CA 92656. 714-879-0549
Borgman, Harry: 39 Hamilton Terr, New York, NY 10031 212-283-3401
Borgman, Joan: 1323A Yale St, Santa Monica, CA 90404 310-453-4821
Boris Image Group: 451 D St, Boston, MA 02210 617-439-3200
Bornstein Design: 2381 NE 193rd St, N Miami Beach, FL 33180 305-933-2300
Bos Assocs, Inc: 411 W Lambert Rd #407, Brea, CA 92621 714-529-8557
Bosha Graphic Design: 921 Childs Ave, Drexel Hill, PA 19026 610-449-1008
Boss Inman Graphic Design, Bo: 1383 S Eudora St, Denver, CO 80222 303-756-0222
Boston Design, Archie: 5707 Aladdin St, Los Angeles, CA 90008. 213-296-2428
Bostrom Design, Cybul: 105 E Burlington, Riverside, IL 60546 708-447-6122
Boszta Costa Adv & Design: 605 W 70th St, Kansas City, MO 64113. 816-333-1165
Botero Assocs, Samuel: 420 E 54th St #34G, New York, NY 10022 212-935-5155
Bottega Design, Inc: 1708 S Crescent, Park Ridge, IL 60068. 847-825-3687
Bottiglieri, Dessolina: 126 E 12th St #6C, New York, NY 10003 212-473-4592
Boullion Graphics: 6423 Willgus Trl, Houston, TX 77066 713-444-5749
Boulton Advertising, Connie: 3242 Caminito Ameca, La Jolla, CA 92037 619-455-5397
Bouthhillier Design Assoc, Lans: 225 Water St S #402, Plymouth, MA 02360 . . 508-747-4973
Bowerman & Collins Adv: 213 W 16th St, New York, NY 10011 212-929-3157
Bowers, John Dallas: 219 Radnor-Chester Rd, Villianova, PA 19085 610-989-9234
Bowers, Karen: 1508 Sanborn Ave, Los Angeles, CA 90027 213-664-5524
Bowles, Aaron: 203 Elden St #401-D, Herndon, VA 22070 703-318-7889
Boyajian & Assocs Design, Carole: 365 W Alameda Ave #308, Burbank, CA 91506 . . 818-848-2595

Boyarski Boyarski: 6958 Edgerton Ave, Pittsburgh, PA 15208 412-362-2626
Boyd Design, Douglas: 6624 Melrose Ave, Los Angeles, CA 90038 213-933-8383
Boylan Assocs: 5 Lakeview Ave, Danvers, MA 01923 508-774-6655
Braatz Studio Inc, Jerry: 4 High St, Valhalla, NY 10595 914-428-0533
Brabner Design: 4517 Dolly Ridge Rd, Birmingham, AL 35243 205-967-6606
Bradbury Assocs, Robert: 26 Halsey Ln, Closter, NJ 07624. 201-768-6395
Bradfield Design, Inc: 215 Long Beach Blvd #427, Long Beach, CA 90802 . . 310-432-2125
Bradford Cout & Jansen Design: 953 N Plum Grove Rd #A, Schaumburg, IL 60173. . 847-619-4777
Bradford, Peter: 928 Broadway #709, New York, NY 10010 212-982-2090
Brady & Paul Comms: 120 E Oakland Pk Blvd #105, Ft Lauderdale, FL 33334. . 954-537-9040
Brady Design Consultants, John: 3 Gateway Ctr #17, Pittsburgh, PA 15222 . . 412-288-9300
Brady, Susan: 1812 Webster St, San Francisco, CA 94115 415-563-4769
Brain Storm, Inc: 3347 Halifax St, Dallas, TX 75247 214-951-7791
Brainard Industrial Design, Robert: 30 Bellair Dr, Danbury, CT 06811. 203-746-5003
Brainstorm Creative: 2015 E State Highway AA, Springfield, MO 65803 417-833-4233
Brainworks Design Group: 2 Harris Court, Monterey, CA 93940 408-657-0650
Braithwaite Communications: 1710 Hayes St #207, Nashville, TN 37203 . . . 615-329-4573
Bram, Brian: 381 Congress St 2nd Fl, Boston, MA 02210 617-338-7770
Bramble Design, Bill: 327 W 11th St, New York, NY 10014 212-929-6289
Bramson & Assocs, Inc: 7400 Beverly Blvd, Los Angeles, CA 90036 213-938-3595
Brand Design: PO Box 30000, Wilmington, DE 19805. 302-888-1648
Brand Equity Int'l: 2330 Washington St, Newton, MA 02162 617-969-3150
Branders Creative Cafe: 1840 E 32nd St, Tulsa, OK 74105. 918-743-6854
Braswell, Lynn: 320 Riverside Dr, New York, NY 10025 212-222-8761
Brauer, Bruce Erik: 131 Midland Ave, Staten Island, NY 10306 718-667-8977
Braun Creative Group: 11051 N Town Sq Rd, Mequon, WI 53092 414-241-8984
Braverman Design, Stan: 200 Rector Pl #14B, New York, NY 10280 212-945-4434
Bravo Multimedia Communications: 325 Huron #404, Chicago, IL 60610 . . . 312-337-9058
Brazell Design: 11447 S 46th St, Phoenix, AZ 85044 602-496-6680
BRD Design: 6525 Sunset Blvd 6th Fl, Hollywood, CA 90028. 213-962-4908
Breakthru Media Group: 20001 Glebe Ln, Charles City, VA 23030. 804-829-2948
Breckenridge Designs: 5225 Wisconsin Ave NW Ste 625, Washington, DC 20015. . 202-686-7100
Bree/Taub Design: 648 Broadway #703, New York, NY 10012. 212-254-8383
Breiner, Joanne: 8 Cornelius Way, Cambridge, MA 02141 617-354-8378
Breiter Concepts Design: 2535 Townsgate Rd #201, Westlake Village, CA 91361. . 818-303-6550
Brejcha, Bart: 312 May St #5F, Chicago, IL 60607 312-433-7786
Brelsford Design, J: 4949 Westown Pkwy #125, West Des Moines, IA 50266 . . 515-282-2655
Brems Eastman Glade: 3131 Elliot Ave #280, Seattle, WA 98121 206-284-9400
Brennan Adv, Patrick: 517 1/2 Potrero Ave, San Francisco, CA 94110 415-864-8520
Brenner Design, Barry: 1636 N Stanley Ave, Los Angeles, CA 90046 213-851-9415
Bressler Design Assoc, Peter: 2400 Market St #4, Philadelphia, PA 19103. . . 215-561-5100
Brett Corp: 8316 Clairemont Mesa Blvd #105, San Diego, CA 92111 619-292-4919
Breuel & Unger Assocs, Inc: 1 Bridge St West Wing, Irvington, NY 10533. . . 914-591-5040
Bricker Design: 9709 Lock Tender Ln, Williamsport, MD 21795 301-223-5282
Bridge: 211 W Wacker Dr #700, Chicago, IL 60606 312-814-0200
Bridges Design: 143 Main St, Rockport, MA 01966 508-546-3149
Brier, David: 38 Park Ave, Rutherford, NJ 07070 201-896-8476
Bright Water Design: 1801 Dove St #104, Newport Beach, CA 92660 714-833-3344
Brill Graphic Design: 8803 Fairway Hill Dr, Austin, TX 78750 512-258-2327
Brilliant Media: 450 Pacific Ave 1st Fl, San Francisco, CA 94133. 415-434-5040
Brinkman Assocs: 21 Pine St, Rockaway, NJ 07866. 201-625-9000
Brinkmann Design, John: 123 S Baldwin Ave, Sierra Madre, CA 91024 818-355-3363
Brittainham Adv/Mullican Design: 4012 Ingraham St, Los Angeles, CA 90005. . 213-383-0232
Britton Design: 737 Broadway Box 1653, Sonoma, CA 95476 707-938-8378
Brochure Art: 1316 3rd St Promenade #101, Santa Monica, CA 90401 310-458-8863
Brochure Masters Creative Dept: 1220 S Bedford St, Los Angeles, CA 90035 . . 310-273-9613
Brock Design, Michael: 8075 W 3rd St #300, Los Angeles, CA 90048 213-932-0283
Brocke Graphic Design, Robert: 425 30th St #25, Newport Beach, CA 92663 . . 714-673-4281
Brody & Co, BL: 7961 Hollenbeck Cir, Parma, OH 44129. 216-842-4484
Brogdon, Chris: 233 E Ontario St #901, Chicago, IL 60611 312-787-0245
Brogren Kelly & Assocs: 234 Columbine St #320, Denver, CO 80206 303-399-3851
Brook Design, Lee Ann: 202 Providence Mine Rd #107, Nevada City, CA 95959 . . 916-265-6817
Brook Group Ltd, The: 8475 Old Frederick Rd, Ellicott City, MD 21043 410-465-7805
Brooks & Pollard Co: 400 W Capital #2900, Little Rock, AR 72201 501-375-5561
Brooks Comm: 1712 Terrace Dr, Belmont, CA 94002. 415-595-1401
Brooks Design, Larry: 5249 College View Ave, Los Angeles, CA 90041 213-467-7922
Brooks Jenkins Design: 1100 Circle 75 Pkwy #650, Atlanta, GA 30339 770-953-8183
Brooks Stevens Assocs, Inc: 1415 W Donges Bay Rd, Mequon, WI 53092 . . . 414-241-3800
Brooks/Cole Publising Co: 511 Forest Lodge Rd, Pacific Grove, CA 93950. . . 408-373-0728
Brookson Design: 1641 E Osborn #7, Phoenix, AZ 85016 602-279-1961
Broom & Broom, Inc: 360 Post St #1100, San Francisco, CA 94108. 415-397-4300
Brothers Bogusky: 11950 W Dixie Hwy, Miami, FL 33161 305-891-3642
Brothers Design: 188 Clintonville Rd, Northford, CT 06472. 203-484-2897
Brouws, Jeffrey T: 30 Prince St, Red Hook, NY 12571 . . . .
Brower Design, Steven: 18 E 16th St 7th Fl, New York, NY 10003 212-633-2356
Brown & Assocs, Janis: 19434 4th Pl, Escondido, CA 92029 619-743-1795
Brown & Assocs, Lynn: 1300 Bristol North #235, Newport Beach, CA 92660 . . 714-756-8018
Brown & Craig, Inc: 407 N Charles St, Baltimore, MD 21201 301-837-2727
Brown Design & Co: 392 Fore St, Portland, ME 04101. 207-879-1714
Brown, Barbara: 791 Colina Vista, Ventura, CA 93003 805-658-2086
Brown, David: 1220 20th St, Birmingham, AL 35205 205-939-1050
Brown, David: 2163 Fair St #1, Chico, CA 95928. 916-891-6682
Brown, Gaines: 1515 S Tryon, Charlotte, NC 28203 704-334-1442
Brown, Gloria: PO Box 335, Poncha Springs, CO 81242 800-372-9465
Brown, Hugh: 4543 Avocado St, Los Angeles, CA 90027 213-661-7767
Brown, Joan: PO Box 60066, Palo Alto, CA 94306 415-493-5773
Brown, Kevin: 5407 Dover St #B, Oakland, CA 94609 510-594-1542
Brown, Kirk Q: 1092 Blake Ave, Brooklyn, NY 11208 718-346-8281
Brown, Lance: 1800 St James Pl #609, Houston, TX 77056 713-622-5720
Brown, Larry: 2800 28th St #125, Santa Monica, CA 90405. 310-452-5502
Brown, Morris R: 1736 Garth Ave, Los Angeles, CA 90035 310-204-2827
Brown, Paula: 11453 Rose Ave, Los Angeles, CA 90066 310-397-4913
Brown, Scott: 323 Chester Ave, Menlo Park, CA 94025 415-473-1123
Brown, Theresa: 53 Danbury Rd, Wilton, CT 06897. 203-222-7040
Brown, Todd: 355 W 52nd St 8th Fl, New York, NY 10019 212-957-7649
Browning Design, Inc: 335 Wilber Ave, Columbus, OH 43215. 614-421-7037
Brubaker Group, The: 10560 Dolcedo Way, Los Angeles, CA 90077 310-472-4766
Bruce Assocs, Taylor: 730 N Franklin #603, Chicago, IL 60610 312-943-5529
Bruno Design Assocs: 120 Kearney Ave, Santa Fe, NM 87501 505-982-5544

Bruno Design Assocs: 151 Kalmus Dr #A104, Costa Mesa, CA 92626 ... 714-545-5424
Bruss Design, Inc, Ellen: 822 E19th Ave, Denver, CO 80218 ... 303-830-8323
Bryant & Assocs: 3838 1/2 Vantage Ave, Studio City, CA 91604 ... 818-762-1433
Bryant & Co: 740 Broadway 8th Fl, New York, NY 10003 ... 212-254-5122
Bryant Assocs, Robert: 4874 Bannock Circle, San Jose, CA 95130 ... 408-370-2121
Bryant, Dane A: 7746 Villa Nova Dr N, Boca Raton, FL 33433 ... 561-447-6744
Bryant, Inc: 740 Broadway 8th Fl, New York, NY 10003 ... 212-254-5122
Buchberger, Brian: 610 N Water St #310, Milwaukee, WI 53202 ... 414-273-8194
Bucher & Russell: 3600 Wilshire Blvd #2035, Los Angeles, CA 90010 ... 213-738-5300
Buckett Assocs, Bill: 10 Gibbs St #310, Rochester, NY 14604 ... 716-546-6580
Buckhorn, Merril: 25 Homedale Rd, Hopkins, MN 55343 ... 612-931-0324
Buckles Design, Timothy: 1800 21st St #100, Sacramento, CA 95814 ... 916-736-1473
Buckley Designs Inc: 310 E 75th St, New York, NY 10021 ... 212-861-0626
Buffalo Brothers Corp: 812 S Tejon St, Colorado Springs, CO 80903 ... 719-389-1230
Buffalo Brothers Studios West: 27 Parker Way, Santa Barbara, CA 93101 ... 805-963-0904
Bugdal Group: 7308 SW 48th St, Miami, FL 33155 ... 305-665-6686
Buhl, Taber: 4308 Goodrich Hill Road, Locke, NY 13092 ... 315-497-0288
Buivid Photo Design: 1551 E River Rd, Grafton, WI 53024 ... 414-377-5118
Bullseye Productions: 2 San Marino Ct, San Rafael, CA 94901 ... 415-460-6824
Bumacod Concept & Design: 1029 W 210th St, Torrance, CA 90502 ... 310-328-7384
Bunzel & Assocs: 2276 S Beverly Glen Blvd #108, Los Angeles, CA 90064 ... 310-286-0969
Burbott Design, Matthew: 8740 Willis #12, Panorama City, CA 91402 ... 818-893-4265
Burch Assocs, Dan: 2338 Frankfort, Louisville, KY 40206 ... 502-895-4881
Burch Design Group: 660 J St #490, Sacramento, CA 95814 ... 916-558-4900
Burdick Group, The: 35 S Park, San Francisco, CA 94107 ... 415-957-1666
Bureau Design: 333 Bryant St #190, San Francisco, CA 94107 ... 415-495-4197
Burg Design: 150 Shoreline Hwy #B21, Mill Valley, CA 94941 ... 415-332-9318
Burgund Design, Kathleen: 18 W Custis Ave, Alexandria, VA 22301 ... 703-683-8084
Burke Design: 2060 Avenue de los Arboles #118, Thousand Oaks, CA 91362 ... 310-280-3488
Burke Graphic Design, Angie: 1266 Camino Palomera, Santa Barbara, CA 93111 ... 805-964-1945
Burke, Michael: 1131 16th St, Baywood Park, CA 93402 ... 805-528-6754
Burkley Studios: 1526 Edison St, Dallas, TX 75207 ... 214-746-6336
Burnett Communication, Roberta: 607 E Loyola Dr, Tempe, AZ 85282 ... 602-966-4900
Burney Design: 409 Hillsborough, Raleigh, NC 27613 ... 919-833-4819
Burns & Assocs, Inc: 2700 Sutter St, San Francisco, CA 94115 ... 415-567-4404
Burns Design Assocs: 9747 Business Park Ave #203, San Diego, CA 92131 ... 619-566-9166
Burns, Rhonda: 13049 Hartsook St, Sherman Oaks, CA 91423 ... 213-913-1929
Burstein/Max Assoc: 271 Madison Ave #903, New York, NY 10016 ... 212-986-2080
Burton & Differding: 897 Woodruff Pl/East River, Indianapolis, IN 46201 ... 317-636-0925
Burton, Matthew L: 440 East 57th St #GC, New York, NY 10022 ... 212-486-1002
Bush Graphics, Robert: PO Box 4830, Long Beach, CA 90804 ... 310-434-1697
Business Graphics: 7321 Beverly Blvd #6, Los Angeles, CA 90036 ... 213-930-4899
Business Information Graphics: 200 Park Ave S #1112, New York, NY 10003 ... 212-477-4288
Business Office, The: 8645 Twin Rivers Dr, Ventura, CA 93004 ... 805-659-2186
Business Presentation Services: 40 Cameron Ave, Sommerville, MA 02144 ... 617-666-1161
Bussolati Assocs: 7000 B Carroll Ave, Tacoma Park, MD 20912 ... 301-891-1062
Butler & Butler, Inc: 1404 S Quaker Ave, Tulsa, OK 74120 ... 918-592-4151
Butler Designs: 4617 Montrose Blvd #228, Houston, TX 77006 ... 713-526-3182
Butler Group, The: 940 N Highland Ave #C, Los Angeles, CA 90038 ... 213-469-8128
Butterfield Design, Christy: 480 Gate Five Rd #201, Sausalito, CA 94966 ... 415-332-8591
Butz Gaskins Art Studio: 1994 Madison Rd, Cincinnati, OH 45209 ... 513-321-7002
Butzko & Rosenthal Design: 214 Greenbriar Rd, Fairfield, CT 06430 ... 203-334-7396
Buz Design Group: 8952 Ellis Ave, Los Angeles, CA 90034 ... 310-202-0140
Buzzo, Marge: 4620 Santa Lucia Dr, Woodland Hills, CA 91364 ... 818-340-5640
BWEH Graphics: 630 Rose Ave, Venice, CA 90291 ... 310-392-9636
By Design: 4606-A E State Blvd, Ft Wayne, IN 46815 ... 219-482-2815
By Design: 271 Madison Ave, New York, NY 10016 ... 212-661-0962
By Design Productions: 211 Cypress Point Dr, Mountain View, CA 94043 ... 415-968-8407
Bydalek Spence Kittner: 1000 Geyer Ave, St Louis, MO 63104 ... 314-621-8002
Byerly, Thomas & Kim: 2870 Cynthia Dr, Medina, OH 44256 ... 330-722-4181
Byrne Design, Susan: 27 W 24th St #602, New York, NY 10010 ... 212-807-6671
Byrne Marketing & Adv, Peter: 25002 Paseo Cipres, El Toro, CA 92630 ... 714-859-3262
Byrne, Chuck: 5528 Lawton Ave, Oakland, CA 94618 ... 510-658-6996
Byte Knights: 410 W Webster, Chicago, IL 60614 ... 773-327-9251

C

C & S Creative Services: PO Box 4082, Park City, UT 84060 ... 801-649-1234
C & W/Iola, Inc: 748 Hwy 206 S, Bellemeade, NJ 08502 ... 908-359-1600
C Gay Petach Studio: 2500 Woodlawn Dr, Nashville, TN 37212 ... 615-292-3691
C/O Keith Berr Productions: 1420 East 31st St, Cleveland, OH 44114 ... 216-566-7950
CA Design Inc: 1188 Bishop St #2611, Honolulu, HI 96813 ... 808-533-2888
Cabat Studio: 627 N 4th Ave, Tucson, AZ 85705 ... 602-622-6362
Cabazon Design: 322 N W 5th Ave #312, Portland, OR 97209 ... 503-220-8236
Caber Graphic Design, Jennifer: 4950 N Calle Esquina, Tucson, AZ 85718 ... 602-577-1063
Cable Design, Jerry: 133 Kuhl Rd, Flemington, NJ 08822 ... 908-788-6750
Cadence Design Systems: 2655 Seely Ave 7A1, San Jose, CA 95134 ... 408-944-7135
Cadmus Creative: 5301 Louis Rd, Sandston, VA 23150 ... 804-236-4500
Caesar Studios: 2602 Pickwick Ln, Austin, TX 78746 ... 512-329-5110
Cagle Design: 5353 Hinton Ave, Woodland Hills, CA 91367 ... 818-340-2887
Cagney & McDowell: 751 S Clark #200, Chicago, IL 60605 ... 312-461-0707
Cahan & Assocs: 818 Brannan St #300, San Francisco, CA 94103 ... 415-621-0915
Cahill Dittrich Advertising: 40 Grove St, Wellesley, MA 02181 ... 617-235-2782
Cahn, Jeff: 6200 SOM Center Rd #D25, Cleveland, OH 44139 ... 440-349-1270
Calanché, Maqué: 545 Belvedere St, San Francisco, CA 94117 ... 415-664-9541
Calderhead, Richard: 821 Broadway 11th Fl, New York, NY 10003 ... 212-673-6200
Caldwell Design, John: 901 El Centro St, S Pasadena, CA 91030 ... 213-682-2809
Calfo Assocs: 156 Fifth Ave #500, New York, NY 10010 ... 212-627-3800
Calico Creations Ltd: 9340 Eton Ave, Chatsworth, CA 91311 ... 818-407-5200
California Coast Advertising: 8439 White Oak Ave #109, Rancho Cucamonga, CA 91730 909-948-7025
California Design: 219 Broadway #254, Laguna Beach, CA 92651 ... 714-831-2188
California Design Int'l: 123 Townsend St #465, San Francisco, CA 94107 ... 415-243-0980
Calko & Lakich: 704 Traction Ave, Los Angeles, CA 90013 ... 213-620-8641
Callahan Design, Bob: 181 Thornridge Dr, Stamford, CT 06903 ... 203-329-0425
Callahan, Tom: 7964 S Madison Ave, Burr Ridge, IL 60521 ... 630-789-1022
Callanta & Assocs, Al: 13010 Miller Ave, Norwalk, CA 90650 ... 310-921-8684
Calleia, Michael: 184 E Second St #4E, New York, NY 10009 ... 212-505-9073
Calligraphics By Julie Ann: 3511 E Capri Ave, Mesa, AZ 85204 ... 602-531-5747
Calligraphy By Rachael: 5800 Lake Murray Blvd # 86, La Mesa, CA 91942 ... 619-465-5566
Calligraphy West Studio: 3101 Federal Ave, Los Angeles, CA 90066 ... 310-837-3604
Callison Partnership, The: 1420 5th Ave #2400, Seattle, WA 98101 ... 206-623-4646
• **Callow, Barbara: pg 927** 1839 Ninth St, Alameda, CA 94501 ... **510-769-1421**
e-mail: ldmreps@prodigy.net / fax: 510-521-1674
Callygraphics: 15848 Sanctuary Dr, Tampa, FL 33647 ... 813-975-0823
Calo'oy & Co: 3889 Clover Ln, Dallas, TX 75220 ... 214-902-8044
Calori & Vanden Eynden Ltd: 130 W25th St, New York, NY 10001 ... 212-929-6302
Calvello, Tony: 515 Alvarado St, San Francisco, CA 94114 ... 415-647-1603
Calviello & Cohen Multimedia: 133 Cedar Rd, E Northport, NY 11731 ... 516-368-2031
Camacho, Dennis: 55 Broad St, New York, NY 10004 ... 212-378-4985
Cambridge Prepress Service: 215 First St, Cambridge, MA 02142 ... 617-354-1991
Camera Ready Graphics: 225 Center St, San Rafael, CA 94901 ... 415-457-5699
Cameron, Inc: 9 Appleton St, Boston, MA 02116 ... 617-338-4408
Camozzi, Teresa: 170 Capp St, San Francisco, CA 94110 ... 415-863-2733
Campbell & Assocs, Tom : 2018 Meadow Valley Ter, Los Angeles, CA 90039 ... 213-661-9288
Campbell Art Studio: 2145 Luray Ave, Cincinnati, OH 45206 ... 513-221-3600
Campbell Design: 209 Hillside Ave, Mill Valley, CA 94941 ... 415-331-3939
Campbell Design: 94 Pike St #30, Seattle, WA 94107 ... 206-622-4294
Campbell Fisher Ditko Design: 3333 E Camelback Rd #200, Phoenix, AZ 85018 ... 602-955-2707
Campbell Harrington & Brear: 352 W Market St, York, PA 17401 ... 717-846-2947
Campbell, Grady: 900 N Franklin #310, Chicago, IL 60610 ... 312-642-6511
Campbell, JC: 7777 Bonhomme #2000, St Louis, MO 63105 ... 314-726-5858
Campisi Design Inc, Ronn: 118 Newbury St, Boston, MA 02116 ... 617-236-1339
Campos Design, Mike: 1804 Marion Ave, Novato, CA 94945 ... 415-892-1573
Canciani International: 461 Second St #C227, San Francisco, CA 94107 ... 415-442-0261
Cancilla Design, Joseph: 3534 Huntertown Rd, Allison Park, PA 15101 ... 412-443-8698
Canfield Design: 45 Newbury St, Boston, MA 02116 ... 617-247-3869
Cannan & Co, Bill: 301 Mortimer Ave, Rutherford, NJ 10036 ... 201-933-9883
Canright & Paule: 1425 W Summerdale Ave, Chicago, IL 60640 ... 773-275-8895
Cantere Assocs, Lee: 1553 Euclid St, Santa Monica, CA 90404 ... 310-395-3221
Cantor Design: 875 Ave of America #10001, New York, NY 10001 ... 212-629-0130
Cantor, Andrew: 4 W 37th St 6th Fl, New York, NY 10018 ... 212-629-0130
Caplin Design: 35 Medford Street #203, Somerville, MA 02143 ... 617-627-9050
Caprs Cleveland Design: 673 Boylston St, Boston, MA 02116 ... 617-267-7957
Caravello Studios: 165 W 18th St 3rd Fl, New York, NY 10011 ... 212-620-0620
Cardi Assocs: 23010 Lake Forest Dr #281, Laguna Hills, CA 92653 ... 714-768-3024
Cardinal Comms Group: 545 W 45th St, New York, NY 10036 ... 212-489-1717
Carew Design: 49 Sunset Way, San Rafael, CA 94901 ... 415-331-8222
Carey & Assocs, Bob: 10 Topaz Way, San Francisco, CA 94131 ... 415-826-3497
Cariddi, Marianne K: 100 Indian Rock Rd, Merrimack, NH 03054 ... 603-424-0337
Carino Graphic Design, Mercedes: 76C Belvedere St, San Rafael, CA 94901 ... 415-485-9299
Carleton Design: 777 San Antonio Rd #96, Palo Alto, CA 94303 ... 415-858-2508
Carling Design: 257 Water St #2A, New York, NY 10023 ... 212-393-9430
Carlisle/Carre Design: 1301 Montana Ave #A, Santa Monica, CA 90403 ... 310-394-5330
Carlo Assocs: 417 E 9th St #14, New York, NY 10009 ... 212-420-1110
Carlson: 3054 Fite Cir #108, Sacramento, CA 95827 ... 916-447-2277
Carlson Design: 107 SW 99th Terr, Gainesville, FL 32607 ... 904-332-4917
Carmel, Abraham: 7 Peter Beet Dr, Peekskill, NY 10566 ... 914-737-1439
Carnase, Tom: 30 E 21st St, New York, NY 10010 ... 212-777-1500
Carpenter Advertising & Design, JL: 4457 Benfield Ct, San Diego, CA 92113 ... 619-527-2850
Carpenter Design, Inc: 10020 National Blvd, Los Angeles, CA 90034 ... 310-837-0732
Carpenter Graphic Design: 72 Spring St 10th Fl, New York, NY 10012 ... 212-431-6666
Carpenter Photo/Design: 20 Granada Way, Los Gatos, CA 95030 ... 330-374-1750
Carpinelli Graphic Design, Janet: 934 Minnesota St, San Francisco, CA 94107 ... 415-826-5509
Carr Design Assocs: 817 A St NE, Washington, DC 20002 ... 202-546-2611
Carrara, Richard: 218 Lorraine Ave, Upper Montclair, NJ 07043 ... 201-783-2872
Carriage House Design: 216 Radnor Chester Rd, Villanova, PA 19085 ... 610-293-1555
Carron Design, Ross: 9787 Mill Station Rd, Sebastopol, CA 95472 ... 415-440-4191
Carsello, Margaret: 516 N Vine, Hinsdale, IL 60521 ... 630-794-9120
Carson & Co: 517 Mercury Lane, Brea, CA 92821 ... 714-990-1500
Carson Design, David: 432 F St #503, San Diego, CA 92101 ... 619-338-8080
Carstens, Daren: 342 Grove #201, Wood Dale, IL 60191 ... 708-238-8505
Carta Communications, Joyce: 2181 NW 99th Ave, Pembroke Pine, FL 33024 ... 954-433-1391
Carter Cosgrove & Co: 345 S Patrick, Alexandria, VA 22314 ... 703-836-2900
Carter Design: 555 Sutter St #401, San Francisco, CA 94102 ... 415-781-7325
Carter Design, David: 4112 Swiss Ave, Dallas, TX 75204 ... 214-826-4631
Carter Design, Inc: 814 E 19th Ave, Denver, CO 80218 ... 303-832-1537
Carter Industrial Design, Don W: 8809 E 59th St, Kansas City, MO 64133 ... 816-356-1874
Carter, Calvin W: 1950 Stemmons Fwy #3207, Dallas, TX 75207 ... 214-746-4266
Carter, Julie: 2890 Westshire Dr, Los Angeles, CA 90068 ... 213-962-2521
Carter, Richard N: PO Box 208, Del Mar, CA 92014 ... 619-792-6473
Carver Letcher Miller: 3940 Spring Dr #11, Reno, NV 89502 ... 702-828-4700
Casal, Linda: 210 E 15th St, New York, NY 10003 ... 212-353-2060
Case: 11 Dupont Cir NW #400, Washington, DC 20036 ... 202-328-5900
Casey & Company Graphic Design: 76 N Eastner Blvd #24, Nashua, NH 03062 ... 603-594-0758
Casey, Jim: 33 W 17th St 7th Fl, New York, NY 10011 ... 212-929-2886
Casey, Jim: 33 W 17th St 7th Fl, New York, NY 10011 ... 212-929-2886
Casper Design Group: 903 University Ave, Berkeley, CA 94710 ... 510-549-1300
Cassidy, Darrell: 2700 Simpson Rd #240, Richmond, BC ... 604-276-0838
Castells, Jaime: 100 Juergens Ave, Cincinnati, OH 45220 ... 513-221-3377
Catalano Design: 374 Congress St, Boston, MA 02210 ... 617-338-7447
Catalog Design & Production, Inc: 1825 A Egbert, San Francisco, CA 94124 ... 415-468-5500
Cates, Randy A: 421 Pendleton Ln, Londonderry, NH 03053 ... 603-437-3759
Cathey Assocs: 3322 Shorecrest Dr #100, Dallas, TX 75235 ... 214-352-6399
Cats' Pajamas, Inc: 344 Ramsey St, St Paul, MN 55102 ... 612-227-2240
CBI Advertising: 8160 E Butherus Dr #6, Scottsdale, AZ 85260 ... 602-948-0440
CCBS Design: 1604 Mclendon Ave NE, Atlanta, GA 30307 ... 404-371-8586
CCMR ADV: 260 Fair St, Kingston, NY 12401 ... 914-331-4620
CCW Group: 133 Coulter Ave, Ardmore, PA 19003 ... 610-642-3330
CD Squared: 418 Meadow St, Fairfield, CT 06430 ... 203-334-3330
Cejka Design: PO Box 4048, Crestline, CA 92325 ... 909-338-2245
Center For Advanced Whimsy: 61 Crosby St, New York, NY 10012 ... 212-219-0342
Centermedia: 186 South St, Boston, MA 02111 ... 617-451-9902
Central Advtg Agcy: 1 Tandy Cir #300, Fort Worth, TX 76102 ... 817-390-3011
Cerulli, Andrew: 82-31 63rd Ave, Middle Village, NY 11379 ... 718-803-2321
Cesaroni Design Assocs, Inc: 1865 Grove St, Glenview, IL 60025 ... 847-724-8840
Cetta, Al: 111 Bank St, New York, NY 10010 ... 212-989-9696
Chadick & Kimball Design: 1025 Conn Ave NW #311, Washington, DC 20036 ... 202-452-8112

Chambers Co, H: 1010 N Charles St, Baltimore, MD 21201 ... 410-727-4535
Chambers Group, The: 1631 16th St, Santa Monica, CA 90404 ... 310-452-5551
Chambray Design: 770 Madison Ave, New York, NY 10021 ... 212-535-0307
Champ Design Assocs, John: 1049 Camino Del Mar #C, Del Mar, CA 92014 ... 619-481-2991
Champ, Heather: 37 E Seventh St, New York, NY 10003 ... 212-995-8494
Champaigne Lafayette Comm: 7 Strathmore Rd, Natick, MA 01760 ... 508-651-0400
Chan Design: 1334 Lincoln Blvd #150, Santa Monica, CA 90401 ... 310-393-3735
Chan Design, Kimiko: 407 Jackson St #202, San Francisco, CA 94111 ... 415-399-9665
Chandler & Assocs: 744 Flume St, Chico, CA 95928 ... 916-343-1127
Chandler, Jeff: 1010 N Windomere Ave, Dallas, TX 75208 ... 214-946-1348
Chaney Co: 272 E Deerpath Rd #200, Lake Forest, IL 60045 ... 847-615-2602
Chang, Ivan: 30 E 10th St, New York, NY 10003 ... 212-777-6102
Chaparos Productions Ltd: 1112 6th St NW, Washington, DC 20001 ... 202-289-4838
Chaparral Graphics Group: 921 E 66th St, Lubbock, TX 79404 ... 806-745-9292
Chapleston, Isabel: 3122 S Durango Ave #6, Los Angeles, CA 90034 ... 310-838-9425
Chaplin Graphics: 164 Edward Dr, Swedesboro, NJ 08085 ... 609-467-5992
Chapman & Partners: 14 Imperial Pl #501, Providence, RI 02903 ... 401-454-3456
Chapman, Sandra S: 122 Ashland Pl #7E, Brooklyn, NY 11201 ... 718-855-7396
Charles Design Group, Richard: 54 Roast Meat Hill Rd, Killingworth, CT 06417 ... 203-663-2754
Charles, Milton: 199 Ravine Rd, Califon, NJ 07830 ... 908-832-7076
Charlier, Mark: 33 E Cedar #5C, Chicago, IL 60611 ... 312-421-2668
Charysyn & Charysyn: Route 42, Westkill, NY 12492 ... 518-989-6720
Chase Design, David O: 1400 E Genesee St, Skaneateles, NY 13152 ... 315-685-8941
Chase Design, Margo: 2255 Bancroft Ave, Los Angeles, CA 90039 ... 323-668-1055
Chateau de Loxley: PO Box 953, Loxley, AL 36551 ... 334-964-6972
Checkman Design, Inc: 149 Fifth Ave 12th Fl, New York, NY 10010 ... 212-674-4464
Chen Design Inc, David: 2211 Newton Drive, Rockville, MD 20850 ... 301-460-6575
Chen, Henry L: 115 Old Short Hills Rd #279, West Orange, NJ 07052 ... 973-736-2379
Chen, Shih-chien: 2839 35th St, Edmonton, AB T6L 5K2 ... 403-462-8617
Cheng Design, Mary Ann: 1092 Potrero Ave, San Francisco, CA 94110 ... 415-647-7382
Cheren Design: 233 Harvard St #32, Brookline, MA 02146 ... 617-734-1194
Chermayeff & Geismar: 15 E 26th St 12th Fl, New York, NY 10010 ... 212-532-4499
Cherry Pie Graphics: 1171 Homestead Rd #220, Santa Clara, CA 95050 ... 408-261-8210
Chesapeake Display & Pkgng Co : 1225 Grand Central, Glendale, CA 91201 ... 818-507-7477
Chesapeake Group, The: 655 Eden Park Dr #525, Cincinnati, OH 45202 ... 513-345-6300
Chesire Designs: 2492 Flair Knoll Court NE, Atlanta, GA 30345 ... 404-633-8330
Cheskin & Masten: 255 Shore Line #100, Redwood City, CA 94065 ... 415-802-2100
Chesler Design Assocs: 23052 Sunfield Dr, Boca Raton, FL 33433 ... 561-477-1525
Chestnut Creative: 610 Lake Medlock Ct, Alpharetta, GA 30202 ... 770-813-0508
Chew Assocs, HR: 1900 N Vine St #108, Los Angeles, CA 90068 ... 213-464-0156
Chiappetta, Gary: 117 S Morgan St 3rd Fl, Chicago, IL 60607 ... 312-738-2611
Chiaro Design: 5 Thompson Rd, Patterson, NY 12563 ... 203-746-0100
Chicago Show: 345 Lakewood Ave, Waukegan, IL 60085 ... 847-263-2210
Children's Television Workshop: 1 Lincoln Plaza, New York, NY 10023 ... 212-875-6905
Chillingworth Raddind: 35 E 21st St 6th Fl, New York, NY 10010 ... 212-674-4700
Chilton Design Group: 1008 Camino San Acacio, Santa Fe, NM 87501 ... 505-820-1865
Chin Assocs, ET: 226 E 54th St #308, New York, NY 10021 ... 212-645-6800
Chinnici Assocs: 49 W 27th St 5th Fl, New York, NY 10001 ... 212-685-0564
Chirping Bird Communications: 1337 W Estes Ave #27, Chicago, IL 60626 ... 773-274-0224
Choe Design: 307 Orchard City Dr #210, Campbell, CA 95008 ... 408-364-1080
Chong, YC: 499 Jln 22, Kuala Lumpur, Salak, Malaysia, 57100 ... 03-7835681
Christensen Media: 3638 Auburn Blvd #F, Sacramento, CA 95821 ... 916-487-4722
Chroma Design & Communications: 115 Indian Spring Dr, Silver Spring, MD 20901 ... 301-585-5880
Chronicle Type & Design: 1255 23rd NW, Washington, DC 20036 ... 202-466-1090
Chu & Co Ltd, HL: 39 W 29th St, New York, NY 10001 ... 212-889-4818
Chu, Collins: 430 W Main St, Tustin, CA 92680 ... 714-731-7200
Chun Graphic Design, Milton: 4946 Kilauea Ave #4, Honolulu, HI 96816 ... 808-735-6436
Church & Main: 30 Main St, Keene, NH 03431 ... 603-357-5898
Church Street Design: 151 Winnona Dr, Decatur, GA 30030 ...
Churik Design, Bennardo: 1601 Mary's Ave, Pittsburgh, PA 15215 ... 412-782-1351
Chute Gerdeman Group: 130 E Chestnut #102, Columbus, OH 43215 ... 614-469-1001
Chwast, Seymour: 18 E 16th St 7th Fl, New York, NY 10003 ... 212-255-6456
Cia Creative Group: 6430 Sunset Blvd #1001, Hollywood, CA 90028 ... 213-461-5959
Ciavarra Design: One Design Ctr Pl #728, Boston, MA 02210 ... 617-439-4223
Ciesa, Inc: 201 Ann St, E Lansing, MI 48823 ... 517-351-2453
Cimarron Bacon O'Brien: 758 N Highland Ave, Hollywood, CA 90038 ... 213-461-5850
Cinema Concepts: 2030 Powers Ferry Rd #214, Atlanta, GA 30339 ... 770-956-7460
Ciphers: 245 El Cajon Way, Los Gatos, CA 95030 ... 408-356-9983
Cipriani Kremer Design: 2 Copley Pl, Boston, MA 02116 ... 617-236-1422
CKS Interactive: 10443 Bandley Dr, Cupertino, CA 95014 ... 408-366-5100
Clare Graphics, George: 815 Sea Spray Ln #214, Foster City, CA 94404 ... 415-349-4103
Clark Art Direction & Design: 4539 Loren Von Dr, Salt Lake City, UT 84121 ...
Clark Illus, Tim: 1256 25th St, Santa Monica, CA 90404 ... 310-453-7613
Clark, Linda: 28 Precita Ave, San Francisco, CA 94110 ... 415-282-7955
Clarke/Thompson: 30 W 22nd St #3rd Fl, New York, NY 10010 ... 212-645-8990
Clarkson Creative: 1472 S 800 East, Salt Lake City, UT 84105 ... 801-467-9993
Clasen Design: 3700 Katella Ave #201B, Los Alamitos, CA 90720 ... 310-596-2202
Clavenna, Barbara: 6000 Stone Ln, Birmingham, AL 35242 ... 205-991-8909
Clayton Design: 4808 Nevada Ave, Nashville, TN 37209 ... 615-383-4687
Cleary Design: 118 A N Division St, Salisbury, MD 21801 ... 301-546-1040
Clebenger & Co: 514 W 26th St #2W, Kansas City, MO 64108 ... 816-471-3311
Clemans & Partners: 1248 Homestead Ave, Walnut Creek, CA 94598 ... 510-938-3224
Clementi Assocs Design: 46 Lincoln St, Waltham, MA 02154 ... 617-899-1661
Clementino Design, Ann: 145 Lakewood Cir N, Manchester, CT 06040 ... 203-649-3669
Cleveland Design, John: 2433 28th St #B, Santa Monica, CA 90405 ... 310-450-2133
Cliff & Assocs: 715 Fremont Ave, S Pasadena, CA 91030 ... 818-799-5906
Clockwise Design: 594 Broadway #904, New York, NY 10012 ... 212-226-5686
Cloud Assocs, Gregory: 2116 Arlington Ave #236, Los Angeles, CA 90018 ... 213-484-9479
Clune Design, Quinby : 1035 Cherokee St #A, Denver, CO 80204 ... 303-620-0070
CM Jackson Assoc: 85 Oxford Dr, Moonachie, NJ 07074 ... 201-807-1500
CM Media: 254 Dolores St #4, San Francisco, CA 94103 ... 415-552-5176
CMA: 1207 Dunlavy St, Houston, TX 77019 ... 713-834-0180
CMG: 11260 Simpson Rd, Monmouth, OR 97361 ... 503-838-2328
CMG Inc: 1200 Kings Ave, Jacksonville, FL 32207 ... 904-346-0010
Cnet: 150 Chestnut St, San Francisco, CA 94111 ... 415-395-7800
CO Design Services: 224 N 5th Ave, Phoenix, AZ 85003 ... 602-252-7296
Coak, Steve: 2870 N Haven Ln, Altadena, CA 91001 ... 818-797-5477
Coakley Heagerty Co, The: 1155 N First Ave #201, San Jose, CA 95112 ... 408-275-9400
Coastline Studios: 545 Delaney Ave #1, Orlando, FL 32801 ... 407-246-1970

Coates Agency: 34 NW 1st Ave #400, Portland, OR 97209 ... 503-241-1124
Cocchiarella, Nino: 201 NW 4th St #114, Evansville, IN 47708 ... 812-423-2500
Coddington Beyer Design: 36 Albany St, Cazenovia, NY 13035 ... 315-655-5500
Coe Design Assocs, Laura: 4918 N Harbor Dr #206A, San Diego, CA 92106 ... 619-223-0909
Coffman, Claudia: 70 E Lake St #415, Chicago, IL 60601 ... 312-236-8545
Cogno Centi Design: 149 Fifth Ave 7th Fl, New York, NY 10010 ... 212-529-0857
Cohen & Co: 3210-2 Peachtree Rd NE, Atlanta, GA 30305 ... 404-233-7331
Cohen & Godefroy: 956 Granville Ave, Los Angeles, CA 90049 ... 310-447-9320
Cohen Design, Inc, Michael: 65-76 162nd St, Fresh Meadows, NY 11365 ... 718-380-4990
Cohen Design, Norman: 201 E 28th St #8K, New York, NY 10016 ... 212-679-3906
Cohen Studio, Steve: 560 W 43rd St #37J, New York, NY 10036 ... 212-279-0246
Cohoe/Baker Design: 256 W 93rd St, New York, NY 10023 ... 212-787-0943
Coker Golley Ltd: 127 Peachtree Road #900, Atlanta, GA 30030 ... 404-523-8805
Colangelo Assocs, Ted: 340 Pemberwick Rd (The Mill), Greenwich, CT 06830 ... 203-531-3600
Colavecchio Design: 684 Main St, Winsted, CT 06098 ... 203-379-9893
Cole & Co Visual Comm: 4981 W Catalpa Dr, Boise, ID 83703 ... 208-345-9962
Cole Design Group: 73 River Rd, Collinsville, CT 06022 ... 860-693-1980
Coleman Group West, The: 125 E Sir Francis Drake Blvd, Larkspur, CA 94939 ... 415-925-8000
Collins, Thomas: 54 W 21st St #604, New York, NY 10010 ... 212-627-1656
Color Age: 900 Middlesex Tpke Dr Bldg 8, Billerica, MA 01821 ... 508-667-8585
Color Assocs-Creative Imaging: 10835 Midwest Industrial Blvd, St Louis, MO 63132 ... 314-423-8111
Color Forms Studio: 24200 Woodward Ave, Pleasant Ridge, MI 48069 ... 248-399-0060
Colorado Film & Television Studios: 2400 N Syracuse St, Denver, CO 80207 ... 303-388-8500
Colorforms Illustration: 24200 Woodward Ave, Pleasant Ridge, MI 48069 ... 248-399-0060
Colorplay Design Studio: 323 W 13th Avr, Eugene, OR 97401 ... 541-687-8262
Colquitt & Kibler Design: 4 E Madison St, Baltimore, MD 21202 ... 410-837-7070
Comadres Comm & Graphics: 55 W Wacker Dr #700, Chicago, IL 60601 ... 312-332-2233
Comark Commulications: 1636 Abbot Kinney Blvd, Venice, CA 90291 ... 310-396-8626
Comark Group, Inc, The: 400 Renaissance Ctr #6060, Detroit, MI 48243 ... 313-567-5100
Comcorp: 542 S Dearborn 9th Fl, Chicago, IL 60605 ... 312-939-6424
Command P: 634 W Sunset, San Antonio, TX 78216 ... 210-821-6006
Communica: 31 North Erie St, Toledo, OH 43624 ... 419-244-7766
Communication Arts: 129 E Pascagoula, Jackson, MS 39201 ... 601-354-7955
Communication Arts Multimedia Inc: 2013 Wells Branch Pkwy #201, Austin, TX 78728 ... 512-251-0074
Communication By Design: 25 Sturges Rd, Sharon, MA 02067 ... 617-784-6000
Communication Connection, The: 2137 Mt Vernon Rd, Atlanta, GA 30338 ... 770-395-7483
Communication Design: 1604 Hodges Ct, Marina, CA 93933 ... 408-883-1361
Communication Design, Inc: 8950 Calif Ctr Dr #235, Sacramento, CA 95826 ... 916-362-0400
Communication/Design: 139 Peterborough Rd, Hancock, NH 03449 ... 603-525-4726
Communications Company: 100 W Rincon Ave #209, Campbell, CA 95008 ... 408-379-5356
Communications Consultants Grp, Inc: 929 Harrison Ave #301, Columbus, OH 43215 ... 614-297-5050
Communications Design, Inc: 5875 Old Millstone Rd, Rockford, IL 61114 ... 815-633-0577
Communications Via Design: 437 D St Ste 4B, Boston, MA 02210 ... 617-204-9500
CommuniCreations: 2130 S Bellaire, Denver, CO 80222 ... 303-759-1155
Comp Art of Louisville: 981 S Third St #300, Louisville, KY 40203 ... 502-589-2557
Compass Design: 510 First Ave N #202, Minneapois, MN 55403 ... 612-339-1595
Computer Graphics Group: 1450 Manhattan Beach Blvd #B, Manhattan Beach, CA 90266 ... 310-372-3228
Comvision: 60 E 42nd St #1365, New York, NY 10165 ... 212-687-2708
Conber Creations: 3326 NE 60th, Portland, OR 97213 ... 503-288-2938
Concept & Design Assocs: 1585 Alameda #300, San Jose, CA 95126 ... 408-993-2272
Concept Design: 154 Brushy Hill Rd, Danbury, CT 06810 ... 203-797-0504
Concept Design Work: 1835 W 6th St #13, Tempe, AZ 85281 ... 602-968-4125
Concept Packaging, Inc: 5 Horizon Rd, Ft Lee, NJ 07024 ... 201-224-5762
Concepts Corp, The: 120 Kedron Ave, Holmes, PA 19043 ... 610-461-1600
Concepts Design Group: 8000 West Ave #1, San Antonio, TX 78213 ... 210-342-0270
Concepts Unlimited, Inc: 1250 Capital of Texas Hwy S/B3#350, Austin, TX 78746 ... 512-328-3576
Conceptual Annual Reports: 65 Bleecker St, New York, NY 10001 ... 212-505-1607
Concrete, Inc: 633 S Plymouth Ct #208, Chicago, IL 60605 ... 312-427-3733
Confluence Comm: 263 Chuckanut Point Rd, Bellingham, WA 98226 ... 360-733-2005
Conflux Design: 2819 Ware Rd, Rockford, IL 61114 ... 815-282-4066
Connelly Design: 444 N Wabash #410, Chicago, IL 60611 ... 312-565-0760
Connick Creative Svcs, Jack: 1935 8th Ave West, Seattle, WA 98119 ... 206-284-1142
Conrad Graphic Design: 1133 Millcreek Ln, Columbus, OH 43220 ... 614-442-1880
Conrad Jorgensen Studio: 1219 Folsom St, San Francisco, CA 94103 ... 415-626-9878
Constable, Janice: 11 Woodstock Ct, San Raphael, CA 94903 ... 415-472-5530
Consultants In Design: 32 W 40th St #7B, New York, NY 10018 ... 212-921-1524
Contempo Design: 212 Railroad Ave, Milpitas, CA 95035 ... 408-956-9555
Context Design Research Dvlpmt: 2601 Meade Ct, Ann Arbor, MI 48105 ... 313-622-0072
Contours Consulting Design Group: 864 Stearns Rd, Bartlett, IL 60103 ... 630-837-4100
Conway Design: 118 Magazine St, Cambridge, MA 02139 ... 617-864-9838
Conyard, Scott O: Rochester, NY ...
Cook & Shanosky Assoc: 401 S State St, Newtown, PA 18940 ... 215-860-8800
Cook Design, Chris: 3836 Piute Dr, Grandville, MI 49418 ... 616-531-5474
Cook Design, Mickey: 1647 Kitchener Dr, Sunnyvale, CA 94087 ... 408-738-8277
Cook Design, Robert: PO Box 639, Bellaire, TX 77402 ... 713-227-8350
Cooke & Co, Bill: 314 main St, Great Barrington, MA 01230 ... 413-528-3808
Cooke Design, Alice: 1 East Ave, Norwalk, CT 06851 ... 203-847-7109
Coon Design Assocs: 3711 W 12th St, Erie, PA 16505 ... 814-838-1528
Cooney Design: 875 3rd Ave 4th Fl, New York, NY 10022 ... 212-303-7604
Coons/Beirise Design Assocs: 313 Hilton Pl, Cincinnati, OH 45219 ... 513-751-7459
Cooper Assocs, Scott: 35 Pinelawn #212E, Melville, NY 11747 ... 516-249-9700
Cooper Design Assocs: 1360 S Coast Hwy, Laguna Beach, CA 92651 ... 714-497-5081
Cooper Graphic Design, Sam: 101 Linden, Ft Collins, CO 80524 ... 970-484-7440
Cooper Software, Inc: 2345 Yale St, Palo Alto, CA 94308 ... 415-855-0250
Copeland Hirthler Design & Comm: 40 Inwood Circle, Atlanta, GA 30309 ... 404-892-3472
Corcetto Enterprises: 3 Skywind Dr, Reinholds, PA 17569 ... 610-678-0867
Corchia Woliner Assocs: 130 W 56th St, New York, NY 10019 ... 212-977-9778
Cordaro Design Inc, Rubin: 115 N First St, Minneapolis, MN 55401 ... 612-343-0011
Cordella Design: 55 Westland Terrace, Haverhill, MA 01830 ... 617-437-9198
Cordesign: 3904 Jefferson, Austin, TX 78731 ... 512-371-1230
Corey Mcpherson Nash: 9 Galen St, Watertown, MA 02172 ... 617-924-6050
Cornelius/Keener Creative: 3326 Mapleridge Ct, Suwanee, GA 30174 ... 770-623-3986
Cornerstone Design Group: 444 Park Ave S #202, New York, NY 10016 ... 212-686-6046
Cornoyer Hedrick, Inc: 2425 E Camelback Rd #400, Phoenix, AZ 85016 ... 602-381-4848
Corpographics,Inc: 47 West St, New York, NY 10006 ... 212-483-9065
Corporate 3 Design: 2723 S 87th Ave, Omaha, NE 68124 ... 402-398-3333
Corporate Design Assocs: 3450 Princeton Pike, LAwrenceville, NJ 08648 ... 609-844-9797
Corporate Design Group: 256 Fifth Ave 2nd Fl, New York, NY 10001 ... 212-889-7696
Corporate Graphics: 51-04 39th Ave, Woodside, NY 11377 ... 718-651-4689

Corporate Graphics, Inc: 1633 Broadway 27th Fl, New York, NY 10019. 212-887-8181
Corporate Image, The: 43 Wensley Dr, Great Neck, NY 11021. 516-773-3131
Corporate Reports: 6 Lenox Pointe NE, Atlanta, GA 30324 404-233-2230
Corporate Visuals, Inc: 515 El Bosque, Laguna Beach, CA 92651 714-494-6269
Corrente, Linda: 45 E 62nd St, New York, NY 10021. 212-486-3015
Corson Design, Madeleine: 25 Zoe St, San Francisco, CA 94107 415-777-2492
Cory Adv: 2083 Main St, Stratford, CT 06497. 203-380-5240
Cosgrove Assocs, Inc: 225 E 31 St 1st Fl, New York, NY 10016 212-889-7202
Costello & Co: 250 Summit Ave, Greensboro, NC 27401 910-273-9028
Costello Communications: 2657 N Bosworth Ave, Chicago, OH 60614. 773-327-1386
Cotler, Inc, Sheldon: 568 Broadway #803, New York, NY 10012 212-719-9590
Cottle Communications, Inc: 8 S Michigan Ave #2212, Chicago, IL 60603. 312-922-7009
Cotton Communications, Jim: 38 Vestry St, New York, NY 10013 212-431-1930
Counihan Graphics, Gerald: 200 Mercer St, New York, NY 10012 212-477-7925
Cousins & Assocs, Morison S: 599 Broadway 8th Fl, New York, NY 10012. 212-751-3390
Cover To Cover: 26 W 17th St *th Fl, New York, NY 10011 212-675-5550
Covey, Traci O'Very: 7 Washington St, Beverly, MA 01915. 978-921-0887
cow.: 1522 Cloverfield Blvd #E, Santa Monica, CA 90404 310-264-2430
Cowen Design, Melinda: 3841 NE 2nd Ave, Miami, FL 33137 305-573-9838
Cox & Hall: 4901 Behrens Rd, Collieville, TX 76034 817-267-2340
Cox Adv, Jim: 391 S Madison, Pasadena, CA 91101 818-584-9363
Cox, Stephen: 299 Miller Rd #69, Mauldin, SC 29662 864-458-8289
Coy Los Angeles: 4230 Lafayette, Culver City, CA 90232 310-837-0173
Coyne Beahm: 8518 Triad Dr, Colfax, NC 27235. 910-996-1255
Coyne Comms: The Penthouse/10 Park Pl, Morristown, NJ 02960 201-984-1800
CPF Marketing Communications: 22015 Marine View Dr South, Seattle, WA 98198 206-824-0688
Cpm 95 Inc: 95 Fifth Ave 4th Fl, New York, NY 10003 212-924-3815
CPS: 267 W 70th St #1A, New York, NY 10023 212-724-6700
CPS Group/Timerlane Mclane: 125 E Carpenter Frwy #600, Irving, TX 75062 214-869-3370
Crabtree & Jimison: 1137 N Highland St, Arlington, VA 22201 703-525-7798
Crabtree & Strussion Design Inc: 1712 Graham Rd, Reynoldsburg, OH 43068 614-577-1712
Craen, Inc, John : 520 Madison, San Antonio, TX 78204 210-224-9751
Craig Design, Susan: 3118 Amherst Ave, Columbia, SC 29205 803-252-6558
Crane, Doug: 1732 NW Quimby St, Portland, OR 97209 503-223-6794
Cranford & Assocs, Johnson: 1st Commercial Bldg #2200, Little Rock, AR 72201 501-376-6251
Craven, Linda: 1737 Connecticut Ave NW, Washington, DC 20009 202-232-4838
Crawford Mikus Design: 887 W Marietta St NW #T-101, Atlanta, GA 30318 404-875-7753
Crawshaw Design, Todd: 120 Bayview Dr, San Rafael, CA 94901 415-456-5544
Create 12: 12 Lois Ave, E Brunswick, NJ 08816 908-238-5051
Creative Avenue: 500 S Clinton St 8th Fl, Chicago, IL 60607 312-922-4500
Creative Concepts In Design: 1638 S Bayshore Ct, Miami, FL 33133. 305-899-8464
Creative Dept: 5002 92nd Ave SE, Mercer Island, WA 98040. 206-236-4548
Creative Dept: 1708 Scott Ave, Charlotte, NC 28203 704-339-0497
Creative Dept, The: 130 S 17th St, Philadelphia, PA 19103 215-988-0390
Creative Design: 1273 Old Dixie Highway, Lake Park, FL 33403 407-848-6666
Creative Design & Marketing: 48 Free St, Portland, ME 04101. 207-774-7528
Creative Design Board: Hancock/875 N Michigan #2205, Chicago, IL 60611. 312-266-2200
Creative Design Center, Inc: 1091 N Granada Dr, Orange, CA 92869 714-771-7124
Creative Group, The: 3201 W Sahara Suite G, Las Vegas, NV 89102. 702-248-6334
Creative Ink Design: 26 Park Rd, Shorts Hills, NJ 07078 201-467-5396
Creative Only: 610 Emory Ave, Campbell, CA 95008 408-379-0151
Creative R & D: 321 Pharr Rd #6, Atlanta, GA 30305. 404-261-1724
Creative Resource Center: 3621 Bury Dr #10, Eden Prairie, MN 55346 612-937-6000
Creative Services: 2109 St James Rd, Raleigh, NC 27607 919-781-5366
Creative Solutions: 205 Rutgers St, Maplewood, NJ 07040. 201-378-3800
Creative Works, Inc: 304 3rd St, Jupiter, FL 33458 407-745-7050
Creatives NYC: 27 W 24th St #500, New York, NY 10010. 212-675-9592
Creativeworks Studios, Inc: 10 E 23rd St #300, New York, NY 10010. 212-477-5610
Cricket Contrast: 2301 N 16th St, Phoenix, AZ 85006 602-258-6149
Crisp, Alan: 1430 Mercy St, Mountain View, CA 94041 415-965-8966
Critz, Anita: 2255 Cumberland Pkwy NW Bldg 1400 #A1, Atlanta, GA 30339. 770-436-6092
Crockadre Studio: 170 S Brownell Rd Suite A, Williston, VT 05495 802-865-6233
Cronan Design: 42 Decatur St, San Francisco, CA 94103 415-522-5800
Cronan, Michael Patrick: 1 Zoe St, San Francisco, CA 94107. 415-543-6745
Crosby, Bart: 676 St Clair St, Chicago, IL 60611 312-951-2800
Crossroads Graphics, Inc: 235 Monroe Tnpke, Monroe, CT 06468. 203-268-2255
Crouch & Fuller,Inc: 853 Camino Del Mar, Del Mar, CA 92014. 619-450-9200
Crow-Quill Studios: 1026 Walker Ave, Oakland, CA 94610 510-832-8931
Croxton Design: 2121 N California Blvd #530, Walnut Creek, CA 94596 510-935-7003
Crum Designs, Inc, Don : 4607 W Lovers Ln, Dallas, TX 75209 214-352-1384
Cruz Design: 423 Tehama St #C, San Francisco, CA 94103 415-495-5999
CSF Design: 3658 Perada Dr, Walnut Creek, CA 94595 510-682-9967
Csoka Benato Fleurant, Inc: 134 W 26th St, New York, NY 10001 212-242-6777
Cuccia Design, Christine: 2350 Taylor St, San Francisco, CA 94133 415-771-1072
Cuerden Advertising Design: 1730 Gaylord St, Denver, CO 80206 303-321-4163
Cuh2A: 211 Carnegie Center, Princeton, NJ 08540 609-452-1212
Cukjati Designs: 2735 Rocky Heights Dr, Colorado Springs, CO 80921. 719-481-4686
Culbert Lavery Russman, Ross: 15 W 20th St 9th Fl, New York, NY 10011 212-206-0044
Cully, Mike: 345 W Erie St, Chicago, IL 60610 312-440-9208
Cummings & Good: 3 N Main St/Box 570, Chester, CT 06412 860-526-9597
Cummings Design Group: 95 Argonaut #140, Aliso Viejo, CA 92656. 949-598-0800
Cunningham & Welsh Design Grp: 633 W Main, Madison, WI 53703 608-258-1988
Curium Design: 83 Divisadero St, San Francisco, CA 94117 415-255-1877
Curr Design, Jane: 745 Walnut Dr, Paso Robles, CA 93446. 805-227-4240
Curran & Connors: 140 Wood Rd #200, Braintree, MA 02184 617-963-7540
Current, Inc: 1005 E Woodman Rd, Colorado Springs, CO 80920 719-594-4100
Curry Design: 1501 Main St/Mezzanine, Venice, CA 90291. 310-399-4626
Curry, Steve: 1501 Main St Mezzanine, Venice, CA 90291 310-399-4626
Curtis & Co: 928 Broadway #1104, New York, NY 10010. 212-475-3680
Curtis Design: 3328 Steiner St #1, San Francisco, CA 94123 415-567-4402
Curtis Design: 698 Bedford Rd, Armonk, NY 10504. 914-234-3574
Curtis, Todd: 2032 14th St #7, Santa Monica, CA 90405 310-452-0738
Custom Designers, Inc: 5866 Old Centerville Rd, Centerville, VA 22020. 703-830-8582
Cutro Assocs, Inc: 47 Jewett Ave, Tenafly, NJ 07670. 201-569-5548
CWA, Inc: 4015 Ibis St, San Diego, CA 92103 619-299-0431
CyberLive: 409 Utica Ave #D44, Huntington Beach, CA 92648 714-536-7014

D

D & D Creative Concepts: 59 Farnell Rd, Weston, CT 06883 203-227-9232
D Wilkinson Advertising: 55 W Chestnut St #1703, Chicago, IL 60610. 312-951-0159
D'Addario: 595 Smith St, Farmingdale, NY 11735. 516-391-5440
D'Anastasio Art Studio: 458 Boonton Turnpike, Lincoln Park, NJ 07035 201-872-4593
D'Art Studio, Inc: PO Box 299, N Scituate, MA 02060 617-545-7313
D'Astolfo Design, Frank: 80 Warren St #32, New York, NY 10007. 212-732-3052
[data-rocket] + [industries]: 2 N Main St #B332, Beacon Falls, CT 06403. 203-720-1603
D-Zine: 34 W 15th St 3rd Fl, New York, NY 10011 212-691-6700
Dakota Design, Inc: 2160 Swedeford Rd, Malverne, PA 19355 610-647-9898
Dale, Inc, Colopy: 850 Ridge Ave, Pittsburgh, PA 15212. 412-332-6706
Dale, Terry: 2824 Hurst Terr NW, Washington, DC 20008. 202-244-3866
DaLee, Dianne: 2029 Santenay Dr, Marietta, GA 30060 770-425-4222
Daley Graphics: PO Box 138, Margaretville, NY 12455. 914-586-4253
Daly & Daly Graphic Design, Inc: 233 Harvard St, Brookline, MA 02146 617-738-7181
Daly Design, Joan: 622 Central Ave, Wilmette, IL 60091 847-256-5042
Dangremond Design Assocs: 6064 N Kirkwood, Chicago, IL 60646 773-205-2222
Danhausen Group Design: 2183 Fairview Rd #103, Costa Mesa, CA 92627 714-574-0303
Daniel, Inc: 3301 Hamilton #106, Fort Worth, TX 76107 817-334-0039
Daniels Design: 104 E 40th St #503, New York, NY 10016. 212-889-0071
Daniels Graphics: 131 Sweeten Creek Rd, Asheville, NC 28803. 704-277-8250
Danube Design, Louy: E 12348 Halweg Rd, Merrimac, WI 53561. 608-493-2797
Danziger, Louis: PO Box 660189, Arcadia, CA 91066 818-446-7717
Darby, Kevin: 6604 Six Forks Rd #201, Raleigh, NC 27615. 919-676-3261
Darden Graphics, Clare: 5422 Bellingham Ave #201B, N Hollywood, CA 91607 818-762-5673
Darden Lentz: 164 W Mariposa, San Clemente, CA 92672 714-361-2807
Darold Designs: 216 F St #145, Davis, CA 95616 916-758-1379
DaSilva, Silvio: 78 Manhattan Ave #2D, New York, NY 10025 212-665-3670
Davenport Design: 3677 Voltaire St, San Diego, CA 92106 619-224-6004
Davenport Design Assocs, Alan: 220 Montgomery St #1035, San Francisco, CA 94104. . 415-362-8333
Davidson Production Design, Peter: 836 Ashland Ave #1, Santa Monica, CA 90405 310-581-9335
Davies & Assocs: 1440 Terrace Dr, Tulsa, OK 74104 918-744-1101
Davies Assocs: 9424 Dayton Way #217, Beverly Hills, CA 90210. 310-247-9572
Davis Adv & Design, Scott: N2806 Walden Ln, Lake Geneva, WI 53147. 414-248-3608
Davis Delaney Arrow, Inc: 141 E 25th St, New York, NY 10010 212-686-2500
Davis Design: 1499 Blake St #1F, Denver, CO 80202 303-455-0357
Davis Design: 1055 Hillside, Naperville, IL 60540 630-305-3982
Davis Design Adv: 1790 Fifth St, Berkeley, CA 94710. 510-649-2777
Davis Design, Carla: 674 10th St #G-Fl, Brooklyn, NY 11215. 212-924-6464
Davis Design, Neil: 119 W 57th St #615, New York, NY 10019. 212-245-4436
Davis Design, Pat: 455 university Ave #360, Sacramento, CA 95825. 916-920-9025
Davis Group: 14730 NE Eighth St #105, Bellevue, WA 98007. 206-641-5758
Davis Group: 4631 Brown Ave, Jacksonville, FL 32207 904-398-1704
Dawson & Company: 21 Dean St, Assonet, MA 02702 508-644-2940
Dawson & Company: 49 Monroe Ctr NW, Grand Rapids, MI 49503 616-458-8022
Dawson Design: 7250 Beverly Blvd #101, Los Angeles, CA 90036. 213-937-5867
Dawson Design: PO Box 369, Maumee, OH 43537 419-866-1119
Dawson Designers Assocs: 21 Dean St, Assonet, MA 02702. 617-644-2940
Dawson, Chris: 7250 Beverly Blvd #101, Los Angeles, CA 90036. 213-937-5867
Day & Assocs, David: 2152 S 109th St, Omaha, NE 68144 402-398-1108
Day Design & Assocs, David: 1310 Pendleton St #204, Cincinnati, OH 45210. 513-621-4060
Day, Brian: 646 Fillmore St, San Francisco, CA 94117 415-621-4934
Dayne, Jeff: 731 NE Everett, Portland, OR 97232 503-232-8777
Dazel Corp: 301 Congress Ave #1100, Austin, TX 78701. 512-494-7300
DB Design: 101 S Jennings #303, Fort Worth, TX 76104 817-870-2941
DBD Intl Ltd: 406 Technology Dr W, Menomonie, WI 54751. 715-235-9040
DD Graphics: 44 Queens St, Rochester, NY 14609. 716-288-8315
De Cesare Design: 15 Waverly Rd, Darien, CT 06820. 203-655-6057
De Goede, Jan: 3826 N Marshfield Ave, Chicago, IL 60613 773-525-6500
De Heer Rose Design: 350 Brannan St 3rd Fl, San Francisco, CA 94107 415-512-7710
De Marting Design: 37 Main St #3, Cold Spring, NY 10516 212-941-9200
De Napoli Studio, Inc: 454 W 46th St #5ES, New York, NY 10036. 212-333-3357
De Olivera Creative: 1750 Lafayette St, Denver, CO 80218 303-837-8717
De Pasque Graphic Design, Diane: 511 Ave Of The Americas, New York, NY 10011 212-229-9201
De Plano Design, Inc: 1 Madison Ave 26th Fl, New York, NY 10010 212-213-2224
De Santis Design: 116 E 27th St 8th Fl, New York, NY 10016 212-725-2655
De Sherbinin Design: 7 Washington St, Beverly, MA 01915. 508-927-6119
De Witt/Anthony Co: 126 Main St, Northhampton, MA 01060. 413-586-4304
Dean Design Assocs: 1007 Nissley Rd, Lancaster, PA 17601 717-898-9800
Dean, Jane: 1007 Nissley Rd, Lancaster, PA 17601. 717-898-9800
Debrey Design: 6014 Blue Circle Dr, Minnetonka, MN 55343 612-935-2292
DeBrey, Robert J: 6014 Blue Circle #D, Minneapolis, MN 55343 612-935-2292
Decampi Inc, Denis: 1201 Delaware Ave, Wilmington, DE 19806 302-656-0460
Decorage: 600 Hadley Rd, S Plainfield, NJ 07080. 908-755-2600
Decrosta Design, George: 902 Upper State St, New Haven, CT 06511 203-776-1155
Deep Design/Div Austin Kelley: 5901 Peachtree Dunwoody #200C, Atlanta, GA 30328 . . 770-396-6666
Dees Group, Inc: 12 Norcross #210, Roswell, GA 30075. 770-522-8430
deFine Design: 415 Central Pk W, New York, NY 10025. 212-316-2599
Defrin Design Inc, Bob: 140 Riverside Dr, New York, NY 10012. 212-799-4793
Degnen Assocs: 181 Thurnman Ave, Columbus, OH 43206 614-444-3334
Dekker Babian: 39 W 14th St #204, New York, NY 10011 212-242-1359
Dekrone Design: 70 E First St #3, New York, NY 10003 212-647-9870
Dektas Eger, Inc: 30 W Third St, Cincinnati, OH 45202 513-621-7070
DeLeeuw, Jeff: 23116 77th Ave SE, Woodinville, WA 98072 206-718-2075
DeLellis, Chris-Anthony: 417 Canal St 2nd Fl, New York, NY 10013 212-431-5300
Deleon Design, Inc: 3301 Edloe #204, Houston, TX 77027 713-963-0060
Delgado Design: 1133 Broadway #1614, New York, NY 10010. 212-645-0097
Dellaporta Adv & Graphic: 2020 14th St, Santa Monica, CA 90405. 310-452-3832
Delor Design Group: 732 W Main St, Louisville, KY 40202 502-584-5500
Demark Keller & Gardner: 141 W 28th St 9th Fl, New York, NY 10001 212-714-1731
DeMartin Marona Cranstoun Downes: 450 Seventh Ave 39th Fl, New York, NY 10123 . . 212-268-5450
DeMartino Design: 584 Broadway, New York, NY 10012 212-941-9200
Dennard Creative, Inc: 5050 Quorum #300, Dallas, TX 75240. 214-233-0430
Denning & Denning Design: 2077 S Gessner #100, Houston, TX 77063 713-789-2076
Denny: 3613 Rolridge Rd, Richmond, VA 23233. 804-360-7623
Denton Design Assocs: 491 Arbor St, Pasadena, CA 91105. 818-792-7141
Deponte Design: 95 N Main St, Petersham, MA 01366 508-724-8823
DeRose, Andrea Legg: 1942 Shiver Dr, Alexandria, VA 22307 703-768-3193

Desert Graphics: 303 N Indian Canyon Dr, Palm Springs, CA 92262 ... 619-325-2333
Desgrippes Gobe &Assocs: 411 Lafayette St, New York, NY 10003 ... 212-979-8900
Design & Direction: 872 5th St, Manhattan Beach, CA 90260 ... 310-937-3669
Design & Graphics: 330 E 13th St, Tucson, AZ 85701 ... 520-623-8802
Design & Image Comm: 1900 Wazee #200, Denver, CO 80202 ... 303-292-3455
Design & Prod: 9434 Hunts End Dr, Sandy, UT 84092 ... 801-943-6771
Design & Time: 1026 Anclote Dr, Tarpon Springs, FL 34689 ... 813-938-5107
Design 291: 1903 Kalorama Pl NW #19, Washington, DC 20009 ... 202-234-6908
Design Alliance: 418 N Pitt St, Alexandria, VA 22314 ... 703-549-8881
Design Alliance, Inc: 105 Stearns Ave, Cincinnati, OH 45215 ... 513-621-9373
Design Art: 6311 Romaine St #7311, Los Angeles, CA 90038 ... 213-467-2984
Design Arts: 2343 W Estrella Dr, Chandler, AZ 85224 ... 602-786-9411
Design Assocs: 430 N Park #402, Indianapolis, IN 46202 ... 317-636-8053
Design Assocs: 6117 N Winthrop Ave, Chicago, IL 60660 ... 773-338-4196
Design Assocs, Inc: 2819 Detroit Ave, Cleveland, OH 44113 ... 216-696-1060
Design Assocs, Martin: 1960 E Grand Ave #610, El Segundo, CA 90245 ... 310-414-9558
Design Assocs, Riley: 380 Diablo Rd #201, Danville, CA 94526 ... 510-552-1590
Design At Work: 17047 El Camino Real #221, Houston, TX 77058 ... 713-280-8635
Design Axis: 12 Westerville Sq #330, Westerville, OH 43081 ... 614-448-7995
Design Basics: 1027 Monroe Dr NE, Atlanta, GA 30306 ... 404-876-6475
Design Board: 1380 E South Temple #110, Salt Lake City, UT 84102 ... 801-521-7090
Design Center: 734 W 800 S, Salt Lake City, UT 84104 ... 801-532-6122
Design Center, Inc: 15119 Minnetonka Blvd, Minnetonka, MN 55345 ... 612-933-9766
Design Central: PO Box 2207, North Bend, WA 98045 ... 206-747-4115
Design Central: 8737 Colesville Rd #304, Silver Spring, MD 20910 ... 301-588-6994
Design Co: 250 State St, North Haven, CT 06473 ... 203-230-9566
Design Co, Inc: 26 E Exchange St #315, St Paul, MN 55101 ... 612-221-1030
Design Comp, Inc: PO Box 23, Meriden, CT 06450 ... 203-235-9809
Design Consultants: PO Box 40894, Chicago, IL 60640 ... 773-907-5500
Design Core: 1352 N Formosa Ave Ste 2, Los Angeles, CA 90046 ... 323-874-5700
Design Corps: 501 N Alfred St, Los Angeles, CA 90048 ... 213-651-1422
Design Corral: 723 E Woodbury Rd, Altadena, CA 91001 ... 818-798-8275
Design Design, Inc: 1333 N Kinsbury #201, Chicago, IL 60622 ... 312-944-0099
Design Direction: 109 N Church St, West Chester, PA 19380 ... 610-436-5382
Design Direction Group: 747 E Union #102, Pasadena, CA 91101 ... 818-792-4765
Design Dynamics: 1681 94th Lane NE, Minneapolis, MN 55449 ... 612-780-4911
Design Edge: 316 N Lamar, Austin, TX 78703 ... 512-477-5491
Design Element: 8624 Wonderland Ave, Los Angeles, CA 90046 ... 213-656-3293
Design Farm: 14 Northridge Lane, Lafayette, CA 94549 ... 510-284-3316
Design Five: 180 Varick St 15th Fl, New York, NY 10014 ... 212-727-8899
Design For Business: 435 Buckland Rd, South Windsor, CT 06074 ... 860-644-3690
Design For Industry, Inc: 341 Linwood Ave, Buffalo, NY 14209 ... 716-883-2095
Design Force: 104 Ganttown Rd, Turnerville, NJ 08012 ... 609-232-7927
Design Form: 8250 Electric Ave, Stanton, CA 90680 ... 714-952-3700
Design Group: 5801 Iris Ave, Las Vegas, NV 89107 ... 702-878-6559
Design Group: 1229 S Washington, Royal Oak, MI 48067 ... 810-546-4390
Design Group: 3444 N Washington Blvd, Indianapolis, IN 46205 ... 317-924-2444
Design Group of Boston: 437 Boylston St, Boston, MA 02116 ... 617-437-1084
Design Group West: 853 Camino Del Mar, Del Mar, CA 92014 ... 619-481-5398
Design Group, The: 4411 W Market St #100, Greensboro, NC 27407 ... 910-856-0815
Design Group, The: 48700 Pointe Lake View, New Baltimore, MI 48047 ... 810-725-2254
Design Group, The: 2976 Triverton Pike, Madison, WI 53711 ... 608-274-5393
Design Horizons: 3055 Cardinal Dr #200, Vero Beach, FL 32963 ... 407-234-8001
Design Horizons Intl: 520 W Erie #330, Chicago, IL 60610 ... 312-664-0006
Design House: 711 E Wardlow Rd #203, Long Beach, CA 90807 ... 310-424-0433
Design III: 333 St Charles Ave #1213, New Orleans, LA 70130 ... 504-558-0333
Design Imports: 260 Narragansett Park Dr, East Providence, RI 02916 ... 401-438-6300
Design Kitchen: 1040 W Huron 1st Fl, Chicago, IL 60622 ... 312-455-0388
Design Kupiec: 48 W 25th St 12th Fl, New York, NY 10010 ... 212-675-2405
Design Logic: 804 Pleasant Hill Rd, Wallingford, PA 19086 ... 610-876-9995
Design Logix, Inc: 345 Queen St #410, Honolulu, HI 96813 ... 808-524-5055
Design Loiminchay: 390 Broadway 3rd Fl, New York, NY 10013 ... 212-941-7488
Design Management: 4930 Morris Ave #4229, Addison, TX 75001 ... 214-239-6280
Design Marks Corp: 1462 W Irving Park, Chicago, IL 60613 ... 773-327-3669
Design Media: 18123 Tarzana St, Tarzana, CA 91356 ... 818-986-5134
Design Metro: 3502 SW Jerald Ct, Portland, OR 97221 ... 503-274-0696
Design Moves, Inc: 1073 Gage St #3, Winnetka, IL 60093 ... 847-661-0999
Design North : 8007 Douglas Ave, Racine, WI 53402 ... 414-762-1320
Design Office: 95 Minna St 2nd Fl, San Francisco, CA 94105 ... 415-543-4760
Design Office: 95 Minna St 2nd Fl, San Francisco, CA 94105 ... 415-543-4760
Design Office Inc, The: 1 Bridge St, Irvington, NY 10533 ... 914-591-5911
Design On Devine: 3103 Devine St, Columbia, SC 29205 ... 803-252-8069
Design One: 437 Marshman St, Highland Park, IL 60035 ... 847-433-4140
Design Online: 804 Desnter St, Evanston, IL 60202 ... 847-328-2733
Design Partners, Inc: 9540 Brink Rd/Po Box 86122, Gaithersburg, MD 20886 ... 301-840-9525
Design Partnership, The: 111 3rd Ave S #150/Mill Place, Minneapolis, MN 55401 ... 612-338-8889
Design Perspective: 3170 Fourth Ave #200, San Diego, CA 92103 ... 619-296-8266
Design Plus: PO Box 1140, Aquebogue, NY 11931 ... 631-722-4384
Design Resource: 700 S Henderson Rd #308B, King of Prussia, PA 19406 ... 215-265-8585
Design Sense Studios: 341 Van Buren St, N Babylon, NY 11703 ... 516-587-0623
Design Services: 2308 O'Keeffe Place, Davis, CA 95616 ... 916-758-3344
Design Services, Inc: 7777 Jefferson Hwy 2nd Fl, Baton Rouge, LA 70809 ... 504-926-2000
Design Studio: 1128 Tahoe Dr, Belmont, CA 94002 ... 415-508-9980
Design Studio: 907 Cunningham Rd, Salem, OH 44460 ... 330-337-0842
Design Studio II Assocs: 1107 NW 14th Ave, Portland, OR 97209 ... 503-223-8058
Design Studio, The: 4600 Post Oak Pl #260, Houston, TX 77727 ... 713-965-0100
Design Tekneka: Box 2510, Decatur, GA 30031 ... 404-378-7900
Design Touch: 2208 River Run Dr #56, San Diego, CA 92108 ... 619-281-9015
Design Trends: 4 Broadway PO Box 119, Valhalla, NY 10595 ... 914-948-0902
Design Tribe: 525 Brannan #201, San Francisco, CA 94107 ... 415-495-3113
Design Trust: 142 Danbury Rd, Wilton, CT 06897 ... 203-761-1412
Design Twenty-Five Twenty-Five: 6220 S Orange Blossom Trl #175, Orlando, FL 32809 . 407-856-2525
Design Two Ltd: 600 N McClurg Ct #330, Chicago, IL 60611 ... 312-642-9888
Design Vectors: 725 Greenwich St 4th Fl, San Francisco, CA 94133 ... 415-391-0399
Design Works: 1042 W Hedding St #100, San Jose, CA 95126 ... 408-922-0788
Design Works, The: 292 S La Cienega Blvd #400, Beverly Hills, CA 90211 ... 310-360-9292
Design Workshop, Inc: 7430 SW 122nd St, Miami, FL 33156 ... 305-378-1039
Design, Christopher: 3308 Church Rd, Cherry Hill, NJ 08002 ... 856-667-7433
Design, Inc: 9304 St Marks Pl, Fairfax, VA 22301 ... 703-273-5053

Designation, Inc: 53 Spring St 5th Fl, New York, NY 10012 ... 212-226-6024
Designers Three: 25 W 43rd St, New York, NY 10036 ... 212-221-5900
Designframe: 116 E 16th St 10th Fl, New York, NY 10003 ... 212-924-2426
Designing Interiors Design Co: 401 E 80th St #12A, New York, NY 10021 ... 212-517-5428
Designmark, Inc: 4640 W 71st st, Indianapolis, IN 46268 ... 317-291-0300
Designology: 7641 E Gray Rd, Scottsdale, AZ 85260 ... 602-443-3227
Designs For Business: 721 Wilson St, Pomona, CA 91768 ... 909-626-4472
Designs, Inc: 762 Purdy Alley, Columbus, OH 43206 ... 614-443-3321
Designspace: 476 Broadway 7th Fl, New York, NY 10013 ... 212-925-9696
Designspeak: 15_0 W 25th St #900, New York, NY 10001 ... 212-675-4477
Designteal: 500 Molina St #307, Los Angeles, CA 90013 ... 213-485-1204
Designxavier: 13 Inverness Way So, Englewood, CO 80112 ... 303-799-6640
Deskey: 50 E River Ctr Blvd #1700, Covington, KY 41011 ... 606-655-2300
Deskey Assocs: 145 East 32nd St, New York, NY 10016 ... 212-447-9400
Desktop Graphic Services: 2265 Westwood Blvd #105, Los Angeles, CA 90064 ... 310-391-5275
Desmarais Design: 108 Ponemah Rd, Amherst, NH 03031 ... 603-673-0053
Desola Group, Inc: 477 Madison Ave 23rd Fl, New York, NY 10022 ... 212-832-4770
Deutsch Design: 25 Mercer St 2nd Fl, New York, NY 10013 ... 212-966-7710
Devaney Murata Design: 17125 S Dalton Ave, Gardena, CA 90247 ... 310-782-8736
Devault Design: 2400 Sunset Pl, Nashvile, TN 37212 ... 615-269-0202
Devries Communications: 10750 Aurora Ave, Des Moines, IA 50322 ... 515-270-3838
Dezine Media: 1629 Wagon Wheel Dr, Plano, TX 75023 ... 214-669-9230
Dezinno, Richard: 348 Neipsic Rd, Glastonbury, CT 06033 ... 203-659-1624
Dfo Creative Consultants: 767 Third Ave, New York, NY 10017 ... 212-980-2900
DFS Creative Services: 12 Maple Ridge Dr, Burlington, MA 01803 ... 617-229-8858
DGF Design: 3280 Cahuenga Blvd W 3rd Fl, Los Angeles, CA 90068 ... 213-851-2244
DH Assocs: 402 E Main St, Palmyra, NY 14522 ... 315-597-0022
Di Bacco Design: 46 Highwood Dr, Avon, CT 06001 ... 203-675-6488
Di Giovine Design: 100 North State St #A, Newton, PA 18940 ... 215-504-2244
di Liberto, Lisa: 413 3rd St #4, Brooklyn, NY 11215 ... 718-768-3212
Dialog Design, Inc: 260 Montague Rd, Leverette, MA 01054 ... 413-548-8198
Diamond Art Studio Ltd: 11 E 36th St 9th Fl, New York, NY 10016 ... 212-685-6622
• **Dickens, Holly: pg 933** 50 E Bellevue Pl #406, Chicago, IL 60611 ... **312-280-0777**
e-mail: holly@hollydickens.com / url: www.hollydickens.com
Dickerson Group: 274 Summer St, Boston, MA 02210 ... 617-426-7555
Diefenbach Elkins: 50 Rockefeller Plza 15th Fl, New York, NY 10020 ... 212-332-3500
Diehl Design, Michael: 1415 Norton, Glendale, CA 91202 ... 818-552-4110
Dietrich, Lance: 119 N Chestnut St, Palmyra, PA 17078 ... 717-838-9590
Digital Art Exchange: 360 Newbury St, Boston, MA 02215 ... 800-329-6266
Digital Corp: 13620 Sunrise Dr NE, Bainbridge Is, WA 98110 ... 206-587-0286
Digital Dirigible, Inc: 38 Vestry St, New York, NY 10013 ... 212-431-1925
Digital Instincts, Inc: 405 Tarrytown Rd #370, White Plains, NY 10607 ... 914-422-5883
Digital Media: 7694 S Madison Ave, Burr Ridge, IL 60521 ... 708-789-1100
Digital Media World: 10 Barley Mow Passage, London, England, UK W4 4PH ... 181-995-3633
Digital Pulp, Inc: 220 E 23rd St #607, New York, NY 10010 ... 212-679-0676
Digital Tribe, Inc: 16 Charity, Irvine, CA 92715 ... 714-854-5400
Dimensional Illustrators: 362 2nd St Pike #112, Southhampton, PA 18966 ... 215-953-1415
Dimmick, Gary: 47 Riverview Ave, Pittsburgh, PA 15214 ... 412-321-7225
Dinardo Design: 64 Palmer Way, Carlisle, MA 01741 ... 508-371-0111
Direct Mail Design: 707 S Snoqualmie, Seattle, WA 98108 ... 206-622-7474
Distler Design, Joshua: 1221 Oak Grove Ave #105, Burlingame, CA 94010 ... 415-343-3940
Dittman & Assocs, Tom: 493 S Robertson Blvd, Beverly Hills, CA 90211 ... 310-273-2197
Dittmann Graphic & Adv Design: 8202 14th Ave NE, Seattle, WA 98115 ... 206-523-4778
Dittrick & Dittrick: 23 W 89th St, New York, NY 10024 ... 212-724-5241
Dixon & Assocs: 3359 Karen Ave, Long Beach, CA 90808 ... 310-433-8710
Dixon & Parcels Assocs: 521 Fifth Ave 39th Fl, New York, NY 10175 ... 212-697-2522
Dixon, Ted: 594 Broadway #902, New York, NY 10012 ... 212-226-5686
Dm Design Lab: 4420 Bunken Circle, Las Vegas, NV 89121 ... 702-221-2808
DM&A Graphics: 3132 W Spuce Ave, Fresno, CA 93711 ... 209-497-8023
DMCD, Inc: 450 7th Ave 39th Fl, New York, NY 10123 ... 212-268-5450
DMRC: 201 Summer St, Holliston, MA 01746 ... 508-429-3300
DMTG : 350 7th Ave #702, New York, NY 10001 ... 212-924-6774
Doctor Design: 10505 Sorrento Valley Rd, San Diego, CA 92121 ... 619-457-4545
Doerr Assocs: 8 Winchester Pl, Winchester, MA 01890 ... 617-729-9020
Dogpaw Creative: 460 N Crooks, Clawson, MI 48017 ... 810-444-4634
Dolan, Michael B: 6120 NW 38th Terr, Gainsville, FL 32653 ... 352-372-1777
Dole Assocs, Inc: 3 Essex Square, Essex, CT 06426 ... 203-767-0773
Dole Design, Tom: 22 W 23rd St, New York, NY 10010 ... 212-924-9100
Doliber Skeffington Design: 8324 Rednock Ln, Miami Lakes, FL 33016 ... 305-828-8252
Domus Advertising: 200 S Broad st 2nd Fl, Philadelphia, PA 19102 ... 215-772-2800
Don Juan Prods & Adv: 17448 Burma St, Encino, CA 91316 ... 818-996-4628
Donahue Studios: 1274 Minhette Dr, Roswell, GA 30075 ... 404-998-5562
Donaldson Makoski: 1 Waterville Rd, Farmington, CT 06032 ... 860-677-9777
Doneger Group: 463 Seventh Ave, New York, NY 10018 ... 212-560-3787
Donmich Design Studio: PO Box 148, Newton, NJ 07860 ... 201-927-7723
Donovan & Green, Inc: 71 Fifth Ave 4th Fl, New York, NY 10003 ... 212-989-4050
Donovan Design: 2076 N Elston #301, Chicago, IL 60614 ... 773-227-0050
Dorenenburg Design: 1010 Farmington Ave, West Hartford, CT 06107 ... 860-231-1310
• **Doret, Michael: pg 931** Hollywood, CA ... **323-467-1900**
New York, NY ... **212-929-1688**
url: www.michaeldoret.com
Doss Design, Charles: 168 Jackson St, San Jose, CA 95112 ... 408-947-7001
Dot System, Inc: 10730 E Bethany Dr #204, Aurora, CO 80014 ... 303 337-5952
Dottinger Design: 20 Passaic Ave, Pompton Lakes, NJ 07442 ... 201-616-9696
Doty Design, David: 661 W Roscoe, Chicago, IL 60657 ... 773-348-1200
Double D Assocs, Inc: 12579 W Custer Ave, Butler, WI 53007 ... 414-783-4800
Double Space: 170 Fifth Ave 2nd Fl, New York, NY 10010 ... 212-366-1919
Double Vision Products: 2902 Pasatiempo Pl, Sacramento, CA 95833 ... 916-921-6986
Douglas Design, Barry: 300 E 71st St #4H, New York, NY 10021 ... 212-734-4137
DouPonce, Kirk: 801 Coit NES, Grand Rapids, MI 49508 ... 616-456-1118
Downey Weeks & Toomey: 519 Eighth Ave 22nd Fl, New York, NY 10018 ... 212-564-8260
Downing, Allan: 50 Francis St, Needham, MA 02192 ... 617-449-4784
Downtown Digital: 32 Avenue of the Americas, New York, NY 10013 ... 212-387-4856
Doyle Logan Company, The: 7836 Santa Monica Blvd, W Hollywood, CA 90046 ... 213-848-8492
Doyle Lynch Design: 60 Spectacle Ln, Wilton, CT 06897 ... 203-762-2789
Drabkin, Leonard: PO Box 567, North Haven, CT 06473 ... 203-288-7957
Draeger, Deanne: 518 E 13th St, New York, NY 10009 ... 212-475-1316
Drake & Boucher: 175 Fifth Ave #805, New York, NY 10010 ... 212-982-3565
Drate, Spencer: 160 Fifth Ave #613, New York, NY 10010 ... 212-620-4672

Draw The Line: 10955 Lowell #200, Overland Park, KS 66210 ... 913-451-6116
Drebelbis Studio, Inc, Marsha: 8150 Brookriver Dr #606, Dallas, TX 75247 ... 214-951-0266
Drebelbis, Marsha: 8150 Brookriver Dr #606-S, Dallas, TX 75247 ... 214-951-0266
Drenttel, William: 1123 Broadway, New York, NY 10010 ... 212-463-8787
Dresser Design, John: 180 Crescent Knoll E, Libertyville, IL 60048 ... 847-362-4222
Drew Hill Graphic Design Grp, Inc: Drawer 607, Fair Haven, NY 13064 ... 800-724-8973
Dreyfuss Assocs, Henry: 114 W 26th St 5th Fl, New York, NY 10001 ... 212-242-6500
Driscoll, Dennis: 101 Main St, Cambridge, MA 02142 ... 617-520-7241
Drive Communications: 133 W 19th St 5th Fl, New York, NY 10011 ... 212 989-5103
Drobenkaite, Ruta: PO Box 17701, San Diego, CA 92177 ... 858-274-3533
Dryden Rubino: 2 Elmhurst Rd, Baltimore, MD 21210 ... 410-243-2140
Duane, Thomas S: 28 W 25th St 5th Fl, New York, NY 10010 ... 212-924-5700
Dubins Design, Milt: 353 W 22nd St, New York, NY 10011 ... 212-691-0232
Dubrow Assocs, Oscar: 18 E 48th St, New York, NY 10017 ... 212-688-0698
Dudervision: PO Box 10416, Oakland, CA 90272 ... 510-893-5889
Duffy Design Group: 901 Marquette Ave S #3000, Minneapolis, MN 55402 ... 612-339-3247
Dufour & Assocs: 532 S 8th St/PO Box 414, Sheboygan, WI 53081 ... 414-457-9191
Duke & Assocs, Charles: 1023 St Paul St, Baltimore, MD 21202 ... 301-539-7916
Duke Marketing Communications: 5333 N Seventh St #C-226, Phoenix, AZ 85014 ... 602-604-8818
Dula Designs, Michael: 17880 Skypark Cir Ste 170, Irvine, CA 92614 ... 949-852-1397
Dumont Design, Don: 285 N Mclean, Memphis, TN 38112 ... 901-278-3188
Dunkelberger, David: 281 Barberry Rd, Southport, CT 06490 ... 203-255-7928
Dunn & Rice Design: 16 N goodman St #100, Rochester, NY 14607 ... 716-473-2880
Duo Graphics: 3907 Manhattan Ave, Ft Collins, CO 80526 ... 970-463-2788
Dupre Design: 415 2nd St, Coronado, CA 92118 ... 619-435-8369
Durrell Design, Clauida: 9 Williams Rd, Bethel, CT 06801 ... 203-744-3511
Dutko, Deborah: 245 Roselle St, Fairfield, CT 06432 ... 203-579-1715
Dvorak Design Ltd: 36 Lexington Dr, Croton on Hudson, NY 10520 ... 914-271-7706
Dvorak Goodspeed & Assocs: 165 Lexington Ave, New York, NY 10016 ... 212-475-4580
Dyad Communications: 303 N Third St, Philadelphia, PA 19106 ... 215-925-7835
Dyer Cahn: 8360 Melrose Ave 3rd Fl, Los Angeles, CA 90063 ... 213-937-4100
Dyer Mutchnick Group: 8360 Melrose Ave 3rd Fl, Los Angeles, CA 90069 ... 213-655-1800
Dykstra Group, William: 01845 W Leonard, Grand Rapids, MI 49544 ... 616-677-1208
Dyna Pac: 7926 Convoy Ct, San Diego, CA 92111 ... 619-560-0117
DynacomInc: 875 N Michigan #2948, Chicago, IL 60611 ... 847-263-9636
Dynamic Diagrams: 12 Bassett St, Providence, RI 02903 ... 401-331-2014
Dynamic Graphics: 6000 N Forest Park Dr, Peoria, IL 61614 ... 309-688-8800
Dysart, Patty: 274 Cross St, Winchester, MA 01890 ... 617-391-3516
Dzignlight Studios: 800 Forrest St, Atlanta, GA 30318 ... 404-355-0755
DZN The Design Group: 470 S San Vicente Blvd 1st Fl, Los Angeles, CA 90048 ... 213-951-7377

E

EActive: 25 Barry Ln, Simsbury, CT 06070 ... 203-651-3345
Eade Creative Services, Inc: 7905 Byrchmont Pl, Charlotte, NC 28210 ... 704-643-7335
Eagle Graphics: 1220 Broadway, New York, NY 10001 ... 212-629-0858
Eagle River Interactive: 411 SW Second Ave, Portland, OR 97204 ... 503 223-2262
East Design, Roger: 600 Townsend St #415W, San Francisco, CA 94103 ... 415-552-2300
East West Creative: 401 Fifth Ave 4FL, New York, NY 10016 ... 212-951-7220
Easterly & Company: 2001 Kirby #500, Houston, TX 77019 ... 713-529-2949
Eaton & Assocs Design: 708 S Third St #420, Minneapolis, MN 55415 ... 612-338-2266
Eaves Design: 4869 Elmhurst Ave, Norfolk, VA 23513 ... 804-853-0675
Ebersol, Rob: 734 Clairemont Ave, Decatur, GA 30030 ... 404-687-8889
Echo Communications: 7801 Norfolk Ave #207, Bethesda, MD 20814 ... 301-652-0504
Eclipse Graphics: 2020 Del Amo Blvd, Torrance, CA 90501 ... 310-328-2255
Eddins Madison & Spitz: 6121 Lincolnia Rd #410, Alexandria, VA 22312 ... 703-750-0030
Edelson, Doug: 340 W Passaic St, Rochelle Park, NJ 07662 ... 201-909-8760
Eden Matrix, The: 101 W Sixth St #210, Austin, TX 78701 ... 512-478-9000
Edge: 20 W 22nd St 11th Fl, New York, NY 10010 ... 212-691-7021
Edge, Dennis: 900 Broadway 5th Fl, New York, NY 10003 ... 212-420-1110
Edmonds Graphics: 624 University Ave, Palo Alto, CA 94301 ... 415-329-9166
Edquist Design: 4014 48th Ave Ne, Seattle, WA 98105 ... 206-524-5374
EDR Media: 23330 Commerce Park Rd, Beachwood, OH 44122 ... 216-292-7300
Educational Media, Graphics Division: GU Med Ctr 3900 Reservoir Rd, Washington, DC 20007 ... 202-625-2211
Edward Beckett Design: 1051 E Altadena Dr, Altadena, CA 91001 ... 818-791-7954
Edwards Design: 119 W 77th St, New York, NY 10024 ... 212-362-0283
Edwards Design Inc, Sean: 28 W 25th St 5th Fl, New York, NY 10010 ... 212-924-5700
Edwards Studio, Inc: 1907 Sedge Dr, Houston, TX 77080 ... 713-465-7080
Eells Design, Duane: 471 E Main St, Ventura, CA 93001 ... 805-643-4952
Effective Design Studio: 1000 Lenora St #505, Seattle, WA 98121 ... 206-621-8989
Egg Design Partners: 790 Centre St, Boston, MA 02130 ... 617-522-7558
Ehrenfeld, Howard: 1250 Key Highway, Baltimore, MD 21230 ... 410-685-3686
Eiber Design Inc, Rick: 31014 SE 58th St, Preston, WA 98050 ... 206-632-8326
Eickhoff Hannan Rue: 515 Busby Dr, San Antonio, TX 78219 ... 210-828-8003
Eicon/Div E Group: 245 5th Ave #602, New York, NY 10016 ... 212-685-3340
Eidolon Comms: 156 Fifth Ave #707, New York, NY 10010 ... 212-633-0404
Einhorn Design: 1103 Bingham St, Pittsburgh, PA 15203 ... 412-488-3900
Eisenberg & Assocs: 3311 Oak Lawn #300, Dallas, TX 75219 ... 214-528-5990
Eisenman Design Assocs, James: 151 Haven Ave, Port Washington, NY 11050 ... 516-944-6770
Eisenman Graphic Design: 6208 Verne St, Bethesda, MD 20817 ... 301-229-1090
EK Weymouth: 207 Old Forge Rd, Riverton, CT 06065 ... 203-738-3666
Elaine Design: 10 Nassau St, Emerson, NJ 07630 ... 201-261-7528
Eldridge, Paul: PO Box 806, Meredith, NH 03253 ... 603-279-5568
Electa Design: 807 Sanford Day Rd, Knoxville, TN 37919 ... 615-470-2581
Electric Paint: 6335 Homewood Ave, Los Angeles, CA 90028 ... 213-462-4332
Electrokinetics: 380 Lafayette #304, New York, NY 10003 ... 212-473-1125
Electronic Hollywood: PO Box 448, Prince St Station, NY 10012 ... 212-777-4801
Electronic Vision: 5 Depot St, Athens, OH 45701 ... 614-592-2433
Elements: 550 College Ave, Palo Alto, CA 94306 ... 415-493-2018
Eleven: 273 Summer St 7th Fl, Boston, MA 02210 ... 617-204-1100
Elliott Agency: 8229 Boone Blvd #802, Vienna, VA 22182 ... 703-903-8631
Elsey & Assocs, Victor: 314 Joyce Way, Mill Valley, CA 94941 ... 415-383-8199
Ely Design Group: 75 Kings Hwy Cutoff, Fairfield, CT 06430 ... 203-333-9300
Elyria Graphics: 561 Ternis St, Elyria, OH 44035 ... 216-365-9384
Ema Design: 1228 15th St #301, Denver, CO 80202 ... 303-825-0222
Emerson Design Studio: 55134 Cobus Ln, Elkhart, IN 46514 ... 219-262-1997
Emerson Hayes: 125 Hawthorne Ave, Palo Alto, CA 94301 ...
Emerson Marketing Agency: 636 Broadway #1000, New York, NY 10012 ... 212-387-8210
Emerson Wajdowicz Studios, Inc: 1123 Broadway, New York, NY 10010 ... 212-807-8144
Emerson, Larry: 6515 Escondido #A1, El Paso, TX 79912 ... 915-581-0184
Emmart, Weston: 39 Hamilton Terr, New York, NY 10031 ... 212-283-3401
Emmerling Design, Ronald: 206 Claremont Ave, Montclair, NJ 07042 ... 201-783-7888
Emphasis Seven Comm, Inc: 549 W Randolph St #700, Chicago, IL 60661 ... 312-951-8887
Emspace: 7634 Pierce St, Omaha, NE 68124 ... 402-398-9448
Encompass Communications: 374 Congress St #408, Boston, MA 02210 ... 617-357-1800
Encore Design: 181 Longhill Rd Bldg 3 #11, Little Falls, NJ 07424 ... 973-890-7891
Encore Studios: 17 Industial West, Clifton, NJ 07012 ... 800-526-0497
Endres & Eng: 209 10th Ave S #343, Nashville, TN 37203 ... 615-251-3002
Endres, Joan: 54 Points of View, Warwick, NY 10990 ... 914-987-1001
Endres, Michael: 10018 Tenbrook Dr, Silver Spring, MD 20901 ... 301-681-6100
Energy Energy Design: 246 Blossom Hill Rd, Los Gatos, CA 95032 ... 408-379-8858
Eng & Yee Designs: 205 W 80yh St #B1E, New York, NY 10024 ... 212-580-3040
Engelhardt Design: 1738 Irving Ave S, Minneapolis, MN 55403 ... 612-377-3389
Engen, Scott: 9058 Greenhills Dr, Sandy, UT 84093 ... 801-942-3125
Engle & Assocs, Ray: 4726 La Villa Marina, Marina Del Rey, CA 90292 ... 310-822-3224
Engle & Murphy, Inc: 236 E Third St #210, Long Beach, CA 90802 ... 310-983-7270
Engler Design Assocs, Ronald: 605 Allengrove St, Philadelphia, PA 19120 ... 215-722-4895
Englund & Donnelly Design: 2261 Morello Ae #D, Pleasant Hill, CA 94523 ... 510-932-8646
Engstrom, Lynda: 317 W 89th St #2W1, New York, NY 10024 ... 212-724-3961
Enright, Phil: 131 George St, Oakville, ON L6J 3B9 ... 905-339-0750
Enteractive, Inc: 110 W 40th St #2100, New York, NY 10018 ... 212-221-6559
Envion International: 472 Amherst, Nashua, NH 03063 ... 603-881-7873
Environmedia: 617 Vine St #1336, Cincinnati, OH 45202 ... 513-333-0040
Environmental Graphics, Inc: 1101 Southeastern Ave, Indianapolis, IN 46202 ... 317-634-1458
Envision: 23 Pleasant St. #507, Newburyport, MA 01950 ...
Epigraph: 333 Bainbridge, Philadelphia, PA 19147 ... 215-925-4700
Epsilon Interactive: 132 S La Jolla Ave, Los Angeles, CA 90048 ... 213-655-4476
Epstein Gutwiller & Partners: 11427 Bellflower Rd, Cleveland, OH 44106 ... 216-421-1600
Erbe Design, Maureen: 1500 Oxley St, S Pasadena, CA 91030 ... 818-799-9892
Erceg Graphic Design, Joe: 123 NW 2nd Ave #201, Portland, OR 97209 ... 503-227-5915
Erickson Design: 13197 W Iliff Dr, Lakewood, CO 80228 ... 303-989-5058
Erickson, Peter: 46 Pleasant St, Marlborough, MA 01752 ... 508-481-2288
Ernst & Assocs, Inc: 247 Velarde St, Mountain View, CA 94041 ... 415-965-0869
Ervin Advertising & Design: 16400 Pacific Coast Hwy #217, Huntington Beach, CA 92649 ... 310-592-3827
Escott Assocs: 3307 Pico blvd, Santa Monica, CA 90405 ... 310-828-9679
Espinosa, Leo: 150 W 25th St #404, New York, NY 10001 ... 212-982-9411
Esposito Design & Mktg, Bronz: 25 Bank St, Stamford, CT 06901 ... 203-324-1300
Esser Design, Steve: 2025 N Third St #170, Phoenix, AZ 85004 ... 602-257-9790
Essertier, David: 2228 Blackrock Trpk #207, Fairfield, CT 06430 ... 203-226-8850
Essex Two, Inc: 2210 W North Ave, Chicago, IL 60647 ... 773-489-1400
Essinger Design Assocs: 36 Glen Ave, Newton, MA 02159 ... 617-964-8803
Essl, Mike: 216 W 18th St #1204, New York, NY 10011 ... 212-473-0204
Estes Assocs, David: 3400 Montrose #505, Houston, TX 77006 ... 713-523-9717
Estrela Design Group: 357 Medford St#2, Somerville, MA 02145 ... 617-625-3355
Estudio Ray: 2320 N 58th St, Scottsdale, AZ 850257 ... 602-945-1299
Etheridge Palombo Sedewitz: 1500 Broadway, New York, NY 10036 ... 212-944-2530
Eucalyptus Tree Studio: 1745 Circle Rd, Dowlson, MD 21204 ... 410-243-0211
Evans Design Assocs: 3303 Harbor Blvd #D8, Costa Mesa, CA 92626 ... 714-957-6266
Evans Design Assocs: 18 Norfield Rd, Weston, CT 06883 ... 203-226-8553
Evans Design, Leslie: 81 West Commercial St, Portland, ME 04101 ... 207-874-0102
Evans Group: 6116 North Central #1100, Dallas, TX 75206 ... 214-691-6491
Evans, Inc, Mackas: 1450 N Decatur Rd NE, Atlanta, GA 30306 ... 770-938-2777
Evenson Design Group: 4445 Overland Ave, Culver City, CA 90230 ... 310-204-1995
Everett Design: Mtng Hs Offcs/121 Mt Vernon St, Boston, MA 02108 ... 617-227-2354
Everett Studios: 22 Baker Ave, White Plains, NY 10601 ... 914-997-2200
Ewing & Beland: 517 S Ivy Ave, Monrovia, CA 91016 ... 818-930-0977
Excelsior Graphics, Inc: 350 W 31st St 3rd Fl, New York, NY 10001 ... 212-563-6100
Executive Arts: 887 W Marietta St J-105, Atlanta, GA 30318 ... 404-875-8225
Exhibit Group/Giltspur: 200 N Gary Ave, Rosell, IL 60172 ... 630-307-2400
Extreme Color: 1221 Lee Rd #120, Orlando, FL 32810 ... 407-298-6384
Eye & I Design Group: 4703 Longridge Ave, Sherman Oaks, CA 91423 ... 818-501-5439
Eye 4: 4320 W University Ave, Gainesville, FL 32607 ... 904-338-7519
Eye Tv: 270 Magnolia Ave, Larkspur, CA 94939 ... 415-945-1370
Fye-Noise: 1215 E Robinson St, Orlando, FL 32801 ... 407-894-3550
Eymer Design, Inc: 25 Dry Dock Ave, Boston, MA 02210 ... 617-345-5434

F

F P Design: 920 Broadway #905, New York, NY 10010 ... 212-473-0006
F Patrick LaSalle Design: 225 Sheridan St, Rockford, IL 61103 ... 815-963-2089
Fahrenheit Design: 169 West Newton St, Boston, MA 02118 ... 617-536-4482
Faia Design, Don: 130 Camino Pacifico, Aptos, CA 95003 ... 408-662-8857
Fairly Painless Adv: 44 E 8th St #500, Holland, MI 49423 ... 616-394-5900
Falcon Advertising Art: 1138 W 9th St #200, Cleveland, OH 44113 ... 216 621 4327
Falcone Design Group: 5 Division St Bldg A, East Greenwich, RI 02818 ... 401-886-8710
Falk Design Group, Robert: 4425 W Pine, St Louis, MO 63108 ... 314-531-1410
Falls Studio, Inc: 1155 Oak Dale Pl, Boulder, CO 80304 ... 303-442-4877
Faragher Design Group: 700 East Blvd #1, Charlotte, NC 28203 ... 704-333-7424
Farber Design Group, Melvyn: 406 Bonhill Rd, Los Angeles, CA 90049 ... 213-829-2668
Farkas, Bob: 1220 S Bedford St, Los Angeles, CA 90035 ... 310-271-4909
Farleo Design, Joseph L: 4915 Heards Forest Dr, Acworth, GA 30102 ... 770-917-9424
Farley, AC: 20 Stearns Terr, Chicopee, MA 01013 ... 413-594-7302
Farnet Hart Design Studio: 822 Perdido St #202, New Orleans, LA 70112 ... 504-522-6300
Faron Melrose, Inc: 19925 Stevens Creek Blvd #135, Cupertino, CA 95014 ... 408-773-8022
Farrell Design Communicatons: 321 Ellis St, New Britain, CT 06051 ... 203-225-3115
Farrell Design, Colonna: 899 Adams St #H, St Helena, CA 94574 ... 707-963-2077
FASE Productions: 4801 Wilshire Blvd #215, Los Angeles, CA 90010 ... 213-937-9911
Fassino Design: 230 Calvary St, Waltham, MA 02154 ... 617-647-0407
Fattal & Collins: 4640 Admiralty Way #900, Marina Del Ray, CA 90292 ... 310-822-2777
Faville Design: 1123 Bdwy #1012, New York, NY 10010 ... 212-989-1566
Fear Design, Jeffery: 3961 Sepulveda Blvd #201, Culver City, CA 90230 ... 310-398-5717
Fearless Design: 149 Fifth Ave, New York, NY 10010 ... 212-253-9520
Fearless Designs, Inc: 622 E Main St #206, Louisville, KY 40202 ... 502-584-1333
Feigenbaum, Joseph: 1 Bridge St, Irvington, NY 10533 ... 914-591-5911
Feldman Assocs: 505 N Lakeshore Dr, Chicago, IL 60611 ... 312-527-1111
Felix Design: 37 Howard Pl, Brooklyn, NY 11215 ... 718-788-5409

Fenster Assocs, Fred: 29 Davis Rd, Port Washington, DC 11050 . . . 516-944-7108
Fenwick Design: 211 W 56th St #30A, New York, NY 10019 . . . 212-246-9722
Fernandez, Robert: 435 Hudson St, New York, NY 10014. . . 212-462-1500
Ferranti & Schiumo: 655 Third Ave 27th Fl, New York, NY 10017 . . . 212-687-3107
Ferris Design, Peggy: 225 Dawlish Pl, Santa Barbara, CA 93108 . . . 805-969-5502
Fetz Design: 1339 S Main St, Salt Lake City, UT 84115 . . . 801-466-8817
Fevurly, Yvette: 2852 W Greenleaf, Chicago, IL 60245 . . . 773-262-1298
Fiedler & Assocs, Inc: 8012 W Berwyn Ave, Chicago, IL 60656. . . 773-775-0192
Figi Graphics: 3636 Gateway ctr Dr, San Diego, CA 92102 . . . 619-262-8811
Filanovsky, Serge: 275 Clinton Ave, Brooklyn, NY 11205. . . 718-789-1747
Fili Studio, Louise: 71 Fifth Ave 4th Fl, New York, NY 10003 . . . 212-989-9153
Filicori Visual Comms: 4 Gramercy Park W, New York, NY 10003 . . . 212-677-0065
Filippo & Assocs, Adam: 1206 Fifth Ave, Pittsburgh, PA 15219. . . 412-261-3720
Film & Video Service: 1550 Bryant St #200, San Francisco, CA 94103 . . . 415-626-8400
Film Art Representation: 6201 Sunset Blvd #60, Hollywood, CA 90028. . . 213-480-1059
Fina, Barbara: 23 Evergreen Way, Sleepy Hollow, NY 10591 . . . 914-332-9345
Finaly, Steve: 1059 Fairfax Circle W, Lantana, FL 33462. . . 561-965-4728
Financial Communications, Inc: 8001 Wisconsin Ave, Bethesda, MD 20814. . . 301-657-1711
Fine Line Graphics: 237 NW Blue Pkwy #100, Lees Summit, MO 64063 . . . 816-941-2440
Fineberg Assocs: 333 E 68th St, New York, NY 10021. . . 212-734-1220
Finger & Smith Assocs, Inc: 1005 Sansome #240, San Francisco, CA 94111. . . 415-788-2238
Finite Matters Ltd: 2604 Fairground Rd, Goochland, VA 23063 . . . 804-556-6631
Fiorella Graphic Design, Inc: 248 Rushley Way, Media, PA 19063 . . . 610-358-4411
Fiorella, Franke: 1221 Nicollet Mall #230, Minneapolis, MN 55403 . . . 612-338-1700
Fiorentino & Assocs: 134 W 26th St #902, New York, NY 10001. . . 212-243-2236
Firehouse 101: 641 N High St Ste 106, Columbus, OH 43215. . . 614-464-0928
Firestone Design: 4810 Bradford Dr, Annandale, VA 22003. . . 703-354-0247
First Experience Communication: 3011 Main St, Glastenbury, CT 06033. . . 203-657-3815
First Impressions: 4411 W Tampa Bay Blvd, Tampa, FL 33614. . . 813-875-0555
Firstline Creative Resources: 525 Bishop St, Atlanta, GA 30318. . . 404-605-0797
Fischer Creative: 5050 Quorum Dr #700, Dallas, TX 75240. . . 214-663-0520
Fischer Graphic Design Assocs: 3854 Ridgeview Rd, Huntingdon Vall, PA 19006 . . . 215-947-9931
Fish Eng Partners, Inc: 431 S Dearborn #1001, Chicago, IL 60605. . . 312-939-4442
Fitch Design: 10350 Olentangy River Rd Box 360, Worthington, OH 43085. . . 614-885-3453
Fitting Kolbrener: 7 Wood St 5th Fl, Pittsburgh, PA 15222 . . . 412-434-6934
Fitzgerald & Assocs: 23 Franklin Blvd #2E, Long Beach, NY 11561. . . 516-431-7073
Fitzpatrick Design Group: 2109 Broadway #203, New York, NY 10023. . . 212-580-5842
Fiumara Art Direction & Photo: 1307 Harvard Rd NE, Atlanta, GA 30306. . . 404-373-7220
Five Oaks Design: 3533 Hattie Rd, Nashville, NC 27856 . . . 919-459-8908
Flagler Adv, Inc: 143 Beaconsfield Rd, Brookline, MA 02146. . . 617-566-6971
Flaherty Robinson Design: 11 First St, Barrington, RI 02806 . . . 401-245-4236
Flanders & Assocs: 368 Congress St, Boston, MA 02210 . . . 617-423-7019
Fleishman-Hillard, Inc: 200 N Broadway, St Louis, MO 63102 . . . 314-982-1700
Fleming Graphics: 510 First Ave N #6, Great Falls, MT 59401 . . . 406-761-7887
Fleming, Toby: 10 E 6th Ave, Conshohocken, PA 19428 . . . 610-940-2300
Flinchum, Inc: 200 W 57th St #609, New York, NY 10019. . . 212-582-6692
Flink Design, Hans: 224 E 50th St, New York, NY 10022. . . 212-832-3860
Flipside Graphic Design: 5 Mandeville Ct, Monterey, CA 93940 . . . 408-649-5510
Flores Jr, Arnie: 13320 Villa Park Dr, Austin, TX 78729 . . . 512-458-3373
Florio Design, Linda: 245 W 29th St 4th Fl, New York, NY 10001. . . 212-736-1959
Florville Design & Analysis: 226 W 21st St, New York, NY 10011 . . . 212-633-8130
Flyleaf: 611 Broadway #826, New York, NY 10012 . . . 212-473-4710
Flynn Design: 1304 N Hametown Rd, Fairlawn, OH 44333 . . . 330-666-1431
Foca Company: 520 Broadway 11th Fl, New York, NY 10012. . . 212-966-1556
Focus 2, Inc: 2105 Commerce St #102, allas, TX 75201. . . 214-741-4007
Fokes, Quinne: 220 Del Casa, Mill Valley, CA 94941 . . . 415-383-0924
Follis Design: 520 N Fair Oaks Ave, Pasadena, CA 91103. . . 818-792-3590
Follis Design, Dean: 520 N Fair Oaks Ave, Pasadena, CA 91103 . . . 818-792-3590
Font Company, The: 7850 E Evans Rd #111, Scottsdale, AZ 85260. . . 800-442-3668
Force, Peter: 6000 N Forest Park Dr, Peoria, IL 61614 . . . 309-688-8800
Ford & Earl Assocs, Inc: 350 W Big Beaver Rd, Troy, MI 48084. . . 810-524-3222
Fordesign Group: 87 Dayton Rd, Redding, CT 06896 . . . 203-938-0008
Forest Design: 5900 S Eastern Ave, Commerce, CA 90040. . . 213-462-6486
Forethought Solutions: 4 Laurel St, Beverly, MA 01915. . . 508-927-8088
Form & Function: 3394 SE Woodward ST, Portland, OR 97202. . . 503-731-0985
Forma : 215 Glenwood Ave, Raleigh, NC 27603 . . . 919-832-1244
Forman Designs, Yale: 11 Riverside Dr, New York, NY 10023 . . . 212-799-1665
Forman, Thomas: PO Box 3174, Princeton, NJ 08543 . . . 609-275-6077
Forstel Graphic Design, Tom: 753 s Walnut St, Boise, ID 83712 . . . 208-345-6656
Forsythe Design: 142 Berkley St, Boston, MA 02116 . . . 617-437-1023
Fortune Design Firm: 1260 Pine Ave, San Jose, CA 95125 . . . 408-723-1202
Fortune, John & Lani: 414 W Lake Samish, Bellingham, WA 98226 . . . 360-647-8024
Forward Design: 848 Eastman #105, Chicago, IL 60622 . . . 312-335-0540
Forward Design, Inc: 1115 E Maine St/Box 61, Rochester, NY 14609 . . . 716-288-0250
Foster Design Group: 222 Newbury St 3rd Fl, Boston, MA 02116 . . . 617-262-5899
Foster Design, Stephen: 17 51st St #5, Weehawken, NJ 07087 . . . 201-866-9040
Foster, Kim A: 1801 SW 11th St, Miami, FL 33135. . . 305-642-1801
Foundation: 1715 E Olive Way, Seattle, WA 98102 . . . 206-860-8800
Four Corners: PO box 10426, Burbank, CA 91510. . . 818-899-8987
Fowler & Co, Tom: 9 Webbs Hill Rd, Stamford, CT 06903. . . 203-329-1105
Fox Design: 36 Ridge Brook Dr, West Hartford, CT 06107. . . 203-521-8227
Fox Klox: 512 Route 202, Hollis, ME 04042. . . 207-929-8492
Frame One, Inc: 2215 Sanders Rd #360, Northbrook, IL 60062 . . . 847-564-2221
Franek Design Assocs, David: 5101 Wisconsin Ave NW #302, Washington, DC 20016 . . . 202-363-4441
Frank & Assocs Inc, Alan: 1524 S 1100 E, Salt Lake City, UT 84105. . . 801-486-7453
Franke & Fiorella: 1221 Nicollet Mall #230, Minneapolis, MN 55403. . . 612-338-1700
Frankfurt Balkind: 244 E 58th St, New York, NY 10022. . . 212-421-5888
Franklin Architects/Design: 401 N Franklin, Chicago, IL 60610 . . . 312-527-1555
Franklin Street Comms, Inc: 2515 Professional Rd, Richmond, VA 23235. . . 804-320-2000
Franz & Company: 8403 Colesville Rd #865, Silver Spring, MD 20910 . . . 301-589-7199
Fraser & Assocs, Robert: PO Box 39035, Baltimore, MD 21212 . . . 410-433-7191
Frassinelli, Michael: 465 South St #103, Morristown, NJ 07960. . . 800-275-5374
Frazier, Greg: 26 Noble St Unit 3, Toronto, ON M6K2C9 . . . 416-538-3797
Frch Design Worldwide/NY: 860 Broadway 5th Fl, New York, NY 10003 . . . 212-254-1229
Frederking Design, Sarah: 433 North Harvey Ave, Oak Park, IL 60302 . . . 708-386-6886
Freelance Ink: 2924 33rd Pl NW, Washington, DC 20008. . . 202-342-2221
Freeman Design Assocs: 2405 Bartlett St/PO 540543, Houston, TX 77098 . . . 713-523-4302
Freeman, Sean: 2105 Commerce St #102, Dallas, TX 75201. . . 214-741-4007
French Blitzer Scott: 156 Fifth Ave, New York, NY 10010. . . 212-807-1111
French Design Worldwide: 31 Elm St #600, Cincinnati, OH 45202 . . . 513-241-3000
Fresh Design: 5627 Cotton Port Dr, Brentwood, TN 37027 . . . 615-331-1663
Fresh Ideas Daily: 60 E 12th St Apt 11D, New York, NY 10003 . . .
Fresh Produce Studio: 1307 Warwick Dr, Lutherville, MD 21093 . . . 410-828-6675
Freyss Design, Christina: 205 E 22nd St, New York, NY 10010. . . 212-496-0453
Fridrich Design, William: 1918 Princess St, Wilmington, NC 28405 . . . 910-762-3993
Friedland & Assocs, Michael: 1408 4th St #26, San Rafael, CA 94901 . . . 415-331-7638
Friedman, Adam: 820 Second Ave 6th Fl, New York, NY 10017 . . . 212-682-6300
Friedson Design, Stephen: 434 Greenwich St, New York, NY 10013. . . 212-226-2922
Frink Chin Casey, Inc: 505 E Grant, Minneapolis, MN 55404 . . . 612-333-6539
Frink Semmer & Assocs: 505 E Grant, MInneapolis, MN 55404 . . . 612-659-4626
Fritz Creative: 1222 State St #200, Santa Barbara, CA 93101 . . . 805-568-3800
Frogdesign: 1327 Chesapeake Ter, Sunnyvale, CA 94089 . . . 408-734-5800
Froom, Georgia: 62 W 39th St #803, New York, NY 10018. . . 212-944-0330
Fruchter, Dara: 93 Thorndike St, Brookline, MA 02146 . . . 617-232-0386
Fucinato Design, Inc: 12 Front St, Marathon, NY 13803 . . . 607-849-3286
Fuld Group, Inc: 2200 N Lamar #306, Dallas, TX 75202. . . 214-220-0303
Full Circle Design: 2 Butler Rd, Reigerstown, MD 21136. . . 410-366-6305
Full Moon Creations: 81 S Main St, Doylestown, PA 18901. . . 215-345-1233
Fuller Design: 136 W 24th #4R, New York, NY 10011 . . . 212-645-2210
Fulton Design, Jacobs: 745 Emerson St, Palo Alto, CA 94301 . . . 415-328-4669
Fultz, Patrick: 307 Fifth Ave 7th Fl, New York, NY 10016. . . 212-545-7483
Funds Hays Graphic Design: 2901 W Busch Blvd #204, Tampa, FL 33618. . . 813-931-5711
Funk Assocs: 1255 Pearl St, Eugene, OR 97401 . . . 541-485-1932
Funk, Barbara: 3174 Catamore Ln, Dallas, TX 75229. . . 214-350-8534
Funny Bone Studio: 4497 W Streetsboro Rd, Richfield, OH 44286 . . . 216-659-4626
Furniss Design, Stephanie: PO Box 307, San Geronimo, CA 94963 . . . 415-488-4692
Fuse: 483 Moreland Ave NE #4, Atlanta, GA 30307 . . . 404-577-5888
Fuse Design: 2761 Laguna Canyon Rd #102, Laguna Beach, CA 92651. . . 714-376-0438
Fusion Interactive: 77 Mount Ave #411, Toronto, ON . . . 416-507-3300
FXC Communications: 970 S Second St, San Jose, CA 95112. . . 408-293-2000

G

G A Design: 25241 W Warren, Dearborn Hts, MI 48127 . . . 313-561-2530
G B Design: 420 W 7th St, Kansas City, MO 64105. . . 816-842-2115
G Deisgn: 4515 Poplar St #501, Memphis, TN 38117 . . . 901-761-3714
G Design: 151 Second Ave #2B, New York, NY 10003 . . . 212-533-5749
G2 Partners: 209 W Central St #230, Natick, MA 01760 . . . 508-651-8158
Gabanyi, Alexandra: 39 Hamilton Terr, New York, NY 10031 . . . 212-283-3401
Gabeler Design: 74 Varick #301, New York, NY 10013 . . . 212-941-8335
Gable Design Group: 509 E Republican St #7, Seattle, WA 98102 . . . 206-623-0908
Gagarin & Mcgeoch: 493 Seaport Ct #102, Redwood City, CA 94063 . . . 415-367-6008
Gage Design: 80 S Jackson #307, Seattle, WA 98104. . . 206-622-0905
Gailen Design Office, The: 541 N Fairbanks Ct #100D, Chicago, IL 60611 . . . 312-787-0405
Galarneau & Sinn: 378 Cambridge Ave, Palo Alto, CA 94306 . . . 415-329-0110
Galasso Assocs Inc, Gene: 9001 New Hampshire Ave, Silver Spring, MD 20903 . . . 301-439-1282
Galaxy America: 4143 W Nelson St, Chicago, IL 60641 . . . 773-777-8687
Gale, Peter: 3715 N Lakewood Ave, Chicago, IL 60613 . . . 312-348-6779
Galeano, Margaret: 140 Platt Ln, Milford, CT 06460 . . . 203-877-4313
Gallagher, Douglas: 1420 K St NW #300, Washington, DC 20005 . . . 202-789-0920
Gallagher, Rob: 51 E 42nd St #419, New York, NY 10017 . . . 212-986-0120
Gallison Design, Lee: Chamber of Commerce Bldg 117 E. Colorado Blvd #308, Pasadena, CA 91105. 818-796-5915
Galperin Design: 130 East 59th St 12th Fl, New York, NY 10022 . . . 212-758-5409
Galzer Design Assocs: 625 N Maple Ave, Hohokus, NJ 07423 . . . 201-612-8606
Gamarello, Paul: 21 E 22nd St #4G, New York, NY 10010 . . . 212-485-4774
Gannett Design, Martha: 1314 NW Irvine St #702, Portland, OR 97209 . . . 503-241-0033
Gano Design Assocs: 4144 Camino Islay, San Diego, CA 92122 . . . 619-457-4235
Ganz Gross Adv: 330 E 38th St #31L, New York, NY 10016 . . . 212-808-9898
Garbow Graphics: 2265 Shadey Oak Rd, Melbourne, FL 32935 . . . 407-752-9688
Garcia, Kim: 105 Calle Sol, San Clemente, CA 92672 . . . 800-871-0798
Gardisher, Martha: 245 Piermont Ave, Nyack, NY 10960 . . . 914-358-0185
Gardner Assoc, Beau: 541 Lexington Ave 18th Fl, New York, NY 10022. . . 212-832-2426
Gardner Design: 100 N 6th St #901A, Minneapolis, MN 55403 . . . 612-332-2270
Gardner Design Ltd: 20 Executive Park #200, Irvine, CA 92714 . . . 714-863-0404
Gardner Geary Coll & young: 27 Maiden Ln 6th Fl, San Francisco, CA 94108 . . . 415-434-2191
Gardner Keaton, Inc: 1605 Allison St NW, Washington, DC 20011. . . 202-328-0414
Garfinkel, Wendy: 37 Fort Royal Ave, Charleston, SC 29407 . . . 843-571-4049
Gargus Design, Sandra M: 54 Old Eagle School Rd, Strafford, PA 19087 . . . 610-254-9309
Gariepy, Peter: 4500 E Speedway #22, Tucson, AZ 85712. . . 800-482-4567
Garland Ca Ltd: 6901 Mammoth Ave, Van Nuys, CA 91405. . . 818-782-4197
Garland Graphic Design, Nathan: 412 Orange St, New Haven, CT 06511. . . 203-562-9539
Gary Comm & Mktg: 1730 S 11th St #201, St Louis, MO 63104. . . 314-621-1730
Gaskell Assocs, Inc: 728 Post Road East, Westport, CT 06880 . . . 203-222-1001
Gasque Design, Ken: 3195 Leaphart Rd, W Columbia, SC 29169 . . . 803-791-0952
Gast Graphic Design, Vivian: 1411 E Butler Pike, Ambler, PA 19002 . . . 215-628-3100
Gaster, Joanne: 201 E 30th St #43, New York, NY 10016. . . 212-686-0860
Gates, Wesley: 1236 N Lincoln St, Jerome, ID 83338 . . . 208-324-8920
Gatter, Inc: 68 Purchase St, Rye, NY 10580 . . . 914-967-5600
Gecko Imaging: 1229 S Wahington, Royal Oak, MI 48067 . . . 810-548-4624
Gee & Chung Design: 38 Bryant St #100, San Francisco, CA 94105. . . 415-543-1192
Geer & Assocs: 3726 N High St, Columbus, OH 43214 . . . 614-748-1890
Geer Design: 2518 Drexel #201, Houston, TX 77027 . . . 713-960-0808
Geimer Design, Chris: 582 Cortland, Lake Zurich, IL 60047 . . . 847-540-5868
Gelb Company, The: 3709 Broadlawn Dr, Hollywood, CA 90068. . . 818-753-8280
Gellman Graphic Design, Stan: 4509 Laclede, St Louis, MO 63108. . . 314-361-7676
Gemmell Comms: 11214 Peartree Way, Columbia, MD 21044 . . . 301-596-6313
Genesis One Design: 6019 California Ave SW, Seattle, WA 98136 . . . 206-935-5578
Genesis, Inc: 604 W Sixth Ave, Denver, CO 80204. . . 303-825-1230
Genex Media: 10003 Washington Blvd, Culver City, CA 90232 . . . 310-287-3545
Genie Originals: 187 N Evergreen Dr, Ventura, CA 93003 . . . 805-648-5882
Genovese Coustenis Design: 3000 Chestnut Ave #400, Baltimore, MD 21211 . . . 410-467-4672
Gentile Studio: 333 E 46th St, New York, NY 10017 . . . 212-986-7743
Gentry Design Studio, David: 1145 Wisconsin St, San Francisco, CA 94107 . . . 415-824-2920
Geodesign: 30 E Huron St #5604, Chicago, IL 60611 . . . 312-280-6873
George, Hershell: 152 Madison Ave PH, New York, NY 10016 . . . 212-929-4321
Georgetown Design Group, Inc: 1301 20th St NW #102, Washington, DC 20036 . . . 202-857-0060
Georgopoulos/Imada Design: 837 Traction Ave #203, Los Angeles, CA 90013 . . . 213-972-0171

Gerard Design, George: 152 Madison Ave 24th Fl, New York, NY 10016 ... 212-696-0177
Gerbino Advertising, Inc: 933 W Commercial Blvd, Ft Lauderdale, FL 33309 ... 305-776-5050
Gerhardt & Clemons: 848 W Eastman St #201, Chicago, IL 60622 ... 312-337-3443
Gerhardt Design, Roland: 67 Vestry St, New York, NY 10013 ... 212-925-4110
Gerle, Carl: PO Box 99991, San Diego, CA 92169 ... 619-274-4511
Gerson Design Concepts, Janice: 16760 Stagg St #220, Van Nuys, CA 91406 ... 818-786-3398
Gerstman & Meyers: 111 W 57th St 7th Fl, New York, NY 10019 ... 212-586-2535
Gestalt Assocs, Inc: 1509 King St, Alexandria, VA 22314 ... 703-683-1126
Gfi Printing: 118 Smith St, Port Chester, NY 10573 ... 914-937-2823
Ghetti Design: 611 4th St, Belvidere, NJ 07823 ... 908-475-2903
Ghost Star Animation: 130 W 42nd St #605, New York, NY 10036 ... 212-354-4542
Gianakas Design, Chris: 93 Mercer St, New York, NY 10012 ... 212-226-1723
Gianatsis Design: 4801 Areforma Rd, Woodlawn Hills, CA 91364 ... 818-223-8550
Gianfagua Group: 316 4th St, Marietta, OH 45750 ... 614-373-7901
Giannatti, Don: 4217 E Windsong, Phoenix, AZ 85044 ... 602-759-1810
Gianninoto Assocs: 133 E 54th St #2D, New York, NY 10022 ... 212-759-5757
Gibb Design: 3466 Blackhawk Rd, Lafayette, CA 94549 ... 510-283-1959
Gibbs Baronet: 2200 N Lamar #201, Dallas, TX 75202 ... 214-954-0316
Giber, Lauren: 152 E 22nd St, New York, NY 10010 ... 212-473-2062
Gignac Palmer: 4401 Jackman Rd, Toledo, OH 43612 ... 419-478-2211
Gilbert & Assocs, Marsha: 6106 1/2 Ocean View Dr, Oakland, CA 94618 ... 510-658-7222
Giles Design: 429 N St Mary's St, San Antonio, TX 78025 ... 210-224-8378
Gillespie Agency: 3007 Milwood Ave, Columbia, SC 29205 ... 803-779-2126
Giltspur/Boston: 275 Bodwell St, Avon, MA 02322 ... 508-584-2700
Giltspur/Rochester: 1143 Lexington Ave, Rochester, NY 14606 ... 716-254-2970
Gingras, Lisa: 81 S Main St, Doylestown, PA 18901 ... 215-345-1233
Ginsberg Adv/Dsgn, Lynee: 600 Edgewater Blvd #107, Foster City, CA 94404 ... 415-577-8355
Giordano Design: 3605 132nd Ave SE #310, Bellevue, WA 98006 ... 206-641-5003
Giorgi Ehlers, Inc: 6 E Main St, Riverhead, NY 11901 ... 516-369-8285
Giovanitti Design Group: 1 Irving Pl #G10F, New York, NY 10003 ... 212-477-2210
Giovanni Design Assocs: 230 E 44th St #2L, New York, NY 10017 ... 212-972-2145
Girvin Design, Tim: 1601 2nd Ave 5th Fl, Seattle, WA 98101 ... 206-623-7808
Girvin Design, Tim: 501 Fifth Ave, New York, NY 10017 ... 212-490-2450
GK Design International: 4007 Paramont Blvd #110, Lakewood, CA 90712 ... 310-496-1445
GK Good Graphic Design: 17 Tater Hill Rd/Barn Studio, E Haddam, CT 06423 ... 860-526-1600
GL Graphics: 333 N Michigan Ave #901, Chicago, IL 60601 ... 312-782-4456
Glaser, Milton: 207 E 32nd St, New York, NY 10016 ... 212-889-3161
Glassearch: 4306 W Lovers Ln, Dallas, TX 75209 ... 214-351-3335
Glazer & Kalayjian, Inc: 301 E 45th St #18F, New York, NY 10017 ... 212-687-3099
Glenbard Graphics: 400 Fullerton Ave, Carol Stream, IL 60188 ... 630-653-4550
Glenn, Raymond: 39 Edgerton Rd, Wallinford, CT 06942 ... 203-269-5643
Glickman, Frank: 180 Mosshill Rd, Boston, MA 02130 ... 617-524-2200
Global West Studio: 201 N Occidental Blvd, Los Angeles, CA 90026 ... 213-384-3331
Glusker, Erwin: 560 Lexington Ave 18th Fl, New York, NY 10021 ... 212-880-2749
Gluth & Weaver: 2929 Briar Park #100, Houston, TX 77042 ... 713-784-4141
Glyph Media Group: 17 Little West 12th St #305, New York, NY 10014 ... 212-929-2773
Gnu Group: 3470 Mt Diablo Blvd #A150, Lafayette, CA 94549 ...
Go Media: 1711 S Congress Ave, Austin, TX 78704 ... 512-326-8222
Godat Jonczyk Design Consult: 807 S Fourth Ave, Tucson, AZ 85701 ... 520-620-6337
Goetz Graphics: 60 Madison Ave #902, New York, NY 10010 ... 212-679-4250
Gola, Sandra: 397 Hudson St, Hackensack, NJ 07601 ... 201-440-3909
Gold & Assocs: 6000 Sawgrass Village Cir #C, Ponte Vedra Beach, FL 32082 ... 904-285-5669
Gold & Assocs, Allan: 2703 Cheswolde Rd, Baltimore, MD 21209 ... 410-358-9795
Gold Assocs, Keith: PO Box 2659, Ponte Verde Beach, FL 32004 ... 904-285-5556
Gold Ink Design: 136 W 22nd St, New York, NY 10011 ... 212-645-6977
Gold, Susan: 136 W 22nd St, New York, NY 10011 ... 212-645-6977
Goldberg, Amy: 632 Broadway 10th Fl, New York, NY 10012 ... 212-253-7488
Goldner Comm Design: 1810 S Rittenhouse Sq #709, Philadelphia, PA 19103 ... 215-735-8370
Goldner, Linda: 709 Rittenhouse Savoy, Philadelphia, PA 19103 ... 215-735-8370
Goldsholl Design & Film: 420 Frontage Rd, Northfield, OH 60093 ... 847-446-8300
Goldstein Designs/Davids Shoes: 74 E 7th St, New York, NY 10003 ... 212-777-1585
Goldstein Soundtracks, Dan: 2 Val Mar Pl, San Carlos, CA 94070 ... 415-593-8397
Golon, Mary: 19762 Sea Gull Ct, Saratoga, CA 95070 ... 408-252-4390
Gonong Graphics, Inc: 3117 Pamela Pl, Garland, TX 75044 ... 214-495-2200
Gonzales, Dan: 7575 NW 50th St, Miami, FL 33166 ... 305-471-0119
Gonzalez, Dan: 7575 NW 50th St, Miami, FL 33166 ... 305-471-0119
Good Design: 2200 N Lamar #209, Dallas, TX 75202 ... 214-954-0474
Good Design, Peter: Pequot Press Bldg, Chester, CT 06412 ... 203-526-9597
Good Graphics Group: 53 Strathmore Rd, Brookline, MA 02146 ... 617-739-8606
Good Idea: 811 W 15th St #2B, Newport Beach, CA 92665 ... 714-646-7913
Goode, Larry: 4115 Guadalupe, Austin, TX 78751 ... 512-467-7471
Goodman/Orlick Design, Inc: 240 E 27th St #12K, New York, NY 10016 ... 212-779-1585
Gorbatty Design, Norman: 310 Madison Ave #2101, New York, NY 10017 ... 212-599-1665
Gordon & Assoc, Sam: 226 W 4th St, New York, NY 10014 ... 212-741-9294
Gordon, Roger: 10799 N Gate St, Culver City, CA 90230 ... 310-559-8287
Gorelick Design, Alan: 26 Cromwell Dr, Morristown, NJ 07960 ... 210-898-1991
Gorelick, Jill: 1035 Mayfair Way, Plainfield, NJ 07060 ... 908-755-5504
Gorman Assocs, Chris: 305 Madison Ave #2214, New York, NY 10165 ... 212-983-3375
Gorman Copy & Dsgn, Allan: 215 Glenridge Ave, Montclair, NJ 07042 ... 201-509-2728
Gorman, Pat: 20 W 20th St, New York, NY 10011 ... 212-620-0506
Goss, Keller & Martinez: 2195 San Dieguito Dr, Del Mar, CA 92014 ... 619-792-1919
Gotlib Design: 515 Madison ave #905, New York, NY 10022 ... 212-319-5022
Goudreau Illustration: 40 E Main St/Weir River Brick, Ware, MA 01082 ... 413-967-9855
Gould Creative, David: 1412 Pecos, Mesquite, TX 75150 ... 214-686-4851
Gournoe Inc, M: 60 E Elm, Chicago, IL 60611 ... 312-787-5157
Goutas Assocs, Evelyn: 59 W 19th St #3A2, New York, NY 10011 ... 212-627-0101
GR Graphics Audio Visual: 1850 N 15th Ave, Phoenix, AZ 85007 ... 602-252-6525
Graetzer Ackerman, Inc: 17 S Franklin Tpke, Ramsey, NJ 07446 ... 201-236-1600
Graffito, Inc: 601 N Eutaw St #704, Baltimore, MD 21201 ... 410-837-0070
Grafica: 525 E Main St, Chester, NJ 07930 ... 908-879-2169
Graficsmiths: 15 Glendale Rd, Hudson, MA 01749 ... 508-562-5494
Grafik Comm, Inc: 1199 N Fairfax St #700, Alexandria, VA 22314 ... 703-683-4686
Grafix Design: 6562 Ridings Rd, Syracuse, NY 13206 ... 315-463-9175
Graham & Assocs, Critt: 2970 Clairmont Rd #620, Atlanta, GA 30329 ... 404-320-1737
Gram Graphic Design, Anne: 400 Linebrook Rd, Ipswich, MA 01938 ... 508-356-1173
Granados Assocs, Inc: 1810 Byberry Rd #E3, Bensalem, PA 19020 ... 215-244-0999
Grand Design: 1746 Underwood Rd, Gambrills, MD 21054 ... 410-721-9485
Grand Design/Boston: 22-A Franklin St, Marblehead, MA 01945 ... 617-631-5072
Graney, Tom: 7735 Pomeroy St, Richmond, VA 23228 ... 804-648-2324
Granola Graphics: 37 West 20 #902, New York, NY 10011 ... 212-727-0512
Granoski, Dana: 2500 Broadway #300, Santa Monica, CA 90404 ... 310-449-5600
Graphein: 1756 Blake St, Denver, CO 80202 ... 303-298-8009
Graphic Art Resource Assocs: 257 w 10th St #5E, New York, NY 10014 ... 212-929-0017
Graphic Artists Guild: 90 John St #403, New York, NY 10038 ... 212-791-3400
Graphic Arts, Inc: 1020 Bernard St, Alexandria, VA 22314 ... 703-683-4303
Graphic Chart & Map Co: 1 North St #2W, Hastings-on-Hudson, NY 10706 ... 914-478-5074
Graphic Comms: 20 W 38th St 2nd Fl, New York, NY 10018 ... 212-764-6237
Graphic Concepts Group: 1612 Summit Ave #410, Fort Worth, TX 76102 ... 817-332-4600
Graphic Concepts Unlimited: 2109 Hamilton Rd #H, Okemos, MI 48864 ... 517-347-8900
Graphic Consortium: 205 Race St, Philadelphia, PA 19106 ... 215-923-3200
Graphic Decisions, Inc: 318 Bainbridge St, Philadelphia, PA 19147 ... 215-627-6901
Graphic Design Advertising: 10400 Loubet St, Orlando, FL 32817 ... 407-277-7461
Graphic Design Continuum: 502 Wayne Ave, Dayton, OH 45410 ... 937-223-8264
Graphic Design Maui, Inc: 173 Ho-Ohana St #103, Kahului, HI 96732 ... 808-871-8000
Graphic Designers, Inc: 700 N Central Ave #450, Glendale, CA 91203 ... 818-247-5433
Graphic Expression, The: 330 E 59th St, New York, NY 10022 ... 212-759-7788
Graphic Expressions: 695 NW 80th Terr, Margate, FL 33063 ... 305-968-3789
Graphic House, Inc: 23200 14 Mile Rd, Bloomfield, MI 48301 ... 313-647-0011
Graphic Impact: 162 Lower Main St, Sunapee, NH 03782 ... 603-763-9221
Graphic Ink: 333 Church St, Clinton, MA 01510 ... 508-365-5205
Graphic Innovations: Rt 67 Box 168-D, Cullowhee, NC 28723 ... 704-293-9178
Graphic Matters: 2908 Berry Hill Dr, Nashville, TN 37204 ... 615-383-3877
Graphic Shop, Inc: 1012 San Pedro, San Antonio, TX 78212 ... 210-226-1006
Graphic Solution, The: PO Box 747, W Jordan, UT 84084 ... 801-569-8761
Graphic Solutions: 304 Hudson St/4th Fl N, New York, NY 10013 ... 212-645-2700
Graphic Solutions, Inc: 1750 Kettner Blvd, San Diego, CA 92101 ... 619-239-1335
Graphic Specialties, Inc: 6800 Shingle Creek Pkwy, Minneapolis, MN 55430 ... 612-722-6601
Graphic Traffic: 5845 Hollis St, Emeryville, CA 94608 ... 510-428-2808
Graphic Workshop: 80 Eighth Ave 17th Fl, New York, NY 10011 ... 212-633-6333
Graphica: 306 E. Market St., Greensboro, NC 27401 ... 336-230-0575
Graphica: 4501 Lyons Rd, Miamisburg, OH 45342 ... 937-866-4013
Graphica Corp: 3184 Alpine, Troy, MI 48084 ... 313-649-5050
Graphically Speaking: 5 Richmond Hill, Laguna Niguel, CA 92677 ... 714-661-0553
Graphics & Design: 421 S Pugh St, State College, PA 16801 ... 814-238-3136
Graphics By Nostradamus: 250 W 57th St #1128A, New York, NY 10107 ... 212-581-1362
Graphics Depot: 190 Hiawatha Pl, Syracuse, NY 13208 ... 315-472-1272
Graphics Et Al: 14th Fifth Ave #3C, New York, NY 10011 ... 212-475-1757
Graphics Etc: 2460 Rue Burgundy, New Orleans, LA 70117 ... 504-944-2814
Graphics Fifty-Five, Inc: 55 Avondale Ave, Clifton, NJ 07013 ... 201-472-4810
Graphics For Industry: 8 W 30th St 7th Fl, New York, NY 10001 ... 212-889-6202
Graphics III: 131 Roseland Ave, Caldwell, NJ 07006 ... 201-226-4343
Graphics Ltd: 9007 Independence Ave, Canoga Park, CA 91304 ... 818-998-6451
Graphics One Fifty: 150 Speedwell Ave, Morris Plains, NJ 07950 ... 201-267-6446
Graphics Pad: 1108 Concora Box 1155, Mansfield, TX 76063 ... 817-473-3380
Graphics Plus: 50 Merritt St, Port Chester, NY 10573 ... 914-939-0888
Graphics To Go: 133 E 36th St, New York, NY 10016 ... 212-889-9337
Graphics West: 1215 De La Vina St #G, Santa Barbara, CA 93101 ... 805-966-0885
Graphics Workshop: 2401 E Lawn Dr, Midland, MI 48642 ... 517-631-9560
Graphicus Corp: 2025 Maryland Ave, Baltimore, MD 21218 ... 301-727-5553
Graphien Design: 1756 Blake St, Denver, CO 80202 ... 303-298-8009
Graphikco Design Group: 2674 N 1st #206, San Jose, CA 95134 ... 498-435-1115
Graphiti Assocs: 1725 Westlake Ave N #101, Seattle, WA 98109 ... 206-285-9440
Graphix Design: 57 E Liberty St, Girard, OH 44420 ... 330-545-5611
Graphix, Inc: 651 E Paces Ferry Rd NE, Atlanta, GA 30305 ... 404-262-7832
Grasso Assocs, Lou: 425 Madison Ave 19th Fl, New York, NY 10017 ... 212-371-1820
Grau Graphics: 6 W 18th St #2D, New York, NY 10011 ... 212-807-7777
Gravdahl Design: 406 E Lake St, Ft Collins, CO 80524 ... 970-482-8807
Graves Fowler & Assocs: 14301 Layhill Rd #200, Silver Spring, MD 20906 ... 301-598-6414
Gray Studio, Cheri: 522 N Rossmore Ave #301, Los Angeles, CA 90004 ... 213-871-8967
Gray, George: 385 West End Ave, New York, NY 10024 ... 212-873-3607
Graywood Agency, Inc, The: 7 Hilltop Rd, Mendham, NJ 07945 ... 201-543-7700
Grear Designers, Malcolm: 391 Eddy St, Providence, RI 02903 ... 401-331-2891
Greatwork Electronic Ink: 2394 Mariner Sq Dr #137, Alameda, CA 94501 ... 510-721-7659
Grebe, Hank: 8209 Persimmon Hill Ln, Jacksonville, FL 32256 ... 904-348-2349
Greedboam & Company: 120 Cedar Ln, Ossining, NY 10562 ... 914-762-0954
Green Design Studio, Peter: 4219 W Burbank Blvd, Burbank, CA 91505 ... 818-953-2210
Green Graphic Design & Adv, Mel: 145 Richdale Rd, Needham, MA 02194 ... 617-449-6777
Green, Douglas: 251 E 51st St, New York, NY 10022 ... 212-752-6284
Greenberg Assocs, Inc, Jon: 29355 NW Highway #300, Southfield, MI 48034 ... 313-355-0890
Greene & Co: 1655 Valley Center Pkwy #100, Bethlehem, PA 18017 ... 610-868-4100
Greene & Co, H: 230 W Huron, Chicago, IL 60610 ... 312-642-0088
Greenebaum Design: 86 Walnut St, Natick, MA 01760 ... 617-655-8146
Greenfield Design: 1026 ave Of The Americas, New York, NY 10018 ... 212-354-0409
Greenfield, Peggy: 5 Manmar Dr #407, Plainville, MA 02762 ... 508-543-6644
Greenfield/Belser: 1818 n St NW #110, Washington, DC 20036 ... 202-775-0333
Greenhill Productions: 216 E 45th St, New York, NY 10017 ... 212-661-1363
Greenlee Hess Ind Design: 750 Beta Dr, Cleveland, OH 44143 ... 216-461-3881
Gregg & Assocs: 112 W 9th St 2nd Fl, Kansas City, MO 64105 ... 816-421-4473
Gregg, Mutsumi: 249 Alpine St #53, Pasadena, CA 91106 ... 818-449-8909
Gregorio Design: 801 Cooper Landing Rd #A410, Cherry Hill, NJ 08002 ... 609-321-1651
Gregory Design: 23 Kronquist Ct, San Francisco, CA 94131 ... 415-296-9331
Gregory Design, Albert: 21 Hanson St, Boston, MA 02118 ... 617-482-0347
Gregory Group, Inc: Box 191003, Dallas, TX 75219 ... 214-522-9360
Greiner & Assocs, John: 3111 N Ravenswood, Chicago, IL 60657 ... 773-404-0210
Grenier Design Assocs: 617 E Scranton Ave, Lake Bluff, IL 60044 ... 847-615-0505
Greteman Group: 1425 East Douglas #200, Wichita, KS 67211 ... 316-263-1004
Grguric, Alek: 25 Trailwood Dr #2508, Mississauga, ON L4Z 3K9 ... 416-868-9721
Grid, Steve Chang: 18 W 21st St 6th Fl, New York, NY 10010 ... 212-255-1806
Griffin Creative Co: 534 Kingfisher Dr, Sugarland, TX 77478 ... 713-242-1119
Griffin Design: 537 Armour Circle, Atlanta, GA 30324 ... 404-842-9900
Grimes Design, Don: 5635 Ridgedale, Dallas, TX 75206 ... 214-821-9590
Gritz Visual Graphics: 5595 Arapahoe Rd, Boulder, CO 80303 ... 303-449-3840
Groff, Jay Michael: 4650 East West Highway, Bethesda, MD 20814 ... 301-215-7221
Groot Organization: 245 Vallejo St, San Francisco, CA 94111 ... 415-788-6677
Groppi Advertising Design: 10 Forbes Rd, Braintree, MA 02184 ... 781-843-9629
Gross Design Concepts, Mike: 2334 E Beverly Dr, Tuscon, AZ 85719 ... 520-629-0626
Gross Graphic Design, Paul: 732 Springfield Ave, Summit, NJ 07901 ... 908-522-0333
Grossman Design, Steve: 4301 Highway 7 #120, Minneapolis, MN 55416 ... 612-922-4343

Grossman, Ken: 1384 Broadway 10th Fl, New York, NY 10018 . . . 212-883-1090
Groth Design, Donna: 13 Seventh Ave E, East Northport, NY 11731 . . . 631-757-1182
Group 118: 24 Fifth Ave #201, New York, NY 10011 . . . 212-995-8340
Group 33 Design Assocs: 15 W 26th St 9th Fl, New York, NY 10010 . . . 212-337-0333
Group Chicago: One E Delaware Pl #200, Chicago, IL 60611 . . . 312-787-4504
Group Design: 401 N Third St #360, Minneapolis, MN 55401 . . . 612-787-4504
Group Design Assocs: 50 Park Circle S, Farmingdale, NY 11735 . . . 516-420-8796
Group Four Design: PO Box 717, Avon, CT 06001 . . . 203-678-1570
Group M: 1621 Cypress St, Philadelphia, PA 19103 . . . 215-546-1995
Groves Design Company: 515 28th St #109, Des Moines, IA 50312 . . . 515-288-5278
Grunau, Ted: 165 Spadina Ave 3rd Fl, Toronto, ON M5T 2C3 . . . 416-351-0411
Grunder Design, Robin: 27 W 20th St #404, New York, NY 10011 . . . 212-727-7125
GTE Entertainment: 2035 Corte Del Nogal #200, Carlsbad, CA 92009 . . . 619-431-8801
Guancione, Karen: 262 DeWitt Ave, Belleville, NJ 07109 . . . 201-450-9490
Guarino Design: 1348 Cambridge St, Cambridge, MA 02139 . . . 617-661-8567
Gucciardo & Shapokas: 244 Madison Ave, New York, NY 10016 . . . 212-683-9378
Gudzin Design: 153 E 57th St #5E, New York, NY 10022 . . . 212-758-2532
Guerard, Jim: 4223 Glencoe Ave #A223, Marina Del Rey, CA 90292 . . . 213-477-8878
Guerrette, Muriel: 3 Forest Ln, Canton, CT 06019 . . . 203-693-1186
Guliani, Bob: 863 Pavonia Ave, Jersey City, NJ 07306 . . . 201-792-5213
Gunn Assocs: 275 Newbury St, Boston, MA 02116 . . . 617-267-0618
Gunselman & Co, Michael: 1007 N Broom St, Wilmington, DE 19806 . . . 302-655-7077
Gurevich, Dmitry: 381 Congress St 5th Fl, Boston, MA 02210 . . . 617-357-0337
Guzman Designs, R: 21037 Superior St, Chatsworth, CA 91311 . . . 818-700-9893
GVO, Inc: 2370 Watson Ct, Palo Alto, CA 94303 . . . 800-727-4486
Gwen Francis Design: 334 State St #203, Los Altos, CA 94022 . . . 415-949-4343

H

H Plus: 260 Fifth Ave #1201, New York, NY 10001 . . . 212-689-8853
H2D Corporate Image Management: 100 E Wisconsin Ave #2370, Milwaukee, WI 53202 414-226-0321
H2N Design: 1468 W 9th St #630, Cleveland, OH 44113 . . . 216-623-1144
Haapaniemi Design, Inc: 5599 San Felipe, Houston, TX 77056 . . . 713-622-3660
Haas, Jay Charles: 1 Plum Path, Ridgefield, CT 06877 . . . 203-438-3166
Hadden Design, Christopher: 44 Exchange St, Portland, ME 21045 . . . 207-772-9801
Hafeman Design Group, Inc: 566 W Adams St #300, Chicago, IL 60661 . . . 312-829-6829
Hafner Graphic Design, Christine: 68-3743 Ua Noe Pl, Waikoloa, HI 96738 . . . 808-883-9573
Hake Assocs: 212 E 47th St #28E, New York, NY 10017 . . . 212-751-5121
Hal Lewis Group: 1610 Chestnut St, Philadelphia, PA 19103 . . . 215-563-4461
Hale Design, Bruce: 1201 NW Blakely Ct, Seattle, WA 98177 . . . 206-440-9036
Haley Johnson Design: 3107 E 42nd St, Minneapolis, MN 55406 . . . 612-722-8050
Hall Design Group, Carla: 261 W 85th St, New York, NY 10024 . . . 212-799-4850
Hall Design, Kelly: 1021 S Wolf Rd #280, Sunnyvale, CA 94086 . . . 408 720-0431
Hall, Steve: 150 Alhambra Cir #1250, Coral Gables, FL 33134 . . . 305-461-9555
Halle, Doris: 355 South End Ave #4C, New York, NY 10280 . . . 212-321-2671
Halleck Design Group: 470 Ramona St, Palo Alto, CA 94301 . . . 415-325-0707
Halpern Adv & Design, Alan: 18 E 16th St 4TH Fl, New York, NY 10003 . . . 212-633-6505
Halsey, Mike: 2525 Lebanon Rd #B2, Nashville, TN 37214 . . . 615-885-6801
Halvorsen, Everett: 874 58th St, Brooklyn, NY 11220 . . . 718-438-4200
Hamada Design, Gary: 1111 Fort Stockton Dr #H, San Diego, CA 92103 . . . 619-294-9711
Hamer Assocs: Canal House/128 Garden St, Farmington, CT 06032 . . . 203-677-1972
Hamilton Displays: 9150 E 33rd St, Indianapolis, IN 46236 . . . 317-898-9300
Hamilton Group, The: 6001 N Adams Rd #100, Bloomfield Hills, MI 48304 . . . 810-205-2800
Hamilton/Sternglass: 54 W 21st St #705, New York, NY 10010 . . . 212-727-2703
Hammond Design Assocs: 79 Amherst St, Milford, NH 03055 . . . 603-673-5253
Hammond Design, Jean: 1026 Mass Ave, Arlington, MA 02174 . . . 617-641-4386
Hampton Corp Design, David: 3311 38th Ave W, Seattle, WA 98199 . . . 206-283-1350
Hanagriff King Design: 2222 Bissonnet, Houston, TX 77005 . . . 713-522-7783
Hananero Computing Solutions, Inc: 6352 Clayton Rd #100, St Louis, MO 63117 . . . 314-645-5522
Hancock Design/Div Hill Holliday: 200 Clarendon St, Boston, MA 02116 . . . 617-437-1600
Hancock Graphic Design, Tim: 500 Grant Ave, Louisville, CO 80027 . . . 303-665-7335
Hancock Rinek Design: 5019 Lido Sands Dr, Newport Beach, CA 92663 . . . 714-631-4200
Handelan Pedersen Design: 811 W Evergreen Ave, Chicago, IL 60622 . . . 312-664-1200
Handelman Graphics: 555 Madison Ave 29th Fl, New York, NY 10022 . . . 212-350-0000
Handler Group, Inc: 22 W 23rd St 3rd Fl, New York, NY 10010 . . . 212-645-3900
Handler Holden Design, Inc: 17 Ralph Ave, White Plains, NY 10606 . . . 914-997-7592
Hands Ink Adv: 2020 S Jones Blvd, Las Vegas, NV 89102 . . . 702-364-8604
Hanigan Consulting Group: 1250 Broadway 23rd Fl, New York, NY 10010 . . . 212-675-2200
Hanna Design, Jim: 4232 Lynd Ave, Arcadia, CA 91006 . . . 818-446-7558
Hannans Design, Nancy: 6637 Kelsey Point Crl, Alexandria, VA 22315 . . . 804-467-3607
Hannus Design Assocs: 10 Commercial Wharf W #508, Boston, MA 02110 . . . 617-227-3725
Hans Design: 3100 Dundee Rd #909, Northbrook, IL 60062 . . . 847-272-7980
Hansen Andrus Design: 2471 S 1500 East, Salt Lake City, UT 84106 . . . 801-487-8033
Hansen Design Assocs, Ted: 1885 Third Ave, San Diego, CA 92101 . . . 619-233-0422
Hansen Design Co: 2212 5th Ave N, Seattle, WA 98109 . . . 206-467-9959
Hansengraphics, Inc: 3305 SW 9th St, Des Moines, IA 50315 . . . 515-243-0637
Hanson, Ken: 301 N Water St, Milwaukee, WI 53202 . . . 414-347-1266
Hanson/Dodge Design: 301 N Water St 5th Fl, Milwaukee, WI 53202 . . . 414-347-1266
Hara Design, Martin: 501 Fifth Ave #2010, New York, NY 10017 . . . 212-573-6377
Harbaugh Design: 1401 NE Boat St, Seattle, WA 98105 . . . 206-547-0830
Harbor Company: 855 10th St #302, Santa Monica, CA 90403 . . . 310-393-6494
Hard Drives International: 1912 W 4th St, Tempe, AZ 85281 . . . 800-776-3475
Harding & Assocs Design Grp: 377 S Daniel Way, San Jose, CA 95128 . . . 408-345-4545
Hardy Design, Pat: 245 Gay Rd, Groton, MA 01450 . . . 508-448-8648
Hardy Design, Paul: 6 Admiral Dr #A279, Emeryville, CA 94608 . . .
Harley Assocs, Don E: 180 State St, St Paul, MN 55107 . . . 612-455-1631
Harmon Design, Jann: 535 Anton Blvd., #450, Costa Mesa, CA 92626 . . . 714-427-3107
Harne, John: 2169 Oakawana Dr, Atlanta, GA 30345 . . . 404-325-0795
Harrington Group, The: 8 Cattano Ave, Morristown, NJ 07960 . . . 201-326-8877
Harris Design, Inc: 724 Yorklyn Rd #150, Hockessin, DE 19707 . . . 302-234-5700
Harris Magee, Inc: 6333 Reynolds Rd, Horton, MI 49246 . . . 517-563-2100
Harris, Judy: 550 Willow Creek Ct, Clarendon Hills, IL 60514 . . . 630-789-3821
Harrison Design, Inc: 665 Chestnut 3rd Fl, San Francisco, CA 94133 . . . 415-928-6111
Harrison Lettering Design, Allen: 1601 Abbot Kinney Blvd, Venice, CA 90291 . . . 310-396-3202
Hart Communication Assocs: 29 Brewster St, North Andover, MA 01845 . . . 508-681-8844
Hart, Kay: 10818 Midwest Industrial, St. Louis, MO 63132 . . . 314-423-9300
Hartley Metzner Hunick: 3076 S CAlhoun Rd, New Berlin, WI 53151 . . . 414-784-1010
Hartley Studios: 16 Crosby St, New York, NY 10013 . . . 212-925-7269
Hartung & Assocs Ltd: 10279 Field Ln, Forestville, CA 95436 . . . 707-887-2825
Harvey & Daughters, Inc: 116 S W Old Padonida Rd, Cockeysville, MD 21030 . . . 410-628-9220
Hasbrouck Studios: 641 Cricket Hill Trl, Lawrenceville, GA 30244 . . . 770-972-7083
Hasgrove Design Group: 2600 S Gessner #518, Houston, TX 77063 . . . 713-789-9815
Hasten Design Studio: 1629 K St NW #950, Washington, DC 20006 . . . 202-293-1333
Hasto Communications: 2248 Spencerport Rd #A, Rochester, NY 14606 . . . 716-352-7095
Hatten Design, Phil: 526 S Sparks St, Burbank, CA 91506 . . . 818-559-5691
Haugaard Creative Group: 414 N Orleans, Chicago, IL 60610 . . . 312-661-0666
Hauser Assocs, SG: 880 Hampshire Rd #A, Westlake Village, CA 91361 . . . 805-497-5810
Hauser, Sydney: 9 Fillmore Dr, Sarasota, FL 33577 . . . 813-388-3021
Hawthorne/Wolfe, Inc: 1818 Chouteau Ave, St Louis, MO 63103 . . . 314-231-1844
Hayakawa & Assocs, Herb: 22736 Juniper Ave, Torrance, CA 90505 . . . 310-325-7755
Hayes Productions, Bruce: 959 Wisconsin St, San Francisco, CA 94107 . . . 415-282-2244
Haygeman Isobe Johnson Kracke: 2260 Rutherford Rd #110, Carlsbad, CA 92008 . . . 619-931-1982
Hayward & Co, Blake: 1234 Sherman Ave #200, Evanston, IL 60202 . . . 847-864-9800
HC Design: 4630 Montgomery Ave #510, Bethesda, MD 20814 . . . 301-215-7111
Hearn Assocs, Walter: 1099 Deerfield Dr NW, Blacksburg, VA 24060 . . . 540-951-2853
Hearn/Perrell Art Assocs: 23022 Hatteras St, Woodland Hills, CA 91367 . . . 310-394-8373
Heatly Assocs Design: 4131 Spicewood Springs #A8, Austin, TX 78759 . . . 512-343-2284
Hecht Design: 1026 Mass Ave, Arlington, MA 02174 . . . 617-643-1988
Heckler & Assocs: 1226 16th Ave W #200, Seattle, WA 98119 . . . 206-448-4242
Hedstrom/Blessing: 5500 Wayzata Blvd #650, Minneapolis, MN 55416 . . . 612-591-6200
Hegstrom Design: 805 Quail Glen Ct, Auburn, CA 95603 . . . 916-888-7000
Heick, Patrick E: 844 East Ave, Park Ridge, IL 60068 . . . 847-825-1099
Heidelberg USA: 1000 Gutenberg Dr, Kennesaw, GA 30144 . . . 770-419-6500
Heimall Inc, Bob: 1798 Rt 565, Sussex, NJ 07461 . . . 201-702-0075
Heiney & Craig: 235 Montgomery St #956, San Francisco, CA 94104 . . . 415-781-2404
Held & Diedrich Design: 703 E 30th St #16, Indianapolis, IN 46205 . . . 317-926-6161
Helfand, Jessica: 214 Sullivan St, New York, NY 10012 . . . 212-388-1863
Helgesson Ind Design, Ulf: 4285 Canoga Ave, Woodland Hills, CA 91364 . . . 818-883-3772
Helms, Nina: 25 Forest Ln, Westbury, NY 11590 . . . 516-997-6567
Hemisphere: 915 Main St #308, Evansville, IN 47708 . . . 812-429-0878
Hemlock Design: 53 Kirkland Circle, Wellesley Hills, MA 02181 . . . 617-237-0037
Hemman Design: 311 S Chadwick St, Philadelphia, PA 19103 . . . 215-985-1780
Henderson Company, The: 222 W Huron, Chicago, IL 60610 . . . 312-951-8973
Henderson Design, Bill: 1083 Kelly Creek Circle, Oviedo, FL 32765 . . . 407-366-5336
Henderson Tyner Art Co: 315 N Spurce St #299, Winston-Salem, NC 27101 . . . 910-748-1364
Hennelly, Noel: 239 28th St #4C, New York, NY 10016 . . . 212-683-2786
Henneman Design: 365 Canal St #2050, New Orleans, LA 70130 . . . 504-529-1482
Hennes Design Inc, Catherine: 445 Highland Ave, San Mateo, CA 94401 . . . 415-348-8247
Henning Communications: 1910 Pine St #100, St Louis, MO 63103 . . . 314-436-6464
Henry Wolf Production: 167 E 73rd St, New York, NY 10021 . . . 212-472-2500
Hensler Westerkamp Giles: 432 Walnut St #1500, Cincinnati, OH 45202 . . . 513-241-0100
Herbst Lazar Rogers & Bell, Inc: 345 N Canal, Chicago, IL 60606 . . . 312-454-1116
Herman & Assocs, Sid: 36 Ticehurst Ln, Marblehead, MA 01945 . . . 617-631-0662
Herman, Ben: 701 Pennsylvania, Ft Worth, TX 76104 . . . 817-332-7679
Hermine Design Group: 3 Lockwood Ave, Old Greenwich, CT 06870 . . . 203-698-1732
Hernandez, Raymond: 111 E 14th St #228, New York, NY 10003 . . . 212-388-7382
Herring Design, Jerry: 1216 Hawthorne, Houston, TX 77006 . . . 713-526-1250
Hershey Comm NY, Inc: 257 Park Ave S 8th Fl, New York, NY 10010 . . . 212-477-9100
Hess Design: 49 Eliot St, South Natick, MA 01760 . . . 508-650-4063
Hewett, Mike: 339 Palace Rd, Kingston, ON K7L 4T4 . . . 613-546-4232
Hewson Design Assocs: 270 Lafayette St #1110, New York, NY 10002 . . . 212-925-2776
Heyck, Edith: 6 Vernon St, Newburyport, MA 01950 . . . 508-462-9027
HeyerTech: 726 Marion Ave, Palo Alto, CA 94303 . . . 415-325-8522
Hickey & Helper Graphics: 1633 Bayshore Hwy #222, Burlingame, CA 94010 . . . 415-652-4860
Hidalgo, Manny: 29776 Teracina Ave, Laguna Niguel, CA 92677 . . . 714-495-1033
High Design, Richard: 6311 Grovewood, Houston, TX 77008 . . . 713-861-7779
High, Richard: 6311 Grovewood Ln, Houston, TX 77006 . . . 713-861-7779
Hild Nelson Design, Inc: 1400 North Ave, Bannockburn, IL 60015 . . . 847-948-7064
Hill Design: 3512 Lake, Houston, TX 77098 . . . 713-523-7363
Hill Design Group: 6 S Bryn Mawr Ave Ste 208, Bryn Mawr, PA 19010 . . . 610-519-1072
Hill Design, Alan: 214 Sullivan St #6D, New York, NY 10012 . . . 212-614-8893
Hill Design, Martin: 1961 Skyview Dr, Altadena, CA 91001 . . . 818-398-7561
Hill Flaherty Sabol Marketing: 1 Gateway Center, Pittsburgh, PA 15222 . . . 412-471-3700
Hill Shea & Clients: 7955 E Chaparral Rd #134, Scottsdale, AZ 85250 . . . 602-945-7289
Hill, Chris: 3512 Lake, Houston, TX 77098 . . . 713-523-7363
Hillhouse Graphic Design: 249 De Lee Dr, Kingsport, TN 37663 . . . 423-239-9384
Hillis Mackey & Co: 1550 Utica Ave S #745, Minneapolis, MN 55416 . . . 612-542-9122
Hillman Design, Thomas: 193 Middle St, Portland, ME 04101 . . . 207-773-3727
Hillmuth, James: 3613 Norton Pl, Washington, DC 20016 . . . 202-244-0465
Hilscher, Anthony: 1503 Washington Ave S, Minneapolis, MN 55454 . . . 612-332-8634
Hilton Graphics, Inc: 1000 N Washington, Lansing, MI 48906 . . . 517-371-1196
Hirano Design International: 875 N Michigan Ave #3443, Chicago, IL 60611 . . . 312-335-0090
Hirata, Clarice: 795 N Rengstorff Ave #10, Mt View, CA 94043 . . . 415-964-3773
Hirsch Design: 9136 Mormon Bridge Rd, Omaha, NE 68152 . . . 402-455-0383
Hirsch O'Connor Design: 205 W Wacker Dr #622, Chicago, IL 60606 . . . 312-329-1500
Hirschhaut Designs, Bruce: 510 Otteray Dr, Highpoint, NC 27262 . . . 910-841-5666
Hirsh Co: 8051 N Central Park Ave, Skokie, IL 60076 . . . 847-267-6777
Hitchcock, Betsy: 135 Green Meadow Ln, Boulder, CO 80302 . . . 303-444-1336
Hixson Design: 1414 E Fifth St, Charlotte, NC 28204 . . . 704-334-8088
Hjermstad & Assocs: PO Box 1304, Pacifica, CA 94044 . . . 415-738-0405
Hlc Group: 39 W 29th St 11th Fl, New York, NY 10001 . . . 212-889-4818
Hnath, John: 271 Madison Ave #1405, New York, NY 10016 . . . 212-661-0962
Hoashi Communications: 275 madison Ave 18th Fl, New York, NY 10016 . . . 212-697-7208
Hodges Graphic Design: 530 E Main St #301, Richmond, VA 23219 . . . 804-643-1909
Hodges, Alison: 4001 Confederate Point Rd, Jacksonville, FL 32210 . . . 904-778-8568
Hodgson/Myers Adv: 610 Market St #103, Kirkland, WA 98033 . . . 206-827-2506
Hoekstra Graphics, Grant: 18 Nottingham Dr, Lincolnshire, IL 60069 . . . 847-948-7378
Hofer Graphics: 3325 Enterprise Rd, Safety Harbor, FL 34695 . . . 813-725-2426
Hoffar & Co, Barron: 11 E Hubbard 7th Fl, Chicago, IL 60611 . . . 312-922-0890
Hogan Design, Inc: 1415 Thistlewood Ln, Grapevine, TX 76051 . . . 817-481-0808
Hohler Assocs: 6 Faneuil Hall Marketplace, Boston, MA 02109 . . . 617-742-5277
Holdsworth Design & Prctn, Ani: 2433 Willow Springs Ct, Apopka, FL 32712 . . . 407-884-8284
Holl, RJ: 35 Old Chicopee St, Chicopee, MA 01013 . . . 413-594-8188
Holland Design, Robert: 2914 Evergreen Way, Ellicott City, MD 21042 . . . 410-531-2481
Hollander Design, Sara: 1102 Tuckahoe Ln, Alexandria, VA 22302 . . . 703-548-0959
Hollinger Group: 9110 Theysen Dr, Houston, TX 77080 . . . 713-690-6244
Holloway, Martin: 56 Mt Horeb Rd, Plainfield, NJ 07060 . . . 908-563-0169

Hollyn Assocs, Lynn : 522 Ramona St, Palo Alto, CA 94301 415-325-9980
Hollywood Interactive: 32215 Pacific Coast Hwy, Malibu, CA 900265 310-858-0577
Hollywood Online, Inc: 1620 26th St #370, Santa Monica, CA 90404 310-586-2000
Holm Design, Sharon : 6 N Forty Dr, New Fairfield, CT 06812.................... 203-746-3763
Holmes Design & Adv: 6832 S Mitchell Dr, Tempe, AZ 85283.................... 602-413-2454
Holter, Catherine: 721 Broadway #606, New York, NY 10003 212-998-1605
Holtz Design: 539 Polk Blvd #B, Des Moines, IA 50312 515-255-4953
Holzsager Assocs, Mel: 19-19 Radburn Rd, Fairlawn, NJ 07410 201-797-3619
Hom Design, Mary: 9 Eastbrook Farm Ln, Southboro, MA 01772.................... 508-303-8382
Homs, John: 813 W 31st St, Richmond, VA 23225.............................. 804-230-7951
Honanken, William: PO Box 20402 Tompkins Sq Sta, New York, NY 10009........... 212-627-4108
HonBlue, Inc: 501 Summer St #3B1, Honolulu, HI 96817........................ 808-531-4611
Honda Design, Ray: 37 Fairview Terrace, Petaluma, CA 94952................... 707-762-6364
Hopkins Baumann: 236 W 26th St #5NW, New York, NY 10001...................... 212-727-2929
Hopp Design Office: 5245 Knox Ave S, Minneapolis, MN 55419.................... 612-920-2540
Hopsick Design, Frank: 17222 Vashon Hwy Sw/PO Box H, Vashon, WA 98070......... 206-463-5454
Horbochuk & Assocs: 4916 Willow Crest Ave, N Hollywood, CA 91601.............. 818-508-7524
Horizon Arts Unlimithed: 3054 S 44th, Kansas City, KS 66016.................... 913-262-4355
Horizon Communication & Design: 256 Horizon Ave, Venice, CA 90291.............. 310-394-5439
Horizon Image Development: 1250 Addison St #212, Berkeley, CA 94702............ 510-843-0131
Horizons Technology: 3990 Ruffin Rd, San Diego, CA 92123...................... 619-292-8331
Hornbacher, Sara: 1270 W Peachtree St #15 G, Atlanta, GA 30309................ 404-724-0412
Horosz, Carl: 10 Park Ave, Morristown, NJ 07960.............................. 201-359-3410
Horvath & Assocs Studios Ltd: 335 W 12th St, New York, NY 10014................ 212-741-0300
Hosick Design, Frank: PO Box H, Vashon Island, WA 98070...................... 206-463-5454
Hot Tech Multimedia, Inc: 46 Mercer St, New York, NY 10013.................... 212-925-3010
Hough Assocs, Jack: 25 Seir Hill Rd, Norwalk, CT 06850........................ 203-846-2666
Hough Inc, Jack: 25 Seirhill Rd, Norwalk, CT 06850............................ 203-846-2666
Houston Mowry Productions: 5601 N Macauthur 105, Irving, TX 75038.............. 214-550-6147
Hovaness Design: #2 Briarwood Ct, Medford, NJ 08055.......................... 609-988-7027
Howard Design Group: 20 Nassau St #115, Princeton, NJ 08542................... 609-924-1106
Howard Jeldsan Assocs/Concorde: 210 N Peak Dr, Alpharetta, GA 30202............ 770-518-9903
Howard-Stutesman, Deborah: 14378 County Rd S, Lyons, OH 43533................. 419-335-3340
Howell Design: 6319 E Valley Rd, Nashville, TN 37205.......................... 615-356-5020
Howell Design, David: 4616 Windmere Chase Dr, Raleigh, NC 27616................ 919-873-0876
Howry Design: 354 Pine St #600, San Francisco, CA 94104....................... 415-433-2035
Hrivnak, James: 10822 Childs Ct, Silver Spring, MD 20901...................... 301-681-9090
Hsiung & Assocs: 205 West 4th St Ste 900, Cincinnati, OH 45202................. 513-381-8855
Hub Graphics: 18 E 16th St 4th Fl, New York, NY 10003......................... 212-675-8500
Huber Design: 3284 Willow Run Rd, Kutztown, PA 19530.......................... 610-285-2266
Hubler, Olivette: 2631 Commerce, Dallas, TX 75226............................. 214-742-2491
Huddleston Malone Design: 56 Exchange Pl, Salt Lake City, UT 84111.............. 801-595-6808
Huebner Design: 12 Ox Hill Rd, Newtown, CT 06470.............................. 203-270-0732
Huerta Design: 800 N Brand Blvd #260, Glendale, CA 91203...................... 818-243-6800
Huerta Design, Inc, Gerard: 54 Old Post Rd, Southport, CT 06490................ 203-256-1625
Huffaker Graphics: 113 Nooks Hill Rd, Cromwell, CT 06470...................... 203-635-3258
Hughes Design: One Bishop St, Norwalk, CT 06851............................... 203-847-9696
Hughes Design Communications: 22 N Morgan #203, Chicago, IL 60607.............. 312-733-1466
Hughes Design Group: 202 Mill Wharf, Scituate, MA 02066....................... 617-545-0740
Hughes, Dralene "Red": 19750 W Observatory Rd, New Berlin, WI 53146............ 262-542-5547
Hulefeld Assocs: 333 E 8th St, Cincinnati, OH 45202........................... 513-421-2210
Hull Design Group, Caryl: 69 Newbury St, Boston, MA 02116...................... 617-536-1017
Hull, John: 353 W 53rd St #1W, New York, NY 10019............................. 212-682-2462
Human Code: 319 Congress Ave Ste 100, Austin, TX 78701........................ 512-477-5455
Human Element, The: 8120 Penn Ave S #433, Bloomngton, MN 55431................ 612-888-9544
Human Factors/Industrial Design: 575 Eighth Ave 15th Fl, New York, NY 10018...... 212-868-2277
Humangraphic: 4015 Ibis St, San Diego, CA 92103.............................. 619-299-0431
Hume Design, Kendra: 208 SW Stark #500, Portland, OR 97204.................... 503-224-7618
Hunt & Fultz, J: 307 Fifth Ave 7th Fl, New York, NY 10016...................... 212-545-7676
Hunt Creative, David: 1237 Gadsden St #101, Columbia, SC 29201................. 803-252-3003
Hunt Weber Clark Design: 525 Brannan St #302, San Francisco, CA 94107........... 415-882-5770
Hunter Design, Rona: 133 Hillside Ave, Cresskill, NJ 07626.................... 201-871-9434
Hunter McMain: One W Loop S #601, Houston, TX 77027........................... 713-627-1177
Hurd & Assocs: 1250 Pine St #102, Walnut Creek, CA 94596...................... 510-930-8580
Hurd Design, Jim: 722 Lombard St #204, San Francisco, CA 94133................. 415-921-4691
Hutcheson & Co: 3845 FM 1960 W #140, Houston, TX 77068........................ 713-440-0221
Huttner: One Penn Plaza #100, New York, NY 10119.............................. 212-695-4858
Huyssen, Roger: 54 Old Post Rd #2H, Southport, CT 06490........................ 203-256-9192
Hyde, Bill: 751 Matsonia, Foster City, CA 94404............................... 415-345-6955

I

I Catcher: 1140 Terminal Twr, Cleveland, OH 44113............................ 216-696-1686
i2M: 2621 11th St, Santa Monica, CA 90405..................................... 310-396-6664
i3 Information & Imagination: 1599 Postroad E, Westport, CT 06880.............. 203-254-9990
Icon: 1430 Yankee Park Pl, Dayton, OH 45458................................... 937-428-3615
Iconos: 118 E 26th St #201, Minneapolis, MN 55404............................. 612-879-0504
Ida Design: 13530 Fonesca Ave, La Mirada, CA 90638............................ 213-943-2660
IDC Design Group: 1989 W 5th Ave #12, Columbus, OH 43212...................... 614-487-8855
Ideas: 300 Broadway #20, San Francisco, CA 94133.............................. 415-397-2777
Ideas To Images: 5256 Aero Dr #3, Santa Rosa, CA 95403........................ 707-542-4301
Ideaworks Presentations: 1191 Chestnut St, Newton, MA 02164.................... 617-244-0101
Identico: 250 Commercial St #3007, Manchester, NH 03101........................ 603-644-1408
Identity Center: 1340 Remington Rd #5, Schaumburg, IL 60173.................... 847-THE-BEST
Identity Design: 1895 Park Ave, San Jose, CA 95126............................. 408-554-1022
Identity Group, The: 114 N Brand Blvd #200, Glendale, CA 91203................. 818-243-3630
iDEZin Digital Workgroup: 2820 West Lunt #2000, Chicago, IL 60645.............. 773-338-3364
Ignition: 400 Yerba Buena Ave, San Francisco, CA 94127......................... 415-731-9050
Ikkanda Design Group: 2440 S Sepulveda #152/Bldg #2, Los Angeles, CA 90064...... 310-477-8584
Ilium Assocs: 600 108th Ave NE #660, Bellevue, WA 98004........................ 206-646-6525
Illustrated Page, The: 713 Indian Way, St Charles, IL 60174..................... 708-443-9651
Imada Design Group: 814 Fairoaks #B, S Pasadena, CA 91030...................... 818-799-9114
Imag'Inez: 5 Oak Flat Rd, Orinda, CA 94563.................................... 510-254-2444
Image Assocs: 4909 Windy Hill Dr, Raleigh, NC 27609........................... 919-876-6400
Image Axis: 38 W 21st St 2nd Fl, New York, NY 10010........................... 212-989-5000
Image Base Comm, Inc: 430 W Erie #600, Chicago, IL 60610...................... 312-587-8700
Image Design Studio: 837 Traction Ave, Los Angeles, CA 90013.................... 213-617-9001
Image Excellence: 3312 Shore Crest, Dallas, TX 75235........................... 214-352-9958
Image Factory: 1500 San Remo Ave #249, Coral Gables (Miami), FL 33146........... 305-666-5559
Image Factory: 15 Olive Ln, Ownings Mills, MD 21117............................ 410-581-8600
Image Group Studio: 3923 Cole St, Dallas, TX 75204............................ 214-745-1411
Image Services: 1419 Standiford Ave #3, Modesto, CA 95350...................... 209-579-5516
Image Source: 6105 Castle Bay Dr, Las Vegas, NV 89108.......................... 702-647-8487
Images: 833 W Main, Louisville, KY 40202...................................... 502-584-7954
Imagesmith: 335 Rte 202-206/PO Box100, Pluckemin, NJ 07978..................... 908-658-9334
Imageworks Communications: 5353 Topanga Canyon Blvd Ste 105, Woodland Hills, CA 91364... 818-712-9439
Imagicians: 1126 Fairview Ave #107, Arcadia, CA 91007.......................... 818-446-9625
Imagics Design Group: PO Box 7651, Santa Cruz, CA 95061........................ 408-426-1531
Imagigraphics: 9 Grant St, West Newton, MA 02165.............................. 617-965-7788
Imagination Creative Svcs: 80 Justin, San Francisco, CA 94112................... 408-988-8696
Imagination Factory, The: 6161 28th St SE, Grand Rapids, MI 49546............... 616-356-2544
Imagine Co: 4015 80th St, Kenosha, WI 53142................................... 414-942-9355
Imago Image Productions: 1264 S Goodrich Ave, City of Commerce, CA 90040......... 213-728-8852
Imergy: 48 W 38th Street, New York, NY 10018................................... 212 221-8585
Impact Communications Group: 18627 Brookhurst St #314, Fountain Valley, CA 92708 . 714-963-6760
Impact Corp Comm: PO Box 730, Ojai, CA 93024................................... 805-640-2950
Impact Media Group: 1920 Franklin St #7, San Francisco, CA 94109................ 415-563-9083
Impact USA: 2227 Ann Dr, St Josephs, MI 49085................................. 616-983-4170
Impact/FCB: 101 E Erie St 10th Fl, Chicago, IL 60611........................... 312-751-3500
Impress: PO Box 761, Williamsburg, MA 01096................................... 413-268-3040
Impress, Inc: 244 Main St, Northhampton, MA 01060.............................. 413-585-5752
Impressions, Inc: 200 Powerhouse Rd, Roslyn Hts, NY 11577....................... 516-484-2233
In House Graphic Design: 0717 Waterloo-Geneva Rd, Waterloo, NY 13165............ 315-539-9004
Inari Information Services: 804 N College #101, Bloomington, IN 47404............ 812-331-2298
Indiana Design Consortium, Inc: 416 Main St Box 180, Lafayette, IN 47902......... 317-423-5469
Indika NYC: 13-17 Laight St/6th Fl#1, New York, NY 10013........................ 212-226-1272
Industrial F/X: 90 Ship St, Providence, RI 02903............................... 401-831-5796
Industrial Technological Assoc: 30675 Solon Rd, Cleveland, OH 44139.............. 216-349-2900
Industry: 171 South Park, San Francisco, CA 94107.............................. 415-882-9879
Info by Design: 21240 Maira Lane, Saratoga, CA 95070........................... 408-857-2229
Info Use: 2560 Ninth St #216, Berkley, CA 94710................................ 510-549-6520
Information Technology Design: PO Box 28, Northfield, MN 55057.................. 507-645-6551
Ing Design: 214 Homer St, Palo Alto, CA 94301.................................. 415-617-8488
Ing Design, Victor: 5810 Lincoln, Morton Grove, IL 60053........................ 847-965-3459
Ingalls & Assocs: 10 Arkansas St, San Francisco, CA 94107....................... 415-626-6395
Ingenious Multimedia: 815 Wells, Chicago, IL 60610.............................. 312-951-8018
Ingle Co: 11661 San Vicente Blvd #402, Los Angeles, CA 90049.................... 310-820-8841
Ingram Design & Assocs, Inc: 71 W 2nd St, Yuma, AZ 85364........................ 520-782-3844
Inkstone Design: 210 N Higgins Ave #334, Missoula, MT 59802...................... 406-542-0270
Inkwell, Inc: 5 W 30th St, New York, NY 10001.................................. 212-279-2066
Inland Group: 222A N Main St, Edwardsville, IL 62025............................ 618-656-8836
Inner Thoughts: 118 E 25th St, New York, NY 10010............................... 212-674-1277
Inno Design, Inc: 577 College Ave, Palo Alto, CA 94306.......................... 415-493-4666
Innovation Design & Adv: 1424 Fourth St #702, Santa Monica, CA 90401............. 310-395-4332
Innovations: 182 Bernard St, San Francisco, CA 94109............................ 415-474-6385
Innovations & Development, Inc: 115 River Rd, Edgewater, NJ 07020................ 201-941-5500
Innovative Design & Graphics: 1234 Sherman Ave #214, Evanston, IL 60202.......... 847-475-7772
Ins Advertising: 811 NW 19th St, Portland, OR 97209............................. 503-221-5000
Insight: 5335 Bar Hills Ave #310, Dayton, OH 45429............................. 513-438-2815
Insite Communications: 3617 Silverside Rd Suite E, Wilmington, MA 19810.......... 302-478-6345
InSite Design: 36 Leafwood Cir, San Rafael, CA.................................. 415-721-0608
Inspire Graphic House: 98 Canal St #2R, New York, NY 10002...................... 212-233-3757
Integre Advertising By Design: N8 W22323 Johnson Dr #D, Waukesha, WI 53186....... 414-544-8800
Intelplex: 12215 Dorsett Rd, Maryland Hts, MO 63043............................. 314-739-9996
Inter-Active Designs: P.O. Box 4022, Hopkins, MN 55343........................... 612-938-1473
Interactive Data Corp: 4400 MacArthur Blvd #500, Newport Beach, CA 92660......... 213-626-3521
Interactive Design: 1900 Superfine Ln #7, Wilmington, DE........................ 302-429-0143
Interactive Factory: 368 Congress St, Boston, MA 02210.......................... 617-426-0609
Interactive Illusions: 3846 Abbott Ave S, Minneapolis, MN 55410.................. 612 926-5924
Interactive Media Communications: 204 Second Ave, Waltham, MA 02154.............. 617-890-7707
Interactive Media Partners: 50 Eagle St, San Francisco, CA 94114................. 415-861-1672
Interbrand Schecter Group: 437 Madison Ave 10th Fl, New York, NY 10022........... 212-752-4400
InterCom: 3 Grogan's Pk #200, The Woodlands, TX 77380........................... 713-298-1010
Intergate, Inc: 32 Warren St, Columbus, OH 43215................................ 614-421-0004
Intergrated Media: 200 Varick St #606, New York, NY 10014....................... 212-229-1200
International Design & Adv: 5 W 19th St 6th Fl, New York, NY 10011............... 212-633-2388
International Imaging: 175 Kimel Park Dr #250, Winston-Salem, NC 27103........... 336-760-0770
Interrobang Design Studio: 526 W 26th St #803, New York, NY 10001................ 212-463-0195
Intersight Design, Inc: 419 Park Ave S, New York, NY 10016...................... 212-696-0700
Intervision: 401 E 10th Ave #160, Eugene, OR 97401.............................. 503-343-7993
Intrepid Design & Communications: 3850 Klahanie Dr Se #22-301, Issaquah, WA 98029..........
Intrepid Productions: 7 Mt Lassen Dr #A116, San Rafael, CA 94903................. 415-491-4050
Intricate Decisions: PO Box 55661, Riverside, CA 92517.......................... 714-274-9829
Invisions Group Ltd: 4927 Auburn Ave, Bethesda, MD 20814........................ 301-718-3450
IPG: 5611-B Foxwood Dr, Agoura Hills, CA 91301.................................. 818-865-1428
Irish Graphics, Gary: 45 Newbury St, Boston, MA 02116........................... 617-247-4168
Ironwood Assocs: 49 Sabbath Day Hill, S Salem, NY 10590......................... 914-763-9595
Isley Design, Alexander: 4 Old Mill Rd, Redding, CT 06896....................... 203-544-9692
Ison Design: 12574 Barrett Ln, Santa Ana, CA 92705.............................. 714-997-4452
Israel, David: 6055 Barfield Rd #200, Atlanta, GA 30328......................... 404-255-6377
It! Design: 100 W Livingston St, Orlando, FL 32801.............................. 407-857-5462
IVID Communications: 7220 Trade St #201, San Diego, CA 92121..................... 619-537-5000
Ivy League of Design: 156 Fifth Ave #417, New York, NY 10010..................... 212-243-1333
IXAT Graphics/Illustration: 42 Roger Rd, Griswold, CT 06351...................... 203-376-2288
Izquierdo Marketing Design, Inc: 213 W Institute Pl #410, Chicago, IL 60610....... 312-787-9784

J

J Brooks Potters Marketing: 23332 Mill Creek Dr #160, Laguna Hills, CA 92653...... 714-727-7078
Jaap Assocs, Penraat: 315 Central Park W, New York, NY 10025..................... 212-873-4541
Jaben Design, Seth: 47 E 3rd St #3, New York, NY 10003.......................... 212-673-5631
Jablonski, Andrew: 10 W 19th St 6th Fl, New York, NY 10011....................... 212-242-1080
Jaciow Design: 396 Grinnell Court, Santa Clara, CA 95051......................... 408-984-8001
Jackmauh Design: 6 Hazel Terrace, Arlington, MA 02174........................... 617-641-4084
Jackson Design: 300 Tenth Ave S, Nashville, TN 37203............................ 615-255-9335
Jacobs Creative Group: 26 Bridgecourt Ln, Concord, MA 01742...................... 508-369-8611

Korshak Creative Services: 4200 Westheimer #280, Houston, TX 77027 . . . 713-961-5061
Kosaka Design: 729 Sansome #300, San Francisco, CA 94111 . . . 415-398-9348
Kosarin, Linda: 400 W 58th St #5F, New York, NY 10019 . . . 212-261-6500
Kosner Design, Anthony: 660 Vly Rd, Stone Ridge, NY 12484 . . . 914-657-6852
Kotlas, Meri: 2201 Candun Dr #100, Apex, NC 27502 . . . 919-363-4454
Kottler Caldera Group: 1201 E Jefferson #A25, Phoenix, AZ 85034 . . . 602-495-1300
Kovach Design Co: 3530 N Lake Shore Dr #2B, Chicago, IL 60657 . . . 773-935-7422
Kovin Design: 236 Lehigh Dr, Richboro, PA 18954 . . . 215 968-7820
Kowler Assocs: 4706 Nicollet Ave #200, Minneapolis, MN 55409 . . . 612-822-3618
Kramer & Larkin: 1934 Lombard St, Philadelphia, PA 19146 . . . 215-545-2120
Kramer Design, Mya: 604 Mission 10th Fl, San Francisco, CA 94105 . . . 415-777-4433
Kratzer Graphic Design, Karen: 294 Rock Landing Rd, Haddam Neck, CT 06424 . . . 860-267-7441
Krause Assocs: 501 Elm St #300, Dallas, TX 75202 . . . 214-741-7500
Kreger Graphics: 7109 46th St, Chevy Chase, MD 20815 . . . 301-654-6944
Kreidel Design: 11060 Artesia Blvd #C, Cerritos, CA 90703 . . . 310-860-1418
Kremers Advtg Specialtists, Inc: 3854 Crystal SW #A, Grandville, MI 49418 . . . 616-538-0340
Kricket Graphics: 319 E 2nd St, Fredrick, MD 21701 . . . 301-631-0373
Krogstad, Yuguchi: 3378 W 1st St, Los Angeles, CA 90004 . . . 213-383-6915
Kroha Assocs: 573 Newfield St, Middletown, CT 06457 . . . 860-346-4650
Krohn Design: 1304 N Beverly Glen Blvd, Los Angeles, CA 90077 . . . 310-470-3597
Krone Group: 1007 Mumma Rd, Wormleysburg, PA 17043 . . . 717-731-9020
Krukowski & Co, Jan: 74 E 79th St 3rd Fl, New York, NY 10021 . . . 212-794-3929
Ksv Communicators: 212 Battery St, Burlington, VT 05401 . . . 802-862-8261
Kubas 11 Design Assocs, George: 13000 Athens Ave, Lakewood, OH 44107 . . . 216-521-5160
Kubota & Bender: 184 Laurel Ridge, S Salem, NY 10590 . . . 914-533-6391
Kucklick Design: 116 Las Astas Dr, Los Gatos, CA 95030 . . . 408-358-4980
Kuester Group, The: 81 S 9th St #300, Minneapolis, MN 55402 . . . 612-338-6030
Kung Assocs, Hans: 491 Broadway 9th Fl, New York, NY 10012 . . . 212-226-4842
Kuntz Design, Diane: 817 Euclid St, Santa Monica, CA 90403 . . . 310-451-3601
Kunz, Randall: 3633 Blaisdell Ave, Minneapolis, MN 55409 . . . 612-821-0429
Kunz Assocs, Willi: 2112 Broadway #500, New York, NY 10023 . . . 212-799-4300
Kurigraphics: 10770 Minette Dr, Cupertino, CA 95014 . . . 408-725-8064
Kuzich Design, John: 350 Townsend St #304, San Francisco, CA 94107 . . . 415-543-3270

L

La Haye Design, Barney: 611 Broadway, New York, NY 10012 . . . 212-505-6802
La Perle Assocs: 330 Parkview Terrace, Oakland, CA 94610 . . . 510 444-8439
Lacy Assocs Ltd, N Lee: 8446 Melrose Pl, Los Angeles, CA 90069 . . . 213-852-1414
Ladd Assocs, Inc: 517 Georges Rd, N Brunswick, NJ 08902 . . . 908-937-5777
Laidlaw Group, The: 337 Summer St, Boston, MA 02210 . . . 617-423-2801
Laing Communications: 16250 NE 80th St, Redmond, WA 98052 . . . 206-869-6313
Lake Design Co, Joslin: 916 S Wabash Ave #403, Chicago, IL 60605 . . . 312-360-1833
Lam Design Assocs: 409 Manville Rd, Pleasantville, NY 10570 . . .
Lam/Berardin: 461 Second St #109, San Francisco, CA 94107 . . . 415-546-6779
Lamb & Co: 2429 Nicollet Ave, Minneapolis, MN 55404 . . . 612-333-8666
Lampert, Dave: 275 E Central Pkwy #238, Altamonte Springs, FL 32701 . . . 407-695-9000
Lamson Design, Dale: 817 Main St 2nd Fl, Cincinnati, OH 45202 . . . 513-381-6121
Lanahan, John: 39 W 38th St 10th Fl, New York, NY 10018 . . . 212-840-2912
Lancaster Design: 2900 Airport Ave #A, Santa Monica, CA 90405 . . . 310-397-7792
Landes & Assocs: 20313 Mason Court, Torrance, CA 90503 . . . 310-540-0907
Landesberg Dsgn Assocs: 1100 Bingham St, Pittsburgh, PA 15203 . . . 412-381-2220
Landis Design: 653 Bryant St, San Francisco, CA 94107 . . . 415-777-2242
Landkamer Assocs: 444 Dharo St #114, San Francisco, CA 94107 . . . 415-522-2480
Landman & Co, K: 30 W 21st St 3rd Fl, New York, NY 10010 . . . 212-924-4254
Landman, Kathy: 30 W 21st St 3rd Fl, New York, NY 10010 . . . 212-924-4254
Landor Assocs: 1301 5th Ave #1600, Seattle, WA 98101 . . . 206-223-0700
Landor Assocs: 230 Park Ave S, New York, NY 10003 . . . 212-614-5050
Landor Assocs: 1001 Front, San Francisco, CA 94111 . . . 415-955-1200
Landry Creative: 251 S Clarkson St, Denver, CO 80209 . . . 303-446-9329
Lane Advertising: 35 Congress St, Salem, MA 01970 . . . 978-744-1600
Lane Design, Emily: 1397 Kersey Lane, Potomac, MD 20854 . . . 301-424-7979
Lane/Morris: 266 Delaplane Ave, Newark, DE 19711 . . . 302-731-7370
Laney, Ron: 25 Madonna Ct, Highland, IL 62249 . . . 847-654-5142
Lange, Jim: 203 N Wabash #1312, Chicago, IL 60601 . . . 312-606-9313
Langston Cherubino Group Ltd: 835 Broadway #1507, New York, NY 10010 . . . 212-533-2585
Lapham/Miller Assocs: 34 Essex St, Andover, MA 01810 . . . 508-475-8570
Largent Studios, Herron: 3300 NE Expressway #1B, Atlanta, GA 30341 . . . 770-986-0009
Larsen Design Interacitve: 7101 York Ave S, Minneapolis, MN 55435 . . . 612-835-2271
Larson Design, Sarah: 6019 N Paulina, Chicago, IL 60660 . . . 773-465-2993
Larson, Ron: 940 N Highland Ave, Los Angeles, CA 90038 . . . 213-465-8451
Lasky Studio Inc, Carol: 30 The Fenway #C, Boston, MA 02215 . . . 617-353-0500
Latto, Sophia: 723 President St, Brooklyn, NY 11215 . . . 718-789-1980
Laufer, Joseph Mark: 2201 Penn Ave #3, Philadelphia, PA 19130 . . . 215-854-8478
Laughing Dog Design: 1925 N Clybourn Ave Ste 202, Chicago, IL 60614 . . . 312-951-8399
Laughlin/Winker, Inc: 251 A St, Boston, MA 02114 . . . 617-426-7140
Lauritsen Design, Peggy: 700 S Third St #102, Minneapolis, MN 55415 . . . 612-339-5011
Lawrence Design Group, Inc: 126 Fifth Ave #803, New York, NY 10011 . . . 212-675-4838
Lazin & Katalan: 227 W 17th St 5th Fl, New York, NY 10011 . . . 212-242-7611
Le Brun Assocs, Inc: 853 Broadway #1607, New York, NY 10003 . . . 212-477-8969
Le Van Design: 208 Spangsville Rd, Oley, PA 19547 . . . 610-689-4812
Leach Design, Molly: 37 W 20th St 10th Fl, New York, NY 10011 . . . 212-627-8361
Leach, Richard: 62 W 39th St #803, New York, NY 10018 . . . 212-869-0972
Learning Co, The: 6401 Kaiser Dr, Fremont, CA 94555 . . . 510-792-2101
Lebowitz Gould Design: 7 W 22nd St 7th Fl, New York, NY 10010 . . . 212-645-0550
Lebowitz, Mo: 2599 Phyllis Dr, N Bellemore, NY 11710 . . . 516-826-3397
Lecat Design: 6911 N Hamilton, Chicago, IL 60645 . . . 773-465-6580
Leckner Design Assocs: 450 Seventh Ave #2302, New York, NY 10123 . . . 212-564-4250
Ledbetter, James: 10818 Ridge Spring, Dallas, TX 75218 . . . 214-341-4858
Lee & Assocs, Michael: 221 W Ohio St, Chicago, IL 60610 . . . 312-832-1300
Lee Assocs, Alan: 296 S Great Rd, Lincoln, MA 01773 . . . 617-259-0533
Lee Assocs, Inc, Tony: 130 Ward Ave, Trenton, NJ 08609 . . . 609-989-7092
Lee Communications: 11 Conant Valley Rd, Pound Ridge, NY 10576 . . . 914-533-2325
Lee Design Inc, Clarence: 2333 Kapiolani Blvd, Honolulu, HI 96826 . . . 808-941-5021
Lee Design, Steven: 135 S Park, San Francisco, CA 94107 . . . 415-546-1701
Lee, Lilly: 15266 Valley Vista Rd, Sherman Oaks, CA 91403 . . . 818-788-4100
Leed Custom Design: 26 Fishkill Hook Rd, Hopewell Junctin, NY 12533 . . . 914-896-7480
Leeds Studio, Judith K: 14 Rosemont Ct, N Caldwell, NJ 07006 . . . 201-226-3552
Leef & Assocs Inc, Naomi: 12 W 27th St 18th Fl, New York, NY 1001 . . . 212-686-6300
Lees & Assocs, John : 65 Broad St 3rd Fl, Boston, MA 02109 . . . 617-542-0399
Lehrer Designs, Inc, Brad: 81 Pondfield Rd Suite#6, Bronxville, NY 10708 . . . 914-793-3001
Lehrfeld, Gerald: 701 Forum Sq #507, Glenview, IL 60025 . . . 847-297-6907
Leigh & Co, Doug: 11 Tobacco Rd, Weston, CT 06883 . . . 203-226-0779
Lekasmiller Design Inc: 1460 Maria Lane #260, Walnut Creek, CA 94596 . . . 925-934-3971
Leneker Design: 919 Stratford Ave #4, Stratford, CT 06497 . . . 203-375-0830
Lenney, Ann: 3003 Van Ness St NW, Washington, DC 20008 . . . 202-363-2729
Lennon & Assocs: 734 N Highland Ave, Los Angeles, CA 90038 . . . 213-465-5104
Lenweaver Adv & Design: 239 W Fayette St/Seneca Bldg, Syracuse, NY 13202 . . . 315-422-8729
Leong Dsgn, Russell: 847 Emerson St, Palo Alto, CA 94301 . . . 415-321-2443
Leonhardt Group: 1218 Third Ave #620, Seattle, WA 98101 . . . 206-624-0551
Leotta Designers, Inc: 303 Harry St, Conshohocken, PA 19428 . . . 215-828-8820
Lerner & Co: 2o Tower Ln, Avon, CT 06001 . . . 860-677-7744
Les Lamotte: 3002 Keating Ct, Burnsville, MN 55337 . . . 612-894-1879
Lesley-Hille, Inc: 250 E 63rd St #411, New York, NY 10021 . . . 212-759-9755
Lesniewicz Assocs: 222 N Erie St, Toledo, OH 43624 . . . 419-243-7131
Lesser/Etcetera, Joan: 3565 Greenwood Ave, Los Angeles, CA 90066 . . . 310-397-4575
Lester & Butler: 475 Fifth Ave, New York, NY 10017 . . . 212-951-6100
Letter Perfect: PO Box 785, Gig Harbor, WA 98335 . . . 206-956-9422
Letterform Design: 501 N Orange Dr, Los Angeles, CA 90036 . . . 213-932-1875
Levavi & Levavi: 310 W 72nd St #9D, New York, NY 10023 . . . 212-875-8160
Levin Design, Lisa: 124 Locust Ave, Mill Valley, CA 94941 . . . 415-389-9813
Levine & Assocs: 1090 Vermont Ave NW #440, Washington, DC 20005 . . . 202-842-3660
Levine & Co: 228 Main St #5, Venice, CA 90291 . . . 310-399-9336
Levirne, Joel: 203 Mountain Ave, Hawthorne, NJ 07506 . . . 201-423-2277
Levy Design, David: 1801 Piedmont Ave #200, Atlanta, GA 30324 . . . 404-817-7049
Lewis Design: 875 Main St 5th Fl, Cambridge, MA 02139 . . . 617-661-7145
Lewis Group Inc, Hal: 1610 Chestnut St, Philadelphia, PA 19103 . . . 215-563-4461
Lexington Design Group: 2240 N Lexington St, Arlington, VA 22205 . . . 703-533-9163
LF Banks & Co: 834 chestnut St #425, Philadelphia, PA 19107 . . . 215-627-2855
Libby MacDonald Shear: 2 Stmfrd Lndng/68 Southfld Ave, Stamford, CT 06902 . . . 203-975-2500
Libby Perszyk Kathman: 19 Garfield Pl 5th fl, Cincinnati, OH 45202 . . . 513-241-6330
Libera Design Inc: 12020 W Pico Blvd, Los Angeles, CA 90064 . . . 310-477-9336
Lieber/Brewster Design: 19 W 34th St #618, New York, NY 10001 . . . 212-459-9099
Lieberman, Ron: 109 W 28th St, New York, NY 10001 . . . 212-947-0653
Liebert, Bob: 16 W 46th St, New York, NY 10036 . . . 212-840-1350
Liew Design: 200 Blossom Ln 3rd Fl, Mountain View, CA 94041 . . . 415-962-8103
Lifetime Media: 352 Seventh Ave 12th Fl, New York, NY 10001 . . . 212-684-1900
Ligasan Design Assocs: 422 E 77th St #5W, New York, NY 10016 . . . 212-737-4393
Light Intertainment Corp: 225 Santa Monica Blvd #310, Santa Monica, CA 90401 . . . 310-394-8729
Lighthouse Media: 2880 Lakeside Dr #331, Santa Clara, CA 95054 . . . 408-727-8500
Lika Assocs, Inc: 160 E 38th St #30G, New York, NY 10016 . . . 212-490-3660
Lindroth Inc, David: 85 Broadway, W Milford, NJ 07480 . . . 201-697-1965
Linschoten Assocs, Inc: 60 N Berethania St #2709, Honolulu, HI 96817 . . . 808-521-9852
Linsky Design, Clark: 201 Main St, Charlestown, MA 21202 . . . 617-241-7600
Lion & Assocs: 1133 Pamela Rd, Cincinnati, OH 45255 . . .
Lionetti Design, Frank C: 3 Ledge Rd, Old Greenwich, CT 06870 . . . 203-637-4152
Lipman, Hearne: 303 E Wacker Dr #1030, Chicago, IL 60601 . . . 312-946-1900
Lippert, Kevin: 37 E Seventh St, New York, NY 10003 . . . 212-995-8494
Lippincott & Margulies, Inc: 499 Park Ave, New York, NY 10022 . . . 212-832-3000
Lipson Alport Glass & Assocs: 666 Dundee Rd #103 , Northbrook, IL 60062 . . . 847-291-0500
Lipson Assocs, Inc: 2349 Victory Pkwy, Cincinnati, OH 45206 . . . 513-961-6225
Liquid Thought: 780 S Federal #1201, Chicago, IL 60605 . . . 312-409-2622
Lisboa, Michael: 235 South 15th St #204, Philadelphia, PA 19102 . . . 215-985-5812
Liska & Assoc: 521 W 26th St #604, New York, NY 10001 . . . 212-627-3200
Listenberger Design: 1455 N Pennsylvania, Indianapolis, IN 46202 . . . 317-634-5106
Lister Butler Assocs: 475 Fifth Ave 7th Fl, New York, NY 10017 . . . 212-951-6100
Little & Co, Inc: 1201 Marquette Ave S, Minneapolis, MN 55403 . . . 612-375-0077
Little Apple Art: 409 Sixth Ave, Brooklyn, NY 11215 . . . 718-499-7045
Little Hill Design: 300 Brannan St #309B, San Francisco, CA 94107 . . . 415-495-2053
Little Men Studios: 17 Highland Ave, Redding, CT 06896 . . . 203-544-8708
Littlefeild & Co: 39 W 29th St 11th Fl, New York, NY 10001 . . . 212-684-2046
Lively & Assocs, Inc: 4821 N O'Connor Rd #350, Dallas, TX 75062 . . . 214-871-0780
Lizak, Matt: Blackplain Rd RD #1, N Smithfield, RI 02895 . . . 401-766-8885
Lizmar: 3981 Lonesome Pine Rd, Redwood City, CA 94061 . . . 415-364-6452
Lizotte Graphics: PO Box 1738, Concord, NH 03302 . . . 603-783-9585
LKT: 4401 San Leandro St #38, Oakland, CA 94601 . . . 510-532-9213
LO River Arts: 47 Newark St, Hoboken, NJ 07030 . . . 201-216-1613
Loftus Design, Kerry: 48 Elm St, Stoneham, MA 02180 . . . 617-279-1055
Logan Design Inc, Rebecca: 125 W Nelson St, Lexington, VA 24450 . . . 540-463-1120
Logan Design, Polivka: 411 N Wahington Ave #101, Minneapolis, MN 55401 . . . 612-672-9495
Logos Studios: 8611 Whippoorwill Ln, Parma, OH 44130 . . . 216-888-7870
Logowitz & Co: 129 South St, Boston, MA 02111 . . . 617-451-3370
Lohman Assocs: 233 E Wacker Dr #311, Chicago, IL 60601 . . . 312-565-4473
Lohmeier, Michael: 259 Broad St, Portsmouth, NH 03801 . . . 603-431-1863
Lombardi Art Direction & Grphc Dsgn: 1316 Third St Mall, Santa Monica, CA 90401 . . . 213-458-3531
Lonczak Design, John: 14 Park Pl, Newburg, NY 12550 . . . 212-274-8493
Loneys Graphics: 2674 N 1st St #206, San Jose, CA 95134 . . . 408-955-9527
Long Design Assocs: 14 Washington Rd, Princeton Junct, NJ 08550 . . . 609-799-5551
Longhurst Design, Elizabeth: 1846 Berkeley Ave, St Paul, MN 55105 . . . 612-690-0235
Lonier Assocs: 111 Plains Rd Box 190, New Paltz, NY 12561 . . . 914-255-7165
Lonz Photography, Bob: 431 Park St, York, PA 17404 . . . 717-845-3740
Looking: 660 South Ave 21 #5, Los Angeles, CA 90031 . . . 213-227-1450
Loose Design, Dave: 620 E Oregon Rd, Lititz, PA 17543 . . . 717-569-6568
Lopez Design, Dick: 200 E 78th St #19E, New York, NY 10021 . . . 212-988-3850
Lopez Needleman Design: 1529 Louisville Ave, St Louis, MO 63139 . . . 314-647-6308
Lord Design, Marcia: 91 Clifford St, Cambridge, MA 02140 . . . 617-492-7028
Lorence Design: 724 Longleaf Dr NE, Atlanta, GA 30342 . . . 404-266-2711
Losch Design, Juile: 134 Charles St, New York, NY 10014 . . . 212-929-2547
Lose Design: 533 W Hortter St, Philadelphia, PA 19119 . . . 215-849-7635
Lose, Hal: 533 W Hortter St Toad Hall, Philadelphia, PA 19119 . . . 215-849-7635
Loturco Ind Design Inc, Raymond A: 11506 W Youth Camp Rd, Columbus, IN 47201 . . . 812-342-4995
Louey/Rubino Design Group: 2525 Main St #204, Santa Monica, CA 90405 . . . 310-396-7724
Louie Design, Lorraine: 80 Varick St #3B, New York, NY 10013 . . . 212-941-7329
Louie, Lisa: PO Box 4112, Foster City, CA 94404 . . . 415-341-1525
Love Graphic Design, Sara: 2188 N Capital, Inianapolis, IN 46202 . . . 317-925-3275
Love, Robin: 628 Broadway 4th Fl, New York, NY 10012 . . . 212-777-3113
Lovelace Design, Tom: One Allentown Pkwy, Allen, TX 75002 . . . 903-364-2866

Loveless Design, JR: 31454 Montgomery Ave, Nuevo, CA 92567 . . . 909-928-0763
Lowe Runkle Co: 301 NW 63rd St #590, Oklahoma City, OK 73116 . . . 405-848-6800
Lowry & Assocs: PMB 116 7 Avenida Vista Grande B7, Santa Fe, NM 87505 . . . 505-466-2920
Lubell, Robert: 2946 E Lincolnshire, Toledo, OH 43606 . . . 419-531-2267
Lubell/Brodsky Graphics: 21 E 40th St #1806, New York, NY 10016 . . . 212-684-2600
Luby & Co, Jodi: 808 Broadway, New York, NY 10003 . . . 212-473-1922
Lucas Art & Design: 5763 Ada Dr SE, Grand Rapids, MI 49546 . . . 616-676-2771
Luciano Creative: 30 Brookside Dr, Greenwich, CT 06830 . . . 203-629-8044
Luebbers & Dundom: 8616 Germantown Ave 2nd Fl Rear, Philadelphia, PA 19118 . . . 215-567-2360
Lukasiewicz Design, Inc: 119 W 57th St, New York, NY 10019 . . . 212-581-3344
Lum Design, Winni: 1736 Stockson St #6, San Francisco, CA 94133 . . . 415-399-8882
Luma Design: 500 Commercial St Ste 302A, Manchester, NH 03101 . . . 603-641-5176
Lumel Design, Inc: 12517 Chandler Blvd #101, N Hollywood, CA 91607 . . . 818-769-5332
Lundgren Graphics, Ray: 1133 Broadway #608, New York, NY 10010 . . . 212-255-0713
Lundgren, Alvalyn: 5530 Tanoak Lane #284, Agoura, CA 91301 . . . 818-707-0635
Lundquist Design: 147 W 24th St 4th Fl, New York, NY 10011 . . . 212-366-4373
Lusignan Design: 145 Fourth Ave #5K, New York, NY 10003 . . . 212-533-2181
Lussier, Mark: 38 Cove Ave, E Norwalk, CT 06855 . . . 203-852-0363
Luxon Carra: 649 Front St, San Francisco, CA 94111 . . . 415-981-1492
Luxuria & Apparatus: 99 Atlantic Ave #410, Toronto, ON M6K 3J8 . . . 416-538-8352
Luzuriaga, Denis: 39 Hamilton Terr, New York, NY 10031 . . . 212-283-3401
Luzzi Ltd: 19 W 21st St 10th Fl, New York, NY 10010 . . . 212-255-4953
LVB Design, Inc: 834 Griegos NW #2, Albuquerque, NM 87107 . . . 505-345-7447
Lvr Graphic Design & Prod: 77 Leehigh Dr, Lincroft, NJ 07738 . . . 908-758-9588
Lynas, Gerald: 233 W 83rd St #4A, New York, NY 10024 . . . 212-799-0675
Lynch Studios: 123-50 146th St, S Ozone Park, NY 11436 . . . 718-322-4752
Lynch, David: 8800 Venice Blvd #216, Los Angeles, CA 90034 . . . 310-287-0440
Lyndon Design: 31 Ripley St, Newton Centre, MA 02159 . . . 617-244-6192
Lyons, Jonathan Lee: 2302 W Indianhead Dr, Tallahassee, FL 32301 . . . 850-942-9442
Lyons, Lisa: 9 Deane St, Gardiner, ME 04345 . . . 207-582-1602
Lytle, Dana: 605 Williamson St, Madison, WI 53703 . . . 608-256-0000
Lyzak Design, Matt: 849 Black Plain Rd, N Smithfield, RI 02896 . . . 401-769-7619

M

M & Co: 225 Lafayette St #904, New York, NY 10012 . . . 212-348-2408
M & M Design: 6789 Wales Ave NW, N canton, OH 44720 . . . 330-494-2263
M Group: 2512 E Thomas Rd #7, Phoenix, AZ 85016 . . . 602-957-7557
M Space: 56 Meadow Lane, Katonah, NY 10536 . . . 914-232-8593
M2 Design: 545 Fifth Ave 8th Fl, New York, NY 10017 . . . 212-687-4000
M2 Unit: 33 W17th St 9th Fl, New York, NY 10011 . . . 212-627-5376
Mabry Design, Michael: 212 Sutter St, San Francisco, CA 94108 . . . 415-982-7336
Mac Art Direction: 7100 Sunnyslope Ave, Van Nuys, CA 91405 . . . 818-764-6222
MAC Media: The Media Center 2955 Village Dr Box 774328, Steamboat Springs, CO 80477 . 970-879-5250
Macal Design, Joseph: 20 W 20th #701, New York, NY 10011 . . . 212-255-9120
Machado Design: 43353 Mission Blvd #B, Fremont, CA 94539 . . . 510-770-8817
Machlica Creative: 1501 S Garfield, Denver, CO 80210 . . . 303-759-0175
Machura Design Inc, Raymond: 307 N Michigan Ave #1013, Chicago, IL 60601 . . . 312-346-4196
MacIntosh, Rob: 60 State St, Boston, MA 02109 . . . 617-742-9100
MacKenzie-Smith, Gail: 4758 Forman Ave #14, Toluca Lake, CA 91602 . . .
Mackerel & Assocs: 1736 Braddock Ct, San Jose, CA 95125 . . . 408-559-1020
Mackin & Dowd Design, Inc: 3110 Juneau Place, Baltimore, MD 21214 . . . 410-426-8010
Maclay & Shoemaker Graphics: 375 Highland Dr, Mountville, PA 17554 . . . 717-285-4042
MAD: PO Box 190, Sausalito, CA 94956 . . . 415-331-1023
Mad : 237 San Carlos Ave, Sausalito, CA 94965 . . . 415-331-1023
Mad Kat Studio, Inc: 12 Lakeview Ave W, Cortlandt Manor, NY 10566 . . . 914-736-0660
Maddocks & Co: 2011 Pontius Ave, Los Angeles, CA 90025 . . . 310-477-4227
Maddox Assoc, Eva: 300 W Hubbard #201, Chicago, IL 60610 . . . 312-670-0092
Mader & Assocs, Ted: 2562 Dexter Ave N, Seattle, WA 98109 . . . 206-270-9360
Madison Group/Y & R: 285 Madison Ave 18th Fl, New York, NY 10017 . . . 212-210-3700
Madridejos, Fernando: 130 W 67th St #1B, New York, NY 10023 . . . 212-724-7339
Madsen Co: 314 E 41st St #703B, New York, NY 10017 . . . 212-297-1815
Madson & Huth: 1004 Olde Oneida St, Appleton, WI 54915 . . . 414-731-5787
Maesteri: 217 Pine St 12th Fl, Seattle, WA 98101 . . . 206-622-4322
Magazine Group: 1707 L St NW #350, Washington, DC 20036 . . . 202-331-7700
Maggio Assocs Inc, Ben: 305 E 46th St 17th Fl, New York, NY 10017 . . . 212-838-8791
Maggio Design Assocs Inc, JP: 561 Broadway, New York, NY 10012 . . . 212-725-9660
Magi Group: 2459 152nd Ave NE, Redmond, WA 98052 . . . 206-869-5411
Maglio, Mark: PO Box 872, Plainville, CT 06062 . . . 203-793-0771
Magna Graphics: 2230 Park Ave, Cincinnati, OH 45206 . . . 513-221-2230
Magnet Creative: 1229 S Washington, Royal Oak, MI 48067 . . . 810-548-3038
Magnet Interactive Studio, Inc: 3255 Grace St NW, Washington, DC 20007 . . . 202-625-1111
Mahan Graphics, Michael: PO Box 642, Bath, ME 04530 . . . 207-443-6110
Mahoney, Carol: 19 Juniper Rd, Norwalk, CT 06853 . . . 203-853-2787
Main St Interactive Multimedia: 3005 Main St #419, Santa Monica, CA 90405 . . . 310-625-1111
• **Maisner, Bernard: pg 924,925** 108 E 35th St, New York, NY 10016 . . . **212-889-3337**
e-mail: gerald@rappart.com / url: www.theispot.com/artist/ / fax: 212-889-3341
Major Assocs: 6734 Charles Street Ave, Baltimore, MD 21204 . . . 410-825-5420
Makela, P Scott: 1221 N Woodward Ave #710, Bloomfield Hills, MI 48304 . . . 612-381-1297
Makon Design, Joy: 41 Fuller Place, Brooklyn, NY 11215 . . . 718-499-8370
Malavis Creative Services, Ellie: 4444 Westheimer #369, Houston, TX 77027 . . . 713-961-0665
Malish Design: 623 S 3rd St, Philadelphia, PA 19147 . . . 215-972-5340
Mallicoat Enterprises: 2269 Chestnut St #265, San Francisco, CA 94123 . . . 415-922-1587
Malone Design Works: 11350 Mcmorick Rd Exec Plz 1, Hunt Valley, MD 21031 . . . 410-584-9040
Man Bites Dog: 577 2nd St #101, San Francisco, CA 94107 . . . 415-356-8280
Mandle, James: 300 Forest Ave, Paramus, NJ 07652 . . . 201-967-7900
Manger & Assocs: Executive Plz One #901, Hunt Valley, MD 21031 . . . 410-785-4971
Mani Graphics: 303 S Paterson St #A, Madison, WI 53703 . . . 608-255-5300
Manning Studios, Inc: 613 Main St, Cincinnati, OH 45202 . . . 513-621-6959
Mannix Design: 95 Wisconsin St, Rochester, NY 14609 . . . 716-654-6721
Manwaring, Michael Office: 111 Crescent Rd, San Anselmo, CA 94960 . . . 415-421-3595
Manzo Finalborgo Assocs: 8 Jagger Ln, South Hampton, NY 11968 . . . 212-683-4405
Marc Rubin Design Assocs: 421 West Church St, Elmira, NY 14901 . . . 607-734-1058
March, Sue: 21 N Harrison Ave #302, Campbell, CA 95008 . . . 408-370-1788
Marcolina, Dan: 1100 E Hector St #400, Conshohocken, PA 19428 . . . 610-940-0680
Marcus & Assocs: 10000 N Central Expwy #1000, Dallas, TX 75231 . . . 214-987-2400
Marcus & Assocs Inc, Aaron: 1144 65th St #F, Emeryville, CA 94608 . . . 510-601-0994
Marcus, Sarna: 4450 Montgomery Ave #602N, Bethesda, MD 20814 . . . 301-951-7044
Marcy Design Group: 50 W Broad St #1903, Columbus, OH 43215 . . . 614-224-6226
Marietta Corp Design Group: 37 Huntington St, Cortland, NY 13045 . . . 800-431-3023
Marion Designs: 418 New W Townsend Rd, Lunenberg, MA 01462 . . . 508-345-4428
Marion Graphics: 2900 Weslayan #150, Houston, TX 77027 . . . 713-623-6444
Maritz Communication Co: 1515 W 190th St #300, Gardena, CA 90248 . . . 310-930-0955
Mark Design, Heather: 330 Hawthorne Rd, Green Oaks, IL 60048 . . . 847-367-9644
Mark Graphics, S: 1518 N Mohawk St, Chicago, IL 60010 . . . 312-573-1666
Market Force: 109 N Boylan Ave, Raleigh, NC 27603 . . . 919-828-7887
Market Street Group: 116 Market St, Lewisburg, PA 17837 . . . 717-524-2367
Market To Market: 3000 Gibbons Dr, Alameda, CA 94501 . . . 510-865-6136
Marketing Arts: Bridge St/Market Place, Waitsfield, VT 05673 . . . 802-496-4488
Marketing Arts: 1244 Canterbury Rd #304, Shakopee, MN 55379 . . . 612-496-2647
Marketing Creative Support Services: 813 Francis St, St Joseph, MO 64501 . . . 816-279-5869
Marketing Design Consultants: 1259 W Belden Ave, Chicago, IL 60614 . . . 773-404-5444
Marketing Design Group: 420 Walnut Ave, San Diego, CA 92103 . . . 619-298-1445
Marketing Out-Of-The-Box: 7200 Oak Park Ave, Niles, IL 60714 . . . 847-869-8250
Marketing Partners: 1109 Hinman Ave, Evanston, IL 60202 . . . 847-492-5180
Markofski & Assocs, Don: 106 W Lime Ave #200A, Monrovia, CA 91016 . . . 818-359-4248
Markone Visual Communiications: 2500 Camino Diablo #202, Walnut Creek, CA 94596 . 510-945-1414
Markos, Michael: 1118 Sixth St NE, Minneapolis, MN 55413 . . . 612-379-2133
Marks Communication: 2400 N Edgemont, Los Angeles, CA 90027 . . . 213-664-2864
Marks Designs, Terry: 91 1/2 Pine St #24, Seattle, WA 98101 . . . 206-628-6427
Marks, David: 726 Hillpine Dr NE, Atlanta, GA 30306 . . . 404-872-1824
Marks, Garson: N14W24 200 Tower Pl, Waukesha, WI 53188 . . . 414-523-3940
Markworks Graphic Design: 1623 Cravens Ave, Torrance, CA 90501 . . . 310-782-8121
Marquis Graphic Design Assocs: 1509 King St, Alexandria, VA 22314 . . . 703-519-7916
Marsh & Co: 34 W Sixth St #1100, Cincinnati, OH 45202 . . . 513-421-1234
Marshall , Alex: 810 E Gutierrez St #C, Santa Barbara, CA 93103 . . . 805-962-9854
Marshall Adv Design, Pat: 3325 m St NW, Washington, DC 20007 . . . 202-342-0222
Marshall Design & Assocs: 1109 Quail St, Newport Beach, CA 92660 . . . 714-756-0806
Marshall Design, June: 3234 Beechwood Blvd, Pittsburgh, PA 15217 . . . 412-521-2877
Marshall, Catherine: 56 Gloucester Rd #333, Kensington, London, England, UK SW7 4UB 1715-447485
Martin Design Group: 33 College Hill Rd #29C, Warwick, RI 02886 . . . 401-822-8530
Martin Design Inc, Lynn: 435 W North Ave, Chicago, IL 60610 . . . 312-787-3717
Martin Design, Virginia: 47 Beverley Rd, Upper Montclair, NJ 07043 . . . 201-744-6989
Martin Graphics: 8328 Shadyside Ave, Whittier, CA 90606 . . . 310-695-7675
Martin Scott, Bruce: 83 Sunken Meadow Rd, Ft Salonga, NY 11768 . . . 516-757-9593
Martin, Amy: 173 E 90th St #4D, New York, NY 10128 . . . 212-987-2395
Martin, Janet: 1112 Pearl, Boulder, CO 80302 . . . 303-442-8202
Martinez, Fernando: 1376 Bank St #202, Ottawa, ON K1H 7Y3 . . . 613-526-1795
Martucci, John: 116 Newbury St, Boston, MA 02116 . . . 617-266-6960
Marx Design: 751 Adobe Rd NW, Albuquerque, NM 87107 . . . 505-345-9171
Mascia Design: 155 E 31st #10A, New York, NY 10016 . . . 212-725-2630
Masi Design Consultants, Inc: 8908 SW Cemetery Rd, Vashon Island, WA 98070 . . . 206-463-6627
Masoff And Scolnik Design: 39 Fields Ln, N Salem, NY 10560 . . . 214-277-7722
Mason, Marlise: 22974 Twin Pines Rd, Bozman, MD 21612 . . . 410-745-6742
Mass Design, JoAnne: 326 Sixth Ave, Salt Lake City, UT 84310 . . .
MASSA Design: 115 Sawsome St #1250, San Francisco, CA 94104 . . . 415-543-5700
Master Graphics: PO Box 370247, Denver, CO 80237 . . . 303-694-0253
Mateka, Jerry: 172 Madison Ave #306, New York, NY 10016 . . . 212-984-3149
Mathew, Mathew K: 5801 Chinquapin Pkwy, Baltimore, MD 21239 . . . 410-433-0035
Matjasich & Assocs: 408 Bluebird Ln, Deerfield, IL 60015 . . . 847-541-0443
Matrix Graphic Design, Inc: 3350 Cork Oak Way, Palo Alto, CA 94303 . . . 415-852-9316
Matrix Int'l: 50 S Steele #875, Denver, CO 80209 . . . 303-388-9353
Matson Navigation: 333 Market St 3rd Fl/POB 7452, San Francisco, CA 94120 . . . 415-957-4534
Matsumoto Design: 220 W 19th St 9th Fl, New York, NY 10011 . . . 212-807-0248
Matt Designs: 40 Devoe Rd, Chappaqua, NY 10514 . . . 914-238-1082
Matthews, Robert: 1101 Boise Dr, Campbell, CA 95008 . . . 408-378-0878
Mattingly Design, George: 820 Miramar Ave, Berkeley, CA 94707 . . . 510-525-2098
Mauck & Assocs, Inc: 303 Locust St, Des Moines, IA 50309 . . . 515-243-6010
Mauk Design: 39 Stillman St, San Francisco, CA 94107 . . . 415-243-9277
Maurer Graphics, Glenn: 4014 Wexford Dr, Kensington, MD 20895 . . . 301-933-9527
Maurice Assocs, Paul: 138 Spring St 6th Fl, New York, NY 10012 . . . 212-925-4224
Max Graphics: 1820 Poplar Ave, Redwood City, CA 94061 . . . 415-322-2647
May & Co: 1600 Pacific Ave #1525, Dallas, TX 75201 . . . 214-528-4770
Maya Design Group: 2100 Wharton St, Pittsburg, PA 15203 . . . 412-488-2900
Mayeda, Scott: 1908 Wandering Rd, Encinitas, CA 92024 . . . 619-284-9692
Mayer Assocs, Gene: 9 Depot St 2nd Fl, Milford, CT 06460 . . . 203-882-5990
Mayfield Design: 616 Ramona St #1, Palo Alto, CA 94301 . . . 415-322-2647
McAlick, Michael: 209 Louis Ave #2L, South Bound Brook, NJ 08880 . . . 732-271-9329
Mcbee, Scott: 39 Hamilton Terr, New York, NY 10031 . . . 212-283-3401
McCall Assocs, Anthony: 11 Jay St, New York, NY 10013 . . . 212-925-5821
McCargar Design: 3906 Silverado Trail, Calistoga, CA 94515 . . . 707-942-2292
McCarthy Designs: 1851 Heritage Ln #281, Sacramento, CA 95815 . . . 916-927-7000
McCarthy, Sally: 38 Montvale Ave #225, Stoneham, MA 02180 . . . 781-438-8812
Mccauley Coren Design Grp: 150 Chestnut St, Providence, RI 02903 . . . 401-831-1290
McCausland Design & Comm: 108-110 Kenwood Dr/POB 191, Belmont, NC 28012 . . . 704-825-0665
McChesney Design: 122 Madison, San Antonio, TX 78204 . . . 210-227-0225
McChesney Design: 8 Laurel Way, old Saybrook, CT 06475 . . . 860-388-2349
McClanahan Graphics, Inc: 405 West Searcy St, Heber Springs, AR 72543 . . . 501-362-4038
McCord Graphic Design: 2014 Cherokee Pkwy #O, Louisville, KY 40204 . . . 502-451-0383
McCord, David: 3890 Potters Rd, Ionia, MI 48846 . . . 800-997-9913
McCoy & McCoy Assocs: PO Box 2001, Buena Vista, CO 81211 . . . 719-395-4036
McCulley Group, The: 415 S Cedros Ave #240, Solana Beach, CA 92075 . . . 619-236-8700
McCulley, Mike: 4041 Bosque Dr, Plano, TX 75074 . . . 214-423-0703
Mccullough Design: 15 Lakeridge Dr, Marlborough, CT 06447 . . . 860-295-8145
McDill Assocs: 2901 San Jose Rd Box 100, Soquel, CA 95073 . . . 408-462-3198
McDonald Design, Daniel: 623 Carroll St, Brooklyn, NY 11215 . . . 718-783-9757
McDonald Design, Jim: 5703 E Evans Dr, Scottsdale, AZ 85254 . . . 602-494-0747
McDonough & Co: 40 Lowell St #21, Peabody, MA 01960 . . . 508-532-5959
McElligott, Fallow: 79 Fifth Ave 14th Fl, New York, NY 10003 . . . 212-206-7900
McGrath Design, Michael: 17815 Windflower Way #107, Dallas, TX 75252 . . . 214-644-4358
McGuire Design, Robert L: 7943 Campbell, Kansas City, MO 64131 . . . 816-523-9164
McGurren Weber Ink: 705 King St 3rd Fl, Alexandria, VA 22314 . . . 703-548-0003
McHorney Marketing: 4725 E Cholla, Phoenix, AZ 85258 . . . 602-953-9768
McKee Design, Inc: 1415 Trestle Glen Rd, Oakland, CA 94610 . . . 510-893-6933
McKiernan Studio: 3591 Long Beach Blvd, Long Beach, CA 90807 . . . 310-426-1888
McLaughlin, Kim: 921 SW Morrison #530, Portland, OR 97205 . . . 503-225-9957
McLuckie Design Assocs: 74 Old Hart Rd, Barrington, IL 60010 . . . 847-382-8111

McMichael Design, Scott: 247 Claremont Ave, Montclair, NJ 07042 201-746-9709
McMillan Assocs: 130 Washington St, West Dundee, IL 60118 847-426-3500
McMillin Giacalone Thompson: 12 New Providence Rd, Watchung, NJ 07060 908-322-7707
McNall Adv & Design: 739 E Walnut St #200, Pasadena, CA 91101 818-796-0495
Mcnally Temple, Inc: 1817 Capital Ave #A, Sacramento, CA 95814 916-447-8186
McNamee Group, Inc: 39-19 45th St, Sunnyside, NY 11104 718-784-4373
McNeir, Kyle A: 2902 Galt Pl, Kennesaw, GA 30144 770-419-9901
Mcwilliams Assocs, George: 600 Montgomery St 27th Fl, San Francisco, CA 94111 415-983-4195
MDB Communications, Inc: 932 Hungerford Dr Bldg 24, Rockville, MD 20850 301-762-4474
Mdg Design Group: 236 Hamilton Ave, Palo Alto, CA 94301 415-322-5696
Me Myself & I, Inc: 150 S 600 East #8C, Salt Lake City, UT 84102 801-322-0665
Meadows & Fowler, R: 2200 Lakeshore Dr, Birmingham, AL 35209 205-870-5211
• **Mecca Studios: pg 928,929** 166 Fifth Ave, New York, NY 10010 .... **212-633-1999**
e-mail: info@meccastudios.com / url: www.meccastudios.com
Medechi Design, Inc: 480 Canal St 6th Fl, New York, NY 10013 212-941-9111
Media Concepts: 25 N Main St, Assonet, MA 02702 617-437-1382
Media Direct: PO Box 302, Tenafly, NJ 07670 201-894-5548
Media Five Ltd, Inc: 345 Queen St 9th Fl, Honolulu, HI 96813 808-524-2040
Media Loft: 333 Washington Ave N #210, Minneapolis, MN 55401 612-375-1086
Media Mix: 3898 Filion St, Los Angeles, CA 90065 213-344-3714
Media of the Minds: 701 Minnesota St #202, San Francisco, CA 94107 415-201-1179
Media Process Group: 770 N Halstead St #507, Chicago, IL 60622 312-850-1300
Media Services Corp: 10 Aladdin Ter, San Francisco, CA 94133 415-928-3033
Media Shop: 158 Elm St #2, Cambridge, MA 02140 ....
Media Studio, Inc: 1115 Erie St, Oak Park, IL 60302 708-386-7562
Media Wave Resources: 215 W 91st St #57, New York, NY 10024 212-787-0700
MediaDesign International: PO Box 731, Redondo Beach, CA 90277 310-798-3668
MediaFour, Inc: 7638 Trail Run Rd, Falls Church, VA 22042 703-573-6117
MediaSense: 383 Arkansas St, San Francisco, CA 94107 415-285-7655
MegaMedia, Inc: 137 S Easton Rd, Glenside, PA 19038 215-576-7050
Melanson Assocs, Donya: 437 Main St, Charlestown, MA 02129 617-241-7300
Melia Design Group: 905 Berninia Ave, Atlanta, GA 30307 404-659-5584
Mellish Creative Svrcs, David: 5020 Rosario Ave, Atascadero, CA 93422 805-462-1104
Melone Adv & Graphic Design: 615 First St, Canonsburg, PA 15317 412-746-5165
Melone, Michael: RD 3 Box 123, Canonsburg, PA 15317 412-746-5165
Menasha Corparte Art Center: N83 W13280 Leon Rd, Menomonee Falls, WI 53051 414-253-8681
Mendez, Nancy: 9816 Rosensteel Ave, Silver Spring, MD 20910 301-608-8075
Menghan, Patti: 665 Third St, San Francisco, CA 94107 415-243-8244
Mentken, Robert: 51 E 97th St, New York, NY 10029 212-534-5101
Mentler & Co: 4819 Broadway, Dallas, TX 75248 214-233-1414
Mentus Incorporated: 8910 University Cntr Ln #750, San Diego, CA 92122 619-455-5500
Mercer Design: 6730 El Carmen, Long Beach, CA 90815 310-431-5974
Mercury Creative Services: 825 Eighth Ave 26th Fl, New York, NY 10019 212-603-7901
Mercury Int'l Corp: 19 Alice Agnew Dr Box 222, N Attleboro, MA 02761 508-699-9000
Meridian Creative Group: 5178 Station Rd, Erie, PA 16510 814-898-2612
Merrifield Communications: 233 E Wacker Dr #4003, Chicago, IL 60601 ....
Merrill Design, David: 4 N Pasture Rd, Westport, CT 06880 203-222-1781
Merrill, John: 123 Albany Shaker Rd, Albany, NY 12211 518-447-5660
Merry Men Design: 13 Water St, Holliston, MA 01746 508-429-0755
Merten Design Group: 3235 F Second Ave, Denver, CO 80206 303-322-1451
Mervil Paylor Design: 1917 Lennox Ave, Charlotte, NC 28203 704-375-4435
Mesmerize: 701 Santa Monica Blvd #300, Santa Monica, CA 90401 310-656-1200
Messing & Assocs: Viamonte 640 4th Fl, Buenos Aires, Argntn, ... 541-322-6948
Meta Design: 350 Pacific Ave, San Francisco, CA 94111 415-627-0790
Meta-4: 311 W superior #504, Chicago, IL 60610 312-337-4674
Metafor Imaging, Inc: 3962 Ince, Culver City, CA 90232 310-287-3777
Metagraphics: 43-27 222 St, Bayside, NY 11361 718-428-2718
Metal Studio, Inc: 1210 W Clay #13, Houston, TX 77019 713-523-5777
Metropolis Dsgn & Adv: 167 Cherry St #453, Milford, CT 06460 203-878-2600
Meyer, Bonnie: 259 Collignon Way #2A, River Vale, NJ 07675 201-666-5763
Meyers Design, Ann: 24 Fifth Ave #1201, New York, NY 10011 212-995-8340
Meyrowitz Design, Randy: 9404 Fox Hollow Dr, Potomac, MD 20854 301-299-2923
MG Design: 3 Forest Ln, Canton, CT 06019 860-693-1186
MGK Design: 20 Roe Ave, East Patchogue, NY 11772 516-475-8661
MH Segan & Co: 18 E 16th St, New York, NY 10003 212-741-0002
Michaelis Carpelis Design: 60 E 42nd St #1730, New York, NY 10165 212-867-8190
Micolucci Design Assocs: 515 Shoemaker Rd, King Of Prussia, PA 19406 610-265-3320
MicroColor, Inc: 2345 Broadway #638, New York, NY 10024 212-787-0500
Middleton Design: 1200 South Church St #10, Mt Laurel, NJ 08054 609-722-1411
Middleton Design, David: 4536 N Sacramento Ave, Chicago, IL 60625 773-463-4690
Mig Design Works: 800 First Ave, Berkeley, CA 94710 510-849-0560
Mihaesteanu, Lucian: 39 Hamilton Terr, New York, NY 10031 212-283-3401
Miho Co: 1045 Fifth Ave, New York, NY 10028 212-288-2070
Mikell, Don: 9909 Highway 36 E, Lacey's Spring, AL 35754 205-880-7435
Milan Concept & Design, Inc: 26 Lawrence Dr, Groton, MA 01450 508-448-3958
Miles Fridberg Molinaroli: 4401 Connecticut Ave NW #701, Washington, DC 20008 202-966-7700
Mill Race Studio: Durham Rd/Brick House Opp Po, Durham, PA 18039 610-346-8117
Miller & Assocs, Bob: 1831 V St, Sacramento, CA 95814 916-448-3878
Miller & White Adv: 328 S 5th St, Terre Haute, IN 47807 812-232-2875
Miller Assocs: 361 Forest Ave #202, Laguna Beach, CA 92651 714-497-2384
Miller Brooks Assocs: 11712 N Michigan Rd, Zionzville, IN 46077 317-873-8100
Miller Design, Victoria: 10650 Kinnard Ave #311, Los Angeles, CA 90024 310-473-3489
Miller Designs, Inc, Randy: 4137-A South Harbor, Tulsa, OK 74135 918-744-9621
Miller Designworks: 200 Lincoln Ave #230, Phoenixville, PA 19460 610-917-0100
Miller, Edward: 231 Willow Ave #1L, Hoboken, NJ 07030 201-420-6457
Miller-Hobbs, Nancy: 474 Marine St, Boulder, CO 80302 303-444-5508
Miller/Zell Design Center: 4715 Frederick Dr SW, Atlanta, GA 30336 404-691-7400
Mills Design: 4400 Chippewa Dr, Boulder, CO 80303 303-494-2109
Millyard Design Assocs, Ltd: 6 Claybrook Rd, Dover, MA 02030 508-785-9843
Milwaukee Design: 735 Wyenel Dr, Elm Grove, WI 53122 414-797-9420
Mind of the Machine: 41 Tamara Dr, Roosevelt, NJ 08555 609-448-5036
Mind's Eye Design: 11666 Goshen Ave, Brentwood, CA 90049 310-444-7387
Minkus & Assocs: 100 Chetwynd Dr #200, Rosemont, PA 19010 610-525-6769
Mint Visual Comm: 927 Rose Ave, Oakland, CA 94611 510-601-8188
Mirenburg, Barry L: 301 E 38th St, New York, NY 10016 212-573-9200
Mires Design Inc: San Diego, CA 619-234-6631
Mirror Ball Studios: 707 N Lincoln St, Arlington, VA 22201 703-243-5335
Miska, John: 192 E Wallings Rd, Cleveland, OH 44147 216-526-0464
Mistretta, Tony: 223 W Erie St #5EC, Chicago, IL 60610 312-751-4005
Mitchell & Co: 11221 Riverview Dr, Potomac, MD 20854 301-765-0979
Mitchell & Witchell: 1101 Stinson Blvd NE, Minneapolis, MN 55413 612-379-1649
Mitchell Design, Dean: 10219 Caminito Pitaya, San Diego, CA 92131 858-566-1032
Mitchell Design, Inc: 1199 Yorkshire Dr, Cupertino, CA 95014 408-257-8291
Mitchell Design/CA: 728 Emerson, Palo Alto, CA 94301 415-463-1938
Mitchell Studios Dsgn Cnsltnts: 1111 Fordham Ln, Woodmere, NY 11598 516-374-5620
Mitten Design: 604 Mission St #820, San Francisco, CA 94105 415-896-5386
Mittlemam/Robinson: 3 W 18th St 2nd Fl, New York, NY 10011 212-627-5050
Mixit Productions: 465 Washington St, New York, NY 10013 212-966-4910
Miyasaki Assocs: 291 E Pondarosa Ln, Anaheim, CA 92802 714-750-9610
Miyawaki Creative: 1201 1st Ave S #326, Seattle, WA 98134 206-587-6530
Mize Advertising Art, Charles E: 633 Battery St #200, San Francisco, CA 94111 415-421-1548
Mizerek Design: 318 Lexington Ave 2nd Fl, New York, NY 10016 212-689-4885
Mizrahi, Robert: 6256 San Harco Cir, Buena Park, CA 90620 714-527-6182
MJH Design: 1839 rustic Oak, Chesterfield, MO 63017 314-532-5127
Mkr Design: 250 W Broadway, New York, NY 10013 212-343-8611
Mlawer, Barbara: 477 Roy St, W Hempstead, NY 11552 516-564-1193
MLH Communications Group: 51 Madison Ave #1201, New York, NY 10010 212-576-5916
Mlodock Hansen: 350 W Ontario #601, Chicago, IL 60610 312-943-1800
MM Design 2000: 20 W 20th St 4th Fl, New York, NY 10011 212-206-0323
Mobium: 200 World Trade Center #2000, Chicago, IL 60654 312-527-0500
Mobium Corp: 200 World Trade Ctr, Chicago, IL 60654 ....
Mobius Design Assocs: 715 Broadway #320, Santa Monica, CA 90401 310-458-9458
Mock Design Assocs Inc, Mark: 1738 Wynkoop St #303, Denver, CO 80202 303-292-0801
Modern Media Ventures: 1317 Hyde St, San Francisco, CA 49109 415-928-7564
Moderns, The: 900 Broadway #903, New York, NY 10003 212-387-8852
Modino, Maureen: 225 Lafayette St #511, New York, NY 10012 212-431-4354
Modular Graphic Services, Inc: 621 N Fourth St, Wilmington, NC 28403 910-791-1441
Modus Exhibit Group: 1011 W 2610 S, Salt Lake City, UT 84119 801-531-7775
Modus Interactive: 5101 Wisconsin Ave NW #302, Washington, DC 20016 202-537-0323
Moewe, Thomas: 4613 Philips Hwy #204, Jacksonville, FL 32207 904-778-8568
Mok Designs, Clement: 600 Townsend St PH, San Francisco, CA 94103 415-703-9900
Molecular Design Ltd: 5347 Lenore Ave, Livermore, CA 94550 510-373-9952
Mollica Design: 850 3rd Ave 11th Fl, New York, NY 10011 212-508-3446
Molten Cube Graphics and Sound: 4647 Bloomsbury Dr, Syracuse, NY 13215 315-469-3317
Mom & Pop Web Services: 6503 38th NE, Seattle, WA 98116 206-528-5676
Monaco Viola, Inc: 351 W Hubbard #602, Chicago, IL 60610 312-245-7400
Monderer Design, Stewart: 10 Thacher St #112, Boston, MA 02113 617-720-5555
Monigle & Assocs Inc, Glenn: 150 Adams, Denver, CO 80206 303-388-9358
Monkeyhouse Design: 5430 LBJ Freeman #1100, Dallas, TX 75240 972-776-8066
Monnens Addis Design: 2515 9th St, Berkeley, CA 94710 510-704-7500
Monogram Group, The: 205 W Wacker #900, Chicago, IL 60606 312-726-4300
Monroe Creative Partners: 1435 Walnut St #600, Philadelphia, PA 19102 215-563-8080
Montano Solaria: 1499 Blake St #1-I, Denver, CO 80202 303-825-3300
Montiero Design: 3 Winslow St, Plymouth, MA 02360 808-747-6236
Moonink, Inc: 205 N Michigan Ave #1300, Chicago, IL 60601 312-565-0040
Moore & Assocs: 7 Riedesel Ave, Cambridge, MA 02138 617-497-1277
Moore & Price Design Group, Inc: 163 Everett Ave, Palo Alto, CA 94301 415-322-9796
Moore Design, Inc, Dave: 3232 E Campbell, Phoenix, AZ 85018 602-955-0775
Moore Design, Julie: 535 Ramona St #33, Palo Alto, CA 94301 650-323-9297
Moorhead Design: 116A Research Dr, Milford, CT 06460 203-874-6441
Morales Adv & Design, Frank: 12770 Coit Rd #905, Dallas, TX 75251 214-233-0667
Moran Design Corp: 438 Fayette St, Hammond, IN 46240 219-931-2825
Moran, Jeffrey: 1596 Glasco Tpke, Woodstock, NY 12498 914-679-8065
Morava Oliver Berte: 2054 Broadway, Santa Monica, CA 90404 310-453-3523
Moravick, Don: 229 W Illinois St 5th Fl, Chicago, IL 60610 312-645-4500
Morey & Waddell: 8440 Woodfield Crossing Blvd #550, Indianapolis, IN 46240 317-469-2222
Morgan & Co: 340 E Palm Ln #120, Phoenix, AZ 85004 602-256-0036
Morgan Interactive: 450 Mission St #5, San Francisco, CA 94105 415-693-9506
Morgan-Burchette Assocs: 6935 Arlington Rd, Bethesda, MD 20814 703-549-2393
Morgenstern, Andrea: 8841 Ashcroft Ave, W Hollywood, CA 90048 310-288-0575
Mori & Kei Designs: 30 E 20th St #202, New York, NY 10002 212-260-2328
Moriber & Company: 420 Lexington Ave #2034, New York, NY 10170 212-599-2277
Morla Design: 463 Bryant St, San Francisco, CA 94107 415-543-6548
Morris Design Assocs, David: 66 York St, Jersey City, NJ 07302 201-434-7797
Morris Design, Alan: 0074 Sunset Dr #2A, Basalt, CO 81621 970-927-8838
Morris Design, Don: 106 E 19th St 8th Fl, New York, NY 10003 212-228-3364
Morris, Carroll: 6323 Mill Point Cir, Dallas, TX 75248 214-931-5762
Morris/Stylism, Dean: 307 E 6th St #4B, New York, NY 10003 212-420-0673
Morrow, Michael: 5508 Dorset Shoals Rd, Douglasville, GA 30135 770-949-2745
Mortensen Design: 416 Bush St, Mountain View, CA 94041 415-988-0946
Mortier, R Shamms: Rocky Dale, Bristol, VT 05443 802-453-4293
Morvil Design, Inc: 3803 Wrightsville Ave #11, Wilmington, NC 28403 910-791-1441
Mosaic Creative: 2702 McKinney Ave #203, Dallas, TX 75204 214-943-6913
Mosaic Design: 38 Montvale Ave #225, Stoneham, MA 02180 617-438-8812
Moser Design Group, Inc: 153 South State St, Hampshire, IL 60140 847-683-7080
Moshier, Harry: 15 E 12th St 2nd Fl, New York, NY 10003 212-645-7554
Moskof & Assocs: 928 Broadway #807, New York, NY 10010 212-473-1707
Moss Hartman: 3013 Washington Blvd, Marina del Ray, CA 90292 310-306-3605
Moss, John C: 4805 Bayard Blvd, Chevy Chase, MD 20816 301-320-3912
Mossberg Design, Stuart: 11 W 73rd St, New York, NY 10023 212-873-6130
Mosseau Graphic Design: 202 Ardsley Dr, Dewitt, NY 13214 315-446-4699
Mossman Assocs: 1600 NW 2nd Ave #14, Baton Raton, FL 33432 407-368-5668
Mosswarner Comms, Inc: 56 Arbor St, Hartford, CT 06106 203-233-5641
Moulton Assocs: 17 Harding Ave, Falmouth, ME 04105 207-781-5243
Mountain Adv, Patrick: 59 N Santa Cruz Ave #M, Los Gatos, CA 95030 408-395-0017
Moving Graphics: 2276 S Beverly Glen Blvd #108, Los Angeles, CA 90064 310-286-0969
Mozdren, Jim: 1121 E Main St #150, St Charles, IL 60174 630-513-555
MPC: 4 W 20th St, New York, NY 10011 212-463-8585
Mraz Design, Anderson: 103 E 1st Ave, Spokane, WA 99202 509-624-4029
Mrk&R: 1940 Fifth Ave, Pittsburgh, PA 15219 412-471-2323
Muccino Design Group: 448 S Market St, San Jose, CA 95113 408-993-1870
Mueller & Wister Studio: 801 E Germantown Pike #J-4, Morristown, PA 19401 610-278-7260
Muhlhausen Design, John: 1146 Green St, Roswell, GA 30075 770-642-1146
Muller & Co: 4739 Belleview Ave, Kansas City, MO 64112 816-531-1992
Muller Design: 1124 De Haro St #700, San Francisco, CA 94107 415-642-9481
Muller-Munk Assocs, Peter: 501 Martindale St, Pittsburgh, PA 15212 412-323-2992
Mulligan, Donald: 418 Central Park W #81, New York, NY 10025 212-666-6079
Multimedia Business Presentations: 4350 17th St, San Francisco, CA 94114 310-785-0512

Multimedia Connection, The: 3517 Manhattan Ave, Manhattan Beach, CA 90266 310-785-0512
Multimedia Mason: 158 Staples Ave, San Francisco, CA 94112 415-586-4718
Multimedia Strategies, Irving: 3720 Millswood Dr, Irving, TX 75062 214-650-1986
Multimedia Works Group: 27 Red Coat Rd, Westport, CT 06880 203-221-8352
Mulvany, Mark: 6770 W 19th Pl #6-208, Lakewood, CO 80214 303-233-7610
Mumford Design: 20 Broad St, Red Bank, NJ 07701 732-741-0030
Murphy & Friends, Harry: 58 Hickory Rd, Fairfax, CA 94930 415-454-1672
Murphy Design, Daina: 26 Seaview Ave, Marblehead, MA 01945 617-639-1264
Murphy Epson: 130 E Chestnut St, Columbus, OH 43215 614-221-2885
Murphy Graphic Design, Rosemary: 1216 Arch St #2C, Philadelphia, PA 19107 215-977-7093
Murray & Assocs: 1520 Brookside Dr #3, Raleigh, NC 27604 919-828-0653
Murray Lienhart Rysner & Co: 58 W Huron Ave, Chicago, IL 60610 312-943-5995
Musgrave & Friends: 444 Pearl #A-5, Monterey, CA 93940 408-649-3122
Mutsumi Gregg Design: 249 Alpine St #53, Pasadena, CA 91106 818-449-5752
MVP : 111 3rd Ave S #230, Minneapolis, MN 55401 612-332-8939
Mydlach Design: 1260 N Prospect Ave #708, Milwaukee, WI 53202 414-276-7090
Myers & Assocs, Loren: 4553 Glencoe Ave #365, Marina Del Rey, CA 90292 310-306-7626
Myers Assocs, Gene: 5575 Hampton, Pittsburgh, PA 15206 412-661-6314
Mystic View Design: 88 Captains Row, Chelsea, MA 02150 617-889-3030

N

N Vision III: 739 A St #B, San Rafael, CA 94901 415-459-5077
NACA: 13 Harbison Way, Columbia, SC 29212 803-732-6222
Nadeau Copy & Design, Greg: 65 Christian Hill Rd, Amherst, NH 03031 603-673-9366
Naganuma Design & Direction: 1100 Montgomery St, San Francisco, CA 94133 415-433-4484
Naganuma Design, Tony K: 1100 Montgomery St, San Francisco, CA 94133 415-433-4484
Nagel, Jan: 9340 Eton Ave, Chatsworth, CA 91311 818-727-2120
Nak, Inc: 29 E 10th St 5th Fl, New York, NY 10003 212-505-9290
Nancekivell Group, The: 400 N First St #100, Minneapolis, MN 55401 612-341-8003
Napoleon Art: 460 W 42nd St 2nd Fl, New York, NY 10036 212-967-6655
Napoleon Art Studio: 460 W 42nd St, New York, NY 10036 212-279-2000
Napoles Design Group, Inc: 89 Madrone Ave, Lark Spur, CA 94939 415-927-8600
Napolitano & Co: 433 E 82nd St, New York, NY 10028 212-988-3686
Nassar Design: 560 Harrison Ave, Boston, MA 02118 617-482-1464
Naughton & Assocs, Carol: 213 W Institute Pl #708, Chicago, IL 60610 312-951-5353
Navratil Art/Design: 717 Liberty Ave/1305 Clark Bld, Pittsburgh, PA 15222 412-471-4322
Nearing Design: 100 Park Blvd #56B, Cherry Hill, NJ 08034 609-354-2328
Needham Design: 22323 Kittridge St, Woodland Hills, CA 91303 818-348-6704
Negin Editorial & Design Svcs: 1545 18th St NW #712, Washington, DC 20036 202-332-8676
Nehmen & Kodner: 1507 McCausland, St Louis, MO 63117 314-644-0114
Neiger Design: 1104 Asbury Ave, Evanston, IL 60202 847-328-1648
Neill, Richard: 9724 Olive St, Bloomington, CA 92316 714-877-5824
Nellis, Ryan: 1101 S Tremaine Ave, Los Angeles, CA 90019 213-934-7118
Nelson Assocs, Louis: 80 University Pl, New York, NY 10003 212-620-9191
Neoscape, Inc: 700 Massachusetts Ave, Cambridge, MA 02139 617-354-1085
Nesheim & Assocs: 3741 Stewart Ave #A, Los Angeles, CA 90066 310-390-6900
Nesnady & Schwartz: 10803 Magnolia Dr, Cleveland, OH 44106 216-791-7721
Nestor/Stermole Design: 19 West 21st St #602, New York, NY 10010 212-229-9377
Network Design Studio: 276 Bowery 3rd Fl, New York, NY 10012 212-431-4675
Neuhaus/Griffin: 488 Julian Ln, Maitland, FL 32751 407-599-7925
Neumann & Friends, Steve: 2405 Bartlett St, Houston, TX 77098 713-629-7501
Neville Graphic Design: 892 Worchester St, Wellesley, MA 02181 617-235-2727
New Concepts Product Design: 7960 Convoy Ct, San Diego, CA 92111 619-576-7222
New Dawn Productions: 675 Line Rd, Matawan, NJ 07747 908-583-0610
New Idea Design: 3702 S 16th St, Omaha, NE 68107 402-733-6169
New Media Designs: 1 Little John Lane, Danbury, CT 06811 203-791-8599
New World Media: 14568 Fancher Ave, Fair Haven, NY 13064 315-947-6016
New York Agency: 10 Gibbs St #200, Rochester, NY 14604 716-232-7060
New York Film & Animation Co, Ltd: 420 Lexington Ave, New York, NY 10170 212-986-5680
New [Media] Directions: 808 Broadway, Nashville, TN 37203 615-742-1490
Newman Design, Inc, Susan: 620 Bloomfield St, Hoboken, NJ 07030 201-420-8205
Newman, Andrew: 54 Winding Cove Rd, Marstons Mills, MA 02648 508-420-1161
NewOrder Media: 209 10th Ave S #450, Nashville, TN 37203 615-248-4848
Newsome, Gregory: 75 St Nicholas Pl #6A, New York, NY 10032 212-283-0871
Nexus Design & Marketing: 710 Wilshire Blvd #510, Santa Monica, CA 90401 310-394-5143
Ngs Assocs: 112 Crockett Rd, King of Prussia, PA 19406 610-337-2745
Nicholas Assocs: 213 W Institute Pl #704, Chicago, IL 60610 312-951-1185
Nichols Graphic Design, Inc: 80 8th Ave #900, New York, NY 10011 212-727-9818
Nichols, Mary Ann: 80 Eighth Ave #900, New York, NY 10011 212-727-9818
Nicholson Design: 364 Second St #2, Encinitas, CA 92024 619-942-9000
Nicholson Partnership: 353 W 53rd St 4th Fl, New York, NY 10019 ...... 212 246-4864
Nickel Design, Rich: 130 W Liberty Dr #205, Wheaton, IL 60187 630-653-2925
Nicolini Assocs: 4046 Maybelle Ave, Oakland, CA 94619 510-531-5569
Nicosia Creative Expresso Ltd: 16 W 56th St 3rd Fl, New York, NY 10019 212-489-6423
Nicosia, Davide: 355 W 52nd 8th Fl, New York, NY 10019 212-957-7649
Niehaus, Don: 2380 Malcolm Ave, Los Angeles, CA 90064 213-279-1559
• **Nielsen, Cliff: pg 227** Chicago, IL **312-364-0244**
London **011-44-207-636-1064**
Los Angeles **323-874-5700**
Washington, DC **410-349-8669**
url: www.shannonassociates.com
Nielubowicz & Assocs: 1900 Glengary St, Sarasota, FL 34231 941-924-5077
Nieshoff Design: 15 Depot Square Suite #1, Lexington, MA 02173 617-864-3664
Niimi Design Assocs: 451 N Racine 2nd Fl, Chicago, IL 60622 312-666-8383
Nimeck, Fran: RD 4/ 358-A Riva Ave, North Brunswick, NJ 08902 908-821-8741
Niven Marketing Group: 1850 Greenleaf Ave, Elk Grove Village, IL 60007 847-640-0300
Nix Design: 426 S Dawson St, Raleigh, NC 27601 919-829-4901
Noel Design, Chris: 1010 Rockville Pike #400, Rockville, MD 20852 301-838-9001
Noi Viva Design: 34 Old Mill Rd, Chappaqua, NY 10514 914-238-3708
Nolan Design: 1211 16th Ave, Belmar, NJ 07719 732-449-6953
Nomadic Display: 3628 Westchase Dr, Houston, TX 77042 713-977-8788
Noneman & Noneman Design: 230 E 18th St, New York, NY 10003 212-473-4090
Norman Gollin Design: 9048 Wonderland Pk Ave, Los Angeles, CA 90046 213-656-2398
Norr Design, Brad: 400 N First Ave #312, Minneapolis, MN 55401 612-339-2104
Norris Reynolds & Denham: 112 N Beechwood Ave, Baltimore, MD 21228 410-788-9229
Norstar Design Star: 2720 Loker Ave W #R, Carlsbad, CA 92008 619-929-0948
North Amer Thought Combine: 270 Lafayette St #903, New York, NY 10012 212-219-1000
North American Aerox, Inc: 14 Engineers Lane, Farmingdale, NY 11735 516-752-0088
North Charles Street Dsgn Org: 222 W Saratoga St, Baltimore, MD 21201 410-539-4040
North, Ron: 566 Dutch Valley Rd, Atlanta, GA 30324 404-892-6232
Northwest Media Design: 326 W 12th Ave, Eugene, OR 97401 503-343-6636
Notovitz Design, Inc: 47 E 19th St 4th Fl, New York, NY 10003 212-677-9700
Nottingham Spirk Design: 11310 Juniper Rd, Cleveland, OH 44106 216-231-7830
Nourse, Bill: 301 N Water St 6th Fl, Milwaukee, WI 53202 414-278-7717
Nova Marketing Communications: 165 W Central Rd, Schaumburg, IL 60195 847-202-6682
Novation: 6612 Gunn Dr, Oakland, CA 94611 510-339-8769
Novus Visual Communications, Inc: 18 W 27th St, New York, NY 10001 212-689-2424
Noyes Assocs Inc, Macey: 232 Danbury Rd, Wilton, CT 06897 203-762-9002
Nuance: 378 Gypsy Hill Rd, Lancaster, PA 17602 717-293-0171
Nuart: 49 Richmondville Ave, Westport, CT 06880 203-222-8181
Nuf Said: 2564 Paintbrush Ln, Lafayette, CO 80026 303-665-8188
Number Seventeen: 285 W Broadway #650, New York, NY 10013 212-966-9395
Nunez Group: 480 Mikasa Dr, Alpharetta, GA 30202 770-475-3980
Nuttall Design & Comm: 52 E Vernon St, Phoenix, AZ 85004 602-257-4458
Nwaise & Assocs: 300 Berkley Dr #R5, Madison, TN 37115 615-868-8065
NZD Designworks: 1542 Woodbine Ct, Deerfield, IL 60015 847-945-2225

O

O & J Design, Inc: 10 W 19th St 6th Fl, New York, NY 10011 212-242-1080
O'Brien Design: 301 N Poverty Rd, Southbury, CT 06488 203-262-1121
O'Brion Design: 10 New Meadows Rd, Winchester, MA 01890 617-729-3893
O'Mara Design Group: 4505 La Virgenes Rd #201, Calabasas, CA 91302 818-880-9220
O'Neil Communications: 1 Bridgeview Cir, Tyngsboro, MA 01879 508-649-7538
O'Very Covey, Traci: 7 Washington St, Beverly, MA 01915 978-921-0887
Obata & Co, Kiku: 5585 Pershing Ave #240, St Louis, MO 631112 314-361-3110
Obata Design: 1610 Menard, St Louis, MO 63104 314-241-1710
Oberg, Richard: 327 15th Ave, Moline, IL 61265 319-359-3831
Oberhand Studios: 20124 Citronia St, Chatsworth, CA 91311 818-775-1999
Ocean Graphic Design, Inc: 273 E Olive St, Long Beach, NY 11561 516-889-1667
Octane Media: 470 W Hwy 96 #260, Shore View, MN 55126 612-482-0700
Odam Design, John: 2163 Cordero Rd, Del Mar, CA 92014 619-259-8230
Odd World Inhabitants: 869 Monterey St, San Luis Obispo, CA 93401 805-781-6220
Odell Group: 7060 Hollywood Blvd #614, Hollywood, CA 90028 213-469-8805
Oden & Assocs: 22 N Front St, Memphis, TN 38103 901-578-8055
Odyssey Communications Group: 9441 LBJ Freeway #510, Dallas, TX 75243 972-997-9052
Odyssey Visual Design: 4413 Ocean Valley Ln, San Diego, CA 92130 619-793-1900
Offenhartz Inc, Harvey: 531 Main St, New York, NY 10044 212-319-5961
Ogando, David: 270 Park Ave S #11C, New York, NY 10010 212-353-0577
Ogdemli/Feldman Design: 1911 Magnolia Blvd #39, N Hollywood, CA 91607 818-760-1759
Oglesby Design, Carla: 289 Stonebrook St, Simi Valley, CA 93063 805-579-8823
Ohalla Design, Inc, Anna: 1812 Camp Ave, Rockford, IL 61103 815-968-1533
Ohman, Diann: 150 W Jefferson #100, Detroit, MI 48226 313-983-3600
Oka Design, Kathy: 120 Fair Oaks, San Francisco, CA 94110 415-647-5652
Okland Design Assocs: 1970 SW Temple, Salt Lake City, UT 84115 801-484-7861
Oldachi Design, Mark: 3316 N Lincoln Ave, Chicago, IL 60657 773-477-6477
Olenik, Sandra: 2096 Durham Rd, Madison, CT 06443 203-421-4867
Olivares, Elena: 41 Union Square W #209, New York, NY 10003 212-645-7858
Olive Design: 918 W 3rd St, Austin, TX 78703 512-457-0207
Oliver Design: 2054 Broadway, Santa Monica, CA 90404 310-453-3523
Oliver, Mark: One W Victoria St, Santa Barbara, CA 93101 805-963-0734
Olivette Hubler Design: 2631 Commerce, Dallas, TX 75226 214-742-2491
Ollio Studio: 2710 Phillips Ave, Glenshaw, PA 15116 412-486-6516
Ollman, Raoul: 470 Potrero Ave #3, San Francisco, CA 94110 415-552-1941
Olsen Muscara Design Group: 60 madison Ave #1010, New York, NY 10010 212-684-4580
Olson Design, Bruce: 14775 Northern Ave, Guerneville, CA 95446 707-869-1066
Olson Design, Inc: 853 Camino Del Mar, Del Mar, CA 92014 619-450-9200
Olthaus Designs, Larry: 1149 Devil's Backbone Rd, Cincinnati, OH 45233 513-451-2815
Olver Dunlop Assocs: 222 W Huron #2001, Chicago, IL 60610 312-337-2323
Omega Design Communications: 717 Lexington Ave, New York, NY 10022 212-319-4859
Omega Group, The: 1028 Route 23, Wayne, NJ 07470 201-628-1996
Omni Graphic Media: 21385 Marina Cove Circle #E12, Miami Beach, FL 33180 305-935-1718
Omni Media, The: 2855 Boardwalk, Ann Arbor, MI 48104 313-761-8872
On Graphics: 5127 Cerrillos Dr, Woodland Hills, CA 9164 818-716-9228
On Line Design: 555 Theodore Fremd Ave #B103, Rye, NY 10580 914-967-7100
On Line Design/Visual Stratgs: 41 Pollard Pl, San Francisco, CA 94133 415-296-9702
Ondesign: 451 D St #305, Boston, MA 02210 617-261-4820
One Flight Up Design: 150 River Rd Suite J-4, Montville, NJ 07045 201-257-9500
One World Arts: 1831 Pearl St, Boulder, CO 80302 303-444-6996
Optimum Design: 38 Clifton Place, New York, NY 11238 718-638-2137
Optimum Group: 9745 Mangham Dr, Cincinnati, OH 45215 513-563-2700
Optisys: 8620 N 22nd Ave #109, Phoenix, AZ 85021 800-327-1271
Orak Design: 4373 25th St, San Francisco, CA 94114 415-550-7101
Orange & Blue Design Group: 80 W 40th St #72, New York, NY 10018 212-354-9833
Orbis Productions: 837 Rosary Ln, West Chester, PA 19382 610-692-0921
Origin Instruments: 854 Greenview Dr, Grand Prairie, TX 75050 214-606-8740
Originators, The: 3600 S Harbor Blvd #155, Oxnard, CA 93035 805-985-4664
Orion Communications: 2323 W Schantz Ave #217, Dayton, OH 45409 937-297-0044
Orlov, Christian: 42 W 69th St, New York, NY 10023 212-873-2381
Orr & Assocs, Michael: 75 W Market St/Hawkes Bldg, Corning, NY 14830 607-936-4607
Orr Assocs, R: 22282 Pewter Ln, El Toro, CA 92630 714-770-1277
Ortiz, Jose Luis: 66 W 77th St, New York, NY 10024 212-877-3081
Orton, Michael Jones: 6800 The Sunset Ridge #200, W Hills, CA 91307 818-716-7300
Osborne Design Illustration: 4801 Nevada Ave, Nashville, TN 37209 615-385-4476
Osborne Design, Michael: 444 De Haro #207, San Francisco, CA 94107 415-255-0125
Osborne-Tuttle: 1259 Belden, Chicago, IL 60614 773-404-5444
Oshima, Carol: 1659 E Sachs Place, Covina, CA 91724 818-966-0796
Osland Design: 145 Ave Of Americas 2nd Fl, New York, NY 10013 212-627-1280
Oslund Design: 125 Lawrence St, Eugene, OR 97401 541-686-9833
Ostrander & Chu, Inc: 900 Manakea St, Honolulu, HI 96817 808-524-4700
Our Design: 3501 Trimble Rd, Nashville, TN 37215 615-783-0093
Out Of The Blue, Inc: 1906 Wellbourne Dr NE, Atlanta, GA 30324 404-897-5817
Outside Line Studio: 225 S Owasso Blvd, Roseville, MN 55113 612-483-5761
Outside The Box Interactive: 133 W 19th St #10B, New York, NY 10011 ...... 212 463-7160
Ovation Marketing: 201 Main St, La Crosse, WI 54601 608-785-2460

Over CC Design: 599 Broadway 8th Fl, New York, NY 10012 ... 212-925-2456
Overton, Janet: 3616 Regent Dr, Dallas, TX 75229 ... 214-357-1272
Ovryn Design, Nina: 142 Grove Ave, Woodbridge, NJ 07095 ... 908-602-0568
Ovryn, Ken: 2619 Windsor St #1000, Chicago, IL 60625 ... 773-866-0866
Owen/Garritson: 603 Business Pkwy, Richardson, TX 75081 ... 972-671-1255
Owens & Assocs Advtg, Inc: 6530 N 16th St #101, Phoenix, AZ 85016 ... 602-230-7557
Owens Marketing Design: 5 Hunt Field Court, Owings Mills, MD 21117 ... 410-235-3327
Oxford & Drozoa: 12555 High Bluff Dr, San Diego, CA 92130 ... 619-481-3446

P

Pace & Partners: 2417 N Cedar St, Holt, MI 48842 ... 517-694-9711
Pace Design Group: 466 Geary St #200, San Francisco, CA 94102 ... 415-495-3600
Package Deal: 18211 Beneta Way, Tustin, CA 92680 ... 714-541-2440
Packaging Network: 985 Old Eagle School Rd Ste 508, Wayne, PA 19087 ... 610-964-9017
Paganucci Design, Bob: 142 E 37th St/Grd Fl, New York, NY 10016 ... 212-779-3560
Page Arbitrio & Resen, Inc: 317 Madison Ave 17th Fl, New York, NY 10017 ... 212-922-9266
Page Design: 1900 29th St, Sacramento, CA 95816 ... 916-457-0108
Pagliaro Design, Joseph: 434 Hidden Valley Ln, Cincinnati, OH 45215 ... 513-761-7707
Pagliuco Design Co: 213 W Institute Pl #707, Chicago, IL 60610 ... 312-943-4281
Pahmer, Mark: 8 W 30th St 7th Fl, New York, NY 10001 ... 212-889-6202
Paige Johnson Design: 290 Lowell Ave, Palo Alto, CA 94301 ... 415-327-0488
Paige Smith Group: 2412 Genesee St, Utica, NY 13502 ... 315-733-2313
Paine Bluett Paine, Inc: 4041 Powder Mill Rd #105, Calverton, MD 20705 ... 301-595-1855
Paine Pomeroy: 209 Tenth Ave S #303, Nashville, TN 37203 ... 615-242-5546
Painter/Cesaroni Design, Inc: 1865 Grove St, Glenview, IL 60025 ... 847-724-8840
Palazzolo Design Studio: 6410 Knapp/The Grange, Ada, MI 49301 ... 616-576-9979
Palk Design Group: 4425 W Pine, St Louis, MO 63108 ... 314-531-1410
Palladino & Roberts Design Assocs: 625 Hillcrest St, Orlando, FL 32803 ... 407-648-1801
Palladino, Tony: 400 E 56th St, New York, NY 10022 ... 212-751-0068
Pallango, E: 37 E 28 St#600, New York, NY 10016 ... 212-213-1880
Palmer Design: 4450 N 12th St #250, Phoenix, AZ 85014 ... 602-277-3361
Palmer Graphics: 231 La Rue France, Lafayette, LA 70508 ... 318-235-6382
Pan & Assocs, Inc: 263 Hatch Ln, Burlingame, CA 94010 ... 415-344-1312
Panebianco, Inc: One E Wacker Dr #2810, Chicago, IL 60601 ... 312-832-0100
Pangborn Design Ltd: 275 Iron St, Detroit, MI 48207 ... 313-259-3400
Pangolin Graphics: 470 Broome St, New York, NY 10013 ... 212-966-6222
Panke, Nick: 116 Wintonbury Ave, Bloomfield, CT 06002 ... 203-242-6576
Paolini Design, Thibault: 19 Commercial St, Portland, ME 04101 ... 207-871-1813
Papagalos & Assocs: 5333 N 7th St #222, Phoenix, AZ 85014 ... 602-279-2933
Paper Crane Design: 2980 College Ave #9, Berkeley, CA 94705 ... 510-849-9477
Paradigm Communciations Group: 250 Production Plaza, Cincinnati, OH 45219 ... 513-381-7100
Paradigm Design: 375 Southend Ave, New York, NY 10280 ... 212-488-8338
Paradigm Productions: PO Box 770188, Memphis, TN 38177 ... 901-685-7703
Paradowski, Alex: 303 N Broadway, St Louis, MO 63102 ... 314-241-2150
Paragon Design International: 541 N Fair Banks Ct #1000, Chicago, IL 60610 ... 312-832-1030
Paragraph Design: 417 N 8th St #3, Philadelphia, PA 19123 ... 215-423-5202
Paragraphs Design: 414 N Orleans #310, Chicago, IL 60610 ... 312-828-0200
Paral X Design: 6 N Michigan Ave #1501, Chicago, IL 60602 ... 312-696-0400
Parallel Group, Inc: 211 Beverly Rd, Atlanta, GA 30309 ... 404-873-2008
Paramount Technical Service, Inc: 31811 Vine St, Cleveland, OH 44094 ... 216-585-2550
Parham Santana: 7 W 18th St 7th Fl, New York, NY 10011 ... 212-645-7501
Parise Design: 5 Schuman Rd, Millwood, NY 10546 ... 914-941-7467
Parker Davis Graphics: 518 Ronalds St, Iowa City, IA 52245 ... 319-354-0418
Parker Design: 212 Haddon Ave, Westmont, NJ 08108 ... 609-854-8008
Parker Design, Laura: 1235 De Haro St, San Francisco, CA 94107 ... 415-282-1711
Parks Communication, Dick: 2414 Drexel St, Vienna, VA 22180 ... 202-255-5500
Parola, Michael: 816 E Fern Ave, Fresno, CA 93728 ... 209-441-7544
Parsons Schl Of Dsgn-Pub Dsgn: 2 W 13th St #810, New York, NY 10011 ... 212-229-8905
Partners & Simons: 25 Drydock Ave 8th Fl, Boston, MA 02210 ... 617-330-9393
Partners By Design: 24300 Town Center Dr #380, Valencia, CA 91355 ... 661-255-5502
Partners Design: 187 Koenig Rd, Bernville, PA 19506 ... 610-488-7611
Pasinski Assocs, Irene: 6026 Penn Circle S, Pittsburgh, PA 15206 ... 412-661-9000
Pate Int'l: 2350 Taylor St, San Francisco, CA 94133 ... 415-928-4400
Patel Design, Harish: 218 Madison Ave, New York, NY 10016 ... 212-686-7425
Patrick Partners, Michael: 532 Emerson, Palo Alto, CA 94301 ... 415-327-3185
Patsy, David: 9 W 14th St, Minneapolis, MN 55403 ... 612-871-5503
Pattee Design, Inc: 3200 Ingersoll Ave #D, Des Moines, IA 50312 ... 515-255-6801
Patterson And Partners, Todd: 100 First Ave #105, Pittsburgh, PA 15222 ... 412-281-9228
Patterson Design, Linda: 55 Laurel Dr, Needham, MA 02192 ... 617-444-1517
Patterson Wood Partners: 133 W 19th St 5th Fl, New York, NY 10011 ... 212-691-7734
Patterson, Margaret: PO Box 1291, Boston, MA 02117 ... 617-424-1236
Patton Design: 8 Pasteur #170, Irvine, CA 92718 ... 714-753-1595
Paul Co, Thomas J: Bldg/1061 Rydal Rd, Rydal, PA 19046 ... 215-886-3220
Paulsen Design: 20 W Maxwell Dr, West Hartford, CT 06107 ... 203-521-4350
Payne, Geof: 817 Prairie Ln, Columbia, MO 65202 ... 314-443-1995
PBS Graphic Art & Design, Inc: 6339 11th Ave S, Richfield, MN 55423 ... 612-866-8159
Peabody Museum/Yale University: 170 Whitney Ave, New Haven, CT 06511 ... 203-432-5004
Peace Design, John: 4 Ellsworth Rd, Larchmont, NY 10538 ... 914-834-2349
Pearson Design, Christine: 4200 Windfield Dr, Charlotte, NC 28205 ... 704-535-5383
Pearson Design, Dennis: 1505 E Fourth St, Charlotte, NC 28204 ... 704-372-6434
Peckolick Inc, Alan: 30 E 21St #2B, New York, NY 10010 ... 212-505-1242
Pegasus Design, Inc: 13831 Northwest Fwy #180, Houston, TX 77040 ... 713-690-7878
Pegasus Productions: 222 S Meramec Ave #300, St Louis, MO 63105 ... 314-727-7707
Peiler, Karl: 36 Horatio St #4B, New York, NY 10014 ... 212-255-3879
• **Pelavin, Daniel: pg 926** 80 Varick St #3B, New York, NY 10013 ... **212-941-7418**
e-mail: daniel@pelavin.com / url: www.pelavin.com / fax: 212-431-7138
Pelican Bay Studio: 17115 Lorillard St, Grenada Hills, CA 91344 ... 818-366-6192
Pelico & Assocs: 11423 Washington Blvd, Los Angeles, CA 90066 ... 310-390-8083
Pellegrini & Assocs: 134 Spring St #5A, New York, NY 10012 ... 212-925-4224
Pen and Ink Creative Svcs: 112 Gorden St, Poughkepsie, NY 12601 ... 914-485-4232
Penfield Design, Inc: 2220 High Pointe Ct, St Paul, MN 55120 ... 612-683-0827
Pensare Design: 729 15th St #200, Washington, DC 20005 ... 202-638-7700
Pentagram Design: 387 Tehama St, San Francisco, CA 94103 ... 415-896-0499
Pentagram Design: 1508 W 5th St, Austin, TX 78703 ... 512-476-3076
Pentagram Design: 212 Fifth Ave 17th Fl, New York, NY 10010 ... 212-683-7000
Pentimento Design: 853 Broadway Ste 606, New York, NY 10003 ... 212-995-2990
Perego Design: 1912 Innwood Rd, Atlanta, GA 30329 ... 404-329-0212
Performance Enhancement & Education Corp: 6810 Horrocks St, Philadelphia, PA 19149 215-745-6629
Perich & Partners Ltd: 117 N First, Ann Arbor, MI 48104 ... 313-769-2215
Perillo Inc, Mary: 125 Cedar St #8S, New York, NY 10006 ... 212-608-3943
Perkins/Boyer Advertising: 1377 Fulton St #3, San Francisco, CA 94117 ... 415-346-8806
Perlman-Withers: 305 E 46th St 15th Fl, New York, NY 10017 ... 212-935-2552
Perlow, Paul: 123 E 54th St #6E, New York, NY 10022 ... 212-758-4358
Perolio, Inc: 311 W Superior #310 , Chicago, IL 60610 ... 312-266-9131
Perr Design, Janet: 135 Eighth Ave, New York, NY 10011 ... 212-620-0896
Perry Townsend Design Inc, Jill: 117 N Young Dr, Otis, OR 97368 ... 503-996-6289
Persona, Inc: 1637 35th St NW, Washington, DC 20007 ... 202-333-1937
Perspectives In Communications: 1637 Harvard St NW, Washington, DC 20009 ... 202-667-7448
Pertuit Assocs, Jim: 601 Julia St, New Orleans, LA 70130 ... 504-568-0808
Pesanelli & Co, David: 14508 Barkwood Dr, Rockville, MD 20853 ... 301-871-7355
Peters Design, James: 866 Kawaiahao St, Honolulu, HI 96813 ... 808-596-2280
Peterson & Assocs, Tom: 4312 2nd Ave NW, Seattle, WA 98107 ... 206-789-7848
Peterson & Co: 2200 N Lamar #310, Dallas, TX 75202 ... 214-954-0522
Peterson Assocs: 17 W 220 22nd St, Oakbrook Terrace, IL 60181 ... 630-530-2600
Peterson Design, Scott: 13385 SW Barberry Ln, Beaverton, OR 97005 ... 541-643-7421
Petertil Design Partners: 1456 N Dayton #201, Chicago, IL 60622 ... 312-642-9131
Petrick Design: 828 N Wolcott St, Chicago, IL 60622 ... 773-486-2880
Petro Graphic Design Assocs: 315 Falmouth Dr, Rocky River, OH 44116 ... 216-356-0429
Pettis, Valerie: 88 Lexington Ave #17G, New York, NY 10016 ... 212-683-7382
Petty, Daphne: 1460 Belmont St NW, Washington, DC 20009 ... 202-667-8222
Pevnick Design: 2602 E Hampshire St, Milwaukee, WI 53211 ... 414-961-8818
Pezzutti's Studio: 496 Lake Shore Dr, Duluth, GA 30136 ... 770-441-9373
Pfeiffer Plus Co: 1910 Pine #130, St Louis, MO 63101 ... 314-621-0899
PHD: 1524A Cloverfield Blvd, Santa Monica, CA 90404 ... 310-829-0900
Pheasant Hill Design: 11 Pheasant Hill Rd, Halifax, MA 02338 ... 617-293-7009
Phelps & Hollander, Inc: 2334 Boca Chica Blvd, Brownsville, TX 78521 ... 956-541-4909
Philion Design: 93 Petersen Rd, Granby, CT 06035 ... 203-653-9838
Phillips Design: 25 Dry Dock Ave, Boston, MA 02210 ... 617-423-7676
Phillips Design Group: 930 Meridian St, Indianapolis, IN 46204 ... 317-955-8435
Phillips Design, Steve: 37 W 17th St 7th Fl, New York, NY 10011 ... 212-242-2626
Phippen Design Group: 2200 Bridgeway, Sausalito, CA 94965 ... 415-331-2250
Phoenix Creative Sevices: 611 N 10th St 7th Fl, St Louis, MO 60101 ... 314-421-5646
Phoenix Graphics: 273 Closter Dock Rd #7, Closter, NJ 07624 ... 201-784-8889
Phoenix Printing & Adv: 300 Maple Ave, Trenton, NJ 08618 ... 609-392-0226
Phoenix Printing & Design: 2809 Pomona Blvd, Pomona, CA 91768 ... 909-594-5831
Phon Graphics, Thomas: 21 Crestmont Rd, West Orange, NJ 07052 ... 201-736-4681
Photo Group Productions: 88 Lexington #15E, New York, NY 10016 ... 212-213-9539
Photon Dreams, Inc: 1054 Golf Ave, Highland Park, IL 60035 ... 847-43-0633
Piccirilli Group: 502 Rock Spring Rd, Bel Air, MD 21014 ... 410-879-670
Pictogram Studio: 1711 U St Nw #2, Washington, DC 20009 ... 202-483-4279
Pierre Logos Inc, Keith: 1202 SW 82th Ave, North Lauderdale, FL 33068 ... 305-726-0401
Pierre Rademaker Design: 738 Higuera St #F, San Luis Obispo, CA 93401 ... 805-544-7774
Piland Goodell, Inc: 5010 Dinkins St 1st Fl, Houston, TX 77005 ... 713-527-9255
Piland, Gary: 3630 SW Burlingame Rd, Topeka, KS 66611 ... 913-267-4712
Pilkington Advertising Design: 1117 N Navajo Dr, Flagstaff, AZ 86001 ... 520-774-0048
Pilz, Misty: 8 Huntington St #331, Huntington, CT 06484 ... 203-922-1811
Pinfold, Miles: ExLibris Nineveh Rd/Holbeck Leeds, W Yorkshire, England, UK LS11 ... 1132-448549
Ping, Cliff: 911 Main St #1717, Kansas City, MO 64105 ... 816-474-4366
Pinkhaus Design Corp: 2424 S Dixie Hwy #201, Miami, FL 33133 ... 305-854-1000
Pinkston & Others, Steve: 212 W Miner St, Westchester, PA 19382 ... 610-692-2939
Pinnacle Design Group: 7910 Woodmont Ave #1050, Bethesda, MD 20814 ... 301-951-5200
Pinto Design: 1416 Simpson Ferry Rd, New Cumberland, PA 17070 ... 717-774-5718
Pinzke Design, Herbert: 1935 N Kenmore, Chicago, IL 60614 ... 312-528-2277
Pioneer Video Manufacturing, Inc: 1041 E 230th St, Carson, CA 90745 ... 310-518-0710
Piper Studios, Inc: 118 N Clinton #403, Chicago, IL 60661 ... 312 454 0259
Pipitone Design Inc, Scott: 61 Riverview Ave, Pittsburgh, PA 15214 ... 412-321-0879
Pisarkiewicz Mazur & Co: 1 Wall St Ct #400, New York, NY 10005 ... 212-668-8400
Pitcock Design: 210 S Michigan #100, South Bend, IN 46601 ... 219-233-8606
Pittenger Design Assocs, Lenore: 2146 Wharton Rd, Glenside, PA 19038 ... 215-881-9426
Pivot Design: 223 W Erie, Chicago, IL 60610 ... 312-787-7707
Pixel Light Communication: 375 Carmita Ave, Rutherford, NJ 07070 ... 201-804-0606
Pixel Press Interactive: 2105 Commerce St #102, Dallas, TX 75201 ... 214-748-5901
Pixelspace: PO Box 2411, Hickory, NC 28603 ... 704-495-3640
Pkg Design Group: 333 Park Ave S 2nd Fl, New York, NY 10010 ... 212-420-0210
Pkg Graphics: 22 Lynn Court, Hampton Bays, NY 11946 ... 516-728-9739
PKI Design: 525 Augusta, Chatham, IL 62629 ... 217-483-4698
PL&P Advertising Studio: 1280 SW 36th Ave, Pompano Beach, FL 33069 ... 307-977-9327
Plaga Design Group: 2858 Wycliff Rd, Raleigh, NC 27607 ... 919-881-0680
Plainspoke: 18 Sheafe St, Portsmouth, NH 03801 ... 603-433-5969
Planet Design Co: 605 Williamson St, Madison, WI 53703 ... 608-256-0000
Planet Works: 4964 Hollywood Blvd, Hollywood, CA 90027 ... 213-663-9956
Plataz, George: 516 Martin Bldg, Pittsburgh, PA 15212 ... 412-322-3177
Platinum Design: 14 W 23rd St 2nd Fl, New York, NY 10010 ... 212-366-4000
Platinum Productions: 8100 N High St, Columbus, OH 43235 ... 614-888-4181
Platinum X: 385 E Lemon Ave E116, Walnut, CA 91789 ... 909-598-3398
Platt Advertising Art, Don: 1399 SE 9th Ave, Hialeah, FL 33010 ... 305-888-3296
Plume, Joe: 1872 N Clybourn #404, Chicago, IL 60614 ... 773-935-8840
PM Design: 62 Robbins Ave, Berkeley Hghts, NJ 07922 ... 908-665-6878
PMCI: 918 Woodley Rd, Dayton, OH 45403 ... 937-252-1122
PNS Graphics: 175 Varick St, New York, NY 10014 ... 212-627-0251
Point Of View Productions: 38 New Friendship Rd, Howell, NJ 07731 ... 908-901-8920
Point Zero Design: 4223 Glencoe Ave #A223, Marina del Ray, CA 90292 ... 310-823-0975
Points of View: 12248 Santa Monica Blvd #B, Los Angeles, CA 90025 ... 310-207-8584
Polan & Waski Design: 1 Liden Pl, Great Neck, NY 11021 ... 516-829-7001
Poletti Design, Inc: 1680 The Alameda #205, San Jose, CA 95126 ... 408-280-0466
Polizos Assocs, Arthur: 220 W Freemason St, Norfolk, VA 23510 ... 804-622-7033
Pollack, Chris: 103 Oakcrest Dr, Verona, VA 24482 ... 540-248-1235
Pollard Design: 17 Luccock Park Rd, Livingston, MT 59047 ...
Pollman Marketing Arts: 2060 Broadway #210, Boulder, CO 80302 ... 303-440-4827
Pominville, Susan: 5075 N Burkhart Rd, Howell, MI 48843 ... 517-545-5000
Ponce: 5205 Airport Blvd #106, Austin, TX 78751 ... 512-467-7471
Pont Street, Inc: 114 W Denny Way #285, Seattle, WA 98119 ... 206-283-9029
Poole Promotional Designs, Lee: 5818 Savoy Ln, Greensboro, NC 27410 ... 910-855-8693
Popiela Creative: 1985 W Big Beaver #210, Troy, MI 48084 ... 810-637-2898
Port Miolla Assocs: 23 S Main St, S Norwalk, CT 06854 ... 203-855-0830
Portable Products: 5200 Quincy St, St Paul, MN 55112 ... 612-717-4400

Porter/Matjasich Assocs: 408 Bluebird Ln, Deerfield, IL 60015 ... 847-541-0443
Portiko Digital: 338 S Main St, St Charles, MO 63301 ... 314-940-8181
Positive Negative: 59 Wareham St #8, Boston, MA 02118 ... 617-423-2212
Positively Main St Graphics: 290 Coconut Ave #7, Sarasota, FL 34236 ... 941-366-4959
Post Edge: 111 Lincoln Rd #805, Miami Beach, FL 33139 ... 954-894-9900
Pouget, Evelyn: 23 E 7th St, New York, NY 10003 ... 212-228-7935
Poulakis, Susan: 32 W 31st St #7, New York, NY 10001 ... 212-239-1502
Poulin, Richard: 286 Springs St 6th Fl, New York, NY 10013 ... 212-675-1332
Poulos Design, Rikki: 8305 Yucca Trl, Los Angeles, CA 90046 ... 213-656-6987
Powell Street Studio: 2135 Powell St, San Francisco, CA 94133 ... 415-986-6564
Power Graphics, Inc: 11701 Commonwealth Dr, Louisville, KY 40299 ... 502-267-0772
Powers Creative: 418 Christopher Way, Windsor, CA 95492 ... 707-837-8673
Powers Design International: 828 Production Pl, Newport Beach, CA 92663 ... 714-645-2265
Pragma Design: 4 Peabody Rd Annex, Derry, NH 03038 ... 603-437-2010
Prather & Assocs: 111 Dennis Dr, Lexington, KY 50403 ... 606-278-5980
Pratt Design, Ellis: 361 Newbury St, Boston, MA 02115 ... 617-266-3282
PRB Design: 4522 Clarcoma Ocoee Rd, Orlando, FL 32810 ... 407-578-1259
Precision Mktg Assocs: 1 Garden Way, Rancelear, NY 12144 ... 518-391-7799
Premis Design: 600 N 95th St, Milwaukee, WI 53226 ... 414-778-1845
Prentice Design: 264 Old Farms Rd, Simsbury, CT 06070 ... 203-651-3056
Presentation Resource: 109 E Cary St, Richmond, VA 23219 ... 804-648-7854
Preslicka, Greg: 5000 Edgewater Dr, Savage, MN 55378 ... 612-432-2166
Pressello Design Inc, John: 7317 Reynolds Rd, Mentor, OH 44060 ... 216-951-8573
Pressley Jacobs Design, Inc: 101 N Wacker Dr #100, Chicago, IL 60606 ... 312-263-7485
Prettyman Design, Claude: 13402 Flint Dr, Santa Ana, CA 92705 ... 714-838-0081
Price & Assocs, Nina: 3405 Waverly St, Palo Alto, CA 94306 ... 415-279-4094
Price Design, Rob: 160 Hodge St, Buffalo, NY 14222 ... 716-884-3304
Price Webber Marketing Comm: 2101 Production Dr, Louisville, KY 40299 ... 502-499-9220
Pride & Performance: 944 Cobb Rd, St Paul, MN 55126 ... 612-487-1000
Pridgen, Bill: 306-200 Parham St, Raleigh, NC 27601 ... 919-833-3767
Primadonna Design: 31771 Topper Ct, Beverly Hills, MI 48025 ... 810-258-8714
Prime Design: 1059 Redmond Ave, San Jose, CA 95120 ... 408-268-4854
Principia Graphica: 2520 NW Upshur St, Portland, OR 97210 ... 503-227-6343
Printmakers Ltd: 2505 N 24th St, Omaha, NE 68110 ... 402-453-7550
Printz: 444 De Haro St #112, San Francisco, CA 94107 ... 415-252-8100
Prism Design, Inc: 4900 Woodway #730, Houston, TX 77056 ... 713-871-8376
Prisma: 200 First Ave, Pittsburgh, PA 15222 ... 412-261-6815
Pro Graphics: 420 Elwood Ave, Hawthoren, NY 10532 ... 914-747-9877
Procaccino Design: 6944 Pawling St, Philadelphia, PA 19128 ... 215-482-7223
Product Genesis: 300 Bent St #200, Cambridge, MA 02141 ... 617-661-3552
Product Solutions, Inc: 447 New Grove St, Wilkes-Barre, PA 18702 ... 717-825-9196
Product Systems International: 40 N Cherry St, Lancaster, PA 17602 ... 717-291-9042
Production Corp, The: 9457 Las Vegas Blvd S #G, Las Vegas, NV 89123 ... 702-263-0933
Production Studio: 382 Channel Dr, Port Washington, NY 11050 ... 516-944-6688
Professional Video Services: 2030 M St NW #400, Washington, DC 20036 ... 202-775-0894
Profile Design: 151 Townsend, San Francisco, CA 94107 ... 415-979-0780
Profile Press, Inc: 40 Greenwood Ave, E Islip, NY 11730 ... 516-277-6319
Project Center Type Design: 8 Executive Park E, Atlanta, GA 30329 ... 404-320-3003
Prokell Design: 26 Marylea Ave #300, Pittsburgh, PA 15227 ... 412-884-5850
Proof Positive/Farrowlyne Assocs: 1620 Central St, Evanston, IL 60201 ... 847-866-9570
Prop Art: 1535 Northwestern Ave, Chicago, IL 60622 ... 773-252-2244
Propaganda, Inc: 245 Turnpike Rd, Southborough, MA 01772 ... 508-303-8585
Propp & Guerin: 550 15th St, San Francisco, CA 94103 ... 415-621-8644
Proxima Corp: 9440 Carol Park Dr, San Diego, CA 92121 ... 619-457-5500
PS Studios: 377 Monarch St, Louisville, CO 80027 ... 303-673-9092
Psl Graphics: Po Box 221459, Carmel, CA 93922 ... 408-625-6379
Publication Services: 101 Belle View Ave, Petaluma, CA 94952 ... 707-763-5707
Puches Design: 260 Fifth Ave 5th Fl, New York, NY 10001 ... 212-684-4545
Puder Design: 2 W Blackwell St, Dover, NJ 07801 ... 201-361-1310
Pugh & Company: 5430 Glen Lakes #240, Dallas, TX 75231 ... 214-691-5665
Pugh Design: 4090 Prospect Rd, Whiteford, MD 21160 ... 410-692-2829
Pugh Design, Dave: 3106 Parkside Dr, Baltimore, MD 21214 ... 410-426-8323
Purington, Camille & Mark: 3539 E Easter, Littleton, CO 80122 ... 303-843-0877
Purple Monkey Studios, Inc: 124 S Marion, S Marion, IL 60302 ... 708-386-3086
Purviance Marketing Comm, George : 7404 Bland Dr, Clayton, MO 63105 ... 314-721-2765
Pygoya: 2119 N King St #206, Honolulu, HI 96819 ...

Q

Q30 Design, Inc: 489 King St W Ste #400, Toronto, ON MJV 1K4 ... 416-596-6500
Qually & Co, Inc: 2238 Central St #3, Evanston, IL 60601 ... 847-864-6316
Quantic Comms: 3 Riverside Dr, Andover, MA 01810 ... 508-681-1500
Quantum Design: 364 Stelle Ave, Milltown, NJ 08850 ... 908-846-6730
Quantum Graphix, Inc: 18097 Live Ln, Eden Prairie, MN 55346 ... 612-934-1134
Quantum Leap Productions: 8439 Jamieson Ave, Northridge, CA 91325 ... 818-881-8548
Quantum Works: 15860 Dartford Way, Sherman Oaks, CA 91403 ... 818-906-3322
Quarasan Group: 214 W Huron St, Chicago, IL 60610 ... 312-787-0750
Queener Design: 65 High Ridge Rd #249, Stamford, CT 06905 ... 203-322-1680
Quinn, Chris: 8775 Cloudleap Court, Columbia, MD 21045 ... 207-772-9801
Quon Design: 10960 Wilshire Blvd 8th FL, Los Angeles, CA 90024 ... 310-444-7000
Quon Design Office, Mike: 568 Broadway #703, New York, NY 10012 ... 212-226-6024
Quon Design, Mike: 53 Spring St 5th Fl, New York, NY 10012 ... 212-226-6024
Quorum Design Inc/San Diego: 1775 Hancock St #190, San Deigo, CA 92110 ... 619-298-3500
Quorum, Inc: 113 Catherine St, Ann Arbor, MI 48104 ... 313-668-1695

R

R & W Creative Services: 6 Morgan Ste 160, Irvine, CA 92618 ... 949-453-0679
R Studio T: 106 Charles St, New York, NY 10014 ... 212-929-8851
Raffert Communications: 1518 139th Ln NW, Andover, MN 55304 ... 612-755-8488
Ragghianti & Assocs, Inc: 4959 Thunder Rd, Dallas, TX 75244 ... 214-788-0914
Raines, Jackie: 16 N Peoria St, Chicago, IL 60607 ... 312-738-5100
Rainwater Communications: 6522 E Montgomery, Cave Creek, AZ 85331 ... 602-948-0770
Rainwater Design: 63B Congress St, Hartford, CT 06114 ... 203-278-6185
Rajcula, Vincent: 176 Long Meadow Hill, Brookfield, CT 06804 ... 203-775-2420
Rakatansky Studio, Mark: 3432 Oakland St, Ames, IA 50014 ... 515-296-0139
Ramie Design, Don: 35982 Cabral Dr, Fremont, CA 94536 ... 510-791-6842
Rampion Visual Products: 316 Stuart St, Boston, MA 02116 ... 617-574-9601
Ramsey Design, Scott: 14881 Waverly Down's Way, San Diego, CA 92128 ... 619-485-8017
Rand Inc, Paul: 87 Goodhill Rd, Weston, CT 06883 ... 203-227-5375
Randazzo Design, Sal: 826 Bellerose Dr, San Jose, CA 95128 ... 408-244-1541
Rank, Jerry J: 5727 Walnut Hill, Des Moines, IA 50312 ... 515-274-5826
Rankin Design, Bob: 9 103rd St NE, Bellevue, WA 98004 ... 206-455-0886
Rappy & Co: 150 W 25th St 5th Fl, New York, NY 10001 ... 212-989-0603
Rasic Creative: 1287 Marquette St #300, Cleveland, OH 44114 ... 216-432-0771
Rasor & Rasor: 1004 White Meadows Dr, Fuquay Varina, NC 27526 ... 919-467-3353
Rattan Design, Joseph: 5924 Pebblestone Ln, Plano, TX 75093 ... 214-931-8044
Rauchmann & Assocs: 5210 SW 60th Pl, Miami, FL 33155 ... 305-663-9432
Rauffenbart, Bruce: 39 Hamilton Terr, New York, NY 10031 ... 212-283-3401
Rauscher Design, Inc: 1501 Story Ave, Louisville, KY 40206 ... 502-589-3900
Ravenna Design: 2321 Hollywood Blvd, Hollywood, FL 33020 ... 954-923-6571
Rayfield/Corporate Design, Robert: 5072 Peck Hill Rd, Jamesville, NY 13078 ... 315-446-5216
Raynsford Solazzo: 34179 Golden Lantern #304, Dana Point, CA 92629 ... 714-489-0044
RBA Design: 487 College St, Wadsworth, OH 44281 ... 330-337-6700
Rea, Donald: 315 Market St, Sudbury, PA 17801 ... 717-286-1111
Read Studio: 2636 North West 14th, Oklahoma City, OK 73107 ... 405-524-4063
Reade Assocs, Herbert: 205 W 19th St, New York, NY 10011 ... 212-242-8085
Realm Communications: 110 Cambie St #300, Vancouver, BC V6B 2M8 ... 604-689-3383
Rebus, Inc: 632 Broadway 11th Fl, New York, NY 10012 ... 212-505-2255
Red Design, Inc: 5 E 19th St, New York, NY 10003 ... 212-475-3711
Red Herring Design: 449 Washington St, New York, NY 10013 ... 212-219-0557
Red Sky Interactive: 60 Green St, San Francisco, CA 94111 ... 421-0927
Red Square Design: 1133 Broadway #1401, New York, NY 10010 ... 212-620-0363
Reddy & Assocs: 14135 N Cederburg Rd, Mequon, WI 53097 ... 414-377-8448
Redgrafix Design Studio: 19750 W Observatory Rd, New Berlin, WI 53146 ... 414-542-5547
Redgull Images: PO Box 1052, Antigonish, NS B2G 2S3 ... 902-783-2772
Redmond Design, Patrick: PO Box 75430, St Paul, MN 55175 ... 651-646-4254
Reece Graphics: PO Box 2529, Tijeras, NM 87059 ... 505-255-3383
Reed, Veronica: 503 Lake Dr, Virginia Beach, VA 23451 ... 804-422-0371
Reel Design: 1035 5th St #10, Santa Monica, CA 90403 ... 310-395-4327
Reeves Design, Dick: 705 Baylor, Austin, TX 78703 ... 512-477-1652
Reichelt, Carol: 123 E Kane St, Port Washington, WI 53071 ... 414-377-3484
Reichgut, Mitchell: 45 W 36th St 2nd fl, New York, NY 10018 ... 212-629-6800
Reid, Scott: 432 State St, Santa Barbara, CA 93101 ... 805-963-8926
Reinbold Studio: 133 S Franklin St, Allentown, PA 18102 ... 610-437-4943
Reinch Design, Michael: 32 D Bow Cir, Hilton Head Island, SC 29928 ... 803-785-9393
Reliable Design Studios: 611 Broadway #742, New York, NY 10012 ... 212-529-5488
Renaissance Communications: 7835 Eastern Ave, Silver Spring, MD 20910 ... 301-587-1505
Renaissance Multimedia: 90 John St #309, New York, NY 10038 ... 212-619-0051
Rene Sheret Design: 101 E Greene St #15, Pasadena, CA 91105 ... 818-577-5088
Renquist & Assocs: 2300 Washington Ave, Racine, WI 53408 ... 414-634-2351
Rep Graphic: 18424 S Dalton, Gardena, CA 90248 ... 310-532-0244
Resource Marketing: 515 N Park St, Columbus, OH 43715 ... 614-621-2888
Rettich Design: 875 Ave Of The Americas, New York, NY 10001 ... 212-947-6276
Reuter Design: 657 Bryant St, San Francisco, CA 94107 ... 415-764-1699
Rev Group: 690 Sugartown Rd, Malvern, PA 19355 ... 610-644-4698
ReVerb: 5514 Wilshire Blvd #900, Los Angeles, CA 90036 ... 213-954-4370
Rex Packaging, Inc: 136 E Portroad, Jacksonville, FL 32218 ... 904-757-5210
Rey International, Michael: 4120 Michael Ave, Los Angeles, CA 90066 ... 310-305-9393
Reynolds Design, Nager: 5 Lowlyn Rd, Westport, CT 06880 ... 203-222-1990
Reynolds Keating Assocs: 10 Lomard St #408, San Francisco, CA 94111 ... 415-433-7170
Rhombus Design: 22 Jefferson Ave SE, Grand Rapids, MI 49503 ... 616-235-0030
Ribeck & Co: 570 Mt Pleasant St, W Rockport, ME 04865 ... 207-785-4165
Ricchio Design: 801 B Central Ave, Sealbeach, CA 90740 ... 310-598-1350
Rich & More: 600 Haverford Rd #103, Haverford, PA 19041 ... 610-658-2820
Rich Assocs, Harry: 648 Oakwood Ave, W Hartford, CT 06110 ... 203-953-2990
Richards & Swensen: 350 S 400 East #300, Salt Lake City, UT 84111 ... 801-532-4097
Richards Design Group: 4722 Old Kingston Pike, Knoxville, TN 37919 ... 615-584-3319
Richards Group, The: 7007 Twin Hill #200, Dallas, TX 75231 ... 214-987-4800
Richardson, Hank: 1575 Northside Dr 100Tch #210, Atlanta, GA 30318 ... 404-636-0567
Richardson/Smith, Inc: 10350 Olentangy River Rd, Worthington, OH 43085 ... 614-885-3453
Richland Design Assocs: 357 Harvard St, Cambridge, MA 02138 ... 617-868-1384
Richman, Mel: 15 N Presidential Blvd, Bala Cynwyd, PA 19004 ... 215-667-8900
Richmond Jones Graphics: 2530 W Eastwood Ave, Chicago, IL 60625 ... 773-588-4900
Rickabaugh, Eric: 384 W Johnstown Rd, Gahanna, OH 43230 ... 614-337-2229
Riddick Corp Marketing: 700 E Main St #1801, Ricmond, VA 23219 ... 804-780-0006
Ridgely Curry & Assocs: 87 E Green St #309, Pasadena, CA 91105 ... 818-564-1215
Ridgeway, Inc, Ronald: 530 Broadway 4th Fl, New York, NY 10012 ... 212-966-9696
Ridgeway, Ronald: 530 Broadway 4th Fl, New York, NY 10014 ... 212-966-9696
Rieb, Robert: 24 Narrow Rocks Rd, Westport, CT 06880 ... 203-227-0061
Rigsby Design Inc, Lana: 2309 University, Houston, TX 77005 ... 713-660-6057
Ringel Design, Leonard: 18 Wheeler Rd, Kendall Park, NJ 08824 ... 908-297-9084
Rio Station Graphics, Inc: 78 Manhattan Ave #2D, New York, NY 10025 ... 212-665-3670
Ritola Design, Roy: 431 Jackson St, San Francisco, CA 94111 ... 415-788-7010
Ritta & Assocs: 568 Grand Ave, Englewood, NJ 07631 ... 201-567-4400
Ritter Design, Richard: 651 Park Ave, King of Prussia, PA 19406 ... 610-354-9200
Ritz Design: 5024 N 83rd St, Scottsdale, AZ 85250 ... 602-949-5348
Riverhouse Graphics, Inc: 1650 Kendale Blvd #115, E Lansing, MI 48823 ... 517-337-2882
RKD: 853 Alma St, Palo Alto, CA 94301 ... 415-324-1355
RKM, Inc: 5307 29th St NW, Washington, DC 20015 ... 202-364-0148
RL Roberson: 12307 Cross Creek, Dallas, TX 75243 ... 214-669-9088
RL Studios: 327 Chestnut St, Roselle Park, NJ 07204 ... 908-241-6464
Rmda, Inc: 212 Roosevelt Way, San Francisco, CA 94111 ... 415-255-1221
Robbins-Tesar, Inc: 925 Brewster St, Bridgeport, CT 06605 ... 203-335-7886
Roberts & Assocs: 402 E Unaka Ave, Johnson City, TN 37601 ... 423-929-7773
Roberts Design, Jillian: One Port Cortcolden Rd, Washington, NJ 07882 ... 908-835-0694
Robertson Design: 219 Ward Cir #4, Brentwood, TN 37027 ... 615-373-4590
Robertson Stephens & Co: 555 California St #2600, San Francisco, CA 94104 ... 415-781-9700
Robertz & Kobold: 35 E Wacker Dr #3900, Chicago, IL 60601 ... 312-236-5522
Robie Design Assocs, James: 152 1/2 N La Brea Ave, Los Angeles, CA 90036 ... 213-939-7370
Robinson Design, Elton: 15 Nordica Dr, Croton on Hudson, NY 10520 ... 914-271-2718
Robinson Job: 415 Delaware, Kansas City, MO 64105 ... 816-474-2228
Robinson Kurtin Comm: 201 E 42nd St, New York, NY 10017 ... 212-983-5757
Robinson Pritchard & Boyer: 9409 Park Hunt Ct, Springfield, VA 22153 ... 703-548-6770
Robison Advertising Design: 191 University Blvd. #246, Denver, CO 80206 ... 303-355-2255
Rockel, Dana: 2 N Main St #B332, Beacon Falls, CT 06403 ... 203-720-1603
Rodney Creative Services, Deborah: 1635 16th St, Santa Monica, CA 90404 ... 310-450-9650

Rodriguez Jr, Emilio: 8270 SW 116 Terr, Miami, FL 33157 . . . 305-235-4700
Rodriguez, Syl: 11516 Sixth Ave, Seattle, WA 98177 . . . 206-364-9077
Roecker Design Group, Inc: 2401 15th St #350, Denver, CO 80202 . . . 303-455-4800
Roerden, Doug: 588 Tremont St, Boston, MA 02118 . . . 617-262-4868
Roessner & Co, Inc: 16 Heath Dr, Basking Ridge, NJ 07920 . . . 908-658-9700
Rogers Design Group: 6233 W 83rd Pl, Los Angeles, CA 90045 . . . 310-393-4014
Rogers Design, Pam: 40 Proctor St, Hopkinton, MA 01748 . . . 508-435-6975
Rogers Seidman Design: 20 W 20th St #703, New York, NY 10011 . . . 212-741-4687
Rogow & Bernstein Dsgn: 5971 W 3rd St, Los Angeles, CA 90036 . . . 213-936-9916
Rohrer Design, Curt: 822 Appletree Lane, Mechanicburg, PA 17055 . . . 717-732-5127
Rojas Design: Po Box 542, Boonville, CA 95415 . . . 707-895-2663
Rokfalusi Design: 2953 Crosswycke Forest Cir, Atlanta, GA 30319 . . . 404-262-2561
Romanelli Advertising & Design: 2 College St Box 227, Clinton, NY 13323 . . . 315-853-3941
Romax Studio: 32 Club Cir, Stamford, CT 06905 . . . 203-324-4260
Romeo Empire Design, Donna: 154 Spring St 3rd Fl, New York, NY 10012 . . . 212-274-0214
Romero Design Group, Javier: 24 E 23rd St 3rd Fl, New York, NY 10010 . . . 212-420-0656
Ronan Design: 1608 N Milwaukee Ave #501, Chicago, IL 60647 . . . 773-252-6624
Roos Design, Roz: 220 Bodega Ave, Petaluma, CA 94952 . . . 707-763-3939
Roose Design Inc, Rich: PO Box 539, Ketchum, ID 83340 . . . 208-622-7924
Root, Laurie: 481 Carlisle Dr, Herndon, VA 22070 . . . 703-318-7225
Ropeik & Assocs, Inc: 9518 Evergreen St, Silver Spring, MD 20901 . . . 301-589-5159
Rose Design, Fay: 310 Centennnial Dr, Blue Bell, PA 19422 . . . 610-292-9595
Rose Graphics: 3 Rose Ct, Colonia, NJ 07067 . . . 908-382-0593
Rosebush Visions: 154 W 57th St #826, New York, NY 10019 . . . 212-398-6600
Roselius Design, Marty: 8 Newell St, Seattle, WA 98109 . . . 206-282-8926
Rosenberg Design, Leslie: 2400 Lakeview Ave #2905, Chicago, IL 60614 . . . 773-929-6277
Rosenthal Assocs, Herb: 207 E 32nd St, New York, NY 10016 . . . 212-685-1814
Rosiak & Assocs: 199 Main St, Matawan, NJ 07747 . . . 908-290-1000
Ross Creative Group, Kim: 86 Seminole Way, Rochester, NY 14618 . . . 716-244-5384
Ross Design: 29160 Heathercliff Rd #200, Malibu, CA 90265 . . . 310-589-3100
Ross Design: 4450 Erie Ave, Cincinnati, OH 45227 . . . 513-561-5542
Ross Inc, Kallir Phillips: 333 E 38th St, New York, NY 10016 . . . 212-856-8400
Ross Roy Communications: 100 Bloomfield Hills Pkwy, Bloomfield Hills, MI 48304 . . . 810-433-6000
Ross-Tomey, Stephanie: 710 N Tucker Ave #512, St Louis, MO 63109 . . . 314-241-3811
Rosser, Toby: 4 Main St, Purdys, NY 10578 . . . 914-277-1064
Rosumat Graphic Design: PO Box 23019, Riyadh, Saudi Arabia, 11426 . . . 9661476-9282
Rotella Assocs: 301 S State St, Newtown, PA 18940 . . . 215-968-3696
Roth Inc, JH: 13 Inwood Ln E, Peekskill, NY 10566 . . . 914-737-6784
Roth, Judee: 712 Main St, Boonton, NJ 07005 . . . 973-316-5411
Rotheiser, Jordan I: 3075 University St, Highland Park, IL 60035 . . . 847-433-4288
Rothschild, Joyce: 305 E 46th St 15th Fl, New York, NY 10017 . . . 212-888-8680
Rothstein & Memsic: 332 N La Brea, Los Angeles, CA 90036 . . . 213-936-7209
Roundtable Media: 121 W Goose Alley, Urbana, IL 61801 . . . 217-367-6028
Rowntree 3D, Inc: 883 Boylston St, Boston, MA 02116 . . . 617-424-0610
Royter/Snow Design: 1537 S Main St, Salt Lake City, UT 84115 . . . 801-484-0419
Rozier Studio: 270 Lafayette St, New York, NY 10012 . . . 212-431-7070
Rozoff Dsgn: 430 Communipaw Ave, Jersey City, NJ 07304 . . . 212-620-4110
RP Communications: 2301 Kirk Ave, Baltimore, MD 21218 . . . 410-467-9200
RP Hibberd, Inc: 5 E 22nd St 21st Fl, New York, NY 10010 . . . 212-358-0447
RPM Commmunications: 601 Boston Post Rd, Milford, CT 06460 . . . 203-878-2611
Rubin Design, Marc: PO Box 440, Breesport, NY 14816 . . . 607-739-0871
Rubin Inc, Gary : 931 E 86th St #206, Indianapolis, IN 46240 . . . 317-251-5330
Rubinrolt Design: 1891 Main St Rear, S Windsor, CT 06074 . . . 203-289-4248
Ruby Shoes Studio: 12A Mica Ln, Wellesley, MA 02181 . . . 617-431-8686
Rudoy, Peter: 1619 Broadway 10th Fl, New York, NY 10019 . . . 212-265-7600
Ruemmele, Steve: 4602 Sylvan Rd, Indianapolis, IN 46228 . . . 317-972-0606
Ruggles Interactive Media: 35-45 78th St #52, Jackson Heights, NY 11372 . . . 718-476-3692
Rumble & Rumble Design: 1512 W Main St, Richmond, VA 23220 . . . 804-359-2598
Rush, Judy: 9854 Ash Dr, Overland Park, KS 66209 . . . 913-652-0125
Rushing & Assocs: PO Box 300219, Fern Park, FL 32730 . . . 407-679-4876
Russell Adv & Dsgn Inc, Emelene: 6312 S Fiddlers Gr Cir #415N, Englewood, CO 80111 303-741-4488
Russell Communications Group: 6167 Bristol Pkwy #450, Culver City, CA 90230 . . . 310-216-1414
Russell Design Assocs: 584 Broadway, New York, NY 10012 . . . 212-431-8770
Russo, Wondriska: 11 Talcott Notch Rd, Farmington, CT 06032 . . . 860-677-6161
Rusty Kay & Assocs, Inc: 2725 Macadamia Ln, Santa Barbara, CA 93108 . . . 310-392-4569
Rutter, Lance: 855 W Blackhawk St, Chicago, IL 60622 . . . 312-787-6831
RWR Designs, Inc: 5025 Arapahpo #502, Dallas, TX 75248 . . . 214-423-7111
Ryan Co, John: 303 Excelsior Blvd #500, MInneapolis, MN 55416 . . . 612-924-7700
Ryan Design, Thomas: 400 8th Ave S, Nashville, TN 37203 . . . 615-254-5374
Ryan, Debby: 21 Arts Center Ct, Avon, CT 06001 . . . 860-677-9777
RYSing Media: 154-10 Ash Ave, Flushing, NY 11355 . . . 718-358-6559
Rysner, Murrie Lienhart: 58 W Huron, Chicago, IL 60610 . . . 312-943-5995
Rytter & Assocs, Robert: 3618 Falls Rd, Baltimore, MD 21221 . . . 410-889-8400
RZA, Inc: 3 Harriot Pl, Harrington Park, NJ 07640 . . . 201-391-8500

S

S & N Design: 121 N 8th St, Manhattan, KS 66502 . . . 913-539-3931
Sabanosh, Michael: 433 W 34th St #18B, New York, NY 10001 . . . 212-947-8161
Sabatella, Paschal: 58 Maybeck St, Novato, CA 94949 . . . 415-883-9219
Sackett Design: 2103 Scott St, San Francisco, CA 94115 . . . 415-929-4800
Sackheim Enterprises, Morton : 1125 Daniels Dr, Los Angeles, CA 90035 . . . 310-276-5418
Sage Graphic Design & Mrkting: 545 Oriole Ln, Corona, CA 91719 . . . 909-279-0330
Sage Interactive: 624 Northern Ave, Mill Valley, CA 94941 . . . 415-381-4622
Saggese Design: 37 Stonehenge Dr, Ocean Township, NJ 07712 . . . 908-922-3282
Sagmeister Design: 22 W 14th St #15A, New York, NY 10011 . . . 212-647-1789
Said Design, Jason: 939 Greenbrier Trace, Nashville, TN 37214 . . . 615-316-9592
Saiki & Assocs: 13 Cutter Mill Rd #366, Great Neck, NY 11021 . . . 516-466-1229
Sailsman Graphics: 137 Varick St 6th Ave, New York, NY 10013 . . . 212-463-7245
Sakin, Sy: 443 Park Ave S 4th Fl, New York, NY 10016 . . . 212-889-4489
Sakowich Design: 99 Tower Rd, Lincoln, MA 01773 . . . 617-259-9601
Saks Assocs, Arnold: 350 E 81st St 4th Fl, New York, NY 10028 . . . 212-861-4300
Saks, Arnold: 350 E 81st St 4th Fl, New York, NY 10028 . . . 212-861-4300
Saksa, Cathy: 10 Hidden Hollow Dr, Hamilton Township, NJ 08620 . . . 609-259-7792
Salavetz, Judith: 160 Fifth Ave #613, New York, NY 10010 . . . 212-620-4672
Salisbury & Salisbury, Inc: 130 W 30th St, New York, NY 10001 . . . 212-268-5893
Salmon, Paul: 5826 Jackson's Oak Ct, Burke, VA 22015 . . . 703-250-4943
Salpeter Design: 142 E 37th St, New York, NY 10016 . . . 212-779-3566
Salvato & Coe Assocs, Inc: 2015 W Fifth Ave, Columbus, OH 43212 . . . 614-488-3131
Samaritan Design, Inc: 1441 N 12th St, Phoenix, AZ 85006 . . . 602-495-4254
Samata Assocs: 101 S First St, W Dundee, IL 60118 . . . 847-428-8600
Sametz Blackstone Assocs, Inc: 40 W Newton St, Boston, MA 02118 . . . 617-266-8577
Sams Design, Stan: 2636B S 13th St, St Louis, MO 63118 . . . 314-664-0797
Samson Kelly Design: 5757 Central Ave #F, Boulder, CO 80301 . . . 303-444-4496
San Diego Art Prdctns: 2752 Imperial Ave, San Diego, CA 92102 . . . 619-239-6666
Sanchez: 138 S 20th St, Philadelphia, PA 19103 . . . 215-564-2223
Sanchez/Kamps Assocs: 60 W Green St, Pasadena, CA 91105 . . . 818-793-4017
Sanders & Co/Dsgn, Robert: 100 Loma Vista Dr, Senoma, CA 95476 . . . 707-996-3532
• **Sanders, Terry W.: pg 923** New York, NY . . . **212-980-1893**
e-mail: lonelaser@aol.com
Sandstrom Design: 808 SW Third Ave, Portland, OR 97204 . . . 503-248-9466
Sanft Design: PO Box 3368, Scottsdale, AZ 85271 . . . 602-966-4311
Sanoski Design: 166 E Superior St, Chicago, IL 60611 . . . 312-664-7795
Santora Design: 295 Madison Ave 43rd Fl, New York, NY 10017 . . . 212-922-0344
Santos Design: 104-37 43rd Ave, Corona, NY 11368 . . . 718-458-2564
Sargent & Berman: 1337 Third St Promenade #203, Santa Monica, CA 90401 . . . 310-576-1070
Sargent Design Company: 397 Campbell Flat Rd, Norwich, VT 05055 . . . 802-649-3230
Sasaki: 41 madison Ave 13th Fl, New York, NY 10010 . . . 212-686-5080
Sasaki Assocs, Inc: 64 Pleasant St, Watertown, MA 02172 . . . 617-926-3300
Satagata/Vollmer: 308 E 8th St, Cincinnati, OH 45202 . . . 513-651-4443
Sater Comms & Dsgn: 4204 Roland Ave, Baltimore, MD 21210 . . . 410-889-4043
Saueressig Design: 222 W Custer Pk, Bismarck, ND 58501 . . . 701-223-3529
Savage Design Group: 4203 Montrose Blvd, Houston, TX 77006 . . . 713-522-1555
Savage Design, Liz: 11201 Longwood Grove, Reston, VA 20194 . . . 703-471-0166
Savion Advtg, Elias: 2424 CNG Tower, Pittsburgh, PA 15222 . . . 412-642-7700
Savlin/Petertil: 1335 Dodge Ave, Evanston, IL 60201 . . . 847-328-3366
Sawyer Studios: 115 W 27th St 8th Fl, New York, NY 10001 . . . 212-645-4455
Sawyer, Sandra: 616 Texas St #101, Ft Worth, TX 76102 . . . 817-332-1611
Sayles Design: 308 8th St, Des Moines, IA 50309 . . . 515-243-2922
Scabrini Design, Janet: 50 Washington St, S Norwalk, CT 06854 . . . 203-853-6676
Scannell Inc, Peter: 250 W 19th St #7L, New York, NY 10011 . . . 212-989-6010
Scaramozzino, Phil: 38 Montvale Ave #220, Stoneham, MA 02180 . . . 617-438-8575
Schaefer Advertising: 39609 Golden Cedar Ln, Oconomowoc, WI 53066 . . . 414-789-9952
Schaefer Assocs: 635 Butterfield Rd, Oak Brook Terrace, IL 60181 . . . 630-932-8787
Schaefer Television Art, Robert: 738 N Cahuenga, Hollywood, CA 90038 . . . 213-462-7877
Schaffer Design: 474 Third Ave, Salt Lake City, UT 84103 . . . 801-364-1717
Schaffer Design, Stephanie: 175 W 87th St Fl 14A, New York, NY 10024 . . . 212-580 1570
Schechter Group, Inc: 437 Madison Ave 10th Fl, New York, NY 10022 . . . 212-752-4400
Scheinzeit, Teri: 27 W 24th St, New York, NY 10010 . . . 212-627-5355
Schell Horn Design: 465 Prospect Ave, Piscataway, NJ 08854 . . . 908-424-1234
Schell, Paul: 1608 E 51st St, Brooklyn, NY 11234 . . . 718-951-8976
Schlaifer Nance & Co, Inc: 11 Piedmont Ctr #404, Atlanta, GA 30305 . . . 404-231-0684
Schlesinger Design: 1231 State St #204, Santa Barbara, CA 93101 . . . 805-966-2970
Schlossberg Inc, Edwin: 641 Avenue of the Americas, New York, NY 10011 . . . 212-691-0290
Schmalz Creative Svcs, Charles: 271 Santa Rosa Ave, San Francisco, CA 94112 . . . 415-586-0866
Schmidt Assocs: 20296 Harper Ave, Harper Woods, MI 48225 . . . 313-881-8075
Schmidt, Alberto: 2200 N Lamar Ave #104, Dallas, TX 75202 . . . 214-871-2747
Schneider & Assocs, Howard: 87 N Raymond Ave #210, Pasadena, CA 91103 . . . 818-795-5258
Schneider Assocs, Inc, Ken: 2 Bending Oak, Houston, TX 77024 . . . 713-464-0322
Schneider Design: 2633 N Charles St, Baltimore, MD 21218 . . . 301-467-2611
Schneider Design, Deborah: 900 N Franklin St #505, Chicago, IL 60610 . . . 312-642-3756
Schnider Design, Oscar: 568 Broadway #804, New York, NY 10012 . . . 212-431-3253
Schoeneberg Design: 551 Sherman Ave, Evanston, IL 60202 . . . 847-869-4180
Schoenfeld, Cal: 6 Colony Ct #B, Parsippany, NJ 07054 . . . 201-263-1635
Schopper, Bernie: 2415 Windbreak Dr, Alexandria, VA 22306 . . . 703-765-4652
Schowalter Design: 1133 Broadway #1610, New York, NY 10010 . . . 212-727-0072
Schrecongost, Paul: 284 Liberty St, Salem, WV 26426 . . . 304-782-3499
Schreer Design, Don: 1641 E Osborn Rd #3, Phoenix, AZ 85016 . . . 602-230-1350
Schreiber & Assocs Inc, David: PO Box 1580, Media, PA 19063 . . . 610-566-7575
Schreiber, Laszlo: 39 Hamilton Terr, New York, NY 10031 . . . 212-283-3401
Schubert Media Design: 176 King St, Redwood City, CA 94062 . . . 415-365-6878
Schulte Design: 2132 24th st, San Francisco, CA 94107 . . . 415-647-5623
Schulwolf, Frank: 524 Hardee Rd, Coral Gables, FL 33146 . . . 305-665-2129
Schum & Stober: 1750 Old Meadow Rd, McLean, VA 22102 . . . 703-448-8150
Schutz, Thomas: 9710 Ferris Ave, Morton Grove, IL 60053 . . . 847-965-7100
Schwartz Graphic Design: 2941 Fourth Ave, San Diego, CA 92103 . . . 619-291-8878
Schwartz, Bonnie & Clem: 2941 4th Ave, San Diego, CA 92103 . . . 619-291-8878
Schwarz Design: 2301 Hickory St, St Louis, MO 63104 . . . 314-773-1181
Sciorilli, Tony: 200 First Ave, Pittsburgh, PA 15222 . . . 412-261-6815
Scotko, Mike: 240 route 38 #C, Moorestown, NJ 08057 . . . 609-273-3255
Scotton Design, Dianne: 72 Tavern Cir, Middletown, CT 06457 . . . 860-344-8472
SCR Design Organization: 305 E 46th St 5th Fl, New York, NY 10017 . . . 212-421-3500
Screamin Lobster Studio: 20 W 20th St #802, New York, NY 10011 . . . 212-229-1275
Sea Studios, Inc: 810 Cannery Row, Monterey, CA 93940 . . . 408-649-5152
Seabright & Assocs, William: 3330 Old Glenview Rd #16, Wilmette, IL 60091 . . . 847-853-8120
Seaman Design Group: 1027 N Central Ave, Glendale, CA 91202 . . . 818-240-2674
Sebastian, James: 116 E 16th St 10th Fl, New York, NY 10011 . . . 212-924-2426
• **Seeley, Dave: pg 229** . . . **212-333-2551**
Los Angeles, CA . . . **323-874-5700**
Washington, DC . . . **410-349-8669**
Chigago, IL . . . **312-364-0244**
London . . . **011-44-207-636-1064**
url: www.shannonassociates.com
Segura, Carlos: 1110 N Milwaukee Ave, Chicago, IL 60622 . . . 773-862-5667
Seidenberg & Assocs: 300 S Duncan Ave #215, Clearwater, FL 34615 . . . 813-447-7635
Seidman, Gene: 20 W 20th St #703, New York, NY 10011 . . . 212-741-4687
Seiniger Advertising: 9320 Wilshire Blvd, Beverly Hills, CA 90212 . . . 310-777-6800
Seip Graphic Design: 916 Medina Ave, Coral Gables, FL 33134 . . . 305-448-6169
Selame Design Assocs: 2330 Washington St, Newton Lower Falls, MA 02162 . . . 617-969-6690
Selbert Design, Clifford: 2067 Massachusetts Ave, Cambridge, MA 02140 . . . 617-497-6605
Selfe Design, Mark: 604 Mission St #830, San Francisco, CA 94105 . . . 415-243-8118
Selfridge, Mary: 817 Desplaines St, Plainfield, IL 60544 . . . 815-436-7197
Selig Group, The: 44 Hawthorne Rd, Milton, MA 02186 . . . 617-426-0075
Seltzer Design & Illus, Meyer: 744 W Buckingham Pl, Chicago, IL 60657 . . . 773-883-0964
Selz Seabolt Communications: 221 N LaSalle St 35th Fl, Chicago, IL 60601 . . . 312-372-7090
Seman Design Group: 7434 Washington Ave, Pittsburgh, PA 15218 . . . 412-242-1775
Sendecke, Reed: 240 W Gilman St, Madison, WI 53703 . . . 608-256-5000

Seneca Design & Consulting: 3540 N Leavitt, Chicago, IL 60618 ... 312-248-3531
Serio Design, Jeff: Salt Lake City, UT ... 801-328-4925
Seroti Group, The: PO Box 470670, San Francisco, CA 94147 ... 415-776-4242
Service Station Design: 167 Perry St 2B, New York, NY 10014 ... 212-229-0988
Sessions Design, Steven: 5177 Richmond #500, Houston, TX 77056 ... 713-850-8450
Sestito Design, Joe: 387 Danbury Rd, Wilton, CT 06897 ... 203-762-9815
Seta Appleman Showell: 2145 Luray Ave, Cincinnati, OH 45206 ... 513-221-3600
Setian Design: 392 Porter Rd, E Longmeadow, MA 01028 ... 413-525-1102
Sexton Design: 151 Kalmus Dr #A203, Costa Mesa, CA 92626 ...
Sexton Graphics: 2800 Griswold, Port Huron, MI 48606 ... 810-982-0420
SFMultimedia Development Group: 2601 Mariposa St, San Francisco, CA 94110 ... 415-553-2300
SGB Partners: 1725 Montgomery St, San Francisco, CA 94111 ... 415-391-9070
SGI: 437 Fifth Ave 11th Fl, New York, NY 10016 ... 212-481-5666
Shades Of Gray: 917 S Cooper, Memphis, TN 38104 ... 901-725-0308
Shalit Designs, Eric: 5428 49th Ave SW, Seattle, WA 98136 ... 206-938-1449
Shapiro, Deborah: 150 Bentley Ave, Jersey City, NJ 07304 ... 201-432-5198
Shared Knowledge Systems: 1806 W Beltline, Cdar Hill, TX 75014 ... 214-293-9151
Shari Finger Design: 555 Milton Rd, Rye, NY 10580 ... 914-967-0854
Shaver Melahn Studios: 138 W 25th St 12th Fl, New York, NY 10001 ... 212-366-9784
Shaw Design, Susan: 150 Nassu St, New York, NY 10038 ... 212-732-6792
Shaw, Paul: 785 West End Ave #16A, New York, NY 10025 ... 212-666-3738
Shawver Assocs: 555 Peters Ave #100, Pleasanton, CA 94566 ... 510-484-4052
Shea Design, Eddie: 3044 N Evergreen St, Phoenix, AZ 85014 ... 602-258-9269
Shea, Michael: 47 Maple St, Burlington, VT 05403 ... 802-864-5884
Sheaff Dorman Purins: 460 Hillside Ave, Needham Heights, MA 02194 ... 617-449-0602
Shear Partnership, The: 2 Stamford Landg/68 Southfldave, Stamford, CT 06902 ... 203-323-6200
Shear, Richard: 68 Southfield Ave #2-290, Stamford, CT 06902 ... 203-323-6200
Sheibley Design: 320 N Kensington, LaGrange Park, IL 60526 ... 708-354-2094
Sheldon Cotler & Assocs: 568 Broadway #402A, New York, NY 10012 ... 212-941-0005
Sheldon Studios Ltd: 170 W Sixth Ave, Vancouver, BC V5Y 1K6 ... 604-874-9363
Shelly Design, Roger: 39 Laurel Grove Ave, Kentfield, CA 94904 ... 415-453-4379
Shen Advertising & Design, Coryn: 550 15th St 3rd Fl, San Francisco, CA 94103 ... 415-864-8200
Shen Design: 707 S Snoqualmie St #3A, Seattle, WA 98108 ... 206-623-3312
Shepard Assocs Design: 816 West Francicso, San Rafael, CA 94901 ... 415-485-0384
Shepard Design: 900 N Franklin #504, Chicago, IL 60610 ... 312-280-8538
Sherard Design: 2040 W Platt St, Tampa, FL 33606 ... 813-254-0068
Sheridan Assocs, Keith: 236 W 27th St 8th Fl, New York, NY 10001 ... 212-645-6400
Shibata-Schwartz Dsgn, Michelle: 5727 Amy Dr, Oakland, CA 94618 ... 510-601-1606
Shields Design: 415 E Olive Ave, Fresno, CA 93728 ... 209-497-8060
Shields Design Group, Inc: 155 Mcclleland Rd, Cannonsburg, PA 15317 ... 412-873-1499
Shiels Design, Inc: 2909 Cole Ave #105, Dallas, TX 75204 ... 214-871-0593
Shilt Graphic Design, Jennifer: 401 S Edgewood Ave, Lomard, IL 60148 ... 630-620-9313
Shimokoshi/Reeves Design: 4465 Wilshire Blvd #305, Los Angeles, CA 90010 ... 213-937-3414
Shinobu Ishizuka Design: 11835 W Olympic Blvd #825, Los Angeles, CA 90064 ... 310-478-4454
Shipps & Assocs, Inc: 410 Fairfax, Birmingham, MI 48009 ... 810-644-5446
Shiramizu Graphic Design, Inc: 1442 Market St #D, Denver, CO 80202 ... 303-623-2211
Shirley/Hutchinson: 707 N Franklin St #100, Tampa, FL 33602 ... 813-229-6162
Shishkoff Design, Debra: 7734 SW Canyon Ln, Portland, OR 97225 ... 503-297-9105
Shostak Studio, Mitch: 57 E 11th St 7th Fl, New York, NY 10003 ... 212-979-7981
Shoulak Graphics, Joel: 5621 Ocean View Dr #2, Oakland, CA 94618 ... 510-450-0298
SHR Perceptual Management: 7702 E Doubletree Ranch Rd #200, Scottsdale, AZ 85258 ... 602-483-3700
Shreeve Design, Draper: 28 Perry St, New York, NY 10014 ... 212-675-7534
Shriver Waterhouse Design, Inc: 1030 W Byron #1W, Chicago, IL 60613 ... 773-871-4015
Shuler Graphic Design, Gil: 231 King St, Charleston, SC 29401 ... 803-722-5770
Shum & Assocs: 1749 Old Meadow Rd #440, Mclean, VA 22102 ... 703-448-8150
Shupe, Rich: 115 E 34th St #8E, New York, NY 10016 ... 212-725-7576
Shurtz/ Capriotti: 604 Mission St 5th Fl, San Francisco, CA 94105 ... 415-546-1677
Shuster Design Assocs, Inc: 1401 E Broward Blvd #103, Ft Lauderdale, FL 33301 ... 305-462-6400
Shyaco Creative Services: 5827 Falkirk Rd, Baltimor, MD 21239 ... 410-532-7870
Sibley Peteet Design : 3232 McKinney Ave #1200, Dallas, TX 75204 ... 214-969-1050
Side Door Multimedia: 784 Columbus Ave #9D, New York, NY 10025 ... 212-222-2322
Sidjakov, Nicolas: 1725 Montgomery St, San Francisco, CA 94111 ... 415-931-7500
Sidney, Douglas: 10 Ritters Ln, Owings Mills, MD 21117 ... 410-363-6555
Siebers Retoucher/Illustrator: 10182 Whitnall Ct, Hales Corners, WI 53130 ... 414-425-6405
Siebert Design: 1600 Sycamore St, Cincinnati, OH 45210 ... 513-241-4550
Siegel & Gale: 10 Rockefeller Plaza, New York, NY 10020 ... 212-730-0101
Siegel Assocs: 74 Laurel Hollow Ct, Edison, NJ 08820 ... 908-753-9722
Siegel Design, Bhote: 3231 Thayer St #LL, Evanston, IL 60201 ... 847-424-1500
Siegel/Incocendio: 33 Vanderwater St #302, San Francisco, CA 94133 ... 415-433-5817
Siero Design, Inc: 112 High Ridge Rd, Avon, CT 06001 ... 860-673-2784
Sierra Web Pages: 2907 Baronet Way, Sacramento, CA ... 916-736-6700
Sigalos Design, Alex: 916 N Prospect Ave, Park Ridge, IL 60068 ... 847-698-9161
Sightworks Creative Development: 414 N Shaffer St, Orange, CA 92666 ... 714-744-8983
Sigler Group: 9059 Havasu St, Ventura, CA 93004 ... 805-647-8356
Sigma 6: 1435 Randolph St #403, Detroit, MI 48226 ... 313-963-2115
Signal Design: 905 W Main St #23E, Durham, NC 27701 ... 919-688-7878
Signcom: 527 W Rich St, Columbus, OH 43215 ... 614-228-9999
Signworks: 7710 Aurora Ave N, Seattle, WA 98103 ... 206-525-2718
Silva Design: 236 Gardiner Rd, Quincy, MA 02169 ... 617-472-8113
Silver Creek Design: 31815 NE 162nd St, Duvall, WA 98019 ... 206-788-6578
Silver Shoe Graphics: 2639 N charles St, Baltimore, MD 21218 ... 410-366-5976
Silverman Design: 45 Clearview Rd, E Brunswick, NJ 08816 ... 908-254-3959
Silverman Design, Bob: 216 E 49th St 2nd Fl, New York, NY 10017 ... 212-371-6472
Silverman Design, Gail: 579 Seventh St 2Fl, Brooklyn, NY 11215 ... 718-499-2036
Silverman Group: 700 State St 3rd Fl, New Haven, CT 06511 ... 203-562-6418
Silverstein, Ted: 245 E 54th St #28S, New York, NY 10022 ... 212-371-0613
Silvia Design Group, Ken: PO Box 2840, Orleans, MA 02653 ... 508-240-2600
Silvio Design, Sam: 633 S Plymouth Ct #204, Chicago, IL 60605 ... 312-427-1735
Simanis, Vito: 4N013 Randall Rd, St Charles, IL 60175 ... 630-584-1683
Simantel Group: 321 SW Constitution Ave, Peoria, IL 61602 ... 309-674-7747
Simgraphics Engineering Corp: 1137 Huntington Dr #1A, S Pasadena, CA 91030 ... 213-255-0900
Simmons, Elaine: 4628 W Browning Ave, Tampa, FL 33629 ... 813-831-9575
Simmons, Suzanne: 39 Hamilton Terr, New York, NY 10031 ... 212-283-3401
Simon & Cirulis: 329 N Euclid, St Louis, MO 63108 ... 314-361-8180
Simon & Co, Rick: 720 N Franklin #401, Chicago, IL 60610 ... 312-951-7252
Simons Industrial Design, IW: 975 Amberly Pl, Columbus, OH 43220 ... 614-451-3796
Simpkin Design, S: 23332 Mill Creek Dr #155, Laguna Hills, CA 92653 ... 714-830-2177
Simpkins Design Group: 3042 Highland Dr, Carlsbad, CA 92008 ... 619-434-1940
Simpson Booth Designers: 14 Arrow St, Cambridge, MA 02138 ... 617-661-2630
Sims, Ronald Bennett: 10609 Sandpiper Dr, Houston, TX 77096 ... 713-271-3703
Singer Design: 18 Porter Pl, New Providence, NJ 07974 ... 908-665-8491
Singer Design: 401 E 34th St #S-11C, New York, NY 10016 ... 212-481-3452
Singer Design, Beth: 1910 1/2 17th St NW, Washington, DC 20009 ... 202-483-3967
Singer Design, Paul: 494 14th St, Brooklyn, NY 11215 ... 718-449-8172
Siren Design: 10 Jay St #7, Tenafly, NJ 07670 ... 201-871-1127
Sirrine, JE: PO Box 5456, Greenville, SC 29606 ... 803-298-6000
Siskind Design, Stewart: 7 E 14th St #917, New York, NY 10003 ... 212-627-0021
Siteline: 180 Varick St, New York, NY 10014 ... 212-929-0505
Sitespecific: 132 W 21 St 12th St, New York, NY 10011 ... 212-206-6600
Sixth Gear: 55 Broad St 11th Fl, New York, NY 10004 ... 212-378-4985
Sji Assocs: 1133 Broadway #635, New York, NY 10010 ... 212-727-1657
Skaar, Melinda: 225 Santa Monica Blvd #311, Santa Monica, CA 90401 ... 310-394-8729
Skelton Design, Claude: 11 E Saratoga St, Baltimore, MD 21202 ... 410-576-8886
Skilling, Johanna: 39 E 20th St 7th Fl, New York, NY 10003 ... 212-254-3344
Skjei Design, Michael: 806 Mount Curve Ave S, Minneapolis, MN 55403 ... 612-374-3528
Sklaroff Design Assocs, William: 124 Sibley Ave, Ardmore, PA 19003 ... 610-649-6035
Skolos Wedell, Inc: 529 Main St, Charlestown, MA 02129 ... 617-242-5179
Skrobisz, Jan: 15017 Oak Crest Ct, Montclair, VA 22026 ... 703-680-3670
Skunta & Co, Karen: 1382 W Ninth St, Cleveland, OH 44113 ... 216-687-0200
Skwarczek, Dave: 1000 N Milwaukee 2nd Fl, Chicago, IL 60622 ... 773-342-7747
Skylight Graphics: 139 Willard Ave, Bloomfield, NJ 07003 ... 201-440-3909
Slam Design: 117 42nd St, Manhattan Beach, CA 90266 ... 310-545-5019
Sleeper Graphic Design: 3460 Cowper Ct, Palo Alto, CA 94306 ... 415-493-5628
Sloan, William: 236 W 26th St #805, New York, NY 10001 ... 212-463-7025
Slover Design, Susan: 584 Broadway #903, New York, NY 10012 ... 212-431-0093
Small Wonder Design, A: 8424 A Santa Monica Blvd #103, W Hollywood, CA 90069 ... 213-658-8353
Smarilli Exhibits & Graphics: 602 N Front St, Wormleysburg, PA 17043 ... 717-737-8141
Smart Concepts: 4525 S Jamestown St, Tulsa, OK 74135 ... 918-747-6006
Smart Design & Co: 137 Varick St 8th Fl, New York, NY 10013 ... 212-807-8150
Smc Falcone: 225 Christiani St, Cranford, NJ 07016 ... 908-272-0660
Smetts Design, Bonnie: 1798 Fifth St, Berkeley, CA 94710 ... 510-644-1313
Smidt, Sam: 666 High St, Palo Alto, CA 94301 ... 415-327-0707
Smit Ghormley Lofgreen: 4251 E Thomas, Phoenix, AZ 85018 ... 602-381-0304
Smith & Dress, Inc: 432 W Main St, Huntington, NY 11743 ... 516-427-9333
Smith & Hall Design, Inc: 2006 Wakefield St, Petersburg, VA 23805 ... 804-861-9660
Smith Group Communications: 614 SW 11th St #405, Portland, OR 97205 ... 503-224-1905
Smith Hinchman Grylls Assocs, Inc: 150 W Jefferson #100, Detroit, MI 48226 ... 313-983-3722
Smith Junger Wellman: 920 Abbot Kinney Blvd, Venice, CA 90291 ... 310-392-8625
Smith, Agnew Moyer: 503 Martindale St, Pittsburgh, PA 15212 ... 412-322-6333
Smith, Boo : 3416 Northview Pl, Richmond, VA 23225 ... 804-560-1757
Smith, Christine: 20 Baycrest Ct, Newport Beach, CA 92660 ... 714-729-1099
Smith, Edward: 1133 Broadway #1614, New York, NY 10010 ... 212-255-1717
Smith, Glen: 119 N 4th St #411, Minneapolis, MN 55401 ... 612-338-8235
Smith, Lauren: 920 Guinda St, Palo Alto, CA 94301 ... 415-322-1886
Smith, Marcia: 1703 W 9th Ave, Spokane, WA 99204 ... 509-456-6982
Smith, Mark: 28 N 20th St #A, Richmond, VA 23223 ... 804-643-2908
Smith, Pam: 584 Broadway #304, New York, NY 10012 ... 212-431-4361
Smith, Paul: 400 N Broadway 5th Fl #500, Milwaukee, WI 53202 ... 414-271-8582
Smith, Steve: 1620 Taylor #100, Portland, OR 97205 ... 503-233-5068
Smith, Terry: 880 C Mawde Ave, Mountain View, CA 94043 ... 415-938-1111
Smith, Thom: 308 SW 1st Ave #181, Portland, OR 97204 ... 503-243-3499
Smith, Tyler: 127 Dorrance St, Providence, RI 02903 ... 401-751-1220
Smith-Felver Prime: 4497 Mechanicsville Rd, Doylestown, PA 18901 ... 215-794-8937
Smolan & Assocs, Carbone: 22 W 19th St 10th Fl, New York, NY 10011 ... 212-807-0011
Smullen Design, Maureen: 85 N Raymond #280, Pasadena, CA 91103 ... 818-405-0886
Smullen, Mark: 57 Corfield Dr, Kitchener, ON N2A 3W8 ... 519-894-9890
Snow, Aaron: 7 Wooster Pl #3, New Haven, CT 06511 ... 203-821-2376
Snowden, George: 8608 Red Coat Ln, Potomac, MD 20854 ... 202-362-8944
Snyder Design: 18 E 16th St 5th Fl, New York, NY 10003 ... 212-691-4146
Sochynsky, Ilona: 200 E 36th St, New York, NY 10016 ... 212-686-1275
Sol Design: 623 W Drummond Pl #10, Chicago, IL 60614 ... 773-404-5882
Solazzo Design Agency: 114 Fifth Ave 18th Fl, New York, NY 10011 ... 212-242-0300
Solo Design: 2115 Vestridge Ln, Birmingham, AL 35216 ... 205-823-2474
SoloMat: 652 Glen Brook, Stamford, CT 06906 ... 203-325-9104
Sonderman Design, Joe: P O Box 35146, Charlotte, NC 28204 ... 704-376-0803
Sonneman Design Group: 20 North Ave, Larchmont, NY 10538 ... 914-833-0128
Sons, Dana: 1320 19th St NW #600, Washington, DC 20036 ... 202-835-0177
Soohoo Design: 425 Bush St #203, San Francisco, CA 94108 ... 415-392-3457
Soohoo Designers, Patrick: 19191 S Vermont Ave #400, Torrance, CA 90502 ... 310-324-0590
Sooy & Co, Brian: 419 Hampton Dr, Elyria, OH 44035 ... 216-366-5415
Soree, Sal: 97 Forest Hill Rd, W Orange, NJ 07052 ... 201-325-3591
Sorel Inc, Elaine: 640 West End Ave #8-A, New York, NY 10024 ... 212-873-4417
Sorensen Industrial Design, Hugh: 841 Westridge Way, Brea, CA 92621 ... 714-529-8493
Sosin, Bill: 415 W Superior St, Chicago, IL 60610 ... 312-751-0974
Soss, Johnathan Gregory: 653 Stanley Ct, Escondido, CA 92026 ... 619-735-5890
Soto Assocs: 97 South 2nd St #200, San Jose, CA 95113 ... 408-288-7686
Soundlight Productions: 1915 Webster St, Birmingham, MI 48009 ... 810-642-3502
Source & Co: 116 S Michigan 16th Fl, Chicago, IL 60603 ... 312-236-7620
Spangler Assocs: 1908 Seventh Ave W, Seattle, WA 98119 ... 206-467-8888
Spangler Design Team, The: 4207 Excelsior Blvd, St Louis Park, MN 55416 ... 612-927-5425
Spangler, Peter James: 7495 NW 4th St/Mark 4 Bldg, Plantation, FL 33317 ... 305-587-2842
Sparkman & Assocs, Don: 1120 Connecticut Ave #270, Washington, DC 20036 ... 202-785-2414
Spartan Graphics, Inc: 200 Applewood Dr, Sparta, MI 49345 ... 616-887-8243
Spatafore & Assocs: 50 South 600 East #100, Salt Lake City, UT 84102 ... 801-364-8759
Spatial Graphics, Inc: 7131 W Lakefield Dr, Milwaukee, WI 53219 ... 414-545-4444
Speare, Ray: 1462 Irving Pk Rd, Chicago, IL 60613 ... 773-327-9102
Spectrum Boston: 85 Chestnut St, Boston, MA 02108 ... 617-367-1008
Spectrum HoloByte: 2490 Mariner Sq Loop #100, Alameda, CA 94501 ... 510-522-3584
Spectrum Sight & Sound: 2801 Hyperion Ave #109, Los Angeles, CA 90027 ... 213-462-0812
Spectrum Studio: 1503 Washington Ave S 3rd Fl, Minneapolis, MN 55454 ... 612-332-2361
Spencer Zahn & Assocs: 2015 Sansom St, Philadelphia, PA 19103 ... 215-564-5979
Spencer, Greg: 5400 Legacy Dr, Plano, TX 75024 ... 214-604-7501
Speyrgraphix Design Studio: 24858 Paseo Primario, Calabasas, CA 91302 ... 818-222-5643
Spiekerman Assocs, Roberta: 650 Fifth St #301, San Francisco, CA 94107 ... 415-546-9173
Spilman, Stacey S: 155 Filbert St #240, Oakland, CA 94607 ... 510-839-5835
Spirals, Inc: 197 W Spring Valley Ave, Maywood, NJ 07607 ... 201-846-5150
Spivey Design, William: 515 Larkspur, Corona Del Mar, CA 92625 ... 714-721-1261
Splane Design Assocs: 10850 White Oak Ave, Grenada Hills, CA 91344 ... 818-366-2069

Spot Design: 775 Ave Of Americas 6th Fl, New York, NY 10001 ... 212-645-8684
Spur Design: 3647 Falls Rd, Baltimore, MD 21211 ... 410 235-7803
Square Docks: 201 W Brentwood, Glendale, WI 53217 ... 414-351-6101
Square One Design: 970 Montroe St NW, Grand Rapids, MI 49503 ... 616-774-9048
Squires, James: 2913 N Canton, Dallas, TX 75226 ... 214-939-9194
Srebro Design, Rose: 140 Carlton Rd, Newton, MA 02168 ... 617-244-2110
St Germain Graphics: 4735 Constance St, New Orleans, LA 70115 ... 504-895-2300
St Martin Ltd: 226 W 47th St, New York, NY 10036 ... 212-840-2188
St Vincent Milone & McConnells: 1156 Ave of Americas, New York, NY 10036 ... 212-921-1414
Stabins Design: 2440 S Sepulveda Blvd #152, Los Angeles, CA 90064 ... 310-478-1708
Stahl Design: 6219 N Guilford Ave, Indianapolis, IN 46220 ... 317-255-6900
Stahl, David: 116 E 48th St, Indianapolis, IN 46205 ... 317-283-5000
Stalinsky Design: 10000 Memorial Dr #170, Houston, TX 77024 ... 713-680-9723
Stalror: 341 B Blvd, Athens, GA 30601 ... 706-548-9349
Stampscapes: 7451 Warner Ave #E124, Huntington Beach, CA 92647 ... 714-968-5541
Stan & Lou: 720 N Post Oak Rd #605, Houston, TX 77024 ... 713-683-8000
Stanard Inc, Michael: 1000 Main St, Evanston, IL 60202 ... 847-869-9820
Standlee Design, Michael: 32962 Calle Miguel, San Juan Capist, CA 92675 ... 714-240-9140
Stanley Design, Steve: 2472 Bolsover #364, Houston, TX 77005 ... 713-522-2645
Stansbury Ronsaville Wood, Inc: 17 Pinewood St, Annapolis, MD 21401 ... 301-261-8662
Star Design, Inc: PO Box 30, Moorestown, NJ 08057 ... 609-235-8150
Starbright Graphics: 200 Hudson St 9th Fl Rm901, New York, NY 10013 ... 212-966-3200
Starke Photo Imaging, Herrmann: 9017 E Mendenhall Ct, Columbia, MD 21045 ... 410-290-3917
Starletta Polster Design: 144 Bain Dr, La Vergne, TN 37086 ... 615-793-4573
Starlin, Jim: 376 John Joy Rd, Woodstock, NY 12498 ... 914-679-8065
Starr Seigle McCombs, Inc: 1001 Bishop Sq #19 Pacific Twr, Honolulu, HI 96813 ... 808-524-5080
Steam/Willardson: 103 W California, Glendale, CA 91203 ... 818-242-5688
Stebbins, John R: 6318 Latona Ave NE, Seattle, WA 98115 ... 206-985-0956
Stecko, Dan: 627 Broadway #504, New York, NY 10012 ... 212-539-1680
Steel Art Co, Inc: 75 Brainerd Rd, Allston, MA 02134 ... 617-566-4079
Steel Design: 4217 E Windsong Dr, Phoenix, AZ 85044 ... 602-759-1810
Steel Point Graphics: 8507 E Indianola Ave, Scottsdale, AZ 85251 ... 602-947-7450
Steele Design: 641 W Lake St, Chicago, IL 60661 ... 312-831-1200
Steinberg Miller Design: 167 Melroseb St, Newton, MA 02166 ... 617-332-2505
Steiny Assocs: 828 N June St, Los Angeles, CA 90038 ... 213-463-1024
Stentz, Nancy: PO Box 19412, Seattle, WA 98109 ... 206-634-1880
Stepan Design: 1849 Barnhill Dr, Mundelein, IL 60060 ... 847-566-0488
Stephens Design, Kirby: 219 E Mt Vernon St, Somerset, KY 42501 ... 606-679-5634
Stephenz Group: 150 Almaden Blvd, San Jose, CA 95113 ... 408-379-4883
Sterling Group: 800 Third Ave 27th Fl, New York, NY 10013 ... 212-371-1919
Sternbach, Ilene: 1385 York Ave #11E, New York, NY 10021 ... 212-737-4999
Stettler Design, Wayne: 565 Glenmore Ave, Elkins Park, PA 19117 ... 215-235-1230
Stevers Design, Martin: 1595 Avenida De Los Lirios, Encinitas, CA 92024 ... 619-634-3056
Stewart Creative: 3290 S Cherry St, Denver, CO 80222 ... 303-759-1445
Stewart Daniels: 24092 Marathon, Mission Viejo, CA 92691 ... 714-586-1658
Stewart Design: 86 Milland Dr, Mill Valley, CA 94941 ... 415-389-1239
Stewart Lopez Bonilla: 550 W Kentucky St, Louisville, KY 40203 ... 502-583-5502
Stillon Interaction Design: 3206 Brasswood Court #3, Greenville, NC 27834 ... 919-321-3071
Stitt, Thomas: 864 W 4th St, Winston-Salem, NC 27101 ... 910-724-1803
Stockton Design: 2 Piney Point Ave, Croton on Hudson, NY 10520 ... 914-271-1058
Stoltze Design: 49 Melcher St 4th Fl, Boston, MA 02210 ... 617-350-7109
Stone Design Assocs: 2345 Washington St #201, Newton Lower Fa, MA 02162 ... 617-964-6882
Stone Yamashita: 355 Bryant St #408, San Francisco, CA 94107 ... 415-536-6600
Stout Design: 320 SW Stark St #418, Portland, OR 97204 ... 503-223-7740
Stoutt Creative Services, JC: 2817 Stratford Ln, Flower Mound, TX 75028 ... 214-539-8455
Stoyan Adverstising & Design: 2482 Newport Blvd #8D, Costa Mesa, CA 92627 ... 714-631-6314
Straightline: 60 Madison Ave, New York, NY 10010 ... 212-779-2626
Strategies In Design: 1911 W Wabansia Ave, Chicago, IL 60622 ... 773-276-3252
Strauss, Ross: 2367 Frankel Blvd, Merrick, NY 11566 ... 516-546-2807
Strawbridge, Ray: 4850 Parkglen Ave, Los Angeles, CA 90043 ... 310-559-4377
Streamline Graphics: 210 Eleventh Ave 6th Fl, New York, NY 10001 ... 212-633-0021
Streamline Interactive: 1406 N Benton Way, Los Angeles, CA 90026 ... 213-413-2406
Stress-Lab, Inc: 212 Third Ave N #385, Minneapolis, MN 55401 ... 612-376-7500
Stribiak & Assocs, John: 11160 Southwest Hwy, Palos Hills, IL 60465 ... 708-430-3380
Strickland Design Group Inc, Michael: 3355 W Alabama #100, Houston, TX 77098 ... 713-961-1323
Stroh Inc, Don: 8015 S Zephyr Way, Littleton, CO 80123 ... 303-973-1476
Stromberg Visual Design, Gordon H: 5423 Artesian, Chicago, IL 60625 ... 773-275-9449
Strong Productions: 101 2nd St SE #904, Cedar Rapids, IA 52401 ... 319-364-8859
Strong, David: 14727 NE 87th St, Redmond, WA 98052 ... 206-883-8684
Stuart, Neil: RD 1 Box 64, Mahopac, NY 10541 ... 914-618-1662
Stubenrauch & Partners: 1007 N Crane Ave, St Helena, CA 94574 ... 707-967-0433
Studio & Co: 9555 Trulock Ct, Orlando, FL 32817 ... 407-671-1717
Studio 203: 323 E Matilija #110-203, Ojai, CA 93023 ... 805-646-7877
Studio 42: 3109 Ave K, Brooklyn, NY 11210 ... 718-377-3686
Studio 609: 609 N 10th St 2nd Fl, Sacramento, CA 95814 ... 916-443-5001
Studio 7: 2440 State St NE, N Canton, OH 44721 ... 216-877-6774
Studio A: 1736 Stockton St #5, San Francisco, CA 94133 ... 415-956-8429
Studio A: 6274 Peachtree St, Los Angeles, CA 90040 ... 213-721-1802
Studio A Design: 1019 Queen St, Alexandria, VA 22314 ... 703-684-7729
Studio Architype: 600 Townsend St PH, San Francisco, CA 94103 ... 415-703-9900
Studio Blue: 9 W Hubbard 2nd Fl, Chicago, IL 60610 ... 312-222-0858
Studio Bolo: 4764 55th Ave SW, Seattle, WA 98116 ... 206-933-1157
Studio Doctor: 6056 Bennetts Corner Rd, Memphis, NY 13112 ... 315-672-8018
Studio Dog Eat Dog, Inc: 506 Theater Pl, Buffalo, NY 14202 ... 716-856-0142
Studio Flux: 739 N Edgemont St, Los Angeles, CA 90029 ... 213-660-4323
Studio G, Inc: 1007 W 6th St, Marshfield, WI 54449 ... 715-384-0092
Studio Goodwin Sturges: 146 W Newton St, Boston, MA 02118 ... 617-262-0591
Studio Grafika: 675 Drewry St NE #2, Atlanta, GA 30306 ... 404-874-3277
Studio Group, The: 1713 Lanier Pl NW, Washington, DC 20009 ... 202-332-3003
Studio Izbickas: 43 Winter St 8th Fl, Boston, MA 02108 ... 617-695-0606
Studio KaMa, Inc: 3 Robin Hood Rd, Pound Ridge, NY 10576 ... 212-355-7830
Studio Marz: 66 Crosby St Studio #4A, New York, NY 10011 ... 212-941-7799
Studio Mongo: 5900 119th Ave SE #B58, Bellevue, WA 98006 ... 206-603-9669
Studio Morris: 55 Van Dam #901, New York, NY 10013 ... 212-366-0401
Studio One: 7300 Metro Blvd #400, Edina, MN 55439 ... 612-831-6313
Studio One Graphics: 16329 Middlebelt, Livonia, MI 48154 ... 313-522-7505
Studio S: 7 Cerrito Pl, Redwood City, CA 94061 ... 415-261-9051
Studio Six Design: 6 Lynn Dr, Springfield, NJ 07081 ... 201-379-5820
Studio Star: 2637 McGee Ave, Berkeley, CA 94703 ... 510-848-0901
Studio Studio: 607 27th Ave, San Francisco, CA 94121 ... 415-221-3525
Studio W: 17 Vestry St Grd Fl, New York, NY 10013 ... 212-274-8744
Studio Wilks: 2148 Federal Ave #A, Los Angeles, CA 90025 ... 310-478-4442
StudioGraphics: 4 West 4th Ave Ste 501, San Mateo, CA 94402 ... 650-344-3855
Studiosoftware: 2140 E Seventh Pl North A2S, Los Angeles, CA 90021 ... 213-614-1126
Sturdevant Studios: 255 Third St #301, Oakland, CA 94607 ... 510-834-5938
Stymest, Brian: 39 Hamilton Terr, New York, NY 10031 ... 212-283-3401
Subjective Technologies: 1106 Second St, Encinitas, CA 92024 ... 619-942-0928
Sugiyama, Kazlinn: 5924 N Washtenaw Ave, Chicago, IL 60659 ... 773-271-9026
Sulewski, Connie: 2472 Bolsover #200, Houston, TX 77005 ... 713-630-0454
Sullivan Perkins Design: 2811 McKinney Ave #320 LB111, Dallas, TX 75204 ... 214-922-9080
Sullivan Scully Design Group: 23 E Fine Ave, Flagstaff, AZ 86001 ... 520-779-1020
Sullivan, Jerry : 1512 N Fremont #101, Chicago, IL 60622 ... 312-951-5510
• **Sullivan, Michael: pg 433** 227 Godfrey Rd, Weston, CT 06883 ... **203-222-8777**
e-mail: jp@artcoreps.com / url: www.artcoreps.com / fax: 203-454-9940
232 Madison Ave #512, New York, NY 10016 ... **212-889-8777**
e-mail: gt@artcoreps.com / url: www.artcoreps.com / fax: 212-447-1475
Summerford Design, Inc: 3200 Maple Ave #411, Dallas, TX 75201 ... 214-748-4638
Summers Studio: 230 E Ontario St #2306, Chicago, IL 60611 ... 312-943-2533
Summit Comms: 15 N Michigan St, Toledo, OH 43624 ... 419-242-6300
Summit Design: 381 Red Tail Trl, Evergreen, CO 80438 ... 303-425-3478
Summit Marketing, Inc: 125 Park Ave 8th Fl, New York, NY 10017 ... 212-479-2354
Sundberg & Assocs: 30 W 26th St 12th Fl, New York, NY 10010 ... 212-691-5477
Sundberg Ferar: 4359 Pineview Dr, Waldlake, MI 48390 ... 810-360-3800
Sundin Design: 25 Whittlemore Rd, Farmingham, MA 01701 ... 508-877-2771
Sundog Studios: 31 Greenfield Rd, Ballstonspa, NY 12020 ... 518-884-8144
Sunshine Graphic: 11455 Paramount Blvd #H, Downey, CA 90241 ... 310-861-0244
Suntar Designs: PO Box 1901, Prescott, AZ 86302 ... 520-778-2714
Super Graphics: 353 Concord Ave, Lexington, MA 02173 ... 617-674-9821
Superior Graphic Systems: 1700 W Anaheim St, Long Beach, CA 90813 ... 310-433-7421
Sussman & Prejza: 8520 Warner Dr, Culver City, CA 90232 ... 310-836-3939
Sussna, Brenda: 67 Potomac, San Francisco, CA 94117 ... 415-431-6616
Suzuki Design, Tom: 140-A W Jefferson St, Falls Church, VA 22046 ... 703-237-0244
Swack Design Assocs, Terry: 49 Melcher St, Boston, MA 02210 ... 617-423-7926
Swalwell, Brian: 707 Park Meadow Rd, Columbus, OH 43081 ... 614-890-9558
Swan Graphics, Inc: 110 N College St #4, Ft Collins, CO 80524 ... 970-224-3259
Swanson & Swanson Dsgn Studio, Inc: 5801 Roberta Circle, Tampa, FL 33604 ... 813-238-1915
Swatek & Romanoff Design: 156 Fifth Ave #1100, New York, NY 10010 ... 212-807-0236
Sweeny Graphic Design, Ken: PO Box 1532, New Canaan, CT 06840 ... 203-972-0920
Sweetlight Creative Partners: 11516 6th Ave NW, Seattle, WA 98177 ... 206-364-9077
Swieter Design: 3227 McKinney #201, Dallas, TX 75204 ... 214-720-6020
Swimmer Design: 15 E Palatine Rd #109, Prospect Height, IL 60070 ... 847-215-0900
Swoger Grafik: 12 E Scott St, Chicago, IL 60610 ... 312-943-2491
Synstelien Design, Ben: 851 Baker St, San Francisco, CA 94115 ... 415-922-5651
Sypher, Alan E: 1400 NW 101 Terr, Plantation, FL 33322 ... 305-370-2159
Syzygy Design Group, Inc: 7037 Matilija Ave, Van Nuys, CA 91405 ... 818-785-4989
Szabo, Michelle: PO Box 2034, Danbury, CT 06813 ... 203-791-8599
Szeto, Gong: 841 Broadway, New York, NY 10003 ... 212-533-4467
Szollose, Bradley: 207 W 25th St PH, New York, NY 10001 ... 212-255-7731

T

T6R17 Design Prtnr Ship: 900 Parkway Dr, Boulder, CO 80303 ... 303-494-8465
Taber, Russell G: 1952 Cleveland Ave, Wyoming, MI 49509 ... 616-245-3830
Tackett Barbaria Design: 1990 Third St #400, Sacramento, CA 95814 ... 916-442-3200
Taff, Barbara: 33 W 67th St PH, New York, NY 10023 ... 212-874-1007
Takatsuki Design, Kondziolka: 5158 W Ainslie St, Chicago, IL 60630 ... 773-777-5091
Takigawa Design, Jerry: 225 Canery Rd #G, Montery, CA 93940 ... 408-372-7486
Talala Design Studio, Mshuja: PO Box 153, Palo Alto, CA 94302 ... 415-964-2890
Tam Design, Julia: 2216 Via La Brea, Palos Verde, CA 90274 ... 310-378-7583
Tana & Co: 9 Claridge Court, Montclair, NJ 07042 ... 973-655-0643
Tanaka & Co: 1 Main St SE #209/Riverplace, Minneapolis, MN 55414 ... 612-378-3928
Tanenbaum Graphic Design, Jill: 4701 Sangamore Rd #235 S, Bethesda, MD 20816 ... 301-229-1135
Tangent Design Communications: 25 Sylvan Rd South #D, Westport, CT 06880 ... 203-221-1013
Tangram Design Group, Inc: 348 W 36th St #6N, New York, NY 10018 ... 212-629-3778
Taras Design, Lander: 115 Mulberry , Stamford, CT 06907 ... 203-968-0058
Tasi & Assocs, Peter D: 21 Southgate Ave, Annapolis, MD 21401 ... 410-269-1326
Tassian, George Org: 702 Gwynne Bldg, Cincinnati, OH 45202 ... 513-721-5566
Tate Designs, Susan: 1201 Executive Dr E #101, Richardson, TX 75081 ... 972-889-8556
Taurins Design Assocs: 280 Madison Ave #1402, New York, NY 10016 ... 212-679-5955
Tauss, Jack George: 484 W 43rd St #40H, New York, NY 10036 ... 212-279-1658
Taussig & Assocs: 331 Hoffman Rd, Tully, NY 13159 ... 315-696-8913
Taylor & Assocs, Carole: 112 Maywood Way, San Rafael, CA 94901 ... 415-485-4431
Taylor & Ives: 1001 Ave of Americas 14th Fl, New York, NY 10018 ... 212-921-9300
Taylor Corporation: 8601 Urbandale Ave, Des Moines, IA 50322 ... 515-276-0992
Taylor Inc, Pat: 3540 S St NW, Washington, DC 20007 ... 202-338-0962
Taylor Inc, Stan: 300 Northern Blvd, Great Neck, NY 11021 ... 516-466-5707
Teague Assocs, Walter Dorwin: 14727 NE 87th St, Redmond, WA 98052 ... 206-883-8684
Team Design: 301 N Water #620, Milwaukee, WI 53202 ... 414-347-1500
Team Design: 584 Broadway #701, New York, NY 10012 ... 212-431-8770
Team Design: 808 Howell St #600, Seattle, WA 98101 ... 206-623-1044
Technology Publishing, Inc: 2100 Wharton St #310, Pittsburgh, PA 15203 ... 412-431-8300
Tedesco, Bob: 8 Payne Rd, Bethel, CT 06801 ... 203-778-2306
Teitelbaum & Co: 433 W Briar Pl, Chicago, IL 60657 ... 773-871-7740
Tektonic Productions: 3034 M St NW #3A, Washington, DC 20007 ... 202-333-2532
Telesis: 215 W Seminary Ave, Lutherville, MD 21093 ... 301-235-2000
Temel Co: 716 Main St, Boonton, NJ 07005 ... 201-335-6298
Temel West: 1303 W Fort #A, Boise, ID 83702 ... 208-345-7076
Temner Design, Howard: 95 Fifth Ave 4th Fl, New York, NY 10003 ... 212-633-1978
Temp Art, Inc: PO Box 030398, Ft Lauderdale, FL 33303 ... 954-474-7770
Tempus Fugit: 437 Way, St Louis, MO 63122 ... 314-821-2826
Tepper Studio: 183 Bennett St, Bridgeport, CT 06605 ... 203-367-6172
Tepper, Lionel: 449 E 14th St, New York, NY 10009 ... 212-505-0029
Terada Design: 1221 East Pike #200, Seattle, WA 98122 ... 206-726-9909
Terrell Design Group: 804 Amatola #3, Torrance, CA 90501 ... 310-782-6301
Tessing Design: 3822 N Seeley Ave, Chicago, IL 60618 ... 773-525-7704
Tetrad Design: 21 Southgate, Annapolis, MD 21401 ... 410-269-1326
Teubner Kavelaras Assocs: 765 Melody Rd, Lake Forest, IL 60045 ... 847-735-1212

TFW Design: 1225 King St 3rd Fl, Alexandria, VA 22314 703-548-5570
TG Madison, Inc: 3340 Peachtree Rd NE #2850, Atlanta, GA 30326 404-262-2623
Tharler/Opper, Inc: 9 Bradford Rd, Natick, MA 01760 508-653-6840
Tharp and Drummond Did It: 1238 NW Glisan St Ste A, Portland, OR 97209 503-222-7226
Tharp Did It: 50 University Ave #21, Los Gatos, CA 95030 408-354-6726
That's Amorra: 19 Stanley Ave, Crotonville, NY 10562 914-762-7250
Thayer Barton Assocs, Jill: 1626 19th St #11, Bakersfield, CA 93301 805-399-0653
Thayer Industrial Design, Dana: Route 1, Monroe, VA 24574 804-929-6359
Theme Entertainment Creators: 920 Hampshire Rd #A-9, West Lake Village, CA 91361 805-381-0522
Theodore, Bradley: 776 NW 81st St, Miami, FL 33150 305-693-4435
Thien Schmidt: 77 E Main St, Newark, DE 19711 302-454-7233
Thill Design, Phill: 6629 University #206, Middleton, WI 53562 608-831-7447
Think Design: 1457 W Norwood St, Chicago, IL 60660 773-761-7564
Think Design Group: 514 N Third St #201, Minneapolis, MN 55401 612-338-3226
Thom & Dave Marketing Design: 28 W State St, Media, PA 19063 610-566-0566
Thomas & Assocs: 532 Colorado Ave, Santa Monica, CA 90401 310-451-8502
Thomas & Assocs Inc, Robert: 1020 Jamieson Rd, Lutherville, MD 21093 410-494-8945
Thomas Assocs, Greg: 2812 Santa Monica Blvd, Santa Monica, CA 90404 310-315-2192
Thomas Design, Keith: 3176 Pullman #109, Costa Mesa, CA 92626 714-557-1173
Thomas Marketing_, Steve: 112 S Tryon St #1755, Charlotte, NC 28284 704-332-4624
Thomas, Sean: 304 Mulberry St, New York, NY 10012 212-226-0441
Thompson Brothers: 331 W Stone Ave, Greenville, SC 29609 864-241-0810
Thompson Design Group: 725 Greenwich St, San Francisco, CA 94133 415-982-5827
Thompson Graphic Design, Maureen: 3041 S Giovanna Dr, Tucson, AZ 85730 520-885-7526
Thompson, Bradbury: Jones Park, Riverside, CT 06878 203-637-3614
Thomson & Thomson, Inc: 500 Victory Rd, N Quincy, MA 02171 617-479-1600
Thomson Comm Design, Melanie: 100 Market Sq #10, Newington, CT 06111 860-665-1424
Thorbeck & Lambert, Inc: 1409 Willow, Minneapolis, MN 55403 612-871-7979
Thorpe Design & Illust, Peter: Manor Inn 265 Charlotte St #6, Asheville, NC 28801 828-251-5545
Three: 444 E 82nd St #12C, New York, NY 10028 212-988-6267
Three & Assocs: 1726 Young St, Cincinnati, OH 45210 513-621-8100
Three Communication Design: 1807 W Sunnyside Ave #2C, Chicago, IL 60640 773-878-2229
Three, Inc: 236 W 26th St #805, New York, NY 10001 212-463-7025
Thumbnail Graphics: 228 NW 32nd St, Oklahoma City, OK 73118 405-755-7587
Thumbprint Design/Adv: 120 University Pk #200, Winter Park, FL 32792 407-672-0117
Tibbott, Randy: 3501 Trimble Rd, Nashville, TN 37215 615-783-0093
Tiberi, Mindy: 2601 Prairy Ave, Evanston, IL 60201 847-491-1545
Tiedrich Graphic Design: 37 W 20th St #910, New York, NY 10011 .... 212 206-6730
Tieken Design & Creative Services: 3838 N Central Ave Ste 100, Phoenix, AZ 85012 602-230-0060
Tigertt, William D: 1435 Randolph St #403, Detroit, MI 48226 313-963-2115
Tilka Design: 921 Marquette Ave #200, Minneapolis, MN 55402 612-822-6422
Time New Media/Pathfinder: Time Life Bldng-Rockfeller Center, New York, NY 10020 212-645-5577
Tin Box Studio: 3449 Michigan Ave/Lower Level, Cincinnati, OH 45208 513-321-2234
Tipton & Maglione: 19 W 21st St, New York, NY 10010 212-645-5577
Tirpak Design: 32 Jefferson Court, Freehold Townsh, NJ 07728 908-577-9351
Tisdale Design, David: 16 Waverly Pl, New York, NY 10003 212-228-7363
Tko Design Group: 287 S Main St #7, Lambertville, NJ 08530 609-397-5883
TKO Graphics: 1018 Ingraham Ave, Del Ray Beach, FL 33483 561-279-9633
TL Smith & Assocs: 101 First St #79, Los Altos, CA 94022 408-255-5696
TMA Ted Mader Assocs: 2562 Dexter Ave N, Seattle, WA 98109 206-270-9360
To The Point: 273B Auburn St, Auburn Dale, MA 02166 617-244-0515
Tobias Design, William: 35 E 63rd St #3, New York, NY 10021 212-832-7724
Todd Communications: 203 W 15th Ave #102, Anchorage, AK 99501 907-274-8633
Todd, Ann: 317 W 87th St PH, New York, NY 10024 212-799-1016
Todd, Hattie L: 6817 Oak Lake Dr, Indianapolis, IN 46214 317-329-9750
Tolleson Design: 220 Jackson #310, San Francisco, CA 94105 415-626-7796
Tollner Design Group: 111 N Market St #1020, San Jose, CA 95113 408-293-5300
Toma & Assocs: 1201 18th St #210, Denver, CO 80202 303-293-8353
Tomkowiak Design: 886 Washington Rd, Grosse Point, MI 48230 313-881-1734
Tomlinson, Inc: 215 First St, Cambridge, MA 02142 508-462-5545
Tommaso Design Group: 3800 N High St, Columbus, OH 43214 614-784-0020
Toomey, Michael: 345 W 88th St, New York, NY 10024 212-877-5817
Top Draw Productions: 610 N Water St #310, Milwaukee, WI 53202 414-273-8194
Toriello, Gary: 120 E Clinton Ave, Bergenfield, NJ 07621 201-384-0529
Torme, Dave: 1868 Buchanan St, San Francisco, CA 94115 415-931-3322
Torode Design Assocs, Barabara: 511 W Mt Airy Ave, Philadephia, PA 19119 215-242-8442
Torrisi Design: 10 E 23rd St #200, New York, NY 10010 212-777-1414
Total Media, Inc: 3015 Main St, Santa Monica, CA 310-450-1315
Toth Design & Advertising: 30 Monument Sq, Concord, MA 01742 508-369-3917
Toth, Joe: 20000 Eldra Rd, Rocky River, OH 44116 216-356-0745
Toto Images, Inc: 81-83 Franklin St #2D, New York, NY 10013 212-966-3788
Touch Creative Group: 2888 Glenvale Dr, Fairfax, VA 22031 703-560-0193
Touch Design & Communications: 27 Woodhollow Ln, Huntington, NY 11743 516-883-9728
Town Studios, Inc: 1370 Washington Pike, Bridgeville, PA 15017 412-257-8377
Townsend O'Leary, Inc: 18061 Fitch, Irvine, CA 92614 714-855-7870
TR Productions: 1031 Commonwealth Ave, Boston, MA 02215 617-783-0200
Tracer Design, Inc: 612 N 2nd St, St Louis, MO 63102 314-781-7377
Transimage Intrnl Comm: 145 Hudson St 9th Fl, New York, NY 10013 212-274-0501
Traver Company, The: 80 Vine St, Seattle, WA 98121 206-441-0611
Traverso Design Inc, Paulette: 2350 Taylor St, San Francisco, CA 94133 415-771-0611
Travis, William: 415 W Broadway 4th Fl North, New York, NY 10012 212-334-6401
Traxler Grphc Dsgn, Marty: 3189-A Airway Ave, Costa Mesa, CA 92626 714-850-1450
Traylor Multimedia: 437 Newtonville Ave #4, Newtom, MA 02160 617-964-1111
Trebing Design: 808 Lea Ave, Nashville, TN 37203 615-255-5252
Tree Frog Studio: The Opera Hs/67 Merchants Row, Rutland, VT 05701 802-773-8700
Trees Design, Brad: 21 N Harrison Ave, Campbell, CA 95008 408-379-8004
Trejo Graphic Comm: 4045 Bonita Rd #108, Bonita, CA 91902 619-267-7035
Trekk Design, Inc: 424 E State St, Rockford, IL 61104 815-962-2132
Trella- Mendl Design Group: 59 W 19th St #2C, New York, NY 10011 212-645-5605
Trepiccione Design, Inc: 77 Warren St, Boston, MA 02129 617-242-7878
Tri-Arts: 1645 N Vine #320, Hollywood, CA 90028 213-461-4891
Triad Productions: 9400 Misson Rd #101, Prairie Village, KS 66206 913-341-8988
Triad, Inc: 14 E Sir Francis Drake Blvd #B, Larkspur, CA 94939 415-925-3300
Tribe Design: 2444 Times Blvd #230, Houston, TX 77005 713-523-5119
Tribich Design Assocs, Inc: 276 Fifth Ave #808, New York, NY 10001 212-328-0662
Tribotti Design: 22907 Bluebird Dr, Calabasas, CA 91302 818-591-7720
Trios: 5706 Park Ln, Dallas, TX 75225 214-824-2200
Triple Strength Graphics: 1375 Old Forge Rd, Annville, PA 17003 717-838-9590
Tripp Design: 2551 N Clark #302, Chicago, IL 60614 773-880-0245
Troller Assocs, Fred: 12 Harbor Ln, Rye, NY 10580 914-698-1405
Trueman, Gregg: 122 E 42nd St #701, New York, NY 10168 212-986-6335
Trusch/Gilbert Design: 1807 E Broad St, Richmond, VA 23223 804-780-3905
TSA Design Group: 5990 N Sepulveda Blvd #100, Van Nuys, CA 91411 818-780-4700
Tscherny, George: 238 E 72nd St, New York, NY 10021 212-734-3277
TSI: 37H Terrace Ln, Lake Zurich, IL 60047 847-438-7128
Tsuchiya Sloneker Comms: 423 Washington #500, San Francisco, CA 94111 415-986-5365
Tsuruda Group: 888 Brannan St #604, San Francisco, CA 94103 415-863-4006
Tulino Design: 7108 De Soto Ave #205, Canoga Park, CA 91303 818-999-0980
Tumble Interactive: 910 West End Ave #3D, New York, NY 10025 212-316-0200
Tunstull Studio: 201 Clinton Ave #14G, Brooklyn, NY 11205 718-834-8529
Turk Studios, Barbara: 202 Atptour Blvd, Ponte Verdra Beach, FL 32082 904-273-8141
Turner Design: 155 W 19th St, New York, NY 10011 212-255-5501
Turpin Design Assocs, Inc: 2501 Pine Cove Dr, Tucker, GA 30084 770-492-0223
Turtle Island Design: 1035 Garden St #3, Hoboken, NJ 07030 201-656-0874
Tuttle and Tuttle: 1220 N Main St #202, Highpoint, NC 27262 910-841-8901
Twinn Design Form: 4 Water St, Arlington, MA 02174 617-643-3100
Two Twelve Assocs: 596 Broadway #1212, New York, NY 10012 212-925-6885
Tyler Blik Design: 655 G Street #E, San Diego, CA 92101 619-234-4434
Tyska Assocs: 1414 Naples Ct, Bartlett, IL 60103 708-830-0938
Tze, David: 1369 Madison Ave #333, New York, NY 10128 212-633-6649

U

Ultimo, Inc: 41 Union Sq W #209, New York, NY 10003 212-645-7858
Ultimus, Inc: 350 W Hubbard St, Chicago, IL 60610 312-527-3727
Ultra Arts, Inc: 150 E 35th St, New York, NY 10016 212-679-7493
Ultra Design Group: 46 Haywood St #336, Asheville, NC 28801 704-254-7985
Ultra Design, Inc: 4667 Macarthur Blvd #400, Newport Beach, CA 92660 714-476-0456
Ungler Image Cnslt/X Reps, Susan: 417 E 57th St #417, New York, NY 10022 212-688-9603
Unicom: 9470 N Broadmoor Rd, Milwaukee, WI 53217 414-352-5070
Unigraphics: 2700 Oak Lawn, Dallas, TX 75219 214-526-0930
Unit One: 2201 S Poplar St, Denver, CO 80224 303-757-5690
Unitech Prepress Solutions: 2000 Bloomingdale Rd #220, Glendale Heights, IL 60139 630-351-4770
Universal Images: 26011 Evergreen St #200, Southfield, MI 48076 810-357-4160
Unlimited Swan: 272 Riverside Ave, Riverside, CT 06878 203-637-4840
Up Design: 24-26 Church St, Montclair, NJ 07042 201-783-1155
Upshur Graphics, Thomas: 245 Madison Ave, Island Park, NY 11558 516-432-3959
Ushio Design, Kenneth: 1516 W Lake St #225, Minneapolis, MN 55408 612-825-3149
UVG & N Studios: 4415 W Harrison St #410, Hillside, IL 60162 708-449-1500

V

Valende & Co: 349 E 52nd St, New York, NY 10022 212-355-2257
Valentine Design: 4940 Viking Dr #408, Edina, MN 55435 612-835-1960
Valentine Group, The: 17 Vestry St 2nd Fl, New York, NY 10013 212-925-3103
Valk, John: 245 E 24th St, New York, NY 10010 212-889-4490
Vallarta Assocs, Frederick: 875 N Michigan, Chicago, IL 60611 312-944-7300
Valley, Ken: 601 N Eutaw St #704, Baltimore, MD 21201 410-962-0272
Van Acker, Wayne: 350 Hudson St, New York, NY 10014 212-627-9618
Van Auken Margolis & Assocs: 11 N Goodman St, Rochester, NY 14607 716-461-4714
Van Bronkhorst Group: 2900 Lakeside Dr #204, Santa Clara, CA 95054 408-980-8012
Van Der Sluys Graphics, Inc: 3303 18th St NW, Washington, DC 20010 202-265-3443
Van Dyke Company: 85 Columbia St, Seattle, WA 98104 206-621-1235
Van Enck Design, Walter: 9830 N Marshfield Ave, Chicago, IL 60613 773-935-9438
Van Noy Design Group: 19750 S Vermont Ave #205, Torrance, CA 90502 310-329-0800
Van Schouwen Assocs: 1391 Main St #300, Springfield, MA 01103 413-732-6077
Vance Design & Assocs: 315 First Ave S 4th Fl, Seattle, WA 98104 206-382-1522
Vance Wright Adams & Assocs: 930 N Lincoln Ave, Pittsburgh, PA 15233 412-322-1800
VanDam, Inc: 430 W 14th St, New York, NY 10014 212-929-0416
Vandecastelle Artworks: 4448 Morella Ave, Studio City, CA 91607 818-506-0564
Vander Stoep-Karraker, Inc: 2751 N Lincoln Ave, Chicago, IL 60614 773-525-3296
Vanides, Alex: 1440 W North Ave #108, Melrose Park, IL 60160 708-343-6210
Vanides, Steve: 1202 Norwood St, Melrose Park, IL 60160 708-681-0022
Vanis, Luke: 172 Horizon Cir, Carol Stream, IL 60188 630-871-1961
Vann, Bill: 1706 S 8th St, St Louis, MO 63104 314-231-2322
VanNoy & Co, Inc: 19750 S Vermont, Torrance, CA 90502 310-329-0800
Varisco Graphic Design: 1925 Esplanade Ave, New Orleans, LA 70116 504-949-2888
Varnau Creative Group: 6727 Riverview Dr, Indianapolis, IN 46220 317-475-0496
Vaughn/Wedeen Creative, Inc: 407 Rio Grande NW, Albuquerque, NM 87104 713-863-1609
VBMC: 21406 Woodchuck Ln, Boca Raton, FL 33428 407-852-0133
Velazquez, Jose: 227 N Grand Ave, San Pedro, CA 90731 310-833-1719
Vera Steiner Design: 38 E 23rd St 4th Fl, New York, NY 10010 212-529-8022
Vergati & Partner: 931 Springwood Ln, Ducanville, TX 75137 214-298-4060
Vermeer Design Inc, Dale : 1185 Akipola St, Kailua, HI 96734 808-261-2659
Vermilion Design, Inc: 2595 Canyon Blvd #350, Boulder, CO 80302 303-443-6262
Vermmer Productions: 1133 Broadway #712, New York, NY 10010 212-645-3602
Verona Design: 538 Lippincott Dr, Marlton, NJ 08053 609-983-3737
VGI Productions: 23400 Mercantile Rd #6, Beachwood, OH 44122 216-464-3635
Vhl International: 835 Strohson Rd, Cutchogue, NY 11935 516-734-5370
Via Design: 3935 Harney St #203, San Diego, CA 92110 619-220-0470
Via Design: 233 Brackett Rd, Rye, NH 03870 603-641-1819
Via Media: 203 Pine Ave, Long Beach, CA 90802 310-435-6998
Viacom New Media: 1515 Broadway, New York, NY 10036 212-258-6619
Vicar Design & Comms, Mac: 2615-A Shirlington Rd, Arlington, VA 22206 703-979-6575
Victory Productions: 581 Pleasant St, Paxton, MA 01612 508-755-0051
Video Communications: 829 Princeton St, Santa Monica, CA 90403 310-829-6619
Video Snapshots: 731 N Hollywood Way, Burbank, CA 91505 818-558-1900
Villaflor Design: 314 Old E Vine St, Lexington, KY 40507 606-226-0546
Vinick Assocs, Bernard: 211 Wethersfield Ave, Hartford, CT 06114 203-525-4293
Violet Carlon Design, Inc: 3125 Stuart St, Denver, CO 80212 303-477-8440
Virgo Comms: 91 Clinton Rd #2D, Fairfield, NJ 07004 201-808-9800
Visions By Hand: PO Box 27035, Regina, SK 306-569-3982
Vista III Design: 2001 University Ave SE, Bloomington, MN 55414 612-942-6169
Visual Accents Corp: 8821 15th Ave, Brooklyn, NY 11228 212-696-1695
Visual Bionics: PO Box 468, N Hollywood, CA 91603 818-841-9372
Visual Communications: 4475 E Hinsdale Pl, Littleton, CO 80122 303-773-0128
Visual Concepts: 100 Cutler Rd, Greenwich, CT 06831 203-869-1928

Visual Events: 815 Covington Rd, Belmont, CA 94002 ... 415-508 1332
Visual Graphic Comms: 177 Newtown Tpke, Weston, CT 06883 ... 203-222-1608
Visual Image Studio: 353 E Kellogg Blvd, St Paul, MN 55101 ... 612-227-9635
Visual Images, Inc: 1626 Franklin, Denver, CO 80218 ... 303-388-5366
Visual Impact: 33 Ship Ave, Medford, MA 02155 ... 617-395-5575
Visual Marketing Assocs: The Livery/322 S Paterson Blvd, Dayton, OH 45402 ... 937-223-7500
Visual Persuasion: 303 Greenwich St #3L, New York, NY 10013 ... 212-233-0311
Visual Resources: 1556 N Fairfax Ave, Los Angeles, CA 90046 ... 213-851-6688
Visual Services: 2100 N Woodward W #201, Bloomfield Hills, MI 48304 ... 810-644-0500
Visual Strategies, Inc: 4232B Knob Oak Ln, Charlotte, NC 28211 ... 704-362-0832
Visual Symphony: 900 William Pitt Way, Pittsburgh, PA 15238 ... 412-826-3938
Visual Thinking, Inc: 5724 S Kenwood Ave #3, Chicago, IL 60638 ... 312-324-6638
Visualgraphics Design: 1211 NW Shore Blvd, Tampa, FL 33607 ... 813-877-3804
Visualworks: 1100 W Cermak Rd #B-423, Chicago, IL 60608 ... 312-738-0690
Vivid Group, The: 317 Adelaide St W #302, Toronto, ON M5V 1P9 ... 416-340-9290
Vivid Media: 6666 Odana Rd #161, Madison, WI 53719 ... 608-276-8244
Vivid Studios: 510 Third St #200, San Francisco, CA 94107 ... 415-512-7200
Vivo, Inc: 3920 North 30, Tagoma, WA 98407 ... 206-761-8595
VNO Design: 2824 Erica Pl, Nashville, TN 37204 ... 615-269-8924
Volpe, Louie: 53 Meadow Ln, Levittown, NY 11756 ... 516-520-0366
Voltec Assocs: 560 N Larchmont, Los Angeles, CA 90004 ... 213-467-2106
Volz Design, Peter: 915 S Third St, Philadelphia, PA 19147 ... 215-574-9750
Von Brincken, Maria: 11 Ford Rd, Sudbury, MA 01776 ... 508-443-4540
Voss, Henry: PO Box 618036, Orlando, FL 32806 ... 407-894-2795
Vote Graphics Inc, Ray: 1056 E Whitton Ave, Phoenix, AZ 85014 ... 602-285-0440
Voyage Co, The: 578 Broadway #406, New York, NY 10012 ... 212-431-5199
Vra Studios: 1413 Highland Ave, Plainfield`, NJ 07060 ... 908-561-5305
VSA Partners: 542 S Dearborn #202, Chicago, IL 60605 ... 312-427-6413

W

W Design: 411 Wahington Ave N #208, Minneapolis, MN 55401 ... 612-288-0288
W Group: 3075 Charlevoix Dr SE City, Grand Rapids, MI 49546 ... 616-940-3913
Wages Design: 887 W Marietta St/Std S111, Atlanta, GA 30318 ... 404-876-0874
Wagner, Jim: 405 E 6th St #2, New York, NY 10009 ... 212-966-6465
Wai Graphic Design, Stan: 4324 Ewing Ave, Minneapolis, MN 55410 ... 612-925-0546
Waksman Design, Sergio: 4306 Knights Ave, Tampa, FL 33611 ... 813-835-5069
Walcott-Ayers Group: 1396 Park Ave, Emeryville, CA 94608 ... 510-594-1300
Waldman, Matthew: 55 Broad St #20A, New York, NY 10004 ... 212-968-8908
Walker Design: 9708 Stirling Rd, Richland, MI 49083 ... 616-629-4349
Walker Graphics, Inc: 111 Third Ave South, Great Falls, MT 59405 ... 406-727-8115
Walker Group/CNI: 320 W 13th St 5th Fl, New York, NY 10014 ... 212-206-0444
Wallace/Church Assocs: 330 E 48th St, New York, NY 10017 ... 212-755-2903
Wallner Harbauer Bruce & Assocs: 500 N Michigan Ave, Chicago, IL 60611 ... 312-787-6787
Waln Communications Group: 2900 Lively Blvd, Elk Grove, IL 6007 ... 312-951-6363
Walsh & Assocs: 1725 Westlake North, Seattle, WA 98109 ... 206-633-4420
Walter's Designs: 24 E Cota #200, Santa Barbara, CA ... 805-962-3677
Walzak Design: 1123 N Water St, Milwaukee, WI 53202 ... 414-276-7800
Wang/Hunter Design: 604 Mission St 2nd Fl, San Francisco, CA 94105 ... 415-957-0872
Ward Design: 374 Congress St #501, Boston, MA 02210 ... 617-426-3866
Warden, Bill: 438 Wellington Dr, Mesquite, TX 75149 ... 214-634-8434
Warhaftig Assocs: 361 Broadway #300, New York, NY 10013 ... 212-941-1700
Warkulwiz Design Assocs: 2218 Race St 3rd Fl, Philadelphia, PA 19103 ... 215-988-1777
Warner Design Assocs, Inc: 3920 Conde St, San Diego, CA 92110 ... 619-297-4455
Warren Design Inc, David: 1730 Blake St #400, Denver, CO 80202 ... 303-291-1111
Warren Group, The: 622 Hampton Dr, Venice, CA 90291 ... 310-396-6316
Warshaw Blumenthal: 104 East 40th Street #504, New York, NY 10016 ... 212-867-4225
Wasserman Design, Diane: 14 Carter Dr, Farmingham, MA 01701 ... 508-788-3684
Waston Design, Tom: 2172 West Lake Rd, Skaneateles, NY 13152 ... 315-685-6033
Water Shed Graphics: 1320 Lombard St #203, San Francisco, CA 94109 ... 415-771-2861
Watercolor Group, The: 101 1/2 E Front St, Wheaton, IL 60187 ... 708-871-9556
Watermark Design: 621 Wythe St, Alexandria, VA 22314 ... 703-549-0609
Waters Design Assocs, Inc: 3 W 18th St 8th Fl, New York, NY 10011 ... 212-807-0717
Watson Design: 704 Flagaer Ln, Redondo Beach, CA 90278 ... 310-376-9665
Watson Dezin Group: 1809 Birchston Ave, Portage, MI 49002 ... 616-345-7222
Watson/Swope Graphic Comm: 102 1/2 E Front St #303, Traverse City, MI 49684 ... 616-947-7550
Wattigney, Madelyn: 307 Olivier St, New Orleans, LA 70114 ... 504-368-5295
Watts Design, Inc: 444 N Wells St #204, Chicago, IL 60610 ... 312-321-0191
Watts Silverstein: 1931 Second Ave #400, Seattle, WA 98101 ... 206-443-4200
Watzman Info Design: 25 Inman Pl, Cambridge, MA 02139 ... 617-876-0099
Wave Communications: PO Box 5502, Santa Monica, CA 90409 ... 310-399-2831
Wave Design Works: 560 Harrison Ave, Boston, MA 02118 ... 617-482-4470
Wayne Hunt Design: 25 N Mentor Ave, Pasadena, CA 91106 ... 626-793-7847
WBMG Design, Inc: 207 E 32nd St #rd Fl, New York, NY 10016 ... 212-689-7122
Weadock, Rutka: 1627 E Baltimore St, Baltimore, MD 21231 ... 301-563-2100
Web Design Publishing Co: PO Box 508, Opelika, AL ... 334-502-7957
Web Page Design by Kaybee: 1540 Taylor Rd, Dothan, AL ... 334-702-1447
Web Site Creations: 1175 Harrison St, Santa Clara, CA 95050 ... 408-261-9024
Webb, Nancy: 101 Kimberlin Heights Dr, Oakland, CA 94619 ... 510-531-1978
Weber Design: 1439 Larimer Sq, Denver, CO 80202 ... 303-892-9816
Weber Design: 30 E 21st St 2nd Fl, New York, NY 10010 ... 212-673-6381
Weber Design, Inc: 705 Kings St 3rd Fl, Alexandria, VA 22314 ... 703-548-0003
Webster &Assocs, John: 1445 Fern Pl, Vista, CA 92083 ... 619-956-6576
Webster Design Assocs: 5060 Dodge St #2000, Omaha, NE 68132 ... 402-551-0503
Webster Design, Inc, Bruce : 545 Suttler St #303, San Francisco, CA 94102 ... 415-956-2252
Webster, Inc, Robert: 220 E 23rd St, New York, NY 10010 ... 212-576-1070
Webster, Shelly: 205 Greenhill Ave, Wilmington, DE 19805 ...
Wechsler & Partners: 71 5th Ave 4th Fl, New York, NY 10003 ... 212-924-3337
Wehrman & Co, Inc: 8175 Big Bend Blvd #250, St Louis, MO 63119 ... 314-962-7953
Weiman Illustration, Jon: 88 Wyckoff St #3C, Brooklyn, NY 11201 ... 718-855-8468
Weiser Design: 167 Hillrise Dr, Penfield, NY 14526 ... 716-377-4064
Weiss Creative, Heaton: 540 Main St #1, Winchester, MA 01890 ... 617-729-3564
Weiss, Jack: 1103 Mulford St, Evanston, IL 60202 ...
Weissman, Walter: 463 West St #B332, New York, NY 10014 ... 212-989-9694
Weller Inst For Cure of Design: 1575 W Highway 32 Box 518, Oakley, UT 84055 ... 801-783-5378
Wells, John: 407 Jackson St, San Francisco, CA 94111 ... 415-956-3952
Wells, Toby: 240 Poverty Hollow Rd, Redding, CT 06896 ... 203-938-8483
Wendt Graphic Design, Peter: 2914 W Pratt Ave, Chicago, IL 60645 ... 773-338-5877
Werner Design Werks: 126 N Third St #400, Minneapolis, MN 55401 ... 612-338-2550
Werremeyer Creative: 15 N Gore, St Louis, MO 63119 ... 314-963-0505
Werther Creative, Beth: 3600 Knollwood R, Nashville, TN 37215 ... 615-297-0333
Wertman, Chuck: 559 Pacific Ave, San Francisco, CA 94133 ... 415-433-4452
Wesko, David: 6430 Southpoint Dr, Dallas, TX 75248 ... 972-931-5091
Wesson & Assocs: 103 W Capitol #1215, Little Rock, AR 72201 ... 501-374-9257
West & Assocs: 1420 Springhill Rd #325, Mclean, VA 22102 ... 703-893-0404
West Design Studio, Harlan: 1843 Woodside, Thousand Oaks, CA 91362 ... 805-493-4049
West Design, Suzanne: 555 Bryant #282, Palo Alto, CA 94301 ... 415-324-8068
West Design, Timothy: 1397 Saddleridge Dr, Orlando, FL 32835 ... 407-299-9748
West Office Exhibition Design: 225 3rd St, Oakland, CA 94607 ... 510-622-7800
West, Harlan: 1834 Woodside Dr, Thousand Oaks, CA 91362 ... 805-493-4049
Westchester Graphic Group: 4 Jeremy Dr, New Fairfield, CT 06812 ... 203-746-8654
Westcom Creative Group: 2295 Coburg Road #105, Eugene, OR 97401 ... 503-484-4314
Westdal Design: 1805 A Second St, Berkeley, CA 94710 ... 510-540-1116
Western Graphics: 3535 W First Ave, Eugene, OR 97402 ... 451-686-2200
Weston Communications: 175 Derby St #31, Hingham, MA 02043 ... 617-749-0944
Westwood Studios: 2400 North Tenata Way, Las Vegas, NV 89128 ... 702-228-4040
Wetzel Assocs, Joseph A: 77 N Washington St, Boston, MA 02114 ... 617-367-6300
Weymouth Design: 332 Congress St 6th Fl, Boston, MA 02110 ... 617-542-2647
Whelan Design Office: 155 W 19th St, New York, NY 10010 ... 212-727-7332
Whibley Assocs: 216 Brewster Ave, Silver Spring, MD 20901 ... 301-587-5944
White Design: 249 E Ocean Blvd #500, Long Beach, CA 90802 ... 310-597-7772
White Design: 2001 Sul Ross, Houston, TX 77098 ... 713-520-0478
White III, Charlie: 9 1/2 Wavecrest Ave, Venice, CA 90291 ... 310-452-1912
White, Dana C: 2623 29th St, Santa Monica, CA 90405 ... 310-450-9101
White, Tom: pg 582, 583, 920, 921 70 Columbus Ave #2E, New York, NY 10025 ... **212-866-7841**
e-mail: tom@twimages.com / url: www.twimages.com
Whitefleet Design, Inc: 440 E 56th St, New York, NY 10022 ... 212-319-4444
Whitford, Kim: 242 Mead Rd, Decatur, GA 30030 ... 404-371-0860
Whittington & Company: 605 W 18th St, Austin, TX 78701 ... 512-474-9045
Why Design: 55 Brandford St #300, Providence, RI 02903 ... 401-421-7622
Wickham & Assocs: 1700 K St NW #1202, Washington, DC 20006 ... 202-296-4860
Wides + Holl: 866 Broadway, New York, NY 10003 ... 212-533-6882
Widmeyer Design, Inc: 911 Western #305, Seattle, WA 98104 ... 206-343-7170
Wiggin Design: Six Thorndal Cir, Darien, CT 06820 ... 203-655-1920
Wijtvliet, Inc: 440 E 56th St, New York, NY 10022 ... 212-319-4444
Wilbanks, Inc: 2256 E Mercer, Phoenix, AZ 85028 ... 602-788-4696
Wilcher Design: 18210 Redmond Way, Redmond, WA 98052 ... 206-882-2300
Wildenradt Design Assocs: 2525 Hartrey Ave, Evanston, IL 60201 ... 847-328-2482
Wiley Design: 2150 Capitol Ave #220, Sacramento, CA 95816 ... 916-447-4633
Wilke Design, Jerry: 15 Mallard Ln, Westport, CT 06880 ... 203-255-7705
Wilkins & Peterson Design: 43212 Second Ave NW, Seattle, WA 98107 ... 206-624-1695
Wilkins Design, Warren: 4927 49th Ave S, Seattle, WA 98118 ... 206-725-7500
Willey & Assocs: 6722 W Carnial Dr, McCordsville, IN 46055 ... 317-335-2445
Williams & Assocs, Bryan: 118 E 25TH St 4th Fl, New York, NY 10010 ... 212-647-1277
Williams & Assocs, Inc, Morgan: 400 First Ave N, Minneapolis, MN 55401 ... 612-339-5000
Williams & Ziller Design: 330 Fell St, San Francisco, CA 94102 ... 415-621-0330
Williams Entertainment, Inc: 10110 Mesa Rim Rd, San Diego, CA 92121 ... 619-658-9500
Williams McBride Design: 344 E Main St, Lexington, KY 40507 ... 606-253-9319
Williams, Christina: 5 Bixby Ln, Westford, MA 01886 ... 508-692-5178
Williamson, Richie: 514 W 24th St, New York, NY 10011 ... 212-807-0816
Williamson, Skip: 620 Groton Dr, Burbank, CA 91504 ... 818-955-9875
Willis Design Group, Remen: 2964 Coltin Rd, Pebble Beach, CA 93953 ... 408-655-1407
Willoughby Design Group: 602 Westport Rd, Kansas City, MO 64111 ... 816-561-4189
Wilmer Fong & Assocs, Inc: 155 Filbert St #240, Oakland, CA 94607 ... 510-839-5835
Wilson Adv & Design: 4021 N Rosewood, Muncie, IN 47304 ... 317-288-5444
Wilson Design, Peter: 23 E Colorado Blvd #203, Pasadena, CA 91105 ... 818-795-0126
Wilson Design, Scott: 497 Washington St, Brookline, MA 02146 ... 617-734-9077
Wilson Graphic Design, Bo: 4705 Brookline Dr, Bartlesville, OK 74006 ... 918-333-8391
Wilson Ink: 5417 Shoreline Ct, Holly Springs, NC 27540 ... 919-567-8144
Wilson, Gavin: 239 Elizabeth St #3, New York, NY 10012 ... 212-966-0040
Wilson, Inc: 716 Crescent Blvd, Glen Ellyn, IL 60137 ... 630-790-1052
Wilson, Mark: 18 River Rd, W Cornwall, CT 06796 ... 203-672-6360
Wilson, Rex Co: 330 Seventh Ave, New York, NY 10001 ... 212-594-3646
Wilsonwork Design: 1825 T St NW #607, Washington, DC 20009 ... 202-332-9016
Winberry Digital Design, Bob: PO Box 13023, Long Beach, CA 90803 ... 310-439-3841
Wind Horse Design: 128 Highland Blvd, Hayward, CA 94542 ... 510-886-5165
Windlight Studios: 702 N First St, Minneapolis, MN 55401 ... 612-943-1029
Windy City Communications: 1462 W IRving Park Rd, Chicago, IL 60613 ...
Wingate Industrial Design, Barry: 4934 Bel Escou Dr, San Jose, CA 95124 ... 408-559-4065
Winker Productions: 71 Laurel St, Marlborough, NH 03455 ... 603-876-3325
Winslow Studios: 18051 Whitman Ln, Lansing, IL 60438 ... 708-895-1048
Winter Design, Carol: 61 W 74th St #3A, New York, NY 10023 ... 212-724-1971
Winters, Michele: 1133 Broadway #816, New York, NY 10010 ... 212-367-8512
Wisconsin, Jonathan: 31 N Main St, Marlborough, CT 06447 ... 860 295-0225
Wisdom Ware, Inc: 841 Greneda Ln, Foster City, CA 94404 ... 414-574-2683
Wise Design: 75 13th St, Atlanta, GA 30309 ... 404-897-5200
Withers Graphic Design, Bruce : 305 E 46th St 15th Fl, New York, NY 10017 ... 212-935-2552
Witherspoon Design: 1844 W 5th Ave, Columbus, OH 43212 ... 614-486-5428
Wittenberg Inc, Ross: 301 W 18th St 4th Fl, New York, NY 10011 ... 212-255-7450
Witus, Ted: 1809 7th Ave #1710, Seattle, WA 98101 ... 206-447-1600
Wohler, Luann: 6201 Leesburg Pike #403, Falls Church, VA 22044 ... 703-536-1773
Wohlmut Media Services: 2600 Central Ave #L, Union City, CA 94587 ... 510-487-1073
Wolen, Merle: 150 E Huron St, Chicago, IL 60611 ... 312-787-9040
Wolf, Anita: 26 Golden Ave, Arlington, MA 02174 ... 781-646-4502
Wolf, Inc, Henry: 167 E 73rd St, New York, NY 10021 ... 212-472-2500
Wolfe Design, Leonard: PO Box 486, Wilton, CT 06897 ... 203-454-0566
Wolff Co, Rudi: 135 Central Park W #12NC, New York, NY 10023 ... 212-873-5800
Wolfson Ink: 853 Broadway #1208, New York, NY 10003 ... 212-475-9510
Woloch Design, Dennis: 1700 York Ave, New York, NY 10128 ... 212-427-1746
Wong & Assocs, Steve: 425 Bush St Ph Level, San Francisco, CA 94105 ... 415-421-3303
Wong & Yeo: 146 Eleventh St, San Francisco, CA 94103 ... 415-861-1128
Wong Design, Benedict: 450 Sansome St #1600, San Francisco, CA 94111 ... 415-781-7590
Wong Design, Christina: 215 W 92nd St #6-I, New York, NY 10025 ... 212-496-0453
Wong Mechanicals/Div Grey, Fran: 58 Maiden Lane, San Francisco, CA 94108 ... 415-743-9400
Wong, George: 935 W Chestnut #500, Chicago, IL 60622 ... 312-733-2391
Wong, Rick: 379-A Clementina, San Francisco, CA 94103 ... 415-243-0588
Woo, Calvin: 4015 Ibis St, San Diego, CA 92103 ... 619-299-0431

Wood Design c/o Louis Dreyfuss: 405 Lexington Ave 57th Fl, New York, NY 10174 212-490-2626
Wood, Tom: 3925 Peachtree Rd NE, Atlanta, GA 30319 404-262-7424
Wood, William: 68 Windsor Pl, Glen Ridge, NJ 07028 201-743-5543
Woods &Woods: 414 Jackson St #304, San Francisco, CA 94111 415-399-1984
Word of Mouth: 495 West End Ave, New York, NY 10024 212-724-8302
Work, Inc: 2019 Monument Ave, Richmond, VA 23220 804-358-9366
Working Design: 3423 Piedmont Rd NE Ste 410, Atlanta, GA 30305 404-261-7813
Worthington, Carl A: 3773 Wonderland Hill Ave, Boulder, CO 80302 303-444-1699
Wow Digital: 520 Broadway, New York, NY 10012 212-941-4600
Wozney Design, Greg: 80 Eighth Ave #1308, New York, NY 10011 212-620-7776
Wright Art Direction: Rte 7-303 Lazy O Ranch, Brazoria, TX 77422 409-798-6574
Wright Communications: 67 Irving Pl 12th Fl, New York, NY 10003 212-505-8200
Wright Design Assocs: 898 Main St, Acton, MA 01720. 978-635-9997
Wright Design Inc, Krueger: 6409 City West Pkwy #207, Eden Prairie, MN 55344 612-827-7570
Wright Design, Thomas: 6349 Torrington Rd, Nashville, TN 37205 615-356-2515
Wright Graphic Design, Evan: 332 Pine St PH, San Francisco, CA 94104 415-421-2520
Write Design: 2261 Market St #325, San Francisco, CA 94414 415-431-5646
Writeline: 19 Bridle Rd, Billerica, MA 01821 617-866-3832
Wu, Brian: 149 Fifth Ave 8th Fl, New York, NY 10010. 212-691-0352
Wunderlich Design: 1802 Lantana Dr, Minden, NV 89423 702-782-7666
Wurman, Richard Saul: 180 Narragansett Ave, Newport, RI 02840 401-848-2299
WW3 Papagalos & Assocs: 5333 N Seventh St #222, Phoenix, AZ 85014 602-279-2933
Wyant Simboli Group, The: 96 East Ave, Norwalk, CT 06851 203-838-0191

X

Xavier Studios, Gae: 9818 Timber Ridge Pass, Austin, TX 78733 512-263-9822
Xeno Group: 465 10th St #100, San Francisco, CA 94103 415-436-0100
Xilinx, Inc: 2100 Logic Dr, San Jose, CA 95124. 408-559-7778

Y

Yacinski Design: 18 W Windsor Ave, Alexandria, VA 22301 703-683-3079
Yamada Design Consultants, Tom: 801 Franklin St #603, Oakland, CA 94607 510-839-2468
Yamaguma Assocs: 255 N Market St #120, San Jose, CA 95110 408-279-0500
Yamamoto Moss, Inc: 252 First Ave N, Minneapolis, MN 55401 612-375-0180
Yanovick Coburn: 312 Washington Ave N #A, Minneapolis, MN 55401 612-375-0092
Yashi Okita Design: 2355 3rd St #220, San Francisco, CA 94107 415-255-6100
Ybarra Design: 2235 Laguna St #201, San Francisco, CA 94115 415-923-1758
Yee Design, Ray: 424 N Larchmont Blvd, Los Angeles, CA 90004 213-465-2514
Yellow Ink: 1038 Washington St, Holliston, MA 01746. 508-429-7904
Yeo Design: 146 11th St, San Francisco, CA 94103 415-861-1128
Yerkey Design Group: 340 Bryant St #201, San Francisco, CA 94107 415-882-9400
Yip Studio, Gene: 559 Pacific Ave #24, San Francisco, CA 94133 415-788-7074
Yonezawa Design: 4300 Aurora Ave N #101, Seattle, WA 98103 206-545-8018
Yoshimura-Fisher Design: 60 E 42nd St #1003, New York, NY 10165 212-431-4776
Young & Lynch Design: 1328 Emerald St, San Diego, CA 92109 619-270-4214
Young & Roehr Adv: 28 SW 1st Ave #500, Portland, OR 97204 503-222-0626
Young & Thomas: 7 Birch Hill Rd, Weston, CT 06883 203-227-5672
Young Assocs, Robert: 78 N Union St, Rochester, NY 14607. 716-546-1973
Young Goldman Young, Inc: 320 E 46th St, New York, NY 10017 212-697-7820
Yurdin Industrial Design, Carl: 2 Harborview Rd, Port Washington, NY 11050 516-944-7811

Z

Z Group: 105 Hudson St #300, New York, NY 10013. 212-941-9272
Z-Group Design: 2121 First Ave #102, Seattle, WA 98121. 206-728-2105
Zahn & Assocs, Spencer: 2015 Sansom St, Philadelphia, PA 19103 215-564-5979
Zahor & Bender: 200 E 33rd St #3E, New York, NY 10016 212-532-7475
Zahra Design Group: 2811 McKinney Ave #218, Dallas, TX 75204. 214-855-1255
• Zaidi, Nadeem: pg 928, 929 166 5th Ave, New York, NY 10010 . . . . **212-633-1999**
Zaine, Carmile: 110 E 17th St, New York, NY 10003. 212-674-0375
Zaino Design: 110 E 17th St, New York, NY 10003. 212-674-0375
Zamchick, Gary: 56 Hillside Ave, Tenafly, NJ 07670. 201-568-3727
Zamparelli & Assocs: 1450 Lomita Dr, Pasadena, CA 91106. 818-799-4370
Zaprauskis Assocs, Levinson: 15 W Highland Ave, Philadelphia, PA 19118. 215-248-5242
Zaref, Marc: 135 W 26th St, New York, NY 10001 212-989-6631
Zarek Packaging & Design: 769 N Ascan St, Elmont, NY 11003 516-825-3608
Zaremda Visual Comms: 927 Main St, Louisville, CO 80027 . . . .
Zastrow Studios: 10555 N Port Washington Rd #202, Mequon, WI 53092 414-241-8828
Zazula Inc, Hy: 2 W 46th St 2nd Fl, New York, NY 10036 212-581-2747
Zebra Design: 5 Beatrice Cove, Fairport, NY 14450 716-223-0150
Zeewy Design: 19 Cobblestone Dr, Paoli, PA 19301 610-644-7150
Zeitsoff, Elaine: 241 Central Park W, New York, NY 10024 212-580-1282
Zender & Assocs: 2311 Park Ave, Cincinnati, OH 45206 513-961-1790
Zeni & Assocs, Bob: 425 N Park Rd, Lagrange Park, IL 60525 708-352-4700
Zenn Graphic Design: 1639 McCollum St, Los Angeles, CA 90026 213-413-4369
• Zero Up: pg 932 PO Box 20828, Baltimore, MD 21209. **800-570-5204**
  e-mail: showcase@zero-up.com / url: www.zero-up.com
Ziba Design: 334 NW 11th Ave, Portland, OR 97209 503-223-9606
Ziegler Assocs, Inc: 107 E Cary St, Richmond, VA 23219 804-780-1132
Ziegler Design Works, Nancy: 1542 Woodbine Ct, Deerfield, IL 60015 847-945-2225
Zierhut Industrial Design: 2014 Platinum, Garland, TX 75042 214-276-1722
Ziga Design: 24 Harstrom Pl, Rowayton, CT 06853 203-852-1640
Ziller & Assocs, Barbara: 330 Fell St, San Francisco, CA 94102 415-621-0330
Zimmerman Crowe Design: 90 Tehama St, San Francisco, CA 94105. 415-777-5560
Zimmerman Design, Roger: 234 W 14th St #2F, New York, NY 10011 212-741-4687
Zimmerman Graphic Design, Amy: 19 Salem Ln, Port Wasington, NY 11050 516-767-7302
Zimmermann & Assocs: 317 N 11th St #1101, St Louis, MO 63101 314-241-3939
Zoe Graphics: 32 N Main St, Pennington, NJ 08534 609-730-0500
Zoom Computer Art Center: 800-A School St, Napa, CA 94559 707-226-7808
Zu Design: 150 Chestnut St, Providence, RI 02903 401-272-3288
Zukor Graphics: 666A State St, San Diego, CA 92101 619-235-8191
Zuzzolo Graphics, Inc: 316 Princeton Rd, Rockville Centr, NY 11570 516-763-1249
Zygote Media Group: New York, NY 212-333-2551